The Geology of Scotland

Society books reviewing procedures

The Society makes every effort to ensure that the scientific and production quality of its books matches that of its journals. Since 1997, all book proposals have been refereed by specialist reviewers as well as by the Society's Books Editorial Committee. If the referees identify weaknesses in the proposal, these must be addressed before the proposal is accepted.

Once the book is accepted, the Society has a team of Book Editors (listed above) who ensure that the volume editors follow strict guidelines on refereeing and quality control. We insist that individual papers can only be accepted after satisfactory review by two independent referees. The questions on the review forms are similar to those for *Journal of the Geological Society*. The referees' forms and comments must be available to the Society's Book Editors on request.

Although many of the books result from meetings, the editors are expected to commission papers that were not presented at the meeting to ensure that the book provides a balanced coverage of the subject. Being accepted for presentation at the meeting does not guarantee inclusion in the book.

Geological Society Special Publications are included in the ISI Index of Scientific Book Contents, but they do not have an impact factor, the latter being applicable only to journals.

More information about submitting a proposal and producing a Special Publication can be found on the Society's web site: www.geolsoc.org.uk.

It is recommended that reference to all or part of this book should be made in one of the following ways:

TREWIN, N. H. (ed.) 2002. *The Geology of Scotland*. The Geological Society, London.

STRACHAN, R. A., HARRIS, A. L., FETTES, D. J. & SMITH, M. 2002. The Highland and Grampian terranes. *In*: TREWIN, N. H. (ed.) *The Geology of Scotland*. The Geological Society, London, 81–148.

The Geology of Scotland

FOURTH EDITION

EDITED BY

N. H. TREWIN

Department of Geology and Petroleum Geology, University of Aberdeen

2002

Published by

The Geological Society

London

THE GEOLOGICAL SOCIETY

The Geological Society of London (GSL) was founded in 1807. It is the oldest national geological society in the world and the largest in Europe. It was incorporated under Royal Charter in 1825 and is Registered Charity 210161.

The Society is the UK national learned and professional society for geology with a worldwide Fellowship (FGS) of 9000. The Society has the power to confer Chartered status on suitably qualified Fellows, and about 2000 of the Fellowship carry the title (CGeol). Chartered Geologists may also obtain the equivalent European title, European Geologist (EurGeol). One fifth of the Society's fellowship resides outside the UK. To find out more about the Society, log on to www.geolsoc.org.uk.

The Geological Society Publishing House (Bath, UK) produces the Society's international journals and books, and acts as European distributor for selected publications of the American Association of Petroleum Geologists (AAPG), the American Geological Institute (AGI), the Indonesian Petroleum Association (IPA), the Geological Society of America (GSA), the Society for Sedimentary Geology (SEPM) and the Geologists' Association (GA). Joint marketing agreements ensure that GSL Fellows may purchase these societies' publications at a discount. The Society's online bookshop (accessible from www.geolsoc.org.uk) offers secure book purchasing with your credit or debit card.

To find out about joining the Society and benefiting from substantial discounts on publications of GSL and other societies world-wide, consult www.geolsoc.org.uk, or contact the Fellowship Department at: The Geological Society, Burlington House, Piccadilly, London W1J 0BG: Tel. + 44 (0)20 7434 9944; Fax + 44 (0)20 7439 8975; Email: enquiries@geolsoc.org.uk.

For information about the Society's meetings, consult *Events* on www.geolsoc.org.uk. To find out more about the Society's Corporate Affiliates Scheme, write to enquiries@geolsoc.org.uk.

Published by The Geological Society from:
The Geological Society Publishing House
Unit 7, Brassmill Enterprise Centre
Brassmill Lane
Bath BA1 3JN, UK

(*Orders*: Tel. +44 (0)1225 445046
         Fax +44 (0)1225 442836)
Online bookshop: http://bookshop.geolsoc.org.uk

British Library Cataloguing in Publication Data
A catalogue record for this book is available from the British Library.

ISBN 978-1-86239-105-5 (hardback)
ISBN 978-1-86239-126-0 (softback)

Reprinted October 2008

Typeset by Aarontype Ltd, Bristol, UK
Printed by Cromwell Press, Trowbridge, Wiltshire, UK

Distributors
USA
  AAPG Bookstore
  PO Box 979
  Tulsa
  OK 74101-0979
  USA
Orders: Tel. +1 918 584-2555
          Fax +1 918 560-2652
          E-mail: bookstore@aapg.org

India
  Affiliated East-West Press PVT Ltd
  G-1/16 Ansari Road, Daryaganj,
  New Delhi 110 002
  India
Orders: Tel. +91 11 327-9113
          Fax +91 11 326-0538
          E-mail: affiliat@nda.vsnl.net.in

Japan
  Kanda Book Trading Co.
  Cityhouse Tama 204
  Tsurumaki 1-3-10
  Tama-shi
  Tokyo 206-0034
  Japan
Orders: Tel. +81 (0)423 57-7650
          Fax +81 (0)423 57-7651

Contents

Acknowledgements

Every reasonable effort has been made by the authors to identify and acknowledge the copyright owners of material reproduced in this book. If further acknowledgement is required, this will be done at the earliest opportunity.

The authors gratefully acknowledge assistance from the following in the preparation of individual chapters, the reading of manuscripts, supply of information, and useful discussion.

Chapter 1. Professor B. J. Bluck, Dr J. R. Mendum, Dr G. J. H. Oliver, Professor G. Park, Dr. R. A. Strachan and G. S. Kimbell.
Chapter 2. Professor G. Y. Craig, Robert Dott Jr., Dr B. R. Bell, Richard Gillander, Graham McKenna, the late Patricia Lapworth.
Chapter 3. Dr J. R. Mendum.
Chapter 4. Dr A. G. Leslie.
Chapter 5. Dr G. Rogers, Dr T. J. Dempster.
Chapter 6. Professor G. Kelling, Dr T. B. Anderson.
Chapter 7. Dr N. J. Soper.
Chapter 8. Professor B. P. J. Williams.
Chapter 10. Shell UK Ltd for sponsorship of colour figures.
Chapter 11. Dr A. J.Hartley, Dr N. Morton.
Chapter 14. Dr R. J. Preston, Dr M. J. Hole
Chapter 15. Sheila Thomas for editorial assistance.
Chapter 16. Dr M. J. Russell, Dr C. G. Smith
Chapter 20. Dr J. E. Gordon, K. F. Leys, R. G. Lees.

The Director of the Geological Survey (NERC) is thanked for permission to reproduce numerous NERC copyright photographs and figures from the BGS archives and publications (Permit No. IPR/32-21C). Photographs are individually acknowledged in the figure captions. Also acknowledgement is given for permission to use borehole logs, maps and sections, for permission to quote from an unpublished manuscript by George Barrow, and to allow modification of a BGS original of the colour geological map in Chapter 1. Thanks also to Tom Bain for prompt attention to requests for material.

Contributions to this volume by K. E. Rollin, M. Smith, P. Stone, M. A. E. Browne, D. Stephenson, I. T. Williamson and R. W. B. O'Knox are made with the permission of the Director of the British Geological Survey (NERC).

The following organisations are thanked for permission to reproduce figures and and for access to archive material. Acknowledgements for sources of colour photographs are given in captions.

American Geophysical Union
Blackwell Science
British Coal
British Geological Survey (NERC)
Center for Global Change and Earth Observations, Michigan State University
D. C. Thomson, publishers
Edinburgh Geological Society
Elsevier Science
Geological Society of America
Gerald Duckworth and Co. Ltd
Haslemere Educational Museum (Geikie archive)
Joint Nature Conservation Committee
The Geological Society of London
The Royal Society of Edinburgh
Yorkshire Geological Society.

The Editor is extremely grateful to colleagues in the Department of Geology and Petroleum Geology at the University of Aberdeen for answering numerous questions during the preparation of this volume. Particular thanks to Barry Fulton for his expertise in drafting figures for Chapters 1 (especially for patience with the geological map), 8, 10, 11, 16, and 19, and for edits on many others. Thanks also to Judith Christie for (much needed) assistance with computing, and to Walter Ritchie for photography. Colin D. Will has continued his long association with this title with expert compilation of the index.

Above all, special thanks go to my wife, Margie Trewin, for many, many hours of patient editorial assistance during the preparation of this volume.

Contributing authors

B. R. Bell
Department of Geography and Topographic Science, Division of Earth Sciences, University of Glasgow.

B. J. Bluck
Department of Geography and Topographic Science, Division of Earth Sciences, University of Glasgow.

G. S. Boulton
Department of Geology and Geophysics, University of Edinburgh.

M. A. E. Brown
British Geological Survey, Edinburgh

S. Brown
Innexus Consulting Ltd. 9, Buckstone Road, Edinburgh.

D. J. Fettes
British Geological Survey, Edinburgh.

K.W. Glennie
Department of Geology and Petroleum Geology, University of Aberdeen.

C. D. Gribble
Department of Geography and Topographic Science, Division of Earth Sciences, University of Glasgow.

B. Hamilton
Olrig, Kirk Road, New Galloway, Castle Douglas.

S. D. Harker
Total Fina Elf Exploration UK, 1 Claymore Drive, Aberdeen.

A. L. Harris
Department of Earth Sciences, University of Cardiff.

J. D. Hudson
Department of Geology, University of Leicester.

R. W. O'B. Knox
British Geological Survey, Keyworth, Notts.

A. McKirdy
Scottish Natural Heritage, Edinburgh.

D. R. Oldroyd
28 Cassandra Avenue, St. Ives, New South Wales 2075, Australia.

G. J. H. Oliver
School of Geography & Geosciences, University of St. Andrews.

R. G. Park
Blackpark, Edderton, Tain, Ross-shire.

J. D. Peacock
18 McLaren Road, Edinburgh.

M. Pye
Department of Trade and Industry, Atholl House, Aberdeen.

W. A. Read
School of Earth Sciences and Geography, University of Keele.

C. M. Rice
Department of Geology & Petroleum Geology, University of Aberdeen.

J. Rippon
4 Ashmore Close, Lichfield, Staffs.

K. E. Rollin
British Geological Survey, Keyworth, Notts.

M. Smith
British Geological Survey, Edinburgh.

D. Stephenson
British Geological Survey, Edinburgh.

A. D. Stewart
Paoluccio, 05020 Porchiano del Monte, Italy.

P. Stone
British Geological Survey, Edinburgh.

R. A. Strachan
Department of Geology, Oxford Brookes University.

D. G. Sutherland
2, London Street, Edinburgh.

M. F. Thirlwall
Department of Geology, University of London: Royal Holloway College.

N. H. Trewin
Department of Geology & Petroleum Geology, University of Aberdeen.

B. G. J. Upton
Department of Geology & Geophysics, University of Edinburgh.

I. T. Williamson
English Nature, Grantham, Lincolnshire.

D. T. Wright
Department of Geology, University of Leicester.

Preface to the fourth edition

The first three editions of this book (1965, 1983, 1991) were ably edited by Gordon Craig and provide a fascinating insight into the development of modern views on the Geology of Scotland. Over the years contributors have had to incorporate the unifying theory of plate tectonics and incorporate increasing knowledge of offshore geology provided by the oil industry. The increasing sophistication of radiometric age dating is providing a current revolution, to the extent that some authors were reluctant to put pen to paper in the midst of revolution!

At the onset of the preparation of this edition a working party comprising Roger Anderton, Henry Emeleus, Douglas Fettes, Grahame Oliver and myself discussed the aims, organisation and content of this volume. A new plan was adopted, aimed at producing an integrated account of the geological history of Scotland.

This greatly expanded edition now has 34 contributors, with teams working on many chapters. This factor reflects modern specialisation in laboratory-based research and a distinct reduction in broad-based field geology. As geological science has expanded in content and complexity, it becomes well nigh impossible for one person to master all aspects of the geology of a time interval, or a region. As might be expected there are no authors from the first edition contributing to the 4th, but one author (congratulations to Tony Harris) remains from the 2nd and five from the 3rd edition. Hence in this edition there are 29 new contributors and a fresh organisation of the contents resulting in a total of 20 chapters. In order to save space, and to avoid repetition, a consolidated reference list is presented for the whole volume, rather than for individual chapters. Thus the 3rd and 4th editions of the Geology of Scotland are very different in authorship and organisation.

The most radical change adopted in this edition has been to treat each of the major Precambrian to Early Palaeozoic terranes of Scotland as separate entities up to (roughly!) the time of their assembly into their present relative positions at the end of the Caledonian orogeny. Thus chapters have been introduced on the Hebridean, Grampian–Highland, Midland Valley and Southern Uplands terranes. These terranes have been assembled through large-scale tectonic processes such as subduction and ocean closure, and movement on major strike-slip faults. The aim is to provide the reader with an account of the rock record and a summary of events affecting each terrane, rather than follow the rocks of (say) the Ordovician over the whole area that is now Scotland.

A further plan has been to try and link igneous, metamorphic and sedimentation histories in an integrated manner within the chapters. There are positive and negative aspects to this, or any other approach. The reader is provided with an account with a great variety in content, and may find information on igneous petrology, sedimentology and palaeontology for a particular place and time on the same page. The consequence is that those seeking a specialist account of only sedimentation or igneous activity through time have to dip into several chapters. This difference in approach is intended to emphasise a holistic approach to the geology of Scotland. Readers may wish to refer back to the excellent contributions of the 3rd edition to pick up different geological themes.

From the Late Silurian–Early Devonian, when the terranes were assembled, this volume reverts to previous practice, with a chapter for each geological period across the whole of Scotland. The Tertiary igneous rocks retain a chapter of their own, largely on account of their obvious role in the development of Scotland.

Two new topics have been introduced to this edition. The first by Oldroyd & Hamilton gives a flavour of the importance of Scotland and Scottish geologists in the development and demonstration of geological thinking from the time of Hutton. The second new topic is Environmental Geology, introduced by McKirdy, and giving a valuable insight into protection of the environment in relation to the use of geological resources in Scotland.

New data, particularly relating to the offshore geology of Scotland, has resulted in the splitting and expansion of the Mesozoic–Tertiary section into separate chapters on Jurassic, Cretaceous and Tertiary history. There is now a wealth of offshore data, and it has not been the intention of the authors to duplicate or compete with publications describing the stratigraphy, petroleum geology and structural history of the offshore areas. This volume concentrates on the onshore evidence of Scotland's geological history, and attempts to put that history in the broad context of our knowledge of the offshore.

The Economic Geology section has been subdivided to give accounts of Metaliferous Minerals (Rice), Bulk Resources (Gribble), Coal (Rippon) and Hydrocarbons (Pye & Brown). For the reasons outlined above, the Hydrocarbons section is intentionally brief, the reader being referred to the numerous existing publications dealing with the petroleum geology of individual fields in the offshore areas.

The opinions expressed in this volume are those of the authors! The observant reader will note that controversy exists between authors in several areas. As editor I have not attempted to produce a unified opinion, but to ensure that different views are represented.

Scotland probably has a greater variety of geology than any other country of comparable size on Earth. It was also the land in which many of the historically important arguments on the development of geology took place. Scotland has a unique geological heritage, and continues to be a test-bed of recent geological development. Professional, student and amateur geologists visit Scotland from all over the world to experience classic geology in the field. I hope that this volume stimulates their interests.

Nigel H Trewin
Aberdeen 2002

1 Geological history and structure of Scotland

N. H. TREWIN & K. E. ROLLIN

The aims of this chapter are to summarize the geological history of, and to introduce the broad geological and geophysical structure of Scotland. The geological history (NHT) is largely drawn from the contributions to this volume, and the reader will find references in the appropriate chapters. There are significant differences of opinion expressed in the various chapters of this volume, and this author has attempted not to promote any particular view in this account. The deeper structure (KER) has to be modelled on a particular interpretation of structural relationships and rock properties, and models based on a variety of hypotheses could be used. Thus it must be stressed that many aspects of Scottish geology continue to promote vigorous debate, and in some areas there is no common consensus.

The Geological History of Scotland

In the third edition of this work, Tony Harris provided an admirable summary of the geological history of Scotland (Harris 1991). He noted the great changes in interpretation

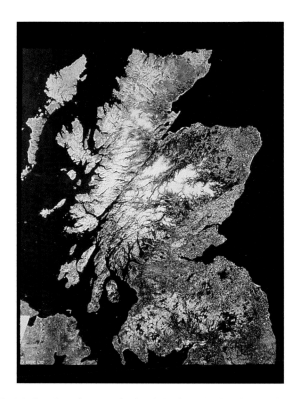

Fig 1.1. Landsat photograph of mainland Scotland and the Hebrides. Reproduced with permission from the Centre for Global Change and earth Observations, Michigan State University.

that had taken place since T. N. George wrote the introductory chapter to the first Edition (George 1965). The same applies 11 years after the third Edition. Continuing advances in isotopic age dating produce results that challenge existing interpretations. Our knowledge of basin structure has greatly improved through advances in seismic interpretation, and the application of sequence stratigraphy has caused some rethinking of traditional views. In this edition, the new layout provides for a summary (Chapter 7) of interpretations of terrane assembly, and hence this summary concentrates on the content of individual chapters. The reader is directed to the appropriate chapters for supporting references and figures. Many authors have assisted in revising material for this contribution, and we thank them for their assistance.

It is appropriate to start this account with a Landsat view of mainland Scotland and the western isles (Fig. 1.1). Key localities are indicated in Figure 1.2, and major terrane-boundary features in Figure 1.3. Comparison of the Landsat image (Fig. 1.1) with the geological map (Fig. 1.4) reveals geological features that have a clear surface expression through topography, vegetation and land use; the Highland Boundary Fault is particularly well-defined.

The assembly of crustal blocks that now comprise the basement of Scotland took place in a series of events extending back into the Archaean. The terranes indicated on Figure 1.3 represent a simplified view, and greater subdivision could be made, for example, within the Midland Valley and Hebridean terranes. It is the more recent events, such as the closure of the Iapetus Ocean, the creation, uplift and erosion of the Caledonian mountains, Mesozoic rifting, and opening of the Atlantic Ocean that have had the greatest influence on the exposed geology of Scotland. A pre-Atlantic reconstruction is illustrated in Figure 1.5, and a summary of events affecting the individual terranes in Figure 1.6.

The Precambrian and Early Palaeozoic terranes of Scotland

The Hebridean terrane

Lying to the west of the Moine Thrust Zone, the Hebridean terrane comprises three distinct rock groups. A dominantly gneissose Archaean to Palaeoproterozoic basement (the Lewisian Complex) is unconformably overlain by Neoproterozoic Torridonian clastics of dominantly fluvial origin, which are in turn unconformably overlain by clastic and carbonate marine shelf deposits of Cambro-Ordovician age. The Torridonian and Cambro-Ordovician rocks are tilted but otherwise undeformed, and to the west of the Moine Thrust Zone form part of the cover of the stable foreland to the metamorphic Caledonides. The thrusting formed at the Caledonian front can be dated as Early Silurian.

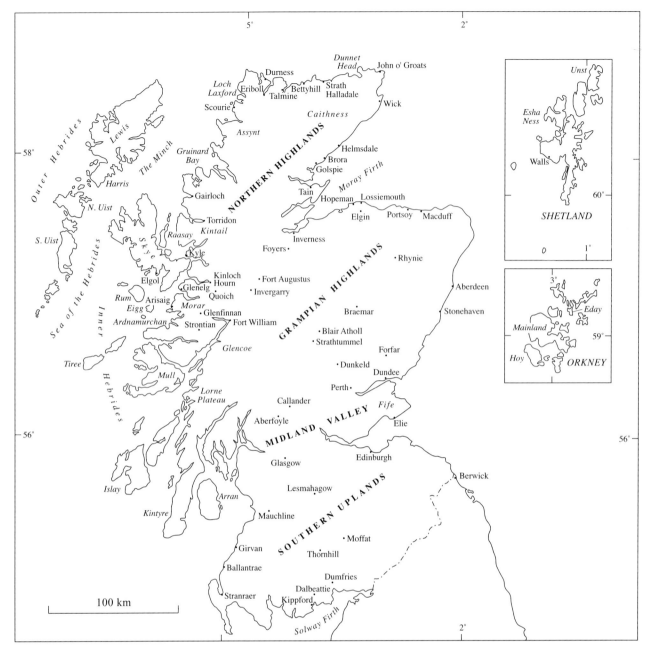

Fig 1.2. General map to show key localities and towns mentioned in the text.

The Lewisian Complex, Mainland Scotland

The complex comprises a variety of gneissose rocks with a complex metamorphic and structural history. From the time of Peach and Horne, research has been directed towards unraveling the history of these rocks. Interpretations based on the results of increasingly sophisticated field methods for interpretation of polyphase deformation are currently being reconciled with new data obtained by radiometric age dating.

The simple view of an early Scourian event separated from a later Laxfordian event by intrusion of the Scourie dyke swarm has now been considerably refined, particularly by the recognition of an event named the Inverian that postdates the granulite facies Scourian event and predates the Scourie dykes. A further factor is the recognition that several basement blocks with significantly different histories have been structurally assembled, and that events recorded within these blocks (e.g. the Northern, Central and Southern blocks of the mainland, and the Outer Isles) cannot necessarily be correlated between

the blocks. Modern methods of age dating (e.g. Sensitive High Resolution Ion Microprobe (SHRIMP) ages) are necessitating reinterpretations as recently presented by Friend & Kinny (2001). Considerable dating work is required before a modified interpretation of the whole region can be made. Park's account (Chapter 3) of these rocks illustrates the new interpretations, and the uncertainties that exist as a result of recent new age dates.

The Scourian gneisses are typically grey and banded with a tonalitic, trondhjemitic or granodioritic (TTG) composition. The grey gneisses are thought to represent deformed and metamorphosed plutonic rocks, but rare metasedimentary rocks are also present, and the basic enclaves may be fragments of ocean crust. In the Central Region the Scourian gneisses are of granulite-facies metamorphic grade. Protoliths of grey gneisses in the Central Region give isotopic ages of 2.96–3.03 Ga, and the granulite metamorphism is dated at 2.49–2.48 Ga (Badcallian). Granite protolith gneiss ages in the

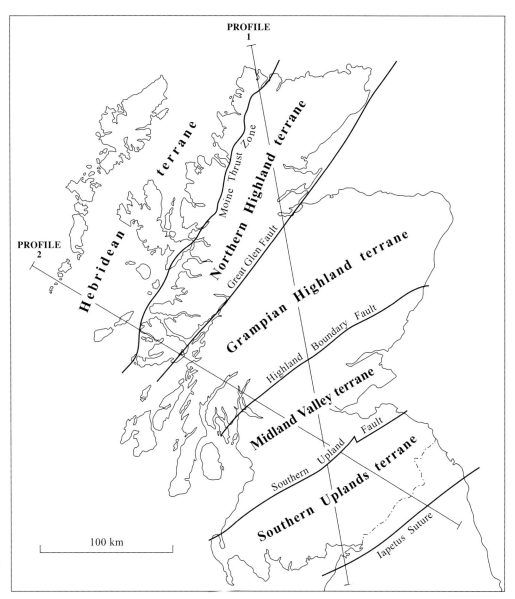

Fig. 1.3. Simplified map to show the major terranes of Scotland, together with the lines of profiles illustrated in Figs 1.10 and 1.11.

Northern (2.68–2.84 Ga) and TTG protolith ages in the Southern Regions (2.73–2.82 Ga) may indicate that there are three distinct crustal blocks in the area that were brought together in the Palaeoproterozoic.

The Inverian event postdates post-Badcallian pegmatites (2.48–2.49 Ga) and predates the earliest Scourie dykes (c. 2.42 Ga). The Inverian resulted in retrogression to amphibolite-facies, and the formation of extensive shear zones up to 4 km wide.

The Scourie dykes, dominantly quartz dolerites, were intruded over a considerable period, with the main swarm dated at c. 2.40 Ga and intruded at depths of 10–20 km. The lack of accurate dates for dyke swarms in all regions means that there is some doubt on correlation. There is no clear-cut break in events and 'Inverian' and 'Laxfordian' possibly overlap the earliest and latest of the Scourie dykes.

The Loch Maree Group of the Southern Region was deposited at c. 2.0 Ga and includes meta-greywackes, quartzite, marble, banded iron formation and amphibolite sheets. The environment is considered to have been marine and whilst the greywackes accumulated close to a continental source, the rare-earth chemistry of the amphibolites indicates an affinity with oceanic plateau lavas.

The term Laxfordian is generally applied to structures that modify the Scourie dykes. An early (D1/D2) phase was associated with amphibolite-grade metamorphism; this was followed by granite and pegmatite intrusion, and D3/D4 retrogression to greenschist-facies. The main, high-grade deformation took place at 1.63–1.86 Ga. Again it is likely that 'Laxfordian' events in the three regions have significantly different timing. Later ages of c. 1.1 Ga are Grenvillian, and the margin of the Grenville belt probably affected NW Scotland.

The Lewisian of the Outer Hebrides
Although the island of Lewis gave its name to the Lewisian Complex, most of our detailed knowledge comes from the Mainland area. In the Outer Isles, the traditional view has been that grey gneisses of the Scourian have been largely reworked by Laxfordian deformation. The Scourie dyke swarm, represented by amphibolite sheets, has fewer dykes than on the mainland, and they are greatly deformed. The dates of Scourian gneiss formation ranges from 2.75 to 3.12 Ga, and the gneisses resemble those of the Laxfordian Northern and Southern Regions of the Mainland. Recent work by Friend & Kinny (2001) suggests that the Outer Isles basement shows more affinities with the east coast of Greenland than with the Scottish mainland.

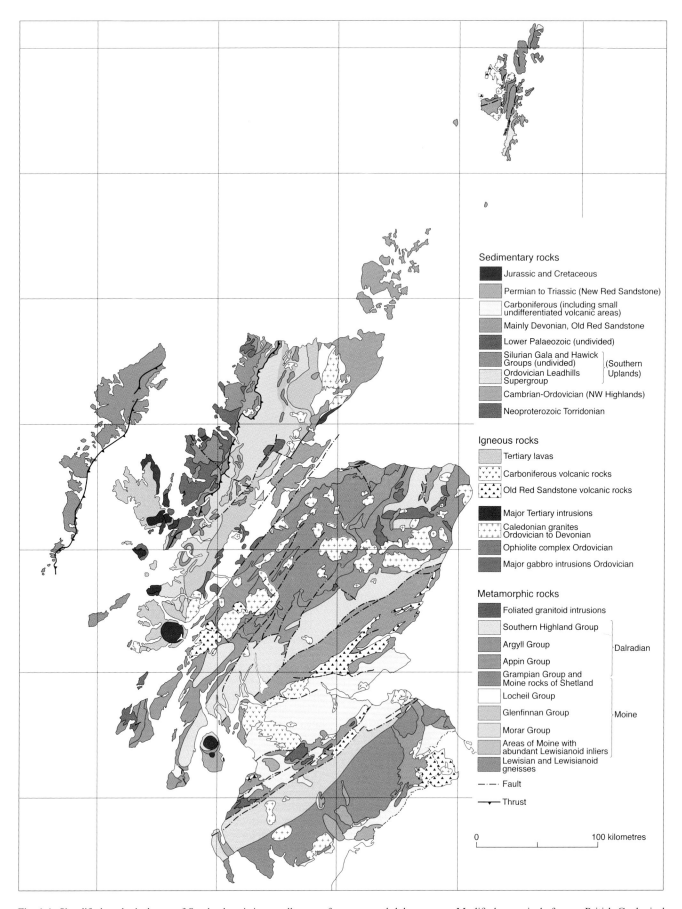

Fig. 1.4. Simplified geological map of Scotland omitting small areas of outcrop and dyke swarms. Modified extensively from a British Geological Survey original.

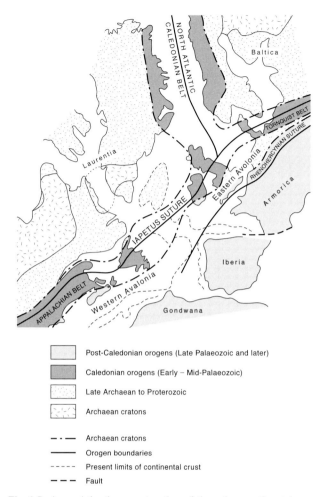

Fig. 1.5. A pre-Atlantic reconstruction of the palaeocontinental areas around Scotland. Modified from Woodcock & Strachan (2000).

Post-Scourian granites and supracrustal rocks including quartzites, marbles, graphitic shists, pelites and gneisses of sedimentary origin and meta-volcanic amphibolites make up a significant proportion of the outcrop area. The Corodale gneiss is a large granulite-facies meta-gabbro to meta-diorite that lies above the Outer Hebrides Fault and occupies most of South Uist.

The Inverian event in the Outer Isles saw the emplacement of 'late Scourian' intrusions that cut Scourian gneissose banding and are dated at $c.2.55$ Ga. They comprise a group of diorites, and a group of K-rich granites, monzonites and pegmatites; both groups show alkaline trends. They are best seen in Barra where they have escaped the most intense Laxfordian reworking.

The meta-sediments occur in the Leverburgh and Langavat belts of South Harris; no clear field relations are seen with the Scourian; lithologies are similar to those of the Loch Maree Group of the Mainland, but the ages do not agree. The South Harris Igneous Complex and the Ness Anorthosite are also of similar age.

Palaeoproterozoic events are widespread in the Outer Isles, strongly affecting most Scourian gneisses and dykes; deformation at $c.1.80$–1.90 Ga resulted in high pressure granulite-facies metamorphism. Temperatures of up to 950 °C affected the South Harris Igneous Complex and associated gneisses, with a more general metamorphic level of $c.$ 800 °C and 13–14 kbar. The late Laxfordian event imprinted amphibolite-facies metamorphism over most of the area and was associated with granite and pegmatite intrusion. Cooling temperatures

(hornblende) after the late Laxfordian event show a wide range of ages from 2.10–1.50 Ga in the south to 1.70–1.60 Ga in the north. In some areas biotite closure ages as young as 1.15 Ga possibly indicate Grenvillian tectonic activity.

The Outer Hebrides Fault Zone (Fig. 1.4) trends NNE–SSW and dips at 20–30° ESE beneath the Minch. Ductile thrusting north of the Langavat belt may have a Grenvillian age, and brittle thrust movements are possibly synchronous with the Moine Thrust Zone of the mainland. Strike-slip movement probably resulted from late Caledonian events, and in the Early Mesozoic it was reactivated as an extensional fault bounding the Hebrides Mesozoic basins.

The Torridonian sandstones
Lying unconformably upon an irregular Lewisian erosion surface with up to 300 m of relief, the Torridonian red arkosic sandstones form spectacular mountain scenery in NW Scotland (Chapter 3). Precise direct dating is difficult but the age must lie between the metamorphic and cooling ages of the basement gneiss ($c.1.9$–1.1 Ga) and the Lower Cambrian ($c.540$ Ma) that unconformably overlies tilted Torridonian. A Pb–Pb age of $c.1.2$ Ga from the Stoer Group of the Torridonian, and dates in the range of $c.950$–1000 Ma from the Torridonian Group indicate periodic deposition over a span of $c.250$ Ma. The Torridonian is considerably more extensive than outcrops reveal, the subcrop extends west to the Minch Fault, and for 125 km SW of Rum. Blocks occur in Tertiary igneous rocks on Canna and Eigg.

These sandstones, up to 6 km thick in places, were deposited in continental rifts or on forelands of the continent Rodinia, near the Grenville orogenic belt and prior to the opening of the Iapetus Ocean. A passive continental margin possibly lay to the east, but it is concealed beneath the Moine. The Stoer Group (to 2 km) forms the oldest part of the Torridonian and is unconformably overlain by the Torridon Group (to 5 km). In Skye the Sleat Group (3 km) conformably underlies the Torridon Group.

The Stoer Group comprises a variety of conglomeratic, sandy and muddy facies. Locally derived breccias mantle the irregular Scourian gneiss surface. Breccias may pass laterally into muddy sandstones with evidence of desiccation. Conglomerates tens of metres thick form fining-up sequences, generally trough cross-bedded, and representing shallow braided channel deposits. Deposits of aeolian dunes, and of temporary lakes are also present. Reversal of current directions probably reflects fault controlled tilting within a rift-valley situation.

The Sleat Group comprises some 3 km of grey sandstones and shales that are within the Kishorn nappe. They may have formed in a separate rift, since they are nowhere in contact with the Stoer Group, and conformably underlie the Torridon Group. Originally the Sleat Group was probably red in colour, but low grade metamorphism has changed the colour by conversion of haematite to magnetite; green colours are due to chlorite and epidote. Again topographic relief of the unconformity surface is evident, and a variety of fluvial, alluvial fan and lacustrine facies are recognised. There is a possibility that marine deposition may have taken place.

The Torridon Group carries a different clast assemblage from the Sleat Group, indicating changes in source and drainage. Around Loch Maree the basal unconformity relief is up to 600 m but declines to 100 m near Cape Wrath where ancient weathering profiles are preserved beneath the unconformity. Facies are again dominated by fluvial deposits that were deposited on eastward-sloping fans or bajada derived from the present position of the Outer Hebrides.

The Torridonian is considered to have been deposited at a latitude of about 10° based on palaeomagnetic data.

Post-Caledonian orogens (Late Palaeozoic and later)

Caledonian orogens (Early – Mid-Palaeozoic)

Late Archaean to Proterozoic

Archaean cratons

— · — Archaean cratons

——— Orogen boundaries

- - - - - Present limits of continental crust

— — — Fault

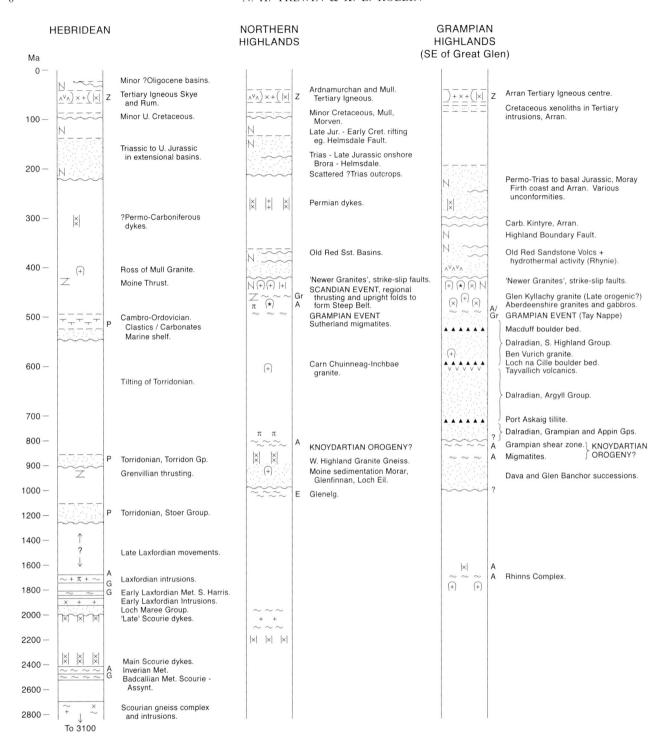

Fig. 1.6. Table of geological events in the terranes of Scotland. Modified from Harris (1991) by Bluck, Oliver, Park, Strachan and Trewin.

Mudstones with similarities to vertisols are present, indicating by modern comparisons, latitudes of 10–30° and seasonal rainfall of 300–1200 mm with summer drought. The abundance of detrital plagioclase is consistent with these conditions.

Formation within a rift lying between the Minch Fault in the west and normal faults in the east; later reactivated as the Moine Thrust Zone is favoured by Stewart (Chapter 3). Palaeocurrents are largely orthogonal to the postulated bounding faults. There are similarities in facies and age with Laurentian rift basins of Canada. An alternative view of the Torridon Group sees it as deposited by large braid-plain rivers originating in Canada and carrying sediment eroded from the Grenville orogenic belt (see Chapter 7)

The Cambro-Ordovician shelf deposits

The clastic and carbonate rocks of the Cambro-Ordovician (Chapter 3) rest unconformably on Torridonian and Lewisian, and are intensely involved in the imbricate structures of the Moine Thrust Zone. The outcrop extends 250 km from the north coast to Sleat in Skye; the conformable succession ranges in age from Early Cambrian to Llanvirin, and is well exposed in the Durness area. This would appear to support a Late Arenig–Llanvirn age for the Grampian Orogeny that brought an end to this lengthy period of shelf sedimentation.

The succession is dominated by clastic rocks in the lower part (Eriboll Group), with carbonates (Durness Group) above. This marine shelf sequence with a thickness of about 1000 m

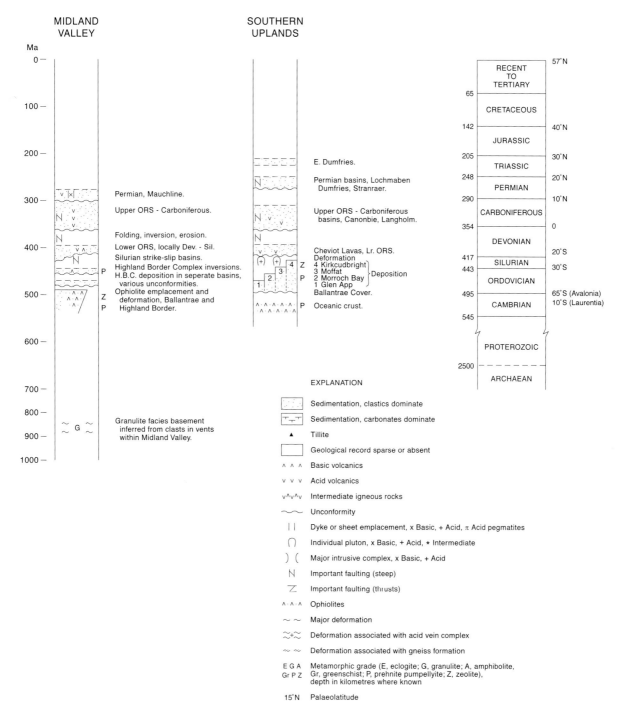

Fig. 1.6. (*continued*).

accumulated on the passive Laurentian (northern) margin of the Iapetus Ocean. The succession was eventually disrupted by the thrusting of metamorphic rocks over the succession during Caledonian deformation following the closure of the Iapetus Ocean.

The Eriboll Group commences with the Basal Quartzitic Member. A thin conglomerate overlies the surface of marine planation, and passes up into cross-bedded quartzite of tidal and shoreface origin. The succeeding Pipe Rock Member is characterized by abundant *Skolithos* burrows, and provides an excellent example of the classic *Skolithos* ichnofacies of the Early Palaeozoic. Water depth gradually increased on the shelf in the NW Highlands as transgression proceeded further into

Laurentia, and the Pipe Rock is succeeded by the Fucoid Beds and Saltarella Grit of the An-t-Sron Formation. The Fucoid beds are dolomitic siltstones with abundant sub-horizontal burrows and the trilobite *Olenellus* that provides an Early Cambrian age, and a strong link with North American faunas. The lithologies and faunas of the Eriboll Formation correlate closely with successions in western Newfoundland, eastern Greenland and Spitzbergen, indicating the wide geographical extent of the marine transgression.

The Durness Group carbonates are mainly dolostones with intervals of limestone, chert is frequently present. These shelf carbonates were deposited in a variety of shallow marine environments with oolite shoals, stromatolites and intraclast breccias. Early dolomitization probably destroyed much fossil material, but some units retain cephalopods and sponges, and bioturbation is common, with burrows preferentially replaced by dolomite.

The tropical equatorial climate, stable shelf situation, and apparent low run-off from land favoured the development of the carbonate shelf. Microbial activity was high giving frequent stromatolites and thrombolites. Lagoonal and sabkha environments with pseudomorphed evaporites are also recognized. It is likely that deposition was not continuous from Lower Cambrian at the base of the carbonates to Late Arenig to Early Llanvirn (based on conodonts) at the top of the succession, and it has been proposed that time gaps may be present in the sequence. Middle and Late Cambrian faunas have not been recognized, but barren strata 200 m thick may cover this time interval, thus there is no accepted evidence for a major break in the sequence.

Northern Highland and Grampian Highland terranes

Northern Highlands
Between the Moine Thrust Zone and the Great Glen Fault, the Caledonian metamorphic rocks of the Moine Supergroup dominate the geology. Inliers of late Archaean orthogneiss dated at c. 2.9 Ga (Friend et al. 2002b) represent basement on which Moine Supergroup sediments were deposited at c. 1000–900 Ma. The Supergroup is divided into the Morar, Glenfinnan and Loch Eil groups that were deposited as sands, silts and muds, under shallow marine conditions. Deposition is inferred to have taken place in NNE–SSW trending extensional half-grabens faulted at their western margins. This is reflected in westward thickening of the sedimentary sequences. The groups are distinguished on differing proportions of sand and mud, now psammite and pelite. The psammitic Morar Group is considered to be the western proximal equivalent of the more pelitic Glenfinnan Group, and the Loch Eil Group probably accumulated in a separate half-graben. Subsequent deformation has dismembered the original grabens so that the preserved sections of the graben fills now lie between westerly directed thrusts (e.g. Moine and Sgurr Beag thrusts).

The Moine sediments do not seem to have been derived from the Lewisian, since detrital zircons give ages of c.1900–1000 Ma. Palaeocurrents imply a southerly source. This is consistent with the recognition of a crustal discontinuity some 15 km east of the Moine Thrust Zone which possibly represents the eastern limit of the exposed Lewisian. The Moine sediments were possibly derived from a more easterly block than the exposed Lewisian. On the question of the possible equivalence in age of the Moine and Torridonian it can be noted that the Stoer Group is older than the Moine. Whilst the Torridon Group and the Moine may be of similar age, differences in dates of detrital zircons in the two successions may indicate deposition in separate basins.

Metamorphism of the Moine is polyphase representing three main orogenic events. The first, Knoydartian, is dated at c. 820–870 Ma and is associated with amphibolite-facies metamorphism and pegmatite intrusions. In the southwest Morar Group temperatures reached c. 700°C and pressures of up to 14 kbar (Vance et al. 1998), conditions consistent with crustal thickening. The second event to affect the area is the Grampian orogenic event in the Mid-Ordovician. This affected both Grampian and Highland areas and so the Great Glen Fault does not appear to have separated fundamentally different crustal blocks, but provides a convenient geographical subdivision. In the third, Scandian event, of Silurian age thrusting took place under high grade metamorphic conditions, and the thrusts are represented by thick (hundreds of metres) mylonites. The region is divided by the Sgurr Beag thrust into the Moine and Sgurr Beag–Naver nappes. Movement on the Moine Thrust was tens of km and intense recumbent folding of the Moine resulted. More than one period of movement created polyphase folding with early recumbent folds deformed by upright folds of the north Highland steep belt. In an alternative view (Chapter 7), the Sgurr Beagg Thrust is considered to be an important regional boundary separating the Morar from the Glenfinnan and Loch Eil groups, such that the latter two groups are the debris derived from the Knoydartian orogeny.

Grampian Highlands
To the SE of the Great Glen Fault in the Grampian Highlands the metamorphic Dalradian Supergroup is dominant, but exceptions are the Dava and Glen Banchor successions south of Inverness. These resemble parts of the Moine, contain detrital zircons with ages similar to those in the Moine, and also underwent a metamorphic event at c. 840 Ma (Noble et al. 1998). They are overlain by Dalradian strata, possibly unconformably, but shearing makes interpretation uncertain.

The Dalradian Supergroup comprises the Grampian, Appin, Argyll and Southern Highland groups; the total thickness is quoted at 25 km, but this does not represent sediment thickness at one place but migration of depocentres during basin fill. Whilst the Dalradian groups are defined on lithostratigraphy, the presence of boulder beds of glacial origin (Port Askaig Tillite, Loch na Cille Boulder Bed) that can be widely traced implies a measure of chronostratigraphic control due to climatic variation.

Much of the Supergroup is of Sturtian to Vendian age. The Port Askaig Tillite is considered to be Sturtian c. 720–760 Ma (Brasier & Shields 2000; Dempster et al. 2002), thus the base of the Supergroup may date to c. 800 Ma, and the sediment could represent debris of the Knoydartian Orogeny. The Tayvallich Volcanics in the Argyll Group date to 600 Ma, and if the Leny Limestone is included in the Dalradian the top is younger than Early Cambrian (509 Ma). An absolute top limit is provided by dates of c. 470 Ma on basic intrusions of NE Scotland that metamorphose the Southern Highland Group.

The sedimentation history of the Dalradian begins with rifting and basin deepening as Grampian Group sediments commence with shallow marine deposition, but pass rapidly up into turbidites of deep basinal facies. Progressive shallowing is then recorded culminating in psammites of nearshore, possibly tidal origin.

The succeeding groups of the Dalradian display a wide variety of facies, controlled by basin faulting to create accommodation space, and by sediment supply. Phases of rapid subsidence (and/or sea level rise) resulted in anoxic basin deposits (e.g. Ballachulish and Cuil Bay Slates of Appin Group) and turbidite fills (e.g. Easdale Slates of Argyll Group; Macduff Slates of Southern Highland Group). At times when supply matched subsidence thick tidal shelf quartzites accumulated (e.g. Jura Quartzite of the Argyll Group). Tidal flats are also represented by limestones and dolomites, some of which are stromatolitic.

The Tayvallich Group includes up to 3 km of volcanics. Basaltic pillow lavas, tuffs and deep water turbidites and shales are associated with sills and dykes intruded into wet sediment. The igneous activity is associated with a possible pull-apart basin associated with the NW–SE Cruachan Lineament. The repeated rifting and extension associated with Dalradian sedimentation probably led to continental breakup and the formation of the Iapetus Ocean.

The glacial Port Askaig Tillite has been variously interpreted as a result of grounded ice, or floating ice. The Loch na Cille

Boulder Bed in the lower part of the Southern Highland Group (Fig. 1.6) is probably equivalent to the c. 590 Ma younger Varanger Tillite of Norway. Situated close to the top of the Southern Highland Group, the Macduff Boulder Bed is clearly a glacial dropstone deposit and may date to 560–570 Ma (see Brasier & Shields 2000). A younger Late Cambrian or Early Ordovician age is possible for the Macduff Slates (Chapter 4), but cannot be correlated with any known glaciation affecting the region at that time.

During the Grampian orogenic event the Dalradian was folded on NE–SW lines into large tight to isoclinal folds that form a fold fan; folds facing NW in the NW, and SE in the SE. A large area of the SE side is occupied by the Tay Nappe, in which much of the succession is inverted. Secondary upright folds, also NE–SW, refolded the earlier structures. Later deformation, particularly in the form of shear zones affects NE Scotland. The classic work of Barrow (1893) on metamorphic zonal index minerals was perfomed in the Dalradian. The peak of metamorphism is dated by Sm–Nd on garnets at 470 Ma (Oliver et al. 2000; Baxter et al. 2002). Metamorphic grade is highly variable, but large areas have been uplifted 25–35 km. However, metamorphic grade is relatively low in the Southern Highland Group in the southwest of the Grampian Highland terrane, and in the Macduff Slates. Understanding the structures controlling exhumation of the Highlands is the key to explaining the post-Caledonian history of the region.

The 'basic masses' (e.g. Huntly, Insch, Portsoy) of NE Scotland are gabbros, frequently with igneous layering, and were intruded under peak metamorphic conditions at about 470 Ma; contact metamorphism producing classic metamorphic aureoles and partial melting of country rock. The 'Older Granites', such as the Aberdeen granite, were also intruded at this time. Uplift and cooling from 470–400 Ma is indicated by Rb–Sr and K–Ar biotite ages.

The cause of the Grampian event is discussed in Chapters 4 and 7, but a possibility is the collision of the margin of Laurentia with a volcanic arc that was partly obducted onto the continent. Ophiolites in Shetland (Unst) and the Midland Valley (Ballantrae; Highland Border Complex) may be remnants of this arc. The apparent absence of a Scandian event in the area may indicate that this region was located to the south of the collision zone.

'Newer Granites' suite

Following the Grampian orogeny the Northern Highland and Grampian terranes had differing histories. In the Grampian area uplift and cooling followed the orogeny and the intrusion of the 'Older Granites'. In the Highlands the Scandian orogeny (c. 435–425 Ma) produced intense deformation and amphibolite facies metamorphism. The 'Newer Granites' of Read (1961) date from c. 425–400 Ma, straddling the Silurian–Devonian boundary, and were intruded into both the Northern Highlands and Grampian Highlands. Rapid uplift and erosion followed and they were unroofed prior to deposition of the Lower ORS. Granite intrusion was contemporaneous with volcanic activity (e.g. Glencoe), resulting in the lavas of the Lower ORS. Geochemically the granites are calc-alkaline I-type granites typical of continental arcs. They can be divided into three suites: Argyll and Northern Highland, Cairngorm, and South Grampian on the basis of isotopic and chemical characters (Chapter 4). Intrusion of the granites was in part controlled by deep crustal features, with the result that the granites are situated along faults or lineaments (Fig. 1.4, and see geophysical evidence below). The 'Newer Granites' are considered to have formed above a subduction zone that plunged beneath the margin of Laurentia.

Midland Valley terrane

Exposure of pre-Old Red Sandstone strata in the Midland Valley is poor, and concentrated mainly along the southern and northern margins. There is considerable scope for speculation on this important area lying between the clearly subduction-related rocks of the Southern Uplands and the metamorphic Grampian Highland terrane to the NW of the Highland Boundary Fault. Whilst the Midland Valley now has a rift-like form, it is clear that it was not a simple rift in Early Palaeozoic times.

Along the northern margin the Highland Border Complex forms a narrow outcrop parallel to the Highland Boundary Fault. There is debate on the relationship of the Highland Border Series to the Dalradian, with arguments for a faulted or a conformable contact. Bluck (Chapter 5) presents evidence from faunas in the Highland Border Series and from cooling ages in the Dalradian that the two have geological histories that are incompatible, indicating that they were not adjacent in the Ordovician. However, in Chapter 7 Oliver favours the interpretation that they were adjacent from the Caradoc onwards.

The Highland Border Series contains pillow lavas, serpentinites, gabbros and conglomerates with trondhjemite and diorite boulders, suggesting remnants of a fragmented ophiolite. The oldest 'assemblage' (Chapter 5) comprises the c. 540 Ma Bute amphibolite and the Early Cambrian Leny Limestone. However Oliver (Chapter 7) prefers the evidence that places the Leny Limestone within the Southern Highland Group of the Dalradian. Ophiolite obduction appears to have taken place before the Mid-Arenig. The Arenig Dounans Limestone of the Aberfoyle area contains a shelly Laurentian fauna and is in tectonic contact with ophiolitic rocks. Higher in the sequence black shales and pillow lavas rest unconformably on the older rocks and are thought to be Llanvirn–Ashgill in age. The youngest rocks are arenites and carbonates, the arenites contain ophiolitic debris, and also metamorphic and acid plutonic clasts. Detrital garnets in the arenites are of Barrovian type and might have been derived from the Grampian Highland terrane. The Complex appears to have been an eroded low relief area prior to deposition of the Wenlockian Cowie Formation of the Old Red Sandstone at Stonehaven.

The Highland Boundary Complex consists of structurally fragmented blocks with differing histories brought together along major faults. Unconformities at different levels within the sequences indicate that several phases of movement took place over a long period of time. The basin(s) in which the Complex accumulated received sediment in the Ordovician, at a time when the Dalradian metamorphic block was cooling during uplift.

The best outcrops of the southern margin of the Midland Valley are those of the Girvan area where the post-Arenig Ordovician sequence rests unconformably on the eroded ophiolitic Ballantrae Complex. Three basins, controlled by contemporaneous faulting, contain conglomerates that fine to the SE into thick greywacke sequences. On fault controlled topographic highs shallow water clastics and fossiliferous limestones (e.g. Craighead Limestone) accumulated. The basin fills became progressively younger to the NW. The Ordovician faunas of the Girvan succession show strong Laurentian affinities, but this provinciality decreases up the succession as the Iapetus Ocean was progressively eliminated.

Silurian outcrops in the Midland Valley are more extensive than those of the Ordovician, stretching from Girvan in the SW to the Pentland Hills in the NE. In these two areas the Old Red Sandstone unconformably overlies Silurian, but in other Silurian inliers (e.g. Lesmahagow) there is an upward transition from marine to continental sedimentation near the base of the Wenlock. The Silurian inliers contain remarkable arthropod and fish faunas, particularly in the strata of the marine to non-marine transition. Old Red Sandstone facies of the Stonehaven area extends down as far as Wenlock, thus there is a record of shallowing and environmental change that eliminates marine deposition from the basins of the Midland Valley.

The derivation of the sediment that fills the basins of the Midland Valley provides valuable clues for palaeogeographic reconstruction. Detailed work reveals that clasts in conglomerates, derived from the south, cannot be matched in the adjacent Southern Uplands, and it is likely that the various basins have been assembled to their present positions along strike-slip faults. This view is strengthened by the presence of abundant granitic clasts derived from the south in the Old Red Sandstone of the Stonehaven succession, indicating 'hidden' source areas within the Midland Valley.

Xenoliths derived from lamprophyre dykes indicate that by the Early Devonian there was continental crust beneath the Midland Valley. Views differ as to whether this was Laurentian crust onto which the Southern Uplands rocks had been thrust, or part of the underthrust northern margin of Avalonia.

The Midland Valley contains remnants of ocean crust rocks, 'hidden' source areas, and evidence of long continued intermittent volcanic activity from the Ordovician to the Carboniferous, and extreme contraction in width. The terrane was a region of extensive strike-slip tectonics in the Palaeozoic. By Devonian times, continental crust was emplaced beneath the Midland Valley, and the Southern Uplands, Midland Valley and Grampian Highland terranes were assembled in essentially the same position we find them today.

The Southern Uplands terrane and Ballantrae Complex

The Southern Upland terrane (Chapter 6) is bounded to the south by the presumed trace of the Iapetus suture, the line of closure of the Iapetus Ocean following collision between Laurentia and Avalonia (Fig. 1.3). Unfortunately the junction is buried beneath younger rocks and cannot be directly observed. To the north the terrane is separated from the Midland Valley and the ophiolitic Ballantrae Complex by the Southern Upland Fault.

Ordovician and Silurian greywackes and shales form the bulk of exposure in the Southern Uplands. The dip is steep, and the area is cut by NE–SW strike-parallel faults that divide the region into structural tracts. One of the fundamental observations that has dominated discussion of the area is the sedimentological evidence that the beds generally young to the NW, but biostratigraphic zonation based on graptolites indicates that the youngest strata are in the SE of the area. It is the tract-bounding faults that hold the key to this apparent paradox; the region is interpreted as an imbricate thrust belt in which the original thrust faults have been rotated into a near-vertical orientation.

There is continued speculation on the origin of the thrust belt. One hypothesis is that it represents an accretionary prism that developed at the margin of Laurentia as northward subduction closed the Iapetus Ocean. In this model the imbricate thrust system developed as slices of the sedimentary pile were sheared from the descending ocean plate and thrust beneath similar slices to form the accretionary stack.

A second model proposes that the sequence was initiated in a back-arc basin. This model accounts for derivation of andesitic material into the basin from the south. Collision of Avalonia with the volcanic arc is envisaged to have caused compression in the back-arc basin. Eventually the arc remnant was thrust beneath Laurentia and the thrust stack, and then developed as a foreland basin fold and thrust complex at the southern margin of Laurentia. A third model proposes that the Southern Uplands represent a rifted continental margin.

It is likely that there is no 'correct' answer. If a volcanic arc was discontinuous, elements of the first two models could be regarded as correct. We only have preserved a small, and not necessarily typical, section of the ancient continental margin from which to gather and interpret evidence. However, the detailed study of biostratigraphy, and provenance studies in the greywackes provide evidence that has to be incorporated in any proposed model.

The Ballantrae Complex and its associated Lower Palaeozoic cover sequence in Ayrshire have been the subject of detailed study for many decades, and the resulting literature is voluminous. The unusual and diverse igneous rocks of the complex are the greatly dissected remains of part of an ophiolite, originating as ocean crust. Thus this fragmented ophiolite is considered to have been obducted onto the Laurentian margin. The ophiolite had been emplaced and eroded by Late Llanvirn, and the lavas within the complex appear to range in age from Late Cambrian to Mid-Arenig.

The lavas are dominated by island-arc and ocean-island tholeites, and are associated with abundant volcanogenic sediments together with cherts, black shales, conglomerates and breccias. Evidence such as hyalotuff deltas and rounded clasts indicate a shallow water origin for lava sequences up to 2 km thick, implying accumulation during subsidence.

Blocks of garnet pyroxenite within a mélange in the complex were obducted from great depth, possibly up to 60 km. Other blocks, including gabbros, trondhjemites, serpentinites and blueschist were being eroded and incorporated in olistostromes by the Late Arenig, indicating that rocks from a great variety of depths and metamorphic conditions had been obducted into juxtaposition probably within the 15 Ma of Arenig time.

The great variety of oceanic rocks may have been brought together as a series of slivers in a strike-slip regime. Three phases of accretion and uplift are recognized; at c. 576 Ma, at c. 505 Ma in the Late Cambrian, and in Late Arenig and pre-Late Llanvirn. Repeated tectonism is implied by the presence of igneous rocks at different depths and with different histories. The fragments that comprise the Ballantrae Complex are interpreted as parts of a disrupted marginal basin with associated arcs similar to the present-day western Pacific.

The sedimentary cover to the Ballantrae Complex consists of a series of Llanvirn to Caradoc conglomerates that progressively transgressed northwards. The conglomerates are channelled into underlying rocks that comprise sequences of shallow water limestones and conglomerates that grade up into deeper water sandstones and shales. Sediment supply also came from the north with Caradocian fan complexes prograding SE, possibly fed by rivers originating in the Grampian Highland terrane. Llandovery conglomerates with marine sandstone and shale rest unconformably on the Ordovician and contain abundant Barrovian-type metamorphic detritus. Normal fault control is evident in their distribution, probably representing reactivation of earlier Ordovician faults.

The faunas of the cover sequences record a wide variety of environments from shallow carbonate shelves to deep marine situations. In particular the shelly shelf faunas of the Caradoc show strong similarities to North America faunas and have little relation to Anglo-Welsh faunas, leading to the conclusion that a significant Iapetus Ocean still existed in the Caradoc.

The post-Caledonian history

The Old Red Sandstone

As the Caledonian mountains were eroded and the Iapetus Ocean was finally eliminated, the Scottish part of the Old Red Sandstone continent was created. Scotland drifted north from about 30°S to 20°S of the equator during the Devonian, and frequently experienced semi-arid conditions. At the start there was little life on land, but by the start of the Carboniferous lowland forests with complex ecosystems were well established. This was a period of great change!

'Old Red Sandstone' is retained in preference to 'Devonian' as the title for this chapter in acknowledgement of the problems involved in fixing the base or top of the Devonian in the Scottish successions. Thus ORS facies extend down into the Silurian, probably as far as Wenlock in the Stonehaven Basin, and successions in the Midland Valley, as at Lesmahagow, show an upward gradation in the Silurian from marine to red-bed deposition. The transition from marine to non-marine strata took place at different times in different areas as individual basins became isolated from marine influence. With the closure of Iapetus the oblique convergence and docking of the continental blocks resulted in considerable local re-organization of blocks, faulting, and consequent changes in patterns of erosion and deposition. These events are most evident in the successions of the Midland Valley where basement source areas that are now hidden, shed sediment northwards onto the Grampian Highland terrane. Much of this material was later reworked back in to the ORS of the Midland Valley, along with debris from the Grampians.

From Wenlock to Emsian times ORS facies, dominantly of fluvial, alluvial and lacustrine origin, accumulated in the Midland Valley area and spilled north and south onto the adjacent terranes. The main drainage was axial with large rivers flowing to the southwest. Structural activity resulted in several phases of basin creation, as for example in the NE of the Midland Valley where the Stonehaven, Crawton and Strathmore basins are now recognized as successively younger structures. To the north of the Midland Valley deposition commenced in the Lorne area in Late Silurian, at Rhynie in the Pragian, and further north in Caithness and Orkney probably in the Emsian.

Extensive subduction-related andesitic volcanic activity characterizes the Lower ORS (the Midland Valley and Lorne areas), and minor volcanics occur at Rhynie, and andesitic clasts are present in the Lower ORS of Caithness. Granites connected with the andesitic volcanicity have Silurian to Early Devonian cooling ages. At least some of these granites were unroofed in the Early Devonian as evidenced by ?Emsian overlying the eroded Helmsdale granite (c. 420 Ma). The granites of Deeside were probably exposed, with uplift creating an E–W watershed between the Midland Valley and Orcadian Basin.

A major change is seen above Emsian strata. In the Midland Valley, Southern Uplands and to the north of the HBF in the west there is a major unconformity with no strata of Mid-Devonian or Frasnian age. During this time the Midland Valley underwent compression and Lower ORS sediments were folded (e.g. Strathmore Syncline), uplifted and eroded.

Deposition of Middle ORS took place within faulted basins forming part of the Orcadian Basin (s.l.). In basin margin areas there is a marked unconformity between Middle and Lower ORS, accompanied by a change in clast composition (e.g. Turriff Basin and eastern Caithness) but in basin central areas deposition may have been continuous from Emsian into the Mid-Devonian.

The most remarkable feature of the Orcadian Basin is the development of cyclic lacustrine deposits representing environments ranging from deep lake to exposed playa. The deep lake deposits consist of organic-rich laminites, and some beds (e.g. the Achanarras and John o'Groats fish beds) contain distinctive fish faunas allowing widespread correlation. The cyclicity is postulated to have a Milankovitch control, but precise assignment of cycle durations is still a matter for debate.

Evidence of volcanicity in the Middle ORS is absent in the south of the Orcadian Basin, but there are minor volcanics associated with the Eday Group in Orkney. In Shetland there was extensive volcanic activity accompanied by granite intrusion which affects Middle ORS strata and is Eifelian–Givetian in age.

The traditional use of the term Upper ORS is easily followed in Central and Southern Scotland where a marked unconformity is present at the base. The fluvial and aeolian Upper ORS passes conformably up into the Carboniferous and ORS facies rocks with abundant caliche are now assigned to the basal Carboniferous (Kinnesswood Formation).

Within the Orcadian Basin area Upper ORS is recognized south of the Moray Firth in the Elgin area, in Easter Ross, and to the north as the Hoy and Dunnet sandstones. In previous editions of this volume the Upper ORS is interpreted to be unconformable on Middle ORS or older strata. This relationship is seen on Hoy in Orkney. However, palynological evidence, together with seismic data and well logs indicate that the Upper ORS is, in general, conformable with Middle ORS in basinal areas. The instances where unconformity can be demonstrated being ascribed to erosion following footwall uplift at the margins of faulted basins. Combining evidence from the Midland Valley and Orcadian areas, Upper ORS facies of fluvial and aeolian sandstones appear to extend from Late Givetian to the base of the Carboniferous without any recognized break, a period of some 20 Ma.

Carboniferous

As noted above, the Devonian–Carboniferous boundary cannot be accurately fixed in Scotland because generally unfossiliferous red-bed facies of the Upper ORS spans the boundary of the two periods. In the Midland Valley the base of the Carboniferous is taken at the incoming of abundant calcretes in the Kinnesswood Formation.

The northward movement of Scotland continued in the Carboniferous during which time it crossed the equatorial belt from south to north. Thus the Carboniferous (Chapter 9) commences with red-bed deposition, followed by deposits of the wet equatorial belt characterized by marine limestones with abundant corals in areas away from clastic supply, and by richly vegetated delta tops and thick shale-rich successions in areas of major clastic input. At the end of the Carboniferous, Scotland lay north of the equator and entered the northern arid belt, heralding a return to red-bed deposition of the New Red Sandstone. Undoubtedly the uplift and erosion of the Variscan mountains to the south also affected climate, the mountains possibly blocking monsoonal southerly winds and leaving Scotland in a rain shadow.

There have been several interpretations of the plate tectonic setting in the Carboniferous, many with radical differences! In the south the destructive boundary lay between the eastern Avalonian and Armorican microplates. As the Variscan orogenic belt developed with its northern margin lying E–W through Southern Eire and England, the European–Baltica block was pushed against Greenland to the NW. The area north of the Variscan front seems generally to have been in tension, resulting in syn-sedimentary faulted basins, of which those of the Midland Valley of Scotland dominate the account given here. However, stress fields changed several times during the Carboniferous, probably as a result of interaction of the various crustal blocks. Thus basins, faults and folds have several orientations produced in response to the changing stress fields. During the Carboniferous folding moved steadily northwards in response to the progressive development of the Variscides in the south.

A major result of the reorganization of the continental blocks, possibly associated with thinned crust north of the Variscides, was the establishment of major intra-plate volcanicity following a generally quiet period of some 50 Ma since Early Devonian. Particularly active volcanism affected the Midland Valley in the Viséan and continued intermittently for about 100 Ma into the Permian. The intraplate magmas were mostly transitional to highly alkaline, and silica-undersaturated in character, but in the Stephanian a widespread episode of tholeiitic basalt intrusion took place. The Carboniferous volcanism produced some spectacular features in the Midland Valley such as the Clyde Plateau Lavas, and the dissected volcano of Arthur's Seat in Edinburgh. Numerous hills in the region owe their scarp features to intrusions such as the Midland Valley Sill, and prominent peaks such as East and West Lomond are formed of resistant igneous rocks in volcanic vents.

There is a vast quantity of stratigraphic data available on the Carboniferous, particularly in the coal basins of the Midland Valley where extensive mining and exploration has taken place. Read *et al.* (Chapter 9) provide the reader with a general background to the stratigraphy as a basis for an account that focuses on palaeoenvironments, palaeogeography, the influence of structural activity on the sedimentary succession and volcanicity. Those seeking stratigraphic detail are referred to the sheet memoirs and reports of the British Geological Survey.

In Chapter 9 the Carboniferous has been divided into three sections. The first section takes the reader from the base of the Carboniferous up to the Mid-Brigantian Hurlet Limestone which represents the first widespread marine transgression in the Midland Valley. The red fluvial sandstones and calcrete palaeosols of the Kinesswood Formation are succeeded by the Ballagan Formation dominated by grey mudstones and siltstones with fluvial sandstones. The finer-grained lithologies were deposited in lakes and marginal marine flats. The introduction of saline water resulting in deposition of evaporites.

The succeeding Viséan strata are dominated in the west of the Midland Valley by the thick lavas of the Clyde Volcanic Formation. Eruptions came from small shield volcanoes and possibly from fissures. Large strata volcanoes may also have developed to form features such as the 8 km wide Misty Law trachytic centre in the SW of the Clyde Plateau Lavas outcrop. In the Lothian region the Arthur's Seat volcano was probably 5 km across and rose 1000 m above the surrounding forests on the alluvial plain. The volcanics of Arthur's Seat and the Garleton Hills are succeeded by shales and sandstones of the Gullane Formation. Fluvial cycles are present, together with occasional coals and marine bands. The overlying West Lothian Oil-shale Formation with its thin developments of oil-shale was mainly formed under lacustrine conditions, but there is evidence for periodic marine influence. The basins in which the oil-shales and associated strata accumulated clearly had a periodic, but tenuous, connection to marine conditions resulting in some unusual palaeontological features such as the famous 'shrimp beds' and the first record of the conodont animal. At East Kirkton, lake deposits, probably associated with hydrothermal activity have yielded a rich biota, including the proto-reptile *Westlothiana* ('Lizzie').

Major thickness and facies changes in the Viséan of the Midland Valley reflect activity on NE–SW faults of general 'Caledonoid' trend. Thus basins also tend to have a similar trend. Areas with contemporaneous lavas, and sites of Devonian volcanic activity tended to act as relatively high areas with respect to the basins.

The second sub-division of the Carboniferous ranges from Late Brigantian (Hurlet Limestone marine band) through the Namurian to the base of the Lower Coal Measures. The formations recognized can be traced throughout the Midland Valley on the basis of the marine bands, representing sea level highs or 'maximum flooding surfaces' of sequence stratigraphic nomenclature. Sedimentation became more uniform throughout the Midland Valley and correlation can be made more easily with the Scottish Borders and England. A new stress regime was initiated and new basins such as the Kincardine Basin formed, whilst those active in the Early Carboniferous ceased to subside and became positive areas. Volcanicity continued, but generally in new localities, particularly on new structural highs and at basin margins.

The most striking feature of the Lower Limestone formations is the spectacular cyclicity of the sediments; the major marine transgressions are marked by shale or limestone marine bands that can be traced into England and Europe. Following marine deposition each cycle coarsens up through shales and sandstones to be capped by coal and palaeosols. These are prograding fluvio-deltaic deposits filling the accommodation space created by sea level rise. The extensive nature of the marine bands attests to the low gradients of the deltaic plain. Lowstands of the sea resulted in the erosion of incised valleys that became filled with thick fluvial sandstones as base-level rose. Interfluvial areas were exposed for long periods and mature soil profiles formed.

The cyclicity reflects both glacioeustatic changes in sea level that may have a Milankovitch periodicity, and cycles of purely sedimentational origin reflecting the building and abandonment of local delta lobes. Scotland lay far from the open ocean to the south and there are fewer marine horizons in the Scottish succession than in the south, reflecting the fact that only the major sea level rises caused transgressions that reached Scotland.

The Passage Formation is variable in character but dominated by fluvial sandstones, most of the cyclicity has an autocyclic control. There was considerable tectonic activity, with a new structural pattern resulting in formation of new basins. Strike-slip fault activity was responsible for basin inversions and formation of basins on former highs. Some basins such as the Westfield Basin are small and local in extent. Although biozonation is difficult to achieve in these rocks it appears that the Chokerian and Alportian stages of the Namurian may be absent, representing a major Mid-Namurian hiatus that may be equivalent to the Mississippian–Pennsylvanian break in North America. Whilst the Southern Uplands formed a general high, Viséan and Namurian strata occur in the Loch Ryan, Sanquhar and Thornhill outliers, showing that some areas were drowned by the accumulating sediment. Typical cyclic deposition continues in the Southern Borders, but there is also tectonic activity within the Namurian.

The upper part of the Carboniferous, the 'Coal Measures', is truncated by the sub-Permian unconformity, and there is no Stephanian recognized onshore. The base of the Coal Measures is taken at the Lowstone Marine Band in the Midland Valley, the *Gastrioceras subcrenatum* marine band that defines the base of the Westphalian in England being absent in Scotland. The Coal Measures are generally grey with upward-coarsening cycles from mudstone to sandstone with a seatearth and coal at the top. The coarsening-up cycles are broadly fluviodeltaic, but the marine influence is slight with fewer marine bands than seen in the Limestone Groups. Fluvial channels have erosive bases and have a fining-up sandstone fill. As strata are traced to the margins of basinal areas, the coal seams tend to die out, and there is an increase in palaeosols and fluvial channel sandstones. These thinner successions covered parts of the Southern Uplands, Highlands and the Mid-North Sea High. The widespread biostratigraphic correlation possible in the Westphalian indicates that much of Western Europe was subject to the same control, probably of a eustatic nature. There was less tectonic activity in the Westphalian and lateral variation in the strata is thus reduced.

During the Westphalian Scotland was moving north from the wet equatorial belt, and into a belt with seasonal rainfall. At the end of the Carboniferous Scotland entered the semi-arid climatic belt, heralding deposition of the red beds and evaporites of the Permian. The closure of the ocean between Laurussia and Gondwana and the rising Variscan mountains probably accelerated the climatic change at this time. The lycopod coal swamps were replaced by drier environments dominated by seed ferns.

At the end of the Westphalian Variscan tectonic activity resulted in major basin inversion in the Midland Valley, and general uplift and erosion resulting in the sub-Permian unconformity. Beneath the unconformity the coal measures, shales and mudstones were intensely oxidized, frequently to varied pink, red and purple hues – as seen at Corrie Shore on Arran.

Permian

Following Hercynian deformation, Carboniferous basins were generally inverted and eroded and the deposits of the New Red Sandstone (Chapter 10) rest on older rocks with marked unconformity. Onshore in Scotland the only place where apparent conformity is seen is the Mauchline Basin in Ayrshire.

Major faulting and subsidence in Permian times established large depositional basins in what are now offshore areas (Northern Permian Basin, Moray Firth Basin, West Scotland). The Viking and Central Grabens were established, and smaller fault-bounded basins controlled Permian deposition in southern Scotland (Stranraer, Dumfries, Lochmaben). Scottish Permian outcrops represent either basin-marginal locations as in the Hopeman–Elgin area at the southern margin of the Moray Firth Basin, or faulted basin fills as in southern Scotland. The evaporitic and playa lake facies of the North Sea basins are not seen onshore in Scotland.

Scotland lay c.15° north of the Permian equator and experienced what are frequently described as 'desert' conditions. Aeolian dune deposits are characteristic (Hopeman, Mauchline, Dumfries) and are associated with water-lain sandstones. Onshore outcrops in Britain and in the Southern North Sea generally indicate winds from the east, but offshore in the North Permian Basin wind was generally from the NW. Dunes were larger and coarser-grained than those being constructed by winds in similar latitudes today, and wind speeds were greater, probably due to compression of air-pressure belts towards the equator during glacial periods as documented for the Pleistocene (discussion in Glennie 1998a).

There was a varied reptile fauna in Scotland during the Permian, mainly evidenced by trackways in dune and waterlain sandstones at Hopeman and Dumfries, and also by the famous fauna of reptiles from the Elgin area. Clearly vegetarian reptiles were surviving, and there was sufficient water at basin margins to support vegetation; but conditions were not generally conducive to preservation of the biota.

Volcanic activity continued from the Carboniferous (e.g. Mauchline lavas), and most Permian extrusives in Scotland have Early Permian ages. The teschenite and dolerite sills of the Midland Valley are chemically similar to the extrusives and are also thought to be of Permian age (see Chapters 9, 10). Permian dyke swarms are present in the Midland Valley and occur as alkaline lamprophyres in Caithness and Orkney. This activity marks the end of intra-plate volcanicity that commenced in the Early Carboniferous.

Triassic

Triassic deposits onshore in Scotland (Chapter 10) are generally a precursor to Jurassic marine transgression, and it is not usually possible to date red-beds underlying undoubted marine Jurassic. Most of the present area of Scotland was land undergoing erosion during the Triassic, but large quantities of sediment accumulated offshore in the North Sea, Moray Firth and basins on the west coast from the Minches in the north to the Irish Sea in the south.

In the Northern North Sea rifting was taking place, and thick sequences of fluvio-lacustrine red sandstones and mudstones accumulated. Similarly, thick Triassic sequences are present in the Hebrides basins, thickening westwards into the Minch Fault.

Triassic sequences bordering the Moray Firth at Lossiemouth and Golspie show fluvial and aeolian sandstones overlain by mudstones including a thick mature calcrete below Jurassic strata. Similarly, calcretes are present in cyclic fluvial sequences beneath Jurassic in the Western Isles (Skye, Raasay) showing that a semi-arid climate and minimal deposition preceded the invasion of the Jurassic seas to western Scotland and the Moray Firth. On Skye thin patches of red (presumed) Triassic strata beneath marine Jurassic reveal an irregular topography with locally derived alluvial and fluvial deposits at the depositional edge of the Hebrides Basin. The marine transgression reached Arran in Rhaetic times, but further north the first marine deposits are of Jurassic age.

Jurassic

The basins and rifts established in Permo-Triassic times continued to be active in the Jurassic (Chapter 11), and once again the Scottish onshore outcrops represent the margins of basins that have their main depocentres offshore. A change to a wetter, more temperate Jurassic climate is illustrated by grey-green shales with plants and spores in non-marine lithologies as at Golspie. In the Western Isles excellent Jurassic sections are preserved beneath the protective cover of Tertiary volcanics, but around the Moray Firth only basin margin relics of the Jurassic are present. However, these include the spectacular Kimmeridgian boulder beds at Helmsdale; deposited adjacent to the basin-bounding Helmsdale Fault.

Thus the main Jurassic sequences are offshore, and there is a wealth of data available from oil exploration and production activities (see Underhill 1998; Evans et al. 2003). Complexities and inconsistencies in lithostratigraphic names have led to the adoption of a sequence stratigraphic approach for correlation, generally based on the recognition of 'maximum flooding surfaces' represented by marine shales that can be picked on well logs. Such correlation surfaces have been related to biostratigraphic zones through palynology, and ultimately to ammonite zones.

The main elements in the North Sea are the rift systems of the Viking Graben, Central Graben and the Witch Ground Graben that joins westwards with the Inner Moray Firth. Perhaps the most significant feature offshore is the central North Sea dome that was located at the triple junction of the graben system. Doming is thought to have been due to the brief development of a rising plume head, resulting in volcanism in the Bathonian–Early Callovian. The doming resulted in erosion of earlier stratigraphies producing the Mid-Cimmerian Unconformity that can be traced over most of the North Sea, roughly from Norfolk in the south to the level of south Shetland in the north. Deflation of the dome following volcanism resulted in progressive onlap of Late Callovian to Early Kimmeridgian onto the dome. Fluctuations in relative sea level made onlap a stepped process, with regular production of sand bodies at times of lower sea level.

Offshore, the transition from Triassic to Jurassic is recorded in the Statfjord Formation where fluvial and alluvial deposits with caliche soil horizons pass upwards into shallow marine shoreface sands and offshore marine shelf muds. The alluvial system prograded northward parallel to the Viking Graben axis, before rising sea level outstripped sedimentation and marine trangression took place.

Onshore in the Moray Firth at Golspie the basin margin setting shows thick caliche at the top of the Trias being reworked into Hettangian fluvial and lagoonal deposits, and fully marine conditions are delayed until the Sinemurian. To the west of the Scottish landmass the junction is not exposed, but there is apparent conformity between fluvial cycles with caliche and the overlying marine shales and limestones of the Broadford Beds. Contemporaneous faulting in the west coast basins produced great thickness variations in the Lower Jurassic deposits, the exposed sections in southern Skye being thin shallow water deposits in contrast to a very thick mud-dominated sequence penetrated in northern Skye (Upper Glen No 1).

In the Mid-Jurassic a great variety of facies are developed. Of greatest economic importance is the Brent Delta System in the Viking Graben, and both marine and paralic sandstone facies surround the central North Sea dome. Bathonian fluvial deposits seen at Brora are typical, but the Bajocian is missing here, probably cut out by the Mid-Cimmerian Unconformity. To the west of Scotland a full Mid-Jurassic succession is seen with Bajocian strata in a variety of shallow marine facies, including spectacular tidal cross-bedded sandstones at Elgol on Skye. The Bathonian of the Hebrides comprises the Great Estuarine Group, with a variety of fluvial, lacustrine, lagoonal and restricted marine facies, and containing a fascinating array of salinity-controlled faunas. A much-reduced section of similar facies is seen at Brora on the east coast.

A major marine transgression in the Callovian brings non-marine conditions to an end, and produces a rapid transition to deep water open marine conditions. This event is recorded in successions in Skye in the west and at Brora in the east. This sea-level rise corresponds with the onset of rapid extension and subsidence in the Northern North Sea. Shallow marine sandstones (e.g. Beatrice Field, Oxfordian reservoir) developed as marine conditions proceeded to cover the North Sea dome, but eventually subsidence and increasing sea levels drowned the dome and marine mudstone deposition became dominant.

In the Kimmeridgian rapid extension was taking place across the Viking Graben, and organic-rich marine muds were deposited under open marine conditions. These muds, buried in basin areas, provide the main source for Scotland's hydrocarbons. Migrated hydrocarbons are trapped in a variety of lithologies, but particularly in the Brent Group sandstones within tilted fault blocks bordering the Viking Graben.

Active rifting at this time resulted in basin-bounding faults penetrating the sea bed, and fault-controlled sedimentation at the margins of land areas such as the East Shetland Platform (Brae Fields), and along the Helmsdale Fault bordering the northern Scottish land area. The Helmsdale Boulder Beds and associated deposits were shed off an active submarine fault scarp that controlled the NW margin of the Inner Moray Firth Basin, and provide a spectacular field example of fault-controlled sedimentation. Oxfordian to Kimmeridgian marine shale facies is also seen in the Hebrides basins, and existed to the west of an Outer Hebrides landmass in a proto-North Atlantic. The Jurassic ends with basins underfilled and with deep water, particularly in the area of the former North Sea Dome.

Cretaceous

The onshore rock record of the Cretaceous in Scotland is sparse, but abundant data are available from the offshore areas, summarized by Harker (Chapter 12). In many basinal areas organic-rich shale deposition continued from the Late Jurassic to Early Cretaceous, but a major seismic marker in the Rhyazanian, frequently referred to as the 'Base Cretaceous Unconformity' (but it does not define the base of the Cretaceous) corresponds to the Late Cimmerian tectonic episode. This event marks a change from E–W extension in the Jurassic to compression from the south due to the Austrian orogeny in the Early Cretaceous. The combination of these forces transmitted through the various crustal blocks, affected sedimentation in different ways in different areas. Some active Jurassic faults continued in extensional (or transtensional) mode, whilst others locked up. Different faults became active in the Early Cretaceous resulting in new sources of erosion products to be transported as turbidites into the existing deep basins. This is particularly well seen in the Moray Firth and Witch Ground Graben areas of the North Sea (Captain and Scapa Fields). Similar fault-controlled Early Cretaceous deep water clastics occur in basins to the west of Scotland.

The Scottish landmass was subaerially exposed in the Early Cretaceous, and shoreline and shallow marine clastics fringed the coast. A remnant of these clastics occurs at Moreseat near Peterhead in NE Scotland, and glacial erratics of Lower Cretaceous sandstones transported onshore from the Moray Firth occur in the Buchan region and in Caithness.

In the Late Cretaceous the Scottish landmass was progressively inundated by globally rising sea level, and may have been briefly covered by marine conditions. Remnants of Cretaceous nearshore deposits remain in the Hebrides, indicating the presence of a thin clastic shoreline fringe, rapidly followed offshore by carbonates, clearly little clastic material was being supplied from the Scottish landmass at this time. Scotland was enjoying a relatively dry sub-tropical climate that was progressively becoming more temperate at the end of the Cretaceous. Chalk dominates in southern Britain, but further north in colder boreal waters around Shetland chalk is replaced by calcareous mudstone, indicative of greater clastic input.

The Late Cretaceous saw a reduction in tectonic activity with only a few faults remaining active, and deposition was dominantly fine-grained. Atlantic opening with sea-floor spreading was in progress between Greenland and North America at this time.

Tertiary

The Tertiary rocks of onshore Scotland are mainly represented by the spectacular dissected volcanic centres and extensive lava sheets of the Tertiary Igneous Province of the west coast, forming the classic scenery of Skye, Rum, Mull and the Ardnamurchan peninsula (Chapter 14). The volcanics rest on an erosion surface comprising mainly Jurassic strata, but including remnants of Late Cretaceous strata.

To the east of Scotland in the sediment-starved northern North Sea Basin muds and chalk continued to be deposited with little change across the Mesozoic–Tertiary boundary, and water depths in the basin were probably increasing as the rift systems subsided. The major geological influence was the development of a mantle plume (?or plumes) centred on the area that would eventually become Iceland. Uplift took place over a vast area extending from Britain to the west of Greenland. Scotland lies at the southern end of the uplift area, and of the extensive volcanics that are found in basins to the west of Shetland, the Faeroes and east Greenland. At about 55 Ma

(Magnetic anomaly 24, close to Palaeocene/Eocene boundary) the continental crust split through the domed area and sea floor spreading commenced between Britain and Greenland. The hot-spot remained at the new oceanic ridge and still exists today as the Icelandic plume. As sea-floor spreading proceeded, Scotland drifted further from the hot spot and formed part of a new passive continental margin, progressively subsiding as it moved further from the spreading ridge.

Uplift of the Scottish continental margin formed a land area extending north of Shetland and from which sediment was shed southeast into the North Sea basin and northwest into the Faeroe–Shetland Basin. Water depths in the basins probably exceeded 1 km in Palaeocene and Early Eocene times. Sands derived from erosion of the landmass were cycled through deltaic and shoreline environments before being deposited as turbidite fans in deep water. These Palaeocene deep-water clastics form the reservoirs of major oil fields such as Foinavon and Schiehallion in the Faeroe–Shetland Basin, and Forties, Montrose, Nelson, Andrew and Arbroath in the North Sea.

Eight cycles of sedimentation can be recognized through the Tertiary in the offshore areas, reflecting the interplay between changing sea levels and tectonic subsidence. The upward trend is of basin filling, and shallowing of water depths through the Tertiary. The changes in sedimentation and basin fill patterns are admirably illustrated by Knox (Chapter 13).

During the Tertiary there was a general cooling in climate from a climatic peak in the Early Eocene when deep tropical weathering affected Scotland, and was probably responsible for the deep weathering of basic igneous rocks seen in NE Scotland. As cooling proceeded glacial conditions began to affect polar areas, and permanent glaciation had probably been established in Antarctica about 14 Ma ago, but did not affect Scotland until rapid cooling took place in the Pliocene to give glacial conditions in northern Europe by 2–4 Ma.

The igneous activity on the west coast of Scotland took place between about 60.5 and 55 Ma, and appears to have been confined to short time spans within this range. Extensive activity took place in Eigg at 60.5 Ma and again at 58.3 Ma. The Skye lava fields date at 58–59 Ma, and those on Mull at 60.5, 58.5 and 55 Ma. The central igneous complexes date from about 60.5 to 55.7 Ma. The lavas are thick (to 2 km) sequences of alkali olivine basalt to trachyte erupted from fissures, represented by the dyke swarms in the area. Lavas were also erupted from the central complexes, which represent the roots of major volcanoes now eroded to expose intrusions that were probably less than 2 km below the volcanic edifice. These central volcanoes are generally sited at lines of weakness created by basinal faulting that accompanied stretching and thinning of the lithosphere in the Mesozoic. Thus the Mesozoic rifts to some extent control the positions of central complexes, dyke distributions and the geometry of the lava fields. However, many of the Mesozoic features are probably reactivations of older crustal features that provided weaknesses along which magma could rise.

At the start of volcanic activity the topography was of low relief and consisted of the planed-off fill of the Mesozoic basins and the adjacent basement. The initial eruptions were frequently into water, with development of tuffs, volcanic breccias, hyaloclastites and pillow lavas. Palynological analysis confirms a freshwater environment, and the presence of upright tree trunks in lavas on Mull attests to terrestrial conditions. The bulk of the lavas appear to have been erupted under terrestrial conditions and red, subaerially weathered, tops to flows are common. In interludes between periods of lava eruption, erosion took place to produce waterlain sediments, some of which (e.g. Ardtun leaf bed on Mull) are rich in floral remains, giving information on climate and possible elevation of the lava fields.

Periods of volcanic activity are also recorded in the North Sea and the Shetland–Faeroes Basin. In the Shetland–Faeroes Basin tuffs and tuffaceous sediments span a range of 62–48 Ma, with a major input at 54–55 Ma. In the North Sea the Balder Tuff (c. 54 Ma) consists of over 200 thin ash-fall layers in 8 m of strata, and forms an important marker on well logs. Tuffaceous material is also found in sandstones of the Palaeocene Sele Formation of the Montrose Group and corresponds with the earlier phase of Hebridean volcanic activity. It appears that volcanic material was either transported from the west of Scotland, or reworked from airfall tuffs deposited on the Scottish landmass.

The thick Tertiary fill of the North Sea and Shetland–Faeroe Basin is mud dominated; sands being generally confined to the marginal areas. The basin fill represents erosion products from the progressive uplift of Scotland and Scandanavia. The elevated surfaces in the Highlands, represented by plateaux and coincident heights of mountains, reflect a series of ancient erosion surfaces possibly dating back to the Cretaceous. Climatic changes and changes in water circulation are reflected in the North Sea sediments. An important event in the Late Eocene saw uplift and significant change from a situation with deep water and a stratified water column to shallow oxygenated conditions. Connection between Atlantic and Arctic ocean waters is believed to have caused widespread erosion and cut large channels. The later deposits in the North Sea Basin are dominated by prograding sediment packages that progressively filled the basin, and were controlled by sea level fluctuations.

In western Scotland small Oligocene basins, probably with sediment fills of freshwater origin, locally rest on the older Tertiary volcanics. In the North Sea marine muds dominate in the Oligocene with marginal glauconitic sands containing bioclastic debris. Mudstones continue to dominate through the Miocene and Pliocene, the only possible onshore deposits being the supposed Miocene/Pliocene Buchan gravels of NE Scotland. In parts of the North Sea there is a remarkable 300 m of Pleistocene representing rapid erosion and sediment transport to central basin areas.

Quaternary

The cooling that culminated in the 'Ice Ages' of the Quaternary began at 35–40 Ma, and from about 14 Ma the Antarctic ice sheet started to form. At about 2 Ma arctic marine microfaunas invaded the North Sea and by about 0.75 Ma sediment dropped from icebergs in the Forth Approaches indicates the existence of a Scottish ice sheet extending into the shallow marine environment. The story is not, however, one of progressive cooling; there were extreme fluctuations producing 'glacial' and 'interglacial' periods.

The periodic locking-up of water in ice sheets 3–4 km thick in Europe and North America resulted in lowering of global sea levels by up to 150 m, exposing large areas of marginal shelves. Rapid changes in climate with a cyclicity of 100 000 years resulted in equally rapid changes in the distribution of biota, and in oceanic and atmospheric circulation. At present we enjoy an interglacial but as Boulton et al. (Chapter 15) point out this is only predicted to last another 5000 years!

The legacy of glacial erosion is admirably preserved in Scotland and influences much of the landscape. Repeated glaciation produced progressively deepened valleys and sea lochs which carried the ice seawards from the ice sheet; the pattern of valleys radiating from Rannoch Moor being a good example. Despite rapid erosion of valleys, the plateau top suffered little erosion, the ice/bedrock boundary being well below freezing point, resulting in preservation of tors and relics of Tertiary weathering.

The corries of the higher mountains, particularly common in the west, generally occur on north and east facing mountainsides and were excavated by small glaciers that repeatedly developed in cold periods on the shaded side of mountains to which snow was blown by winds from the SW. Other major features are the striated and smoothed bare rock surfaces of the upland areas, and oriented elongate drumlins of till formed beneath moving ice. Outwash from the ice sheets produced extensive fluvio-glacial gravels, including large eskers, many now sadly destroyed by extraction of sand and gravel. Around Scotland's coasts 'raised beaches' attest to changing relative levels of land and sea, and the variation in isostatic rebound can be combined with shoreline evidence to estimate the pattern of loading of the crust by earlier ice sheets.

The unravelling of stratigraphy within the Quaternary deposits of Scotland is a complex task; modern methods of stratigraphic and radiometric dating, together with indicators of climatic change, continually produce surprises. Evidence from climatically sensitive beetle faunas suggests that temperature rise at the end of the last glaciation was rapid (c.1°C/decade). There is also evidence that offshore sea temperatures may have risen from near zero to close to modern temperatures in a few decades, coinciding with the return of the warming North Atlantic Drift to our shores. Reports of current slowing down of the North Atlantic Drift may be an indication that we are heading for the next glacial period. Within the last 150 000 years Scotland has at different times been much colder, and also much warmer than at present. In the long term major climatic change is inevitable, and outwith the influence of mankind, who will be powerless to stop the onset of the next glaciation!

The deep structure of Scotland

Having summarized the outcrop areas it is appropriate to review evidence for the deeper structure of Scotland. The exposed geology of the UK ages towards the northwest, with Archaean basement forming most of the Outer Isles. Models of the basement and lithosphere beneath Scotland depend on evidence from: basement-cover relationships, igneous petrology and provenance, mantle xenoliths, and geophysical data.

The well developed patterns of post-Carboniferous extension and uplift seen in the offshore seismic data are likely to extend across the Scottish mainland, but are more difficult to observe. The structural framework observed in the Hebridean terrane and in offshore seismic data can be extended to the Northern Highland and Grampian terranes using geophysical lineaments, signatures, and modelling. Lineaments identify horizontal gradients in gravity (Fig. 1.7) and magnetic (Fig. 1.8) data and can be directly related to boundaries in density and magnetisation. Lineaments, faults, shear zones and localities relevant to this account are shown on Fig. 1.9.

Since the Grampian orogenic event there has been an enormous amount of uplift (c. 30 km) and erosion that has exposed high-grade metamorphic rocks in northern Scotland. This exhumation is thought to have occurred on, or close to, major structures, notably the Outer Isles Fault, the Moine Thrust, the Great Glen Fault, the Highland Boundary Fault and the Portsoy Shear Zone. Images of geophysical data (Figs 1.7, 1.8) reveal lineaments suggesting an extensive set of NNE and ESE structures which may have enabled the uplift and erosion, and which control the present disposition of basement blocks beneath the Caledonian rocks. Even the Southern Uplands terrane has been uplifted c. 13 km, exposing prehnite–pumpellyite facies rocks, and again NE and ESE structures have been involved.

There is considerable evidence for a c. 850 Ma event in the orthotectonic Caledonide rocks north and south of the Great Glen Fault, but debate continues concerning the nature of this event. There are currently two main hypotheses for the nature of the Neoproterozoic–Early Palaeozoic orogenic deformation.

1. Extended Neoproterozoic sedimentation (Moine–Dalradian Supergroups) on a Laurentian margin with Riphean and Vendian extension followed by a focused Grampian orogenic event in the late Arenig (470–460 Ma). In this model, the apparent continuity of stratigraphy (Soper 1994) and structural style are the basis for a single Caledonian convergent event. Migmatites and older granites are the product of extension and partial melting.
2. Neoproterozoic orogeny involving significant compressional shortening, ductile fracture and tectonic uplift during a Knoydartian/Morarian event (c. 850 Ma) followed by the Grampian event at 470–460 Ma. This model requires a significant basement/cover unconformity within the orthotectonic metasedimentary Moine–Dalradian sequence (i.e. along the Grampian Shear Zone) or the recognition of allochthonous metamorphic blocks.

Regardless of the nature and dating of Neoproterozoic deformation events, the focused Grampian event implies significant crustal thickening and topographic building. It may also have been preceded by widespread ophiolite obduction (Dewey & Shackleton 1984). More importantly, the orogeny has been followed by rapid orogenic collapse with coeval intrusion (c. 410 Ma), and subsequently enormous uplift and exhumation.

Geophysical anomalies associated with basement structure

Geophysical potential fields (gravity and magnetic data) integrate the response of source distributions of density and magnetization determined by sedimentary, igneous and tectonic processes throughout the crust. Consequently, much structural information is contained within regional geophysical data. Variations in the rock density and magnetization parameters often occur at geological contacts and produce changes in anomaly gradient and amplitude which can be used as an indication of source distribution and depth. This structural information is often only visible within the gradient data of the fields and is best displayed using the shaded-relief technique. Colour shaded-relief images provide both the gradient and amplitude information of the field and permit simple signature and lineament analysis (Fig. 1.9). Accepting that the surface and buried geology is responsible for the observed geophysical signal the problem is often one of finding a consensus (or otherwise) acceptable geological model which can be used to interpret the observed data and produce realistic and possible solutions.

Regional gravity map
The Bouguer gravity anomaly map (Fig. 1.7) of northern Britain can be interpreted in a structural framework involving a series of sub-parallel footwall basement blocks separated by major NNE trending faults. Offshore, many of these faults show Mesozoic dip-slip movement. The faulted blocks produce a 'saw-tooth' pattern in a NW–SE Bouguer gravity profile across the northern UK. The exposed basement blocks are divided into separate units by transverse NW shear zones and this pattern appears to be repeated beneath the metamorphic orthotectonic Caledonidian rocks.

Across north Scotland interpreted depths to the Moho range from about 22 km off Cape Wrath to over 36 km in the Midland Valley and show only limited correlation with the Bouguer

Fig. 1.7. Shaded relief image of the gravity anomaly map of Scotland (based on BGS 1997*b*). Bouguer gravity anomaly onshore, and free-air anomaly offshore is illuminated from the north at a sun angle of 45°.

gravity anomaly map (Fig. 1.7). In the Midland Valley, regional Bouguer gravity anomalies are close to zero, so that the deep Moho must be linked with a relatively high-density basement or lower crust. The main reasons for the poor correlation of the seismic Moho with the gravity data are voluminous granitic material in the upper crust, low-density psammites in the Moine and Dalradian Supergroups and thick post-Devonian sedimentary basins. At least 4 km of Mesozoic sediment is present in basins within the Inner Moray Firth and at least 6 km of largely Permian and Mesozoic sedimentary rocks in basins offshore NW Scotland.

In NE Grampian, the Dalradian strata east of the Portsoy Shear Zone are associated with a positive regional gravity anomaly. There are local maxima over some of the syn-tectonic basic intrusions but the regional anomaly is probably an indication of the basement. The magnetic basement which is

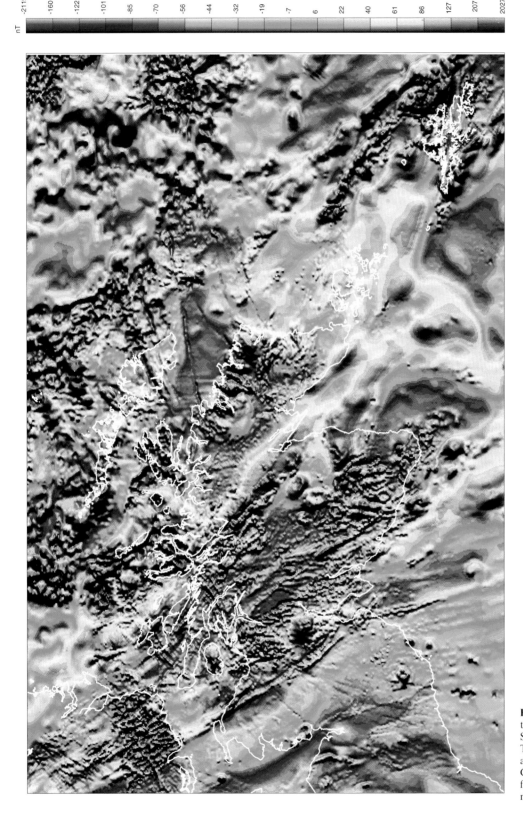

Fig. 1.8. Shaded relief image of the aeromagnetic anomaly for Scotland (based on BGS 1998a). Total field anomaly adjusted to a modified International Geomagnetic Reference Field for 1990 is illuminated from the north at a sun angle of 45°.

the source of the Great Glen and Lossiemouth regional magnetic anomalies is probably absent east of the Portsoy Shear Zone so that Appin and Argyll Group rocks rest on (Midland Valley terrane) basement without Grampian Group strata. The thick low-density siliclastic strata of the Grampian Group appear to be limited to the southwest by the Oban

lineament (cf. Cruachan lineament) which appears to extend across the Great Glen Fault.

Strong positive gravity anomalies associated with the South Harris Complex and the Ness Shear Zone are truncated at the Outer Isles Fault Zone. The continuity of basement terranes is limited by significant uplift along faults active in the Mesozoic

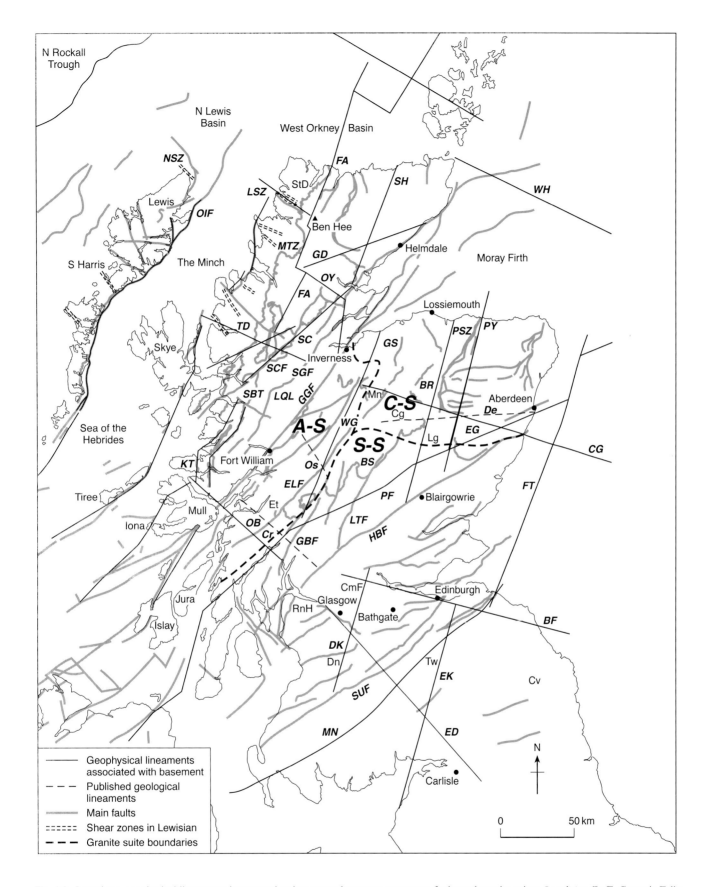

Fig. 1.9. Locations, geophysical lineaments interpreted as important basement structures, faults and granite suites. *Localities*: CmF, Campsie Fells; RnH, Renfrew Hills; StD, Strath Dionard. *Granites*: **A-S,** Argyll suite; **C-S,** Cairngorm suite; **S-S,** South Scotland suite; Cg, Cairngorm; Cv, Cheviot; Dn, Distinkhorn; Lg, Lochnagar; Mn, Monadhliath; Tw, Tweedale. *Faults and structures*: **Cr,** Cruachan; **De,** Deeside; **BS,** Boundary Slide; **ELF,** Ericht–Laidon; **GBF,** Garabal Hill; **GGF,** Great Glen Fault; **GS,** Grampian Slide; **HBF,** Highland Boundary Fault; **KT,** Knoydart Thrust; **LQL,** Loch Quoich; **LSZ,** Laxford Shear Zone; **LTF,** Loch Tay; **MTZ,** Moine Thrust Zone; **NSZ,** Ness Shear Zone; **OIF,** Outer Isles Fault; **Os,** Ossian; **PSZ,** Portsoy Shear Zone; **SBT,** Sgurr Beag Thrust; **SCF,** Strath Conon Fault; **SGF,** Strath Glass Fault; **SUF,** Southern Upland Fault. *Lineaments*: **BF,** Berwick–Forth; **BR** , Braemar; **CG,** Central Graben; **DK,** Distinkhorn; **ED,** Eden–Carlisle; **EG,** East Grampian; **EK,** Ettrick; **FA,** Fannich; **FT,** Forth Approaches; **GD,** Grudie; **MN,** Moniave Shear Zone; **OB,** Oban (Cruachan); **OY,** Oykel; **PF,** Pitlochry–Fyne; **PY,** Portsoy; **SC,** Strath Carron; **SH,** Strath Halladale; **TD,** Torridon; **WG,** West Grampian; **WH,** West Halibut.

rather than by significant strike-slip across the Minch, focused on the Outer Isles Fault Zone. Large strike-slip movement has been proposed, which would relate the Langavat Shear Zone along the SW coast of South Harris, with the Canisp Shear Zone (Piper 1992). Such movement would seem inconsistent with the sinuous trace of the Outer Isles Fault, although there are some linear NE structures in the Minch, inferred from the regional gravity data, which might provide a plane for strike-slip motion.

Regional magnetic map

The observed total magnetic field anomaly over Northern Britain (Fig. 1.8) contains a wide spectrum of frequencies representing the contributions from numerous sources: thin reversely magnetised Tertiary dykes associated with the igneous centres, large polyphase granitic intrusions such as Cairngorm, Monadhliath and Etive, and in places a (Lewisian) basement with significant magnetisation (e.g. Rona Ridge, Coll–Tiree). In addition, the largest amplitude anomalies are over the Tertiary igneous centres of the Inner Hebrides which have strong negative anomalies over the reversely magnetized intrusive components and over the thick early lavas.

A simple model assuming a magnetic basement extending up from a depth of 20 km with a bulk induced magnetisation of 1.0 A/m (susceptibility 0.025 SI) approximates most of the regional magnetic anomaly. This model has basement at the surface in the main areas of exposed Lewisian with significant magnetisation, and shallow magnetic basement under much of the Sea of the Hebrides, Skerryvore Bank and the Inner Hebrides Trough. The basement along the Great Glen Fault onshore is modelled locally within 1 km of surface, predominantly on the northwest side of the fault. In the north Central Highlands this magnetic basement appears to be restricted to the zone close to the Great Glen Fault, suggestive of an uplifted basement block. Shallow basement also occurs in the Inner Moray Firth from near Lossiemouth to the Central Ridge.

Exposed basement

The foreland Lewisian Archean (2.9–2.7 Ga) terrane is partitioned by NE trending major faults which were active in the Mesozoic (Outer Isles Fault Zone, the Camasunary–Rona Fault). NW-trending shear zones partition the footwall highs into regions, each with characteristic properties. On the mainland Northern, Central, and Southern regions are recognized (Chapter 3).

The Northern Region Laxfordian biotite hornblende gneiss with basic and ultrabasic lenses contains numerous lenses and sheets of pegmatite and granite which form up to 20% by volume and are the likely cause of the Strath Dionard magnetic anomaly north of the Laxford shear zone (Figs 1.8, 1.9). The magnetic anomaly of the Central Region reflects the more magnetic pyroxene granulite gneiss.

Exposed Lewisian rocks have a relatively high saturated density (2.78–2.82 Mgm^{-3}) and show several populations of susceptibility with modal values at 0.1, 1, 5, 12 and 24 10^{-3} SI units. This complexity of the exposed Lewisian basement (see above and Chapter 3) provides a model for the likely variety of concealed basement to the orthotectonic rocks. Analysis of lineaments seen in Landsat images (e.g. Fig. 1.1) over the Archaean terrane of the Scottish mainland indicate three sets of orthogonal structures: 020/110; 045/135 and 070/160 degrees. These populations reflect not only the fabric of metamorphic grade but also subsequent extension. The 020/110 set is seen in geophysical data across all the terranes of Scotland.

Northern Highlands

Amphibolite grade Lewisian gneiss, which has a refraction velocity of about 6.1 km/s, forms much of the outcrop on the mainland west coast and occurs at numerous localities throughout the western Moine strata as tectonic inliers of Lewisian-type rocks often along zones of high ductile strain. Locally a basement–cover (Moine–Lewisian) relationship has been suggested. The 6.4 km/s refractor observed beneath the Northern Highlands in the LISPB seismic experiment (Bamford 1979) has been equated with Lewisian granulite-facies gneisses on the Hebridean craton and inferred to underlie much of the Northern Highlands as far south as the Great Glen Fault. Shackleton (1979) suggested that the 6.4 km/s refraction was most likely to be generated from a diachronous series of granulite facies gneisses younging to the south. A deeper 7 km/s refractor beneath northern Scotland was associated with a Poisson's ratio of 0.25 and interpreted as a lower crust of essentially meta-igneous (gabbroic–eclogitic) rocks at garnet-granulite facies (Hall & Al-Haddad 1976).

Evidence now suggests that the eastward extent of the Archaean terrane beneath the Moine rocks is limited. Older rounded detrital zircons in migmatites in the Kirtomy and Naver nappes of the Moine (c. 465 Ma) cluster in two age groups: 1000–1250 and 1500–1750 Ma (Friend et al. 2002b). This suggests a Grenvillian provenance for the Moine rocks and questions the supposed Moine–Lewisian unconformity in the Northern Highlands. Tectonic inliers of Lewisian type rocks are present across much of the Morar Group in the western Northern Highlands, at least west of the Naver Slide, but these are consistent with either of the two models mentioned above.

Geophysical models suggest that the asymmetrical 400 nT magnetic anomaly across the Great Glen Fault (Fig. 1.8) can be interpreted as a footwall high in a magnetic basement which is continuous from the Northern Highlands and into the Grampian Highlands. If basement in the north Central Grampians is early Proterozoic (Rhinnian) in age, then this would suggest continuity of an early Proterozoic basement into the Northern Highlands so that the boundary between Proterozoic and Archaean crust lies north of the Great Glen Fault.

In the Northern Highlands, regional magnetic anomalies associated with the exposed Lewisian granulite gneiss of the Central Region and pervasive granite veining in the Northern Region continue east of the Moine Thrust Zone only for about 10 km. A series of higher frequency linear magnetic anomalies over the western outcrop of the Moine are associated with magnetic zones within psammites of the Morar Group. Near Ben Hee, the magnetic anomalies are truncated at the prominent NNE Fannich lineament seen in the Bouguer gravity anomaly map about 15 km east of the Moine Thrust Zone (Figs 1.7, 1.9). This has been interpreted as indicating post-thrust dislocation of the Moine Nappe by footwall uplift along the Fannich structure. This suggests that the Archaean blocks which make up the North, Central and Southern Regions of NW Scotland only extend eastwards as far as the NNE structure associated with the Fannich gravity lineament. Other NNE structures across the Northern Highland terrane can be related to this model, notably the Strath Halladale lineament and the Walls Boundary Fault in Shetland.

Grampian Highlands

Direct evidence of the basement to the Dalradian of the Grampian Highlands is limited, but on the Rhinns of Islay the quartz-feldspar-hornblende-muscovite gneiss is early Proterozoic (1.8 Ga) in age (Marcantonio et al. 1988) and is derived from juvenile mantle material. This basement was considered to extend across to Inishtrahull and Colonsay and beneath much of the Dalradian Supergroup. This contradicted a model of the BIRPS WINCH profile which had suggested a zig-zag model of obduction across the Islay region (Hall J. 1985).

Dickin & Bowes (1991) confirmed an early Proterozoic age (1.96 ± 0.02 Ga) for the Inishtrahull gneiss and used Sm–Nd isotopic data from Caledonian granites to suggest an early Proterozoic basement block approximately 100 km wide and 600 km long on the south side of the Great Glen Fault. This implied that the Cruachan lineament (Graham 1986a), broadly associated with Vendian volcanic activity in the Dalradian and the southwest limit of Grampian Group strata, was not a fundamental basement boundary.

Stephens & Halliday (1984) had used Sm–Nd and U–Pb isotopic data to identify three distinctive suites (South Scotland, Argyll, Cairngorm) of late-tectonic (390–420 Ma) plutonic rocks which may reflect characteristics of the deeper crust. The suites are all generally I-type granites with low initial $Sr^{87/86}$ ratios (0.704–0.708) formed from a primary mantle-derived melt with crustal contribution. The main intrusions are generally associated with a strong negative Bouguer gravity anomaly (Fig. 1.7) indicating significant mass deficiency within the upper 10 km of crust. Many of the bodies also exhibit annular magnetic anomalies reflecting zoning of the intrusion into separate phases. This is well seen in the Etive, Lochnagar, and Monadhliath plutons, and is implied for the Cairngorm pluton.

Many of the isotopic differences between the granite suites can be explained in relation to orthogonal NNE and ESE late orogenic collapse structures which cross Scotland and define zones of uplift, basement blocks, and hence crustal character. The E–W Deeside lineament (Fettes et al. 1986) is not recognized in the geophysical data and the ESE East Grampian lineament (Fig. 1.9) appears to be the main control on the intrusion of the Cairngorm suite of granites. Similarly the signature of the Argyll suite is essentially a reflection of the crustal structure either side of the NNE West Grampian lineament (Fig. 1.9). The Mid-Grampian line separating the southern suite might therefore be related to a deeper basement boundary separating the Grampian Highland and Midland Valley terranes at depth.

Midland Valley

LISPB identified a distinct velocity structure across the Midland Valley terrane especially the high velocity (6.4 km/s) refractor at about 8 km depth, also associated with a low Poisson's ratio (0.231) typical of intermediate crystalline lithologies. Silurian to Lower Devonian sequences of the Midland Valley contain only minor contributions of Dalradian provenance, the bulk of material coming from sources (now hidden) within the Midland Valley terrane.

Xenoliths from vents in the Southern Highlands and the Midland Valley suggest a metamorphic basement of granulite facies rocks of various compositions including ultramafic, anorthosites and quartz-feldspar granulites. This basement is not terminated at either the Highland Boundary Fault or the Southern Upland Fault, in part confirming the continuity seen in the LISPB 6.4 km/s refractor. A shallow 6.0 km/s refractor seen in seismic experiments (MAVIS, Dentith & Hall 1989, 1990; Southern Uplands Seismic Refraction Profile SUSRP, Hall et al. 1983) in the Midland Valley and northern belt of the Southern Uplands, at depths of about 4 km, has been interpreted as crystalline basement beneath the Lower Palaeozoic strata but might be related to Devonian andesitic units or to ophiolitic remnants. In an alternative hypothesis, Oliver & McKerrow (1984), using the same data, postulated that the

'crystalline' signatures might be a reflection of greenschist-facies metamorphism of the greywackes seen at the surface.

The Highland Border Complex probably underlies in part the Dalradian of the Southern Highlands which masks the hidden terrane boundary. Exposed Lower Palaeozoic sequences in the south of the Midland Valley are possibly about 3–5 km thick above a basement of high velocity (6 km/s) rocks at depths between 4–8 km (Dentith & Hall 1990) and a lower crust of mainly basic meta-igneous granulites, anorthosites and pyroxenites (Upton et al. 1984).

There is circumstantial evidence for the continuation of the Midland Valley terrane northwards beneath the Dalradian of the Southern Highlands and possibly the Buchan region of NE Scotland. This evidence includes gravity modelling across the Highland Boundary Fault; E–W features in the magnetic data of the Southern Highlands; distribution of Late Carboniferous dykes across the Midland Valley, Southern Highlands and in NE Grampian; comparable geophysical textures southeast of Portsoy and in the Midland Valley; and disruption of ENE features by NNE structures seen in gravity and magnetic data.

A discontinuity in the basement across the Portsoy Shear Zone supports the model of orogenic collapse and exhumation across this structure. Continuation of the Midland Valley terrane to Shetland would put the Unst ophiolites in a situation more similar to those at Ballantrae and at the Highland Border.

Southern Uplands

Models of the Southern Uplands as an accretionary prism (discussion in Chapter 6) have been modified by provenance studies for the northern, central and southern belts, the identification of important transcurrent structures and the apparent extension of shallow crystalline crust in the Midland Valley southwards beneath the northern belt. The Southern Upland Fault marks the northern limit of either a thin (1–4 km) accretionary prism development (northern belt) on the metamorphic basement of the Midland Valley terrane, or a thicker prism progressively metamorphosed at depth to greenschist facies. The central and southern belts are either a back arc or successor basin deposited after arc volcanicity ended in the Late Ordovician and accreted at the margin of the Midland Valley terrane. A magnetic basement block, possibly of Avalonian origin, lies beneath the central belt. The northern margin of this block is marked by the Orlock Bridge Fault/Moniave Shear Zone. The Bouguer gravity anomaly increases to the southwest across NW structures (such as the Eden–Clyde line) which appear to have controlled the development of faulted Carboniferous and Permian basins. It is uncertain whether these features affect basement type and terrane. More subtle ENE features such as the Ettrick line appear related to late-Caledonian granites and may control the disposition of basement blocks and exhumation.

Cross sectional profiles

Quantitative modelling of gravity and magnetic data can provide a constrained solution to the observed data in terms of density and magnetization. The constraints are provided by existing or postulated geological models supported by observational or interpreted evidence and the database of physical properties of rocks.

Full crust 2.5D modelling, to a depth of 40 km, incorporates the Moho structure from seismic data or isostasy, an upper mantle density of 3.30 Mgm^{-3}, and a mean lithosheric density (to 40 km depth) of 2.95 Mgm^{-3}. Figures 1.10 and 1.11 illustrate the upper 25 km of two full crust 2D modelled cross sectional profiles of Scotland (Fig. 1.3).

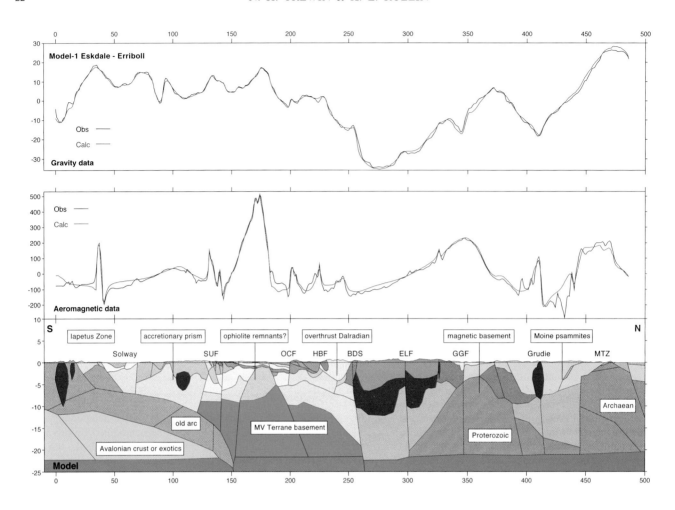

Key to Model 1 Eskdale - Eriboll (N is number of polygons for each code)

	Code	Description	Density	Susceptibility	N
	132	Upper Mantle	3.30	0.0	1
	131	Lower Crust	2.95	0.0	3
	130	Mafic lower crust	3.10	0.0	1
	129	Proterozoic gneiss	2.78	24.0	5
	128	Mafic middle crust	2.85	6.2	4
	126	Southern Uplands basement	2.88	10.0	2
	125	Pre-Dalradian basement	2.79	6.0	5
	122	Dalradian psammites (Drummochter)	2.69	0.0	2
	90	Triassic mudstones, marls	2.61	0.0	5
	82	Carboniferous Westphalian A-B	2.66	0.0	3
	81	Carboniferous Namurian	2.60	0.0	3
	80	Carboniferous Tournaisian, Visean	2.69	0.0	10
	78	Upper Devonian	2.67	0.0	7
	75	Lower Devonian	2.75	0.0	12
	73	Silurian Wenlock	2.78	1.7	7
	72	Silurian Llandovery	2.82	0.0	4
	70	Ordovician Ashgill-Caradoc	2.77	2.5	4
	68	Ordovician Llanvirn, Arenig	2.79	3.6	11
	62	Cambrian quartzite	2.78	5.0	5
	53	Carboniferous basalt and spilite	2.76	31.2	6
	50	Devonian andesitic lava-tuff	2.75	13.6	11
	44	Ordovician andesitic lava, tuff	2.81	2.9	7
	42	Ordovician basalts-spilite-tuff	2.81	25.8	6
	37	Felsite, trachyte	2.72	20.0	1
	34	Granite, syenite	2.74	4.7	7
	20	Dalradian schist, phyllites	2.86	0.0	5
	19	Dalradian grits, schists	2.80	0.0	2
	13	Dalradian psammites and schists	2.79	0.0	4
	11	Moine schists	2.79	1.5	4
	9	Moine psammite	2.79	0.0	11
	1	Lewisian gneiss	2.79	20.0	4

Fig. 1.10. Modelled geological profile from Eskdale to Eriboll (Profile 1 on Fig. 1.3). Observed gravity and magnetic anomalies have been modelled to a depth of 40 km using 2.5D polygons with density and magnetization properties consistent with observed rock properties. Number codes based on the published 1:625 000 BGS geological map.

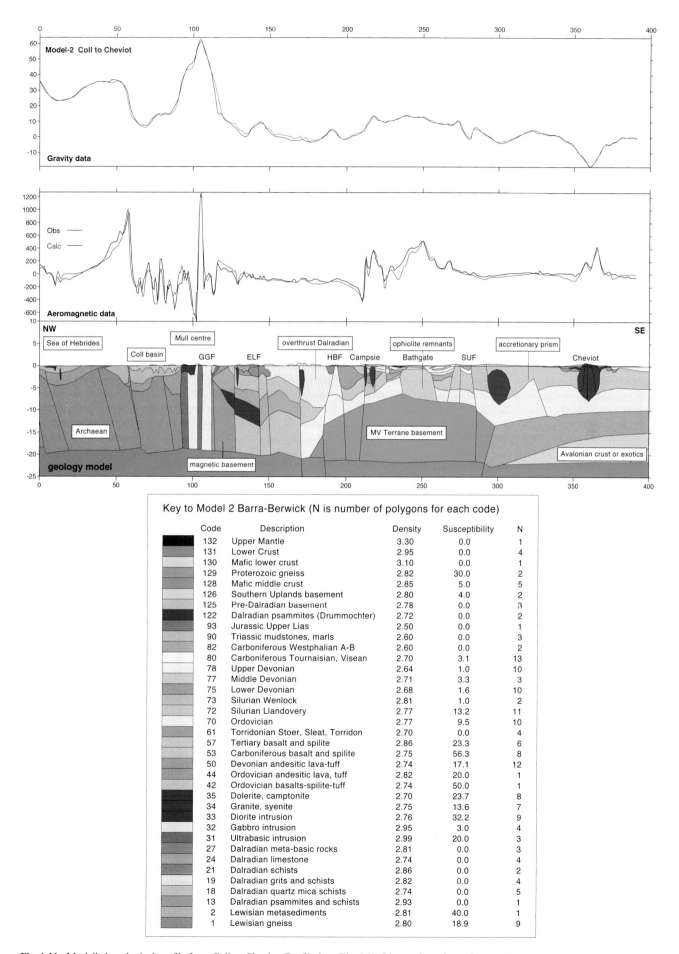

Key to Model 2 Barra-Berwick (N is number of polygons for each code)

	Code	Description	Density	Susceptibility	N
	132	Upper Mantle	3.30	0.0	1
	131	Lower Crust	2.95	0.0	4
	130	Mafic lower crust	3.10	0.0	1
	129	Proterozoic gneiss	2.82	30.0	2
	128	Mafic middle crust	2.85	5.0	5
	126	Southern Uplands basement	2.80	4.0	2
	125	Pre-Dalradian basement	2.78	0.0	3
	122	Dalradian psammites (Drummochter)	2.72	0.0	2
	93	Jurassic Upper Lias	2.50	0.0	1
	90	Triassic mudstones, marls	2.60	0.0	3
	82	Carboniferous Westphalian A-B	2.60	0.0	2
	80	Carboniferous Tournaisian, Visean	2.70	3.1	13
	78	Upper Devonian	2.64	1.0	10
	77	Middle Devonian	2.71	3.3	3
	75	Lower Devonian	2.68	1.6	10
	73	Silurian Wenlock	2.81	1.0	2
	72	Silurian Llandovery	2.77	13.2	11
	70	Ordovician	2.77	9.5	10
	61	Torridonian Stoer, Sleat, Torridon	2.70	0.0	4
	57	Tertiary basalt and spilite	2.86	23.3	6
	53	Carboniferous basalt and spilite	2.75	56.3	8
	50	Devonian andesitic lava-tuff	2.74	17.1	12
	44	Ordovician andesitic lava, tuff	2.82	20.0	1
	42	Ordovician basalts-spilite-tuff	2.74	50.0	1
	35	Dolerite, camptonite	2.70	23.7	8
	34	Granite, syenite	2.75	13.6	7
	33	Diorite intrusion	2.76	32.2	9
	32	Gabbro intrusion	2.95	3.0	4
	31	Ultrabasic intrusion	2.99	20.0	3
	27	Dalradian meta-basic rocks	2.81	0.0	3
	24	Dalradian limestone	2.74	0.0	4
	21	Dalradian schists	2.86	0.0	2
	19	Dalradian grits and schists	2.82	0.0	4
	18	Dalradian quartz mica schists	2.74	0.0	5
	13	Dalradian psammites and schists	2.93	0.0	1
	2	Lewisian metasediments	2.81	40.0	1
	1	Lewisian gneiss	2.80	18.9	9

Fig. 1.11. Modelled geological profile from Coll to Cheviot (Profile 2 on Fig. 1.3). Observed gravity and magnetic anomalies have been modelled to a depth of 40 km using 2.5D polygons with density and magnetization properties consistent with observed rock properties. Number codes based on the published 1:625 000 BGS geological map.

Profile 1 Eskdale–Eriboll. Profile 1 (Fig. 1.10) was selected to avoid most of the voluminous late tectonic granites. It shows the Midland Valley terrane impinged by the basement to the Southern Uplands. The mid-crustal layer of the Southern Uplands includes units thought to be subducted volcanic arcs with bulk magnetisations close to 0.8 A/m. The Northern Belt of the Southern Uplands, immediately south of the Southern Upland Fault is the remnant of an accreted wedge and is here modelled to overlie the basement to the Midland Valley. This includes blocks of high magnetization (1.2 A/m), possibly ophiolitic material, at shallow depth.

In the Midland Valley the Bathgate magnetic anomaly is also modelled as an (ophiolitic?) basement with high magnetization beneath the Carboniferous volcanic rocks. The Midland Valley terrane extends beneath the Dalradian of the Grampian Highlands north of the Highland Boundary Fault approximately as far as the Boundary Slide. North of this, a thick wedge of siliclastic psammites up to 10 km thick lies above an indeterminate basement.

The 250 nT magnetic anomaly at the Geat Glen Fault is modelled as magnetic basement (susceptibility about 0.03 SI) within 2 km of the surface and extending on both sides of the fault. This basement block may be Early Proterozoic (1800 Ma, Rhinnian) by comparison with the magnetic anomalies over Islay. Low-density psammites of the Moine Supergroup overlie this basement to the north and might be up to about 7 km thick near the Grudie granite. Beneath these strata indeterminate basement with low magnetization is adjacent to the Lewisian terrane of the northern belt. Lewisian rocks extend only 10–20 km southeast of the Moine Thrust Zone.

Profile 2 Coll–Cheviot. Profile 2 (Fig. 1.11) runs southeast from near Mingulay in the Outer Hebrides, across the Sea of the Hebrides and Coll, across north Mull, through the Loch Ba centre and across the hidden Great Glen Fault in Loch Spelvie. It crosses Dalradian strata near Kerera and then the Devonian lavas of the Lorne Plateau before crossing the metavolcanic Tayvallich subgroup rocks near Loch Awe. It crosses the Garabal Hill Fault near Loch Fyne, the flat belt of the Southern Highlands and the Highland Boundary Fault near Loch Lomond. The profile crosses the Dungoil volcanic centre in the Campsie Fells and the central coalfield of the Midland Valley near Bathgate. It crosses the Midlothian coalfield, the Pentland Hills and the east Lothian coal basin and the Southern Upland Fault near to Leadburn, and continues across the Moorfoot Hills, the northeast Southern Uplands and the Cheviot granite.

In the Sea of the Hebrides, Permian–Mesozoic rocks to depths of about 1.5 km overlie Torridonian strata modelled to depths of about 4 km. The lower crustal zone commences at a depth of about 18 km beneath the basin. A prominent magnetic anomaly with a magnitude of 1000 nT on the east side of Coll is partly due to magnetite bearing phases in the Precambrian metasedimentary sequence. In the Coll Basin, a variable thickness of Palaeocene lavas overlie the Mesozoic and Torridonian rocks to 4–5 km depth, the variation in amplitude of the anomaly reflected in the thickness of the reversely magnetized lavas. The Mull Tertiary centre has several phases of polarity reversal but has been modelled approximately as a sub-cylindrical mass to depths of about 18 km.

At the Great Glen Fault, which has been invaded by the Mull centre, the magnetic basement on the southeast side is modelled at a depth of about 4 km but deepens rapidly to the southeast to over 12 km. Magnetic basement might not extend as far southeast as the Ericht–Laidon Fault passing through Loch Awe. Beneath the Lorne Plateau lavas a wedge of Siluro-Devonian rocks might be preserved. The Dalradian rocks of the Southern Highlands are modelled to a depth of about 12 km above a basement of unknown affinity, possibly Rhinnian. Southeast of the Garabal Hill Fault the Dalradian rocks are modelled as overthrust on to the Midland Valley terrane, with Early Palaeozoic sequences (Highland Border Series).

The Devonian strata at the Highland Boundary have been modelled as up to about 6 km thick in contact with Highland Border Series at the fault. The Midland Valley basement extends north beneath the Dalradian rocks. There is a regional magnetic low across much of the Southern Highlands with minimum values just northwest of the Campsie Fells lavas. The regional gravity and magnetic high over the central part of the Midland Valley has been modelled as Carboniferous lavas above a magnetic basement block on top of a high density, high velocity (6.4 km/s), basement at a depth of about 8 km. This basement extends southeast of the Southern Upland Fault and into the northern belt of the Southern Uplands.

A magnetic layer at depth 10–15 km in the Southern Uplands might be volcanic arc remnants or fragments of Avalonian crust thrust beneath the accreted strata. The Tweeddale granite has been modelled in the region northeast of Peebles to depths of about 6 km. The Cheviot granite is modelled as a deeper intrusion to depths of about 8 km with significant marginal dioritic phases and associated Devonian volcanic rocks.

Conclusions

The obduction, nappe stacking and topographic development focused in the Grampian and Scandian events (Fig. 1.6) has been largely obliterated by subsequent uplift and exhumation. Much of this uplift may have been enabled on major structures initiated as late-Caledonian transtensional structures, coeval with late intrusive activity and subsequently involved in orogenic collapse and significant Mesozoic extension. Many of the main structures need to be reassessed in terms of uplift and extension features with predominantly vertical dip-slip movements.

A complementary set of NNE and ESE structures can be identified in the geophysical data for north Scotland (Fig. 1.9). The NNE structures can be dated by association with appinitic and granitic rocks as c. 425 Ma, close to the late movements at the orogenic front. Some of the NNE structures are linked to Mesozoic faults offshore and are probably sites of post-Caledonian extension and footwall uplift across the Highlands. The depth to basement and the distribution of basement type is largely controlled by these structures and highlighted by residual gravity and magnetic anomalies.

1. The exposed Archaean rocks are separated into a series of basement footwall highs by major Mesozoic faults. This basement has a relatively high density so that the positive regional gravity anomalies identify the main basement highs on the Hebrides Shelf and the West Shetland Platform. On the Hebrides Shelf, the basement highs are divided into blocks of differing lithology, grade and age by northwest trending Palaeoproterozoic shear zones. Gravity data indicate that the South Harris Shear Zone and the Ness Shear Zone can be traced across the Hebrides Shelf but are terminated at the Outer Isles Fault.

2. The magnetic signature of the Archaean basement blocks is variable and can be the product of basic gneisses or intrusive granite-pegmatite vein complexes. North of Loch Laxford, the amphibolite grade migmatised biotite-hornblende (Laxfordian) gneiss is intruded by a red pegmatite-granite vein complex which is the most likely source of the prominent aeromagnetic anomaly centred on Strath Dionard. The Laxford Shear Zone

and other shear zones represent important basement boundaries. Regional magnetic maps identify a number of zones of magnetic basement on the Hebrides Shelf and the West Shetland Platform.

3. East of the Moine Thrust Zone, the exposed Archaean footwall block extends eastwards only as far as the NNE structure associated with the Fannich gravity lineament. This steep straight (and thus probably late) structure shows evidence of post Moine Thrust dislocation since high frequency magnetic anomalies associated with magnetic psammites in the Moine Nappe are truncated at the Fannich gravity lineament. East of this structure the basement to the Moine Supergroup is likely to be either Archaean–Proterozoic basement to an overridden foreland or a basement melange associated with allochthonous Moine strata assembled after the Grampian event.

4. The disposition and nature of the Caledonian orogenic front depends on the interaction of the shallow late thrusts (or slides?) with the steep NNE structures. The orthotectonic strata are thin-skinned west of the Fannich structure and thicker-skinned to the east. Across much of the West Orkney Basin and the West Shetland Platform the orogenic strata west of the Foula ridge are essentially thin-skinned. Some of the NNE structures are collinear with mapped faults in the West Orkney Basin which show clear evidence for Mesozoic extension. This suggests that onshore, the NNE structures may also have been involved in Mesozoic extension.

5. NNE structures cross the Northern Highlands, the Grampian Highlands and the Midland Valley terrane. Locally the NNE structures are coeval with appinites and related to late-Caledonian transtension and transpression and subsequently orogenic collapse. The presence of the NNE structures across many of the amalgamated Caledonian terranes suggests that they are not related to Proterozoic basin extension structures that controlled deposition of Torridonian and Moine strata.

6. The asymmetric magnetic anomaly along parts of the Great Glen Fault Zone can be modelled as a basement formation of relatively high magnetisation (1.0–1.2 A/m) locally within 1 km of ground level. This basement can be modelled as extending across the Great Glen Fault and therefore questions the significance of the fault as a major strike-slip boundary and as the southern limit of Archaean basement. The associated

gravity anomalies are inconsistent with a low-density late granite, but possible sources are a root zone network of leucocratic granite veins (as exposed in the Rosemarkie Complex) or a high-grade gneissose basement. The Rhinnian terrane has suitable geophysical properties and a similar geophysical signature. The Lossiemouth–Moray Firth magnetic anomaly may also have a similar source.

7. Generally, the signature of the Great Glen Fault offshore is a high frequency free-air gravity anomaly minima with associated discontinuous asymmetric magnetic anomaly. Using this signature the Great Glen Fault, or a splay fault, in Shetland most likely runs northeast through the southern arm of the Unst basin, and hence the Walls Boundary Fault north of Shetland might be a NNE transtensional structure which forms an important basement boundary.

8. In the Grampian Highlands the NNE West Grampian lineament forms an important basement boundary which is recognisable in isotopic data for the main granite suites, while the NNE Portsoy Shear Zone marks an important geophysical boundary. Both these are complementary structures to the ESE East Grampian lineament which has been the focus of late tectonic granites in the Grampian Highlands. This feature extends into the North Sea as the Central Graben Transform and arguably across the Highlands and into the Rockall Trough. This and other prominent ESE structures may have been involved in strain partitioning of the lithosphere during Cretaceous opening of the Rockall Trough.

9. The Midland Valley terrane extends northwards beneath the Dalradian of the Southern Highlands at least as far as the Boundary Slide. This terrane might also occur east of the Portsoy Shear Zone in NE Grampian and in the outer Moray Firth. The same terrane is modelled beneath the northern belt of the Southern Uplands. NNE structures such as the Forth lineament are present in the gravity data for the offshore part of the Midland Valley terrane. Truncation of magnetic anomalies in the Midland Valley suggests that NNE structures also extend through Distinkhorn and into the Grampian Highlands. High-amplitude magnetic anomalies in the Midland Valley terrane show broad correlation with Carboniferous volcanic activity but can also be interpreted as tilted blocks of magnetic basement some of which may be remnants of an early (Grampian) obducted ophiolite.

2 Themes in the early history of Scottish geology

D. R. OLDROYD & B. M. HAMILTON

In this chapter, new to this edition of *The Geology of Scotland*, we discuss some of the more interesting and important themes and personalities relating to the early history of Scottish geology. The topic is vast, and clearly it is impossible to cover all possible themes. A 'regional' approach is adopted, concentrating on selected areas of particular importance.

Present debates are necessarily rooted in the past. They grow from a complex intertwining of geographical, theoretical, personal, social, methodological, institutional and economic factors. We have sought to refer, albeit briefly, to all such aspects, but different features receive different emphases in the different regional accounts. The emphasis is chiefly on 19th century geology, but in most cases discussion has been carried through to the early 20th century, and in some cases we have briefly indicated how matters developed closer to the present. Although the material is organised chiefly by regions, an effort has also been made, as far as the subject matter allows, to provide a historically integrated account. Thus, we hope to offer a useful historical background to the more technical topics that appear in following chapters. The aim, however, is not to see the past from the eyes of the present; rather to see the present with the assistance of some knowledge of the past. Reversing the old adage, we should like to show that 'the past is the key to the present'.

Founding fathers

The history of geology delights in heroes, and James Hutton (1726–1797) and Charles Lyell (1797–1875) have long been counted among the greatest names in the history of the science. It has been usual, since the time of Archibald Geikie (1835–1924), to refer to the 'Scottish School of Geology,' with the physician, farmer, businessman, chemist, geologist, philosopher and gentleman scholar, James Hutton, as its founder. The claim that Hutton was the 'founder of modern geology' has been recently reaffirmed by his biographer, Dennis (D. R.) Dean (1992).

Hutton studied medicine at Edinburgh and Paris and took his M.D. in Leyden where, in 1749, he presented a dissertation 'On the circulation of the blood in the microcosm' (Donovan & Prentiss 1980). He also studied chemistry. But instead of undertaking a medical career, Hutton devoted himself to farming as one of the 'Improvers'. As shown by Jones (1985), Hutton had a hard time breaking in his land on his two farms in Berwickshire, and during his agricultural years he observed that soil was constantly being washed into the sea. It seemed that in time there might be none left, unless replenished in some way.

Given to metaphysical speculation, Hutton is usually thought to have been an exponent of the 'argument from design' (although Şengör (2001) has suggested that Hutton's 'design' passages were a 'front for agnosticism or even atheism'). As traditionally understood, Hutton believed that the earth was specially produced by Divine wisdom for mankind's well being, as could be known by appearances of design in the natural world. Unconstrained by 'biblical' ideas about the earth's age, Hutton argued that there must be some process whereby soil is renewed, otherwise the design would be imperfect. Soil, he thought, could be replenished by weathering of the underlying rock. But what might replenish the rock?

In response to this conundrum, Hutton devised his celebrated theory of the earth (Hutton 1785, 1788, 1795, 1899) which, in its final form, proposed a cycle of geological processes. The earth had an intensely hot interior beneath its solid external crust. By weathering and erosion, sediments were washed into the sea and consolidated to rock by heat and pressure. Eventually, the sediments became so heated, perhaps as air becomes heated when compressed, that expansion of subterranean material might occur, with molten magma being intruded into the overlying sedimentary rock, uplifting or tilting it and producing both large and small igneous intrusions of such rocks as granite or trap (basalt, which could also be extruded). Such changes might elevate rock previously below sea level, producing hills or even mountains. Then, by weathering and erosion, the crystalline rock might be exposed and weathered, eventually yielding agricultural soil and further sediment. As said, the process was supposedly cyclic, a model that may have appealed to Hutton because of his work on the circulation of the blood. The system was open-ended: 'we find no vestige of a beginning, no prospect of an end' (Hutton 1795, Vol. 1, p. 200). Hutton (1788, p. 217) also held that '[i]n examining things present, we have data from which to reason with regard to what has been seen'; a position that later came to be known as 'uniformitarianism'.

It is a nice question whether Hutton's theory preceded or followed his observations (Leveson 1996). Certainly it had predictive power. Rising magma supposedly heaved up overlying strata; and their exposed parts might subsequently be worn down by weathering and erosion. At some later stage, the truncated strata might lie below sea level, again covered by sediment. Then, following subsequent upheaval, one might have exposures of inclined strata topped by horizontal sediments, giving 'unconformities', as such structures were later termed.

Following his retirement from agriculture to Edinburgh about 1767, Hutton travelled with friends to various parts of Britain; and in 1785 he presented a preliminary account of his theories to the Royal Society of Edinburgh, arguing particularly for the internal heat of the earth on the basis of selected hand specimens (Hutton 1788). Subsequently, he recorded unconformities at several localities: in Arran (1787), at Jedburgh (1787), and, most notably, at Siccar Point (Plate 16), north of his Berwickshire farms (1788). In a famous excursion in 1788, made with the Edinburgh mathematics professor John Playfair (1748–1819) and Sir James Hall of Dunglass (1761–1832), they sailed along the coast until the party reached a junction between the 'primary micaceous schistus' (now called Silurian greywacke), and a 'covering of red horizontal sandstone' (our Old Red Sandstone). If the structure were formed as Hutton envisaged, it would take vast periods of time to be brought into being. As Playfair put it: 'The mind seemed to grow giddy by looking so far into the abyss of time' (Playfair 1805, p. 73). So the Scottish School of Geology, early on, provided both theoretical and empirical argument for the great age of the earth.

Hutton was undoubtedly looking for the unconformable contact at Siccar Point in the light of his theory. He already had information from 'Mr Hall of Whitehall' that a contact was to be found in 'Tour Burn' (now Tower Burn), near Siccar Point, and the friends did not merely examine the famous coastal site but made a systematic search for the line of unconformable contact in the whole neighbourhood (Hutton 1795, Vol. 1, pp. 453–467). Theory and observation were beautifully intertwined.

The notion of intrusive emplacement of granite, so important in Hutton's theory, was supported by his observations at Glen Tilt (1785) and Arran (1787). At the former he found veins of granite, apparently associated with an adjacent mass of that rock, penetrating and ramifying through 'schistus' and limestone on the valley floor. Many of his observations were drawn by his friend, John Clerk of Eldin (1728–1812) (Craig et al. 1978), who had practical interests in the mining industry.

In Arran, besides observing an unconformity (not so called) at Loch Ranza, Hutton developed the idea of the granite of Goat Fell having intruded the overlying strata, heaving them into a great dome; the granite being subsequently exposed by erosion. The idea was wonderfully depicted by Clerk in drawings reproduced in Craig et al. (1978).

Hutton's health was failing after 1793 and he did little further fieldwork. But Playfair extended his mentor's investigations, describing, amongst others, unconformities at Tor Bay (Devonshire), Thornton Force (Yorkshire), near the outlet of Ullswater (Lake District), and Cullen (Banffshire) (Playfair 1802; Tomkeieff 1962). Playfair and his friend Lord Webb Seymour also collected specimens at Glen Tilt (still held by the Hunterian Museum, Glasgow), illustrating Hutton's theory (Webb Seymour 1815).

Hutton's theory depended on the ability of weathering and erosion to produce major changes in landforms, given sufficient time. Water and wind acted as denuding agents, and the idea of glaciers having been larger in the past than at present was also considered: arising, for example, from the Alps having formerly been higher (Hutton 1795, Vol. 2, pp. 218–219). Playfair also discussed erosive processes and, like Hutton, thought rivers could carve their own valleys. Valleys were not produced by great *débacles*, as some of Hutton's critics such as the Swiss, Jean de Luc, contended. The theory of Hutton and Playfair was not without problems, however, given the existence of lakes in many regions. How could a river form a hollow for a lake? Playfair invoked ad hoc argument, supposing hypothetically that in some instances there might be subterranean water-soluble materials such as salt beds (Playfair 1802, p. 365).

Both Playfair and Hutton explained the earth's past in terms of presently observable processes. They thought that conditions were much the same in the past as at present (though in a manuscript on 'The Principles of Agriculture,' held at the National Library of Scotland, Hutton envisaged evolution, and even natural selection). Hutton was particularly concerned to deny that there was evidence for the condition of the earth's surface 'in the beginning'. Thus he rejected the existence of 'primitive' strata; the oldest observable strata might be called 'primary'(i.e. the most ancient ones recognizable after the long series of geological cycles), but nothing could be said to be primaeval or 'primitive'.

Hutton's theory was testable experimentally as well as in the field; but he showed little enthusiasm for geological experimentation and it was only after his death that Hall published the results of his experimental investigations. He showed that by *slow* cooling of molten basalt a substance was obtained that approximately resembled the original material (instead of a glass); that by heating powdered limestone under pressure a substance approximating to marble was produced, without loss of 'carbonic acid air'; and that by baking sand under brine a substance like sandstone could be obtained such as might be formed in sediments buried deep beneath the ocean, receiving heat from the earth's interior (Hall 1805, 1812, 1826). However, it proved impossible to produce granite in the manner that basalt was 'made', and even dolerite, melted and slowly cooled, produced a substance only approximately resembling the original material, as the samples from Hall's experiments, displayed at Edinburgh University, reveal.

Hutton, Playfair and Hall believed in the importance of heat in producing rocks, and came to be known as 'Vulcanists'. But there was a rival theory with which the Huttonian theory had to contend (Geikie 1905). Abraham Gottlob Werner (1749–1817), lecturer at the Freiberg Mining Academy, had taught that the crystalline rocks were precipitated from a primaeval ocean onto the surface of an irregular terrestrial core. As deposition proceeded, a mixture of mechanically-derived material and crystalline matter was deposited ('Transition Strata'); and eventually material of wholly mechanical origin ('*Floetz*' or 'Layered' Strata). However, the sequence of events was complicated by ad hoc changes of level of the hypothetical universal ocean, and by changing conditions of storm or calm; and the theory was physically implausible (Ospovat, in Werner 1971).

However, Werner's 'Neptunist' theory had the merit of proposing an ordered sequence of strata. And (in Thomas Kuhn's language) it provided a paradigm for the 'normal scientist'; i.e. Werner's Saxon/Thuringian sedimentary sequence served as an exemplar for studying the stratigraphic column elsewhere in the world. And his students spread and applied his ideas. Robert Jameson (1774–1854), Professor of Natural History at Edinburgh, a student of Werner from 1800 to 1804, actively promoted his teacher's ideas in Scotland, establishing a Wernerian Natural History Society in Edinburgh. But Jameson espoused 'Neptunist' ideas before his sojourn in Germany. They were initially derived from lectures by John Walker in Edinburgh, and from Richard Kirwan in Ireland (Sweet & Waterston 1967). Even before he went to Germany, Jameson claimed evidence from Portrush, Antrim, where ammonites had been found beneath, and apparently merged with, a basalt flow (Jameson 1796, *fide* Sweet & Waterston 1967, p. 95). On examination by Huttonians in Edinburgh the fossils were judged to be in 'a sort of hornstone' baked by the lava (Playfair 1802, p. 287) 'a sufficient refutation of the volcanic opinion'.

Like Werner, Jameson was an able mineralogist. He was also an energetic field geologist. It should be noted that at the beginning of the 19th century the same field observations could be, and sometimes were, interpreted equally well through the lenses of either Huttonian or Wernerian theories (Rudwick 1962). For example, Hutton's section through Arran could, apart from the granitic veins and the hypothetical magma chamber shown in Clerk's drawings, be construed quite satisfactorily in terms of Werner's theory as well as Hutton's (Oldroyd 1971). It is interesting, then, that Jameson knew about unconformities (as at Loch Ranza), and introduced the terms 'conformable' and 'unconformable' (Jameson 1805, pp. 37–38), the term 'unconformity' being a translation of the Wernerian term '*abweichende Lagerung*' or 'deviating stratification' (Tomkeieff 1962). Jameson (1805, pl. 4, fig. 2) figured

'Newer Floetz Sandstone' (Upper Old Red Sandstone) lying unconformably on folded 'Transition Rocks' (Silurian Greywacke) at Birrenswark Hill, Ecclefechan.

In his autobiography, Darwin (1887, Vol. 1, p. 41) described Jameson's lectures as 'incredibly dull'; and he was almost put off geology by Jameson's interpretation of the igneous rocks of Salisbury Crags in Neptunist terms. Jameson has also been seen as providing a link between Neptunism, the 'catastrophist' ideas of Georges Cuvier, and ideas about the Deluge (Gillispie 1959, p. 68). To be sure, Jameson encouraged the English translation by Robert Kerr of Cuvier's 'Preliminary Discourse' (Cuvier 1813) and furnished it with notes and an account of Cuvier's geological discoveries; but by the 1827 edition 'Jameson was in favor neither of the Mosaic flood nor of sudden Cuvierian revolutions as major geological agents' (Secord 1991). In fact, Jameson had some sympathy for evolutionary ideas. Moreover, in his later years, as editor of the *Edinburgh New Philosophical Journal*, he supported the introduction of important Continental geological theory into Scotland, notably Louis Agassiz's ideas on glaciation (Agassiz 1838).

Scotland was one of the first countries to be geologically surveyed, albeit sketchily. In 1808, a crude geological map of Scotland was presented to the Geological Society by the Genevan, Louis Albert Necker de Saussure (1786–1861), who studied in Edinburgh under Jameson in 1806 and spent his later years in Skye. In Ireland, Richard Griffith prepared a preliminary map ready as early as 1814 (published 1838). In England, William Smith published his first full map of the country (with parts of Scotland) in 1815. In Scotland, it was John Macculloch (1773–1835) who almost singlehandedly surveyed Scotland and published (posthumously) a simple map covering the whole country (Macculloch 1836).

Born in the Channel Islands, Macculloch trained in medicine at Edinburgh, where he also studied chemistry and became interested in geology. He was employed as chemist to the Board of Ordnance, and became geologist to the Trigonometric Survey from 1814 to 1821, to make an 'examination of mountains with a view to the discovery of a situation geologically fit for the repetition of the experiment on the attraction of mountains' (Cumming 1985, p. 78). During his work for the Trigonometric Survey, Macculloch also compiled much geological information, and in 1825 succeeded in obtaining Treasury funds for a geological survey of Scotland. By Macculloch's death in 1835 (following a fall from his coach during his honeymoon, poor man) there was enough information for publication of a 'broad-brush' geological map of Scotland. Jameson, however, was aggrieved, thinking that he should have been contracted for the task.

Macculloch's most detailed work was in the Hebrides. His *Description of the Western Islands* (Macculloch 1819) attracted favourable attention, and he was elected FRS (1820). He mapped the 'traps' of Skye and other islands of the Inner Hebrides, and raised the question of the relative ages of the Black and Red Cuillin Hills. In the Northwest Highlands, Macculloch mapped outcrops of sedimentary rocks (quartzrock, fucoid beds, and limestone) from Durness and Eriboll southwards to Skye. He made no distinction on his map between (Lewisian) gneiss and (Moine) schist, and he conflated the sandstones of the west coast (Torridonian Sandstone) and the east coast (Old Red Sandstone). He proposed a simple conformable arrangement for the structure of the Northwest Highlands, with a straightforward sequence of strata, dipping from west to east, between Durness and Eriboll. Macculloch's ideas set the scene for subsequent debates about these rocks. In his later years, Macculloch (1831) tended towards 'scriptural geology' and his early reputation (Geological Society President, 1816) was not maintained. However, one must admire his remarkable effort in constructing even a very general view of Scotland's geology.

While Macculloch's reputation waned, Lyell's flourished remarkably. Much of his work lies outside the scope of the present review, as it was done outside Scotland. Even so, he was arguably the most distinguished 19th century Scottish geologist, renowned for his *Principles of Geology* (1831–1833). Son of a wealthy gentleman, with property at Kinnordy, Forfarshire, Lyell's family settled in Hampshire, and he made only occasional visits to Scotland.

In 1817, Lyell made a field excursion to the Inner Hebrides, sailing round Mull and visiting Staffa, where he was able to provide information useful to his teacher at Oxford, William Buckland, who did not accept a hypothesis propounded by a recent visitor, Leopold von Buch, that Fingal's Cave was formed along the line of a dyke intruded into the columnar basalt (Wilson 1972, p. 53).

One of Lyell's first researches (though carried out in part with Buckland) involved a careful survey of the region round Kinnordy House, situated near Kirriemuir, just south of what is now called the Highland Boundary Fault. His large geological map of the counties of Forfar and Angus, coloured onto a topographic map by John Ainslie (1794) and made to assist Macculloch's work, survives at Kinnordy House. The main features appear in Lyell (1829), which also has some coloured sections. The map shows the general NE–SW strike of the strata. The Grampians are shown as 'micaceous schist', with a band of 'greywacke and clay slate' on the southern margin. Interestingly, Lyell also depicted a narrow parallel exposure of 'dike of serpentine'. This is very pronounced in field exposures, and its presence is accounted for today by a complex theory involving subduction occurring at a zone associated with the fault. Lyell could only surmise that the serpentine might represent an igneous dyke. He could hardly have picked a more difficult place to cut his teeth in geology, and one may wonder whether it put him off 'hard-rock' studies! The fault-complex was not recognized: Lyell's section simply had the younger strata 'curved up' against the serpentine rock.

However, Lyell had much more success for the southern area of his map, with his account of the marls associated with the small lochs near Kinnordy. He showed that at Kinnordy Loch the lime was the product of springs rising from underlying sandstones and was ultimately derived from accumulated freshwater shells and algae. At Forfar Loch, he could see the limestone actually being formed; and hence he had a present-day example of the formation of strata analogous to those described by Brongniart and Cuvier for the Paris Basin. Thus past and present processes and products were deftly tied together. So Lyell's work in his home region provided one of the warrants for his subsequent well known 'uniformitarian' methodology (previously adumbrated by Hutton). In his figured section, Lyell also showed that he understood the general structure of the region with the sandstones forming a 'trough' in Strathmore, where Kinnordy was situated, and a 'saddle' in the Sidlaw Hills to the south. He later used these to illustrate the concepts of 'anticlinal' and 'synclinal' in his *Elements of Geology* (Lyell 1838, pp. 99–101).

However, perhaps Lyell's most interesting Scottish contributions related to glacial theory. The 'drift' deposits over many parts of northern Britain had been thought by Buckland (e.g.) to be residua of the biblical Deluge. Lyell found this idea unsatisfactory as it conflicted with his belief that past conditions were essentially the same as those of the present, and certainly that present processes should be used as the guide to understanding the earth's geological history. His idea was, rather, that 'drift' deposits were, as their surviving name suggests, emplaced by drifting icebergs, which could deposit great loads of transported debris when they eventually melted. This hypothesis accorded with Lyell's 'uniformitarianism'.

Despite initial opposition to Agassiz's theory of an *Eiszeit*, Lyell countenanced some substantial climatic changes, according to the distribution of land and sea at any given epoch. (In Lyell's thinking, land was always rising and falling in different regions; and the occurrence of an unusually large amount of high land near the poles would cause global cooling.) Agassiz visited the British Association meeting in Glasgow (1840), and his eloquent arguments successfully converted a number of British geologists, notably Buckland, to the notion of glaciers being responsible for 'drift' deposits (or 'diluvium'). For a time, Lyell was a convert, especially when Buckland visited him at Kinnordy after the Glasgow meeting and was able to show him glacial moraines, and 'perched lakes', such as Loch Kinnordy, that could be ascribed to glacial influences on the topography. Lyell (1838–1840 (1840)) renounced his earlier view of a general submergence, with floating icebergs depositing their cargoes of erratic blocks. He envisaged, rather, that there had been glacially dammed lakes, and that stratified sands and gravels had been deposited therein.

But influential geologists, such as Roderick Murchison, William Whewell, and George Greenough, rejected Agassiz's view, and before long Lyell (1841) recanted. He wavered back towards Agassiz's theory in 1858 (K. M. Lyell 1881, Vol. 2, p. 279), and eventually in his *Antiquity of Man* (1863) he fully adopted the glacial theory. But by then he had accepted Darwin's evolutionary arguments (in the tenth edition of the *Principles*). In so doing, Lyell made radical changes to his general worldview, and his long-held geological beliefs were substantially modified.

The next generation of Scottish geologists, such as the Geikie brothers (Archibald and James), Andrew Ramsay (1814–1891), Benjamin Peach (1842–1926), and John Horne (1848–1928) all adhered to glacial doctrine. Even in the 1840s, the physicist James Forbes (1809–1868) (1846) was making close investigations of glacial phenomena in Skye.

The amateur tradition

Amateur geologists made important contributions to the study of geology in Scotland in at least the first half of the 19th century, though after the beginnings of official Survey work in 1854, and the establishment of the Scottish Branch of the Survey (1867) under Archibald Geikie, the relative significance of amateur work declined.

The words 'amateur' and 'professional' were used somewhat differently in the 19th century from today's usage. The Surveyors thought of themselves as the professionals, and all other geologists, from university professors to local collectors, were amateurs. This was not necessarily a derogatory epithet, however, and amateurs contributed much to early Scottish geology. Through his Wernerian Natural History Society, and the *Edinburgh New Philosophical Journal*, Jameson did much to encourage amateur geological enquiry. Another important outlet for amateur publication was the *Transactions of the Highland and Agricultural Society of Scotland*.

Some of the early amateur geologists undertook useful mapwork. Necker travelled extensively, and, as mentioned, produced a 'geognostic' map of Scotland as early as 1808 (Eyles 1948). Based on Wernerian principles, granite was represented as 'Unstratified Primitive'. The great mass of the Highlands and the gneiss of the Outer Hebrides were represented as 'Stratified Primitive'. The Southern Uplands greywackes were given as Transition rocks. The Midland Valley sediments, the Old Red Sandstones of the east coast, and the sediments of the north of

Skye were represented as Secondary or *Floetz* rocks. The basalts of the Inner Hebrides were called 'Trap'. The (Torridonian) sandstones of the northwest were not represented, revealing that the region was geologically unknown at that time. Later Necker (1821) published his *Voyage en Écosse*, giving a good geological conspectus of the country as then known.

Ami Boué (1794–1881), a man of Swiss extraction, studied medicine in Edinburgh and learned Wernerian geology from Jameson. However, after work in Central France, he adopted a Vulcanist perspective, and in a volume on Scottish geology (Boué 1820), gave a detailed account of his travels and the geology of the country. He interpreted the 'trap' rocks of the Midland Valley (such as those of the Ochil Hills) as the outpourings of ancient volcanoes. His book included a geological map of Scotland, which represented the Old Red rocks of Fife as 'grès houiller'.

In 1826, Roderick Murchison (1792–1871), who had only recently taken to geology, visited Scotland, and the following year he made an extensive tour with the Cambridge geologist Adam Sedgwick (1785–1873), the two travelling together round the northern part of the country (Sedgwick & Murchison 1828*a, b, c*). Not long before (1822–1824), Sedgwick had been teaching himself how to study unfossiliferous rocks of complex structure in the Lake District. There, he had prepared field maps, looking for rocks of different lithologies, and indications of their dips and strikes ('bearings'). He was attempting to discern some general structural patterns, and eventually he thought that he had enough evidence to support the theory of Élie de Beaumont, that different mountain ranges were formed at different times in specific directions, arising from a patterned contraction of a cooling earth (Sedgwick 1831). This was the only way to proceed at that time in unfossiliferous strata.

However, given that much of Sedgwick and Murchison's journey was made round the coast by sea, they naturally gave attention to the sedimentary deposits as they appeared in the coastal regions, and they were on the lookout for fossils in what they took to be Secondary strata. Their most detailed section (Sedgwick & Murchison 1828*a*) was along the northeast shore of Arran, and it is interesting that they depicted a great anticline in the northern part of the island, with Old Red Sandstone at the centre, extending to New Red Sandstone on the northern and southern flanks. Schist and granite (Goat Fell) were depicted in the background; but there was no apparent causal connection between the folding and alteration of the strata and the intruded granite, such as Hutton had earlier envisaged.

The symmetry of northern Arran seems to have appealed, for Sedgwick and Murchison also envisaged that the sandstones of the mainland west coast (Torridonian) and east coast (Old Red Sandstone, and what they took to be New Red Sandstone at Dunnet Head) were essentially one and the same. The sandstones 'framed' the central mountainous regions of supposed ancient rock. But no close examination was made of the west-coast sandstones, Macculloch's work being relied on in this area. Later, the correlation of the eastern and western sandstones was cause of much of the misunderstanding of the structure of the Northwest Highlands.

In Sedgwick's Lakeland work, he correlated strata with similar structural features and lithologies; and perhaps he was trying to do this with respect to the eastern and western sandstones of northern Scotland. There was a tension in the Sedgwick/Murchison papers, however, for if the eastern and western sandstones were one and the same they should perhaps have had opposed dips (as at Arran), rather than similar ones (as on the surrounds of the Highlands). Of course, no fossils were found in the western sandstones, but the travellers gave close attention to the fossil fish that were by then being discovered in the strata of the east coast, and some specimens were figured, having been transmitted to Cuvier in Paris for identification.

While Sedgwick and Murchison did not do enough work in the Northern Highlands to get a clear understanding of the structure of the region, there was one amateur who mapped the area in the 1830s with remarkable success. This was Robert Hay Cunningham (1815–1842), another Jameson student. He did fieldwork in the Inner Hebrides, Kirkcudbrightshire, the Lothians, Banffshire and the Northwest Highlands, publishing in the *Memoirs of the Wernerian Society* (1831–1837), and in prize essays for the Highland and Agricultural Society. One of these, 'Geognostic Account of the County of Sutherland' (1841), was a remarkable achievement, and there exists also an impressive manuscript geological map of Sutherland, dated 1838, held at the Royal Scottish Museum (Waterston 1957). Hay Cunningham distinguished between the western gneiss and the eastern 'mica slates' (Moine schists) and noted their different strikes. He observed (as had Macculloch and Murchison) that the western sandstones ('red conglomerate with sandstone') were unconformable on the gneiss, and he mapped in the Durness Limestone, the brilliant white quartz-rock, and an earthy rock of 'wood-brown appearance' and 'calcareous strata of brownish yellow colour' (later known as the 'serpulite grit' and the 'fucoid beds'). He also remarked that the quartz-rock lay unconformably on the western sandstones. (See Chapter 3.)

However, in some localities, as at Loch Eriboll, Hay Cunningham recorded gneiss overlying quartz-rock; whereas east of Ben Arkle he found quartz-rock atop gneiss. This was a puzzle, and Macculloch's suggestion that there were two gneisses, one above and the other below the quartz-rock, was followed. Hay Cunningham also followed Sedgwick and Murchison in supposing that the eastern and western sandstones of northern Scotland belonged to the same unit. Hay Cunningham's achievements in mapping in Sutherland over three seasons were remarkable, but he died young at 27.

Regarding fossils, Andrews (1982) has suggested that there may have been collections as far back as the 17th century. In the 19th century, there were early newspaper reports of findings of fossil fish, and it is known that Sir George Sinclair, a Caithness MP, sent specimens to Jameson in 1826 (Anon 1826). Further, Andrews has shown the considerable extent of searches for fish and reptile remains in the next few decades, especially in the region of the Moray Firth and in Caithness. Here, amateurs did sterling work, making large numbers of specimens available to the metropolitan experts.

Among the amateur collectors and naturalists, one may mention the Reverend David Ure, Glasgow; James Christie, a Banff solicitor; John Fleming, Minister of Flisk on the south of the Tay, and later professor at Aberdeen and the Free Church College, Edinburgh; the Reverend John Anderson, Minister of Newburgh; Dr John Malcolmson of Elgin; Dr Samuel Hibbert, Edinburgh physician and professor of natural history at the University; Robert Dick, the famed 'baker of Thurso'; his friend Charles Peach, of the coastguard service at Wick; Sir John Robison, Secretary of the Royal Society of Edinburgh; Patrick Duff, town clerk of Elgin; the Inverness solicitors George and Peter Anderson; George Gordon, Minister of Birnie near Elgin; Sir William Jardine of Applegarth near Dumfries; William Cole, Earl of Enniskillen; John Martin, land surveyor; the Reverend Henry Duncan, Minister of Ruthwell near Dumfries; and most famously Hugh Miller (1802–1856), the stonemason from Cromarty and later editor of the evangelical newspaper *The Witness,* whose writings did more than those of any other early Victorian naturalist to popularize geology and natural history. Of the amateur collectors, the Englishman Sir Philip de Grey Egerton developed the most

significant private collection and wrote the most important theoretical papers.

Collection of fossil fish and other vertebrate remains, and fossil footprints, was a special interest of the Scottish amateurs. Anderson recorded in a Perth newspaper (1829) that he had found specimens at Clashbinnie. Subsequently Anderson (1841) described discoveries at what came to be a famous site: Dura Den, between Cupar and St Andrews (see Chaper 8). But the best known fish collector was Hugh Miller, through his book *The Old Red Sandstone* (1841). Miller has recently attracted renewed attention, and many aspects of his life, work, and character have been analysed (Shortland 1996). Miller was an autodidact who, though he came from a middle-class family, deliberately chose the career of stonemason. Thereby, he observed rocks of many kinds, and became interested in the fossils he had found in the Liassic and Old Red Sandstone strata near Cromarty. Many fine specimens were collected and where necessary were reconstructed on 'architectural' principles (Oldroyd 1996a).

Miller's work was initially encouraged by the Anderson brothers in Inverness, later by Malcolmson, and eventually by such notables as Murchison and also Agassiz, the authority on fossil fish. Information and specimens were supplied to these distinguished experts. In his middle career, Miller began to engage in church politics, and was invited to Edinburgh in 1840 to edit *The Witness*, which published accounts of his scientific investigations. *The Old Red Sandstone* first appeared in its pages in serial form.

In *The Old Red Sandstone*, Miller proposed that the fossil record showed 'progress' (though it was discontinuous and seemed to betoken separate creations). For example, the Old Red began with the little *Pterichthys* and culminated with the large *Megalichthys*. But in 1848 Miller visited the Orkneys, and saw there the giant *Asterolepis* which occurred in the *lower* beds of the Old Red Sandstone (not Lower ORS as presently defined).

So, reconsidering his theory of progress, Miller (1849) suggested that the fossil record did not display continuous progress; as his opponent Robert Chambers (1802–1871), anonymous author of *Vestiges of the Natural History of Creation* (1844), maintained. It now seemed to Miller, in the light of the Orkney evidence, that the 'chain' of Nature was periodically broken. Organic change occurred in forward leaps, followed by retrogressions (Oldroyd 1996a). Such linkage of contemporary religious and social beliefs was not attempted so directly by other geologists, either amateur or professional. The precise nature of Miller's intellectual programme has been explored only recently (Henry 1996).

In his geological explanations, Miller consistently used analogies from everyday life, and was a consummate exponent of the principle that the 'present is the key to the past', an idea which he probably passed on to his protege, Archibald Geikie, who popularized the maxim in his *Founders of Geology* (1905). However, though skilled at extracting and reconstructing fossils, Miller's ventures into stratigraphy were not a success. He had an excellent idea of the geological structure of the region round Cromarty (which he naively thought was a geological 'epitome' for the whole world), but like Sedgwick and Murchison, and Hay Cunningham, Miller believed that the sandstones of the east and west coasts of north Scotland belonged to the same formation.

Some of the most interesting amateur research occurred in the Elgin area, through the investigations of the Reverend George Gordon (1801–1893) and his circle. Indeed, as has been shown by Collie (1991), Collie & Diemer (1995), Keillar & Smith (1995), Collic (1995) and Collie & Bennett (1996), the group of Moray amateur naturalists played a significant role in the discovery of fossil reptiles in the district, in sorting out the stratigraphy of the area, and assisting front-rank figures such as Huxley and Murchison in their studies of the region. Through his network of correspondence, Gordon served as an important 'clearing-house' for information on the study of natural history in northeast Scotland.

When Murchison and Sedgwick visited the Elgin area in 1827 they regarded the sandstones as Old Red, equivalent to strata found on the northern side of the Moray Firth, later studied by Miller, and those further north in Caithness (Diemer 1996). Subsequently (1844), unusual fossil remains were discovered at Lossiemouth by a workman named Anderson. Duff initially thought they belonged to a fish, an opinion supported by Agassiz, who named them *Staganolepis robertsoni*. Further material was discovered and passed to Huxley in London, who regarded it as reptilian. Another specimen was discovered at Spynie quarry near Elgin, and identified as a reptile by Gideon Mantell (Mantell & Brickenden 1852): *Telerpeton elginense*. In accordance with the received understanding of the age of the strata, Mantell thought it belonged to the *Old* Red Sandstone; and were this true it would be of profound importance in that the origin of reptiles would be carried right back into the Palaeozoic. It became a matter of pride among the Moray amateurs that their region had such geologically important fossils. Their Devonian age was supported by Murchison, who visited the region with Gordon and others in 1858 and 1859. Murchison advocated the Devonian interpretation in his address to the British Association in Aberdeen in 1859 (unpublished in Report; but see Murchison 1859a).

Gordon himself initially doubted the Old Red determination, but fell in with Murchison. Unfortunately, Murchison (1867) later changed his mind, in response to the discovery of an Elgin-type reptile, *Hyperodapedon*, in an incontrovertibly Triassic bed, the Keuper Sandstone, near Warwick (Huxley 1869). This left the Moray amateurs isolated, their Devonian reptiles transferred to the Triassic; but they could not prevail over the specialists. The Elgin controversy manifested the growing hegemony of professional geology.

Besides studying fossil vertebrate remains, the amateurs also interested themselves in fossil footprints. About 1824, a five-foot slab of red sandstone from Corncocklemuir Quarry, Annandale, Dumfriesshire, was discovered by a Mr Carruthers of Dormont. It bore the impressions of 24 footprints of the fore and hind feet of some short-legged but wide-tracked animal. They were given to Henry Duncan (1776–1846), antiquarian and minister of Ruthwell, near Dumfries. The impressions were unlike anything he had seen previously and after searching the quarry he had casts made and sent to Buckland in Oxford in 1827 (G. Duncan 1848; Hall 1910; Sarjeant 1974).

After a series of experiments, with various animals being made to walk over 'pye-crust, wet sand and soft clay', Buckland announced that the footprints had been made by a tortoise (H. Duncan 1831, p. 202). Buckland was surprised that there might be tortoises at such an early period, and informed Duncan that he regarded his discovery as 'one of the most curious and most important that ha(d) ever been made in geology' (G. Duncan 1848, p. 183).

Such was the early interest in fossil footprints that Sedgwick and Murchison made a southern diversion in their 1827 journey to examine the claims. They went away not completely convinced by the evidence they saw in the quarry. However, in Edinburgh, Professor David Ansted and Sir David Brewster agreed with Buckland as to the value of Duncan's discovery (Hall 1910, p. 88). Duncan also attempted to deduce the conditions in which the animal lived. He was thus reconstructing the environment of Corncocklemuir in the geological past. This indicates that Scottish amateurs were attempting work

similar in kind to that of Cuvier in Paris and of David Ure in Glasgow (1793).

The new fossil discoveries raised the issue of 'extinction' as a significant philosophical and religious problem. The concept of the Deluge as a geological agent was still current and used to explain fossil finds in lieu of better theories for their emplacement. For a clergyman like Duncan, there was a potential conflict in this find. Present-day processes could explain the circumstances of footprints' preservation, but the final uplifted position of the remains was explained by citing Cuvier's 'mighty but mysterious convulsions'.

Further fossil footprints were found in Dumfriesshire. Robert Harkness (1816–1878) (1850) mentioned the Corncocklemuir footprints, and also those found at Locharbriggs and Caerlaverock, together with *Cheirotherium* prints from younger rocks near Annan and Kirkpatrick Fleming. At nearby Applegarth, Sir William Jardine amassed a large collection of footprints, which he housed at Jardine Hall and described in a mammoth, lavishly illustrated book, *The Ichnology of Annandale* (Jardine 1853).

In 1833, footprints had been found in Craigleith quarry in Edinburgh and were described by one George Fairholme in catastrophist terms. Regrettably, they were lost from the Museum of the Royal Society of Edinburgh. However, the most important finds outwith Dumfriesshire were made in 1850 when Captain Lambart Brickenden discovered footprints in Mason's Heugh quarry near Elgin (Brickenden 1850) They were apparently made by a tailed vertebrate quadruped, with hind feet larger than its fore feet. Subsequent work on footprints played a considerable role in the discussions about the age of the east-coast sandstones, at Moray and elsewhere, holding the line temporarily for the Old Red rather than the New Red view for the Elgin reptiles (Diemer 1996).

In the 1830s and 1840s, amateur geologists also accomplished a remarkable amount of mapping. In 1839, the Highland and Agriculture Society established prizes for 'geological surveys and descriptions of various parts of this kingdom', the desire being to establish the relationships between soil types and underlying strata. In response, farmers, architects, lawyers, mining engineers, surveyors, clergymen, estate factors, and private scholars such as Hay Cunningham and James Nicol (1810–1879), produced coloured geological maps and sections of much of Scotland's farming and industrial regions.

Such mapwork was undertaken on a local basis, and colouring was inconsistent, but a considerable amount of surveying was accomplished before systematic official work began in 1854. In this regard, the situation was different from England, where government sponsored survey began in 1835. A few of the Scottish amateurs eventually turned professional or became full-time geologists. Most notably, there was Andrew Ramsay, who produced a study of the geology of Arran (1841), joined the Survey proper that year, and became Director General in 1872; and James Nicol, who produced a survey of Peebles in 1843, worked in the Southern Uplands and the Northwest Highlands with Murchison in 1858, and obtained chairs at Cork (1849) and Aberdeen (1853).

The Southern Uplands

In the 18th century, Hutton studied the rocks from Berwickshire to Wigtownshire, and, as mentioned, based some of his theorising on the evidence of unconformity at Siccar Point. Jedburgh, further south, provided confirmatory evidence. The important Wrae Limestone fossils of Peeblesshire were mentioned in *Theory of the Earth* (Vol. 1, p. 334–336). Jameson (1805) classified the rocks from the Pentland Firth to the Solway Firth as 'Transitional/Grauwacke'. The extreme folding of the area was discussed by Hall, and simulated by demonstration models, in a paper read before the Royal Society of Edinburgh (Hall 1812). He also tried to establish a link between folding and the intrusion of various granite masses, especially with reference to one west of Loch Ken: Cairn Edward.

A second phase in the mapping and understanding of this comparatively wild and inaccessible region began with publications by the amateurs Charles MacLaren (1782–1866) (1839) and John Carrick Moore (1840). Investigating rocks in the northeast of the region, MacLaren found remains of *Orthoceras* and some trilobites, while Carrick Moore found graptolites (so determined by Lyell) at Loch Ryan. Hay Cunningham noted the relations between the folded rocks and intrusions, previously remarked by Hall. In his *Guide to the Geology of Scotland* (1844), Nicol lamented the paucity of fossils, only graptolites and a few shells having been found. The specimens available were insufficient to correlate the rocks with others elsewhere, or even put them in chronological order. However, four years later, in his paper on the geology of the valley of the Tweed and its tributaries (Nicol 1848) he was, with the help of fossils and aided by the Survey Palaeontologist, John Salter, able to make correlations with rocks from Murchison's Welsh Silurians; and in the third edition of *Siluria* Murchison (1859*b*) acknowledged Nicol's work on the relationship between the Wrae fossils and associated schistose masses. Discoveries of graptolites from Grieston (near his home at Traquair) and Thornilee (Thornylee) led Nicol to place these rocks in the Llandeilo (the unit into which Murchison and the Survey officers were inclined to place all graptolite-bearing dark shales). Also, influenced by the French theorist Élie de Beaumont, Nicol deduced the broad structure of the region, as an anticline, with axis running from east of Innerleithen to Loch Skene, north of Moffat (Nicol 1850). Murchison (and later the Surveyors) believed that the Southern Uplands were a mass of conformable strata, over twenty thousand feet thick, of largely uniform lithology and virtually destitute of fossils except for a few graptolites and some brachiopods and other invertebrates in the west.

Harkness (1851) described a fairly detailed succession, and identified three parallel bands of black shales, traced along the strike for many miles in the Hartfell and Grieston area, Dobb's Linn (19th century spelling), Frenchland Burn, Selcoth Burn, and Craigmurchan Scaurs. These sites are distant from one another and separated by drift-covered moorland. Outcrops can only be seen in isolated river-cut cliffs and stream beds, and occasional quarries. The steeply inclined NNW-dipping strata were attributed to parallel *faults*, and repetition of beds was thought to be a possibility. Harkness proposed a second anticlinal axis, different from that envisaged by Nicol, from Dumfries and Kirkcudbright, suggesting the Criffel Granite intrusion as the cause. He found graptolites and *Orthoceras* in the Kirkcudbright area and correlated the strata with the Wenlock Shales. Following such preliminary work, Sedgwick and Murchison, with the knowledge gained from their work on the Lower Palaeozoic of Wales, sought to correlate the Welsh and Scottish rocks.

In 1850, Sedgwick, who had visited the Southern Uplands in 1841 with Carrick Moore, published a succession based on traverses made in 1848, hoping to determine the structure of the area, using the tectonic theories of the American brother geologists, H. D. and W. B. Rogers. Sedgwick distinguished five units based on lithology and fossils (1851) and thus a preliminary stratigraphic framework for the whole area was established.

Murchison revisited the area in 1850, making a number of traverses, collecting many fossils and making correlations with his Welsh units. For structure, Murchison (1851) envisaged a broad anticline passing between Dumfries and Lockerbie, but

tight folding made it difficult to work out a succession. He suggested that folding, not faulting, might cause repetition of the beds. He was inclined to place the rocks of the centre of the anticline below the Llandeilo and Bala, but above the 'lowest Silurian'. He could not be more precise because the only fossils found were graptolites, the potential stratigraphic importance of which had not yet been realised.

By the mid-1850s, more graptolite species were known, and Murchison plotted their stratigraphic distribution and range in the 1859 edition of *Siluria*. There was awareness of great structural disturbances causing repetition of beds, and correlation with the Welsh Silurians was again attempted. One drawback was that the commonly used traverse method of fieldwork, and the use of small-scale maps, could only reveal the broad geological pattern. In the Southern Uplands, with isolated exposures, and a comparatively featureless landscape, which did not reflect the rock types and structures below the 'drift', this procedure was inadequate. But workers such as Murchison and Geikie were under no illusions about this.

From 1854, the Geological Survey began a systematic effort to map the south of Scotland. Ramsay began in Haddingtonshire in the east and by 1867 Archibald and James Geikie, James Young and Benjamin Peach had completed large portions of Haddingtonshire and Berwickshire, the Edinburgh neighbourhood, Peebles and Ayrshire. Their conclusions, emphasizing petrology and structure, were summarized by Geikie (1869). The idea of repetition of beds, as envisaged by Murchison and Harkness, but with different explanations, was accepted, but the French/Bohemian stratigrapher Joachim Barrande's suspect theory of colonies underlay the palaeontological explanations. According to this convenient theory (on which see Perner (1937) and Kriz & Pojeta (1974)), there could be 'colonies' of 'precursorial' forms of various species inhabiting certain areas before the more general introduction of those species from their main centres. This allowed one to discount the basic principles of 'William Smith' stratigraphy. The theory was later discredited by, among others, John Marr (1880), who showed that the faunal repetitions in Bohemia were caused by faulting. Be this as it may, the Survey made rather free use of the hypothesis to account for stratigraphic anomalies in the Southern Uplands (Murchison 1859*b*, p. 400) where, as in Barrande's Bohemia, the apparent palaeontological and stratigraphic anomalies were actually due to faulting and associated structural complexities.

Overall, however, the new Survey work confirmed the earlier findings of Murchison, Sedgwick, Harkness and Nicol. Several thousand fossil specimens were collected by the Survey staff and palaeontological evidence was certainly not overlooked. But graptolites were thought of as abundant only in the Llandeilo, as was also thought to be the case in Wales. Welsh experience coloured the understanding of Scottish geology.

Yet some amateurs were beginning to think in terms of zones. George Haswell (1865, p. 47), Secretary of the Geological Society of Edinburgh, wrote in regard to the Silurian strata of the Esk Inlier, Pentland Hills: 'geologists would do well to arrange the fossils from the different parts of the sections separately ... If they arrange their fossils in this way, they will perhaps find several zones of deposit, each representing a subdivision of the silurian system.' Five years later, David Brown and John Henderson (1870) compiled a substantial table of fossils establishing vertical ranges for the rocks of the Inlier. Several shell types were listed, but brachiopods were regarded as particularly important. The age determinations were based on Murchison's Silurian work, but the list again contained the seed of the idea of stratigraphic zones, suggesting a stratigraphic methodology already in use by Scottish amateurs in the late 1860s.

In 1872, Henry Alleyne Nicholson (1844–1899), then professor at Toronto, but later to occupy chairs at St Andrews
and Aberdeen, published his *Manual of Palaeontology*. Having
worked on Palaeozoic fossils in Canada and Scotland, including the south of Scotland, his statement in the introduction
about the use of fossils, as distinct from lithologies, for
stratigraphic research, was important. He used graptolites as an
exemplar. This was breaking new ground. That Nicholson
became a close friend of Charles Lapworth (1842–1920) during
the latter's work on the Southern Uplands, and later when
Lapworth went to work in St Andrews, is a key factor in the
development of Scottish geology.

This brings us to Lapworth's work in the Southern Uplands.
The countryside around Galashiels, where he moved in 1864,
was composed of grey, slaty, fractured rocks, the few outcrops
usually having steep dips in narrow valleys. Except for noted
dramatic beauty spots such as the Devil's Beeftub and the
Grey Mare's Tail, the hills were rounded, bleak and featureless, and plastered with boulder-clay and peat. Much of the
area was inaccessible to all but the most energetic.

However, in the burgeoning industrial towns such as Galashiels, Hawick, and Selkirk, quarries were extensively worked
and new ones were opened through the 1850s and 1860s. The
new railway cuttings also offered fresh exposures. Even so, it
was a difficult area in which to start, though some important
exposures had been recorded by earlier workers. Lapworth's
first geological work was done with a journalist friend, James
Wilson, who initially had more geological knowledge than
other local amateurs.

Lapworth's early papers (1869–1878) were tentative and used
the nomenclature, succession, and dating of the Geological
Survey, but his celebrated Moffat paper (1878) offered a
complete re-interpretation of the palaeontological evidence,
the stratigraphic succession, and the geological structure of the
area. In drafts of lectures, dated 1878, held in Birmingham
University, Lapworth used the analogy of separate drawers to
describe his procedure for collecting and housing his specimens,
gathered from layer after layer of graptolitic shales, and
carefully recorded up one side of Dobb's Linn (a small valley
near Moffat) and down the other. They were identified and
correlated, and their vertical ranges carefully noted. There are
also family memories of a specially modified waistcoat with
extra pockets on each side, in which different graptolites could
conveniently be placed as rock faces were searched. The
meticulous collection, identification, and recording at a minute
scale, and the analysis of the vertical distribution of specimens,
enabled Lapworth to distinguish different rock units by their
graptolite assemblages.

On this palaeontological basis, Lapworth successfully subdivided the highly condensed anticlinal sequence of rocks at
Dobb's Linn into zones; and, using the same technique, he
confirmed his findings there at many other sites. It did not
matter that beds of rock could not be traced physically along the
strike. They all carried identification in the graptolite species
distributed within them. It no longer mattered if rocks were
upside down, isoclinally folded, or repeated many times by
faulting. Once one key section had been zoned and its correct
'way-upness' determined, all else fell into place. Breaks in the
fossil succession could be recognized where they occurred. Here,
in logical and meticulous application, were the principles laid
down by William Smith many years earlier (and subsequently
developed by the Continental geologists Alcide d'Orbigny and
Albert Oppel).

The results of Lapworth's investigations had wider repercus-
sions. Not only did his work establish a sequence that is retained
to the present, but the condensed nature of the Southern
Upland shales vis-à-vis the Welsh equivalents was established

and a distinct palaeontological break below the Birkhill Shales
(Lower Llandovery) was recognized.

Lapworth did not confine his work to the central and eastern parts of the region. He also looked to the west, where a
different facies was found. Because of the occurrence of some
graptolitic shales, interbedded with limestones containing
brachiopods and larger invertebrates, he was able to establish the stratigraphic grouping of rocks in the Girvan area,
using the methodology employed at Moffat (Lapworth 1882).
It was during this work that he met Mrs Elizabeth Gray (1831–
1924), whose collection of more than thirty thousand specimens
had been amassed using the same principles of careful collection and recording as Lapworth (Cleevely *et al.* 1983). Nicholson, Lapworth, the Survey palaeontologist, Robert Etheridge,
and many others, acknowledged their debt to this redoubt-
able woman.

In the second part of the 1870s and in the 1880s, there
remained one major area of southern Scotland to be elucidated.
The igneous rocks of the west coast, near Ballantrae, were
mapped by Thomas Bonney (1833–1923) (1878). The igneous
nature of the serpentine, gabbro, and pillow lavas of that area
was established, as were the various ages, which were thought
to range from Silurian to Miocene. Subsequently, Lapworth
investigated the same phenomena, and completed, for him, the
work on the Southern Uplands. He found that Murchison had
mistakenly supposed there was a syncline in the Girvan Valley,
whereas in fact the beds in the region were inverted. He was
able to date many of the volcanics as being older than the
Girvan sedimentary sequence by locating volcanic fragments at
the base of the series. Lapworth (1889) established the ages of
these stratified, altered and Ballantrae igneous rocks as ranging
from Arenig through to Llandeilo and post-Ordovician.

All this work stimulated a thorough re-examination of the
Southern Uplands by the Geological Survey. Benjamin Peach,
John Horne and the Survey fossil collector Arthur Macconochie began this in early 1888, using Lapworth's methods, and
their work culminated in the notable Survey memoir on *The
Silurian Rocks of Britain, Vol. 1* (1899). What had been taken
to be a mass of greywacke, of enormous thickness, was now
under palaeontological control, and the fact that strata were
frequently repeated by faulting was recognized, so that a much
thinner sequence was required.

Needless to say, work in the region has continued. Craig
& Walton (1959), for example, revised Lapworth's interpretation of the fold structures of the region, proposing as their
preferred hypothesis a set of faulted monoclinal folds rather
than a synclinorium. And post-war plate tectonics has led
to re-working of the area and reinterpretation of ideas according to notions of terranes and accretionary prisms (Chapter 7). However, the cartographic methodology developed in
the Southern Uplands, the concepts of zoning and condensed
sequences, and enhanced knowledge of graptolites, remain as
outstanding contributions from the work in the region.

Structural geology and the Highlands controversy

As mentioned, early investigations in the Highlands suggested
that there was a 'framing' of the northern mountains by
analogous sandstones, east and west. Macculloch's map (1836)
showed limestones exposed on the northern coast at Loch
Durness, and to the south of this locality at Loch Assynt. Additionally, Macculloch had a line of 'quartz-rock' cropping out
at various places from Loch Eriboll through Assynt, Ullapool,
the head of Loch Maree, down to the southeast of Skye. The
rocks along this line marked what came to be called a 'zone
of complication'.

Macculloch's map made no distinction between gneiss on the west coast and the schists of central Sutherland or other related rocks in the Grampians. In a section running from Loch Durness to Loch Hope (Macculloch 1819, Vol. 3, pl. 32, fig. 1), he showed an ascending sequence: limestone; gneiss; quartz-rock; limestone; quartz-rock; gneiss; quartz-rock – all dipping to the east, and apparently conformable on one another. Repetitions were attributed to repetition of rock-types, not structural complexity. However, Macculloch recognized an unconformity between the western sandstone (Torridonian) and the underlying rock (Lewisian Gneiss) (Chapter 3).

In their reconnaissance of 1827, Sedgwick and Murchison gave little attention to the complications of the far northwest, being chiefly concerned with the sandstones to west and east, though the limestones and other lithologies, at Durness and Eriboll were sketched in. It is interesting that Murchison's hand-coloured map for the north of Scotland for 1827 survives at the Survey Library in Edinburgh (F101). Among its numerous annotations, Murchison remarked, concerning the sandstone gneiss contact south of Cape Wrath: 'Unconformable junction of Old Red with the gneiss of Cape Wrath. O.R. dipping. Gneiss vertical'; and 'Old Red Sandstone dips WNW'.

Apart from work by Hay Cunningham, not much was accomplished in the region in the next two decades. The rocks were apparently without shelly fossils and hence unamenable to the stratigraphic techniques of the period. However, in 1854 fossil shells were discovered in the limestone at Durness on the north coast by the amateur naturalist Charles Peach (1800–1886), of the coast-guard service at Wick, who was examining a wreck near Durness. Specimens were sent to London, and were provisionally dated as Devonian by Murchison. In 1855, Murchison took over as Director General of the Survey and thus turned 'professional'. That summer he went north with Nicol to look into Peach's discovery.

Though their work was hurried, Murchison arrived at a major generalization. While regarding the western sandstones as Old Red, he now interpreted Peach's Durness fossils as Silurian, and boldly suggested that the overlying schists etc. to the east were also Silurian. So he had Silurian running all the way from Durness to the Old Red of the east coast: his Silurian 'kingdom' was thus greatly expanded, but there was the difficulty of the western sandstones. If they were Devonian they ought to lie above the quartz-rocks and limestones, not below. Yet Nicol recorded that he saw the 'Quartzite series' overlying the red sandstone at Assynt.

Nicol (1857) took issue with Murchison's interpretation. For Nicol, the quartz-rock overlay the sandstone unconformably, so that the latter could hardly be Devonian if the Durness fossils were Silurian. In fact, Nicol initially suggested that the fossils in the limestone might be Carboniferous ('Mountain Limestone'); an idea later ridiculed by Murchison. Nicol also noted, near Kinlochewe and elsewhere, a rock that seemed to him to be igneous, and which lay between the eastern schists and the upper quartz-rock.

Nicol, it seems, could make no sense of the idea of the eastern metamorphic rocks having been metamorphosed *in situ*, leaving underlying sediments such as the soft 'fucoid beds' unaltered. So he began to develop the idea that the line between Durness/Eriboll and Skye represented a huge (high-angled) fault, with consequent repetition of the metamorphic rocks, and intrusion of igneous matter along the line of fault. Murchison protested that this disregarded the lithological distinctions between the western and eastern metamorphics, and the fact that the lines of strike of their foliations were manifestly different. Of course, if Nicol were right, Murchison's Silurian kingdom would lose ground in the great tract of Moine schists.

Murchison did further work in the northwest with Charles Peach in 1858 and the same year Nicol traced the supposed line of fault all the way from the north coast to Skye. Murchison went north again with his deputy Andrew Ramsay in 1859 (as too did Nicol, independently), and presented his views at the meeting of the British Association in Aberdeen, in what he called his great 'reform bill' for Scottish geology (report of meeting, *Aberdeen Journal*, 21 Sept. 1859, p. 11). This involved interpreting the unfossiliferous western sandstones as Cambrian, not Old Red (an idea pleasing to Sedgwick, who was present). So the sequence from west to east was: 'Fundamental gneiss'; sandstone (Cambrian); the sediments (quartz-rock, fucoid beds, limestone (Silurian)); schists (Silurian); Old Red Sandstone (Devonian). It seemed to be a simple ascending sequence from west to east. To make things work, Murchison had to rescind his 1827 observation of a WNW dip for the western sandstone. He also required repetition of some units. For example, he had a 'lower' and an 'upper' quartz-rock. But he found sections at Loch Eriboll, Assynt, and Knockan Cliff, south of Assynt, that apparently supported the theory, and which brought needed order to the rocks of the northern Highlands.

Nicol maintained his opposition to Murchison's ideas, and visited the area in 1860. Some conglomerates near Tongue he took to be equivalents of the 'red conglomerates and sandstones of the west coast' (Nicol 1861, p. 93), i.e. the Torridonian Sandstone; further apparent evidence for repetition of strata from west to east by faulting.

The same year Murchison also went north, in the company of Archibald Geikie. Their plan was to re-examine the sections, and try to extend Murchison's theory to the more southerly Grampians. The two geologists had little success in the south, but Geikie concurred with his patron's views about the succession in the northwest.

Geikie's career flourished under Murchison's patronage (Oldroyd 1990). Geikie was appointed director of the Scottish Branch of the Survey in 1867 and, with Murchison's support, he obtained the new chair in geology at Edinburgh in 1871. The positions were held concurrently with considerable success, for Geikie was one of the most able and administratively efficient geologists of his generation. Murchison's reputation benefited by having a favourable posthumous biography penned by Geikie; and the Murchisonian theory, with its expanded Scottish Silurian, held sway through the 1870s. Geikie taught the theory at Edinburgh, and it underpinned the maps of that decade. But Nicol, marginalized in Aberdeen, contended to the last that he was right.

The debate was reopened in 1878 by the Welsh geologist Henry Hicks (1837–1899), possibly as a result of his finding a rock on the west coast that looked to him like the schists to the east; and, near Kinlochewe, he thought he could discern an igneous rock between the quartz-rock and the eastern schists, as Nicol claimed. For Hicks, Murchison's 'Fundamental Gneiss' was Precambrian.

The question being reopened, other geologists such as John Judd (1840–1916), John Blake (1839–1906), Charles Callaway (1838–1915), Thomas Bonney, and the ever-active Lapworth began work in the north. At Loch Broom, Callaway (1883) did more than make two traverses as Geikie had done, and instead of finding evidence of a seeming transition or passage bed into gneiss, such as Geikie and Murchison claimed, he found the ground all sliced up by faulting: 'a pavement of fragments'. At Assynt, there seemed to be definite indications of the action of lateral forces. By more detailed work at Eriboll than Murchison and Geikie had attempted, Callaway found evidence that the quartz-rock had been folded into an S-shaped structure (the Assynt Series was 'folded back on itself'), so that the idea of there being two quartz-rocks was illusory. Also, it seemed that gneiss had in some instances been forced over the quartz-rock by lateral forces. But Callaway did not distinguish between gneiss and schist, as was required to untangle the geometry of the region's rocks and provide an adequate theory of the structure of the Northwest Highlands.

The 'secret of the Highlands' was eventually revealed by Lapworth. As already said, he had gone over the ground in the Southern Uplands, and had concluded that some of the Survey's interpretations were in error, as they had not recognized repetitions of strata due to faulting and folding. His Moffat work led to a chair at Birmingham (1882), and shortly thereafter Lapworth attempted to sort out the unresolved problems in the Northwest Highlands. In two field seasons (1882 and 1883), he undertook detailed mapping at Durness and Eriboll, armed with theoretical ideas from the Continent, notably Albert Heim's idea of how intense S-shaped overfolding could eventually give way to reverse faulting; and the idea of Johannes Lehmann that metamorphism could be produced by pressure acting so as to crush crystals and produce foliations, with new laminar crystals being developed under pressure.

Lapworth worked frenetically, to the extent that his health collapsed. It is said that one night he dreamed of the great mass of the Moines being thrust over him. Be this as it may, he unravelled the succession of the quartz-rock, fucoid beds and Durness Limestone, by examining an anticlinal structure at Eriboll. He recognized that Nicol's 'igneous rock' was in fact bits of Lewisian Gneiss that had become caught up in the earth movements, and partly altered thereby. He developed the idea of low-angle reverse faults (later called thrust-faults by Geikie), such as that which came to be named the Moine Thrust; and he had the idea that the eastern schists were not upper Silurian rocks that had somehow been metamorphosed in situ, without affecting the underlying sediments, but were formed during the course of their emplacement, when shoved over (and concomitantly faulting and folding) the underlying rocks from the east.

Geikie became Survey Director General in 1882 and, knowing that the old theory developed back in the 1860s was being questioned, he sent his best surveyors, Benjamin Peach and John Horne, and later, other field men, to map the Northwest Highlands. According to the recollection of Surveyor, George Barrow (1853–1932) (no date (c. 1930)), Lapworth met the Survey men in the north and showed them his six-inch field maps, convincing them that the whole question of the succession needed to be reopened. By their second season, Geikie's lieutenants arrived at essentially the same theory as Lapworth's, being particularly impressed by the imbricate structures at Eriboll. Geikie travelled to Eriboll in October 1884 and was reluctantly convinced of the essential correctness of the structures envisaged by Lapworth, Peach and Horne, and the revised theory was swiftly announced in *Nature* (Geikie 1884; Peach & Horne 1884). Recently, Oldroyd (1996b) has shown that Geikie was actually well prepared to recant before he saw the Eriboll sections. He had been reading Lehmann's new ideas on metamorphism from Germany, and the field-maps already prepared by Peach and Horne were highly persuasive. In the *Nature* article, Geikie stated that he had been convinced by the new field evidence seen at Eriboll; but he was only there for a few hours in dreadful weather!

Following Geikie's change of heart, the next few years were spent in detailed mapping of the Northwest Highlands and the 'zone of complication', leading to the celebrated Survey Memoir: *The Geological Structure of the North-west Highlands of Scotland* (Peach et al. 1907).

In 1885, Lapworth discovered fragments of the Cambrian fossil *Olenellus* at Comley in Shropshire. The unit in which they occurred lay above the so-called Wrekin Quartzite, and the Longmynd rocks lay at a lower horizon. The Longmynds had been designated Cambrian by the Survey under Murchison, but Lapworth (1888) suggested that the unit might be Precambrian, and equivalent to the Torridonian Sandstone. Thus the sediments situated between the western and eastern metamorphic rocks might plausibly be Cambrian. This conjecture was confirmed when in 1891 the Survey collector Arthur Macconochie discovered specimens of the *Olenellus* fauna in the fucoid beds in the area between Lochs Broom and Maree. Thus the units Murchison had designated Silurian, on the basis of the Durness fossils, were reclassified as Cambrian, and the unfossiliferous Torridonian Sandstone fitted into the stratigraphic column as an upper unit of the Precambrian (Peach & Horne 1892); so Lapworth's conjecture was confirmed.

Lapworth did no more work in the far north. However, the essential problem of the geometrical arrangement of the rocks in the region, the idea of their being affected by thrust-faulting, the notion of the Moine Schists (so named by Geikie 1888, 436) being formed under the action of pressure during the process of their emplacement, and the occurrence of mylonite along the 'zone of complication' were all broadly supported by the surveyors' detailed work prior to the publication (Peach et al. 1907), though already in that publication new ideas were beginning to appear.

Above the Moine thrust-plane, the rocks were subdivided into: mylonized rocks; phyllitic schists, siliceous schists, and limestones; granulitic quartzo-feldspathic schists with garnetiferous mica schist (the 'Moine Schists'); and inliers of gneiss of Lewisian character. The second of these units was thought to represent a metamorphosed sedimentary series; and the third also suggested a sedimentary origin, with evidences of altered pebbles of quartz and feldspar. However, the rocks to the east of the thrust appeared holocrystalline, while those near the zone showed cataclastic structures. So were the rocks of the thrust-zone fractured, previously-formed schists, or were they sedimentary rocks in the process of being converted to schists? The surveyors did not agree on this question. They concurred, however, that there appeared to be two systems of folding, giving a mullion structure. The second folding, at least, appeared to be post-Cambrian.

There was, then, the problem of the source of the rock from which the Moine Schists were constituted. Here Peach and Horne differed. Geikie (1893a, p. 262) reported Peach's idea that the schists south of Loch Carron were metamorphosed Torridonian Sandstone, caught up in a great fold of Lewisian material as they were driven westwards. Also, it appeared from Charles Clough's (1852–1916) work, south of Tarskavaig in Skye, that Moine-type rocks could be found to the *west* of the zone of complication. These rocks were less metamorphosed than normal Moines and appeared to be intermediate between them and the Torridonian. Moreover, as the main body of (eastern) Moines was examined more closely, there appeared, according to Peach, to be traces of false-bedding and pebble bands still visible (Geikie 1897a, p. 16), and lines of heavy minerals, not entirely obscured by the metamorphism, which suggested an original clastic origin (Peach & Horne 1930, p. 147). And Peach (Peach et al. 1913, p. 30) thought he had evidence in Central Ross-shire of rocks in the otherwise Torridonian region to the west of the thrust-zone that had metamorphic features analogous to the Moine Schists proper to the east of the zone.

But the Survey as a whole was sceptical about all the Moines being metamorphosed Torridonian, for the rocks appeared relatively uniform from north to south, compared with the Torridonian (Peach et al. 1910b, p. 46). In the Glenelg sheet memoir (Peach et al. 1910b, p. 46) it was also suggested that the

Moine rocks might have been folded and altered before they were thrust westwards, but that the metamorphism might have been post-Cambrian. Horne pointed out that in the northern area of the 'zone of complication' there was 'classic' Moine present but no neighbouring Torridonian, since the quartz-rock rested directly on the Lewisian. Basal Torridonian conglomerates could be found to the west of the zone, but these appeared to have no equivalent to the east except round the Lewisian inliers; and these Horne regarded as anomalous exceptions. His hypothesis, then, was that the Moine Schists were older than the Torridonian, though they had been altered in the post-Cambrian earth movements that caused the thrust faulting, which movements had produced the mylonites, green schists, and phyllites, found along the line of the thrust-zone.

Later work on the Moines has been bedevilled by difficulties and controversies, and complete understanding and agreement are still not reached. Attention was given to the inliers of Lewisian rock found within the Moines; for example near Tongue and several other places on the north coast; in the region of Strathconon Forest; and at Loch Alsh. It was assumed that the rocks closest to the Lewisian inliers were the oldest. For Peach, these represented pre-Torridonian basal rocks on which sediments that later became schists were deposited. He also claimed Torridonian rocks existed at some localities *east* of the zone of complication, as for example at Ben More Assynt; and he further attempted correlation between Torridonian and Moinian subdivisions.

Views about the Moines developed up to the 1930s were helpfully summarized by Herbert Read (1934a). There was Peach's opinion, supported with qualification by Clough, that they represented metamorphosed Torridonian. There was Horne's view, supported by the Glasgow professor, J. W. Gregory, that the material from which the schists were generated was intermediate in age between the Lewisian and the Torridonian, and were metamorphosed before deposition of the Torridonian. The rocks of Lewisian appearance within the Moine domain were inliers. Gregory (1915) claimed to find Moine pebbles *within* the Torridonian at Little Loch Broom. Barrow thought that all the Highland schists were of Lewisian age, and merely displayed different degrees of metamorphism; an idea congruent with his major theoretical contribution of the notion of metamorphic zones (discussion appended to Tilley (1925)), on which see below. In fact, as early as the mid-1880s Barrow found himself at odds with the 'Lapworth paradigm', taken up by the Survey. For as it appeared to Barrow, though there was mylonitization at the Moine Thrust there was little evidence of recrystallization there, and the schistosity appeared greater further east. So he inferred that the formation of the schists was prior to the thrusting. For Barrow, the divisional planes of the schists were depositional, and the crystallization was essentially thermal. Also, there was the idea of Scandinavian geologists, such as Gustav Frödin (1920–1922), that the schists were a mixture of older materials including Lower Palaeozoics, and were subsequently metamorphosed in the Caledonian movements. This echoed Lapworth's ideas.

Read himself doubted that all the metamorphism occurred in one episode. He distinguished between the 'dislocation metamorphism' (post-Cambrian) in the zone close to the Moine Thrust, and the more general metamorphism and schistosity further east. Thus he thought that mylonitization was superimposed on earlier metamorphic material. However, for the metamorphics of Central Sutherland, it appeared that the Lewisian 'inliers' were part of the same metamorphic complex, with altered intrusive rocks being similar in the western Lewisian proper and in the Moine 'territory'. He inclined to the view, then, that they were of pre-Torridonian age, possibly Lewisian.

In a survey of the problem at the 1948 London International Geological Congress, Sir Edward Bailey leaned towards Peach's views, the Moines supposedly being Torridonian sediments altered by Caledonian metamorphism (Bailey 1950). By contrast, William Quarrier Kennedy (1949) developed ideas akin to Barrow's, with progressive metamorphic zones running roughly parallel to the line of the Moine Thrust in the region between Loch Nevis and Loch Sunart. He suggested that the Torridonian had initially been metamorphosed into the Tarskavaig Moines, and then converted into the Moines proper, with metamorphism increasing to the east of the thrust. Robert Shackleton (1949), in summarizing the views expressed at the Congress, concurred with the emerging consensus that the Moines were metamorphic equivalents of the Torridonian Sandstones.

Consensus did not last long, however. Following lengthy studies of the fabrics and lineations of the Moines, Coles Phillips (1951) was inclined to return to Horne's view of the Moines as pre-Torridonian, and called for radiometric age determinations.

In the event radiometric dating and geomagnetic analyses have revealed that the Moines are by no means a single entity; not a series, but an assemblage (Johnstone *et al.* 1969). Distinctions have been made between the Morar Division to the northwest, the Glenfinnan Division to the southeast of this, and the Loch Eil Division, which is to the southeast again and crosses the Great Glen Fault to run into the Dalradians (see below). So-called 'Old' and 'New' Moines have also been distinguished. The problems that continue to plague the study of Scottish metamorphic rocks are discussed in detail in subsequent chapters.

The Central Highlands

The Central Highlands of Scotland extend from the Great Glen Fault to the Highland Boundary Fault. The metamorphic rocks of this region above the Moines are called 'Dalradian'; a term proposed by Archibald Geikie (1891, p. 75), after the ancient kingdom of 'Dalriada' of Northern Ireland and Scotland. The Dalradian structures and metamorphic features are complex and early workers had great difficulty in making sense of the geology. To a great extent the area was treated as a whole, and this lay at the root of some of the problems, because the region has been subject to varied and extreme geological processes over a long time. The main problems, all interrelated, were: (1) the nature of granite: igneous or metamorphic; magmatic or migmatic?; (2) the role of metamorphism; (3) the folding and dislocation, especially in the sheared rocks and great rock slides; (4) the age of the rocks relative to those of the Northwest Highlands and the Southern Uplands.

The problems associated with the nature of granites and the ages of the rocks of the Central Highlands vis-à-vis the northwest were, and still are considerable, but modern agedating techniques provide a way forward. Gregory (1931) regarded the Dalradian rocks, north of the Highland Boundary Fault, as immediately younger than the Moines. But, as mentioned, some geologists regarded the Moines as altered Torridonian. Research was hindered by the frequent use of local names, which complicated correlation. The whole area was, in effect, a laboratory for metamorphic and tectonic geology, and it took geologists over a century to realise they were dealing with the deep core of mountain chains, exhumed many times by erosion. However, the region stimulated ideas on geological methodology and epistemology (Greenly 1926).

In his work at Glen Tilt, Hutton had estimated that the rocks there were some of the oldest in Scotland and that the granite was younger than the schists into which it was intruded. A fundamental geological age principle was therefore established in this area. Igneous phenomena dominated reconnaissance investigations of the region. For example, Macculloch's (1814a) work and Thomas MacKnight's (1811) both included the Glen Tilt area. Travelling extensively, MacKnight, a Wernerian, observed and recorded the schists and their associated quartz veins, the extreme deformation, and the presence of gneisses and 'granites', which he regarded as younger that the surrounding schists.

Macculloch (1814b), by contrast, envisaged a mechanical rather than a 'precipitate' origin for the quartzites and clay-slates. He later (1817) suggested thermal alteration as a result of granite emplacement. Even at this early date, the origin of the granites of the Ben Nevis region was controversial. However, Macculloch recognized the structures that could be seen in the rocks, investigated their relative ages, together with features related to the concept of metamorphism as introduced by Lyell (1841, p. 221) and he acknowledged the presence of schist included within the Ballachulish 'granite'. Carl von Oeynhausen (1826–1833 (1829), 1830) also observed that 'granite' had apparently forced its way through the schists.

Hay Cunningham (1841) and Nicol (1844) wrote extensively on the Central Highlands. Nicol recognized that the Southern/Central Highlands consisted of rocks that could be traced from coast to coast, and he postulated a succession based on lithological types in the Loch Lomond area, which he considered to be in their original order, in contrast to the inverted succession in the Callander area further east. Sedgwick and Murchison (1828a, p. 125) thought that the quartz-rocks and limestones, associated with and passing under micaceous and gneissose schists, were overlain on the east coast by the Old Red. The sandstone contained fragments of the pre-existing crystalline rocks, which were therefore manifestly older.

Murchison (1851) tried to show that certain bands of 'clay-slate' and 'chloritic and micaceous schist', found in the southern zone of the Highlands, were probably metamorphosed Lower Silurians, similar in age to rocks in southern Scotland. The slates and schists were associated with massive igneous rocks, as well as Old Red Sandstone and the Coal Measures of the 'Great Caledonian Trough'. Murchison's opined that what he called 'the Crystallines' were metamorphosed Lower Palaeozoic. While influenced by what he had seen in the Northwest Highlands, he thought the Central Highlands were a geological extension of the younger rocks further south (Murchison 1859b, p. 179).

Murchison gave a simple, even simplistic, account of the rocks, with many complexities merely accounted for by the influence of igneous intrusions. There was no attempt to reconcile his succession with the evidence of faults, often with high or reversed dips, and highly contorted gneiss, often seemingly conformable on top of limestone. Many such features where explained by the influence of plutonic masses, though (we think) these masses were of metamorphic origin.

Murchison's contemporaries, Harkness and Nicol, with their 'neo-Wernerian' training, gave a strong emphasis to lithologies. The metamorphic nature of many of the rocks was recognized, however, as was an upward sequence of gneiss, mica-slate, chloritic-slate and clay-slate, all altered sediments supposedly from the Lower Silurian sea. Nicol (1863) placed these rocks below the limestone and quartz-rock.

Harkness supported Murchison in the Northwest Highlands and also in the Central area, where he worked out a two-fold succession (Harkness 1861). Schistose rocks were found above a band of limestone, and flaggy quartzite lay below. Geikie, who worked with Murchison in the region in 1860, expressed doubts, and it is clear in retrospect that the true mineralogical

nature of the beds and their stratigraphic succession escaped them (Macnair 1896). Murchison & Geikie (1861) postulated an anticline along the line of Loch Linnhe to explain the succession in the northern part of the Central Highlands. Harkness (1861) extended this work, proposing major broad synclines in the Ballachulish and Appin districts.

By contrast, Nicol's objective in his Southern Grampians paper (1862) was to study the relationships between three great formations: clay-slate, mica-slate and gneiss. He made a shrewd choice of sections in the Creran, Tay and Great Glen regions among others, and recorded observations that Macnair (1908) thought were not surpassed by the Geological Survey 35 years later. Nicol noted the regular occurrence of certain altered sediments, and the phenomena of 'reversed dips', SE–NW, across the Grampians. But such was Murchison's reputation, that it was his ideas, not Nicol's, that dominated research in this area for decades. There is no doubt that the succession was always likely to be problematical, at a time when the degree of metamorphism was commonly linked with age (Hamilton 1989). In addition, overfolding and sliding, though remarked by Murchison, was not sufficiently appreciated. Harkness simply assumed that gneiss must be older than clay-slate, which in its turn must be older than the 'primitive' limestone – a Wernerian legacy. Yet long before, Macculloch (1814b, p. 470) had pointed to the anomaly of the alternation of the supposed 'Primitive' and 'Transition' rocks, forcing reconsideration of definitions or order of lithological succession, according to Wernerian doctrine.

Geikie's *Scenery of Scotland* (1865) attempted an overall Scottish succession, including the Central Highlands, whose rocks he placed below the greywacke slates and limestones of the Southern Uplands and above the Fundamental Gneiss. The 'Lower Silurians' were arranged in great folds, whereby lower rocks were repeatedly brought to the surface. Geikie dated the metamorphism of the Highlands as occurring between the Llandeilo/Caradoc and the Old Red Sandstone. The absence of the Upper Silurian was represented by a gross unconformity.

Both Geikie (1865) and the amateur James Bryce (1876) addressed the problem of the origin of the granites of the Central Highlands. Geikie thought that they might be metamorphic, but Bryce opted for an eruptive origin. In his account of the Lower Palaeozoic volcanoes of the Highlands, Judd (1874, 276) interpreted the 'granite' masses of the area as eroded stumps of huge volcanoes, and also drew attention to the great dyke swarms. However, though he recognized that the 'granites' had been intruded into the surrounding schists, he interpreted the lavas and agglomerates as caps to the granites. This idea remained popular until Maufe's work (1910). In his *Ancient Volcanoes of Great Britain*, Geikie (1897b) did not mention the Ben Nevis area, and the Glen Coe volcanics were simply mentioned as 'picturesque outliers'.

By the end of the 19th century, geological technology had advanced significantly. Accurate base maps were becoming available. The increasingly sophisticated and powerful petrographic microscope and associated techniques of rock and crystal analysis were combined with a more sophisticated theoretical framework. As mentioned, knowledge of the nappe structures of the Alps and elsewhere had already been applied to the Northwest Highlands. Development of such concepts as regional metamorphism, linking heat, pressure and movement on a large scale at depth, over considerable areas, meant that geologists had powerful new ideas that could be applied to the Central and Southern Highlands.

Though the Geological Survey moved into the Aberdeen area as early as 1879–1880, they only entered the Glen Coe–Cuil Bay area south of the Great Glen in 1895. The *Annual Reports* for 1895–1896 and the *Summaries of Progress* from

1897 to 1912 detail the work done in the central region. The differences and links between different areas in the Central Highlands now became apparent, with James Grant Wilson being given the task of identifying the main features as quickly as possible. By 1898, it was realised that spectacular recumbent folding characterized the southern part of the Central Highlands. Grant Wilson was responsible for the Loch Linnhe area, between the foot of Ben Nevis and Loch Creran. James Hill (1861–1927) worked in the Loch Awe district. Henry Kynaston (1868–1915) concentrated on Loch Etive and Ben Cruachan, and Robert Symes mapped the Lorne volcanics and the Oban area. A chain of surveyors was now working across the Highlands. Sometimes there was collaborative work with university specialists such as Alfred Harker (1859–1939). The igneous phenomena studied were mostly small-scale features.

The collective work resulted in important developments in the understanding of magma, its emplacement and differentiation (Hill & Kynaston 1900; Harker & Dakyns 1900). Further east, Barrow worked on the intrusions and associated metamorphics in the Glen Muick and Dee valleys with ground-breaking ideas on metamorphic aureoles, zones of progressive metamorphism, and filter-press action. The association of higher-grade metamorphism with granite was, according to Read (1957), 'the basis on which much modern progress had been established'. But Barrow's iconoclastic ideas met with opposition from his colleagues (one suspects chiefly Peach (Barrow n.d.)), and Barrow was eventually transferred to England.

Barrow (1893) proposed that several masses of intrusive rock were connected underground, and that the highly metamorphosed nature of the surrounding schists was due to thermal metamorphism. Increasing acidity in each intrusion southeastward was explained by phased consolidation, with higher temperatures in the earlier parent igneous bodies. Changes in the minerals of the country rocks were shown to be especially marked in the alumino-silicates and were identified as products of contact metamorphism. Thus the distribution of minerals and the crystalline phases of the rocks were seen as dependent on the distance from the igneous masses. Barrow (1893) showed that an orderly succession of metamorphic zones existed in pelitic rocks, each zone being marked by a significant index mineral. These zones came to be known as 'Barrovian Zones'. They proved to be one of the crucial concepts in interpreting the geological history of the Highlands, though analogous ideas had been developed elsewhere previously, for example in relation to the alteration of the Skiddaw Slates in the Lake District by the Skiddaw Granite.

Also in 1893 Barrow sought to publish a paper arguing that all the Highland schists were pre-Torridonian, a view with which Horne privately concurred; but he did not choose to go out on a limb and support Barrow. Thus the suggestion was regarded as too disruptive of the recently achieved 'Lapworthian' consensus in the Survey and Geikie did not allow Barrow's publication to proceed (Barrow n.d.).

The petrologist Jethro Teall (1849–1924) succeeded Geikie as Survey Director in 1901, and Clough succeeded Peach as District Geologist for Central Scotland in 1904, with more staff committed to the area. Wilson, Bailey, and Maufe worked on the igneous and associated metamorphic rocks. Harkness's earlier correlation of quartzite from Ballachulish to Appin was discounted. Maufe, who completed Clough's survey of 1905, realized the scale of the great recumbent folds and proposed a succession for the area

One outstanding piece of work from this group of geologists was the mapping of the cauldron subsidence of Glen Coe (Clough et al. 1909). The area, which had been described previously by MacKnight (1811), Macculloch (1817), Nicol (1844) and Judd (1874), offered good exposures, left fresh by

glaciation, though access had earlier been difficult. Macculloch had noted the presence of a large number of dykes. In 1900, Kynaston and Peach came to work in the area. Two years later, together with David Tait, they established the age of the Glen Coe Volcanic group as Devonian. The work was completed under Peach, with the age of the Rannoch Moor granite being established and the Glen Coe Subsidence fault traced. The work, which examined structures exposed by deep erosion, contributed to understanding cauldron subsidence and associated stoping processes, the current new working theory.

There were also non-Survey geologists who responded to the challenges of the Central Highlands. Macnair (1892), Curator of Natural History, Glasgow Museums, and Honorary Secretary of the Glasgow Geology Society, endeavoured to establish a large-scale structural framework, choosing the Loch Tay limestone as a datum line. This allowed the complicated isoclinal folds of the area to be traced along the great fold axes, and the multiple deformations, especially the strain-slip structures in schistose rocks, were elucidated.

Bailey, who with Murray MacGregor emerged as the authority on the region, had worked there since 1910. He concentrated on Argyllshire, with tectonic phenomena as the key to his work. Papers on the Glen Orchy Anticline (Bailey 1912) and the Loch Awe Syncline (Bailey 1913) were two major contributions. A prophetic statement in the latter area was to the effect that in the Scottish Highlands one should never assume that present order of superposition represented original order of deposition, for Bailey had experienced grievous problems in finding the 'right-way-up' of the beds. When this problem was solved, everything began to fall into place regarding order and succession.

However, Bailey was at odds with both Hill and Barrow (who was at odds with Peach), and Barrow questioned his findings, some antagonism being evident in the reports of discussions at the Geological Society. The differences remained unresolved and, as mentioned, Barrow was moved out of Scotland. Work in the Ballachulish area, near the head of Loch Creran (Bailey 1914), revealed that systematic re-examination was needed. Bailey (1910a) had distinguished between folds, faults and fold-faults, which he termed 'slides'. The many slides and intense secondary re-folding meant that the original sequence had to be extrapolated from neighbouring areas; and such correlations were uncertain, the intense contact metamorphism from many small intrusions masking original differences in certain rock groups.

In 1930, new light was thrown on the problem of succession and structure by overseas geologists, Thorolf Vogt, Sherwood Buckstaff and Olaf Rove, who had visited Ballachulish in 1924. Though they had insufficient time to verify all Bailey's work on recumbent folds and slides, they established that his succession, as proposed in 1922 (Bailey 1923) was in fact upside down. Bailey, while waiting for Vogt to publish, attended the Princeton Summer School in Canada in 1927 and accepted that the ideas from the Wisconsin School on graded and current bedding (cross-bedding) could and should be applied to Scottish geology to determine the order of succession in areas of folded rocks.

Bailey acted as guide to the Princeton team when they visited Scotland in 1929, and the Cambridge geologist Tressilian Nicholas (who was a member of the party and had also attended the Princeton School in 1927) claimed that he could determine the original succession in the light of cross-bedding he had found in a location different from Vogt. The party then became aware of the possibility of different interpretations of the original section. Careful fieldwork followed, but Nicholas's was regarded as inconclusive. Vogt's section, on the other hand, convinced practically everybody. The whole party, including the Canadian Surveyor Thomas Tanton, who had demonstrated 'way-upness' criteria to Bailey in 1927, went to a third locality and examined an exposure of the Appin Quartzite, and there proved to Bailey and William King the true 'way-up' of the section. Confirmation by other sections led to the whole field programme being changed, so that sections that had puzzled Bailey for years, especially at Loch Leven, could be understood. The new criteria of order of succession made it relatively easy to recognize the essential structure of the district as one of recumbent folding, miles in extent, followed by thousands of feet of steeply-packed folding. Tanton exclaimed: 'The original order of succession is everywhere clear, and everywhere it is upside down!' All this work ultimately stemmed from ideas developed at the University of Wisconsin, where Tanton had done his PhD, the ideas being made known by Leith (1913) and Twenhofel (1926).

After the Second World War, complete re-evaluation of the tectonics and geological environments which governed the rocks in the Central Highlands of Scotland followed the development of the theory of plate tectonics, referred to frequently in later chapters.

Hebridean geology

In the Inner Hebrides, as for so much Scottish geology, Macculloch was the first major figure to take to the field. While working for the Trigonometric Survey, he published two papers on the geology of Skye and a substantial volume on the geology of the Hebrides and the Isle of Man (Macculloch 1816, 1817, 1819). His paper of 1816 contained a rudimentary map of Skye. The book (1819) referred to the Red Cuillins as 'syenite' (= granite) and the Black Cuillins as 'hypersthene rock' (= gabbro). Macculloch also raised the question as to which of these was the older (Macculloch 1819, Vol. 1, p. 368). He recorded veins of syenite in the hypersthene rock in the 'valley of Coruisk' but could not trace them to the Red Cuillins, so the question was not answered. In any case, the veins in question could have been dolerite. The 'trap rocks' of northern Skye were thought to overlie 'Oolitic' rocks along the eastern coast of the island.

Ten years after Macculloch's book, the Germans Carl von Oeynhausen and Heinrich von Dechen (1829) published their work on Skye. They too were interested in the Red/Black Cuillins contact and traced the boundary approximately. In one of their sections, they showed syenite under the *hypersthenfels*, suggesting that the Red Hills were younger; but they may have mistaken a slice of basalt faulted into the Red Hills for the *hypersthenfels*. They were uncertain about the relationship between the *hypersthenfels* and the trap rock (basalt).

Further work in Skye was undertaken by James D. Forbes (1809–1868) in the 1830s and 1840s. He traced the boundary in Glen Sligachan between the 'pale orange felspar rock' and the dark 'hypersthene rock', with the latter apparently overlying the former. The 'hypersthene rock' also seemed to overlie some of the basalt, so Forbes concluded that the basic rock of the Black Cuillins was younger than the acidic rock of the Red. This seemed to accord with the general form of the mountains. The petrographer Ferdinand Zirkel visited Skye in 1868 and concurred with Forbes (Zirkel 1871).

In 1850, fossil leaves were discovered by a Bunessan shopkeeper named McDairmid at Ardtun, Mull, in beds intercalated between basaltic lava flows. The specimens were given to George Campbell, Duke of Argyll, who submitted them to Henry De la Beche in London. They were evidently important,

and the Duke described the finds at the Edinburgh meeting of the British Association (Campbell 1851*a*). The plants were figured by Edward Forbes, who thought they were Miocene (Campbell 1851*b*). But while the Mull lavas were possibly Tertiary, Edward Forbes (1851) thought that there was lava between Middle and Upper Oolite at Loch Staffin in Skye, with only the lower unit showing signs of baking; so the Skye basalts/traps could have been Jurassic. The fossil leaves were re-evaluated by the Belfast palaeobotanist J. Starkie Gardner (1884–1885, 1887) and determined as Eocene. Ever since, the lava flows of the Hebrides have been regarded as Tertiary, including of course such famous sites as Fingal's Cave.

Some of Archibald Geikie's earliest work, as a self-taught teenage geologist, was undertaken in Skye, and after he joined the Survey in 1855, though he was officially mapping in the Lothians, he continued to visit the Hebrides. He visited Eigg in 1864 and published an interesting section in his *Scenery of Scotland* (1865, frontispiece), illustrating his ideas on the origin of the island's famous Sgùrr. Though this mass of columnar 'pitchstone' forms the top of the hill, its lava appeared to have run down a valley, etched into a former land surface of an older volcanic rock. Under the lava could be found shingle and fragments of wood (earlier discovered by Hugh Miller, who probably told Geikie about them). So there was a complete inversion of relief. Geikie used Eigg to exemplify the power of fluvial erosion acting over vast periods of time; and indeed the immensity of geological time. The Eigg work suggested that the basaltic lavas of the Hebrides, parts of the mainland, and also across in Northern Ireland, might be mere fragments of what was formerly one vast tract of basaltic lavas.

For thirty years and more, Geikie studied the remains of ancient British volcanoes, and in Scotland he visited almost every relevant site. His work culminated in the publication of *The Ancient Volcanoes of Great Britain* (1897). This work underscored Geikie's authority as leading British geologist of the day, and the authority on British volcanoes. But his supremacy was challenged by Judd, and an acrimonious debate developed in the 1870s, 1880s, and early 1890s concerning the geology of Skye, which was eventually reduced to the question of whether the Black Cuillins were older than the Red, or vice versa.

Some of Judd's early years were spent in survey work in the English Midlands. He later took up a career as an industrial chemist in Sheffield where he met Henry Clifton Sorby and learnt how to study rocks in thin section. But Judd had to cease work temporarily because of a railway accident, and when he recovered he resumed his interests in Jurassic geology. This took him to northeast Scotland to examine the Brora coal field; then he turned to a study of the Jurassic strata of the Hebrides. This led on to study of the igneous rocks of the region, where he worked for five seasons, concluding that there was evidence of there having once been five great volcanoes in the region: at St Kilda, Ardnamurchan, Mull, Rum, and Skye. The Hebridean basalts, then, represented the outpourings of these great volcanoes.

But on publishing this work, Judd (1874) was stepping into a field where Geikie had been working for about twenty years (though without publishing much). In fact, Geikie stood aside for some time, leaving the field to Judd (Oldroyd & Hamilton 1997), but after a visit to Idaho in 1879, Geikie returned with the idea of 'fissure eruptions' (proposed by Ferdinand von Richthofen 1868), and sought to apply them to the Hebridean case. Ironically, Judd also took from von Richthofen a broad generalization, namely that in extended periods of volcanic action in the same region acidic magma generally preceded the production of basic magma.

Judd's 'type area' was Mull, where he envisaged the production of an outer ring of acidic rock, followed by the formation of a central core of basic rock intruded up approximately the same vent. In Skye, then, it was supposed that much the same sequence had occurred, except that the basic rock had been emplaced next to, rather then through, the older acidic rock. The upshot was that for Judd the Black Cuillins were younger than the Red, whereas for Geikie the order was opposite. In the 1880s, Geikie again returned to the Hebrides and sought to show that their lavas were agreeable to the theory of fissure eruptions, and much of his fieldwork that decade was spent in the region.

As a student of Sorby, Judd's (1889, 1893) investigations became increasingly petrographical in character, and he interested himself in textures. The idea was that the coarser grained rocks such as the Cuillin gabbros could have formed within the depths of a magma chamber, whereas the basalts, of similar chemical composition, being extruded, were finer grained. The debate became ever more closely focused, until it rested on the question of the relative ages of the Cuillins and the Red Hills, and on a particular locality, Druim Hain ('Ridge of Ice'), above Loch Coruisk, where the acidic and basic rock could be seen in contact. We cannot be sure that Judd and Geikie visited precisely the same localities but, whereas in that general area Judd saw inclusions of acidic rock within the gabbro, Geikie saw veins of granitic matter penetrating the gabbro.

While it is uncertain precisely what Judd observed, Geikie (1894) produced photographic evidence of intrusive granitic veins, having organized a large party to visit the area, and give testimony to his views, in 1893. The Geological Society was persuaded of Geikie's interpretations, and concluded that Judd had not investigated the ridge with sufficient attention. He was obliged to withdraw from the controversy and from this area of fieldwork, and his reputation suffered.

As Director General, Geikie had greater resources than Judd (who was however by then a Professor at the Royal College of Science), and over the next few years Geikie employed the distinguished Cambridge petrologist Alfred Harker to make a detailed survey of the Skye mountains. Geikie's interpretation was vindicated: granitic veins from the Red Cuillin mass did seem to intrude the gabbro at Druim Hain. Harker's model (Harker & Clough 1904, p. 93) envisaged a mass of granite emplaced under a mass of gabbro, with veins of the former penetrating the latter and also passing through an intervening deposit of volcanic agglomerate. In addition, Harker (Harker & Clough 1904, pp. 175–193) developed important ideas about the hybridization of acidic and basic magmas through his study of the rocks of Marsco (Chapter 14).

In the 1920s, fundamental work was done by James Richey in his mapping with H. H. Thomas of Ardnamurchan, Mull and Coll (Richey & Thomas 1930; Richey 1932). Following his work in Skye, Harker (1917, p. xciv) referred to 'cone sheets' at Ardnamurchan similar to those that he had envisaged in the Cuillins in Skye. In 1920, Richey saw the Ardnamurchan cone sheets and interpreted them as earlier than the mass of gabbro in the peninsula. More detailed mapping in the next two years revealed three igneous centres, manifested by three sets of 'ring dykes'. These suggested upward flow of magma along fissures produced by caldera subsidence, while the cone sheets could be ascribed to magma exerting a strong upward pressure against the roof of its chamber. Thus was born the classic theory of ring dykes and cone sheets (e.g. stated in Holmes 1944). Richey sought to link his work with Norman Bowen's (1928) ideas on patterns of crystal deposition from molten magmas, and also sought (1932) to apply the ideas from Mull back to Skye. In broad terms, Richey found sympathy with Judd's

old idea of places such as Mull and Ardnamurchan being the 'basal wrecks' of giant volcanoes. Interestingly, Richey thought the roughly linear distribution of the great Hebridean volcanoes (excluding St Kilda) might indicate a line of weakness attributable to Wegener's notion of North Atlantic rifting (Richey 1932).

Reverting to the earlier debates, remapping of the Black and Red Cuillins of Skye by Brian Bell of Glasgow University between 1984 and 1993 has largely confirmed Harker's mapwork. Bell has seen a grain-size reduction in the granite as the nearly vertical granite/gabbro contact is approached at Druim Hain, with spherulitic rhyolite dykes invading the gabbro, apparently being apophyses of the granite (Chapter 14).

The Midland Valley

The rocks of this important economic region have been studied from a practical standpoint for centuries. There are reports of coal being worked for the Abbey of Dunfermline in 1291 (Bald 1812). Today, on the north of the Firth of Forth, one can still see evidence of the workings by the monks for supply of Culross Abbey. These workings extended right under the Firth, and about 1604 an amazing air shaft down to the mine was constructed on a rock-reef a quarter-mile out in the Firth under the direction of Sir George Bruce (Land 1997). There are records of coal seams made by Clerk of Eldin's grandfather in the 17th century; and carefully delineated 18th-century figures of sections of seemingly faulted coal seams made by his father (McIntyre & McKirdy 1997). However, until the early 19th century, and often later, working for coal was not based on scientific knowledge, and was associated with horrific working conditions, as described by Bald (1812). John Williams (1730–1795), initially a Welsh miner who came to work in Scotland and became a successful prospector and consultant (Torrens 1996), authored an important two-volume treatise which dealt, among other things, with the ways of studying coal deposits in a systematic fashion and coal prospecting. He distinguished between ordinary coal, soft coal, and 'creeshy (greasy) blaes'; later called oil-shale (Williams 1789, Vol. 1, p. 82). His book reveals the extensive knowledge of the lie and outcrop of coal seams and associated strata in Scotland in the second half of the 18th century.

The Glasgow University graduate, the impoverished Reverend David Ure (1749–1798), was the first to describe and figure Scottish fossils (Gray 1865). They were collected from coal-measure sites near the present Glasgow city centre (Ure 1793). Additionally, Ure recorded petroleum oozing from an 'argillaceous grit' in the banks of the Calder, and drew up lists of strata at different depths at a number of localities, based on information from borings. He also distinguished between freshwater and marine deposits, but doubted the similarity of past and present conditions. Believing that his observations were compatible with the 'sacred theory given by Moses' he was a determined opponent of Hutton's doctrines. Examples of solitary corals, crinoids ('entrochi'), and other fossils, collected by Ure, are on display at the Hunterian Museum, Glasgow, and may be compared with his illustrations.

Though teaching in Edinburgh, in the social centre of Plutonism or Vulcanism, Jameson's approach to stratigraphy in the Midland Valley was, in the Wernerian tradition, based on lithologies (Jameson 1818, 1821). In his volume on the county of Dumfries he (correctly) challenged the assertion that reddish brown sandstone was never found in the coal formations in Scotland (Jameson 1805, pp. 165–166). This point was taken up by his pupil Hay Cunningham (with whom Jameson did local fieldwork). Referring to Jameson's Dumfries book, Hay Cunningham (1831–1837) thought that the Old Red Sandstone, Mountain Limestone, and Coal Formations could not be distinguished satisfactorily and correlated with counterparts in north England, showing the problems for those who sought to undertake stratigraphic work on Wernerian geognostic principles, rather than Smithian stratigraphy. Hay Cunningham also sought to use Élie de Beaumont's method for determining the relative ages of mountain ranges by considering their orientations, and which strata were heaped up against which. The method did not work particularly well. Nevertheless, he published a creditable map of the Lothians, and his essay was awarded a prize by the Highland and Agricultural Society (Hay Cunningham 1838). His subdivisions for the Lothians were: Transition Series; Red Sandstone Series; White Sandstone Series; Mountain Limestone; Felspar Rocks including Porphyry & Clinkstone; Augitic and Trap Rocks. Perhaps surprisingly, he described, with apparent approval, the experimental work of Sir James Hall. Several other areas of the Midland Valley were described and mapped in prize essays for the H & A Society during the 1830s and 1840s, before the official Survey got to work in Scotland in 1854.

It was noted above that Lyell did not recognize the existence of the Highland Boundary Fault, and the geologists in the 1830s thought of the Midland Valley as an approximately synclinal structure, with similar underlying beds cropping out in the Southern Uplands and the Southern Highlands (Conybeare 1833, frontispiece accompanying: 'Section across Europe from the North of Scotland to the Adriatic').

With all the mining and quarrying that went on in the Midland Valley in the nineteenth century, there were splendid opportunities for amateurs to obtain new and interesting specimens. Samuel Hibbert made a fine collection of fossil fish and other remains, including plants, from the limestone of Burdiehouse quarry, near Edinburgh and interpreted them as freshwater in character (Hibbert 1836). Using his fossils, he regarded the strata as Carboniferous, and supposed that at that epoch there had been alternating marine and freshwater conditions. This was accounted for in terms of Élie de Beaumont's ideas; namely that a cooling earth with a solid crust would contract in its fluid interior, and thus there would be occasional collapses of fractured portions of the crust.

In his book on Fife and the Lothians, Charles MacLaren (1839) recognized that straightforward correlation between the Carboniferous deposits of Scotland and northern England was not possible. He therefore introduced a new unit, the 'Calciferous Sandstone', for beds of sandstone, shale, clay, ironstone, limestone and coal, which seemed to be the equivalent in its lower part to the English Old Red Sandstone, and in its upper to part of the Mountain (Carboniferous) Limestone and part of the Coal Series. So his stratigraphic column for the Midland Valley was: (1) Greywacke and Clay Slate (at margins); (2) Old Red Sandstone (conglomerate); (3) Calciferous Sandstone; (4) Coal Measures; (5) Upper Coal (supposedly equivalent to the English New Red Sandstone).

James Bryce (1859) prepared a booklet on the geology of Clydesdale and Arran for the British Association's 1855 meeting in Glasgow. He regarded the area of the coal beds as a great synclinal trough filled with enormous thicknesses of coal-bearing strata, and intercalated igneous rocks. There was little Carboniferous Limestone, as compared with England, and apparently no Millstone Grit. Bryce's sequence was, then: (1) Old Red Sandstone and Ballagan Series (cementstones); (2) Lower Marine Limestone Series, with intercalated freshwater beds; (3) Lower Coal Series; (4) Upper Marine Series; (5) Upper Freshwater Coal Series; and (6) Upper Red Series

(possibly equivalent to the New Red Sandstone). Bryce differed from Hugh Miller (1854), who had thought that the whole of the Lower Marine Limestone Series was analogous to the Carboniferous Limestone.

In one of the first publications of the Scottish Branch of the Survey (Howell & Geikie 1861), the following classification was adopted: (1) Silurian; (2) Lower Old Red Sandstone; (3) Upper Old Red Sandstone; (4) Basement Beds of Lower Carboniferous Group; (5) Lower Carboniferous Series; (6) Carboniferous Limestone Series (including Midlothian Coalfield); (7) Millstone Grit; (8) Coal Measures. Thus greater analogy with the English deposits was envisaged. The lowest member of the Carboniferous Limestone Series was the Hurlet Limestone, and the Carboniferous rocks below (but not the ORS) formed the 'Calciferous Sandstone Measures'. Such work was undertaken in the light of palaeontological evidence, with vast numbers of fossils being collected from the highly fossiliferous and economically important strata.

Following the notable entrepreneurial and scientific work of James ('Paraffin') Young (1811–1883), who investigated the oil-bearing shale deposits in the Calciferous Sandstones to the west of Edinburgh, obtaining an important patent (1851–1864) for the extraction and purification of oil (useable for candle manufacture, and later gasoline), considerable attention was given to the study of these shales. They were termed the Oil Shale Group by Henry Cadell (1885), and corresponded to Howell and Geikie's Lower Carboniferous Series. Cadell divided the Oil Shales into an Upper and a Lower Group, separated by Hibbert's Burdiehouse Limestone. The development of stratigraphic schemes continued in the 20th century, with those of Cadell (1913) and MacGregor (1928–1929 (1931)) leading towards the modern classification employed in this volume. However, modern lithostratigraphic classifications (e.g. Cameron & Stephenson 1985) differ significantly from those proposed by MacGregor.

With the extension of the Survey's map work northwards towards the Highlands, it became clear that the Midland Valley was not simply a depositional trough, but a region bounded by faults at the northern margin (the Highland Boundary Fault) and southern (the Southern Uplands Fault). It is not clear who was the first to recognize these structural features, but the principal fieldworkers at the northern side in Perthshire, Forfarshire, and Kincardineshire in 1875–1879 were James Geikie, William Irvine and William Skae. Presumably the great fault (complex) of the Highland Boundary became evident as the ground was covered and the maps fitted together. Colonel Ninian Imrie (1806) had noted highly disturbed ground at the spot where the North Esk river crossed the Highland Boundary Fault; but no generalization about the feature was attempted or possible at that early date. So James Geikie (1885) described the Midland Valley as a 'broad depression between two table-lands' with the younger strata (as compared with those of the Southern Uplands and the Grampians) being saved from denudation by downward faulting. Thus, a kind of horst and graben structure was envisaged. This notion held, essentially, until the advent of plate tectonics in the 20th century and the doctrine of terranes, discussed elsewhere in this volume.

Conclusions

It was Archibald Geikie who first wrote about the Scottish School of Geology. As an ardent Scot (though he eventually settled in a salubrious part of Surrey), Geikie was inclined to see the history of geology in the country of his birth from a somewhat nationalistic perspective. We see no harm in this. Scotland was indeed one of the countries that contributed most to the foundation of geological science, and provided some of its most notable founders, both in the field and as theoreticians. It is a small country, but one that is geologically both interesting and perplexing. If Scotland provided an environment highly propitious for the work of the 'founder of geology', James Hutton, the Moines have provided a region that still defies full elucidation. In Scotland, if perhaps we see a definite vestige of a beginning of geological research, there seems to be no prospect of an end in view.

3 The Hebridean terrane

R. G. PARK, A. D. STEWART & D. T. WRIGHT

The Hebridean terrane consists of that part of northwest Scotland, lying west of the Moine Thrust Zone, which formed part of the stable foreland of the Caledonian orogenic belt during the Palaeozoic era. The rocks making up this piece of crust comprise a crystalline, mainly gneissose, Archaean to Palaeoproterozoic basement (the Lewisian complex) overlain by an undeformed or gently tilted sedimentary cover of Neoproterozoic (the Torridonian) and Cambro-Ordovician age.

The present eastern margin of the terrane is formed by the Moine Thrust Zone, of Caledonian age, which itself conceals an earlier inferred boundary of Grenvillian age (~1.1 Ga) separating Lewisian crust with only minor Grenvillian effects in the west from gneisses with a high-grade (eclogite/granulite facies) overprint in the east (cf. Sanders et al. 1984). It also constitutes the western margin of the Knoydartian (~800 Ma) 'orogenic' event (cf. Vance et al. 1998). The nature of this major, long-lived crustal boundary clearly implies that the Hebridean terrane is at least parautochthonous, and may possibly be allochthonous, with respect to the adjacent Northern Highlands terrane.

The crystalline Lewisian basement of the Hebridean terrane was welded together during the Palaeoproterozoic at ~1.9 Ga when it formed part of a large continental assemblage, including much of North America and Scandinavia. Further amalgamation and re-organization of crustal fragments around 1.0 Ga resulted in the supercontinent of Rodinia, which existed during the Neoproterozoic, and during this time the Torridonian deposits formed in intracontinental basins. After the break-up of this sector of Rodinia at the end of the Precambrian, the Hebridean terrane formed part of the passive margin of the Laurentian continent on which the Cambro-Ordovician deposits were laid down. Although the Caledonian orogeny resulted in the addition of a large part of the British Isles onto the Laurentian margin, its effects were felt only peripherally in the Hebridean terrane. The subsequent history of the terrane left little sign in the rock record until the Mesozoic, when extensional basins formed along the western seaboard, heralding the separation of North America and Europe and the opening of the North Atlantic Ocean in the Early Tertiary.

The Lewisian, Torridonian and Cambro-Ordovician rocks will be described in turn. Rocks of Mesozoic and Tertiary age, which also occur within the Hebridean terrane, are described separately (Chapters 10–14).

The Lewisian complex

The main outcrops of the Lewisian complex on land occur on the islands of the Outer Hebrides and on a coastal strip of the mainland from Cape Wrath in the north to Loch Torridon in the south (Figs 3.1 & 3.2). Lewisian rocks also occur on several islands of the Inner Hebrides: Rona, Raasay, Coll, Tiree and Iona. Geophysical and other evidence indicates that these surface outcrops form part of a broad region extending to the west and north of the Hebrides up to the edge of the continental shelf. Lewisian-like rocks also form inliers within the younger

Precambrian Moine Supergroup of the Caledonian orogenic belt, east of the Moine thrust belt (see Chapter 4). The offshore region is crossed by a number of deep seismic reflection profiles including both BIRPS (British Institutions Reflection Profiling Syndicate) and commercial lines. From these and from the geophysical evidence on the physical properties of Lewisian rocks (Hall 1987) it can be concluded that Lewisian or similar rocks probably form the basement to Scotland at least up to the line of the Great Glen Fault (cf. Bamford et al. 1978; Barton 1992).

The disrupted nature of the Lewisian outcrop is mainly attributable to the formation of fault-controlled extensional basins in Mesozoic and Tertiary times, of which the most obvious examples are in the sea areas separating the Outer Hebrides from the mainland (Fig. 3.1).

Stratigraphical subdivision

The first comprehensive account of the Lewisian rocks of the Northwest Highlands appears in the famous Geological Survey 1907 memoir (Peach et al. 1907) in which the Lewisian is described as consisting of a wide range of different igneous rocks of various ages, together with some sediments, subjected to deformation and metamorphism. The nature of the Lewisian outcrop as a 'complex', affected by a series of events over a lengthy time span, was clearly recognized. Peach et al. (1907) established the following simple chronological sequence. An older group of rocks, mainly acid gneisses, which they referred to as the 'fundamental complex', was intruded by a younger group consisting of various intrusions including the basic to ultrabasic dykes of the *Scourie dyke* suite. Both sets of rocks were then affected by deformation, which caused severe modifications to the complex in certain areas, particularly the northern and southern regions of the mainland, but left the central mainland region comparatively unscathed. These movements did not affect the oldest of the overlying sedimentary formations, the Torridonian, and were termed the 'Pre-Torridonian movements'.

The chronological subdivision of the Lewisian, so clearly foreshadowed in the work of Peach and his Survey colleagues, was addressed again half a century later by Sutton & Watson (1951) in a classic paper based on their work on the Loch Torridon and Scourie areas. Sutton & Watson interpreted the chronology of the complex in terms of successive orogenic cycles: the older (corresponding to the fundamental complex of Peach et al. (1907) was termed the *Scourian* and the younger, the *Laxfordian*. These two cycles were separated by the intrusion of the Scourie dykes, which Sutton & Watson regarded as anorogenic and intruded essentially contemporaneously. Thus the concept arose of Scourian rocks, formed during Scourian time, and reworked during Laxfordian time.

This stratigraphic interpretation was complicated by the work of Tarney (1963), Park (1964), Evans & Tarney (1964) and Evans (1965) which showed that a major tectonometamorphic event took place after the granulite-facies event of the central region and before the Scourie dyke emplacement.

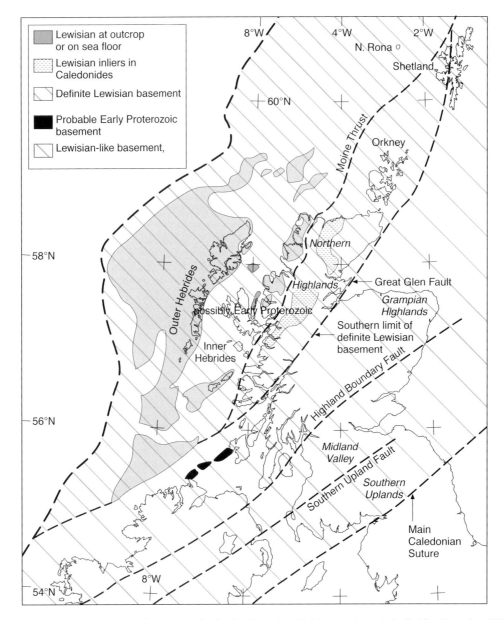

Fig. 3.1. Distribution of the Lewisian complex in northern Scotland and on the adjoining continental shelf. After Dunning (1985).

This event was named the Inverian by Evans (1965) and structural and metamorphic effects attributed to the Inverian have since been recognized throughout much of the Lewisian complex. The similarity of structural style and orientation, and of metamorphic facies, between the Inverian and the Laxfordian has led to considerable confusion and debate.

The first radiometric ages produced on a variety of Lewisian rocks by Giletti *et al.* (1961) provided firm support for Sutton and Watson's chronology. Rocks from the Scourian complex yielded late Archaean while in areas of Laxfordian reworking, granites, gneisses and Scourie dykes gave Proterozoic ages ranging from 1610 to 1160 Ma. More recent radiometric ages record a long and complex history of crustal processes spanning an extensive period of time, around 2 Ga (see below; Fig. 3.3).

The terms Scourian, Inverian and Laxfordian are used here in their traditional sense to label Lewisian rocks and events that fall within broad chronological periods: Scourian corresponding to Archaean, Inverian to earliest Palaeoproterozoic (before the Scourie dykes), and Laxfordian to later Palaeoproterozoic

(after the Scourie dykes). However the continued use of this terminology depends on a consensus that the rocks and events in question, in different parts of the Lewisian complex, are broadly correlatable. Friend & Kinny (2001) suggest that the Lewisian complex may comprise several separate Archaean terranes that only amalgamated during the Palaeoproterozoic and that the terminology in question requires re-evaluation. However until a better geochronological framework exists, and a new consensus emerges, it seems wiser to continue with the traditional usage.

The Lewisian of the Scottish mainland

Following Peach *et al.* (1907), the Lewisian complex of the mainland is divided into three separate regions (Fig. 3.2): Northern, Central and Southern. The *Central Region* extends for ~65 km from north of Scourie to Gruinard Bay, and is composed typically of granulite-facies Scourian rocks relatively unmodified by younger Laxfordian effects. These rocks are

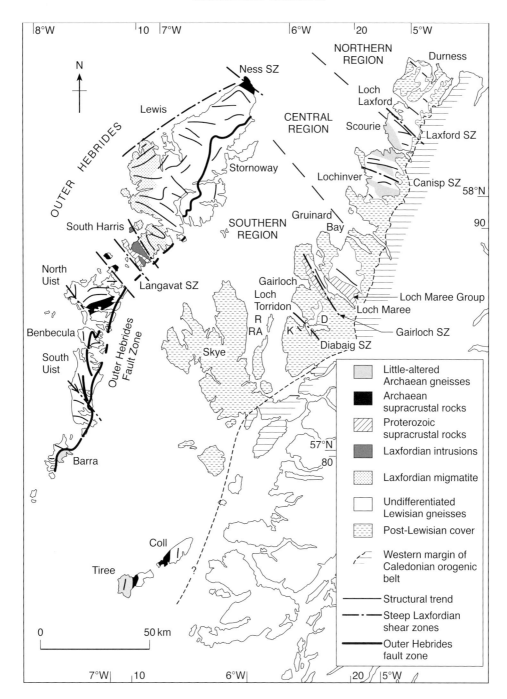

Fig. 3.2. Simpified map of the Lewisian complex showing main rock units and structures, and the regional subdivision. Outer Hebrides modified from Fettes & Mendum (1987). D, Diabaig; K, Kenmore; R, Rona; RA, Raasay; SZ, shear zone.

intruded by mafic and ultramafic dykes of the Scourie dyke swarm with a generally NW–SE to E–W trend. The dykes, although typically metamorphosed to some degree, are generally undeformed or only locally deformed where affected by the numerous narrow shear zones that traverse the region. The northern margin of the Central Region is occupied by a zone of intense deformation, several kilometres wide, in which the granulite-facies gneisses of the Scourian complex are progressively transformed to amphibolite-facies hornblende- and biotite-gneisses (Beach *et al.* 1974).

The Northern and Southern Regions, on the other hand, represent Laxfordian belts where Scourian gneisses have been modified by Laxfordian deformation and amphibolite-facies metamorphism (Fig. 3.2). The *Northern Region* extends from

Loch Laxford to Cape Wrath on the north coast. The *Southern Region* extends from Gruinard Bay to Loch Torridon, and includes the islands of Rona and Raasay. The northern part of this region consists of an 8 km wide zone extending from Gruinard Bay to Fionn Loch, north of Loch Maree, where Inverian deformation and amphibolite-facies metamorphism have severely modified the Scourian gneisses. The Scourie dykes are little affected here by Laxfordian deformation, which only becomes intense at the southern margin of this zone, around Fionn Loch and Loch Maree, and further south. The only known post-Scourian metasediments within these Laxfordian belts form a unit known as the *Loch Maree Group*, which outcrops in the Southern Region at Loch Maree and Gairloch (Fig. 3.2).

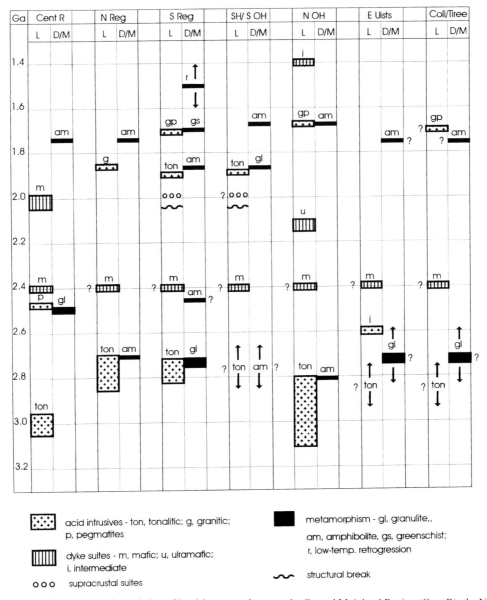

Fig. 3.3. Simplified Lewisian chronology and correlation of Lewisian events between the Central Mainland Region (Cent R); the Northern Mainland Region (N Reg); the Southern Mainland region (S Reg); South Harris and southern Outer Hebrides (SH/S OH); the northern Outer Hebrides (N OH); the Uists and Barra, east of the Outer Hebrides Fault (E Uists); and Coll and Tiree. L, lithology; D/M, deformational and metamorphic event; ? indicates undated event; arrows indicate large uncertainty over date. For sources, see text.

The Scourian gneisses

Lithology. The original extent of the Scourian complex, and the proportion of post-Scourian material within the Lewisian outcrop, have been the subjects of considerable debate in the past. Peach *et al.* (1907) followed by Sutton & Watson (1951) considered that the fundamental or Scourian complex (now known to be Archaean in age) extended throughout the whole of the mainland belt. They based their belief on the presence of amphibolite sheets similar to the Scourie dykes within both the Northern and Southern Regions. Others (e.g. Bowes 1968*b*; Holland & Lambert 1973) suggested that much of the material of the Laxfordian complexes may have represented post-Scourian supracrustal sequences, and that the amphibolite sheets were not all of the same age as the Scourie dykes. However, more recent Sm–Nd data indicate that almost the whole crust of the mainland region originated in the interval 3.0–2.7 Ga (e.g. Whitehouse 1989; Whitehouse *et al.* 1997*b*; Corfu *et al.* 1998) and the Archaean age of the 'fundamental complex' of the mainland is now firmly established.

The Scourian rocks, like those of many other Archaean high-grade terrains, are predominantly banded, or less commonly massive, grey gneisses of tonalitic, granodioritic or trondhjemitic composition, with occasional sheets or lenses of granitic gneiss, and numerous mafic and ultramafic layers and enclaves (Fig. 3.4, Plate 1). The grey gneisses in the unmodified parts of the Central Region make up probably between 75 and 80% of the complex, and contain pyroxene and/or hornblende in addition to plagioclase and quartz as their main constituents. Pyroxene-hornblende gneisses in which hornblende aggregates have replaced pyroxene are the most abundant type. Biotite- and muscovite-gneisses are confined to areas of later reworking in the Central Region, but are universally present in the Northern and Southern Regions, where it is difficult to determine the original nature of the gneisses because of pervasive Laxfordian reworking.

Metasedimentary rocks are comparatively rare in the mainland Scourian outcrops. A few narrow bands consisting mainly of semipelitic gneisses, but including minor calc-silicate rocks

Fig. 3.4. Banding in Scourian gneisses with intrafolial isoclinal folds and lensoid basic inclusions, Scourie. Field of view about 1 m wide. Photograph courtesy of the British Geological Survey.

and possible arkoses, are associated with the mafic/ultramafic layered complexes described below (Okeke *et al.* 1983; Cartwright & Barnicoat 1987). One of the best preserved occurrences, near Stoer in the Assynt region, is described by Cartwright *et al.* (1985). Brown, rusty-weathering gneisses form a layer about 75 m thick within the grey gneisses. These brown gneisses are quartzo-feldspathic, with abundant garnet and biotite, accompanied by either hornblende, with locally abundant cummingtonite, or muscovite. Within this unit are several thin quartz-free layers containing centimetre-sized staurolite, kyanite and corundum porphyroblasts in a white mica matrix. These aluminous layers contain millimetre-scale segregations and veins of alkali feldspar, plagioclase and quartz, which are regarded as the neosomatic product of local partial melting of the host rock (Cartwright & Barnicoat 1987). Pods and layers containing hornblende, epidote and clinozoisite, with biotite-scapolite augen, probably represent calcareous psammites. The metasediments are associated with basic and

ultrabasic orthogneisses. A narrow band of kyanite gneiss occurs within the basement gneisses at Fionn Loch, north of the contact with the metasediments of the Loch Maree Group. This band has yielded a Scourian age (Bickerman *et al.* 1975) and therefore is not an outlier of the Loch Maree Group.

Pegmatites consisting of quartz and perthite, sometimes with graphic intergrowth, and with accessory biotite and magnetite, are widely distributed. These bodies, dated at 2490–2480 Ma (Corfu *et al.* 1994), cut the gneissose banding, and are associated with local retrogression of the granulite-facies assemblage. They are taken as marking the boundary between the Scourian and Inverian events (Evans & Lambert 1974; Fig. 3.3).

The more mafic enclaves within the acid gneisses are collectively known as the *early basic* suite, to distinguish them from the post-Scourian basic intrusions. These masses vary in size from a few centimetres to about a kilometre across, and are particularly common in the Scourie and Assynt areas. In the Central Region, such bodies typically contain both clinopyroxene and orthopyroxene, and variable amounts of hornblende, in addition to plagioclase. Often they are cut or veined by acid gneiss, and sometimes grade into agmatite or, ultimately, to patches of acid gneiss enriched in small mafic clots.

The ultramafic enclaves vary compositionally from monomineralic masses of either hornblende or pyroxene, to large bodies of peridotitic or dunitic material, now largely serpentinized; they are either homogeneous or banded in nature (e.g. Fig. 3.5), with varying proportions of hornblende. The larger ultramafic bodies are often associated with mafic masses (Bowes *et al.* 1964). Ultramafic/mafic masses near Scourie contain anorthosite layers and are intimately associated with pelitic metasediments (Davies 1974). These mafic/ultramafic bodies appear to be generally older than the acid gneisses and to have been invaded by them; Park & Tarney (1987) suggest that they may represent disrupted pieces of oceanic crust.

The relative proportions of these lithological components vary in different parts of the mainland belt. The granulite-facies terrain of Scourie and Assynt in the Central Region is characterized by a high proportion of intercalated ultramafic and mafic material, and the composition of the grey gneisses varies from mafic diorite to tonalite with only a small proportion of silicic trondhjemite (Sheraton *et al.* 1973). On the other

Fig. 3.5. Scourian agmatite, heights of Kinlochewe. Photograph courtesy of the British Geological Survey (hammer for scale).

hand, the northern part of the Southern Region around
Gruinard Bay consists predominantly of amphibolite-facies
trondhjemitic gneisses with numerous mafic enclaves, although
relict granulite-facies assemblages survive locally. The gneisses
of the Northern and Southern Regions in general display a
lower proportion of mafic material, and few ultramafic enclaves
compared with those from the Central Region; they are more
silicic and potassic, with a much higher proportion of granodioritic material. The geochemistry of the gneisses of the Northern
Region led Sheraton et al. (1973) to conclude that they had
not undergone a granulite-facies metamorphism. Some of these
petrological and geochemical variations appear to reflect fundamental differences in crustal history across the Lewisian
outcrop (see below).

Deformation and metamorphism. The extreme heterogeneity
of the complex, coupled with the almost ubiquitous compositional banding, indicates generally intense deformation (e.g.
Fig. 3.4). The banding or foliation is typically sub-horizontal or
gently inclined over large areas of the Central Region (Sheraton
et al. 1973) although it is locally steepened in Inverian shear
zones. In the Southern Region, on the other hand, the banding
is steeply dipping and trends N–S to NE–SW where relatively
unaffected by later deformation.

Granulite-facies metamorphism is a characteristic feature of
the Scourian complex throughout the Central Region, although
local retrogression to amphibolite facies is widespread (see Sills
& Rollinson 1987). This metamorphic event is termed the
Badcallian (Park 1970), and was originally dated at ~2.7 Ga
from Sm–Nd and zircon ages (Pidgeon & Bowes 1972; Lyon
et al. 1973; Humphries & Cliff 1982). However Humphries
& Cliff (1982) dated the closure of the isotopic systems at
2490 Ma, and later work on zircons by Corfu et al. (1998) and
Friend & Kinny (1995) suggests that this disturbance of the
zircon systems at ~2.5 Ga corresponds to the main Badcallian
metamorphism which probably occurred at between 2490 and
2480 Ma.

However this major ~2.5 Ga granulite-facies event could not
be recognized in the U–Pb data from either the Northern
Region (Kinny & Friend 1997) or in the retrogressed granulite-
facies gneisses at Gruinard Bay in the Southern Region (Corfu
et al. 1998) suggesting that it may be restricted to the Central
Region. A hornblende-granulite facies metamorphic event
at ~2730 Ma has however been recognized from U–Pb dating at
Gruinard Bay associated with the steep NE-trending Archaean
fabric (Corfu et al. 1998). It would therefore seem logical to
restrict the term Badcallian to the 2.5 Ga event (since the type
areas for this event are at Badcall and Scourie), rather than
apply it to all late Archaean events throughout the complex, as
in previous usage.

Cartwright & Barnicoat (1987) review the geothermometric
and geobarometric data for the 2.5 Ga granulite-facies event
which indicate peak temperatures of ~1000°C and pressures
of ~11 kbar, with a subsequent decrease in temperature to
~800–900°C.

Origin and age of the gneisses. It is now generally believed that
the bulk of the gneisses are of plutonic igneous origin as
originally suggested by Peach et al. (1907). Geochemical studies
(Weaver & Tarney 1980) indicate that the gneisses have an
essentially bimodal character, where the two components
display different petrogenetic characteristics. The mafic components show a range of Fe/Mg ratios and their trace-element
patterns are consistent with low-pressure tholeiitic crystal
fractionation. The common association of ultramafic/mafic
bodies with metasedimentary layers suggests that this material
represents fragments of ocean-floor crust intercalated tectoni-

Fig. 3.6. Schematic profile illustrating the formation of the Scourian
complex (see text for explanation). After Park & Tarney (1987).

cally within the continental crust. The tonalitic to trondhjemitic
gneisses on the other hand have rare-earth element patterns
consistent with partial melting of a mafic source under high-
pressure hydrous conditions. Tarney & Weaver (1987a) suggest
that a subduction zone is the only environment where large
volumes of mafic material could be melted in order to generate
the tonalitic crustal material. They envisage a process of relatively shallow melting at a low-angle subduction zone where
melts generated under hydrous conditions would yield relatively dense tonalitic magmas which would solidify at deep
levels and progressively thicken the crust by underplating
(Fig. 3.6). Thus the mafic/metasediment (oceanic crust) association would first experience a high-grade metamorphic phase at
the base of the continental crust before being uplifted by further
underplating. Severe tectonic disruption of the deeper parts of
the complex would result from long periods of ductile-shear
deformation affecting the base of the accreting crust as the
underplating proceeded.

The age of the protoliths of the grey gneisses in the Scourie
area has been estimated at ~2930 Ma (model Nd: Whitehouse
1989) and ~2960 Ma (SHRIMP: Friend & Kinny 1995). Whitehouse (1989) records several different Sm–Nd ages of co-genetic
mafic/ultramafic suites ranging from ~2930 Ma at Scourie, to
~2860 Ma at Gruinard Bay, and to ~2780 in the Northern
Region. He suggested that the process of initial crustal accretion and differentiation was diachronous, and that a later and
unrelated tectonic accretion process was probably responsible
for the crustal thickening which led to the granulite-facies metamorphism at ~2.5 Ga. Single zircon and titanite U–Pb data
indicate protolith ages of 2770–2840 Ma for the gneisses of
the Northern Region and 2792–2730 Ma for Gruinard Bay
in the Southern Region compared with the ages of 2960–3030
for the Central Region (Kinny & Friend 1997; Corfu et al. 1998).

The difference in protolith ages between the Central and
Northern Regions, together with the fact that the 2.5 Ga
granulite-facies event could not be recognised in the U–Pb data
from the Northern Region, led Kinny & Friend (1997) to propose that the Northern and Central Regions represent distinct
crustal blocks with different Archaean histories, tectonically
juxtaposed during the Palaeoproterozoic. The Archaean geochronology of the Southern Region is only known from
Gruinard Bay in the north of the region, but the uniformity of
the steep, NE–SW to N–S-trending Archaean foliation from
Gruinard Bay across the Southern Region to Torridon (Park
et al. 1987) suggests that the ~2.8–2.7 Ga event recognized by
Corfu et al. (1998) affected the whole of the Southern Region.
Only the Central Region appears to have experienced the
high-strain, sub-horizontal fabrics and ultra-high pressure
metamorphism of the type Badcallian event. It would appear
therefore that at least two, and perhaps three crustal blocks are
represented in the mainland Lewisian, each with different
Archaean histories.

The Inverian event
The Inverian event (Evans 1965; Evans & Lambert 1974)
is defined as post-dating (but presumed to be closely related to)

a suite of post-Badcallian pegmatites at Scourie dated at 2490–2480 Ma (Corfu *et al.* 1998) and pre-dating the earliest Scourie dykes, dated at ~2420 Ma in age (Heaman & Tarney 1989). According to Humphries & Cliff (1982) ultimate closure of the Sm–Nd isotopic system in the granulites at 2490 Ma is associated with uplift, marking the commencement of Inverian tectonic activity. However, as recognized many years ago by Tarney (1963), the metamorphism affecting the shear zones into which the Scourie dykes were intruded persisted during the emplacement of at least the earlier members of the suite, so that the Inverian event is considered to overlap the dyke emplacement.

Post-Scourian, pre-dyke structures and associated amphibolite-facies retrogressive metamorphism in the Southern Region have been correlated with the Inverian on grounds of general similarity (e.g. Park *et al.* 1987) but Corfu *et al.* (1998) were unable to detect the event in the gneisses at Gruinard Bay; nor has an event of this age been recorded in the Northern Region (Kinny & Friend 1997).

Confusion is inevitable between Inverian and Laxfordian events because of the way that the nomenclature has developed. On the basis of the Sutton & Watson (1951) definition, all post-dyke events are Laxfordian. However since the dyke swarms in the Northern and Southern regions have not been dated, their equivalence to the type Scourie dykes of the Central Region cannot be assumed. Another problem is that it is likely that Inverian deformation and metamorphism may have persisted intermittently at this crustal level, from before the first dykes were emplaced at ~2420 Ma until after the dyke intrusion, thus overlapping the Laxfordian event, as originally defined. It has not so far proved possible to isolate the Inverian part of this activity by radiometric dating, since the isotopic systems used did not become closed until after 1800 Ma. Until more geochronological information becomes available, it is probably useful to restrict the term 'Inverian' to cover events up to 2400 Ma, and 'Laxfordian' for subsequent events, recognizing the possibility that anomalies of nomenclature could arise were later 'Scourie' dykes (~2000 Ma, say) shown to cut early 'Laxfordian' structures.

A major Inverian shear zone has been recognized at the northern margin of the Central Region. This zone is approximately 4 km wide and extends from near Scourie to Loch Laxford (Fig. 3.7) (see Beach *et al.* 1974; Davies 1978). On its southwest side, it cuts undeformed Badcallian structures and causes retrogression of the granulite-facies gneisses to amphibolite facies. On its northeast side, it becomes intensely affected by Laxfordian deformation in the Laxford shear zone. A second major zone is the 1–2 km wide Canisp shear zone (Tarney 1963; Evans 1965; Attfield 1987) that cuts through the middle of the Central Region in the Assynt district (Fig. 3.2). Many minor steep shear zones also occur throughout the region.

Another major shear zone correlated with the Inverian of the Central Region occurs at the northern margin of the Southern Region between the Gruinard River and Fionn Loch, with a width of about 8 km (Fig. 3.8). This zone is over-printed and obscured by a wide Laxfordian belt on its southwest side (Crane 1978). Further south, Inverian structures have also been recognized in a number of areas throughout the Southern Region (Park *et al.* 1987).

The Scourie dyke swarm

Dykes attributed to the Scourie dyke suite (Plate 2) occur throughout the Mainland Lewisian but have been reliably dated only in the Central Region. It is not yet possible to establish whether or not those in the Southern and Northern Regions belong to the same suite as the type Scourie dykes of the Central Region. The dykes are typically steep, with a NW–SE to E–W trend, and for the most part appear to have been emplaced dilationally, implying considerable crustal extension. They are thickest and most numerous between Gruinard Bay and Torridon in the Southern Region but decrease in abundance northwards towards Durness. Within the areas affected by the Inverian deformation, the dykes are partly controlled by the pre-existing structure, being generally concordant, thinner, and more numerous in zones of strongly developed, steep, NW–SE-trending Inverian foliation (Park & Cresswell 1972, 1973). The possibility that the Scourie dyke suite may consist of two or more chronologically separate swarms separated by major tectonic events was put forward by Bowes (1968b). However, there is as yet no reliable evidence to support this view.

Tarney & Weaver (1987b) define four petrological/geochemical types: bronzite-picrites, norites, olivine-gabbros, and quartz-dolerites. The quartz-dolerites are by far the most abundant and correspond to the main 'epidiorite' suite recognized by Peach *et al.* (1907). There is evidence in the Central Region for their emplacement at depth into hot country rock (O'Hara 1961; Tarney 1963).

The timing and duration of Scourie dyke intrusion is still uncertain. The original K–Ar and Rb–Sr dating of Evans & Tarney (1964) gave a range of ages interpreted as indicating a date of ~2200 Ma for the emplacement of the main swarm and ~2000 Ma for two younger alkali-basalt and tholeiite dykes. More recently, Chapman (1979) obtained an Rb–Sr whole-rock age of ~2400 Ma from a combined isochron from three typical quartz-dolerites from Scourie and Kylescu (13 km southeast of Scourie) and Heaman & Tarney (1989) report U–Pb baddeleyite ages from two dykes: $2418 + 7 - 4$ Ma for a bronzite picrite and $1992 + 3 - 2$ Ma for an olivine gabbro. These results

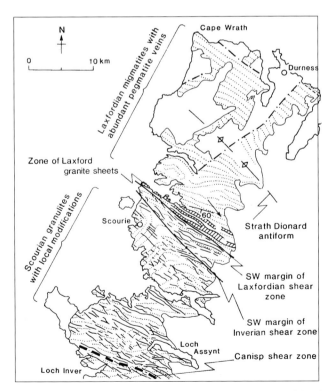

Fig. 3.7. Simplified map of the Northern Region and the transitional zone in the northern part of the Central Region, showing the principal structures and the boundaries of the major Inverian and Laxfordian shear zones. Dotted lines represent trend of banding; Scourie dykes in black; Laxford granite sheets hachured. Note generalized dip of planar fabric and plunge of linear fabric in the Laxfordian shear zone. After Watson (1983).

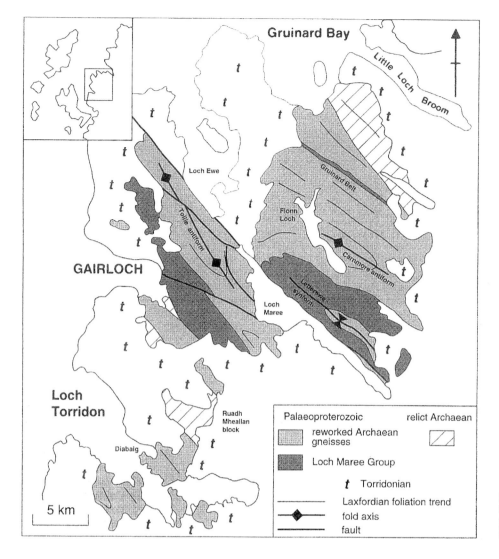

Fig. 3.8. Simplified map of the Southern Region showing the principal structures. After Park *et al.* (1987). Inset map shows location.

support the early suggestions that intrusion of the dyke suite spanned a considerable period of time and are consistent with the interpretation that the main Scourie dyke swarm was emplaced around 2400 Ma ago, at depths of 10–20 km, during the Inverian metamorphism (Dickinson & Watson 1976) and that certain members of the swarm were emplaced much later (~2000 Ma) into cooler crust in the Central Region.

In the Southern Region, several undated sill-like bodies cut supracrustal rocks of the Loch Maree Group dated at ~2000 Ma (see below).

The Loch Maree Group
Two belts of metasediment, intercalated with amphibolite sheets, occupy a combined outcrop area of about 130 km² at Loch Maree and Gairloch in the Southern Region (Fig. 3.8). They were first described in detail by Peach *et al.* (1907) and subsequently became known as the *Loch Maree Group* (LMG). Both outcrops exhibit intense polyphase deformation. Peach *et al.* (1907) were unable to decide whether the sediments were older than the igneous rocks of the fundamental complex, or were unconformable upon them (see discussion in Peach & Horne 1930). They noted that the boundaries were tectonically modified and that gneisses appeared to be thrust over metasediments at Loch Maree. They were unable to find examples of Scourie dykes cutting the metasediments, but speculated as to whether the amphibolite sheets may have been fed by Scourie dykes.

Park (1964, 1965) concluded, from a comparison of the structural and metamorphic history of the LMG with that of the neighbouring gneisses, that the LMG was younger. This view was confirmed by O'Nions *et al.* (1983) who published Sm–Nd model ages of 2490 and 2190 Ma on two samples of clastic metasediment, indicating an important post-Archaean component in their provenance, and establishing a maximum age for the Group of ~2.2 Ga. More recent U–Pb detrital zircon ages recorded by Whitehouse *et al.* (1997) include both Archaean (3.06–2.48 Ga) and Palaeoproterozoic (2.2–2.0 Ga) components, which confirm the earlier data and indicate a probable depositional age of ~2.0 Ga.

The supracrustal sequence comprises several belts of schistose metasediments separated by amphibolite sheets. The metasediments consist mainly of semipelitic quartz–biotite–plagioclase schist, considered to represent metamorphosed greywackes, and include narrow bands of chlorite schist, hornblende schist, banded iron-formation, quartzite, marble and calc-schist, graphite schist and garnet–grunerite schist. The amphibolite sheets are mainly in the form of hornblende schist but also occur occasionally as massive amphibolite. The thicker sheets (250–500 m thick) are thought to represent basic volcanics (see below) but some of the thinner sheets are probably basic sills. Studies of the geochemistry and petrology of the metabasic rocks were carried out by Park (1966), Power & Park (1969) and Johnson *et al.* (1987) and of the metasedimentary schists by Winchester *et al.* (1980) and Floyd *et al.*

(1989). The origin of the suite has recently been reviewed by Park *et al.* (2001).

The geochemical study carried out by Floyd *et al.* (1989) recognized two main groups of semipelite: relatively immature clastic sediments akin to greywackes and more mature lithic sandstones. The intermediate to high silica content and rare-earth element patterns of the Gairloch semipelites were considered to indicate derivation from a continental upper-crustal source, and a basic volcanic component was also recognized in those metasediments closely associated spatially with the meta-volcanic rocks. Park *et al.* (2001) note that the high K/Rb ratios and highly fractionated rare-earth element patterns do not match the local Archaean gneisses and indicate that the sediments were mostly not of local derivation.

Further evidence for the sediment source comes from the zircon study of Whitehouse *et al.* (1997). Zircons from a semipelitic schist sample yield a range of ages which fall into two groups: an Archaean group with ages ranging from ~2.5 to ~3.1 Ga and an early Palaeoproterozoic group with ages clustering around ~2.0 and 2.2 Ga. The Archaean zircons may have been derived from local Archaean basement sources with matching ages, but the early Palaeoproterozoic zircons require a quartzofeldspathic source with ages of ~2.0 and 2.2 Ga, and although mafic igneous activity at ~2.0 Ga has been identified in the Lewisian, no acid source rocks of that age are yet known. Whitehouse *et al.* (1997) consider that the source was a volcanic arc which may have been tectonically displaced during collision. The semipelites are thus considered to represent the immature clastic sediments of an accretionary prism, incorporating both juvenile and older basement source materials.

The origin of those metasedimentary rocks closely associated with the amphibolites is different from that of the semipelites forming the bulk of the sediments. Current views on banded iron-formation favour a shallow-marine, biogenic origin, which would also explain the presence of the associated graphitic schists. The marbles also may have a biogenic origin, although there is no local evidence to support that view. These largely chemical sediments are thought to have formed on a substrate of submarine basalt and the associated quartz–chlorite schists are thought to represent altered basaltic volcaniclastic material to which variable amounts of silica have been added. Several occurrences of stratiform sulphides are associated with the mafic igneous rocks and the chemical sediments, and are considered to be of exhalative origin by Jones *et al.* (1987).

The chemistry of the majority of the LMG amphibolites leaves little doubt that these rocks are of igneous origin and represent tholeiitic basalts (Johnson *et al.* 1987). The intercalation with chemical and clastic sediments of marine type, together with the evidence of associated hydrothermal activity, are strong indicators of a submarine origin and suggest that the basalts were erupted in an active ridge setting. Park *et al.* (2001) note that their rather flat rare-earth patterns and lack of Nb/Ta depletion are characteristic of oceanic plateau lavas. A few amphibolites possess rare-earth element profiles and chemistry similar to those of primitive island-arc basalts (Park *et al.* 2001). These bodies are thin sheets (up to 100 m thick), occasionally displaying relict igneous textures, and are more likely to represent sills than lava flows.

The LMG supracrustal rocks at Gairloch are cut by sheets of tonalitic to granodioritic gneiss, collectively known as the Ard gneisses, which are deformed by early Laxfordian structures. A zircon age of 1903 ± 3 Ma is interpreted as the emplacement date of the gneiss (Park *et al.* 2001) and gives a minimum age for the supracrustal rocks. Chemically, the Ard gneisses have a primitive arc signature (Park *et al.* 2001), regarded as evidence of a Palaeoproterozoic magmatic arc, and indicating contemporary subduction of oceanic material.

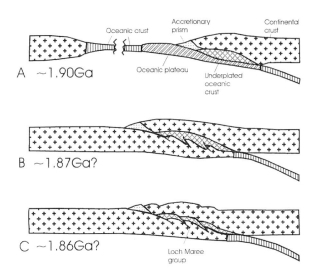

Fig. 3.9. Schematic profile across the Southern Region to illustrate the proposed collisional model for the Loch Maree Group (From Park *et al.* 2001).

The intercalation of the LMG within continental basement suggests that the LMG outcrop occupies a collisional suture zone (Fig. 3.9). Previous lack of evidence of a volcanic arc had been used as an argument in favour of an intraplate model for the LMG (Johnson *et al.* 1987), but this model is no longer sustainable in view of the more recent evidence.

It is not clear whether or not there is a direct relationship between the basic volcanics of the LMG and the adjacent very numerous and densely packed Scourie-type dykes within the basement. If the dykes in the basement are the same age as the 2.4 Ga suite of the Central Region, they are much earlier than, and unrelated to, the LMG, in which case their massive concentration around Gairloch may reflect a zone of basement weakness, or incipient rifting. Alternatively some (or possibly all) of the Scourie dykes of the Loch Maree–Gairloch district may be related to a phase of crustal extension immediately preceding the deposition of the LMG at ~2.0 Ga.

Laxfordian modifications and younger events
The problem of nomenclature for those events post-dating the earlier Scourie dykes and preceding the later has already been discussed. In practice, structures and metamorphism affecting any of the 'Scourie' dykes have been regarded as Laxfordian, following Sutton & Watson (1951). Laxfordian modifications on the mainland can be divided on a very simple basis into an earlier set (D1/D2) associated with amphibolite-facies metamorphism and followed by the emplacement of granites and pegmatites, and a later set (D3/D4) accompanied by retrogressive alteration to greenschist facies or below (Fig. 3.3). The earlier Laxfordian deformations produced fabrics in the dykes associated generally with amphibolite-facies recrystallization of the original igneous assemblages. In many areas, recrystallization has occurred in the absence of deformation, producing the typical 'epidiorite' dyke textures of the Central Region. It is possible that this static recrystallization represents a continuation of the Inverian metamorphic event.

The theoretical older age limit to the earliest Laxfordian events is 2400 Ma, the age of the earlier Scourie dykes in the Central Region. The date of the main (high-grade) Laxfordian metamorphism has been estimated by a set of metamorphic ages, including Rb–Sr whole-rock, lead-isotope and zircon ages, in the range 1860–1630 Ma, concentrating around a date of ~1700 Ma (Lambert & Holland 1972; Lyon *et al.* 1973).

However the younger of these dates are indistinguishable from those of the widespread post-tectonic granitoid intrusions (see below), and may reflect that event. The D1 deformation in the Southern Region post-dates the Loch Maree Group, and is therefore later than ~2000 Ma. Park *et al.* (2001) consider the 1903 Ma date of the synkinematic Ard gneiss intrusion to be an estimate of the age of the D1/D2 event in the Southern Region. The date of the Laxfordian amphibolite-facies recrystallization and deformation of the gneisses in the Northern Region is estimated at ~1740 Ma (from titanite) by Corfu *et al.* (1998) and Kinny & Friend (1997). It is possible therefore that the early Laxfordian events in the Northern and Southern Regions are not correlatable.

D1/D2 structure. The early Laxfordian structures (D1/D2) are very heterogeneous in their development. In the Central Region, they are confined to narrow shear zones, generally of the order of metres in width, with the exception of the Canisp shear zone where the belt of Laxfordian reactivation reaches 750 m in width (Attfield 1987). The main Laxfordian belts are situated in the Northern and Southern Regions (Fig. 3.2). In both regions, the first Laxfordian deformation (D1) is generally sub-concordant with the Scourie dykes, progressing from narrow marginal zones, eventually to encompass the whole width of the dyke, and spreading out into the host gneisses. The development of the first Laxfordian fabric is associated with variable, locally very large, strains, and is typically steep near the margins of the Laxfordian belts. In the Southern Region, Park *et al.* (1987) show that this D1 fabric, with a strong NW–SE elongation lineation, is folded during D2, becoming flat-lying between Carnmore and Gairloch, and south of Loch Torridon (Fig. 3.7). Thorough reworking of the Scourian complex produces a finely banded gneiss containing concordant amphibolite sheets (produced from Scourie dykes), and pervaded by granitic migmatite of Laxfordian age (e.g. Fig. 3.10). 'Laxfordianized' gneisses of this kind are confined to the Northern Region, north of Loch Laxford, the southernmost parts of the Southern Region around Kenmore, and the islands of Rona and Raasay.

According to Coward & Park (1987), the main Laxfordian belts of the mainland are linked in a major mid-crustal shear zone network which separates and encloses more stable crustal blocks (Fig. 3.11). It is considered that the D1 and D2 deformations probably represent earlier and later stages of a progressive deformation involving transport of higher-level crustal blocks relative to lower, on a major sub-horizontal mid-crustal shear

Fig. 3.10. Typical finely banded gneiss, affected by intense Laxfordian deformation, with discordant granite sheets. Near Badcall, Loch Laxford. Photograph courtesy of the British Geological Survey (hammer for scale).

zone, in a NW–SE direction. This major shear zone was thought to be exposed in the Northern and Southern Regions of the mainland, passing beneath the Central Region, and to be widely represented in the Outer Hebrides (see below) at a lower crustal level. The metamorphic event associated with the Laxford shear zone is dated at ~1740 Ma by Kinny & Friend (2001), who believe that the zone, separating the Central and Northern Regions, represents a terrane boundary along which the two Regions (which they term the Assynt and Rhiconich terranes, respectively) were juxtaposed.

Tectonic significance of the LMG. As explained above, the LMG consists of two quite distinct assemblages: one dominated by semipelitic metagreywackes interpreted as an accretionary wedge sequence formed proximally to a continent and influenced by a contemporary magmatic arc; the other consisting of the plateau-type metabasalts and their associated sediments, formed probably in an oceanic setting (see Park *et al.* 2001). Although these two assemblages could have formed in close proximity, it is more likely, given the evidence for an active margin setting, that they have been tectonically juxtaposed and subsequently invaded by the arc-like Ard gneiss. The interleaving of the semipelites with the oceanic assemblage probably reflects the accretion of separate tectonic slices. This process of lateral accretion involved severe tectonic imbrication and mixing of oceanic, volcanic arc and continentally derived components followed by continental collision. The major D1/D2 deformation, which is strongly developed in the LMG, is interpreted as the result of a major, low-angle shear zone with a westerly directed sense of movement. It affects both the LMG and the adjoining gneisses on both sides, and must partly relate to the collision process. However, it is not possible to separate structures formed during the accretion stage from those formed during collision. The Gairloch and Loch Maree outcrops may represent separate thrust-bound slices or may have been isolated by D3 movements (Fig. 3.8).

The LMG and the basement gneisses in the Southern Region share the same Laxfordian deformational and metamorphic history as the Scourie dykes, and the metamorphic assemblages are typical of middle to upper amphibolite facies. Thermobarometric studies on marble, calc-silicate and meta-ironstone from Gairloch (Droop *et al.* 1999) yielded peak metamorphic conditions of $530 \pm 20°C$ and 6.5 ± 1.5 kbar, and a pelite from Loch Maree yielded a rather higher temperature estimate of ~630°C. These conditions indicate burial of the supracrustal assemblages to ~25 km and imply considerable crustal thickening during the early Laxfordian event, consistent with the collisional model proposed.

Granites and pegmatites. Laxfordian granite and pegmatite sheets are widespread throughout the Northern and Southern Regions. They cut the early Laxfordian structures (D1/D2) and in places are affected by D3 structures (e.g. the Tollie antiform at Gairloch). The bodies are typically only metres across but thicker sheets occur at Loch Laxford in the north, where several thick, sub-concordant, sheets of pink, gneissose granite occur within a zone 2–4 km wide. North of the granite sheets, narrow bands of granite and pegmatite are abundant. The bodies are typically granodioritic to granitic in composition and had been dated at ~1700 Ma by a variety of methods (Lyon *et al.* 1973; Taylor *et al.* 1984). However Friend & Kinny (2001) give a Pb–Pb zircon age of 1854 ± 13 Ma for a narrow composite granite–pegmatite sheet north of Loch Laxford, interpreted as the intrusion age of the sheet. A pegmatite body from Loch Tollie, near Gairloch in the Southern Region, has yielded a precise zircon age of 1694 ± 5 Ma, also interpreted as the intrusion age (Park *et al.* 2001).

D3, D4 and Grenvillian events. The D3 Laxfordian structures consist of prominent NW-trending major folds that dominate the outcrop pattern of the Laxfordian belts in both the Northern and Southern Regions (Figs 3.7, 3.8, 3.11). In the north, the Strath Dionard antiform (Dash 1969) (Fig. 3.7) and in the south, the Carnmore, Tollie and Torridon antiforms and the Letterewe synform (Park *et al.* 1987) (Fig. 3.8) belong to this set. The 6 km-wide Gairloch shear zone (Odling 1984; Park *et al.* 1987) (Fig. 3.2) is also attributed to the D3 deformation. Park *et al.* (1987) have linked these D3 structures with the development of a new, locally developed, planar fabric accompanied by retrogression to greenschist facies, with albite–epidote–actinolite assemblages in amphibolite, and albite–epidote–biotite–chlorite–muscovite assemblages in acid gneisses. The development of these retrogressive assemblages appears to have closely followed the emplacement of the granites and pegmatites and is probably responsible for the ~1700 Ma ages referred to above. Holland & Lambert (1995) present an Rb–Sr age of 1663 ± 22 Ma on pegmatites from the Tollie antiform which is believed to reflect D3 recrystallization. Older K–Ar ages on hornblendes also cluster around 1700 Ma and were attributed to cooling of the complex at the end of the main Laxfordian metamorphic phase by Moorbath & Park (1972).

Later, more localized, structures of various styles and orientations, together with crush zones containing pseudotachylite, were assigned to the 'late phase' of the Laxfordian in the Gairloch area by Park (1964). Similar structures have been recognized and described in other parts of the Laxfordian belts (e.g. Bhattacharjee 1968; Dash 1969; Cresswell 1972) and are attributed to D4 by Park *et al.* (1987). These structures may be responsible for a set of younger Laxfordian K–Ar dates of ~1500 Ma recorded by Moorbath & Park (1972).

Two young K–Ar dates of 1148 Ma and 1169 Ma were obtained by Moorbath & Park (1972) from chloritized biotite in acid gneisses from Torridon. These ages are close to a biotite Rb–Sr age of 1160 Ma reported by Giletti *et al.* (1961), and suggested the possibility that some of the later structures in the Lewisian complex (e.g. certain crush belts) may result from Grenvillian movements at around 1100 Ma (Park 1970). More widespread evidence for activity close to 1100 Ma in Lewis, north of the Langavat shear zone, has been presented by Cliff & Rex (1989). Sanders *et al.* (1984) report two Sm–Nd dates of ~1082 and 1010 Ma from an eclogite body in the Lewisian gneiss of the Glenelg inlier, within the Moine thrust zone, and infer a Grenvillian age for the eclogite-facies metamorphism.

The margin of the Mesoproterozoic Grenville belt probably crossed Scotland not far east of the mainland Lewisian outcrop, and it is possible that both the Moine thrust zone and the Outer Hebrides fault zone may have been active at this time.

The Lewisian of the Outer Hebrides

The islands of the Outer Hebrides collectively form the largest Lewisian outcrop in northwest Scotland (Fig. 3.1) and the island of Lewis gave its name to the complex. However they received very little attention from the early geologists, and the chronology was more difficult to interpret because of the absence of large areas of unmodified Scourian gneisses. For these reasons, the main advances in understanding of the Lewisian complex came through studies on the mainland. The early descriptive work was carried out by Jehu & Craig (1923, 1925, 1926, 1927, 1934) and by Dearnley (1962, 1963). The latter extended to the Outer Hebrides the chronological sub-division established by Sutton & Watson (1951) on the mainland. Detailed mapping by the Geological Survey carried out in the 1970s was published at a scale of 1:100 000 in 1981 (Fettes *et al.* 1992) while a summary of the geology of the islands is given by Fettes & Mendum (1987).

Like the mainland Lewisian, the bulk of the Outer Hebrides outcrop is composed of rocks correlated with the Scourian complex, although post-Scourian granites make up a significant proportion of the outcrop area. Amphibolite sheets correlated with the Scourie dyke swarm, on the other hand, are generally less numerous, smaller, and more deformed and disrupted than their mainland counterparts. Two groups of rocks have apparently no precise equivalent on the mainland. These are the *South Harris Igneous Complex* and the *Corodale Gneiss*. The Outer Hebrides also differs from the mainland in containing a significant proportion (about 5% of outcrop area) of supracrustal rocks. The relationship of these rocks to the Scourian complex is uncertain. Their distribution is described by Coward *et al.* (1969) and the main outcrops are shown on the BGS maps (see also Fig. 3.2). They include quartzites, marbles, graphitic schists, kyanite– or sillimanite–garnet–pelites, quartzo-feldspathic gneisses, magnetite-rich gneisses, and fine-grained, banded amphibolites interpreted as metavolcanics.

The Scourian gneisses

The dominant rock types, as on the mainland, are grey, tonalitic to granodioritic gneisses containing a wide variety of

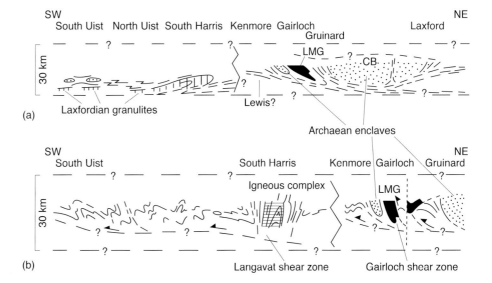

Fig. 3.11. Schematic composite structural profiles across the Lewisian complex. (**a**) Early Laxfordian, showing how the structures may be related to a network of low-angle shear-zones. Note that the movement direction is largely into the page (towards NW). (**b**) Late Laxfordian, showing refolding into upright structures and steep shear zones. From Coward & Park (1987). CB, central block; LMG, Loch Maree Group.

ultramafic, mafic and acid bodies, both as inclusions and as later intrusions (see Fig. 3.3). The date of formation of the gneisses in the southern part of the Outer Hebrides has been estimated by Sm/Nd model ages ranging from 2750 to 2830 Ma with a terrane average of 2770 Ma (Whitehouse 1990), and in Harris by a zircon U–Pb age of 2700 ± 20 Ma (Pidgeon & Aftalion 1972) and more recently by mean Pb–Pb zircon ages of 2834 ± 14 Ma from a tonalitic gneiss and 3125 ± 14 Ma from a migmatitic gneiss by Friend & Kinny (2001).

The general character of these gneisses is more reminiscent of the Laxfordian belts of the mainland than of the Central Region. The gneisses typically contain biotite and/or hornblende as their principal ferromagnesian constituent. Pyroxene-bearing varieties are confined to Barra and South Uist (Coward 1973) where granulite-facies assemblages are preserved, showing varying degrees of retrogression to the amphibolite-facies assemblages typical elsewhere. Granulite-facies rocks also occur in southern South Harris, but are of Laxfordian age (Cliff *et al.* 1983). Extensive areas of migmatite surround the Laxfordian granites of Lewis and South Harris (Fig. 3.2), and are generally more common than on the mainland. Thin bands or lenses of metasediment, a few metres in width, are intercalated with the gneisses in zones traceable for several kilometres; it is not certain whether or not these are an original part of the Scourian complex. Banded basic rocks associated with the metasediments form isolated bodies, usually tens of metres in width, and are traceable for many kilometres along strike. These bodies display banding on all scales from centimetres to metres, and range in composition from ultramafic to anorthositic. The association is similar to that of the ultramafic/mafic bodies of the mainland.

Fettes & Mendum (1987) believe that Scourian granulite-facies rocks were confined to South Uist and Barra, east of the Outer Hebrides Fault Zone, at the present level of exposure, and that the bulk of the Outer Hebrides gneisses, like those of the Northern and Southern Regions of the mainland, represent originally higher crustal levels of the Scourian complex. They suggest that much of the migmatization seen in the west of the Outer Hebrides may be of Scourian age, and represents the high-level consequences of fluid migration from deeper levels undergoing granulite-facies metamorphism.

The early deformation of the Scourian complex, like that of the mainland, is represented by the intense foliation accompanying the Scourian metamorphism. Fettes *et al.* (1992) recognize an earlier foliation confined to the metasediments and pre-dating the emplacement of the plutonic igneous precursors of the acid gneiss complex.

The Corodale Gneiss. A large metagabbroic to metadioritic body, metamorphosed in granulite facies occupies almost the whole Lewisian outcrop in South Uist above the Outer Hebrides fault, and is termed the Corodale Gneiss (Coward 1972). It was tentatively correlated by Dearnley (1962) and Coward (1972) with the pyroxene-granulites of the South Harris complex (see below) but more recently Whitehouse (1993) has recorded whole-rock Sm–Nd and Pb–Pb ages of 2770 ± 140 Ma and 2900 ± 100 Ma respectively, indicating that the Corodale Gneiss belongs to the early Scourian mafic suite and that the granulite-facies metamorphism is Scourian.

The Inverian Event
The period after the end of the Scourian metamorphism and deformation, and before the intrusion of the Scourie dykes, was marked by the emplacement of a suite of 'late Scourian' intrusions which cut the Scourian banding. These intrusions consist of two distinct widespread suites, the first consisting

of diorites, monzodiorites and microdiorites, and the second of potash-rich granites, monzonites and pegmatites. Both exhibit typical alkaline trends. These rocks are best seen in Barra, where the effects of Laxfordian reworking are minimal. Here, a number of diorite dykes, centimetres to metres in width, are cut by members of the younger basic dyke suite (correlated with the Scourie dykes). The late-stage pegmatites have yielded an Rb–Sr whole-rock age of 2555 ± 50 Ma (Moorbath *et al.* 1975) on Barra, and 2576 ± 80 Ma on South Uist (Lambert *et al.* 1970). Further north, on the island of Fuday, one of the dioritic dykes is folded prior to the injection of an undeformed younger basic dyke (presumed to be a Scourie dyke). This outcrop demonstrates the only clear geochronological evidence in the Outer Hebrides of the Inverian event. However, other structures attributed to the Inverian by Fettes & Mendum (1987) comprise regionally developed asymmetrical folds with steep NNE–SSW long limbs, and a number of sub-vertical NW–SE (and occasionally NE–SW) shear zones. Several of these shear zones are intruded by members of the younger basic dyke suite. The intensity of the Laxfordian deformation over most of the Outer Hebrides outcrop precludes any attempt to assess the regional extent or intensity of the Inverian event. However the absence of Inverian deformation in Barra suggests that, as on the mainland, areas of Scourian granulite-facies rocks acted as resistant blocks during both Inverian and Laxfordian deformation.

The younger basic (Scourie dyke) suite
Basic and ultrabasic intrusions believed to correlate with the Scourie dyke suite of the mainland are widespread throughout the Outer Hebrides, and are termed there the 'younger basics' by Fettes & Mendum (1987). They comprise three main groups: (1) ultrabasic bodies; (2) noritic and picritic bodies of the 'Cleitichean Beag' suite; and (3) the abundant metadolerites of the main swarm.

The ultrabasic bodies comprise peridotites and subordinate dunites, and are generally massive. Their age relationship to the other two groups is uncertain. The Cleitichean Beag dykes contain two pyroxenes, (olivine), hornblende, plagioclase and opaques, and are concentrated in two E–W belts in Lewis and Harris. They are broadly similar, petrographically and chemically, to the norites and picrites of the mainland suite (Tarney 1973) and have yielded a ~2400 Ma K–Ar age (Lambert *et al.* 1970). Members of this group are cut by metadolerites of group 3, but reliable intrusion dates of the latter are not available. The Maaruig gabbro, correlated by Tarney & Weaver (1987b) with the olivine gabbros on the mainland, has yielded a 2140 ± 38 Ma Sm–Nd mineral isochron age (Cliff *et al.* 1998).

The Leverburgh and Langavat metasediments
The largest and best preserved outcrops of metasediment in the Outer Hebrides occur in two belts in South Harris, termed the Langavat and Leverburgh belts respectively, flanking the South Harris Igneous Complex (Fig. 3.12). The Langavat belt corresponds to a major shear zone (Coward 1984a) which appears to mark the boundary between two areas of significantly different geological history (Cliff & Rex 1989); the Leverburgh belt shares a distinctive metamorphic history with the South Harris Igneous Complex (see below) but neither belt possesses clearly interpretable contacts with Scourian gneisses. A 2.44 Ga Sm–Nd model age (Cliff *et al.* 1998) on a semipelitic gneiss from the Leverburgh belt, and detrital zircons with Pb–Pb ages in the range 2.15–1.83 Ga from the Langavat belt (Whitehouse & Bridgwater 1999) demonstrate that the South Harris metasediments are of Palaeoproterozoic age, and in that respect resemble the Loch Maree Group on the mainland.

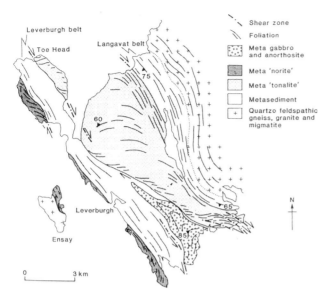

Fig. 3.12. Simplified map of the South Harris igneous complex and the Langavat shear zone. After Graham (1980).

The South Harris Igneous Complex and the Ness Anorthosite
The *South Harris Igneous Complex* consists essentially of a thick sheet of anorthosite and metagabbro, with associated bodies of tonalitic and pyroxene-granulitic gneiss (Fig. 3.12). The complex is emplaced mainly within, and thus post-dates, supracrustal gneisses of the Leverburgh and Langavat belts. Cliff *et al.* (1983) give an Sm–Nd model age of 2200 Ma for the anorthosite from analyses of contiguous whole-rock samples and a younger maximum age of 2060 Ma for the tonalite. More recently, Whitehouse & Bridgwater (1999) report a precise U–Pb zircon age of 1881 ± 13 Ma for the tonalite-diorite. The emplacement of the igneous complex thus falls roughly within the same age range occupied by the Loch Maree Group and the Ard gneiss on the mainland.

The *Ness Anorthosite* (Watson 1969) (Fig. 3.2) has been compared with the South Harris body, and is also associated with high-grade metasediments. Whitehouse (1990) shows that it has a similar early Proterozoic Sm–Nd model age ($\sim$2200 Ma) and suggests that it may have originally been part of the same body, disrupted during early Laxfordian shearing.

Laxfordian modifications
The effects of Laxfordian deformation and metamorphism are more widespread in the Outer Hebrides than on the mainland. Recrystallization of the Scourie dykes to granular fabrics, and Laxfordian deformation in general, are ubiquitous except in small areas of South Uist and Barra. Fettes & Mendum (1987) recognize two metamorphic events, the early and late Laxfordian, following Dearnley (1962).

Six phases of Laxfordian deformation are recognized by Fettes & Mendum (1987) of which only the first three are regionally significant. D1 is confined to planar fabrics in certain Scourie dykes. Fettes & Mendum relate these fabrics to the continuation of activity on the Inverian shear zones during or shortly after dyke emplacement. The main regionally developed phases are D2 and D3 (Fig. 3.11). D2 produced sub-horizontal axial-planar fabrics which, in areas of high Laxfordian strain, become more intense: folds tighten, Scourian structures become rotated into parallelism, and dykes become thinned and boudinaged (e.g. Fig. 3.13). D3 is characterized by upright folds, trending NW–SE, or locally NE–SW, in northwest Lewis. D4 is restricted in extent; D5 and D6 produced open warps, restricted cataclasis and local mylonitization, including early movements on the Outer Hebrides Fault Zone (see below). D2 corresponds to D2 on the mainland (Fig. 3.3); D3 structures are similar in both areas but appear to have different relationships to the granite emplacement (see below, Fig. 3.3). D5 and D6 structures appear similar to the D4 structures of the mainland.

The early Laxfordian. The early Laxfordian metamorphism can be distinguished only in the South Harris Igneous Complex and in its host gneisses, where a high-pressure granulite-facies assemblage characterises a variety of meta-igneous and meta-sedimentary rocks (Dearnley 1963). Cliff *et al.* (1998) give an Sm–Nd mineral isochron age of 1826 ± 16 Ma for this event and Friend & Kinny (2001) give two mean Pb–Pb ages from zircon overgrowths of 1874 ± 29 and 1885 ± 7 Ma. The isotopic data

Fig. 3.13. Boudinage and folding of Scourie dykes intensely deformed in the Laxfordian, South Uist (hammer for scale). Photograph courtesy of the British Geological Survey.

therefore support Dearnley's interpretation of a Laxfordian age
for the granulite-facies metamorphism.

In a detailed study of the granulite-facies pelitic gneisses in
the Leverburgh belt, Baba (1999) estimates peak metamorphic
conditions of ~950°C and >10 kbar, compatible with ultra-
high temperature metamorphism. These conditions are attributed to the emplacement of the South Harris Igneous Complex
and are succeeded by a prograde granulite-facies event at
~800°C involving an up-pressure transition to 13–14 kbar.
The latter event probably corresponds to the widespread
regional early Laxfordian event, and was followed in turn by a
retrogressive phase attributed to decompression at 550–650°C
and 6.5 kbar.

Further north, in Harris and central Lewis, garnet granulite-
facies mineral assemblages are locally developed in younger
basic bodies, although the host gneisses have amphibolite-
facies assemblages.

The late Laxfordian.   Late Laxfordian metamorphism is characterized by general amphibolite-facies assemblages over the
remainder of the Outer Hebrides outcrop, and is associated
with regional migmatization and emplacement of granites and
pegmatites.

The granite–migmatite complexes of north Harris and south
Lewis consist of biotite–granite bodies ranging from porphyritic varieties to leucogranites, aplites and pegmatitic veins. The
emplacement of these rocks is accompanied by extensive metasomatic activity involving particularly, potassium remobilization (Myers 1970, 1971). Sm–Nd whole-rock isotope data on
several members of this suite show that they were derived
almost entirely by remelting of older Scourian crust (Cliff *et al.*
1998). The granite suite is considered to post-date D3, but
shows varying degrees of deformation associated with low-
temperature retrogression, which Fettes & Mendum (1987)
suggest may be contemporaneous with emplacement. Dates of
1750 ± 34 Ma (Rb–Sr whole-rock) and 1715 ± 10 Ma (U–Pb
zircon) were obtained by Van Breemen *et al.* (1971) from the
extensive granite-migmatite complex of north Harris and south
Lewis (Myers 1971) (Fig. 3.2). However Friend & Kinny (2001)
give a rather younger age of ~1675 Ma for the granite sheets of

the injection complex, based on three Pb–Pb zircon concordia.
The youngest Laxfordian intrusions are thin microdiorite
dykes, one of which cuts a pegmatite of the granite-migmatite
suite described above and has yielded a K–Ar mica age of
1409 Ma (Fettes *et al.* 1992). No equivalents of these are known
on the mainland.

Mineral ages generally reflect cooling after the late Laxfordian event. In the southern Outer Hebrides, K–Ar hornblende
ages range from 2100 to 1500 Ma (Moorbath *et al.* 1975) while
in the north, cooling through the hornblende closure temperature appears to have occurred between 1700 and 1600 Ma (Cliff
et al. 1998). Biotite Rb–Sr ages show a sharp break across the
Langavat shear zone (Cliff & Rex 1989); Laxfordian ages of
between 1346 and 1622 Ma are found to the southwest, but to
the northeast, there is a block in which biotite ages are generally
close to 1150 Ma, suggesting significant Grenville-age tectonic
activity (Cliff & Rex 1989).

The Laxfordian metamorphic events in the Outer Hebrides
thus appear to be somewhat different from those on the mainland, although the early granulite-facies event of South Harris
may correlate with the main (D2) Laxfordian amphibolite-
facies event at Gairloch, and the widespread late Laxfordian
amphibolite-facies event giving dates of ~1700 Ma may correspond with the (mostly greenschist-facies) D3 event of the
Southern Region of the mainland (Fig. 3.3). Friend & Kinny
(2001) emphasize the significant differences in the most recently
published dates of the injection complexes between the northern Outer Hebrides and the Northern Mainland Region and
suggest that these two regions represent different terranes. They
also believe that the northern Outer Hebrides (their Tarbert
terrane) only became amalgamated with the Palaeoproterozoic
block of South Harris (their Roineabhal terrane) during the
later Laxfordian.

The Outer Hebrides Fault Zone
This prominent fault zone extends for over 200 km from Sand-
ray, south of Barra, to Tolsta Head in north Lewis (Fig. 3.2),
and continues offshore. The zone trends NNE–SSW, and dips
between 20° and 30° ESE below the Minch. It was termed the
'Hebridean thrust' by Kursten (1957) and has been referred to

Fig. 3.14. Pseudotachylite in crush
breccia from the Outer Hebrides fault,
Barra (hammer for scale). Photograph
courtesy of the British Geological
Survey.

as a thrust, of probable Caledonian age, by most subsequent workers until seismic evidence for normal movement offshore was obtained (Smythe *et al.* 1982).

The fault zone, described in detail by Sibson (1977) and White & Glasser (1987), embraces structures ranging from crushed or brecciated gneiss (e.g. Fig. 3.14) through mylonite, ultramylonite and pseudotachylite, to phyllonite. These authors interpret this sequence as an effect of increasing strain similar to that recorded from faults in other deeply exposed gneiss terrains. Sibson (1977) interpreted the zone as a thrust, but White & Glasser (1987) pointed out that the progressive increase in retrogression into the hangingwall suggested a normal rather than thrust-sense displacement, which was confirmed by the evidence from accompanying minor structures such as fold asymmetry and the orientation of shear bands. More recent work concentrated on the phyllonites (Butler *et al.* 1995) has distinguished several stages of movement, commencing with ductile followed by brittle thrust movements, followed in turn by ductile sinistral strike-slip and finally by extensional movements. The later ductile movements are confined to the phyllonite zones, which are attributed to fault weakening, consequent on the influx of hydrous fluids into the zones causing the development of retrogressive phyllosilicate assemblages.

The age of the brittle thrust movements has been dated by Ar–Ar laser probe on pseudotachylite at 430 ± 6 Ma (Kelley *et al.* 1994) suggesting a link with the Moine Thrust system to the east. The strike-slip phase of movement on the phyllonite zones is attributed by Butler *et al.* (1995) to late Caledonian movements, and the extensional phase to Mesozoic movements associated with the opening of the Minch and Sea of the Hebrides basins. However the distribution pattern of Grenville-age K–Ar and Ar–Ar cooling ages, discussed above, which are an indication of Grenvillian tectonic activity in the Outer Hebrides, suggests that the early ductile thrust movements may be Grenvillian in age.

Lailey *et al.* (1989) reported that mylonitic structures within the fault zone at Scalpay, Harris, are cut by amphibolite sheets correlated with the Scourie dykes, and infer an Inverian age for the initiation of the fault zone. Fettes & Mendum (1987) also suspect older movements and cite as evidence the presence of aplogranitic veins, displaying only slight deformation, cutting strongly sheared granite. They conclude that the initiation of the fault zone was 'closely connected' with the later stages of Laxfordian granitic activity (i.e. ~1700 Ma).

The Lewisian of the Inner Hebrides

Lewisian rocks occur in a number of the smaller islands of the Inner Hebrides: from north to south, Rona, Raasay, Coll, Tiree and Iona (Fig. 3.2). Further south, on Colonsay and Islay, rocks formerly attributed to the Lewisian are now assigned to the Rhinns complex (Muir *et al.* 1994*a*) discussed below. The outcrops on Rona and Raasay are a southward continuation of the Laxfordian belt of the Southern (mainland) Region, and have already been discussed. However the Lewisian rocks of Coll, Tiree and Iona exhibit several distinctive features. Both Coll and Tiree display a broadly N–S arrangement of outcrops of acid and basic gneisses, together with prominent layers of metasediment, comprising quartzites, marbles, calc-silicate rocks and garnet–biotite–(kyanite) pelites (Drury 1972; Westbrook 1972). The rocks exhibit variably retrogressed granulite-facies assemblages correlated with those of the Scourian on the mainland and on nearby Barra. A suite of dykes was correlated with the Scourie dykes of the mainland by Westbrook (1972), although Drury (1972) regarded them as early Scourian. Muir *et al.* (1993) assign the dykes to the Scourie dyke swarm on the basis of their strong geochemical similarity

and field relationships. Sm–Nd whole-rock-mineral ages of ~1.75 Ga are interpreted as dating the growth of garnet during the metamorphism, which is thus Laxfordian rather than Scourian as thought by Drury (1972).

Upper-amphibolite facies metamorphism of Laxfordian age is characteristic of the eastern half of Tiree and of the whole of Coll. Westbrook (1972) recognizes four main phases of deformation (Fig. 3.3), of which D1 is regarded as Scourian, and is cut by the basic dykes. D2 produced the dominant N–S major folds. A set of biotite-pegmatites emplaced between D2 and D3 (Drury 1972) may represent the local equivalent of the ~1700 Ma Laxfordian granite/migmatite suite abundantly developed further north in Raasay and Rona. The D3 structures are associated with widespread retrogression in amphibolite facies, and comprise asymmetric folds producing local attenuation of the pre-existing banding and deformation of the post-D2 pegmatites. The D4 deformation produced monoclines and shear zones, associated with lower-temperature retrogression, and finally crush belts with pseudotachylite. Westbrook (1972) noted similarities between this sequence and that described for the southern Outer Hebrides by Coward *et al.* (1969).

Regional setting

The Lewisian complex of northwest Scotland forms a comparatively small part of a very extensive region of Precambrian continental crust which includes the Laurentian shield of North America and Greenland, and the Scandinavian, or Baltic, shield (Fig. 3.15). The northwestern part of the British Isles became detached from North America during the Early Tertiary opening of the North Atlantic Ocean, and is separated from Scandinavia both by the Caledonian orogenic belt and by extensional rifts and basins of Devonian to Mesozoic age.

The Lewisian complex forms part of a once continuous Palaeoproterozoic belt linking the Eastern Churchill province of the Canadian shield, the Nagssugtoqidian of Greenland, and the Lapland–Kola belt of Scandinavia (Fig. 3.15). The Nagssugtoqidian belt in southeast Greenland, known also as the Ammassalik belt, bears many similarities to the Lewisian complex, and has been compared with it by Wright *et al.* (1973), Myers (1987), Kalsbeek *et al.* (1993) and Park (1994). Comparisons have also been drawn with the Lapland–Kola belt of Finland and Sweden, in the east, and the Torngat belt of the Eastern Churchill Province in the Canadian shield to the west (e.g. Bridgwater *et al.* 1991, 1996; Park 1994). Specific similarities have also been pointed out between the Loch Maree Group in the Lewisian, and supracrustal sequences in the Cape Smith and Labrador belts of the Eastern Churchill Province (Johnson *et al.* 1987; Floyd *et al.* 1989).

The Nagssugtoqidian belt in southeast Greenland consists of reworked Archaean granitoid gneisses cut by mafic dykes and other intrusions (e.g. Kalsbeek 1989). The central part of the belt contains abundant metasediments with a depositional age of around 2.0–1.9 Ga (Bridgwater *et al.* 1996). These metasediments are cut by calc-alkaline tonalitic intrusions dated at 1.90 Ga (Kalsbeek *et al.* 1993), regarded as subduction related, and also by deformed and metamorphosed intrusions of the Ammassalik igneous complex; the latter yield a date of 1.89 Ga (Hansen & Kalsbeek 1989) which is regarded as a metamorphic age and the probable date of collision.

The Nagssugtoqidian belt of southwest Greenland (e.g. van Gool *et al.* 1995) is separated from the Eastern Nagssugtoqidian by the Greenland ice cap but is thought to be continuous with it. The belt is of similar width to the Eastern Nagssugtoqidian and contains reworked Archaean gneisses and Palaeoproterozoic paragneisses, metavolcanics and calc-alkaline plutonic intrusions. Isotopic data from the paragneisses indicate derivation

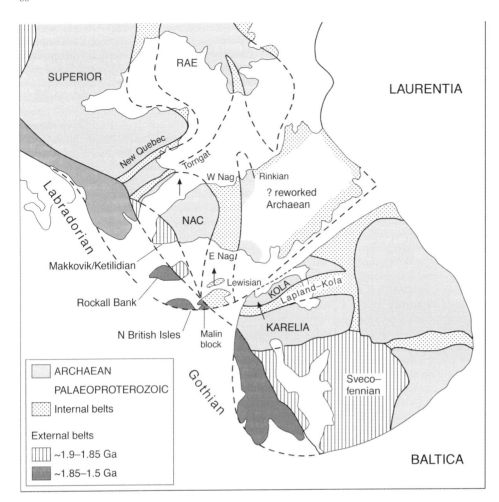

Fig. 3.15. Reconstruction of the Palaeoproterozoic belts and Archaean cratons of the North Atlantic region. NAC, North Atlantic craton; Nag, Nagssugtoqidian (From Buchan *et al.* 2000).

from juvenile Proterozoic sources (Stevenson & Patchett 1990). Calc-alkaline plutonic rocks from the central part of the belt, dated at 1.92 Ga by Kalsbeek *et al.* (1987) are interpreted as a juvenile magmatic arc, from which a collisional origin for the belt was proposed. From dates of between 1.87 and 1.82 Ga on metamorphic zircons in a variety of rocks (Connelly & Mengel 1996), the date of collision may be taken as ~1.87 Ga.

The southward continuation of the belt of Palaeoproterozoic activity along the west side of the North Atlantic craton is known as the Torngat belt (e.g. Wardle *et al.* 1990) (Fig. 3.15). This belt is between 75 and 200 km wide, and consists of re-worked Archaean rocks, Palaeoproterozoic granitic and dioritic plutons, mafic dykes and a band of high-grade metasediment (the Tasiuyak gneiss) thought to have been derived from an accretionary prism (Scott & Machado 1994). Studies of detrital zircons from the Tasiuyak gneiss show that a major proportion of the metasediment was derived from sources younger than 2.1 Ga and that deposition occurred between 1.94 and 1.90 Ga (Scott & Gauthier 1996). Both the metasediments and the western edge of the Nain craton are intruded by a suite of primary, mantle-derived, calc-alkaline plutons ranging in age from 1.91 to 1.86 Ga (Scott & Machado 1995) which are held to indicate easterly subduction beneath the Nain craton. Ub–Pb zircon ages ranging from 1.86 to 1.84 Ga are considered to date the main high-grade metamorphic/deformational event (Scott 1995), attributed to oblique collision between the North Atlan-tic and Rae cratons (Van Kranendonk & Wardle 1994).

The Lapland–Kola belt of Baltica (Bridgwater *et al.* 1991) is between 200 and 400 km wide and separates the Archaean cratons of Kola in the north and Karelia in the south. A narrow zone near the northern margin contains 2.4–2.0 Ga-old vol-

canic and sedimentary assemblages, including an andesitic volcanic arc sequence, and is interpreted by Berthelsen & Marker (1986) as a collisional suture zone. On the south side of this zone, the Inari terrain is interpreted as a juvenile calc-alkaline magmatic arc, dated at 1.95–1.93 Ga (Barling *et al.* 1996). Further south again, the Lapland granulite belt consists of high-grade, deformed, Palaeoproterozoic metasediments intruded by a syntectonic plutonic suite. Zircons from the metasediments yield both Archaean and Palaeoproterozoic source ages of which the youngest group is 2.0 Ga (Sorjonen-Ward *et al.* 1994); this can be taken as the approximate depositional age. Campbell *et al.* (1994) link the metasediments with similar rocks in the Nagssugtoqidian and Torngat belts and suggest a continental margin setting. Peak metamorphism is dated at between 1.95 Ga and 1.87 Ga (Bernard-Griffiths *et al.* 1984; Daly & Bogdanova 1991).

The Palaeoproterozoic Torngat, Nagssugtoqidian, and Lapland–Kola belts are thus broadly coeval with each other and with the Lewisian complex. Detailed comparisons between the tectonic histories of these belts have been made by Bridg-water *et al.* (1991), Kalsbeek *et al.* (1993) and Park (1994) and they are considered to have been linked together in one con-tinuous collisional belt at ~1.9 Ga. Park (1994) has pointed out that the movement directions associated with the main period of high-temperature deformation in these belts correspond best when the belts are arranged as in Figure 3.15.

The main period of tectonic acrivity in these Palaeoprotero-zoic collisional belts appears to have ended by around 1.84 Ga, and calc-alkaline magmatism became concentrated along the SW side (with respect to the present orientation of Scotland) of the large continental mass created by these collisions. This new

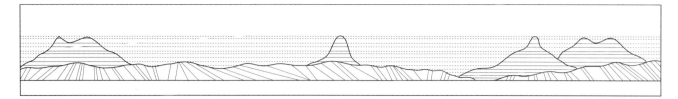

Fig. 3.16. The mountains of northwest Scotland drawn by Dr John Macculloch (1819). The sketch shows the unconformable relationship of the strata to the gneisses beneath, which Macculloch was the first to recognize. The observer looks eastwards from the sea. Quinag is on the left, Suilven in the middle and Cul Mor on the right.

active margin is represented by the Makkovik–Ketilidian belt of Labrador and South Greenland, and by the younger Labradorian-Gothian belt of NE Canada and SW Scandinavia (Fig. 3.15) which was active in the period 1.85–1.50 Ga (see Park 1995 and references therein). This belt is represented in Scotland by the Rhinns complex of Islay (Muir *et al.* 1994), which is part of a largely submerged area of juvenile Proterozoic crust known as the Malin block (Fig. 3.15). It is considered (e.g. Park 1994, 1995) that the late Laxfordian tectonothermal episodes in the Lewisian, such as the emplacement of the granitoid pegmatite suite and the D3 deformation, reflect the imfluence of events taking place at this active margin.

The Torridonian

The deeply eroded Lewisian gneisses of northwest Scotland were buried in the Late Proterozoic by red sandstones, informally called *Torridonian*, relics of which form the the mountains shown in Figure 3.16, and the topography illustrated in Plate 3. These sandstones are the remnants of deposits that once filled rift valleys in the heart of the super-continent Rodinia, near the Grenville orogenic belt, before the opening of the Iapetus Ocean. Closure of Iapetus in the Palaeozoic seems to have transformed some of the old normal faults into thrusts, such as the Ben More Thrust and the Outer Isles Thrust. The Moine nappe probably conceals the passive margin sediments that originally lay farther east.

The outcrop of the sandstones, mainly based on Geological Survey mapping, is shown in Figure 3.17. The subcrop, however, is considerably more extensive. Westwards, as far as the Minch Fault, seismic data show that up to 6 km of Torridonian underlies the ?Carboniferous to Tertiary section (Stein 1992). The Tertiary rocks of Canna, west of Rum, include sub-angular blocks of red sandstone and metamorphics from the underlying basement. Tertiary agglomerate on Eigg also contains blocks of red sandstone from the basement (Harker 1908). To the southwest of Rum, Torridonian rocks form the sea floor for 125 km, reaching as far south as latitude 56°N, west of Colonsay (Evans *et al.* 1982, fig. 1). This explains the occurrence of 'red Torridonian sandstone' and fossiliferous Durness Limestone in the Triassic conglomerates of Mull (Rast *et al.* 1968). The 500 m thick sequence of breccias and sandstones unconformably overlying the Lewisian basement in Iona (Stewart 1962) may also belong to the Torridonian but definite proof is lacking.

Stratigraphically the Torridonian can be divided into two parts (Fig. 3.18). Red beds up to 2 km thick outcropping at Stoer (*Stoer Group*) have been shown to be much older than the rest, from which they are separated by a clear angular unconformity and a 90° change in the direction of magnetization (Stewart & Irving 1974; Smith, R. L. *et al.* 1983). The red beds above (*Torridon Group*), up to 5 km thick, are responsible for the spectacular mountain scenery of northwest Scotland,

especially round Torridon which Nicol (1866) took as the type area for his 'Torridon Sandstone'. Clastic sediments 3 km thick in the Kishorn nappe of Skye and elsewhere (the *Sleat Group*) conformably underlie the Torridon Group. They are not seen in contact with the Stoer Group but are, nevertheless, believed to be younger. They may have accumulated in a sub-graben. The age of the three groups is bracketed by the Laxfordian to Grenvillian metamorphic events in the basement gneisses which generate ages ranging from ~1.9 to 1.1 Ga (Fig. 3.3) and the Lower Cambrian fossils in beds unconformably overlying the Torridon Group, dated at about 544 Ma (Cowie & McNamara 1978; Tucker & McKerrow 1995). A limestone in the Stoer Group gives a Pb–Pb age of 1199 ± 70 Ma (Turnbull *et al.* 1996) whereas phosphate concretions in the Diabaig Formation at the base of the Torridon Group give an age of 994 ± 48 Ma by Rb–Sr and 951 ± 120 Ma by Pb–Pb (Turnbull *et al.* 1996), suggesting that the Stoer and Torridon Groups are about 200 Ma apart in time, in accord with the palaeomagnetic evidence (Smith, R. L. *et al.* 1983). The age of the youngest detrital zircon grains in the overlying Applecross Formation is 1060 ± 18 Ma (Rainbird *et al.* 2001).

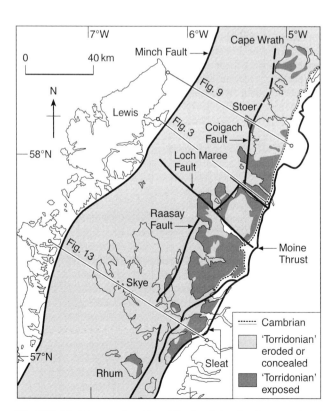

Fig. 3.17. Sketch map of northwest Scotland showing the present and former extent of the 'Torridonian', together with some major faults.

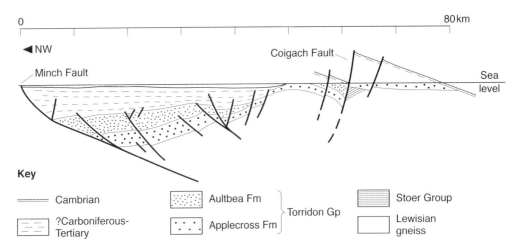

Fig. 3.18. Cross-section of the North Minch Basin from the Eye Peninsula, near Stornoway, to Dundonnell, based on Stein (1992) and Stewart (1993). The section shows the relationship between the 'Torridonian' and the overlying ?Carboniferous–Tertiary sediment. There is no evidence for the existence of the Stoer Group west of the Coigach Fault.

The Stoer Group

The Stoer Group was named from the peninsula of Stoer (Stewart 1969) because the rocks there are sedimentologically representative, structurally simple, and superbly exposed. The main features of the succession at Stoer are shown in Figure 3.19. A formal stratigraphic nomenclature has been provided by Stewart (1991*a*). The key stratigraphic element is the *Stac Fada Member*, a volcaniclastic sandstone about 10 m thick which does not recur in any single succession and is believed, therefore, to be unique. This sandstone identifies outcrops of the Group along the coast south of Stoer, as far as Rubha Reidh. The seven red-bed facies which constitute the succession at Stoer and elsewhere are described briefly below.

The breccia facies

At Stoer, this facies immediately overlies a hilly landscape of Scourian granulitic gneiss with over 300 m of relief. The clasts come exclusively from the Lewisian and it is significant that the proportion of basic and even ultrabasic rocks types in the breccia is similar to that in the basement nearby. The rounding of the clasts suggests transport distances of up to a kilometre, except near the unconformity where the clasts have demonstrably moved only a few metres. The breccia in contact with the Lewisian is usually massive, with clasts up to about half a metre in size. It is clast supported, with a sandy matrix. Stratigraphically upwards a crude stratification appears and the breccias pass into pebbly red sandstones and, rarely, red shale. There can be no doubt that the facies represents a series of fanglomerates. Maximum fan radius seems to have been about 300 m. The upward fining results from upstream fan-head retreat.

The muddy sandstone facies

This consists of reddish-brown massive sandstones, texturally greywackes, with about 40% matrix. These are lateral equivalents of the finer, distal part of the breccia facies, which geochemically they closely resemble. Sedimentologically, however, there are substantial differences. For example, at Clachtoll, the lowest 130 m of the facies is completely devoid of bedding or lamination. This massive development is succeeded upwards by beds of muddy sandstone about half a metre thick, defined

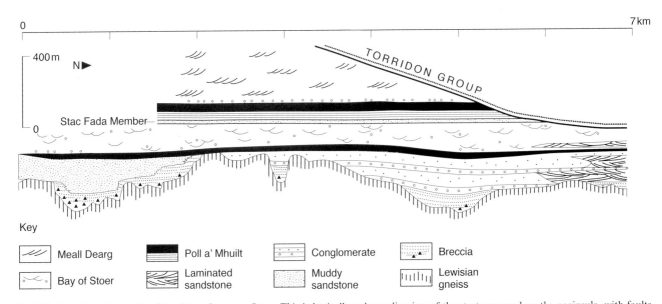

Fig. 3.19. Stratigraphic profile of the Stoer Group at Stoer. This is basically a down-dip view of the strata exposed on the peninsula, with faults removed. The Stoer Group is truncated unconformably by the Torridon Group.

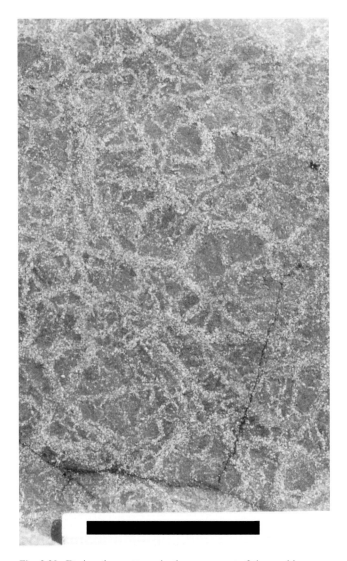

Fig. 3.20. Desiccation patterns in the upper part of the muddy sandstone facies at Clachtoll [NC 037272]. Scale bar 10 cm.

Fig. 3.21. The conglomerate facies at Stoer [NC 047329]. The base of the conglomerate erosively cuts the laminated sandstone facies. The ruler is 20 cm long.

by desiccated sheets of red siltstone or carbonate. The beds of muddy sandstone also show desiccation patterns (Fig. 3.20) suggesting that the massive nature of the facies is due to seasonal wetting and drying of a sediment originally rich in smectitic (swelling) clay. The ponded water mudflats of Hardie *et al.* (1978) would be a suitable setting for the facies, the sediments recording periodic flushes of slightly weathered material from a source area with abundant basic rocks. Percolating groundwater rich in Mg and Ca may also have contributed to smectite production.

The conglomerate facies
This consists of upward-fining sequences of coarse, trough cross-bedded red sandstones, and occasional multi-storey conglomerate. Such sequences are typically tens of metres thick. The bases are erosional (Fig. 3.21) and the tops marked by a metre or so of red siltstone (rarely exposed). The conglomerate clasts are mainly acid gneiss. Small pebbles of fine-grained red sandstone and black dolerite are also present. The former are possibly of intraformational origin while the latter probably come from the chilled margins of Scourie dykes. The composition and rounding of the larger clasts suggests 5–10 km of transport. Acid porphyry pebbles have been reported by Piper & Poppleton (1991).

The facies was probably deposited in shallow braided channels. However, one of the mapped conglomerates occupies the full width of the palaeovalley (see Fig. 3.19), so that conglomerate deposition must have been essentially synchronous over the whole of the flood plain. There is no evidence for lateral accretion in the conglomerate units, so they are thought to reflect episodic source rejuvenation.

The laminated sandstone facies
This facies (formerly the 'Port Cam' facies of the third edition) is striking because of its cross-bedding (Fig. 3.22). The laminae within the cross-beds are are only a few millimetres thick but can be followed for many metres as they asymptotically approach the base of a set. Set thickness is usually a few decimetres, but in places reaches as much as 10 m. The thinner sets persist laterally for tens of metres, but the thicker ones for much further. The cross beds originally dipped eastwards at angles usually less than 20° and only rarely more than 25°. The grains forming the

Fig. 3.22. Cross-bedding in the laminated sandstone facies at Stoer [NC 048328]. The ruler is 20 cm long.

rock are well sorted, subangular in shape, and average 0.2 mm in diameter. The maximum diameter is about 2 mm.

In contrast to these well-laminated red sandstones, there are decimetre- to metre-thick intercalations of relatively massive sandstone with irregular, erosional bases. Occasionally these sandstones incorporate small gneiss clasts, and even lumps of the laminated sandstone which must have been already partially lithified. The intercalations are quite common where the laminated sandstone facies is in contact with the breccia and conglomerate facies (Fig. 3.19). The base of the Bay of Stoer facies (described below) is also highly erosive where it overlies the laminated sandstone facies.

The cross-bedding described above is typical of that formed by migrating barchanoid dunes, while the massive interbedded sandstones evidently record invasions of the dune field by torrential flood water.

The Poll a' Mhuilt facies
This consists of thinly bedded red siltstone and fine sandstone. Wave ripples and desiccation cracks are characteristic. These fine-grained sediments form several intercalations, each only a few metres thick, within the Bay of Stoer facies (described below). Though thin, the intercalations can be traced right across the peninsula of Stoer for about 6 km, with only slight changes in thickness. Deposition of the facies was preceded in every case by a decimetre-thick bed of muddy sandstone. A spectacular example of this association is afforded by the Stac Fada Member and the overlying sequence of red siltstone and sandstone. The Stac Fada Member belongs to the muddy sandstone facies, but differs in containing about 25% of devitrified volcanic glass (Lawson 1972; Young 1999). An analysis of the glass shows that it was olivine normative and probably undersaturated, – a typical feature of rift volcanics. The glass is believed to be air-fall tuff (Stewart 1990, 1991*a*), though Sanders & Johnston (1989, 1990) have suggested that the Member originated as a fluidized peperite.

The silty sediments following the Stac Fada Member, which belong to the Poll a' Mhuilt facies, are about 100 m thick. In addition to the usual red beds there are also limestones (Upfold 1984), laminated black shales containing poorly pre-

served organic-walled microfossils (Cloud & Germs 1971) and abundant gyspum pseudomorphs.

The interpretation of the Poll a' Mhuilt facies by Stewart & Parker (1979), based on sedimentology and the boron content

Fig. 3.23. Contorted bedding in the Bay of Stoer facies at Clachtoll [NC 035272]. The 20 cm ruler marks the top of a cusp.

of illite, is that it formed in temporary lakes. The lake associated with the Stac Fada Member was unusual in covering hundreds of square kilometres and in having had a maximum depth of at least a hundred metres. For the first half of its life it must have been perennial and stratified.

The Bay of Stoer facies

This simply consists of trough cross-bedded red sandstones forming the eponymous formation. Soft-sediment contortions and overturned cross-bedding are common (Fig. 3.23). Well-rounded, centimetre-sized pebbles of gneiss and orthoquartzite, in roughly equal proportions, are sporadically present throughout the facies.

The Meall Dearg facies

This is built entirely of sandstones, petrographically indistinguishable from those in the Bay of Stoer facies. These sandstones constitute the *Meall Dearg Formation*. Planar cross-bedding and planar bedding with extensive wave-rippled surfaces are equally common. Pebbles are absent except at the very base of the facies at Stoer.

Both the Bay of Stoer and Meall Dearg facies are believed to have been deposited by braided rivers, the latter perhaps deposited in wider channels and on gentler palaeoslopes than the former. A modern analogue for the Bay of Stoer sandstones might be the predominantly trough cross-bedded sands deposited by powerful floods in central Australia (Williams 1971). In contrast, the Meall Dearg facies resembles the predominantly planar cross-bedded sands deposited in transverse bars by the relatively sluggish Platte River (Smith 1970).

The three facies found laterally adjacent to basement hills, namely the breccia, conglomerate and laminated sandstone facies, find close modern analogues in areas such as South Yemen (Moseley 1971). There, gravel fans fringe basement hills of Precambrian gneiss 300–600 m high. The gravels interfinger with the fluvial deposits of an ephemeral river system over which drift barchanoid dunes. South Yemen lies at latitude 15°, as compared with 10° deduced from the palaeomagnetism of the Stoer Group (Torsvik & Sturt 1987), and has a semi-arid climate. The idea that the basal breccias could be glacial diamictites (Davison & Hambrey 1996, 1997) can be discounted, for, as described above, they have a typical fluviatile, clast-supported structure and fine upwards into sandstones (Stewart, A. D. 1997; Young 1999).

Palaeocurrents within the Stoer Group at Stoer reverse through 180° at the base of the Bay of Stoer Formation and again at the base of the Stac Fada Member (Stewart 1982), suggesting fault-controlled deposition in a rift valley (Fig. 3.24). The repetition of lacustrine interludes (Poll a' Mhuilt facies) within the fluviatile Bay of Stoer facies can be attributed to episodic fault tilting and disruption of the drainage net.

All the sandstones in the Stoer Group at Stoer are plagioclase-rich arkoses, as would be expected if Scourian granulitic gneisses like those outcropping nearby had formed the source area. However, some of the sandstones in the basal breccia and all those forming the muddy sandstone facies, which might have been expected to most closely resemble the parent gneisses, are relatively enriched in Rb, Mg, Y and Th, suggesting that they have been contaminated by air-fall tuff (Stewart 1991a). According to van de Kamp & Leake (1997) the plagioclase in these sandstones and also in the rest of the Stoer Group has been albitized. They suggest that the soluble elements may have been trapped in a closed basin, so that the Na which was initially lost during the weathering of plagioclase was later consumed during albitization. This is a feasible explanation for the albitisation of plagioclase in the breccias and muddy sandstones, and also the Poll a' Mhuilt facies, but

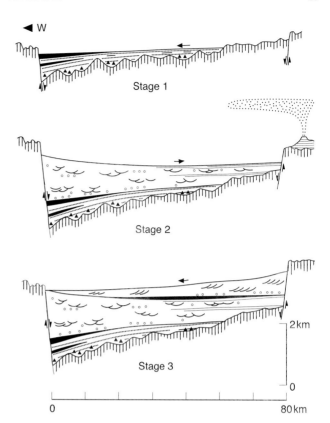

Fig. 3.24. Stages in the development of the Stoer rift. Stage 1 shows locally derived sediments such as the breccia and conglomerate facies. Stage 2 shows the Bay of Stoer facies and Stage 3 the Meall Dearg facies. Stoer is located roughly in the middle of the rift. Arrows show palaeocurrent directions.

another source of Na is needed for the albitization of the fluviatile Bay of Stoer and Meall Dearg formations.

The Sleat Group

The Sleat Group consists of 3500 m of coarse-grained, grey, fluviatile sandstones, with subordinate grey shales, and is best exposed between Loch na Dal and Kylerhea in the Sleat of Skye. Although the beds are confined to the Kishorn nappe, their stratigraphic position is secured by a conformable relationship with the overlying *Torridon Group*, presumed to be only slightly younger. The Sleat Group is nowhere seen in contact with the Stoer Group. The absence of any sequence like the Sleat Group outside the Kishorn nappe may mean that the sediments were deposited in an independent rift, predating the Torridon Group, the western edge formed by a listric normal fault that during Palaeozoic compression, was inverted to form the Kishorn-Suardal thrust.

No isotopic dating of the Sleat Group has ever been attempted because of the lower greenschist facies metamorphism that affected the rocks during the Palaeozoic and probably reset the isotopic systems. This low-grade metamorphism also changed the colour of the rocks from red to grey. The grey colour is not due to the presence of chlorite, which is ubiquitous, but rather to the transformation of hematite to magnetite (Peach *et al.* 1907; Stewart 1991b).

The stratigraphy, palaeocurrent directions and framework mineralogy of the sandstones in the Sleat Group are summarized in Figure 3.25. The brief sedimentological details that follow are mainly based on Stewart (1991b and in Hambrey *et al.* 1991).

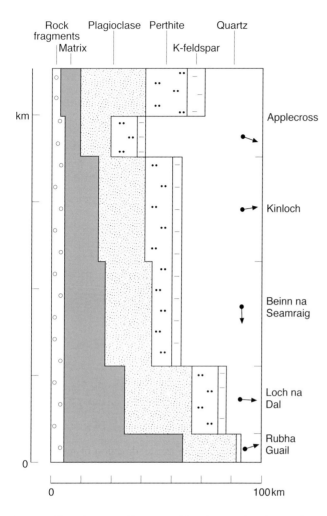

Fig. 3.25. Sleat Group and lower Torridon Group mineralogy and vector mean palaeocurrent directions (see arrows) in Skye. The mineralogy is based on 50 modal analyses by Byers (1972) and the palaeocurrents on 229 cross-bedding directions measured by Sutton & Watson (1960, 1964). The palaeocurrent directions have not been corrected for the 26° clockwise rotation of the Kishorn nappe reported by Potts (1990).

The Rubha Guail Formation

This consists almost entirely of coarse sandstone, coloured green due to its chlorite and epidote content. The sandstone is underlain by gneiss breccia close to the unconformity with the Lewisian 10 km northeast of Kyle of Lochalsh (Peach *et al.* 1907, p. 343), but unfortunately neither unconformity nor breccia is exposed in the type section in Skye. Trough cross-bedding is typical of the coarser beds. Laminated siltstones and fine-grained sandstones, which become more abundant towards the top of the formation, contain wave ripples and desiccation cracks (Sutton & Watson 1960, fig. 7; Stewart 1962, fig. 11). They are followed above by the laminated dark grey siltstones of the Loch na Dal Formation. The upward fining from coarse sandstone into grey shale which the Formation shows in the type section near Rubha Guail suggests that it originated as a large alluvial fan, prograding from the flank of a basement hill or fault scarp into a lake. Basement relief during the deposition of the Rubha Guail Formation was several hundred metres (Peach *et al.* 1907, p. 343).

The Loch na Dal Formation

The lowest 200 m of this formation is composed of laminated dark-grey siltstones, often phosphatic and punctuated by coarse or very coarse sandstone laminae. This unusual juxtaposition of fine and very coarse grain sizes has been noted by several workers (Clough, in Peach *et al.* 1907, p. 354; Sutton & Watson 1964). It is also seen on the south side of Upper Loch Torridon, where shales of the Diabaig Formation (Torridon Group) are within a hundred metres of a basement hill. The upper part of the Loch na Dal Formation is dominated by coarse, and locally pebbly, trough cross-bedded sandstones, that often infill channels up to a metre deep. The shales probably mark the maximum expansion of a lacustrine or shallow marine phase of deposition, terminated by prograding deltas.

The Beinn na Seamraig and Kinloch Formations

These are much alike and can conveniently be considered together. A substantial proportion of both consists of strongly contorted, cross-bedded sandstones. The main difference is that the sandstones of the Kinloch Formation are fine-grained while those of the Beinn na Seamraig are coarse. Ripple-lamination forms metre-thick sequences, especially in the Kinloch Formation. Less commonly there are grey, shaly intercalations like the sediments forming the lower part of the Loch na Dal Formation. In the Kinloch Formation these shales form the upper parts of cycles 25–35 m thick. The two formations are thought to represent braided river deposits with lacustrine or shallow marine interludes.

The upper formations of the Sleat Group closely resemble the overlying Applecross Formation of the Torridon Group, described later. However there are two significant differences. Firstly, the pebble suite in the Sleat Group contains none of the metasedimentary pebbles which are so abundant in the Applecross of Skye and the mainland. The vast majority of Sleat pebbles are porphyry, of rhyolitic or rhyodacitic composition, while the remainder are acid gneiss, typically quartz and plagioclase ± microcline ± biotite. This suggests different source areas for the two Groups. The second important difference lies in the composition of the plagioclase, which has been completely albitized in the Applecross Formation but only partially in the Sleat Group. The source of the Na to accomplish albitization is unknown. The Ca expelled from the original detrital plagioclase (probably andesine) is still present in the Sleat Group as calcite but is lacking from the Applecross.

The Sleat Group clearly derives from an upper crustal source, for geochemical analyses show that the sediments have an average K/Rb ratio of 285. The immature sediments at the base (Rubha Guail Formation) are twice as rich in Fe, Ni, Ti, Ca and Mg as those stratigraphically above, and are thought to come from very local hornblende–biotite gneisses. Upwards through the Group there is a marked increase in quartz and K-feldspar at the expense of plagioclase (Fig. 3.25), together with a reduction in average grain size and whole-rock K/Rb ratios. The sediment in the highest formations of the Sleat Group and the overlying Torridon Group in Skye appears to derive from granite gneisses containing tectonically emplaced slices of quartzite and acid volcanics, eroded from a rising massif to the west (Stewart 1991*b*, fig. 7).

The Torridon Group

The Torridon Group rests on an old land surface with relief of 600 m around Loch Maree, declining to less than 100 m in the Cape Wrath area (Geikie 1888, pp. 400–401; Stewart 1972). An example of the relief on the unconformity, exhumed during the Palaeozoic, is shown in Figure 3.26 and Plate 2. Basement weathering in Torridon Group times may be preserved near Cape Wrath, where it was originally detected by Williams (1968). Williams & Schmidt (1997) have shown that the iron minerals in the weathered profile formed during the late

Fig. 3.26. Precambrian topography exhumed from beneath the gently dipping beds of the Torridon Group on the north side of Quinag – a pen and ink sketch by Sir Archibald Geikie (1906).

Precambrian, but pedogenic smectite and low temperature illite are also present, indicating a burial temperature of <120°C. This poses a problem in view of the deep burial which the rocks have suffered (Retallack & Mindszenty 1994; Stewart 1995a).

The unconformity generally cuts Lewisian gneiss, but near the mainland coast it truncates the westward-dipping beds of the Stoer Group. There are good exposures of the angular unconformity at Stoer (NC042330) (Williams 1966; Stewart in Hambrey et al. 1991, p. 119), Achiltibuie (NC024068) (Stewart in Hambrey et al. 1991), Stattic Point (NG976958) (Lawson 1976), and Rubha Reidh (NG745921) (Lawson 1976). However, the most important locality is Enard Bay (NC035147) (Gracie & Stewart 1967; Stewart in Hambrey et al. 1991) where the superb coastal section shows the Stoer Group, including the Stac Fada Member, overlain by the two lowest formations of the Torridon Group, one of them containing its diagnostic suite of quartzose and volcanic pebbles. Both here, and at Achiltibuie and Rubha Reidh, the direction of magnetization of the beds changes abruptly across the unconformity (Stewart & Irving 1974; Smith, R. L. et al. 1983; Torsvik & Sturt 1987).

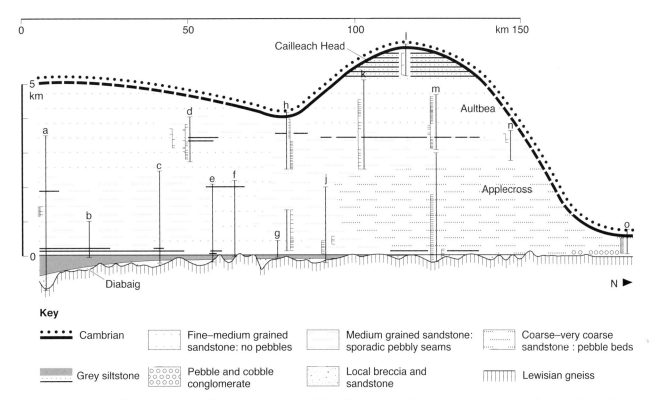

Key

- ●●●●● Cambrian
- Grey siltstone
- Fine–medium grained sandstone: no pebbles
- Pebble and cobble conglomerate
- Medium grained sandstone: sporadic pebbly seams
- Local breccia and sandstone
- Coarse–very coarse sandstone : pebble beds
- Lewisian gneiss

Fig. 3.27. Longitudinal profile of the Torridon Group between Rum and Cape Wrath, perpendicular to the palaeocurrent direction. Key sections are: a, Rum; b, Soay; c, Scalpay; d, Toscaig; e, Raasay; f, Shieldaig to Applecross; g, Diabaig; h, Torridon, west and east of the Fasag Fault; j, Gairloch; k, Aultbea; l, Cailleach Head and Scoraig to Dundonnell; m, Summer Isles and Achiltibuie to Strath Kanaird; n, Rubha Stoer; o, Cape Wrath. The palaeomagnetic stratigraphy is shown with SE positive polarity to the right of the vertical line and NW negative to the left (Irving & Runcorn 1957; Stewart & Irving 1974; Smith, R. L. et al. 1983; Robinson & McClelland 1987).

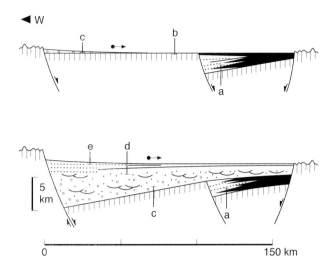

Fig. 3.28. Transverse profiles of the Sleat and Torridon groups in the latitude of Skye. The upper profile illustrates the situation at the end of Sleat Group time while the lower profile shows the end of Torridon Group time. Arrows indicate palaeocurrent directions. Stratigraphy: a, Sleat Group; b, Diabaig Formation; c, Applecross Formation; d, Autbea Formation; e, Cailleach Head Formation.

The Torridon Group has been divided into the *Diabaig, Applecross, Aultbea and Cailleach Head formations*, as shown in restored stratigraphic profiles (Figs. 3.27, 3.28). From these profiles it will be noticed that the Diabaig Formation is confined to the lower parts of palaeovalleys in the underlying gneissose basement. Brief descriptions of the formations follow.

The Diabaig Formation
This is excellently exposed around Loch Torridon (Rodd & Stewart 1992; Stewart in Hambrey *et al.* 1991) and on the Isle of Raasay (Selley 1965*a, b*). There are four component subfacies. *Breccias* (1) mantle the gneiss landscape and choke the lower parts of the palaeovalleys (Fig. 3.29). They are similar to those at the base of the Stoer Group except that the clasts are more angular. The clasts are of sandstone where the facies overlies the Stoer Group but otherwise they are made of local gneiss. Transport distances rarely exceed 3 km eastward from the source rock (e.g. Peach *et al.* 1907, p. 315) and are usually very small. The breccias pass stratigraphically upwards, and also laterally away from the palaeovalley sides, into (2) *tabular sandstones*, usually a few decimetres thick and separated by films of red silt, often showing trough and planar cross-bedding, horizontal lamination and extensive wave-rippled surfaces (Fig. 3.30). Channels up to 300 mm deep are locally common. Stratigraphically upwards and away from the palaeovalley sides this facies interfingers with (3) *grey shales*, which comprise millimetre-thick graded units, possibly seasonal and usually desiccated, together with fine sandstone bands, millimetres to centimetres in thickness, showing wave ripples. The fine sandstones fill the desiccation cracks in the shale. Phosphatic laminae and pods are common. Cryptarchs are abundant in the shale and are particularly well preserved in the phosphate (Naumova & Pavlovski 1961; Downie 1962; Peat & Diver 1982). *Grey sandstone* (4) beds appear in the upper part of the facies, increasing in frequency and thickness towards the top. The sandstones are petrographically subgreywackes and typically form massive beds several decimetres thick with sharp bases (Fig. 3.31). The tops of the beds show ripple-drift lamination generated by palaeocurrents flowing from the west. The interbedded shales contain desiccation cracks indicating lake level changes of the order of 10 m.

Fig. 3.29. Roughly stratified basal breccia of the Diabaig Formation on Beinn Dearg Bheag [NH 020825]. The photograph shows a bedding plane about 30 m laterally from a Lewisian palaeohill. Some of the loose pebbles strewn across the bedding plane have been liberated from the breccia by recent weathering.

The breccias and tabular sandstones are best regarded as fan deposits that accumulated on the flanks of the palaeovalleys, with the grey shales recording ephemeral lakes which occupied the valley centres. The arrival of Applecross rivers (see below) before the end of Diabaig times is evidenced by turbidites (the grey sandstones) in the shales and, geochemically, by the presence of K and Ti in the shales in excess of that which the local gneisses could have supplied. Ultimately these rivers completely filled the lakes with sediment and buried the remaining Lewisian hill tops. The boron content of illite (Stewart & Parker 1979) suggest that the shales were deposited in fresh water, as does the lack of primary carbonate and the absence of evaporites. There is no evidence that the Diabaig Formation was deposited in a hydrologically closed basin as suggested by van de Kamp & Leake (1997).

The limited sediment transport distances in Diabaig times cited above suggest that most of the streams which deposited the breccias and tabular sandstones were small. However, in the Inverpolly–Cam Loch area the Diabaig Formation contains thick cobble conglomerates, including rounded blocks of red sandstone and white quartzite probably derived from the Stoer Group 22 km to the west, demonstrating the existence of a major river here.

The Applecross Formation
This consists of red sandstones with an average grain size over 0.5 mm. Both trough and planar cross-bedding are common.

Fig. 3.31. Grey sandstones and shales near the top of the Diabaig Formation on Diabaig shore [NG 79276027].

Fig. 3.30. Tabular sandstones of the Diabaig Formation showing rippled surfaces, on the south side of Upper Loch Torridon [NG 852547].

The troughs have an average width-to-depth ratio of ten; most are only 1–2 m wide but exceptionally reach 30 m. The average palaeocurrent direction is to the southeast. The sandstones normally contain pebbles, including distinctive types such as jasper and porphyry (Williams 1969b; Anderton 1980). Pebble abundance provides a ready index to the subfacies recognized at Cape Wrath by Williams (1969a, 2001), and also used in Figure 3.27.

The top of the Applecross Formation is formed of finer sandstones, gradational into the overlying Aultbea Formation. One or two grey siltstone beds occur at this stratigraphic level and may be of regional extent for they correlate with a sequence of rapid palaeomagnetic reversals (see Fig. 3.27). The sphaeromorphic acritarchs and filamentous sheaths which occur in these grey shales are perhaps the remains of a lake flora (Zhang Zhongying et al. 1981; Zhang Zhongying 1982).

About a half to three-quarters of the beds in the Applecross Formation show soft sediment contortions. These either take the form of open synclines 0.5–3 m wide, linked by sharp cusps, or recumbently folded cross-bedding. They have been described in detail by Owen (1995, 1996a, b) who concludes that seismic liquefaction of the sediment was the probable cause, despite the inhibiting effect of the coarse grain-size. The structures, how-

ever, are much more abundant than in other red bed sequences deposited in similar tectonic settings. Furthermore, if seismic shaking were the cause it would need to have been almost continuous to affect such a high proportion of beds. The origin of the liquefaction remains obscure.

The Aultbea Formation

This consists of red sandstones with a grain size of less than 0.5 mm. Pebbles are absent except for a mappable lens south of Applecross village. Virtually all the beds are contorted.

The lowest beds of the Applecross Formation at Cape Wrath have a palaeocurrent pattern which shows that they formed part of a giant alluvial fan, with a radius of at least 40 km, which prograded from a source region immediately west of the Minch Fault (Williams 1969a, 2001). However, radial palaeocurrent patterns are not replicated in sediments farther south, suggesting that most of the Applecross and Aultbea Formations formed on a bajada. The interpretation of these sediments as braided river deposits covering a bajada is well established from the studies of Selley (1965a, 1969), Williams (1966, 1969a, 2001) and Nicholson (1993). According to Miall (1977, table 5), Applecross sedimentation was Platte type, with deposition by linguoid and transverse sand bars in very shallow river channels. Nicholson (1993) has shown that channel depths, deduced from bed thickness, were generally 1–3 m deep, and exceptionally 5–9 m. From this he deduces bankfull flood discharges and concludes, by comparison with some present-day European and North American rivers in latitudes of 40–50°, that mean annual discharges of Applecross rivers reached a maximum of

$1800 \, m^3 \, s^{-1}$. However, the comparison with present day rivers in temperate latitudes is misleading. The lack of plant cover in Precambrian times promoted rapid runoff (Schumm 1968) which, together with the palaeolatitudes of 30–40° shown by the palaeomagnetism of the Torridon Group (Stewart & Irving 1974; Smith, R. L. *et al.* 1983; Torsvik & Sturt 1987), makes a comparison with the rivers of present-day semi-arid regions more appropriate. The high discharges calculated by Nicholson were probably infrequent and the mean annual discharges much less than claimed. The significance of this is that the dimensions of the source area for the Applecross rivers calculated by Nicholson, of the order of $100\,000 \, km^2$, are far too large. The dimensions of the Cape Wrath alluvial fan indicate a source area of about $10\,000 \, km^2$, over the present position of the Outer Hebrides block.

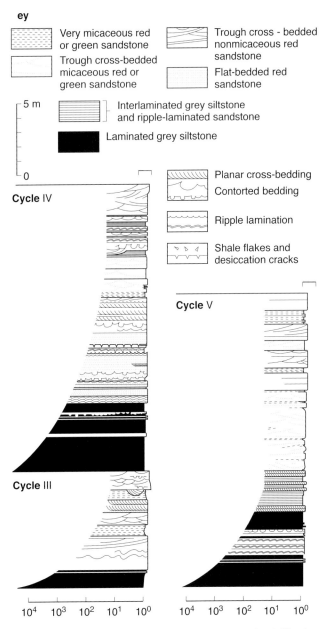

ey

Very micaceous red or green sandstone

Trough cross-bedded micaceous red or green sandstone

Trough cross - bedded nonmicaceous red sandstone

Flat-bedded red sandstone

5 m

Interlaminated grey siltstone and ripple-laminated sandstone

Laminated grey siltstone

0

Planar cross-bedding

Contorted bedding

Cycle IV

Ripple lamination

Shale flakes and desiccation cracks

Cycle V

Cycle III

10^4 10^3 10^2 10^1 10^0 10^4 10^3 10^2 10^1 10^0

Fig. 3.32. Graphic logs of three sedimentary cycles in the Cailleach Head Formation. The base of cycle III is at NG 98499848 and the top of cycle V at NG 98469835. The horizontal scale gives the lateral persistency of the beds, defined as their lateral extent divided by their maximum thickness. The grain size bar represents 0–4 phi units.

The Cailleach Head Formation

This is only exposed on the cliffs at Cailleach Head. The base of the Formation, concealed beneath the sea at this point, may be seen in the north-eastern part of Gruinard Island. The Formation consists of cyclothems averaging 22 m in thickness (Fig. 3.32). Each begins with a major, flat erosion surface, followed by laminated dark-grey shales which pass up into tabular red sandstones, internally containing planar cross-bedding, and typically covered with wave ripples. This tabular facies gives way above to trough cross-bedded sandstones, red or green in colour, and often very micaceous. Deep desiccation cracks commonly occur near the top of the grey shale, but just as in the Diabaig Formation there are no evaporites or carbonates. Teall (in Peach *et al.* 1907, p. 287) described and figured sphaeromorphic microfossils and fibres from phosphatic concretions in the shales, the first Precambrian fossils described in Britain. The sphaeromorphs are usually single vesicles about $10 \, \mu m$ in diameter or, less commonly, aggregates of vesicles up to $50 \, \mu m$ across. Similar forms have been described by Zhang Zhongying (1982) from the underlying Aultbea Formation.

The pattern of sedimentation and the lack of evaporitic minerals or carbonates in the cyclothems suggest that they represent progradation of deltas into a freshwater lake that did not suffer evaporative concentration of salts. The thickness of the tabular sandstone facies suggests minimum water depths of around 5–6 m. There is no sedimentological evidence that the Formation was deposited in a hydrologically closed basin, where evaporites might be expected, as suggested by van de Kamp & Leake (1997).

Torridonian palaeoclimate and tectonic environment

Palaeoclimate

The climate during deposition of the *Stoer Group* can be specified with some confidence from sedimentary structures, mineralogy and geochemistry. The massive muddy sandstones in the Clachtoll Formation and the massive siltstone in the Poll a' Mhuilt Member are analogous to modern vertisols which form in latitudes 10–30° with an annual rainfall of 300–1200 mm and a pronounced summer drought (Stewart 1991*a*). Palaeomagnetic data give similar palaeolatitudes for the Group (Torsvik & Sturt 1987). Van de Kamp & Leake (1997) used the abundance of plagioclase in the sandstones, which is not unlike that in the local source rock, to deduce that Stoer Group sandstones formed in a climate with a long, hot, dry season and annual rainfall of 500–1000 mm, confined to the cool winter. The index of chemical alteration – a measure of the removal of labile components Ca, Na and K from silicates during weathering – gives a similar result (Young 1999). The possibility that the immaturity of the sediment could be due to a glacial climate (Davison & Hambrey 1996) can be rejected on sedimentological grounds (Stewart, A. D. 1997; Young 1999). Nor does the immaturity seem likely to result from high relief and rapid erosion of the source rocks, for basement relief during deposition of the Stoer Group was hundreds rather than thousands of metres (Fig. 3.19).

The lower part of the Sleat Group in Skye (Rubha Guail and Loch na Dal formations) is also very immature, suggesting a dry climate, but the sediments at higher stratigraphic levels are finer grained and have less plagioclase relative to K-feldspar. This could have resulted from more transport and/or more rain (Stewart 1991*b*).

The abundance of plagioclase relative to K-feldspar and quartz in the Torridon Group is much less than in the Stoer Group. According to Van de Kamp & Leake (1997) Diabaig Formation sandstone with a plagioclase/total feldspar ratio of 0.8 is consistent with a temperate climate, while the sandstones in the stratigraphically higher Applecross Formation, with a plagioclase/total feldspar ratio of 0.4, have compositions comparable with modern stream sands in the cool, temperate climate of Pennsylvania and New Jersey.

Tectonic model

Pavlovski (1958) proposed that the Torridonian Basin developed between two active faults, the Minch Fault in the west and a precursor of the Moine Thrust in the east. Rifting was later used by Stewart (1982) to account for the deposition of the Stoer Group, as shown in Figure 3.24. The Sleat and Torridon Groups lack volcanics but nevertheless a rift model accounts for the following features.

1. A conformable sequence of coarse fluviatile sediments is 6 km thick in the Torridon Group on the mainland, and over 4.5 km in the Sleat and Torridon Groups of Skye.
2. Arkosic detritus was eroded from relatively old continental basement. The source rocks for the Torridon Group sanstones were paragneisses of normal upper continental crustal composition (Stewart & Donnellan 1992; Stewart 1995b; Van de Kamp & Leake 1997). Zircon, biotite, feldspar and tourmaline ages in the Torridon Group range from 1100 Ma to about 2700 Ma while the porphyry pebbles give Laxfordian ages (Moorbath *et al.* 1967; Rogers *et al.* 1990; Allen 1991; Rainbird *et al.* 1998).
3. The outcrop is bounded by two major fractures about 80 km apart; a spacing typical of rifts.
4. A uniform supply of pebbly material came from the west throughout the deposition of the Applecross Formation, suggesting recurrent uplift of the source terrain along a western boundary fault, probably the Minch Fault.
5. Normal faults on the eastern boundary were reactivated as thrusts during the Palaeozoic (Butler 1997).
6. Palaeocurrents were orthogonal to the boundary faults. In the Torridon Group most came from the west (Nicholson 1993), but near the Moine Thrust at Quinag they came from the east and southeast.

The alternative hypothesis of a thermal relaxation basin (Nicholson 1993) stems from the idea, rejected above, that the Applecross river basin was very large. The hypothesis is also difficult to reconcile with the coarse, fluviatile nature of the deposits, for the sediment in thermal subsidence basins is typically marine. On the other hand, there is a close resemblance between both the Stoer and Torridon groups and the fluviatile and lacustrine sediments deposited during the Triassic and Jurassic in the active rift basins of eastern North America. The resemblance extends not only to facies types, total thickness of beds, and the relationship of palaeocurrent patterns to the boundary faults (Hubert *et al.* 1978, 1992) but also to the diagenesis (van de Kamp & Leake 1996, 1997).

Correlation

Precambrian lithostratigraphic correlation is virtually impossible except for unusual deposits like tillites. The emphasis has to be, rather, on time-stratigraphic correlation, with the aim of obtaining a regional picture at a point in time. Early attempts at correlation of the Torridonian were based on the lithological similarity of the Torridon Group and the physically adjacent psammitic rocks of the Moine Supergroup, (Geikie 1895; Kennedy 1951; Sutton 1963). The two units, however, had different source areas. This is shown by their diverse detrital zircon suites (MacKie 1923b), and by their very different tourmaline contents, – reflected in the boron content of present-day stream sediments (Plant 1984). Time correlation is conceivable, but if the Moine Supergroup originated far from its present

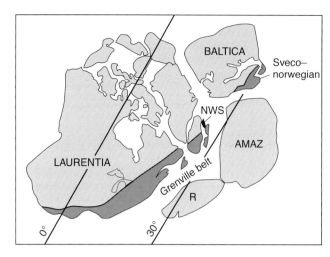

Fig. 3.33. Reconstruction of continents of the North Atlantic region at ~725 Ma showing the position of NW Scotland (NWS) in relation to the Grenville and Sveconorwegian belts. Positions of Laurentia, Amazonia (AMAZ), Rio Plata (R) after Dalziell (1997); Baltica after Buchan *et al.* (2000). Compare Figure 3.15.

position and was thrust by plate convergence onto the Laurentian passive margin (Stewart 1982; Bluck *et al.* 1997) then such correlation would be intercontinental rather than regional. More is to be gained by looking at the eastern margin of the Laurentian plate (Fig. 3.33), to which northwest Scotland was joined prior to the formation of the Iapetus Ocean, for regionally related rifting events contemporaneous with the Torridonian. Three such events can be identified, each associated with sediments which have at some time been correlated with the Torridonian; the Keweenawan (Winchester 1988), the Wakeham Supergroup (Turnbull *et al.* 1996) and the Double Mer Formation (Gower 1988).

The Keweenawan is a 20 km thick sequence of basalts and sandstones deposited in the mid-continent rift that extends about 2000 km from the Grenville front at Lake Erie, through Lake Superior to Kansas. The lavas are reliably dated at about 1100 Ma (Davis & Paces 1990) and yield palaeomagnetic poles that were shown to agree closely with those for the Stoer Group by Stewart & Irving (1974) and Smith, R. L. *et al.* (1983). The Freda Sandstone and Nonesuch Shale near the top of the Keweenawan, dated at roughly 1060 Ma, have palaeomagnetic poles closer to the Torridon Group. The Keweenawan as a whole appears to be slightly older than the Grenville orogen (970–1000 Ma).

The Wakeham Supergroup in north-eastern Quebec is contained in a 200 km long basin tectonically overlying Grenvillian basement. It consists of clastic sediments, rhyolites, basalts and gabbros metamorphosed to greenschist facies and intruded by post tectonic granites dated at about 990 Ma. Rhyolite in the lower part of the Supergroup has been dated at about 1270 Ma (Martignole *et al.* 1994). The Supergroup is supposed to have formed during gravitational collapse of the Grenville orogen (Rivers 1994). It is evidently synorogenic, so that the correlation with the Torridonian suggested by Turnbull *et al.* (1996) is based only on the similarity of the ages.

Of the many late Neoproterozoic rifts which cut the eastern margin of Laurentia (Hoffman 1989), the Lake Melville rift in Labrador was only about 1000 km from Scotland on pre-Iapetus reconstructions. The Double Mer Formation, which fills the rift, consists of unmetamorphosed, cross-bedded reddish-brown sandstones and conglomerates, up to 5 km thick. The sandstones contain about 50% feldspar, of which half is plagioclase. The overall similarity to the Stoer and

Torridon Groups is clear but the Double Mer overlies Grenville basement and so postdates orogenic uplift at about 960 Ma. Furthermore, the Lake Melville rift appears to continue to the southwest into the St Lawrence rift, which is known from contemporaneous intrusions to have developed after 650 Ma. This means that the Double Mer Formation may be too young to be a suitable correlative even for the Torridon Group.

The Cambro-Ordovician

The Cambro-Ordovician rocks of northwest Scotland crop out along a narrow belt stretching some 250 km from Loch Eriboll on the north coast to the Ord window in Skye (Fig. 3.34). In the west, they rest unconformably on Torridonian and Lewisian rocks, and to the east they are truncated by the Moine nappes. The entire succession (Fig. 3.35), which ranges in age from Early Cambrian to Llanvirn, can be seen in the Durness area, where strata are largely undeformed and preserve primary sedimentary structures and fossils. Further south around Assynt, Cambrian quartzites unconformably cap many of the spectacular inselbergs of Torridonian sandstones, which rise, also unconformably, above the Lewisian gneissic basement. At Skiag Bridge, the Cambro-Ordovician succession passes up conformably eastwards as far as the lower Ghrudaidh Formation, the basal unit of the Durness Group, where it is truncated by the Sole Thrust; this thrust is the leading edge of the Moine Thrust Zone, which here comprises stacked thrust packages forming the structure known as the Assynt Bulge. Repeated thrust slices occur above this horizon, and crescentic rock packages separated by minor thrusts can be particularly well seen in the escarpment of Stronchrubie cliffs, formed by strata of the Ghrudaidh and Eilean Dubh formations (Plate 4). These imbricate slices are in turn truncated by major thrusts along which underlying Lewisian and Torridonian as well as Cambrian strata have been transported westwards and piled up into thick, thrust-bound wedges intruded by plutonic complexes. Other locations where parts of the succession are well exposed include Ullapool, Kinlochewe and Ord, on the Isle of Skye.

During the Early Palaeozoic, northwestern Scotland formed part of the Laurentian craton, and enjoyed a tropical climate just south of the equator. The succession developed as the inner belt of an extensive shelf sequence on the northern passive margin of the Iapetus Ocean, which separated Laurentia from Baltica and Gondwana, and was contiguous with parts of what is now western Newfoundland, Spitzbergen and eastern Greenland (Harland & Gayer 1972; Swett & Smit 1972; McKerrow *et al.* 1991, 1992). In northwestern Scotland, the earliest Cambrian rocks unconformably overstep both Archaean (Lewisian) basement gneiss and Proterozoic Torridonian sandstones, recording a marine transgression that continued with minor fluctuations throughout the Cambro-Ordovician. Deformation and tectonic truncation of the succession occurred during westward translation of the Moine Nappe along the Moine Thrust plane and associated structures, mainly in Silurian and Early Devonian times, associated with closure of the Iapetus Ocean and the Caledonian orogeny (McKerrow *et al.* 1991).

The Cambro-Ordovician succession can be divided into a lower dominantly clastic suite, the Eriboll Group, and an upper carbonate sequence, the Durness Group (Fig. 3.35). Reported maximum thicknesses for the Cambro-Ordovician have differed somewhat, with 2100 feet (~670 m) given by Peach & Horne (1930), 1500 m proposed by Swett (1965, 1969), while Wright, S. C. (1985) reports an accumulated thickness of ~750 m for the Durness Group, giving a total of some 1000 m with the Eriboll Group. These differences can be attributed to structural complexities in the exposed sections.

The Eriboll Group

The Eriboll Group (Wright, S. C. 1985) comprises the *Eriboll* and *An-t-Sron* formations, each of which consists of two members.

The Eriboll Formation

The earliest Cambrian unit is the 75–125 m thick, feldspathic to quartzitic *Basal Quartzite Member* (formerly known as the 'False-Bedded Member') of the Eriboll Formation. Current cross-bedding, including herringbone, is the most conspicuous feature, and at its base, a thin conglomerate oversteps both Lewisian gneiss and Torridonian sandstones. Stacked tidal channel deposits with cross-bedding indicating a dominantly eastward palaeoflow direction are overlain by tidally influenced shoreface sands showing bimodal NE and SE current directions. Wave ripples on some bed tops indicate occasional exposure to waves (McKie 1990). By contrast, the overlying, strikingly white, 75–100 m thick Pipe Rock Member is a mature, heavily bioturbated quartzite. This unit is characterized by abundant thin, cylindrical burrows ('pipes') oriented perpendicular to bedding, called *Skolithos* (Fig. 3.36), together with similar burrows with spreite described as *Monocraterion* (Westergard 1931). The two trace fossils were probably produced by the same animal, the trumpet-shaped spreite possibly representing escape structures to prevent sediment burial (Swett 1969). The length of the pipes, generally several centimetres although exceptionally up to 2 m in places, may be related to rates of sediment deposition. Heavy bioturbation masks sedimentary structures, but occasionally well-preserved cross-bedding and vertically graded sandstones suggest tidally influenced bedforms which become increasingly storm-dominated up section (McKie 1990). The geometry and structures of the Basal Quartzite are indicative of barrier-island to tidal-flat environments, with a similar marine origin for the Pipe Rock, which shows gradual transgressive trends culminating in the deposition of the Fucoid Beds of the An-t-Sron Formation (McKie 1989, 1990).

The An-t-Sron Formation

The An-t-Sron Formation consists of the lower *Fucoid Beds* (12–27 m thick) and the upper *Salterella Grit* (up to 20 m thick)

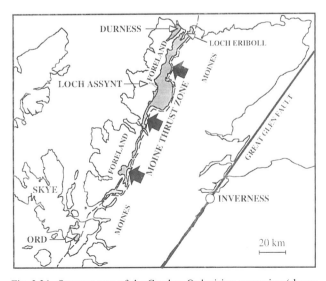

Fig. 3.34. Outcrop area of the Cambro-Ordovician succession (shown in grey) in northwest Scotland.

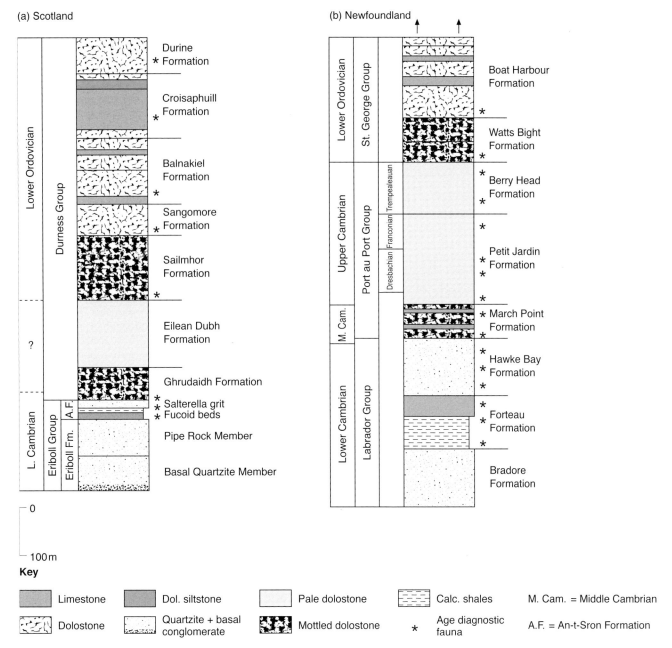

(a) Scotland

(b) Newfoundland

Key

Limestone	Dol. siltstone	Pale dolostone	Calc. shales	M. Cam. = Middle Cambrian	
Dolostone	Quartzite + basal conglomerate	Mottled dolostone	* Age diagnostic fauna	A.F. = An-t-Sron Formation	

Fig. 3.35. Simplified stratigraphy of the Cambro-Ordovician of (**a**) Northwest Scotland and (**b**) western Newfoundland. Note similarity of lithofacies successions between biostratigraphic benchmarks of Lower Cambrian and Lower Ordovician strata.

Fig. 3.36. The Pipe Rock Member of the Eriboll Formation, with abundant vertical white *Skolithos* burrows, Skiag Bridge. Width of view *c.* 70 cm.

members, which are best seen on the eastern shore of Loch Eriboll, and near Skiag Bridge by Loch Assynt.

The Fucoid Beds. These comprise ferruginous, brown coloured dolomitic siltstones with several argillaceous and quartz-rich horizons and minor limestones, with numerous bedding-parallel, sand-filled, *Planolites* burrows, originally considered to resemble fucoids, or seaweed, hence the name of the unit. Pisolitic iron ore has been reported locally (Cowie 1974). This unit contains the trilobite *Olenellus lapworthi* (Lapworth 1888; Cowie & McNamara 1978), and other olenellids (Fig. 3.37), the earliest valid index fossils in the generally poorly fossil-iferous Cambro-Ordovician sequence. Other fossils include *Salterella maccullochi*, *Hyolithes* sp., *Coleoloides* sp., brachiopods, molluscs and echinoderm fragments. Occasional bidirectional ripple structures within a vertical facies association domi-nated by low-angle planar laminated and graded beds indicate a

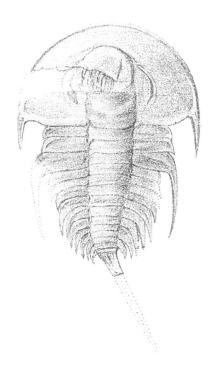

Fig. 3.37. *Olenellus lapworthi*, from the Lower Cambrian Fucoid Beds at Meall a' Ghubhais, Kinlochewe, Ross-shire. Total length 30 mm. Reproduced from Peach (1894, pl. 29, fig. 3).

storm-dominated tidal environment, while the upward increasing proportion of mudstones suggests gradual transgression (McKie 1990).

The Salterella Grit.   This member (formerly the Serpulite Grit) is a white, coarse, mature quartzite with minor arkosic gritty parts. It is characterized by the small conical shells of *Salterella*, but also contains *Skolithos*, so that differentiation from the Pipe Rock may be difficult where the units are exposed in thrust slices. *Salterella* was once believed to represent an early cephalopod, but Yochelson (1977) concluded that it was a unique form, and designated it to its own phylum, Agnata. Shaly layers near the base have yielded *Salterella maccullochi* and *Olenellus lapworthi*, while shales near the top tend to be dolomitic. The Salterella Grit represents a regressive episode during which sandbodies migrated over a muddy shelf and were succeeded by sandsheets indicative of renewed transgression (McKie 1990), which spread to the cratonic interior, followed by prolonged carbonate deposition.

Biostratigraphical and lithostratigraphical evidence (see below) indicates that the Eriboll Formation correlates with similar successions in western Newfoundland, eastern Greenland and Spitzbergen (Bradore, Kloftelv/Lower Bastion and Tokommane formations respectively). The overlying Fucoid Beds Member correlates in the same areas with the Forteau, Upper Bastion and Topiggane Shale formations (Downie 1982; Swett 1981; Cowie *et al.* 1972). The Salterella Grit can be correlated with the Hawke Bay Formation of western Newfoundland (Wright, D. T. & Knight 1995).

The Durness Group

The Durness Group carbonates, frequently but erroneously referred to as the 'Durness Limestone,' are a thick sequence of dolostones, with intervals of limestone and subordinate chert, which conformably overlie the dominantly clastic Eriboll Group. Marble occurs where the carbonates are intruded by igneous plutons in the Assynt area. They were first divided into seven 'groups' by Peach *et al.* (1907), and although the status of these units has varied according to researchers' preferences, they are now referred to as formations following Cowie *et al.* (1972). From base to top, these are the *Ghrudaidh*, *Eilean Dubh*, *Sailmhor*, *Sangomore*, *Balnakiel*, *Croisaphuill* and *Durine* formations. The complete sequence can only be seen in the Durness area, but even here structural complexity makes measurements difficult and, as outlined earlier, reported thicknesses for the succession vary significantly (e.g. MacGregor & Phemister 1972; Swett 1969; Wright, S. C. 1985).

The Ghrudaidh Formation
The Grudaidh Formaton is around 60 m thick, and consists of dark to mid-grey, burrow-mottled and massive structureless dolostones, with oolitic and bioclastic grainstones and rare stromatolites. The depositional environment is interpreted as a low-energy, subtidal shelf, following marine transgression (Wright, S. C. 1985). Cyclicity in the upper part of the formation, where dololaminites and desiccation features are associated with oolitic facies, suggests shoreline progradation behind oolite barrier sands. The Ghrudaidh Formation has yielded no body fossils above the basal 10 m, which contain two horizons of *Salterella maccullochi* suggesting that the base is late Early Cambrian in age (Fritz & Yochelson 1988). Mottled dolostones are common in the Ghrudaidh Formation and have been attributed to bioturbation. However, 3D serial sections show complex patterns incompatible with burrow architecture (Swett 1965). The mottled patches are the result of different grain sizes, and may represent different types and times of dolomitization. They also resemble the clotted fabrics of thrombolites, and may therefore be related to mineralization associated with benthic microbial communities.

The Eilean Dubh Formation
The Eilean Dubh Formation is about 150 m thick, and is characterized by faunally barren, pale grey, flaggy, laminated, often porcellaneous dolostones, with abundant and diverse microbialites. The latter include laterally-linked hemispheroidal, domal, digitate and stratiform stromatolites, and bun-shaped and tabular thrombolites. Intraclast breccias and occasional nodular, lenticular and tabular cherts occur, some of which preserve microbial sediments and ooids (Brasier 1977; Wright, D. T. 1993, 1997a). The distinctive lithological characteristics of particular sections of the Eilean Dubh Formation at Balnakiel Bay are recognizable throughout its outcrop area, which is broadly that of the Durness Group at Balnakiel Bay and along the Moine Thrust Zone from Loch Eriboll in the north to the Ord window in Skye, including Assynt (see Fig. 3.34), and enable the formation to be divided into three subordinate units (Wright, D. T. 1993), the Kyle, Stromatolite and Solmar members.

The Kyle Member.   This comprises about 65 m of dominantly fine-grained, pale-grey and grey massive, structureless and fenestral dolostones and rare cherts. Preservation of ooids, peloids and intraclasts in the cherts indicates that these facies may have been much more abundant, but can no longer be recognized because of fabric-destructive dolomitization. Rare intraformational breccias occur, in which elongate, pale grey mudstone clasts are set in a grainy grey matrix. The tops of some beds are pink-stained. Stromatolites are common in the upper 20 m of the Member (Fig. 3.38), where some occur within metre-scale shallowing-upward cycles (Wright, S. C. 1985; Wright, D. T. 1993).

Fig. 3.39. Weathered upper surface of digitate stromatolite bioherm from the Stromatolite Member of the Eilean Dubh Formation at Balnakiel Bay, showing characteristic pitted, meandrine outlines of cross-sections of digitate columns. Blank areas represent sand, silt and mud. Lens cap 52 mm.

Fig. 3.38. Stratiform and laterally linked hemispherical stromatolites typical of the Kyle Member of the Eilean Dubh Formation. Lens cap 52 mm.

The Stromatolite Member. This is approximately 45 m thick, and contains abundant and diverse stromatolites, as well as thrombolites, intraformational breccias and chert lenses. Several metre-scale shallowing-upward cycles occur in the upper part of the member, typically comprising a basal ripple cross-laminated unit, a thin, intraformational breccia overlain by clotted thrombolites sharply overlain by digitate and/or undulose stromatolites. Digitate stromatolites show characteristic pitted, meandrine outlines on upper weathered surfaces (Fig. 3.39); fenestrae become increasingly abundant upwards, indicating greater desiccation with aggradation, while overlying undulose stromatolites contain abundant detrital siliciclastics, including millet seed quartz. The regionally extensive cycles indicate fluctuating sea level on a broad, shallow shelf, with microbialite build-ups aggrading in a lagoonal setting behind shoal barriers (Fig. 3.40).

The Solmar Member. This comprises similar facies to the Stromatolite Member, but ripple cross-laminated beds predominate and evidence for cyclicity is rare. Tabular, laterally extensive, structureless thrombolitic dolostones also occur. Stromatolites are less abundant and include hummocky, structureless forms not seen in the Stromatolite Member. Cherts, some of which contain poorly preserved ooids, increase in abundance towards the top of the Member, near the contact with the Sailmhor Formation.

The Sailmhor Formation
The dark grey massive dolostones of the Sailmhor Formation, some 130 m thick, sharply overlie the Eilean Dubh Formation, and are characterized by the dark and pale mottled 'Leopard Rock', a texture derived from adjacent fine and coarse grained patches and often attributed to bioturbation. However, the 'burrows' have both vertical and horizontal elements, forming a boxwork structure, which may have a diagenetic origin. Pink and white diagenetic cherts are conspicuous, and may form characteristic 'onion skin' nodules preserving sedimentary and stromatolitic laminations. Stromatolites are abundant, and thrombolite mounds with clotted, stromatactoid and locally laminar, fenestral fabrics occur, which may be onlapped by thin-bedded dolostones. Shallowing-upward cycles 2–10 m thick are abundant (Wright, S. C. 1985), in which mottled dolostones, sometimes with a basal lag, pass up into stromatactoid dolomite overlain by laminated and/or stromatolitic dolomite, typically capped by an emergent surface. The cycles represent progradation into a continually subsiding shallow basin. Deep, breccia-filled fissures extending down to the Eilean Dubh Formation have been reported (Palmer *et al.* 1980; Wright, S. C. 1985) as originating at a karstic surface at the top of the Sailmhor Formation.

The Sangomore Formation
This Formation is about 60 m thick at Balnakiel Bay, and is dominated by pale to dark grey structureless dolostones, but contains thin peloidal limestones, especially in its upper part. Domal microbialites and laterally-linked hemispheroidal and stratiform stromatolites with chert nodules occur, as do pink to cream silicified oolitic grainstones and intraclast breccias.

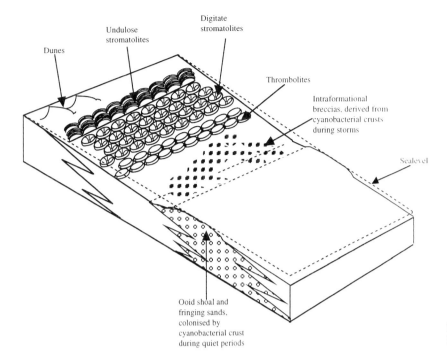

Fig. 3.40. Depositional model for the Stromatolite Member, Eilean Dubh Formation.

Thin beds and nodules of chert occur throughout, whereas ripple cross-laminated dolostones are rare and tepee structures are locally developed. The facies suite indicates shallow subtidal to emergent depositional settings, possibly on a shallow subtidal carbonate platform dotted with a mosaic of exposed low banks and islands. Post-depositional collapse breccias associated with folded, sagging beds occur throughout the Sangomore Formation, but are more abundant in the upper part. They formed after later dissolution of interbedded evaporites and indicate a supratidal sabkha setting. This is supported by milky white quartz nodules in two horizons near the top of the formation which have been interpreted as pseudomorphs after evaporites (Young 1979). Cephalopods and conodonts indicate a Tremadocian to Arenig age.

The Balnakiel Formation
The Balnakiel Formation has a cumulative thickness of 140 m in incomplete coastal and inland exposures at Balnakiel Bay. It comprises wavy-laminated alternating thin beds of dolomite and limestone 'ribbon rock,' dark grey, thinly bedded dolostones and normally paler bioclastic limestones. Stromatolites are abundant, especially in the lower part of the Formation, typically forming bun-shaped mounds with edgewise intraclast breccias concentrated in the intermound pockets. In the lower to middle part, cycles comprise black, bioturbated wackestones, with stromatolitic and thrombolitic boundstones overlain by thinly bedded, irregular mudstone and often capped by dololaminites. Cyanobacteria thus dominated the depositional environment. Dolomite of the ribbon rock is usually laminated, and may represent microbial stabilization of ripple surfaces, followed by microbially-mediated dolomitization (Wright, D. T. 1993, 1997*a*). Higher up, oolitic and peloidal grainstones and packstones are interbedded with intraclast breccias, bioturbated limestones and laminated dolostones, with rare stromatolites. The observed lithologies indicate an intertidal to shallow subtidal setting behind a microbialite reef barrier (Wright, S. C. 1985). Transgression across the Sangomore formation sabkhas led to less restricted marine conditions in which grazing cephalopods reduced the importance of benthic microbial communities. The limestones of the upper part of the formation reflect more open marine conditions, with a relatively diverse fauna. Molluscs and the sponge *Archaeoscyphia minganensis* indicate an Arenig age for the Balnakiel Formation (Peach *et al.* 1907).

The Croisaphuill Formation
The Croisaphuill Formation consists of some 120 m of monotonous, bioturbated, dark grey fossiliferous limestones, with gastropods, cephalopods and the sponge A*rchaeoscyphia minganensis* indicating a Late Arenig age, together with an abundant *Chondrites* and *Planolites* ichnofauna (Peach & Horne 1930; Wright, S. C. 1985). All primary fabrics have been destroyed by bioturbation. Burrows are commonly replaced by sucrosic dolomite, surrounded by a micritic limestone matrix. The rich fauna indicates an open, shallow water subtidal depositional environment.

The Durine Formation
The Durine Formation comprises around 80 m of bioturbated and laminated carbonates, the top of the formation being tectonically truncated by movements along the Moine Thrust Zone. Dolostones become dominant, though burrow-mottled beds similar to those of the Croisaphuill Formation dominate the lower part. Overlying laminated dolostones contain cherts with pseudomorphed evaporitic textures indicative of lagoonal to sabkha environments. The Durine Formation thus records gradual shallowing to intertidal and emergent conditions in an arid environment. Conodonts indicate a Late Arenig to Early Llanvirn age (Higgins 1967; Bergstrom & Orchard 1985).

Diagenesis

The Eriboll Group
Pore space in the Eriboll Sandstone has been severely occluded by silica cementation following pressure solution. Petrographic analysis shows fitted fabrics, fractured grains, syntaxial euhedral overgrowths on rounded grains and highly strained, undulatory extinction patterns in quartz grains. Feldspars commonly display overgrowths that crosscut adjacent sutured quartz grains, indicating development after the principal compaction event (Swett 1969).

The most significant diagenetic feature of the Fucoid Beds is the unusually high K-feldspar content, incorporated as authigenic sanidine, whose origin is controversial. Bowie *et al.* (1966) argued that vigorous erosion of the Lewisian and Torridonian strata supplied the potassium to the Cambrian sea. However, some 200 m of siliciclastic rocks separate the Fucoid beds from the unconformity, making such a source unlikely. Swett (1969) suggested that dolomitzation in overlying carbonates displaced potassium from illite, which was reprecipitated in the Fucoid Beds as orthoclase, notwithstanding the intervening Salterella Grit. The Salterella Grit generally shows evidence of early cementation, with pore space occluded by silica and dolomite cements, but pressure solution and deformed quartz textures are rare.

The Durness carbonates
A complex diagenetic history for the Durness carbonates has been reported by Swett (1969) and expanded upon by Wright, S. C. (1985). Swett's diagenetic sequence comprises five stages:

(1) recrystallization of original calcium carbonate followed by (2) dolomitization, (3) silicification, (4) calcitization and (5) further dolomitization. Dispersed rhombohedra in limestone through to dolostones, plus dolomitized microbial allochems support an authigenic origin for most of the dolomite.

Petrographic, geochemical and cathodo-luminescence analysis of numerous samples indicates that lithification and stabilization of fabrics accompanied early dolomite formation, and that late diagenetic cementation was relatively minor (Wright, S. C. 1985; Wright, D. T. 1993). For example, digitate stromatolites of the Eilean Dubh Formation exhibit a range of fabrics from micritic to coarse spar, which represent a diagenetic sequence. Micritic textures in some stromatolite columns preserve vestiges of the microtopography of the microbial growth surface, whereas other columns in the same colony show coarser textures produced by aggrading neomorphism in which a distinct lamination is seen, caused by differences in grain size. Columns with the coarsest spar show a faint lamination due to trails of inclusions of residual dolomicrite and

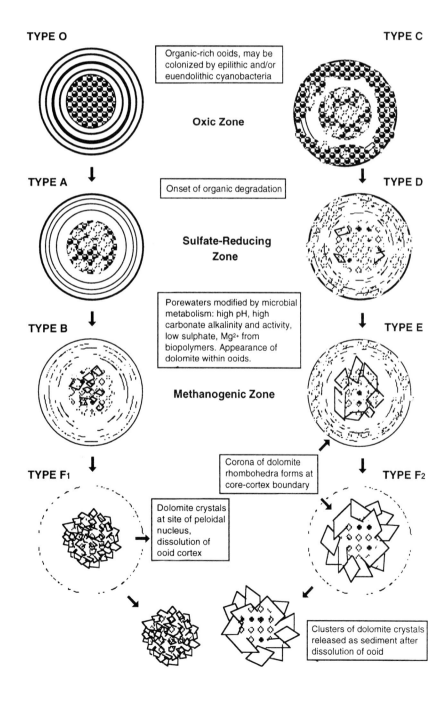

Fig. 3.41. Sequential diagenetic evolution and destruction of the ooids in which organic degradation is accompanied by the appearance and increase in abundance of intragranular authigenic dolomite. Ultimately, packages of dolomite crystals are released as sediment into the environment.

organic material (Wright, D. T. 1993, 1997*b*). Lamination is thus interpreted to be the result of early neomorphic recrystallization of precursor, biologically-influenced micritic fabrics whose original mineralogy may have been Mg-calcite or protodolomite.

Dolomite formation was a major diagenetic process affecting the Durness Group sediments. Recent studies have shown that extensive dolomitization occurred at a very early stage in the diagenetic history of the shallow subtidal to supratidal sediments, and has generally been explained in terms of evaporitic, mixed-water and burial models (e.g. Wright, S. C. 1985). However, there is increasing evidence that widespread dolomite formation was associated with early organic diagenesis. Dolomite precipitation from seawater is normally inhibited by the presence of sulphate, the low activity of the carbonate ion, and the high enthalpy of hydration of the magnesium ion (e.g. Lippmann 1973; Baker & Kastner 1981). In modern microbial sediments, anoxic degradation of cyanobacterial material by sulphate-reducing bacteria can significantly alter ambient water chemistry by increasing pH and carbonate alkalinity to levels necessary for dolomite formation. Gebelein & Hoffmann (1973) reported that cyanobacterial sheaths and mucilage can concentrate magnesium and release it for dolomite formation during diagenetic degradation, while Slaughter & Hill (1991) suggested that magnesium could be supplied from complexed ion pairs in alkaline solutions.

Diagenetic cherts from the lower Eilean Dubh Formation near Loch Assynt preserve uncompacted cyanobacterial microfossils, demonstrating that silicification must have been early, but the presence within the cherts of relict cores of dolomite in silicified rhombs associated with degraded microbial mat and organic-rich ooids shows that dolomite formation here predated silicification (Wright, D. T. 1993, 1997*a*). Further study of thin sections of the cherts has shown that sequential degradation of microbial mat fabrics is associated with the appearance and increase in abundance of dolomite. Silicified oolitic grainstone fabrics preserve various ooid types that form a sequence in which progressive degradation of component microbial material, together with leaching of the original calcium carbonate ooid shell, is accompanied by the appearance and increase in abundance of intragranular authigenic dolomite. Dolomite crystals and rhombohedra formed either within the peloidal nucleus or as a corona at the core-cortex boundary, ultimately to be released as a sediment package after total dissolution of the ooids; this diagenetic sequence is shown schematically in Fig. 3.41. Similar sequences are observed in peloids and intraclasts.

The cherts thus provide preservational 'windows' in which silicified boundstones and ooid grainstones represent ephemeral fabrics that in the normal diagenetic sequence would be replaced by massive, structureless crystalline dolomitic fabrics, as seen in the host rocks of the cherts. Wright (1997*a*) has argued that because microbialites and organic-rich sediments such as ooids, peloids and intraclasts, dominated the environment during deposition of much of the Durness Group, organic diagenesis may have led to widespread and massive dolomitization of rock fabrics in restricted shallow subtidal and peritidal environments.

There is thus substantial evidence that microbial degradational processes, in particular bacterial sulphate reduction, played a hitherto unrecognized but important role in carbonate diagenesis, especially in penecontemporaneous dolomitization in sediments of the shallow subsurface. In this context, it is probably significant that the few limestone intervals are frequently fossiliferous, and their depositional environments represent ecosystems dominated by metazoans. The burrow-mottled limestones of the Croisaphuill Formation underwent

early aragonite dissolution and calcitic cementation. The dolomitic arthropod burrows are thought to have provided the plumbing for dolomitizing fluids of mixing zone origin percolating down from the overlying Durine Formation (Wright, S. C. 1985). However, the abundance of laminated microbial mats and stromatolites throughout the Durine Formation indicate a possible organogenic derivation for these solutions. In the Sangomore and Durine formations, milky white quartz nodules, pseudomorphed evaporitic textures and post-depositional collapse breccias indicate dissolution of interbedded evaporites formed in a supratidal sabkha setting followed by later silicification (Young 1979). Late cherts are found in other formations, for example thin sections of pink cherts from the Eilean Dubh Formation show that they comprise partially leached, pressure-compacted siliciclastic fabrics (Wright, D. T. 1993). Late-stage diagenesis, usually in the form of neomorphism and burial dolomitization, appears to be restricted to structural discontinuities which acted as conduits for hydrothermal solutions (Wright, S. C. 1985).

Stratigraphical problems and correlation

Scottish statigraphy

Although there is a broad biostratigraphical framework for the Cambro-Ordovician of north-western Scotland (Fig. 3.35), problems of dating and correlation of the Eilean Dubh and middle to upper Ghrudaidh formations of the Durness Group persist because

(a) the Eilean Dubh Formation and most of the Ghrudaidh Formation are faunally barren, and

(b) Middle and Late Cambrian faunas are absent from the succession.

An Early Cambrian age has generally been assigned to the Eilean Dubh Formation, based on the view that the greater part of the Middle and Upper Cambrian is unrepresented in the succession because of the total absence of fossils of this age, and the purported presence of unconformities at particular formational boundaries (Grabau 1916; Poulsen 1951; Palmer *et al.* 1980; Wright, S. C. 1983). However, the argument that the Middle and Upper Cambrian strata must be missing simply because there are no fossils of this age is unconvincing, especially when there are some 200 m of barren strata in the Ghrudaidh and Eilean Dubh formations which might reasonably be expected to have been deposited during this period. The preservation of macro- and microscopic sedimentary and microbial lamination in the Eilean Dubh Formation indicates that an infauna was never present. A report by Phemister (1960) of *Salterella* from the Eilean Dubh Formation in the Assynt area proved to be unsubstantiated (Cowie *et al.* 1972; MacGregor & Phemister 1972), while silicified fossils from the lower Eilean Dubh Formation previously assigned to the Early Cambrian (Brasier 1977) are no longer considered to be age-diagnostic (M. D. Brasier, pers. comm. 1989, 1994). Biostratigraphic constraints thus establish only that the age of the Eilean Dubh Formation lies between the Early Cambrian and the Early Ordovician (Fig. 3.35).

Major stratigraphic breaks have been proposed at both the Eilean Dubh–Sailmhor (Poulsen 1951; Wright, S. C. 1985) and Sailmhor–Sangomore (Palmer *et al.* 1980) formation boundaries to represent supposedly missing Middle and Upper Cambrian strata. This is in contrast to other workers who argue that no significant break exists in the succession. Cephalopods reported by Wright, S. C. (1985) from the lower Sailmhor Formation place it in the Early Ordovician, suggesting that any succeeding hiatus is intra-Ordovician. Reappraisal of the field evidence at Balnakiel Bay by Nicholas (1994) led him to interpret the karstic surface at the top of the Sailmhor as a Recent feature. The sharply planar contact between the pale grey dolostones of the Eilean Dubh Formation and the dark grey, mottled, cherty dolostones of the Sailmhor Formation at its only known exposure at Balnakiel Bay, near Durness, shows a clear facies change but offers little evidence for a significant break in deposition. Moreover Nicholas (1994), presenting data from strontium isotope studies, argued that there is no major unconformity within the Cambro-Ordovician succession. This information provides indirect evidence in support of a Late Arenig–Llanvirn age for the Grampian orogeny (Soper *et al.* 1999).

Correlation with western Newfoundland

The similarities of the faunal, sedimentary and diagenetic histories of the Cambro-Ordovician sedimentary successions of northwestern Scotland and western Newfoundland, are well-established (Nicol 1857; Peach & Horne 1930; Swett & Smit 1972) and studies in east Greenland, northwestern Scotland and Spitsbergen have provided compelling evidence to indicate that all these successions evolved contiguously on the same broad, shallow shelf along the eastern, passive margin of Laurentia (Gobbett & Wilson 1960; Cowie 1974; Swett 1981; Wright, S. C. 1985) (Fig. 3.42).

The sedimentary succession in western Newfoundland is constrained within a palaeontologically established chronos-

tratigraphical framework that precludes the possibility of a pre-Tremadocian unconformity (Fig. 3.35). Correlations with those units of the succession in northwestern Scotland that contain age-diagnostic faunas can be made with confidence (Wright, D. T. & Knight 1995) (Fig. 3.35). Biostratigraphical correlation of the lower parts of the successions is firmly based upon the presence of fauna diagnostic of the latest Early Cambrian *Bonnia–Olenellus* Biozone. This zone embraces both the Forteau Formation and the lower part of the Hawke Bay Formation in western Newfoundland, and the more condensed equivalent inner shelf strata of the Fucoid Beds and Salterella Grit together with the lowermost Ghrudaidh Formation in northwestern Scotland. Trilobites from the mixed siliclastic-carbonate Bridge Cove Member of the Hawke Bay Formation on the east side of the Great Northern Peninsula help to date its upper part as earliest Middle Cambrian (*Plagiura* to *Ehmaniella* Biozones; Knight & Boyce 1987). The next biostratigraphically correlatable units are the Lower Ordovician Watts Bight and Sailmhor formations of western Newfoundland and northwestern Scotland respectively (Wright, S. C. 1985; Knight & James 1987; James *et al.* 1989). The two formations are also lithological correlatives, both comprising distinctive dark-grey, burrow-mottled dolostones (the 'leopard stone' of the Sailmhor Formation), abundant mottled thrombolites, stromatolites and abundant cherts. Biostratigraphic correlation between the two successions continues in succeeding formations, and at the top of the Durness Group, the

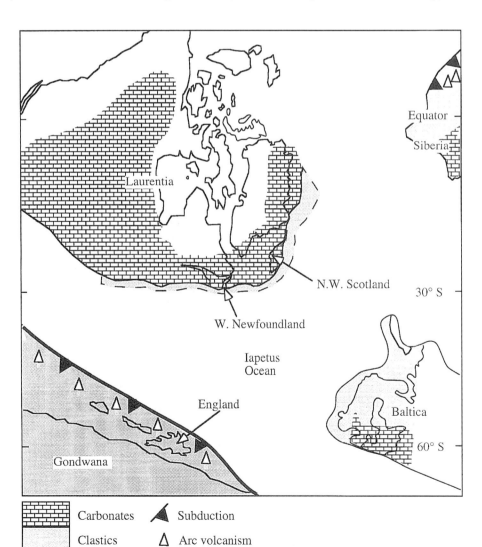

Fig. 3.42. The Cambro-Ordovician of NW Scotland in its North Atlantic context. After McKerrow *et al.* (1991).

Whiterockian conodonts of the Durine Formation are reflected in conodonts and trilobites of similar age in the Aguathuna Formation of western Newfoundland (Stouge & Boyce 1983; Knight & James 1987).

The parallel development of the once-contiguous Cambro-Ordovician successions provides a framework in which to place the faunally barren strata of the Durness Group. An Early Cambrian age for the Eilean Dubh Formation, and for the whole of the Ghrudaidh Formation above the *Salterella* horizons, is at variance with the equivalent stratigraphic position of faunally dated, lithologic correlatives in western Newfoundland (Wright, D. T. & Knight 1995), where the Upper Cambrian is represented by the Petit Jardin and Berry Head formations (Fig. 3.35). Knight (1978) divided the Petit Jardin Formation in the inner shelf of the Great Northern Peninsula, where the Berry Head Formation is not distinguished, into Lower Dolostone, Middle Stromatolite and Upper Dolostone members. These members share lithofacies assemblages with the three members of the Eilean Dubh Formation, and show a sparse faunal content. These characteristics are in marked contrast to fossiliferous Lower Cambrian mixed terrigenous–carbonate strata, which are dominantly bioclastic. This trend is mirrored in the Scottish succession, where richly fossiliferous, bioclastic Lower Cambrian strata pass up into faunally barren strata of the middle and upper parts of the Ghrudaidh and the Eilean Dubh formations.

Where fossils have been found in carbonates of the western Newfoundland succession, they have usually been recovered from limestones in the outer shelf. Dolostones from the inner shelf are dominated by microbialites and although they have yielded fossils of the Dresbachian *Cedaria* to *Crepicephalus* Biozones (Knight & Boyce 1987), they are scarce and generally poorly preserved. The absence of Middle and Upper Cambrian faunas in the Durness Group and rocks of equivalent stratigraphic positions in Spitsbergen and central east Greenland (Gobbett & Wilson 1960; Swett & Smit 1972), and their paucity in the inner shelf of western Newfoundland, may be due to hostile conditions over the formerly contiguous shelf, such that the fauna was scarce and unlikely to be preserved.

Wright, D. T. & Knight (1995) have proposed the correlation of the Eilean Dubh Formation with the Upper Cambrian Petit Jardin and Berry Head formations (Fig. 3.35) based on the equivalent chronostratigraphical positions of lithostratigraphical correlatives bracketed between biostratigraphically controlled benchmarks, together with the similarity of faunal and sedimentological trends in each succession, strontium isotope data and field evidence. This has the corollary that the Ghrudaidh Formation, which also has chronostratigraphic and lithological correlatives in western Newfoundland, probably extends through the Middle Cambrian, indicating that in northwestern Scotland, the Cambrian succession contains no significant breaks. More recently, Huselbee & Thomas (1998) have provided supporting evidence for this argument by recording Ordovician conodonts from near the top of the Eilean Dubh Formation at Balnakiel Bay, showing that the Cambro-Ordovician boundary must lie within this unit. They have concluded that the upper part of the Ghrudaidh and lower part of the Eilean Dubh formations are of probable Middle Cambrian age, and that the upper part of the Eilean Dubh Formation spans the Late Cambrian and earliest Ordovician.

4 The Northern Highland and Grampian terranes

R. A. STRACHAN, M. SMITH, A. L. HARRIS & D. J. FETTES

The Northern Highland and Grampian terranes together comprise an extensive tract of structurally complex and generally high-grade metamorphic rocks within the Caledonian orogenic belt of Scotland (Fig. 4.1). This part of the orogen is dominated by two thick sequences of mainly Neoproterozoic metasedimentary rocks. The older sequence comprises the Moine Supergroup of the Northern Highland terrane, and possibly also the Dava Succession of the Grampian terrane. Both were deposited between c. 1000 Ma and c. 870 Ma, and subsequently affected by a controversial Knoydartian tectonothermal event at c. 800 Ma. The younger Dalradian Supergroup of the Grampian terrane accumulated between c. 800 Ma and the Early Cambrian during the break-up of the late Precambrian supercontinent Rodinia and the formation of the Iapetus Ocean. Inliers of Archaean to Palaeoproterozoic orthogneisses (Fig. 4.1) probably represent fragments of the Laurentian continental basement on which the Moine and Dalradian successions accumulated.

Caledonian orogenesis in the North Atlantic region resulted from the closure of the Iapetus Ocean and the convergence of three crustal blocks: Laurentia, Baltica and Avalonia (Soper & Hutton 1984; Pickering et al. 1988; Soper et al. 1992b). Early orogenic activity along the Iapetan margin of Laurentia resulted from an arc–continent collision that occurred during initial ocean closure in the Early to Mid-Ordovician. This phase of the Caledonian orogenic cycle is known as the Grampian event and it affected both the Northern Highland and Grampian terranes. Ocean closure and final amalgamation of crustal blocks occurred in the Late Silurian. The collision of Laurentia and Baltica resulted in the Scandian orogenic event, the effects of which are widespread in the Northern Highland terrane, but very limited in the Grampian terrane which must have been located some distance from the main collision zone. Final juxtaposition of the two terranes resulted from major sinistral strike-slip movements along the Great Glen Fault during the Late Silurian and Early Devonian.

The Northern Highland and Grampian terranes are bordered by major Caledonian structures. The Moine Thrust Zone limits the Northern Highland terrane to the northwest, and the Highland Boundary Fault limits the Grampian terrane to the southeast. The transcurrent Great Glen Fault separates the two terranes. References to Northern Highland and Grampian 'terranes' in the literature results from uncertainty concerning the magnitude and potential significance of Precambrian and/ or Early Palaeozoic displacements between these two crustal blocks and adjacent blocks to the northwest and southeast (e.g. Gibbons & Gayer 1985). Useage of the term 'terrane' has provided a framework within which the status of the major Caledonian structures could be examined. Are there sufficient contrasts in the coeval geological features of the crustal blocks either side of these structures to justify the proposal that these were acquired far from one another prior to their juxtaposition? If significant contrasts could be demonstrated, useage of the term 'terrane' in the North American sense (e.g. Coney et al. 1980) might be justified.

The Scottish Caledonides is one of the most intensively studied orogenic belts in the world. However, despite the decades of detailed field and laboratory work that have been carried out, there is continued discussion over numerous fundamental issues. These include the role and possible status of the Great Glen Fault, the presence or absence of Neoproterozoic orogenic events within the Scottish Highlands, and the age of deposition of the Dalradian Supergroup. These problems arise at least in part from a lack of chronostratigraphic control, and difficulties in recognizing orogenic unconformities in polydeformed, high-grade metasedimentary successions, and relating radiometric mineral ages to structural and metamorphic events (Tanner & Bluck 1999). In this chapter, we focus initially on the Neoproterozoic evolution of the Northern Highland and Grampian terranes, and then discuss the prolonged history of Caledonian deformation, metamorphism and igneous activity recorded within both crustal blocks.

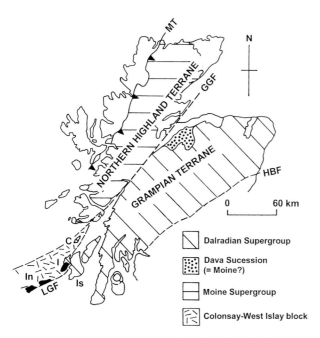

Fig. 4.1. Map showing the main tectonic units and regional structures in the Scottish Highlands (Caledonian igneous complexes omitted). MT, Moine Thrust; GGF, Great Glen Fault; HBF, Highland Boundary Fault; LGF, Loch Gruinart Fault; Is, Islay; In, Inishtrahull; C, Colonsay. Areas in black represent exposures (both on land and on the sea-bed) of the Palaeoproterozoic Rhinns Complex basement. The smaller Archaean basement inliers of the Northern Highland terrane are not depicted.

The Northern Highland Terrane

Early Neoproterozoic marine sedimentation: stratigraphy and basin evolution of the Moine Supergroup

The Moine rocks that dominate the Northern Highland terrane comprise metamorphosed, arenaceous and argillaceous sediments with minor impure calcareous units. The main rock types are psammites, semipelites and pelites, all of which occur in thick formations as well as in striped or banded units characterized by rapid alternations of lithology on centimetric to metric scales. Sedimentary structures are often present in areas of low tectonic strain and provide the evidence on which the original way up of local successions can be established. The presence and relative abundance of minor lithologies such as calc-silicate lenticles and heavy mineral laminae are locally diagnostic of certain units and have been highlighted in early lithostratigraphical studies (e.g. Johnstone *et al.* 1969). Amphibolites are common in many parts of the Moine Supergroup. Although a few might represent metamorphosed ferruginous marls (e.g. Rock & MacDonald 1986), the great majority were intruded as basic igneous sheets early in the geological history (see below).

Age and tectonic setting of Moine sedimentation

The age of the Moine Supergroup, which is completely unfossiliferous, is constrained mainly by isotopic data. Detrital and inherited zircon grains obtained from Moine metasedimentary rocks, as well as migmatites and granites formed by the melting of Moine sources, have given ages which mostly range between *c.* 1800 and *c.* 1000 Ma (Friend *et al.* 1997, 2003; Kinny *et al.* 1999). The Moine rocks were thus probably derived in part from erosion of the *c.* 1.1–1.0 Ga Grenville orogenic belt that developed during the assembly of the supercontinent Rodinia (Fig. 4.2; Dalziel & Soper 2001). A lower limit for Moine sedimentation is provided by ages of *c.* 870 Ma for igneous rocks that intrude the supergroup (see below). Moine sedimentation is therefore constrained to the period between about 1000 and 870 Ma. Dalziel & Soper (2001) have suggested that the Moine rocks were deposited within an aborted rift zone that developed along the eastern margin of Laurentia at the same time as East Gondwana separated from west Laurentia to form the Pacific Ocean (Fig. 4.2).

Regional framework

As a result of the structurally complex nature of the Moine rocks, early studies were mainly limited to establishment of local stratigraphical successions (e.g. Johnstone *et al.* 1969; Tobisch *et al.* 1970; Brown *et al.* 1970). However, in recent years, two interrelated aspects of the geology have been recognized which enable a regional stratigraphy to be erected: the importance of basement-cover relationships, and the thrust-sheet configuration of the Caledonian regional structure (Holdsworth *et al.* 1994).

Basement-cover relationships: Lewisianoid inliers in the Moine Supergroup.

Numerous units of hornblendic orthogneiss that crop out between the Moine Thrust Zone and the Great Glen Fault (Fig. 4.3) are thought to represent tectonically emplaced inliers of the basement upon which the Moine Supergroup sediments were deposited (Flett 1905; Peach *et al.* 1907; Read 1931; Tanner *et al.* 1970; Rathbone & Harris 1979). The inliers consistently lie at the lowest structural levels in the successions when the effects of thrusting and/or folding are removed. Some inliers lie in the cores of isoclinal folds (e.g. Glenelg, Morar), whereas others are carried as allochthonous slices along Caledonian ductile thrusts, notably the Sgurr Beag Thrust

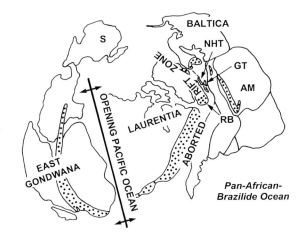

Fig. 4.2. Continental reconstruction for the early Neoproterozoic, following Grenvillian orogenesis and assembly of Rodinia (modified from Dalziel & Soper 2001). The reconstruction depicts the rifting of East Gondwana from west Laurentia to form the Pacific Ocean. At the same time, rifting along the east margin of Laurentia is associated with development of the Torridon Group and Moine Supergroup sedimentary basins. AM, Amazonia; NHT, Northern Highland terrane; GT, Grampian terrane (dashed line separating NHT and GT represents the future location of the Great Glen Fault); RB, Rockall Bank microcontinent; S, Siberia. Stippled areas represent belts of *c.* 1.1–1.0 Ga Grenville orogenic activity.

(e.g. Tanner *et al.* 1970). A fault-bounded slice of basement lies adjacent to the Great Glen Fault at Rosemarkie (Fig. 4.3; Rathbone & Harris 1980). Most inliers are dominated by tonalitic to dioritic, hornblende gneisses. Ultramafic hornblendite, serpentinite and garnet-pyroxene rocks are distinctive minor lithologies. Metasedimentary lithologies such as marble, and aluminium- and graphite-rich pelite occur within some inliers (e.g. eastern Glenelg, Loch Shin and Meadie inliers, Fig. 4.3) and appear to be integral parts of the basement rather than infolds or tectonic slices of Moine lithologies.

In most areas, ductile deformation of the inlier gneisses and the adjacent Moine units has obliterated any traces of sedimentary or structural discordances across the original unconformity (Fig. 4.4). In the western Moine, however, basement is relatively easy to identify because there is a marked contrast in texture and metamorphic grade between the unmigmatized, upper greenschist- to middle amphibolite-facies Moine rocks and the high-grade inlier gneisses. In areas where the intensity of overprinting deformation is moderate or low, the basement rocks may also display greater structural complexity compared with adjacent Moine rocks (e.g. Peach *et al.* 1907; Barber & May 1976). At several localities (e.g. Loch Carron, Glenelg, Strathfarrar, Strath Evelix, Talmine Fig. 4.3), Moine basal conglomerates are preserved in contact with basement gneisses (Peach *et al.* 1910*b*; Ramsay 1958; Strachan & Holdsworth 1988; Holdsworth 1989). At other localities (e.g. Sleitell, Scardroy, Fig. 4.3) cross-bedding is so well preserved in adjacent Moine psammites that it is difficult to interpret the contact as being anything other than an unconformity. However, as metamorphic grade within the Moine cover rises generally eastwards, contrasts between migmatized Moine metasediments and possible basement rocks become difficult to identify. In particular, banded quartzofeldspathic rocks that strongly resemble Moine psammites can be produced by the intense deformation and recrystallization of acid basement gneisses. Consequently, the mapped extent of basement inliers may commonly be conservative.

Correlation of the basement inliers with the Archaean Lewisian Complex of the Hebridean terrane has been generally

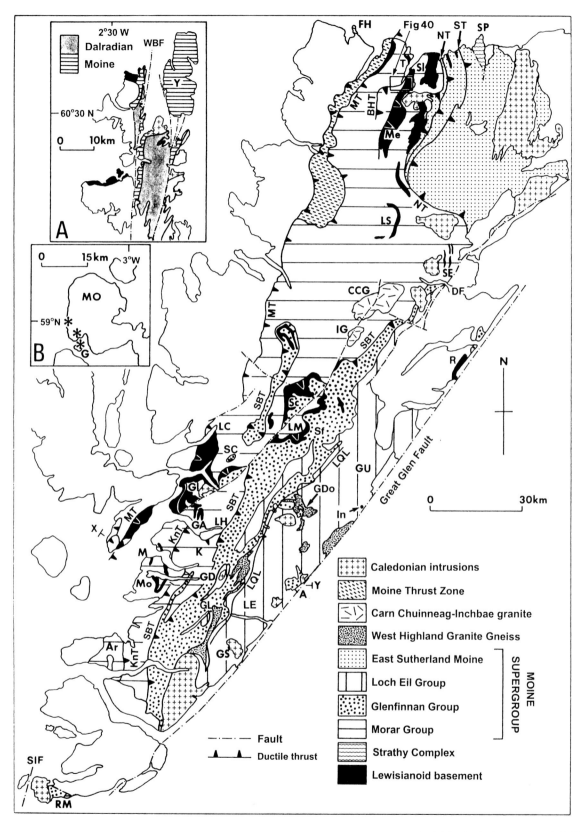

Fig. 4.3. Map showing the distribution of the Moine Supergroup. Place names: A, Achnacarry; Ad, Ardnish; Ar, Ardnamurchan; DF, Dornoch Firth; FH, Faraid Head; G, Graemsay; GA, Glen Arnisdale; GD, Glen Dessary; GDo, Glen Doe; GG, Glen Garry; GL, Glenfinnan; Gl, Glenelg; GS, Glen Scaddle; GU, Glen Urquhart; In, Invermoriston; K, Knoydart; L, Lochailort; LC, Loch Carron; LE, Loch Eil; LH, Loch Hourn; LM, Loch Monar; LS, Loch Shin; Ma, Mallaig; Me, Meadie; Mo, Morar; MO, Mainland Orkney; R, Rosemarkie; RM, Ross of Mull; SC, Sguman Coinntich; Sc, Scardroy; SE, Strath Evelix; Sf, Strathfarrar; Sl, Sleitell; SP, Strathy Point; T, Talmine; Y, Yell. Structures: BHT, Ben Hope Thrust; GGF, Great Glen Fault; KnT, Knoydart Thrust; LQL, Loch Quoich Line; MT, Moine Thrust; NT, Naver Thrust; ST, Swordly Thrust; SBT, Sgurr Beag Thrust; SIF, Sound of Iona Fault; WBF, Walls Boundary Fault. CCG, Carn Chuinneag granite; IG, Inchbae granite. XY shows the line of the cross-section in Figure 4.41. Inset maps show the location of Moine rocks in Shetland (A) and Orkney (B). In inset A, black areas represent basement gneisses; crosses are Caledonian igneous complexes.

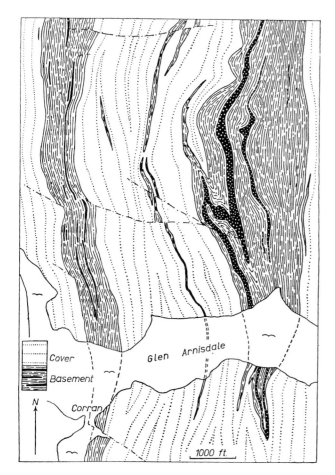

Fig. 4.4. Relations between the Moine rocks and basement units east of Arnisdale (see Fig. 4.3 for location; taken from Ramsay 1963). Note the almost complete obliteration of unconformable relations and the highly ductile nature of the folding in the basement. The black strips within the basement represent metabasic units (Scourie dykes?), and the white stipple denotes eclogitic bands. Scale 1000 ft = 307 m.

accepted on the basis of broad lithological and geochemical similarities (e.g. Winchester & Lambert 1970; Rathbone & Harris 1979; Moorhouse & Moorhouse 1988; Strachan & Holdsworth 1988; Holdsworth 1989), but requires confirmation by modern isotopic techniques. A Rb–Sr whole rock isochron of *c.* 2700 Ma was obtained from the Scardroy inlier (Fig. 4.3) by Moorbath & Taylor (1974) and might correlate with the Badcallian metamorphic event recognized within the Lewisian Complex. The Sm–Nd whole rock and mineral ages of *c.* 1050 Ma obtained by Sanders *et al.* (1984) from eclogites in the eastern Glenelg inlier imply that at least some of the basement inliers were reworked during the Grenville orogeny. The fault-bounded Strathy Complex of east Sutherland (Fig. 4.3) may also represent part of the basement to the Moine Supergroup, although its age is unknown. The complex is dominated by amphibolites and banded siliceous grey gneisses, the protoliths of which were probably a series of bimodal calc-alkaline volcanic rocks (Moorhouse 1979; Moorhouse & Moorhouse 1983; Burns 1994).

Caledonian ductile thrusting. Structural analysis of the Moine rocks is hampered by the monotony of the stratigraphy, the considerable heterogeneity of tectonic strain, and the complex structures produced by polyphase deformation. Local structural histories may commonly involve up to five or six separate phases of folding and associated fabric development (e.g. Ramsay 1958, 1963; Brown *et al.* 1970; Tanner 1970;

Tobisch *et al.* 1970; Powell 1974; Baird 1982; Strachan 1985). Many areas record one or two sets of early isoclinal folds that are typically associated with development of penetrative planar fabrics and strong mineral and extension lineations. These are commonly post-dated by tight-to-open fold sets of varying orientations that are associated with crenulation fabrics. This complexity reflects the prolonged orogenic history of the Moine that, if the results of isotopic dating are correct, has been subject to three major tectonothermal events during the Neoproterozoic and Early Palaeozoic (see below). Early syntheses were mostly concerned with the correlation of fold phases and fabrics within different areas of the Moine (e.g. Brown *et al.* 1970; Tobisch *et al.* 1970; Powell 1974). A regional structural framework emerged through the recognition of major Caledonian ductile thrusts, principally the Sgurr Beag and Naver thrusts (Fig. 4.3). This enabled the Moine to be perceived in terms of a series of thrust nappes, each with a characteristic lithostratigraphy and structural sequence (Tanner *et al.* 1970; Barr *et al.* 1986; Holdsworth *et al.* 1994).

Regional tectonostratigraphy of the Moine Supergroup
The monotonous lithology of the Moine Supergroup provides few distinctive horizons that can be correlated easily over any great distance. Deformation and migmatization have often masked original lithological differences and destroyed some of the evidence on which stratigraphical interpretation could be based. Nevertheless, sedimentary structures are commonly preserved in areas where tectonic strain is relatively low and metamorphism has not resulted in gneissification. Johnstone *et al.* (1969) divided the Moine rocks of western Inverness-shire into three tectonostratigraphical units (from west to east): the Morar, Glenfinnan and Loch Eil divisions. These divisions were not regarded as formal stratigraphical groups as their boundaries were tectonic. The Morar and Glenfinnan divisions were separated by a major ductile thrust, the Sgurr Beag 'Slide' (Tanner 1970; Tanner *et al.* 1970). The Loch Quoich Line separated the steeply dipping Glenfinnan Division rocks from the commonly flat-lying Loch Eil Division (Leedal 1952).

The divisions recognized by Johnstone *et al.* (1969) form the basis of what are now regarded as formal lithostratigraphical groups. Holdsworth *et al.* (1987) recognized that rocks assigned to the Morar Division may pass upwards by stratigraphical passage into Glenfinnan Division rocks on the Ross of Mull (Fig. 4.3). A hint of lateral transition between the Morar and Glenfinnan rocks is also found in eastern Knoydart (Fig. 4.3) in the footwall to the Sgurr Beag Thrust where uppermost Morar Division rocks are succeeded by striped and banded, highly siliceous psammites similar to Glenfinnan-type lithologies. Roberts & Harris (1983) and Roberts *et al.* (1984) also recognized that the Glenfinnan Division rocks in Inverness-shire passed stratigraphically upwards into the Loch Eil Division across the Loch Quoich Line (Fig. 4.3). This structure was recognized by them as the axial surface trace of a late-stage, asymmetric regional scale synform. As a result of this work, the 'Moinian Assemblage' of Johnstone *et al.* (1969) is now known as the Moine Supergroup, made up of the Morar (oldest), Glenfinnan and Loch Eil (youngest) groups (Holdsworth *et al.* 1987, 1994; Roberts *et al.* 1987; Harris & Johnson 1991). The Moine succession in western Inverness-shire is now regarded as the type locality for the supergroup (Holdsworth *et al.* 1994).

The Morar Group stratigraphy in its type area is dominated by a tripartite psammite–pelite–psammite succession that is up to 5 km thick (Fig. 4.5; Johnstone *et al.* 1969; Brown *et al.* 1970). Inliers of basement found at the base of the succession lie in the cores of major early isoclinal folds (Powell 1974). A discontinuous basal pelite comprises a tectonic mélange of Moine semipelite and retrogressed basement gneisses. The

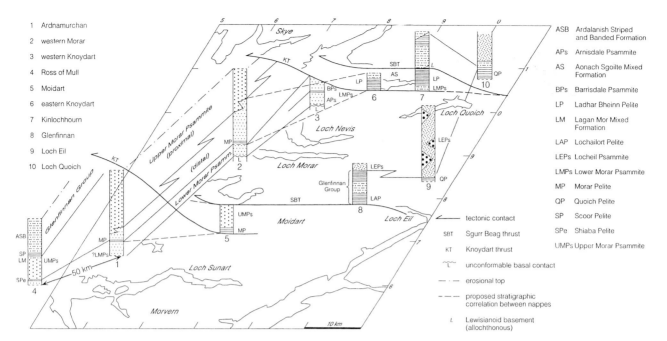

Fig. 4.5. A fence diagram of various stratigraphical successions within the Moine of W Inverness-shire (from Soper *et al.* 1998). Dots represent psammitic lithologies of varying proximality, but coarse dots in column 9 signify quartzite. Close fine dots are Loch Eil Group psammites. Lines represent pelite or semipelite (undistinguished). Dot–dash ornament represents striped and banded pelitic, semipelitic and psammitic units.

Knoydart Thrust is the only structure that disrupts the sequence significantly, although a common succession is recognized in both the footwall and hangingwall of the structure. Large areas record only relatively low tectonic strains, so sedimentary structures are locally abundant. The Glenfinnan Group characteristically comprises striped units of thinly interbanded psammites, semipelites, quartzites and pelites, together with thick pelitic formations (Fig. 4.5). Sedimentary structures are rarely preserved, mainly because of high levels of ductile strain. Original stratigraphical thicknesses are therefore difficult to establish, and estimates vary from 1–4 km (Holdsworth *et al.* 1994). Allochthonous slices of Lewisianoid basement present along the trace of the Sgurr Beag Thrust north of Loch Hourn (Fig. 4.3) are assumed to lie at the stratigraphical base of the Glenfinnan Group. The Loch Eil Group is a monotonous sequence of psammites, although laterally discontinuous quartzite and striped formations are recognized in the Loch Eil area (Fig. 4.5; Stoker 1983; Strachan 1985). Sedimentary structures are locally common and the succession may be as thick as 5 km (Strachan 1985). Outliers of the Loch Eil Group occur as synformal infolds within the steeply dipping Glenfinnan Group (Roberts *et al.* 1984) and migmatitic gneisses adjacent to the Great Glen Fault at Achnacarry probably represent upfolds of the Glenfinnan Group (Fig 4.3; Strachan *et al.* 1988). Other Glenfinnan-type gneisses crop out adjacent to the Great Glen Fault near Invermoriston and northeast of Glen Urquhart (Fig. 4.3), but their spatial limits are uncertain at present.

Following recognition that the Sgurr Beag Thrust extends northwards into Ross-shire (Wilson & Shepherd 1979; Kelley & Powell 1985) and probably correlates with either the Naver or Swordly thrusts in central Sutherland (Barr *et al.* 1986; Strachan & Holdsworth 1988; Fig. 4.3), the type Moine succession has been extended to most of the Northern Highlands (Holdsworth *et al.* 1994; Fig. 4.3). Much of the Morar Group in western Ross-shire is dominated by psammite, with occasional pelite units. In west Sutherland, the total thickness of the Morar Group psammites is less than 500 m once the effects of deformation are removed (Holdsworth 1989). The Moine rocks of eastern Ross-shire comprise Glenfinnan-type pelitic and

psammitic gneisses that pass eastwards into Loch Eil Group psammites. Unfortunately, the Moine rocks of eastern Ross-shire pass underneath Old Red Sandstone cover in the region of the Dornoch Firth (Fig. 4.3) and cannot be linked continuously with the east Sutherland Moine. The Moine rocks above the Naver Thrust in east Sutherland are dominated by psammitic and pelitic gneisses of Glenfinnan aspect; in southeast Sutherland these are overlain by cross-bedded psammites and quartzites of Loch Eil Group aspect (Strachan 1988).

Sedimentation history and basin evolution
Sedimentological studies in areas of low strain have shed light on the depositional environment of the Upper Morar Psammite (Glendinning 1988, 1989) and parts of the Loch Eil Group (Strachan 1986; Strachan *et al.* 1988). Glendinning interpreted the Upper Morar Psammite between the Ross of Mull and Mallaig as a predominantly tidal shelf deposit. The sequence is regressive, with a proximal, locally fluvial facies prograding northwards over a more distal facies. Complex sand waves, bipolar cross-bedding and gravel lag deposits are present and compare closely with those found in modern shelf environments (Fig. 4.6a). A shallow marine environment of deposition is also indicated for the Loch Eil Group in its type area by bipolar cross-bedding, wave ripples, possible lenticular and flaser bedding, and the rarity of channelling (Strachan 1986). In both areas, palaeocurrents deduced from cross-bedding indicate a general direction of flow from south to north.

Soper *et al.* (1998) proposed that the Moine sediments were deposited in two major half-graben basins that were bounded to the west by east-dipping normal faults (Fig. 4.7). In Morar and Ardnamurchan, the Upper Morar Psammite displays a marked westward thickening consistent with deposition in a half-graben (Glendinning 1988). Soft-sediment deformation structures, probably seismically induced, are common in the west outcrop of the unit (proximal to the inferred basin-bounding fault) and absent in the eastern outcrop on the east limb of a major antiform. The unit appears to become progressively more distal eastwards and the striped and pelitic rocks of the Glenfinnan Group may represent a distal facies of the Morar

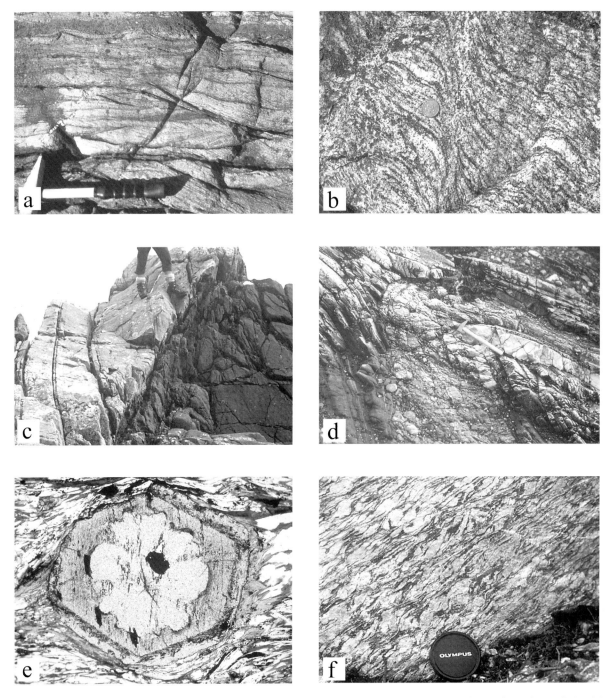

Fig. 4.6. (a) Cross-bedding within the Upper Morar Psammite on the Ross of Mull; (b) West Highland Granite Gneiss at the Loch Quoich dam spillway showing migmatitic segregations parallel to a strong gneissosity; (c) amphibolite discordant to bedding within Moine psammites on the Ross of Mull; (d) folded Knoydartian pegmatite at Ardnish: both the fold and the internal fabric within the pegmatite are probably the result of Caledonian deformation; (e) photomicrograph of a garnet (field of view 7 mm) within the Morar Pelite: it is these garnets that have yielded Sm–Nd ages of 820–790 Ma (Vance *et al.* 1998); (f) the deformed Inchbae granite that has been dated at 611 ± 11 Ma (Strachan & Rogers unpublished data).

Group. The upward transition from Morar to Glenfinnan lithologies preserved on Mull suggests that the mixed and muddy deposits of Glenfinnan type prograded across the tidal shelf represented by the Upper Morar Psammite. Early rift-related sedimentation (Morar Group) may thus have been followed by transgressive, more quiescent deposition (Glenfinnan Group), perhaps reflecting a decline in active rifting and greater control by thermal subsidence. The Loch Eil Group may represent the effects of renewed extensional rifting. An asymmetrical facies distribution and westward thickening of the sequence is again consistent with deposition in a half-graben bounded by an east-dipping normal fault (Fig. 4.7;

Strachan 1986). This rifting phase must have occurred later than the Morar phase because the Loch Eil Group conformably overlies the Glenfinnan.

Moine of Orkney and Shetland

Small inliers of pre-Devonian rocks on Mainland Orkney and Graemsay (Fig. 4.3) are dominated by strongly deformed and metamorphosed granite (Steavenson 1928; Wilson *et al.* 1935). The country rocks are migmatized psammitic gneisses with occasional amphibolite sheets, very similar to the high-grade Moine rocks of east Sutherland and Caithness (Strachan, unpublished data).

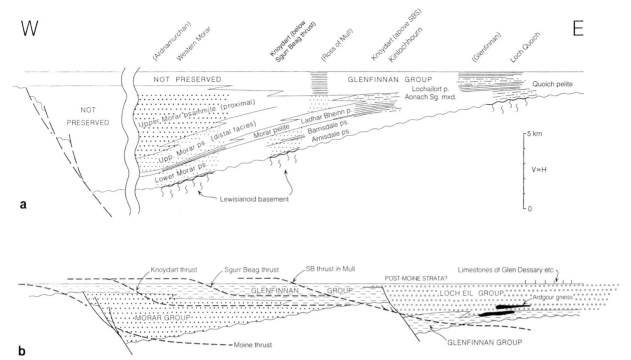

Fig. 4.7. (a) Schematic E–W restored section across western Inverness-shire to show the inferred original stratigraphical relationships of the Morar and Glenfinnan groups and the geometry of the Morar rift basin. (b) Inferred original stratigraphical relationships of the three Moine groups and the basins in which they were deposited, showing the positions of the major thrusts that subsequently disrupted the basin-fills. Taken from Soper *et al.* (1998).

On Shetland, rocks assigned to the Moine Supergroup occur on either side of the Walls Boundary Fault and may have originally been separated laterally by up to 200 km (Flinn 1985). To the west of the fault (Fig. 4.3), psammites are tectonically interleaved with Lewisianoid basement gneisses (Flinn 1988). Despite intense deformation, the rocks exhibit some cross-bedding and conglomerates, leading Flinn (1988) to correlate them with the Morar Group. To the east of the fault, rather different Moine-like rocks known as the Yell Sound Division comprise much of Yell as well as two narrow, north–south trending strips on Mainland Shetland (Fig. 4.3; Flinn 1988). These are dominated by banded, commonly gneissic, psammites with minor layers of quartzite and semipelite and abundant hornblende schists, a lithological assemblage comparable with the Glenfinnan Group (Flinn 1988). Thin slices of Lewisian-type basement gneiss are interleaved with the Moine rocks of Yell.

Post-Moine sedimentary units
The top of the Moine Supergroup is not observed. Possible outliers of a younger sedimentary sequence are preserved at a few localities within the outcrop of the Loch Eil Group. Isolated occurrences of metamorphosed limestones in glens Scaddle, Dessary and Urquhart (Fig. 4.3) are all preserved in association with intrusive rocks that occupy the cores of major synforms (Rock *et al.* 1984). Limestones are not proven to form part of any Moine succession anywhere else in the Northern Highlands and their tectonostratigraphical affinities arc therefore enigmatic at present. It is possible that they represent stoped blocks of a formerly more continuous sedimentary sequence that once overlay the Moine Supergroup. However, the age of this sequence, and hence whether or not it might correlate with either the Cambro-Ordovician platform succession of the Hebridean terrane or any of several Neoproterozoic limestone-bearing successions exposed east of the Great Glen Fault within the Dalradian Supergroup (see below), is currently unresolved.

Relationship to the 'Torridonian': correlation across the Moine Thrust Zone?
The possibility that the Torridon Group of the Hebridean terrane and the Moine Supergroup could represent essentially the same sedimentary succession foreshortened by Caledonian thrusting was first proposed by Geikie (1893b). The Torridon Group was deposited in a major fluvial system that flowed eastwards (Nicholson 1993) and correlation with the marine Moine sedimentary rocks remains an obvious possibility (Soper & England 1995; Soper *et al.* 1998). The available isotopic data suggest that the two sequences were probably contemporaneous (Turnbull *et al.* 1996). Comparison of detrital zircon suites from the two sequences indicates that while they apparently share similar Proterozoic sources, the Moine rocks contain significantly less Archaean detritus (Friend *et al.* 2003). This may preclude correlation and the two sequences might therefore have accumulated in separate basins on the margin of Laurentia (see also Chapter 3).

Regional metamorphic framework of the Moine Supergroup

Metamorphic grade within the Moine is often difficult to establish because of the aluminium-poor nature of pelitic rocks that has inhibited the formation of Barrovian index minerals. Following the pioneering work of Kennedy (1949), metamorphic grade has been defined in terms of mineral assemblages in calc-silicates (Johnstone *et al.* 1969; Winchester 1974; Tanner 1976; Powell *et al.* 1981; Fettes *et al.* 1985). Published maps of the variation in metamorphic grade within the Moine (Fig. 4.8) are based mainly on the anorthite content of plagioclase, enabling correlation with the metamorphic facies defined by Turner (1981). Metamorphic grade within the Morar Group increases rapidly from the greenschist facies in the west, through the epidote–amphibolite-facies and into a broad belt of low amphibolite-facies metamorphism where rare kyanite appears in pelites and calc-silicates show hornblende ± plagioclase assemblages. A central area of high-grade rocks

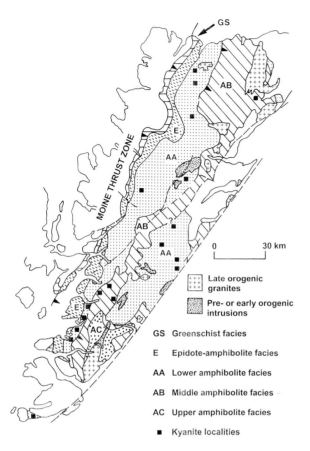

Late orogenic
granites

Pre- or early orogenic
intrusions

GS Greenschist facies

E   Epidote-amphibolite facies

AA Lower amphibolite facies

AB Middle amphibolite facies

AC Upper amphibolite facies

■   Kyanite localities

Fig. 4.8. Metamorphic zones in the Moine of the Northern Highland terrane (modified from Fettes *et al.* 1985).

occupies a narrow north-northeast trending belt, broadly corresponding to the outcrop of the *lit-par-lit* migmatites of the Glenfinnan Group which contain hornblende ± pyroxene–bytownite assemblages in calc-silicates. According to Barr (1985), widespread migmatization was associated with peak metamorphism in the kyanite and sillimanite zones, which gave rise in suitable lithologies to subsolidus, trondhjemitic leucosomes. The western margin of the high-grade belt is broadly coincident with the Sgurr Beag-Naver thrust, consistent with field evidence that regional migmatization of the Glenfinnan Group pre-dated ductile thrusting (e.g. Powell *et al.* 1981; Barr 1985; Strachan & Holdsworth 1988). The eastward decrease in grade into the low amphibolite-facies of the Loch Eil Group is probably a result of the late folding of gently dipping isograds into a broad regional synform, because high-grade Glenfinnan-type migmatites re-emerge locally adjacent to the Great Glen.

The apparent simplicity of the regional metamorphic zonation is, however, illusory since the implication of isotopic studies is that it is composite and polymetamorphic. Isotopic evidence from the SW Moine suggests that Neoproterozoic metamorphism was associated with garnet growth in the Morar Group (Vance *et al.* 1998) and anatexis of the Glenfinnan Group to form the West Highland Granite Gneiss (Friend *et al.* 1997). However, there is no doubt that these early metamorphic events were postdated by widespread recrystallization during the Early Palaeozoic Caledonian orogeny. The high-grade nature of Caledonian metamorphism is indicated by: (1) the manner in which the pyroxene isograd in calc-silcates cuts across early Caledonian ductile thrusts in Inverness-shire (Powell *et al.* 1981); (2) isotopic evidence for widespread

Caledonian migmatization in east Sutherland (Kinny *et al.* 1999); (3) the replacement of contact metamorphic andalusite by kyanite in the vicinity of the *c.* 600 Ma Carn Chuinneag granite in Ross-shire (Wilson & Shepherd 1979); (4) the over-printing of Caledonian lineations by post-kinematic kyanite in west Sutherland (Holdsworth *et al.* 2001); (5) the occurrence in Inverness-shire of locally intense swarms of late- to post-tectonic pegmatites derived from the melting of Moine rocks (e.g. van Breemen *et al.* 1974; Barr 1985; Powell & Glendinning 1988). Conversely, the narrow belt of greenschist-facies metamorphism adjacent to the Moine Thrust Zone (Fig. 4.8) appears to be the result of end-Caledonian retrogression because the diagnostic albite–epidote assemblages in calc-silicates coexist with higher-grade garnetiferous pelites. The complex porphyroblast growth histories deduced for various parts of the Moine (e.g. Brown *et al.* 1970; Tobisch *et al.* 1970; Smith & Harris 1972; MacQueen & Powell 1977) are entirely consistent with a polymetamorphic history, and recent petrological studies have identified evidence for distinct metamorphic episodes (Friend, C. R. L. *et al.* 2000; Zeh & Miller 2001).

Early (*c.* 870 Ma) igneous activity within the Moine Supergroup

The Moine Supergroup was intruded during the mid-Neoproterozoic by igneous rocks which are now thoroughly metamorphosed and deformed and appear to have undergone most, if not all, of the tectonic history of their host rocks. Two main intrusive suites have been identified: a series of metagranites, known collectively as the West Highland Granitic Gneiss, and metabasic rocks of basaltic to gabbroic composition.

West Highland Granite Gneiss

The West Highland Granite Gneiss (Johnstone 1975) comprises a series of separate bodies most of which mainly crop out close to the Glenfinnan Group–Loch Eil Group boundary between Strontian and Glen Doe (Fig. 4.9). In the area east of Loch Quoich and adjacent to the Great Glen Fault at Fort Augustus, granite gneisses occur entirely within the Loch Eil Group. The granite suite is therefore discordant to the regional lithostratigraphy, although contacts with host Moine rocks are invariably concordant at outcrop scale. While sharply defined at some localities, contacts between gneiss and metasedimentary country rock are apparently rapidly transitional at others, especially where the latter are migmatized. The gneiss is a coarsely foliated, microcline–oligoclase–quartz granite with subordinate biotite and local hornblende. Garnet, sillimanite and opaque minerals are important accessories. It carries abundant, sub-concordant quartzofeldspathic lenticles, bordered by biotite selvedges (Fig. 4.6b).

Although Bailey & Maufe (1916) intepreted the augen-gneiss facies of the Ardgour body as a deformed, pre-metamorphic granitic intrusion, the origin of the suite has been controversial. Subsequent workers have variously interpreted the suite as metasomatic (Harry 1953; Dalziel 1963, 1966), magmatic (Mercy 1963) or a tectonically emplaced slice of pre-existing granitic basement (Harris, in discussion of Winchester 1974). More recently, Barr *et al.* (1985) have interpreted the granitic protolith of the gneisses to be a magmatic intrusion formed by anatexis of Moine rocks. This is consistent with the chemistry of the gneisses that have a restricted range of bulk composition with high SiO_2, low Na_2O/K_2O and Fe_2O_3/FeO, an initial $^{87}Sr/^{86}Sr$ ratio of 0.709, and are corundum normative. Other reasons which led Barr *et al.* (1985) to support a magmatic origin for the suite include: (1) the discordance of the suite with the regional lithostratigraphy; (2) the sharpness of contacts

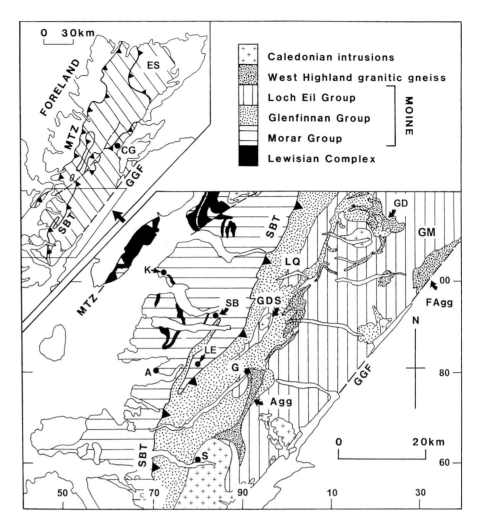

Fig. 4.9. Sketch map of the southern outcrop of the Moine Supergroup (see inset for location) showing the outcrop of the West Highland Granite Gneiss and the location of dated Knoydartian pegmatites at Ardnish (A), Sgurr Breac (SB), Knoydart (K), Loch Eilt (LE) and Carn Gorm (CG). Other abbreviations: G, Glenfinnan; S, Strontian; GD, Glen Doe; GM, Glen Moriston; LQ, Loch Quoich; GDS, Glen Dessary syenite; SBT, Sgurr Beag Thrust; GGF, Great Glen Fault; MTZ, Moine Thrust Zone; ES, East Sutherland; Agg, Ardgour granite gneiss; FAgg, Fort Augustus granite gneiss.

with host metasediments, although some are locally sheeted; (3) the presence of rare inclusions of psammite and hornblende schist, interpreted as xenoliths; (4) the difficulties involved in converting a diverse series of metasediments into a uniform, homogeneous gneiss had its origin been metasomatic.

The granite gneiss suite has assumed critical importance in Moine geology because of isotopic dating that has demonstrated the antiquity both of the suite itself and the host Moine rocks. The results of early isotopic studies were contradictory. A Rb–Sr whole rock isochron of 1028 ± 43 Ma obtained from the Ardgour granite gneiss at Glenfinnan (Brook *et al.* 1976) was interpreted as dating formation of the gneiss during the Grenville orogeny (e.g. Powell *et al.* 1988; Harris & Johnson 1991). However, subsequent U–Pb dating of bulk zircon fractions failed to confirm the Rb–Sr age (Pidgeon & Aftalion 1978; Aftalion & van Breemen 1980). Latterly, dating of individual zircon grains using high-precision TIMS (Thermal Ionization Mass Spectrometry) and SHRIMP (Sensitive High Resolution Ion Microprobe) techniques has yielded more reliable data (Friend *et al.* 1997; Rogers *et al.* 2001). Dating of zircon needles and rims that have overgrown older cores has shown that the granitic protolith of the Ardgour body and its enclosed segregation pegmatites formed at 873 ± 7 Ma, significantly later than the Grenville orogeny (Friend *et al.* 1997). A similar age of 870 ± 30 Ma has been obtained for formation of the granitic protolith of the Fort Augustus granite gneiss (Rogers *et al.* 2001). The data provide a lower age limit for sedimentation of the Moine host rocks that must have occurred prior to *c.* 870 Ma.

Metabasic intrusions

Numerous minor metabasic intrusions occur within the Moine Supergroup (e.g. Winchester 1984; Moorhouse & Moorhouse 1979; Smith 1979; Winchester & Floyd 1983; Rock *et al.* 1985; Millar 1999). They are common within the Glenfinnan and Loch Eil groups but are rare in the Morar Group, except in west Sutherland. The majority are foliated amphibolites or hornblende schists, although metagabbros with relict igneous textures have been recorded locally. Metabasic bodies vary from centimetres to tens of metres thick, and from sheets traceable for several hundred metres to trails of boudins or pods. The largest is the Ben Hope Sill in west Sutherland which is up to 200 m thick and traceable laterally for 15 km. Rock *et al.* (1985) concluded that in the area west of Glen Urquhart (Fig. 4.3), variations in size and fabric are largely a function of country rock competence: metagabbros are mostly confined to host granite gneisses, whereas amphibolite sheets are typical in host psammites, and the smaller, disrupted pods of amphibolite and hornblende schist in host pelites. The original emplacement geometry of the intrusions is difficult to evaluate because of the effects of subsequent ductile deformation. The dominance of concordant or only slightly discordant contacts in some areas of low tectonic strain (e.g. Loch Eil) suggests that here the intrusions were emplaced mainly as dilational sills. In contrast, amphibolites within the Glenfinnan Group rocks on the Ross of Mull (Fig. 4.6c) are often discordant (Holdsworth *et al.* 1987) and may therefore have been emplaced as dykes. In the case of the Ben Hope Sill, it appears to have been intruded along the stratigraphic Moine–basement boundary

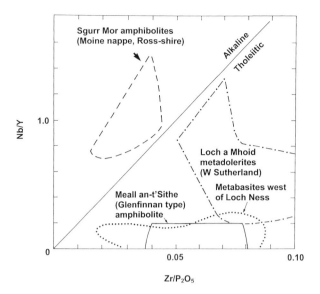

Fig. 4.10. Zr/P_2O_5–Nb/Y plot showing the tholeiitic affinities of the majority of metabasic rocks within the Moine Supergroup (modified from Rock *et al.* 1985).

(Holdsworth 1989). It is generally assumed that the metabasic rocks belong to a single suite: only rarely has the existence of two suites been demonstrated on the basis of cross-cutting relationships (e.g. Rock *et al.* 1985; Millar 1999).

Metabasic rocks throughout the Northern Highlands display a tholeiitic chemistry comparable with modern mid-ocean ridge basalts (Fig. 4.10; Moorhouse & Moorhouse 1979; Winchester 1984; Winchester & Floyd 1983; Rock *et al.* 1985; Millar 1999). Differentiation trends show characteristic strong Fe and Ti enrichment and depletion in Cr and Ni. Metagabbros in the Glen Doe area show more evolved compositions due to contamination with host granite gneiss (Millar 1999). Although it is clear that the metabasic rocks were not emplaced within an oceanic setting *sensu stricto*, since the host Moine rocks were deposited on Archaean basement, the chemistry is also consistent with intrusion into thinned continental crust during extension and rifting. The only isotopic data pertaining to the age of magmatic crystallization of any member of the suite is that of Millar (1999) who obtained a U–Pb zircon age of 873 ± 6 Ma from a metagabbro that intrudes the West Highland Granite Gneiss in Glen Doe (Fig. 4.9). This is very similar to the age obtained for emplacement of the granitic protolith to the Ardgour Granite Gneiss (Friend *et al.* 1997). Provided that the Ardgour and Glen Doe granite gneiss bodies are essentially of the same age, the available data indicate that the two igneous suites must have been emplaced within 13 Ma (the maximum combined error on the two age determinations).

Was the Moine Supergroup affected by Neoproterozoic orogenic activity?

The nature of Neoproterozoic tectonothermal activity within the Moine Supergroup is a highly contentious and unresolved issue. The current debate is focused on whether or not the Moine rocks were affected by one or more orogenic events in the period between *c.* 870 Ma and *c.* 790 Ma.

Origin and significance of the West Highland Granite Gneiss

Barr *et al.* (1985) argued that the granite gneisses were syn-orogenic and formed during regional migmatization, melting and D1 isoclinal folding of the Moine. In support of this, they

drew attention to the absence of a thermal aureole adjacent to the granite gneiss bodies, which implied to them that the country rocks were already at elevated temperatures when the granites were emplaced. Furthermore, they showed that the migmatitic leucosomes within the granite gneisses locally cross-cut the S1 gneissic fabric which must therefore have developed during this high-grade event which was subsequently dated at *c.* 870 Ma by Friend *et al.* (1997).

In contrast, Soper (1994*a*), Soper & Harris (1997), Millar (1999) and Dalziel & Soper (2001) have suggested that the granitic protolith of the gneiss was formed during crustal extension, development of the Moine sedimentary basin(s), and emplacement of the regional metabasic suite. Soper & Harris (1997) and Dalziel & Soper (2001) cite field observations from Glen Moriston and Glen Doe (Fig. 4.10) where the granite gneisses and cross-cutting metabasic sheets have apparently both been affected by all the deformation events recorded in the host Moine rocks. In their view: (1) there is no evidence that there was any regional deformation or metamorphism of the host Moine rocks either prior to or during the emplacement of the protoliths of the granite gneisses, and (2) it is thus quite feasible that all the observed tectonic structures formed during the Caledonian orogeny.

Ryan & Soper (2001) envisage that emplacement of meta-basic intrusions at depth provided sufficient heat to locally melt both the underlying basement and Moine sediments to produce granitic melts that migrated up through the sedimentary pile to their present locations. However, in the absence of reliable *P–T* data to constrain the conditions of melting, the origin of the granitic protoliths, the age of their gneissification, and hence the nature of the *c.* 870 Ma tectonothermal event remain equivocal.

Evidence for a Knoydartian orogeny at *c.* 800 Ma

Rather firmer evidence exists for a younger orogenic event at *c.* 800 Ma. The first indications that the Moine rocks were metamorphosed during the Precambrian were provided by Giletti *et al.* (1961) who dated muscovites from deformed segregation pegmatites at Knoydart and Sgurr Breac (Fig. 4.9). Rb–Sr ages of 690–750 Ma were interpreted as the likely age of early metamorphism of the Moine rocks. Further isotopic dating of these pegmatites and others at Loch Eilt, Carn Gorm and Ardnish (Fig. 4.9) yielded Rb–Sr muscovite ages of *c.* 650–776 Ma (Long & Lambert 1963; van Breemen *et al.* 1974, 1978; Powell *et al.* 1983). The younger of these ages are of uncertain significance because they probably reflect partial resetting of the Rb–Sr system during Caledonian metamorphism (van Breemen *et al.* 1974, 1978). More reliable constraints on pegmatite crystallization were obtained from U–Pb analyses of bulk fractions of monazite and zircon that are less susceptible to resetting. Analyses of monazites for the Sgurr Breac pegmatite were concordant at 780 ± 10 Ma whereas discordant zircon data gave an upper intercept age of 815 ± 30 Ma; zircons from the Loch Eilt pegmatite were also discordant giving an upper intercept age of 740 ± 30 Ma (van Breemen *et al.* 1974, 1978). The pegmatites were thought to have been produced during a regional amphibolite-facies event termed the Knoydartian (Bowes 1968*a*) or Morarian (Lambert 1969) orogeny.

Latterly, Hyslop (1992) has confirmed, on the basis of integrated field and geochemical studies, that pegmatites at Carn Gorm, Knoydart, Sgurr Breac and Ardnish formed essentially *in situ* in localized zones of high strain and melt generation during post-D1 metamorphism at garnet grade and higher. U–Pb analyses of single monazite grains from pegmatites have yielded precise ages of 827 ± 2 Ma (Ardnish pegmatite at Sloch, Fig. 4.6d) and 784 ± 1 Ma (Sgurr Breac pegmatite) (Rogers *et al.* 1998). Sm–Nd ages of *c.* 820–790 Ma obtained from post-D1 Morar Group garnets apparently date the early metamorphism (Vance *et al.* 1998; Fig. 4.6e). The peak pressures of 12.5–14.5 kbar and temperatures of *c.* 650–700°C obtained from the dated garnets (Vance *et al.* 1998) are indicative of crustal thickening. Rb–Sr muscovite ages of *c.* 750 Ma obtained from a range of pegmatites and meta-morphic units in the Northern Highlands are interpreted to date post-metamorphic cooling (Piasecki & van Breemen 1983; Piasecki 1984; Hyslop 1992; Rogers *et al.* 1998). However, various workers have continued to question the reality of a Knoydartian orogenic event, asserting that the pegmatites pre-date any regional deformation and were emplaced during crustal extension and episodic melting of the Moine sedimen-tary pile (Soper & Harris 1997; Dalziel & Soper 2001).

Summary

The reality of a *c.* 800 Ma Knoydartian tectonothermal event within the Northern Highland terrane is now fully established although its significance is still being debated. The current balance of evidence favours the interpretation that the Kno-dartian event is related to orogeny and crustal thickening (Tanner & Bluck 1999). The earliest metamorphic events and D1 isoclinal folding, including the nappe-scale interleaving of Moine rocks and the basement inliers of Glenelg and Morar (Fig. 4.3; Ramsay 1958; Powell 1974) are therefore likely to be Precambrian. The D1 isoclinal folds in the western Moine were originally believed to close and face eastwards away from the Caledonian foreland (Powell 1974). However, it is now clear that these folds have highly curvilinear hinges and probably root from the south or southeast (Soper *et al.* 1998).

The wider tectonic significance of a Knoydartian orogenic event is uncertain at present, partly because Neoproterozoic orogenesis has not been identified in related parts of the Laurentian craton (e.g. east Greenland, northwest Newfound-land) with which northern Scotland is thought to have been contiguous at that time (Soper 1994*b*). A possible solution to this problem is that the Moine Supergroup and its associated basement are an 'exotic' fragment of either the Baltica or Amazonian cratons (see Fig. 4.2) where Neoproterozoic oro-genic events have been recorded (Bluck *et al.* 1997). If correct, this would rule out any correlation of the basement inliers with the Lewisian Complex of the Hebridean terrane.

Late Neoproterozoic augen granites in the Moine Supergroup

The Moine rocks of Ross-shire and Sutherland were intruded by a distinctive suite of granites during the late Neoproterozoic. These include the Carn Chuinneag–Inchbae granite within the Morar Group rocks of Ross-shire, and granite sheets within the east Sutherland Moine (Fig. 4.3). These have yielded U–Pb zircon ages of 611 ± 11 Ma (Inchbae granite), 599 ± 9 Ma and 588 ± 8 Ma (east Sutherland granites) (Kinny, Strachan & Rogers, unpublished data). The Carn Chuinneag intrusion includes a distinctive riebeckite gneiss, minor amphibolites and hybrid rocks formed by the mingling of coexisting acid and basic magmas (Peach *et al.* 1912). All the granites were strongly deformed during the Caledonian orogeny and carry a coarse augen fabric (Fig. 4.6f). The preservation within the contact aureole of the Carn Chuinneag granite of delicate sedimentary structures, including ripple cross-lamination, small slump folds and sedimentary dykelets still normal to bedding appears to rule out a pervasive pre-granite deformation in the Morar Group country rocks (Peach *et al.* 1912; Soper & Harris 1997). If the evidence obtained from the SW Moine in support of a Knoydartian orogeny is correct, the Carn Chuinneag-Inchbae granite must lie within an area of low Knoydartian strain. The tectonic setting of late Neoproterozoic granitic magmatism in

the Northern Highland terrane is uncertain at present. In the context of evidence for contemporaneous anorogenic, bimodal magmatism in the Appalachians and the Norwegian Caledo-nides as a result of the breakup of Rodinia (Bingen *et al.* 1998), the augen granites in Northern Scotland may have resulted from processes related to continental rifting (see also discussion below of the Older Granite suite). Granites form important parts of some rift-related igneous suites in zones of Mesozoic and Cenozoic crustal extension (e.g. Gust *et al.* 1985; Davies & MacDonald 1987).

The Grampian Terrane

Late Neoproterozoic continental break-up and deposition of the Dalradian Supergroup

The break-up of the supercontinent Rodinia during the late Neoproterozoic led to the formation of the Iapetus Ocean (Fig. 4.11; Soper 1994*b*). Extensive passive margin sedimentary sequences were deposited along the eastern side of Laurentia during a prolonged period of continental rifting and ocean widening which lasted possibly from *c.* 650 Ma until the Early Ordovician. Within NW Scotland, this rifting history is re-corded by two separate successions. The first is a thick sequence of deformed and metamorphosed late Neoproterozoic to Lower Ordovician shallow- and deep-water sediments and volcanics, the Dalradian Supergroup of the Grampian Highlands and Shetland (Figs 4.12, 4.13). The Dalradian Supergroup is similar in age to the Fleur de Lys Supergroup in Newfoundland (Ken-nedy 1975) and the Eleonore Bay Supergroup in east Greenland (Soper 1994*b*). The second is the Cambro-Ordovician shelf succession of the Hebridean terrane (see Chapter 3) that can also be correlated with very similar sequences in east Green-land (Higgins *et al.* 2001) and NW Newfoundland (Swett 1969). The Cambrian-Ordovician and Dalradian rocks and their correlatives formed two subparallel sedimentary belts located along the eastern margin of Laurentia, with the shelfal

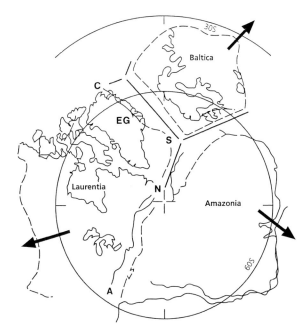

Fig. 4.11. Reconstruction of Baltica, Amazonia and Laurentia in the late Neoproterozoic; A–C, western margin of Appalachian–Caledonian orogen; S, Scotland; EG, East Greenland; N, Newfoundland; arrows indicate directions of relative movement of continental blocks during rifting and opening of the Iapetus Ocean (modified from Soper 1994*b*).

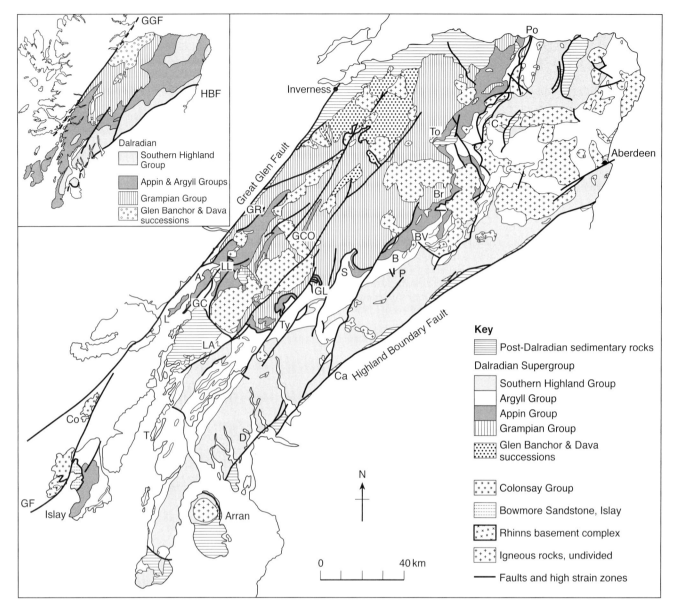

Fig. 4.12. Map showing the distribution of the Dalradian Supergroup and its subdivisions in the Grampian Highlands and Inner Hebrides. A, Appin; B, Blair Atholl; Br, Braemar; BV, Ben Vuirich; C, Cabrach; Ca, Callander; Co, Colonsay; D, Dunoon; GC, Glen Creran; GCO, Geal Charn–Ossian Steep Belt; GF, Gruinart Fault; GL, Glen Lyon; GR, Glen Roy; L, Lismore; LA, Loch Avich; LL, Loch Leven; P, Pitlochry; Po, Portsoy; S, Schiehallion; T, Tayvallich; To, Tomintoul; Ty, Tyndrum. Modified from Stephenson & Gould (1995) with permission of the British Geological Survey.

Cambro-Ordovician rocks lying on the landward side of the generally deeper water Dalradian-type lithologies. These two sedimentary belts are now in much closer proximity due to the effects of crustal shortening during the Caledonian orogeny. Oceanic crust is presumed to have existed to the southeast of the present Dalradian outcrop.

One of the key unresolved issues is the nature of the crust or basement that was stretched and rifted to form the basins into which the Dalradian Supergroup was deposited. Basement rocks within the Grampian terrane are mostly poorly exposed and fault-bounded. Their tectono-stratigraphical affinities are unclear and compounded by frequent tectonic reworking of key contacts with adjacent strata. Remote methods utilizing the inherited geochemical characteristics of igneous intrusions, and crustal-scale geophysical modelling provide a useful framework but are generally non-diagnostic. A number of different basement types are present within the Grampian terrane and it is appropriate to discuss these before dealing with the basin evolution and stratigraphy of the Dalradian Supergroup.

Pre-Dalradian basement within the Grampian terrane

Palaeoproterozoic basement: the Rhinns Complex

Formerly believed to be part of the Lewisian Complex, Palaeoproterozoic basement rocks, known collectively as the Rhinns Complex, crop out between the Great Glen and Loch Gruinart faults in the Colonsay–west Islay block (Figs 4.1, 4.12). The Rhinns Complex is dominated by syenitic gneisses that were affected by deformation and amphibolite-facies metamorphism prior to the intrusion of gabbro sheets. The syenites and gabbros are characterized by major and trace element patterns similar to igneous rocks generated in subduction-related magmatic arcs (Muir *et al.* 1994a). Both consist dominantly of juvenile material derived from a depleted mantle source at *c.* 1.8 Ga (Muir 1990; Daly *et al.* 1991a). U–Pb zircon ages obtained from syenites on Islay (1782 ± 5 Ma; Marcantonio *et al.* 1988) and Inishtrahull (1779 ± 3 Ma; Daly *et al.* 1991a) are interpreted as crystallization ages. An ^{40}Ar/^{39}Ar hornblende age of *c.* 1710 Ma obtained from a gabbro at

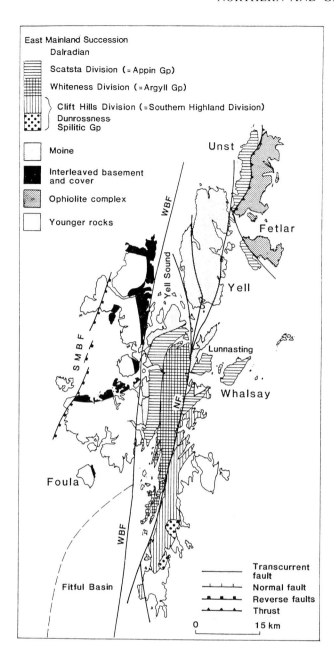

East Mainland Succession

Dalradian

▤ Scatsta Division (= Appin Gp)

▦ Whiteness Division (= Argyll Gp)

Clift Hills Division (= Southern Highland Division)
Dunrossness
Spilitic Gp

☐ Moine

■ Interleaved basement and cover

▨ Ophiolite complex

☐ Younger rocks

Unst

Fetlar

WBF

Yell Sound

Yell

Lunnasting

Whalsay

S M B F

NF

Foula

WBF

Fitful Basin

──── Transcurrent fault
─┼─┼─ Normal fault
─■─■─ Reverse faults
─▲─▲─ Thrust

0   15 km

Fig. 4.13. Map showing the distribution of the Dalradian Supergroup on Shetland (after Flinn 1985). SMBF, St Magnus Bay Fault; WBF, Walls Boundary Fault; NF, Nesting Fault.

Inishtrahull is thought to date cooling following metamorphism (Roddick & Max 1983). The Rhinns Complex is apparently part of an extensive tract of juvenile Palaeoproterozoic crust that includes the Ketilidian belt of southern Greenland and the Gothian belt of Scandinavia (Chapter 3; Park, A. F. 1991; Park, R. G. 1994; Nironen 1997).

The isotopic signatures of Caledonian granites and rare inclusions in Tertiary dykes across the Grampian terrane are consistent with derivation, at least in part, from juvenile Proterozoic crust at depth (Dickin & Bowes 1991; Upton *et al.* 1998). For this reason, it seems likely that the Rhinns Complex or similar rock units form the basement on which much of the Dalradian and older sedimentary rocks were deposited. Unmodified stratigraphical contacts are not, however, preserved between the Rhinns Complex and any younger metasedimentary strata (see below). Combined regional gravity

and magnetic evidence indicate the presence of a distinctively different (non-Rhinnean?) low density, high magnetic basement under the Midland Valley of Scotland extending beneath much of the Dalradian of Perthshire. Highly magnetic basement also underlies much of the NE Grampian (Buchan) region (Rollin 1994, and see Chapter 1).

The Dava and Glen Banchor successions of the Central Highlands: Moine rocks east of the Great Glen Fault?
Southeast of the Great Glen Fault, the stratigraphically and structurally oldest known strata within the Central Highlands comprise thoroughly recrystallized, mainly gneissose and locally migmatitic psammite and semi-pelite with subordinate quartzite. These metasedimentary rocks, formerly referred to as the 'Younger Moines', Central Highland Division (Piasecki 1980) or the Central Highland Migmatite Complex (British Geological Survey 1999*a*; Highton 1999) resemble parts of the Moine Supergroup, notably the Glenfinnan Group (Piasecki 1980). In the absence of sedimentary structures, and by contrast with the Moine Supergroup, an internal stratigraphy has not been identified while the stratigraphical, metamorphic, isotopic and structural relationships between these rocks and the overlying Dalradian rocks of the Grampian Group remains the subject of considerable debate (Piasecki 1980; Harris *et al.* 1994).

In the Glen Banchor and Kincraig districts (Fig. 4.14) these strata occur in the cores of large-scale antiformal structures and are informally termed the Glen Banchor succession (Robertson & Smith 1999; Smith *et al.* 1999). Further north, comparable strata are assigned to the Dava succession (Smith *et al.* 1999) and cover *c.* 90 km^2 bound in part by ductile shear zones (Fig. 4.14). In broad terms, the Dava and Glen Banchor successions comprise a structurally lower unit of banded psammite (Fig. 4.15a), micaceous psammite and subordinate semi-pelite, and an upper, invariably sheared, unit of more varied lithologies including quartzite, arkosic and micaceous psammite and schistose banded semi-pelite. The lithological assemblages and accessory mineral content are consistent with deposition in shallow marine environments. The ages of detrital zircon grains from a sample of the Dava Succession show that the provenance area for the sedimentary protolith included crustal fragments of Palaeoproterozoic and Grenville age (Highton *et al.* 1999).

Isotopic evidence for a Knoydartian event in the Central Highlands. In recent years, a significant body of isotopic evidence has accumulated that indicates that the Glen Banchor and Dava successions were affected by an early Neoproterozoic tectonothermal event at *c.* 840–800 Ma. A U–Pb zircon age of 840 ± 11 Ma obtained from kyanite-grade gneisses of the Dava Succession has been interpreted as dating migmatization (Highton *et al.* 1999). This regional high-grade event was post-dated by development of a series of ductile shear zones, known collectively as the Grampian Shear Zone. These can be traced discontinuously throughout the Glen Banchor and Kincraig inliers and largely delimit the Dava Succession (Fig. 4.14). Individual shear zones are up to several tens of metres wide and are characterized by intense grainsize reduction and destruction of pre-existing gneissose and migmatitic foliations, attenuation of minor folds, porphyroblastesis and muscovitization. Published kinematic indicators suggest a mainly top-to-the-N or NE sense of shear (Piasecki 1980; Piasecki & Temperley 1988*a*; Hyslop & Piasecki 1999). The shear zones have been variously interpreted to represent deformation of an unconformity between basement and (Dalradian) cover (Piasecki 1980), a zone of tectonic interleaving (with nappe scale thrusts) between Dalradian and a migmatite complex (Highton 1992; Hyslop &

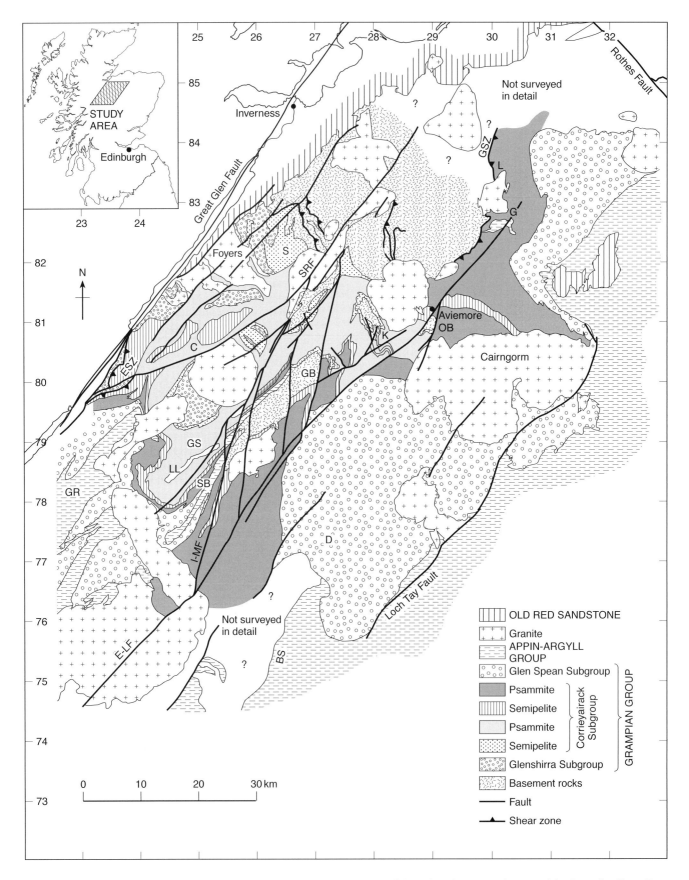

Fig. 4.14. Simplified geological map of the Central Highlands showing distribution of the main subgroups and extent of the Grampian Shear Zone. BS, Boundary Slide; C, Corrieyairick; D, Drumochter; ESZ, Eilrig Shear Zone; E-LF, Ericht–Laidon Fault; G, Grantown-on-Spey; GB, Glen Banchor; GR, Glen Roy; GS, Glenshirra Dome; I-MF, Inverpattack–Markie Fault; K, Kincraig; L, Lochindorb; LL, Loch Laggan; OB, Ord Ban; S, Strathnairn; SB, Geal Charn-Ossian Steep Belt; SRF, Sronlairig Fault (modified from Smith *et al.* 1999).

Fig. 4.15. (a) Folded gneissose psammite of the Glen Banchor succession, Kincraig (BGS photograph D5124); **(b)** A'Bhuidheanaich pegmatite, Kincraig. Mylonitic pegmatite with feldspar augen from the Grampian Shear Zone dated at *c.* 804 Ma (BGS photograph D5123; coin is 1.5 cm in diameter); **(c)** cross-bedded and convolute laminated psammite with feldspar porphyroclasts in the Glenshirra Subgroup (BGS photograph PS18573; lens cap 7 cm in diameter); **(d)** ripple laminated and lensoid quartzose laminated psammite and semi-pelite overlain by massive psammite; note development of minor faults from ripple crests, Strathtummel succession, River Garry section (BGS photograph PS18572).

Piasecki 1999), and a zone of distributed shear located entirely within the Glen Banchor and Dava successions (Smith *et al.* 1999). The latter view is adopted here.

Many of the shear zones incorporate a distinctive suite of syntectonic, mylonitic granitic pegmatite and quartz veins (Piasecki 1980; Piasecki & van Breemen 1979, 1983; Hyslop 1992; Hyslop & Piasecki 1999). U–Pb analyses of monazites from mylonitic pegmatites at A'Bhuideanaich (Fig. 4.15b) and Lochindorb have provided ages of, respectively, 808 + 11/-9 Ma and 806 ± 3 Ma (Noble *et al.* 1996). Monazites from the matrix of the mylonitic gneiss hosting the Lochindorb pegmatite yielded a concordant age of 804 + 13/-12 Ma (Noble *et al.* 1996). These ages confirm that pegmatite formation was contemporaneous with recrystallization and mineral growth in the host mylonitic gneisses at *c.* 806 Ma.

The *c.* 840–800 Ma isotopic ages reported from the Dava and Glen Banchor successions are interpreted to record orogenic activity that has been correlated with the Knoydartian event recognized within the Moine Supergroup (Highton *et al.* 1999). Younger Rb–Sr ages ranging from *c.* 700 to 500 Ma (Piasecki 1980; Piasecki & van Breemen 1983) are now thought to result from variable resetting of isotopic systems during the Caledonian orogeny (Hyslop & Piasecki 1999). It is emphasized that isotopic evidence for a Precambrian (Knoydartian) tectonothermal event is restricted to the Glen Banchor and Dava successions and their mylonitic derivatives: the overlying Dalradian rocks of the Grampian Group record only Caledonian mineral ages.

Relationship with the Grampian Group Dalradian: a cover-basement boundary? In contrast to the Dava and Glen Banchor successions, there is no isotopic evidence for Precambrian tectonothermal activity in the Grampian Group or higher parts of the Dalradian Supergroup. Only Caledonian events are known in these rocks that show an apparently consistent and unbroken pattern of structural facing throughout the Grampian terrane as far as the Highland Border (Treagus 1999; Rose & Harris 2000, Harris & Lindsay, unpublished data). If the Glen Banchor and Dava successions record the effects of an early Neoproterozoic tectonothermal event, whereas the overlying Dalradian rocks record only Caledonian events, then a major orogenic unconformity may exist at or near the base of the Grampian Group. However, identification of this break is fraught with difficulty and has been the subject of much debate and controversy. Piasecki (1980), Piasecki & van Breeman (1979, 1983) and Piasecki & Temperley (1988a) suggested that a major orogenic break was located at or near the base of the Grampian Group. Their evidence was based upon the apparent structural and metamorphic contrasts between an older crystalline basement (essentially the Glen Banchor and Dava successions) that experienced amphibolite-facies migmatization, gneissification and deformation prior to the deposition of a Grampian Group cover sequence. The lines of evidence presented by Piasecki and co-workers have been questioned, partly because it is now evident that the distribution and development of gneissose and migmatitic textures in all rocks is largely compositionally controlled and cannot be used as a discriminant between cover and basement. Thus, during peak metamorphic (amphibolite-facies) conditions, semi-pelite and compositionally suitable psammite of not only the Glen Banchor and Dava successions but also of the Grampian, Appin and Argyll groups may preserve such textures.

Recent BGS mapping has thrown further light on the nature of this boundary. Critical localities in Glen Banchor, Speyside and Lochindorb areas are largely unaffected by intense Caledonian deformation and present map-scale unconformable and overstep relationships of Grampian and Appin group rocks onto the Glen Banchor and Dava successions (Smith *et al.* 1999; Robertson & Smith 1999; BGS unpublished data 2000). This provides fresh evidence for a significant stratigraphical break near the base of the Grampian Group. It is evident that rocks of the Glen Banchor and Dava successions are invariably intensely recrystallized, do not preserve sedimentary structures, and commonly contain intrafolial isoclinal folds that deform the first foliation (usually a gneissosity). In contrast, the overlying Grampian Group rocks are variably recrystallized, structurally less complex, and commonly preserve sedimentary structures. The first foliation, usually a schistosity, deforms bedding. These observations provide support for the original hypothesis of Piasecki and suggest a stratigraphical and structural break at the base of the Grampian Group. However, where both successions are migmatitic or highly deformed this difference is often difficult to detect. The failure of regional metamorphic studies (Phillips *et al.* 1999) to provide evidence of a break may result from the intensity of the Caledonian amphibolite facies overprint and the likelihood that the Glen Banchor and Dava successions, if already dehydrated during an earlier metamorphic event, would have been essentially unreactive (e.g. Yardley & Valley 1997).

The above stratigraphical and structural observations coupled with the isotopic data cumulatively indicate that the Dava and Glen Banchor successions could be interpreted as a metasedimentary basement that was affected by a Knoydartian orogenic event prior to deposition of the overlying Grampian Group. Following the original proposals of Piasecki, it may therefore be appropriate to assign the Glen Banchor and Dava successions to the Moine Supergroup. Further geochemical, provenance and structural studies are required to refine and confirm this model.

Rocks of uncertain affinity: Colonsay Group and Bowmore Sandstone

The Colonsay Group is well exposed on Colonsay and the Rhinns of Islay (Fig. 4.12). It consists of a 5.5–6 km succession of strongly deformed, unfossiliferous, siliciclastic sediments with minor limestone. The oldest part of the group is exposed on Islay where it is inferred to have had an unconformable relationship with the adjacent Rhinns Complex basement. The contact between the Colonsay Group and the basement is a 3–4 m wide mylonite zone that cuts discordantly across lithological boundaries in both units (Fitches & Maltman 1984). The mylonite zone cuts eastwards up the Colonsay Group stratigraphy resulting in an apparent onlap relationship involving the five lowest units seen, and an unknown thickness of the original sequence may therefore be missing. Stewart & Hackman (1973) and Bentley (1988) interpreted the lowest 500 km of the sequence on Islay as deltaic, passing upwards to turbidites. These become increasingly distal as the succession youngs onto Colonsay, possibly reflecting basin deepening. Thereafter, on Colonsay, the turbidites appear to pass up into shallow marine sediments with the topmost units possibly reflecting the onset of renewed deepening. However, Bentley (1988) suggested that the changes identified on the present erosion surface may reflect an oblique, not a vertical cut, through a succession

deposited in a small intracratonic basin. Thus, at least part of the palaeoenvironmental variation may be an artefact. The Colonsay Group cannot be related with any confidence to stratigraphical successions deposited in the wider more extensive Grampian, Appin or Argyll Group basins. On Islay, a fault-bounded succession of feldspathic and coarse-grained sandstones termed the Bowmore Sandstone (Fig. 4.12) is of uncertain stratigraphical affinity. It has been variously correlated with the Moine, the Torridonian and the Dalradian (Grampian and Argyll groups) (Stephenson & Gould 1995). Both the Colonsay Group and the Bowmore Sandstone are thought to have been deformed and metamorphosed during the Ordovician Grampian event.

Stratigraphy and basin evolution of the Dalradian Supergroup

The Dalradian sediments were deposited as a well-differentiated sequence of marine sands, silts, muds and limestones and are readily divided into the Grampian, Appin, Argyll and Southern Highland groups (Harris *et al.* 1978, 1994, Stephenson & Gould 1995; Figs 4.12, 4.16, 4.17). The apparent total thickness of the Dalradian succession is at least 25 km, although it is improbable that the complete vertical thickness was ever deposited at one place. It is more likely that depocentres migrated southeastwards with time. Although the groups are essentially lithostratigraphical units, they approximate to chronostratigraphical units. The columns in Figure 4.17 illustrate that, whereas the formations within the Dalradian succession may be only of local significance, correlation at subgroup level can be sustained over large parts of the depositional area. A number of events that were broadly synchronous on the scale of the Grampian terrane are recognizable; for example, periods of glaciation and rift-related magmatism marked by the Port Askaig Tillite and large volumes of basic volcanic rock in the Argyll Group (Figs 4.16, 4.17) respectively. These key events permit widespread correlation along a 280 km strike length, and the conclusions about the disposition of the older basins and the history of their fill described below complete a picture of basin evolution, some aspects of which have been known for 30 years or more.

Regionally, much of the Dalradian succession has been affected only by low- to medium-grade metamorphism and is not strongly deformed, with the result that its sedimentological history, former basin architecture and the controlling influence of long-lived faults can be deduced. Lithostratigraphical, sedimentological and tectonic studies indicate periods of basin deepening and shallowing which, by analogy with Phanerozoic basins, may correspond to multiple periods of lithospheric stretching, rifting and thermal subsidence (Fig. 4.16). Thickness and facies changes in the upper parts of the Grampian Group and overstep onto older strata constrain basin margins within the Grampian and Lower Appin groups (Glover *et al.* 1995; Goodman *et al.* 1997; Smith *et al.* 1999; Robertson & Smith 1999). In the southwest Highlands, Knill (1963), Borradaile (1979), Litherland (1980) and Anderton (1985) indicated very rapid lateral facies and thickness changes in the Appin and lower parts of the Argyll groups that implied that rapid syndepositional faulting accommodated the deposition of the essentially shallow-water shelf deposits.

Grampian Group

The Grampian Group records the initiation of middle to late Neoproterozoic extension and basin development. The main outcrops are restricted to the Central Highlands (Fig. 4.12) and possible correlatives are also present on the north Grampian coast and on the islands of Shetland (Fig. 4.13) and Islay. Three main lithofacies associations are recognized, and interpreted

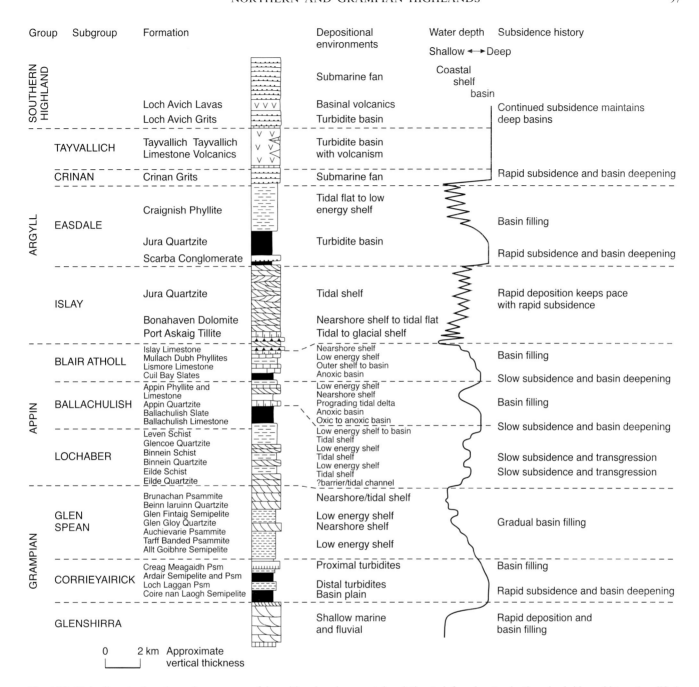

Fig. 4.16. Dalradian stratigraphy and a summary of depositional environments in relation to inferred water depth and subsidence history (modified from Anderton 1985, and Strachan & Holdsworth 2000). The names of the individual formations within the subgroups are mostly derived from the southwest Highlands.

to represent distinct phases of early and syn-rift extension followed by a protracted period of post-rift thermal subsidence. Within the main outcrop, deposition occurred within a series of rift basins bound by major crustal lineaments (Fig. 4.18; Glover & Winchester 1989; Smith *et al.* 1999). Despite pervasive regional deformation and metamorphism to amphibolite-facies conditions, the stratigraphical integrity and overall geometry of these basins has apparently been preserved largely intact. At present, only the Corrieyairack Basin (Fig. 4.18) is known in detail whilst the adjacent Cromdale and Strath Tummel basins are the subject of ongoing research.

Glenshirra Subgroup. The base to the Grampian Group is not exposed. The oldest exposed unit is the Glenshirra Subgroup (Figs 4.14, 4.16, 4.17) that is nowhere in primary undisturbed contact with the underlying Glen Banchor or Dava succession rocks. With a maximum exposed thickness of *c.* 2 km, the Glenshirra Subgroup comprises stacked shoaling sequences of geochemically distinct, immature arkosic psammite and metaconglomerate. The metaconglomerates thicken, up to tens of metres, and increase in abundance both up-section and up-dip towards the Great Glen Fault. Magnetite-rich mineral seams and abundant sedimentary structures including convolute lamination, trough cross-bedding (Fig. 4.15c), ripple lamination and rare hummocky cross-stratification indicate deposition by traction currents in shallow marine environments subject to storms. Parts of the subgroup may represent fluvial deposits. The progressive westward thickening and coarsening of the strata combined with pebble compositions (mainly granite and vein quartz with rare amphibolite, psammite and

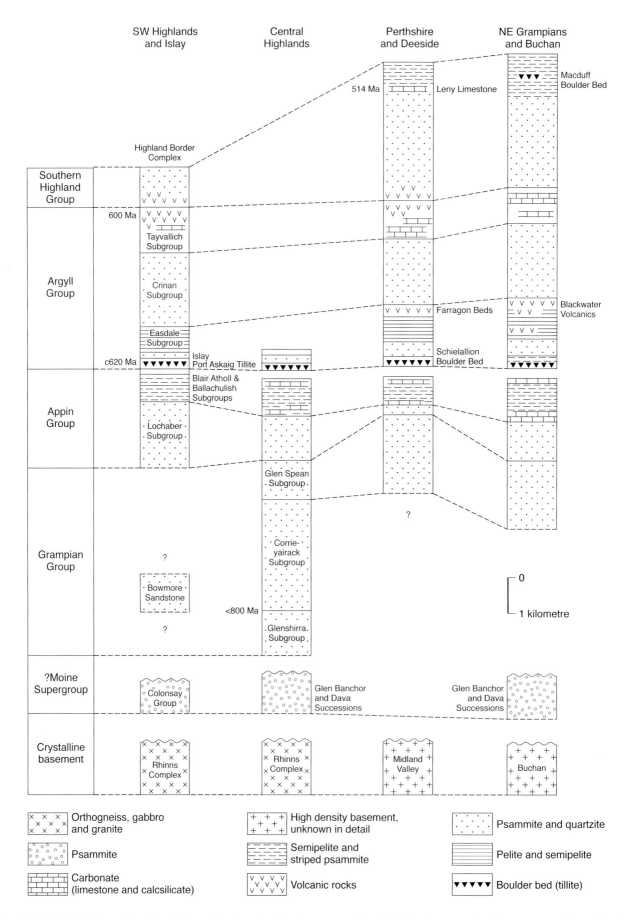

Fig. 4.17. Simplified lithostratigraphical columns for the Dalradian Supergroup of Scotland showing general relationships, question marks denote uncertainty (modified from Harris *et al.* 1994). Thicknesses are approximate and key age constraints are shown.

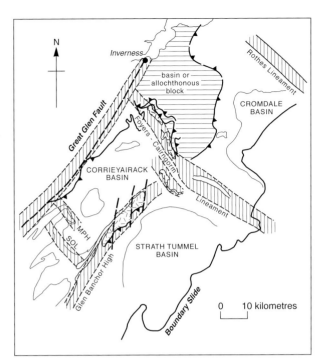

Fig. 4.18. Rift basins and their bounding lineaments in the Grampian Group of the Central Highlands (after Smith *et al.* 1999). MPH, Meall Ptarmigan High; SOL, Strath Ossian Lineament.

quartzite) imply the presence of a basin margin to the west or northwest behind which lay an exposed hinterland of quartzo-feldspathic gneiss and granitic rock. Possible source regions include the Rhinns Complex of Islay or older Proterozoic rocks of Laurentia.

Corrieyairick Subgroup. Within the Corrieyairack and Strath-nairn districts, the Glenshirra rocks are abruptly but conformably overlain by a distinctive and regionally widespread succession of semipelite and striped semipelite and psammite. This marks the base of the overlying Corrieyairack Subgroup (Figs 4.14, 4.16, 4.17) and records a basin-wide flooding event heralding the start of a period of widespread subsidence and rift-related extension. Locally (e.g. Ord Ban, Kincraig), a heterogeneous succession of muscovite-rich semipelite interbedded with calc-silicate rocks, thin quartzite and metacarbonate marks the local base to the Corrieyairack Subgroup. These rocks, previously assigned to the Ord Ban Subgroup (Winchester & Glover 1988) probably represent a condensed basin margin facies reflecting deposition on, or adjacent to, an uplifting high. Comparable lithologies near Grantown-on-Spey, previously of uncertain stratigraphical affinity (McIntyre 1951; Highton 1999), show a distinctly different lithogeochemical signature (BGS unpublished data) and are more likely of Lower Appin Group age as originally proposed by Harris & Pitcher (1975).

Within the western Corrieyairack Basin, a nearly complete rift sequence is preserved. The basal semipelitic strata (Coire nan Laogh Semipelite Formation) are overlain by 4–5 km of siliciclastic deposits (Loch Laggan Psammite Formation) deposited by prograding turbidite complexes. Variations in sediment supply and source area are indicated by changes in plagioclase and K-feldspar abundance, whereas variations in bed thickness and form reflect depositional processes. Bouma sequences are well represented in turbidites within the main depocentre around Loch Laggan.

The overlying Ardair Semipelite Formation records a reduction in sand supply and development of shelf conditions along the basin margins as recorded by the lateral facies change into striped semipelite and psammite. A renewed influx of sand-dominated turbidites (Creag Meagaidh Psammite Formation) was deposited in extensive turbidite fan-lobe systems derived from the northwest, passing south and eastwards in the Glen Roy and Drumochter areas into shelf environments (Glover & Winchester 1989). Rapid local facies and thickness variations indicate contemporary tectonism and together with the progressive overstep onto an interbasin high in the Glen Banchor area, they permit the tracing of outlines of former basin margins (Glover & Winchester 1989; Robertson & Smith 1999).

Glen Spean Subgroup. The turbiditic rocks of the uppermost Corrieyairick Subgroup are conformably overlain by shallow-marine sedimentary rocks of the Glen Spean Subgroup (Fig. 4.14) that prograded into the basin from the NW and SE. Reduced subsidence and relative tectonic stability at this time are interpreted to represent post-rift thermal subsidence (Glover *et al.* 1995). Deposits of the Glen Spean Subgroup dominate the upper 2–3 km of exposed Grampian Group strata that make up the Cromdale and Strath Tummel basins. In the latter basin, geophysical modelling indicates significant thicknesses of older strata at depth (Smith *et al.* 1999). The lithological associations of the Glen Spean Subgroup, combined with well-preserved sedimentary structures (Fig. 4.15d), indicate deposition in shallow-marine shelf environments (Fig. 4.16). These shelf areas were subject to tidal influences and sea-level fluctuations that resulted in extensive reworking of the underlying turbiditic rocks. Locally, spectacular heavy mineral concentrations of zircon, apatite and magnetite are preserved and give rise to distinctive regional stream-sediment geochemical anomaly patterns. Glen Spean strata in the southern and eastern margin of the Corrieyairack Basin show complex diachronous and lateral facies relationships with the younger formations of the Corrieyairack Subgroup (Key *et al.* 1997). Similar relationships have been recognized recently in the Drumochter area. Farther north, psammites and quartzites of the Glen Spean Subgroup are well represented in the northern Cromdale Basin and also form a thick succession of originally channel-dominated quartz sands along the Banff coast.

Appin Group
The Appin Group crops out throughout the Grampian terrane in a broad zone from the type area in the southwest to the north Grampian coast and Shetland. It also occurs in narrow fold hinges in the Central Highlands both in the Glen Roy area, where it represents an extension of the Lochaber stratigraphy, and further to the east in an outlier in the Geal Charn–Ossian Steep Belt. The Appin Group comprises three subgroups (Figs 4.16, 4.17) whose constituent formations can be correlated confidently throughout a 280 km strike length, despite significant lateral facies and thickness variations and local unconformities. This lateral persistence suggests that consistency in sediment supply and processes of deposition within low energy, open marine to lagoonal environments were widespread under a regime of progressive lithospheric stretching (Anderton 1985). Syn-sedimentary growth faults, first identified in the Glen Creran–Loch Leven district (Fig. 4.19), are thought to dominate basin architectures within a series of NE–SW trending basins (Hickman 1975; Litherland 1980). However, at both the local and regional scales, many problems of correlation remain to be resolved as evidenced by past confusion over the identification of the Ballachulish and Blair Atholl subgroup rocks and the relationship between the Lochaber Subgroup and the Grampian Group, as discussed below.

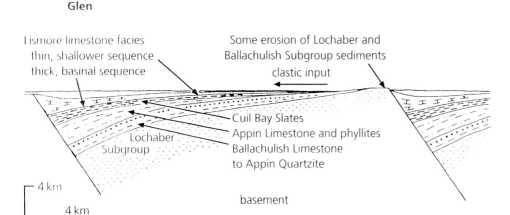

Fig. 4.19. A tectonic cross-section for the Lochaber to Lismore area during deposition of the upper Appin Group (see Fig. 4.12 for location; after Anderton 1985).

Lochaber Subgroup. The basal Lochaber Subgroup records a period of transitional change as the siliciclastic-dominated basin fills of the Grampian Group gradually gave way to widespread deep-water mud and carbonate sedimentation typical of the Ballachulish and Blair Atholl subgroups (Fig. 4.16). Modern regional geochemical (Stone *et al.* 1999*b*), provenance and petrographic data permit a division of the Lochaber Subgroup into two units and support the need for a revision of the subgroup lithostratigraphy. The basal psammites, quartzites and pelites show close affinity with the Grampian Group, whereas the uppermost Leven Schist Formation is comparable with the overlying Ballachulish Subgroup.

The presently defined Lochaber Subgroup with a maximum aggregate thickness of 4.2 km, is represented everywhere by alternating successions of siliceous psammite and quartzite with minor semipelite, pelite and, in its highest beds, rare metacarbonate units. These strata record the continuation of relatively shallow marine conditions from Grampian Group times with the established earlier depocentres continuing to exert a strong influence. The base of the Lochaber Subgroup is diachronous and marked by a marine transgression (Fig. 4.16) and thus shows considerable lateral facies variations along its crop with an overall decrease in thickness to the southwest. In the Central and Southwest Highlands it conformably succeeds the Grampian Group. However, along the main outcrop south of the Cairngorms, this relationship is obscured by the Boundary Slide.

Within the Central Highlands around Glen Roy, the coastal deposits of the upper part of the Grampian Group are succeeded by tidally-dominated, white to light grey, fine- to medium-grained and generally poorly bedded quartzites (Glover *et al.* 1995, Key *et al.* 1997). Farther east, within generally deeper water environments there are complex facies variations both laterally and temporally as these quartzites and associated psammites in turn pass into semipelite (Key *et al.* 1997). Transitional passages into psammites indicate that Grampian Group shelf deposition also continued locally. In the Loch Leven area, the offshore sediments are interbedded with quartzites that thicken to the southwest (e.g. Glencoe quartzite). They are interpreted to represent nearshore tidal sediments extending away from a coastline to the north reflecting periodic basin shoaling events (Glover & McKie 1996). In the Geal Charn–Ossian Steep Belt, comparable sedimentary rocks underlie the glacial Kinlochlaggan Boulder Bed (Treagus 1969, 1981; Evans & Tanner 1996).

Within Central Perthshire, the Lochaber Subgroup comprises highly tectonized slates and schistose semipelite. Recognition of the component formations is hampered by condensed sequences, attenuation and excision along the Boundary Slide and other tectonic breaks. In contrast, north of the Cairngorm Granite, lithofacies are more variable: thin, cleaved calcareous semipelite thicken northeastwards into flaggy micaceous psammite and quartzite. The establishment of local lagoonal environments with marine chemically precipitated limestones is marked by thin muddy metacarbonate beds in the upper parts of several formations (Thomas 1989).

A period of renewed rifting with a gradual deepening and widespread marine transgression marks the upper part of the Lochaber Subgroup (Fig. 4.16) and is recorded by the Leven Schist Formation. In the Central and Southwest Highlands this distinctive unit comprises more than 1 km of laminated pale grey schistose pelite but elsewhere is thin or absent reflecting the developing basin geometry. The Leven Schist Formation is significantly less feldspathic than typical Grampian Group pelites, and has a distinctly different whole-rock chemistry and provenance (Stone *et al.* 1999*b*). In places, significant stratigraphical excision associated with footwall uplift brings the Leven Schist to rest unconformably on the upper parts of the Grampian Group. In the Loch Leven area (Glover 1993) and within and adjacent to the Geal Charn–Ossian Steep Belt, over 1200 m of strata are locally absent (Glover *et al.* 1995, Robertson & Smith 1999).

Ballachulish and Blair Atholl subgroups. As clastic input into the basins waned, the overlying Ballachulish Subgroup sediments record the progressive development of extensive shallow-shelf, tidally influenced sedimentation and anoxic lagoonal environments (Anderton 1985). This change in environment is reflected in a change in lithology to tremolitic calc-silicate rocks with dolomitic and pure calcic limestones (e.g. Ballachulish Limestone Formation), interbanded with graphitic and pyritiferous slates (e.g. Ballachulish Slate Formation). Lithostratigraphical subdivision of the Ballachulish Subgroup can be traced with remarkable continuity from Islay to Banffshire, attesting to widespread stability and relatively uniform subsidence at this time.

Above the Ballachulish Slate Formation, local uplift is reflected by the stratigraphical excision and sporadic distribution of the upward coarsening, deltaically-influenced Appin Quartzite (Fig. 4.16; Litherland 1980). The Appin Quartzite, a locally pebbly quartzite with abundant cross-bedding, can be traced discontinuously northeastwards from its type area to the Central Highlands and Perthshire where it forms a thick and distinctive mappable unit. Farther north it thins rapidly and is absent on the Moray–Buchan coast section. A return to interbedded semipelite, calc-silicate rock and limestone deposition (the Appin Limestone and Phyllite formations) indicates renewed transgression. In the Geal Charn–Ossian Steep Belt, as a result of a combination of non-deposition and erosion on a longstanding footwall 'high', these formations overstep underlying Appin Group lithologies and the entire Grampian Group to rest directly on the Glen Banchor succession (Robertson & Smith 1999).

The Blair Atholl Subgroup marks the continued diversification of lithologies and a change to deeper, poorly oxygenated marine conditions (Fig. 4.16). Complete sequences are present in the Schiehallion, Blair Atholl and Appin–Lismore districts. In the type area, the basal slates and phyllites are in stratigraphical continuity with the underlying Ballachulish Subgroup. However, whilst the dark graphitic pelite–limestone associations typical of the underlying strata continue, successions differ locally (Goodman *et al.* 1997). This may indicate deposition in a series of smaller basins with thinning and lateral facies changes into more semipelitic flags and argillaceous limestones along the basin margins. A distinctive 'pale group' (Smith & Harris 1976) marks the top of the subgroup in the Central Highlands and elsewhere (e.g. Islay and NE Grampians) banded semipelites, phyllites, micaceous psammites and dolostones are characteristic. With an aggregate thickness of up to 1 km individual limestone formations are laterally persistent, contain oolites, stromatolites and lenticles of chert, and in the southwest typically form into limestone–slate cycles. Associated slump folds and intra-formational breccias may indicate instabilities along basin margins. Some hints of volcaniclastic detritus and minor tuff horizons are also recorded in the Tomintoul area.

Argyll Group

Argyll Group rocks are differentiated on the basis of lithology and environment into four subgroups (Figs 4.16, 4.17). The group records the onset of renewed instability with the widespread shallow marine conditions of the Appin Group replaced by cycles of rapid basin deepening. Variable lithofacies and locally thick formations indicate that sediment input kept pace with extension within a series of northeast-trending basins. The main outcrops extend from the Southwest Highlands to the Banff coast and Shetland and include beds of volcanic rocks and volcaniclastic sedimentary rocks. In Perthshire, these strata host economically significant stratabound exhalative sulphide and bedded baryte mineralization (see Chapter 16).

Islay Subgroup. In contrast to the distinctive successions of black pelite, graphitic and tremolitic metacarbonate rock and quartzite of the underlying Appin Group, the Islay Subgroup is dominated by psammite and quartzite lithologies that record a phase of basin deepening. The base of the subgroup is marked by one of the most obvious and readily recognized lithostratigraphical units within the Dalradian succession, a marine tillite or 'boulder bed' termed the Port Askaig Tillite Formation (Plate 5; Spencer 1971). The same unit in Perthshire is known as the Schiehallion Boulder Bed (Fig. 4.17). Being of glacial origin and therefore the product of, in geological terms, a relatively brief episode and everywhere succeeded by thick sequences (up to 9 km) of remarkably pure quartzite (e.g. the Islay/Jura Quartzite of the Inner Hebrides, the Schiehallion Quartzite of Perthshire and the Durnhill Quartzite of Banffshire), this tillite and its associated dolomitic strata are of immense lithostrati-

graphical and chronological value throughout the Irish and Scottish Dalradian. In Shetland, the absence of a tillite and matching stratigraphies at this level hampers effective Appin Group/Argyll Group boundary correlations with the mainland Dalradian successions.

The tillite, with up to 47 individual beds identified (Spencer 1971), is essentially a sequence of sandstone, siltstone and conglomerate. Varved siltstones with probable dropstones are thought to have been derived from floating ice possibly brought in from the southeast. Clast compositions in the lower parts are dominated by Appin Group lithologies but in the upper parts are subsumed by extrabasinal granitoids and gneissose granite (Fitches *et al.* 1990). The exact age of the tillite is unknown and the long accepted correlation with the Varangerian tillites of Norway (c. 630–590 Ma, Gorokhov *et al.* 2001) has been recently questioned by Prave (1999) and Brasier & Shields (2000) in favour of a Sturtian (c. 720 Ma) age.

The succeeding warm-water Bonahaven Dolomite or 'cap dolomite' includes sandstones, pelites and impure dolomitic rocks with stromatolites (Spencer & Spencer 1972; Fairchild 1980, 1985). The overlying Jura Quartzite is a massive fine- to medium-grained cross-bedded quartzite with conglomerate beds, limestone and pelite towards the base. Well exposed in the southwest, the formation dies out northeastwards before reappearing in the Schiehallion and Perthshire districts. This absence may indicate a basin margin in the vicinity of the Etive Granite Complex (Etive lineament?). North of Braemar and further into the northeast Grampians, correlations (Durnhill Quartzite Formation) locally are less certain in detail with interdigitating sequences of semipelite, pelite, limestone and dolostone. Minor basic tuff bands and pillow lavas have been recognized immediately below the tillite.

Easdale Subgroup. The base of the Easdale Subgroup is marked by a wide range of generally finer-grained lithologies including black graphitic pelite, and semipelite commonly associated with pebbly quartzite and sheets of basic meta-igneous rock of varying abundance, and indicate a phase of renewed rapid deepening (Fig. 4.16). Important facies changes between Islay, Loch Leven and Perthshire indicate that, in contrast to the Appin Group, deposition occurred within more discrete fault-bounded basins (Fig. 4.20) subject to periodic influxes of coarse-grained mass flow and turbiditic sediment.

The contact with the Islay Subgroup is not everywhere clearly defined. Towards the west, the first lithology to appear in the subgroup is a pebbly quartzite (the Scarba Conglomerate or Carn Mairg pebbly facies). However, in central Perthshire, 2–3 kilometres of strata comprising a mixed assemblage of schistose semipelitic lithologies, some graphitic, and with locally significant pebbly quartzite (Killiecrankie Schist) intervene between the top of the white Schiehallion (Jura) Quartzite and the main crop of the Carn Mairg pebbly quartzites. These are followed in turn by black pelites that have only localized incursions of pebbly quartzite. Towards Braemar and Tomintoul, the pebbly quartzites are essentially absent, their place being taken by semipelitic lithologies, while, at Portsoy, thick pelites, some of which are graphitic, are present. These variations could be interpreted as a trend, with fining from west to east and northeast while mafic volcanism probably occurred locally in Perthshire. They emphasize the uncertainties in the identification of the base of the Easdale Subgroup that may be most appropriately marked by the upward disappearance of the white quartzite facies.

The continuous tracing of the subgroup from the SW Highlands through Perthshire to the northeast is facilitated by a distinctive sequence of micaceous and garnetiferous schistose semipelite, feldspathic, locally pebbly, quartzite and graphitic

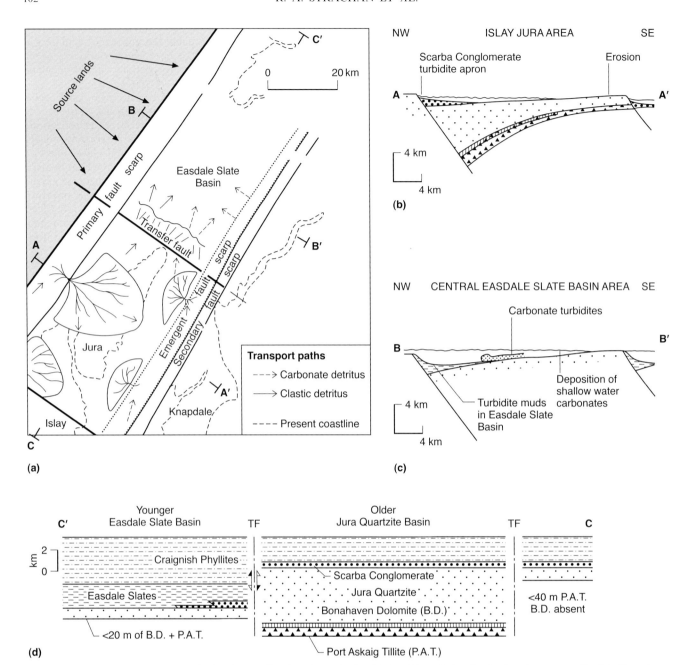

Fig. 4.20. (**a**) Suggested palaeogeography for the Argyll seaboard area in the vicinity of Jura during Scarba Conglomerate to Easdale Slate times, showing location of submarine fans and directions of sediment transport; (**b, c**) tectonic cross-sections for early Easdale Subgroup times, see (a) for locations of sections; (**d**) NE–SW longitudinal section of the Islay and Easdale subgroups in the area of map (a) showing how movement along transfer faults can account for thickness variations (the latter shown schematically)(from Strachan & Holdsworth 2000, modified from Anderton 1985).

pelite (Easdale Slate, Killiecrankie Schist, Carn Mairg Quartzite, Ben Eagach Schist, Ben Lawers Schist). Within this succession, exhalative saline brines gave rise to a laterally persistent bed of stratabound sulphide, baryte and vein mineralization near the top of the Ben Eagach Schist (Chapter 16; Stephenson & Gould 1995).

The topmost strata of the Easdale Subgroup are marked by greater uniformity as the Craignish Phyllite Formation, characterized by calcareous pelite with subordinate limestone and quartzite, can be recognized throughout the whole basin. The first indications of a developing major volcanic episode are heralded in Perthshire by the Farragon Beds (Fig. 4.17; Sturt 1961) and in the Cabrach area by the Blackwater Formation (Fig. 4.17) that includes mafic and ultramafic pillowed lavas interbedded with psammite and semipelite (Goodman & Winchester 1993; Fettes *et al.* 1991).

Crinan and Tayvallich subgroups. Individually thick formations and deep water turbiditic facies characterize the Crinan Subgroup (Figs 4.16, 4.17). The very coarse-grained basal Crinan Grit facies with its more siliceous equivalent, the Erins Quartzite, gives way eastwards to finer-grained micaceous semipelite (Ben Lui and Stonefield Schist formations). In the northeast, as the metamorphic grade increases, these strata locally are prone to migmatization as indicated by the Cowhythe gneisses of Banffshire, the Inzie Head gneisses of Buchan and the Duchray Hill Gneiss of Central Perthshire. Volcanic activity is not widespread but in the Tyndrum–Glen Lyon area dolomitic and magnesite schists with nickel and chrome testify to the erosion of ultramafic ophiolitic rocks (Fortey & Smith 1986; Power & Pirrie 2000).

The overlying Tayvallich Subgroup (Figs 4.16, 4.17) is dominated by carbonates, locally accompanied by thick extrusive

Fig. 4.21. Deformed pillow lavas of the Tayvallich Subgroup, Point of Rubha na Cille, Tayvallich Peninsula (BGS photograph PO34372).

mafic volcanic rocks and sub-volcanic sills marking perhaps for the first time rupturing of the continental crust during rifting. At its type locality, a change and reduction of sediment source occurs as the coarse siliceous Crinan Grits give way to massive carbonate beds with dispersed clastic carbonate containing siliciclastic material. Intervening beds of graphitic pelite are common, while upwards the sequence is intercalated with concordant mafic sheets that may represent high-level sill complexes. On the northwest coast of the Tayvallich peninsula and Loch Avich area, these submarine sills can be seen to have broken through the limestones to breach the water/sediment interface, pillowing in the topmost, unconsolidated sediments and the overlying water (Fig. 4.21). The younger limestone beds comprise several irregular layers of volcanic debris, including fragments of pillows, set in a carbonate matrix. Ash fall tuffs suggest that volcanism evolved upwards into a subaerial environment. Felsic tuffs within the Tayvallich Volcanic Formation have been dated at 601 ± 4 Ma (U–Pb zircon, Dempster *et al.* 2002). Rapid lateral variations in facies and thickness associated with unconformities, overstep relations and pebbly beds typify this part of the succession.

In its type area, the Tayvallich Volcanic Formation includes the glacial Loch na Cille Boulder Bed that has also been recognized in Donegal (Condon & Prave 2000). This potentially important stratigraphical marker unit may correlate with the *c.* 620–590 Ma Varangerian tillites of Norway (Condon & Prave 2000) if the Port Askaig Tillite proves to be Sturtian in age. Prave (1999) and Alsop *et al.* (2000) have pointed to the presence within the boulder bed of cleaved clasts of metsedimentary rock with up to two deformational fabrics; they suggest that these may represent the results of the erosion of an older (Moine?) metamorphic source.

The Tayvallich Limestone Formation and its correlatives usually mark the top of the Tayvallich Subgroup and the base of the Southern Highland Group. In the far southwest and in Banffshire this calcareous unit is poorly represented and replaced by psammites. It is recognized widely in Scotland and Ireland and is thought to extend into Shetland as the Laxfirth Limestone, the youngest limestone of the Shetland Dalradian. Variation in the thickness of the limestone and intercalations of semipelite and graphitic schist indicate deposition by low density turbidity currents, with beds of schistose amphibolite marking the continuation of volcanic activity, probably located to the southwest.

Southern Highland Group

The top of the known Dalradian succession is marked by a *c.* 4 km pile of coarse-grained turbiditic sedimentary and volcaniclastic strata lying immediately above the Tayvallich/Loch Tay Limestone and termed the Southern Highland Group (Figs 4.16, 4.17). These sediments mark a return to rapid basin deepening which persistently stayed ahead of the sedimentary and volcanic fill and was probably sourced from the north and northwest. Much of the outcrop of the Southern Highland Group lies in the inverted limb of a major Caledonian fold known as the Tay Nappe (see below) and is severely deformed. Thus over much of its crop, lateral correlation and evidence for the original nature of its sediments and bedforms is obscured by tectonic strain and compounded by a lack of reliable marker bands (Harris & Fettes 1972; Mendum & Fettes 1985; Rose & Harris 2000). However, in the cores of major synforms in Banffshire and Argyllshire, and in a strip up to 5 km wide along the Highland Border (i.e. at the highest structural levels in the Tay Nappe complex), the original nature of the deposits is best preserved.

As described by Harris *et al.* (1976, 1978), Anderton (1980, 1985) and BGS (unpublished data 2001), the metagreywackes are typically coarse-grained, poorly sorted, graded, turbiditic sandstones, commonly composite, with minor silty beds, carring graded and ripple lamination. Pelitic facies (slates and phyllites) typical of the lower parts are probably diachronous and thin limestones are preserved locally in the Dunoon area. The coarse-grained sediments were probably laid down in slope apron or ramp settings with channels on the lower slopes and inner zones of deep-water submarine fans with the finer sediments being laid down as overbank deposits or as outer fan facies. The bases of the coarser sandstones commonly display large saucer-shaped loadcasts. Some of the channels are manifestly asymmetrical with steep banks occasionally showing evidence that slumps collapsed into the channels. The sub-rounded to subangular clasts in the coarse-grained sedimentary rocks are of quartz, K-feldspar, and sparse muscovite and chlorite. Interbedded and gradational with the metasediments are a series of distinctive units rich in chlorite and epidote and termed the Green Beds. These units, most prevalent in the lowermost 1 km, essentially comprise a mixture of siliciclastic and basic igneous detritus in varying proportions. They are interpreted as recording, in part, the erosion of the underlying basic volcanics, but may also result from contemporaneous volcanism in the hinterland.

Information critical to the biostratigraphical age of the highest preserved parts of the Southern Highland Group is preserved in the Callander area (Fig. 4.12; Tanner 1995). Tanner concluded that two units of black slate with thin chert bands and subordinate grey limestone lie within a newly established Keltie Water Grit Formation that is transitional over several tens of metres stratigraphically downwards into grits of the Southern Highland Group. He traced the more persistent of these slate units from the Keltie Water to Leny Quarry where they appear to be in stratigraphical and structural continuity with the Leny Limestone that contains topmost Lower Cambrian *Pagetia* trilobites (Fig. 4.17; Pringle 1940; Stubblefield 1956; Cowie *et al.* 1972; Rushton & Owen 1999). This sequence is discussed further in Chapter 5.

The youngest sedimentary rocks of the Buchan area (Macduff Slate Formation) comprise thin-bedded turbidites displaying Bouma sequences, turbidite fan channels filled with coarse, poorly-sorted pebble arenites, and mudstones with slump units. Within the Formation, the Macduff Boulder Bed contains exotic, extra-basinal ice-rafted clasts up to a metre in diameter (Plate 6; Sutton & Watson 1956*a*; Trewin 1987*d*; Stoker *et al.* 1999). A sample of the Macduff Slates has yielded a possible Lower Ordovician acritarch (Molyneux 1998).

Age and stratigraphical continuity of the Dalradian Supergroup

Age constraints on the initiation of Dalradian sedimentation are poor. The Grampian Group must be younger than the *c*. 800 Ma pegmatites in the Glen Banchor and Dava successions. How much younger is conjectural at present. Sr/Sr whole rock isotope data from Grampian Group metacarbonate rocks at Kincraig (BGS unpublished data 2000) yield values consistent with the global late Neoproterozoic (Vendian) strontium sea-water signature younger than 800 Ma and possibly as young as *c*. 670 Ma. If the latter were to be correct, this would conflict with the proposed correlation of the Port Askaig Tillite with tillites of the Sturtian glaciation dated at *c*. 720 Ma (Brasier & Shields 2000; Condon & Prave 2000) but support correlation with the Varangerian tillites of Norway at 620–590 Ma (Gorokhov *et al.* 2001).

The time span represented by the Dalradian succession could be over 300 Ma if the base of the Grampian Group is *c*. 800 Ma *and* the Early Ordovician age for the Macduff Slate Formation proves robust. On the other hand, if the base of the Grampian Group is as young as *c*. 670 Ma and the late Early Cambrian age of the Leny Limestone proves to be a more reliable indicator of the age of the uppermost part of the Dalradian, then the time span of the succession is reduced to 150 Ma. It has been generally assumed that the Dalradian succession is broadly continuous and no conclusive evidence has yet been produced for any major breaks. The succession has long been interpreted to represent the result of a prolonged period of continental rifting that culminated in development of the Iapetus Ocean (Fig. 4.22; Anderton 1985). The structural continuity of the succession certainly appears to rule out any regional orogenic unconformity. Nevertheless, the presence of undetected stratigraphic breaks or periods of non-deposition in the Dalradian succession cannot be precluded (Prave 1999; Alsop *et al.* 2000; Dempster *et al.* 2002).

Significance of the 'Older Granite' suite

A series of deformed and metamorphosed granites intrude the Dalradian rocks near Pitlochry in Perthshire (Fig. 4.12) where they form part of the 'Older Granite' suite of Barrow (1893). Traditionally grouped with the Older Granites are small sheets of augen granite in the Portsoy area in Aberdeenshire (Fig. 4.12). These granites mainly comprise K-feldspar, plagio-clase, biotite and quartz and have been interpreted as S-type, crustal melts. The results of U–Pb zircon dating show that the Ben Vuirich granite in Perthshire was emplaced at 590 ± 2 Ma (Rogers, G. *et al* 1989), the Portsoy granite at 600 ± 3 Ma and the Keith granite at 601 ± 4 Ma (J. Mendum pers. comm.). These granites are therefore broadly similar in age to the Carn Chuinneag–Inchbae and east Sutherland augen granites that intrude the Moine Supergroup (see above). Other deformed granites in Perthshire have only been dated using the less reliable Rb–Sr whole rock system, but nonetheless may form part of the 'Older Granite' suite (e.g. the Glen Clova–Rough Craig granite, 549 ± 44 Ma (Robertson 1994)).

The structural setting of the Ben Vuirich granite has been controversial. The granite was formerly thought to have been emplaced after the main D2 nappe folding in the host Dalradian rocks (Bradbury *et al.* 1976). The *c*. 590 Ma U–Pb zircon age provided by Rogers, G. *et al.* (1989) was therefore thought to indicate that regional D1 and D2 deformation events must have occurred during a previously unrecognized Neoproterozoic orogeny. However, subsequent studies revealed that the granite was emplaced prior to regional D2 deformation, and that the early 'D1' fabric present within the contact metamorphic aureole represents bedding modified by intrusion-related deformation (Tanner & Leslie 1994; Tanner 1996). This permits the main nappe-scale folding and associated regional metamorphism of the Dalradian to be reassigned to an Early Palaeozoic Grampian event (see below).

Tanner (1996) concluded that the Ben Vuirich granite was emplaced during continental rifting and Dalradian sedimentation. The contact metamorphic assemblages (cordierite and andalusite) within the aureole of the granite indicated emplacement at 7–14 km depth, consistent with an estimated overburden of *c*. 9 km of Argyll Group sediments (Tanner 1996, see also Ahmed-Said & Tanner 2000, and discussion in Dempster *et al.* 2002). A rift-related origin for the Portsoy and Keith granites also seems very likely given that they are precisely the same age as the Tayvallich Volcanic Formation.

Mid-Ordovician orogenic activity: the Grampian event

In the Cambrian and Early Ordovician, the Laurentian margin in northern Scotland consisted of a shallow-water carbonate shelf that probably passed southeastwards into the deep marine

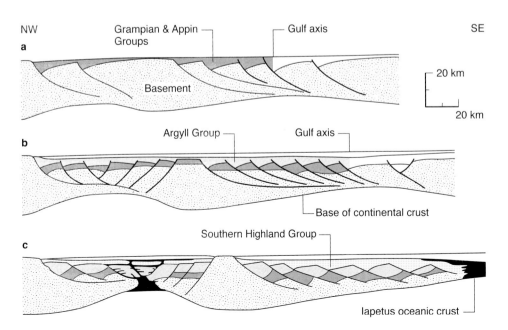

Fig. 4.22. Schematic cross-sections to show the progressive development of the rifted Laurentian margin in Scotland in (**a**) late Appin Group times; (**b**) Crinan Subgroup (Argyll Group) times, and (**c**) Southern Highland Group times (modified from Anderton 1985). Basaltic intrusions and volcanic rocks (in black) in (c) only.

turbidite basins of the Southern Highland Group (Fig. 4.22). Sedimentation was halted in the Mid Ordovician by the Grampian orogenic event (Lambert & McKerrow 1976; Soper *et al.* 1999). A possible model for the Grampian event in Scotland involves convergence of the Laurentian continental margin with an intra-oceanic subduction zone and a volcanic arc that developed during closure of the Iapetus Ocean (Fig. 4.23). Parts of this arc are exposed in western Ireland (Dewey & Ryan 1990), and there is indirect evidence that such an arc is buried beneath the post-Grampian sedimentary cover in the Midland Valley of Scotland (Bluck 1983, 1984). Collision of the Laurentian margin with the arc is thought to have resulted in overthrusting of an exotic ophiolite nappe, and regional deformation and Barrovian metamorphism of the Dalradian and Moine rocks (Fig. 4.23; Dewey & Shackleton 1984; Dewey & Ryan 1990). A remnant of this exotic nappe is thought to be preserved in Unst, NE Shetland where a substantial ophiolite slice structurally overlies Dalradian rocks. Other ophiolites along the Highland Border and at Ballantrae may also have been obducted at this time (see Chapter 5). A similar tectonic model has been proposed for early Mid-Ordovician orogeny in the Appalachians of eastern North America, where the Taconic event resulted from the thrusting of major ophiolite nappes onto the Laurentian margin during arc-continent collision (Dewey & Shackleton 1984). In North America (e.g. Newfoundland) the ophiolites are preserved as thrust klippe that overlie Cambro-Ordovician shelf carbonates similar to those

exposed on the Caledonian foreland in northwest Scotland. It therefore seems likely that in the Appalachians, ophiolites must have originally overlain a large part of the orogenic belt but have now been largely removed by erosion. Such a scenario may be equally valid for the Grampian and Northern Highland terranes in Scotland.

Grampian regional deformation of the Dalradian Supergroup
The Grampian event affected all of the Dalradian and older rocks of the Grampian Terrane. Peak deformation culminated in the formation of major fold stacks or nappe complexes and associated zones of attenuation with individual fold traces extending for hundreds of kilometres. The lateral persistence of the Dalradian lithostratigraphy described above precludes large-scale thrusting at the present erosion level. Later deformation phases record the final uplift, collapse and extension of the orogenic pile. Subsequent more brittle deformation may have been associated with the Silurian Scandian event recorded mainly by the rocks of the Northern Highland Terrane (see below).

Remarkably, the identification and spatial distribution of the major folds has survived essentially intact with only minor modification since the original descriptions of Bailey (1910*b*, 1922, 1934). However, reconstructing the evolution of this event remains a challenging task. The non-orthogonal nature of the collision resulted in the diachronous development of structures and associated tectono-metamorphic fabrics across

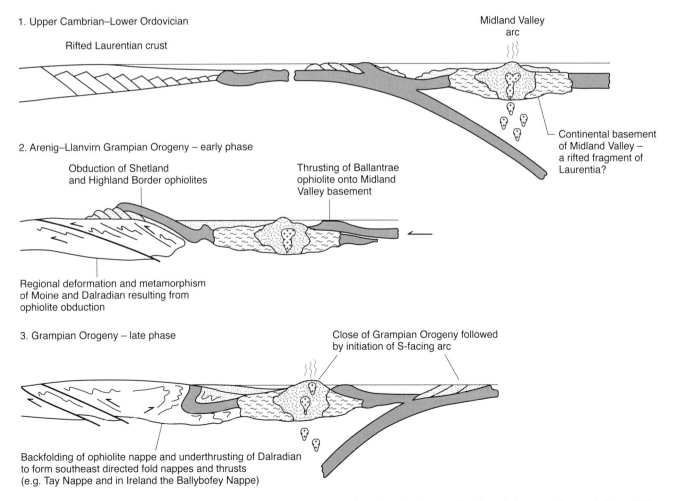

Fig. 4.23. A possible tectonic model for the Grampian event in Scotland (from Strachan 2000, with acknowledgment to Dewey & Ryan 1990). See text for discussion.

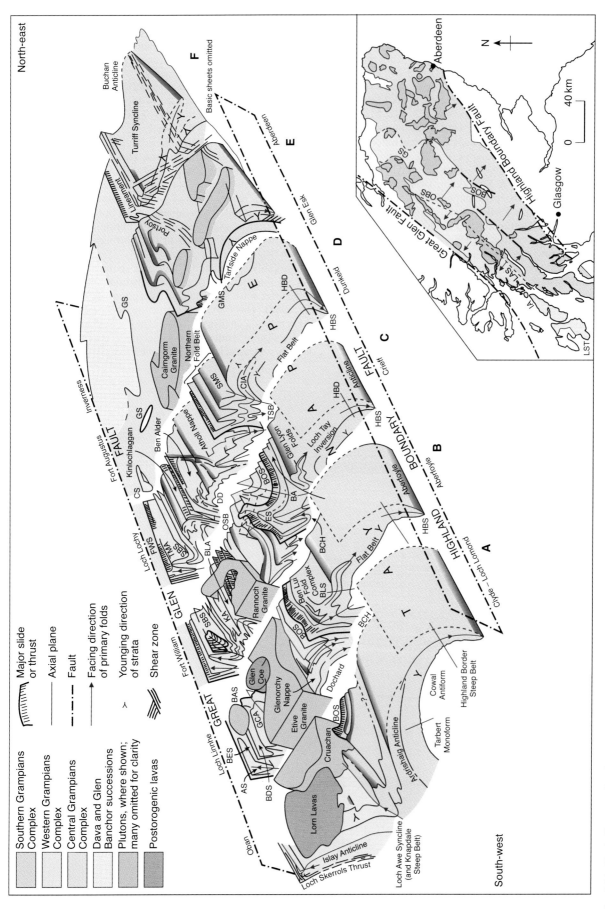

Fig. 4.24. Block diagram of major structures in the Grampian Highlands, reproduced from Stephenson & Gould (1995) with permission of the British Geological Survey. Brittle faults and minor intrusions are not shown. Sections A, B, C and D are from Thomas (1979). AS, Appin Syncline; BA, Bohespic Antiform; BCH, Beinn a Chuallaich Folds; BAS, Ballachulish Slide; BDS, Beinn Don Syncline; BES, Benderloch Slide; BLA, Beinn na Lap Synform; BLS, Ben Lawers Synform; BOS, Boundary Slide; CIA, Creag na h'Iolaire Anticline; CS, Corrieyairick Syncline; DD, Drummochter Dome; ES, Errochty Synform; FWS, Fort William Slide; GCA, Glen Creran Anticline; GMS, Glen Mark Slide; GS, Grampian Slide; HBD, Highland Border Downbend; HBS, Highland Border Steep Belt; IA, Islay Anticline; KA, Kinlochleven Anticline; LAS, Loch Awe Syncline; LST, Loch Skerrols Thrust; OSB, Geal Charn–Ossian Steep Belt; SBS, Stob Ban Synform; SMS, Sron Mhor Synform; TMA, Tom Meadhoin Anticline; TSB, Tummel Steep Belt.

the Grampian terrane showing complex overprinting relationships. Changes in the collision vectors and in the geometry and character of the colliding plate boundaries resulted in a range of coeval tectonic regimes including compression, extension, transpression and transtension. In Scotland, we can only study an oblique section through this orogen ranging from the deeply eroded levels (>25 km) in the Central and Southwestern Highlands to shallower levels (10–20 km) in the northeast.

In combination, these factors have produced local complexity in the geology and provided controversy that hampers regional correlation (Roberts & Treagus 1977b, Hickman 1978, Thomas 1979, Soper et al. 1999, Dewey & Mange 1999). Stephenson & Gould (1995) provide an excellent summary and description of the main structures. Their unique 3D block diagram (after Thomas 1979) visualizing the key elements is reproduced here (Fig. 4.24) and with cross sections (Figs 4.25, 4.26) that assign folds and their axial traces to episodes, D1, D2 and D3, and indicate the complexity and facing azimuth of the individual large-scale D1 structures.

The deformational sequence
Crustal shortening during the Grampian event is traditionally subdivided into four main episodes or phases of deformation (D1–4). These are developed with variable intensity within the progressively uplifting and deforming orogenic pile. In general, D1 structures are considered to be widespread but often transposed and hence difficult to detect except in the south and southeast. D2 (main phase) structures are common to all Dalradian strata. D3 structures first appear about 5–10 km to the

northwest of the Highland Boundary Fault (HBF), whereas D4 structures are restricted to the Highland Border Steep Belt and the Buchan area. Regional lineation trends are highly variable due to the effects of superimposed folding. Folds and interference patterns are common at all scales. Kinematic indicators indicative of tectonic transport imply a general sense of top-to-the-north to northwest transport. Sedimentary structures are locally well preserved and provide invaluable controls on facing and fold geometries.

Onset of deformation (D1). During Early Ordovician times as overthrusting of the Laurentian margin commenced, the initial strains are manifest by originally close-to-tight D1 major folds, ductile shears and associated tectonic fabrics. Where largely unaffected by later deformations, for example in the Southern Highland Group rocks of the Highland Border Steep Belt (see below), these folds have a dominantly NE–SW trend. This D1 deformation was accompanied by greenschist-facies metamorphism and pressure solution appears to have had an important role in balancing the effects of potentially different strain rates among diverse lithologies, and transporting or redistributing material in solution. This resulted in distinctive spaced cleavages in the more psammitic lithologies and a penetrative, locally slaty cleavage in pelitic rocks.

There is no direct evidence regarding the original attitude of the D1 folds (i.e. upright or recumbent) and interpretation depends upon their relationship to the Tay Nappe. If the Tay Nappe (described below) is essentially a D1 structure then F1 folds were originally recumbent (e.g. Mendum & Fettes 1985),

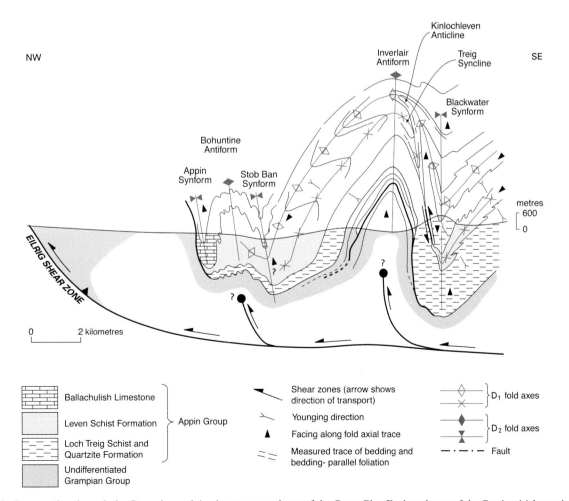

Fig. 4.25. Cross-section through the Grampian and Appin groups southeast of the Great Glen Fault and west of the Corrieyairick granite complex. From Key *et al.* (1997) and reproduced by permission of the British Geological Survey.

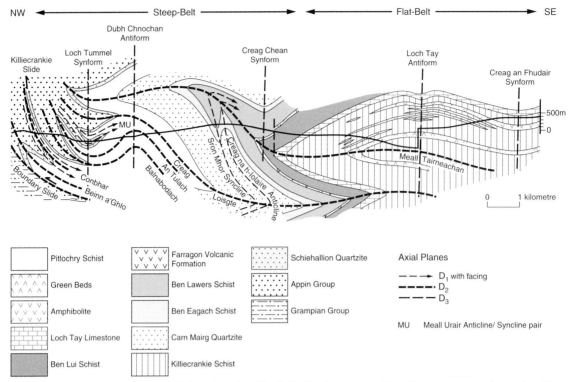

Fig. 4.26. Cross-section east of the Loch Tay Fault through rocks of the Dalradian Supergroup. From Treagus (2000) and reproduced by permission of the British Geological Survey.

alternatively, if the Tay Nappe formed as a result of D2 folding and shearing (e.g. Harris *et al.* 1976; Treagus 1987; Krabbendam *et al.* 1997; Rose & Harris 2000), then the F1 folds may have been originally upright.

Peak deformation (D2) and metamorphism. Continued overthrusting of the ophiolite nappe and impingement of the volcanic arc produced rotation and stacking of fold nappes. This stacking and overthrusting produced the crustal thickening that generated the classic Barrovian metamorphism in the Grampian Highlands. D2 folds are widespread and typically close to isoclinal, strongly asymmetrical and associated with the dominant foliation S2. With the possible exception of the Geal Charn–Ossian Steep Belt, D2 structures probably developed originally with a recumbent to low-angle attitude. Later steepening by D3 and D4 structures occurred in the Tummel and Highland Border Steep Belt respectively (Fig. 4.24). Most authors agree that D2 deformation was highly non-coaxial (i.e. it had a high simple-shear component). S2 varies from pressure-solution striping to crenulation cleavage commonly becoming an intense penetrative schistosity or gneissosity, depending on lithology, metamorphic grade and amount of strain. Locally, D2 high strain zones are marked by extremely platy, sub-mylonitic fabrics. These D2 high strain zones, commonly termed 'tectonic slides' (Hutton 1979) generally comprise the attenuated limbs of large-scale, often highly asymmetrical F2 folds.

Waning deformation and metamorphism (D3). The D3 deformation phase is dominated by upright structures formed under lower to middle amphibolite-facies conditions and is associated with locally high temperatures producing minor granitic melts and pegmatite in fold hinges and along S3 crenulations. D3 folds fold the dominant S2 schistosity and vary from open to tight, with moderately inclined to vertical axial planes. They are responsible for the formation of the Tummel Steep Belt

(Fig. 4.24) and the major arcuation of strata around the southwestern edge of the Buchan Block. D3 folds display highly variable orientations of axial planes, fold axes and vergence; in some places they are coaxial with D2 folds, but elsewhere show non-coaxial interference structures with D2 folds.

Late deformation (D4). The last expressions of the Grampian event are weak and take the form of broad upright folds and late crenulation and (chevron style) minor folds and brittle structures. In the Buchan area, in the southwest and along the Highland Border they are responsible for the downturning of the hinge zone and part of the lower limb of the Tay Nappe into the Highland Border Steep Belt, a zone that ultimately will be the site of the Highland Boundary Fault. Deformation is associated with widespread crustal block movements indicated by transpressive strike-slip movements on many of the major Caledonoid faults. In the NE Grampian Highlands, D4 structures are mainly open to close folds, with gentle plunges and NE–SW striking axial planes, and are often difficult to separate from D3 structures. Generally, axial planar fabrics are not developed although locally poorly to well-developed crenulation cleavages occur in the more pelitic lithologies, particularly within the hinge zone of the Highland Border Downbend.

Key structures of the Grampian Event
For ease of description, the Grampian terrane is subdivided into two structural regions: (1) the Grampian Highlands, including the Southwest Highlands, Perthshire and the Central Highlands, and (2) the Buchan Block, which contains Dalradian stratigraphy but is different in its metamorphism, deformational sequence and crustal geophysical signature. With the exception of the basement rocks of the Central Highlands that contain evidence for earlier Knoydartian tectonothermal events, these areas are dominated by a series of

large-scale features including the Tay Nappe and associated folds, steep belts, domes and shear zones. Some of these key structures are described below.

Grampian Highlands
Tay Nappe. The Tay Nappe (Fig. 4.24) is the largest single structure of the Grampian Terrane; 10 to 20 km in width, it can be traced northeast from the Isle of Arran to Stonehaven. It is not recognized within the Buchan Block. The present day erosion level only preserves the shallowly inclined inverted rocks of the lower limb(s). These reveal little of the changing fabrics and structures with depth in the Tay Nappe. Fortunately, evidence for the upper limb that would have contained a right-way-up sequence, several kilometres above the present land surface, is preserved within the steeply downturned strata of the Highland Border Steep Belt in the SW Highlands.

In the SW Highlands (Fig. 4.24, cross section A), a central zone coincides with the composite Loch Awe Syncline that is characterised by open to close, upright and upward-facing D1 folds on all scales from metres to kilometres. To the northwest, the D1 folds and associated cleavages become progressively and gradually overturned, verging towards the major Islay Anticline which is overturned and faces towards the northwest. Its axial surface dips at *c.* 45°. The lower, overturned limb of the anticline rests on the southeast-dipping Loch Skerrols Thrust, which overlies the Bowmore Sandstone. Southeast from the upright central zone, the Ardrishaig Anticline becomes rapidly overturned towards the southeast. It is inferred to pass over the late-stage (?D3) upright, open Cowal Antiform to face downwards as the Aberfoyle Anticline (Synform) towards the Highland Border (Fig. 4.24). From the hinge zone of the Ardrishaig Anticline to the hinge zone of the Aberfoyle Anticline, the rocks at crop, across some 30 km of strike, lie on the inverted limb of the Tay Nappe. From Cowal, this major zone of inversion extends northeastwards, although the arch-like geometry of the Cowal Antiform diminishes rapidly, and the inverted rocks become generally gently undulating to sub-horizontal, known colloquially as the Flat Belt, as far to the northeast as Glen Esk. The width of the Flat Belt varies, but it is some 18 km wide in Central Perthshire. That the rocks are not everywhere inverted has been shown by Krabbendam *et al.* (1997) and Treagus (1999) who identified km-scale D1 isoclines within the Flat Belt of Perthshire.

In Perthshire, the roles of the Boundary Slide and the Ben Lui Fold Complex are important in controlling the disposition and hence the facing of the major folds. For example, in cross-section B (Fig. 4.24), the D1 folds initially face upwards and northwest above the Boundary Slide, but their facing direction is reversed to sideways and southeast about the hinge of the Ben Lui Fold. In cross-section C (Fig. 4.24), the D1 folds in the Appin Group initially face down to the southeast above the Boundary Slide, as indeed they do in the Grampian Group exposed below it to the northwest (Thomas 1979). Extrapolating cross-section C northeastwards across the Loch Tay Fault, (cross section D, Fig. 4.24), Treagus (1999) has re-interpreted the (Loch) Tummel Belt as zone of strong interference between D1, D2 and D3 folds, with sub-recumbent D2 folds again playing an important role in controlling the disposition and facing of the D1 folds (Fig. 4.26). By this means, a long-standing problem has been resolved that stemmed from the lack of a major reversal of younging consistent with the core of the Tay Nappe in the area between Pitlochry and the Loch Tay Fault.

Northeastwards from Glen Esk, rocks become right-way-up. This is thought to occur in the Tarfside culmination (Harte & Hudson 1979) that exposes the Tarfside Nappe, which is structurally *below* the Tay Nappe (Fig. 4.24). The Tarfside Nappe is separated from the Tay Nappe by the by the Glen Mark Slide.

The arch of the Tarfside culmination essentially terminates the Flat Belt to the northeast, while the amplitude of the Tay Nappe itself seems also to diminish markedly northeastwards. Restoration of the Highland Border Steep Belt to the horizontal by unbending the Highland Border Downbend brings the D1 and D2 folds and fabrics to their inverted pre-Downbend disposition. D2 structures become congruent with the D2 structures in the Flat Belt, while the restored D1 structures predictably face sub-horizontally southeastwards, or in the Glenshee area, gently up towards the SE.

There are conflicting views relating to the mechanisms of formation of the Tay Nappe. Was the sense of D2 shear top-to-the-SE or NW? Was the original attitude of F1 folds recumbent or upright, and is the Tay Nappe essentially a D1 structure slightly modified by D2, or mainly the product of strong D2 shearing and folding? Discussion of these various points are provided by Mendum & Fettes (1985) and Rose & Harris (2000 and references therein).

Highland Border Steep Belt. Along the entire Highland Border in Scotland, a zone of steeply dipping rocks intervenes between the Highland Border Fault, or its supposed trace below the Old Red Sandstone cover, and the Flat Belt (Fig. 4.24). This zone forms the steep limb of an important, regional-scale fold structure where the inverted rocks of the Flat Belt pass across the axial surface trace of the Highland Border Downbend into a steep orientation (Shackleton 1958).

The Highland Border Downbend is thus an asymmetrical, late-stage antiform, of variable geometry, commonly accompanied by strong crenulation cleavage modifying earlier S1 and S2 cleavages. The steeply dipping rocks are referred to collectively as the Highland Border Steep Belt. To the southwest the downbend is little more than a continuation of the arch of the Cowal Antiform, but northeast of Loch Lomond it becomes a more distinct monocline on the steep limb of which, the strata become vertical. In Perthshire at Dunkeld, strata are overturned, so that some 5 km of formerly inverted rocks dip at around 60° to the northwest and are once more right-way-up. The Highland Border Downbend generally does not refold D3 structures. However, Crane *et al.* (2002) describe gentle, open warps near Kirkmichael parallel to the structure that do refold D3 folds and thus it is considered a regional D4 structure.

Structures between the Tay Nappe and the Boundary Slide. The fundamental divergence of facing as seen in Figure 4.24, cross-section A, persists to the northeast, albeit with increasing complexity, as the regional WSW plunge brings lower structural levels to the surface. Studies immediately to the northeast of the Cowal to Islay region (Fig. 4.24, cross-section A) as far as Glen Orchy, Appin and Ballachulish, originally led Roberts & Treagus (1977*a*) to the conclusion that the apparently simple high-level manifestation of the structural geometry of the nappe complex gives way downwards to a much more complicated configuration. This required the recognition of polyphase deformation involving a second set of structures, notably the Ben Lui Fold, and the modification of the early patterns of structural facing, without fundamentally changing the primary divergence about a central upward-facing zone.

An abrupt change in dips from flat lying or near horizontal strata into steep to vertical strata occurs east of the Loch Tay Fault in northern Perthshire to form the Tummel Steep Belt. This structure is *c.* 10 km wide and dominated by tight, upright folds. Its origin, age and significance has been the source of controversy, but Treagus (1999) demonstrated convincingly that the steepening is the result of late ENE-trending (D3) flexuring, and corrugation of a pre-existing flat belt composed of recumbent D1 and D2 structures (Fig. 4.26). The F3 folds are commonly coaxial with earlier folds and as a result, D1, D2 and D3 fold closures in the Steep Belt are not readily distinguished.

In the area between Glen Shee and Cairngorm, Upton (1986) and Crane *et al.* (2002) documented a similar steep belt, the Cairnwell Steep Belt, separated from the Tummel Steep Belt by the Carn Dallaig Transfer Zone, a complex NW–SE trending zone probably with a D2 strike-slip component. The structural interpretation of the Cairnwell Steep Belt by Upton (1986), and Crane *et al.* (2002) is similar to that of Treagus (1999): effectively a steepening of a pre-existing flat belt by folding of D3 age.

The Central Highlands. Immediately beneath the Boundary Slide (see below) the Grampian Group rocks between Glen Orchy and Blair Atholl are disposed in a series of large-scale D1 and D2 recumbent folds (Thomas 1979); these face downwards to the southeast and display complex D1/D2 interference patterns. The nappes are arched by the D3(?) Glen Orchy Antiform and Drummochter Dome (Fig. 4.24, cross-section D; Lindsay *et al.* 1989; Roberts & Treagus 1979)

Farther west into the Monadhliath district, the regional structure is complex but different. Various D2 tectonic elements display contrasting orientations, geometries and interference patterns. In the northern Central Highlands, a 3–4 km wide zone extending from the Foyers Granite to the eastern end of the Cairngorm Granite and nearly normal to the regional Caledonoid trend carries NW–SE-trending foliation related to SW-verging and sideways-facing to upright D1 and D2 folds (Smith *et al.* 1999). In the Corrieyairack to Stob Ban Synform area, D2 folds are upright and facing to the northwest and fold plunges are typically gentle to sub-horizontal, curvilinear and associated with a prominent lineation. Where S1 strikes northeast on D3 fold limbs, then similar style D2 structures are indistinguishable from D3 folds. In marked contrast, in the Drummochter–Strathtummel area, D2 folds are inclined to recumbent and consistently downward facing to the SE. Hook interference patterns between D2 and D3 folds, often seen at outcrop are rarely present on a kilometric scale as seen elsewhere (e.g. in the Northwest Highlands).

Grampian Group rocks show S1 schistosity, usually steeper than bedding and most clearly displayed in semipelites and micaceous tops to graded psammite beds. This fabric which pre-dates all the intrusive granitic bodies of the area, crenulates and transposes the earlier gneissosity of the basement rocks (Glen Banchor and Dava successions). In lithologies of suitable composition it is associated with the production of lit-par-lit migmatites.

The broad arch of the post-D2 Glenshirra Dome separates a zone of complex top-to-the-southwest folding to the north from top-to-the-northwest folds and thrusts to the south. In the southwestern Central Highlands, D1 nappe folds are restricted to the Ben Nevis–Loch Treig area (Fig. 4.24 cross-section C, Fig. 4.25). Here they are recognized by changes in minor fold vergence, inversion of local stratigraphy on D2 fold limbs and changes in trend of mapped lithostratigraphical boundaries. S1 is a schistosity axial planar to the early folds. Further north, such folds have not been identified and cannot be traced through the Glen Roy district (Key *et al.* 1997).

Geal Charn–Ossian Steep Belt The Geal Charn–Ossian Steep Belt is a prominent 2–4 km wide linear zone of steeply dipping (>60°) rocks and highly attenuated folds that can be traced for more than 50 km across the Central Highlands. It is most clearly defined in the southwest (Fig. 4.24, cross-section D), where it affects upper Grampian Group and Appin Group strata. To the west of Ben Alder, the Steep Belt widens and

becomes more diffuse northwards, affecting strata of the lower part of the Grampian Group and the Glen Banchor succession.

The Geal Charn–Ossian Steep Belt, first described by Thomas (1979), contains a series of spectacularly developed isoclinal folds and co-planar tectonic fabrics (Fig. 4.27) associated with ductile shear zones or slides that are most clearly displayed in the Appin Group strata in the core of the Kinlochlaggan Synform. The intense focusing of deformation into such a narrow zone and evidence of opposing facing directions for recumbent folds on either side led Thomas (1979) to interpret the Steep Belt as a root zone to the Grampian nappes. The completion of the primary mapping of the Dalwhinnie district (Robertson & Smith 1999; BGS 2000) has confirmed the importance of the Steep Belt as a primary upright deformation zone that separates two contrasting structural domains: the upright to steeply inclined folds of the Loch Laggan–Glen Roy area to the west, and the gently inclined, overturned and flattened rocks of the Drummochter–Strathtummel area to the east. The steep belt probably resulted from its location adjacent to a faulted rift basin margin and subsequent buttressing of the Grampian and Appin strata against a rigid upstanding block of the Glen Banchor succession (Fig. 4.28; Robertson & Smith 1999).

Three phases of deformation are recognized in the Steep Belt. D1 and D2 are essentially coplanar and separated by kyanite grade metamorphism (Robertson & Smith 1999). During D2, an increase in temperature to form sillimanite was associated with significant grain coarsening and migmatization of psammitic lithologies particularly close to slides. D3 in the Steep Belt is characterized by an upright crenulation fabric and an absence of new metamorphic mineral growth.

Fig. 4.27. Opposed verging fold pairs separated by a vertical high-strain zone in Glen Spean subgroup psammites in the Geall Charn–Ossian Steep Belt, slopes NE of Loch a'Bhealaich Leamhain, Ardverkie Forest. BGS photograph P508351.

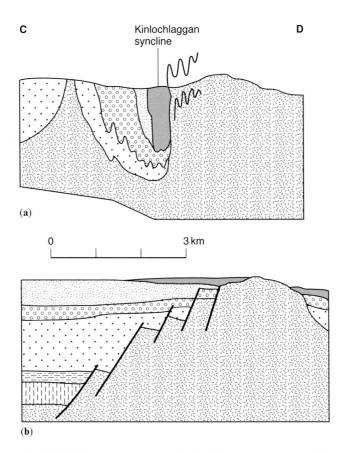

Fig. 4.28. (a) Cross-section across the Geall Charn–Ossian Steep Belt. Random dashes are Glen Banchor succession, other ornaments represent strata of the Grampian and Appin groups; (b) basin reconstruction along the same line of section (modified from Robertson & Smith 1999). The steep belt is thought to have formed as a result of compression of the Grampian and Appin strata against the upstanding basement block of Glen Banchor succession.

Shear zones and tectonic slides. Tectonic slides (Bailey 1910; Hutton 1979) are typically ductile faults that formed during an episode of folding and fabric formation. Several of these structures are recognized at different stratigraphical levels in the Grampian terrane where they may interupt and/or repeat the stratigraphical succession.

The Boundary Slide is one of the largest ductile fault structures in the Grampian terrane (Fig. 4.24). It is everywhere broadly coincident with the Grampian–Appin group boundary and may therefore mark the site of an early, primary extensional structure. It is best developed in the Schiehallion area, but is traceable throughout Perthshire and the Southern Highlands from Dalmally in the southwest to Braemar in the northeast. It has not been recognized north of the Cairngorms. The structure was formerly regarded as a major dislocation that separated two contrasting sequences. However, the identification within the shear zone of a near complete Appin Group succession, albeit with whole subgroups represented by a few metres of rock, has served to lessen its importance (Treagus 1999). The slide zone is a zone of extreme attenuation marked by strong S2 schistosity imposed by top-to-the-NW D2 shear demonstrated by rotated garnet porphyroblasts and deformed quartz veins and pebbles.

The Eilrig Shear Zone (Fig. 4.25; Phillips *et al.* 1993; Key *et al.* 1997) has been recognized over a strike length of only *c.* 30 km between Loch Lochy and Loch Tarff and brings younger Grampian Group rocks to rest on the Glenshirra Subgroup. Microstructures indicate a consistent northwest-

directed sense of shear. There is no evidence for a major change in fold facing across this structure but metamorphic conditions change from amphibolite grade in the upper Grampian Group rocks to greenschist below the shear zone. Phillips *et al.* (1993) suggest that the Eilrig Shear zone may represent the surface expression of a major basal decollement or floor thrust to many of the structurally higher slides and shear zones.

The effects of Grampian shearing are thought to have extended structurally downwards into the basement rocks of the Glen Banchor and Dava successions. It is evident in places that the Neoproterozoic ductile shear zones (Grampian Shear Zone, see p. 93 above) were reworked strongly during the Grampian Orogeny. The dominant fabric within parts of the shear zone network results from the transposition of an older mylonitic foliation during the first phase of deformation to affect nearby Grampian Group lithologies.

The Buchan Block
In the NE Highlands, stratigraphy, sedimentary facies, and structural, metamorphic and geophysical crustal signatures define a separate and distinct crustal unit termed the Buchan Block. This records essentially the same sedimentary history as the rest of the Dalradian. It is bounded by large ductile shear zone structures (Portsoy and Deeside lineaments) and is largely unaffected by the complex recumbent D1 and D2 fold stacks of the Tay Nappe (Fig. 4.24). D1 structures generally face upwards although their attitude varies with structural level and the effects of later folds. Inverted rocks are recorded in Central Deeside and in the Stonehaven–Collieston areas. A major monoformal structure termed the Boyndie Syncline has been variously described as an early or late structure (Sutton & Watson 1956b; Treagus & Roberts 1981). D2 folds and fabrics are locally dominant and formed on the limbs of the early large-scale structures in association with ductile thrusting and shearing, including the regionally important Portsoy–Duchray Hill lineament (Ashcroft *et al.* 1984; Fettes *et al.* 1991). D3 structures, although sometimes difficult to distinguish from D2, are characteristically monoclinal and associated with crenulation cleavages.

The Portsoy–Duchray Hill Shear Zone or Portsoy Lineament (Figs 4.24, 4.29) is a major linear zone of movement and relative uplift with a kinematic history that extends from at least Argyll Group times (630–720 Ma) to the Silurian (Fettes *et al.* 1991). It effectively forms the western boundary to the Buchan Block and shows evidence for compressional, transtensional, transpressional and extensional activation in both ductile and brittle modes. Up to *c.* 10 km wide it can be traced from the coast at Portsoy for *c.* 100 km southwards to Duchray Hill where its effects on the regional stratigraphy and structure become muted. The Portsoy Lineament, and a sub-parallel structure to the northwest, the Keith Shear Zone, appear to have acted as pathways for magma at various times, influencing the location of Argyll Group metavolcanics and the emplacement of both basic and granitic sheets. A number of other shear zones are recognized within the Buchan Block where they are thought to accompany and post-date the emplacement of major gabbro sheets during the Grampian event (see below; Ashcroft *et al.* 1984).

Significant changes in structure and metamorphism occur across the Portsoy Lineament. A coherent sequence of Barrovian metamorphic and tectonic events is present to the west in Speyside and can be extended southwards into the Southern Highlands. To the east, the correlation with structural phases in the Buchan Block is more problematical and here metamorphism is dominated by high temperature, low pressure (Buchan) conditions. The southern margin of the Buchan Block is defined by an imbricated zone containing a number of east–west trending shear zones including the Glen Mark Slide that Harte & Hudson (1979) considered to replace the axial zone of a major upward facing nappe.

Ordovician magmatism in the Grampian terrane

Several suites of Ordovician plutonic rocks were intruded into the Dalradian rocks of the NE Grampian Highlands during regional deformation and metamorphism (Fig. 4.29). These include a syn- to late-tectonic suite of basic and ultramafic plutons (the 'Newer Gabbros' of Read 1961), and two suites of late-tectonic diorites and granites.

Syn- to late-tectonic basic and ultramafic intrusions of the NE Grampians: the 'Newer Gabbros'

A major suite of variably deformed and metamorphosed gabbroic plutons within the Dalradian rocks of NE Scotland (Figs 4.29, 4.30) has been the focus of much research since the pioneering investigations of H. H. Read (1923*a,b*, 1935, 1956; Read *et al.* 1961, 1965). The apparent alignment of members of the suite, either along N–S or E–W trending lineaments (Fig. 4.29), some of which correspond to zones of intense D3 deformation (e.g. the Portsoy Lineament), suggests a tectonic control on their emplacement. Most contacts with host Dalradian rocks are tectonic and coincident with large-scale ductile shear zones (Ashcroft *et al.* 1984; Fettes *et al.* 1991). Other important shear zones are developed within plutons (e.g. Huntly and Portsoy (Munro & Gallagher 1984)).

The basic suite has tholeiitic geochemical affinities (Stephenson *et al.* 1999). The parent magma is thought to have been basaltic with normative hypersthene, and the cumulate succession follows a tholeiitic differentiation trend. This is consistent with the widespread occurrence of orthopyroxene, the absence of olivine in intermediate fractionation stages, and by the presence of quartz in the most evolved rocks. Many plutons (e.g. Belhelvie, Insch, Huntly and Morven–Cabrach) contain cumulates and layering thought to have formed by gravity settling of crystals precipitated from the parent magma (e.g. Ashcroft & Boyd 1976; Wadsworth 1982; Munro 1984; Stephenson *et al.* 1999). Wadsworth (1982) divided the cumulates into lower, middle and upper zones ranging in composition from peridotites (olivine cumulates) and troctolites (olivine–plagioclase cumulates), through gabbros (opx–cpx–plagioclase cumulates), to 'syenogabbros' (cpx–opx–plagioclase–alkali feldspar cumulates). This is a generalized fractionation sequence, although all three zones are only found in the Insch pluton. Many of the plutons contain

quartz–biotite norites that occur as distinct bodies of homogenous basic rocks without cumulate textures. These are interpreted as parts of the same tholeiitic parent magma that crystallized *in situ* under relatively hydrous conditions.

The effects of post-emplacement deformation and metamorphism of the basic suite are widespread but heterogeneous. Development of steep ductile shear zones on all scales up to 1–2 km width (Fig. 4.30) was associated with conversion of peridotites and gabbros to serpentinites and amphibolites respectively (e.g. Mongkoltip & Ashworth 1986) under amphibolite-facies metamorphic conditions. Zones of intense deformation are characterized by development of schistose metagabbros and mylonites. Some shear zones are cut by largely undeformed sheets of granite and pegmatite.

The plutons are spatially associated with areas of peak high-temperature, low-pressure Buchan metamorphism (see below, Fettes 1970; Ashworth 1975; Kneller & Leslie 1984), and produced locally a sillimanite overprint of regional metamorphic assemblages prior to involvement in D3 folding and ductile shearing. Distinctive xenolithic complexes occur along the margins and/or roof zones of the Huntly and Arnage plutons, and also locally at Insch. These comprise a variety of hornfels fragments in a cordierite norite matrix (Gribble 1968, 1970; Gribble & O'Hara 1967). The fragments are interpreted as the refractory residues resulting from partial melting of the Dalradian host rock as it was heated by the basic magma; the matrix material probably represents the partial melt component which may have mixed with the basic magma in places. The contact metamorphic aureoles are commonly incomplete as a result of later deformation (Munro 1984; Ashcroft & Boyd 1976; Ashcroft & Munro 1978; Leslie 1984; Ashcroft *et al.* 1984). Intense D3 shearing has, for example, removed much of the aureole along the southern margin of Insch pluton (Fig. 4.30). Isolated fault- and shear zone-bounded slices of hornfels rocks up to several kilometres from the nearest basic pluton are thus interpreted as displaced segments of aureoles (Ashcroft *et al.* 1984).

The timing of Buchan metamorphism and D3 deformation in Aberdeenshire are constrained indirectly by the isotopic dating of components of the 'Newer Gabbro' suite. The Insch pluton has yielded a U–Pb zircon age of 470 ± 9 Ma (Dempster *et al.* 2002). A Rb–Sr mineral age of 462 ± 5 Ma obtained from a pegmatite which cross-cuts sheared gabbro within the Belhelvie pluton (van Breemen & Boyd 1972) places a lower limit on the age of D3 shearing that was probably initiated shortly after emplacement and continued during cooling of the plutons and their host rocks.

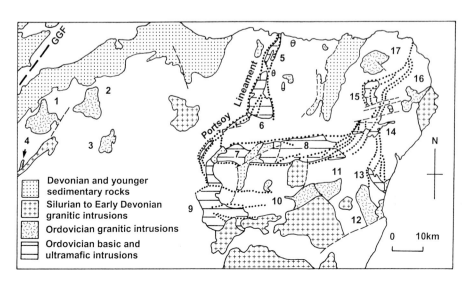

Fig. 4.29. Sketch map of the Ordovician intrusions of the Grampian Highlands. Dashed lines are faults (GGF, Great Glen Fault); dotted lines are shear zones. Numbers correspond to individual intrusions as follows: 1, Moy; 2, Ardclach; 3, Grantown; 4, Kyllachy; 5, Portsoy; 6, Huntly; 7, Boganclogh; 8, Insch; 9, Morven–Cabrach; 10, Tillyfourie; 11, Kemnay; 12, Aberdeen; 13, Belhelvie; 14, Haddo–Arnage; 15, Maud; 16, Forest of Deer; 17, Strichen.

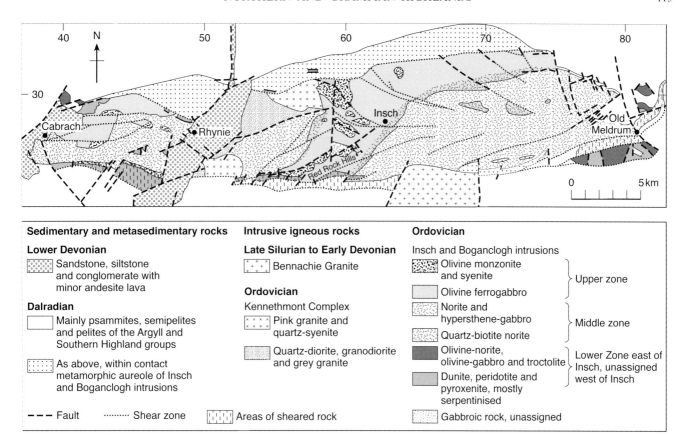

Fig. 4.30. Map of the Insch, Boganclogh and Kennethmont intrusions (from Stephenson *et al.* 1999, with permission of the Joint Nature Conservation Committee).

Many of the plutons are only poorly exposed, but gravity and magnetic data can be used to determine the subsurface dimensions and extent of some of the plutons (Stephenson & Gould 1995). The Portsoy, Knock and Huntly plutons extend no deeper than about 1 km depth, whereas the northern part of the Morven–Cabrach pluton, the southwestern part of the Boganclogh pluton and the intervening area are underlain by *c.* 5 km of basic rock (Gould 1997). The Morven–Cabrach pluton steadily thins to the south and is underlain at shallow depths by the much younger Ballater granite. The Insch mass is *c.* 2 km thick and its sheared southern margin dips north. The Belhelvie pluton continues for *c.* 10 km to the south-southeast beneath post-Caledonian cover. Prominent gravity anomalies between the Haddo House pluton and Fraserburgh imply the presence of basic igneous rocks at depth along this lineament.

Late-tectonic granites of the northern Grampians
NE Grampians. Various granitic rocks (*sensu lato*) are spatially associated with the 'Newer Gabbro' suite in the NE Grampians (Fig. 4.29), but are slightly younger and late-tectonic in relation to D3 shearing and folding. They comprise two suites. The first comprises a group of biotite–muscovite granites that include the Kenmay, Aberdeen, Strichen and Forest of Deer plutons (Fig. 4.29). Where emplaced into low-grade country rocks (e.g. Aberchirder), these are unfoliated and have contact metamorphic aureoles. In contrast, where the country rocks are at higher metamorphic grades the granites display primary magmatic foliations, have transitional contacts and migmatitic aureoles (e.g. Aberdeen and Strichen). Although the granites postdate regional migmatization and the basic suite, they still record localized solid-state shearing during D3 (Kneller & Leslie 1984; Boyd & Munro 1978; Harrison 1987). The granites have S-type characteristics, including

peraluminous chemistry, high intial $^{87}Sr/^{86}Sr$ ratios (>0.71) and inherited zircons (Pankhurst 1974; Pidgeon & Aftalion 1978; Harmon 1983), all features indicative of a crustal origin. They probably originated by the melting of Dalradian rocks at shallow depths just below the present level of exposure (Kneller & Aftalion 1987), possibly as a result of heat advected from the basic suite. A genetic relationship between the two suites is supported by isotopic dating which has provided ages of 470 ± 1 Ma for the Aberdeen granite (U–Pb monazite, Kneller & Aftalion 1987) and 467 ± 6 Ma for the Strichen granite (U–Pb zircon, Oliver *et al.* 2000).

The second suite consists of the diorites, tonalites and granodiorites of the Kennethmont, Syllavethy, Tillyfourie and Correnie intrusions and associated vein complexes (Sadashivaiah 1954; Read & Haq 1965; Busrewil *et al.* 1975; Harrison 1987; Gould 1997). Some of the intrusions are foliated and many are highly xenolithic. The chemistry and isotope characteristics of the suite indicate a mantle or lower crustal igneous source (I-type). A preliminary $^{206}Pb–^{207}Pb$ zircon evaporation age of 457 ± 0.9 Ma for the undeformed Kennethmont granite provides an upper limit on the timing of D3 deformation. (Oliver *et al.* 2000).

NW Grampians. A series of late tectonic granitic intrusions crop out in the NW Grampians, including the Moy, Grantown and Glen Kyllachy granites (Fig. 4.29; van Breemen & Piasecki 1983; Highton 1999). These mostly comprise variably foliated and recrystallized granites and granodiorites with subordinate leucogranite and pegmatite. Initial $^{87}Sr/^{86}Sr$ ratios of the intrusions are in the range 0.714 to 0.718, indicating that they are S-type granites derived from melting of a metasedimentary protolith (Stephenson & Gould 1995). No reliable intrusion ages have been obtained for any member of the suite, but their great similarity to the Aberdeenshire granites described above suggested that they also formed towards the end of Grampian orogenic activity, possibly as a result of decompression melting during uplift (Oliver 2001).

Grampian metamorphism of the Dalradian Supergroup

The metamorphic grade or facies of the Grampian Highlands was traditionally referred to index minerals in pelitic rocks. Barrow (1893, 1912), working in the SE Highlands, first established a zonal sequence indicative of progressive metamorphic grade. This scheme, slightly modified by Tilley (1925), became the classical *Barrovian zones* (chlorite → biotite → garnet → staurolite → kyanite → sillimanite). In the NE Highlands, Read (1952) recognized a different style of metamorphism evidenced by a progressive mineral sequence that formed the *Buchan zones* (biotite → cordierite → andalusite → sillimanite). The pattern of metamorphic zonation across the Central Highlands was established principally by Elles & Tilley (1930), Kennedy (1948), Chinner (1966), Dewey & Pankhurst (1970) and Winchester (1974). The nature of the reactions defining the zonal boundaries has been studied extensively. A discussion of these is beyond the present description but summaries are given by Atherton (1977), Harte & Hudson (1979) and Hudson (1980).

Read (1952) regarded the Barrovian and Buchan metamorphisms as quite separate events. However, Fettes *et al.* (1976) demonstrated that the Buchan zones were part of a progressive decrease in the pressure of metamorphism (or increase in the geothermal gradient) from the southwest to the northeast Highlands. The transition from the Barrovian to the Buchan areas was detailed by Harte & Hudson (1979) who defined a series of four zonal sequences reflecting decreasing pressure, namely: *Barrovian* (biotite → garnet → staurolite → kyanite → sillimanite), *Stonehavian* (biotite → garnet → chloritoid + biotite → staurolite → sillimanite, *West Buchan* (biotite → cordierite → andalusite → staurolite → kyanite) and *East Buchan* (biotite → cordierite → andalusite → sillimanite → sillimanite + K-feldspar). More recently, the metamorphic grade has been illustrated by means of conventional facies (Fettes *et al.* 1985; Harte 1988). The basis of the correlation between the mineral zones and the facies is given by Fettes *et al.* (1985, table 1)

Distribution of metamorphic facies

The distribution of metamorphic facies is shown in Figure 4.31. This shows a general increase in grade from greenschist-facies in the SW Highlands, northeastwards through epidote–amphibolite-facies to predominantly amphibolite-facies. The greenschist-facies wedges out as two arms running, respectively, along the Highland Boundary and Great Glen faults. The greater part of the higher grade rocks lie in the lower amphibolite-facies, characterized by kyanite + staurolite and andalusite + cordierite assemblages. In the Monadhliaths and Eastern Highlands, the rocks reach middle and upper amphibolite conditions characterized by sillimanite + muscovite and sillimanite + K-feldspar assemblages.

Some earlier zonal maps differentiated areas of 'migmatites' (e.g. Dewey & Pankhurst 1970; Fettes 1979). These rocks are characterized by the presence of quartzo-feldspathic lenses, pods or stringers and are generally associated with sillimanite-bearing amphibolite-facies rocks. Barrow (1912) originally considered the migmatites as the heat source for the metamorphism, a view echoed by Kennedy (1948) and Read (1955). However subsequent studies (e.g. Ashworth 1976, 1979; Atherton 1977) have shown that the 'migmatites' encompass a variety of products including coarse sillimanite-gneisses and true anatectic melts. These products derive from a number of rela-

tively high-grade metamorphic and metasomatic processes. The presence or absence of 'migmatites' at the local scale is largely controlled by the chemical composition of the host lithologies. As such they can be regarded as by-products of high-grade metamorphism with no direct significance in terms of the pattern of metamorphic facies

Superimposed on the main metamorphic facies is a regional zone (Fig. 4.31), running from Loch Tay to Kintyre, which is marked by the development of late stage albite porphyroblasts (Watkins 1983). The boundaries of the facies or the isogradic surfaces, are broadly flat lying over the greater part of the Central Highlands but steepen markedly against the Highland Boundary Fault particularly in the SE Highlands. This pattern of facies and facies boundaries led Kennedy (1948) to propose the concept of a 'thermal anticline' whose core was marked by the higher grade rocks and which plunged southwestwards. The distribution of the metamorphic facies is generally considered to represent the peak conditions during the Grampian event. No significant areas of retrogressive metamorphism are present.

Age of metamorphism in relation to deformation events

The age of metamorphism was considered by early workers in relation to the main deformation as indicated by the relative attitude of the lithostratigraphical and metamorphic zonal surfaces. Thus, Elles & Tilley (1930) suggested that the metamorphism was broadly coincident with the early deformation but that no metamorphism accompanied the later folds, which demonstrably folded the isograd surfaces. Later workers placed emphasis on the textural relationship between porphyroblast growth and deformational fabrics (for example, Rast 1958; Johnson 1962, 1963; Sturt & Harris 1961; Harte & Johnson 1969; Fig. 4.32a, b, c). This work broadly showed that blastesis started during the early deformation and that the peak of porphyroblast growth took place after the main nappe forming or crustal thickening phases and before the later uplift phases. This late deformation was only accompanied by limited retrogression due to relatively rapid uplift of the succession. Although there is considerable local variation (see below) this relationship is essentially true for the whole of the Central Highlands.

Facies variations in space and time

Although the pattern of the Grampian metamorphism is broadly uniform throughout the Central Highlands there are significant variations. Fettes *et al.* (1976) documented changes in the geothermal gradients from the SW to the NE Highlands. Subsequent *P–T* estimates have quantified these variations. Thus temperatures of *c.* 550°C were recorded for lower amphibolite-facies conditions across the Central Highlands but at markedly different pressures: namely 9–10 kbar in the Schiehallion area (Baker 1985), 7–8 kbar in western Aberdeenshire (Baker 1985) and in the Monadhliaths (Phillips *et al.* 1999), 5–6 kbar in Angus (Dempster 1985), 3–4 kbar in Banffshire (Beddoe-Stephens 1990). Also, Graham (1983) recorded pressures of 8–10 kbar for epidote–amphibolite-facies rocks in the SW Highlands whereas similar facies rocks in Buchan record pressures of 2–3 kbar (Hudson 1985; Beddoe-Stephens 1990). Although these figures indicate systematic variations across the Central Highlands, there is also significant variation in style and timing at a local scale with marked kinks in the *P–T–t* loops. Harte (1988) categorized these variations into six regions that are characterized by different metamorphic and tectonic styles. He regarded the boundaries to the six regions as partly marked by major lineaments (Ashcroft *et al.* 1984; Fettes *et al.* 1986). Harte's regions are used below for descriptive purposes.

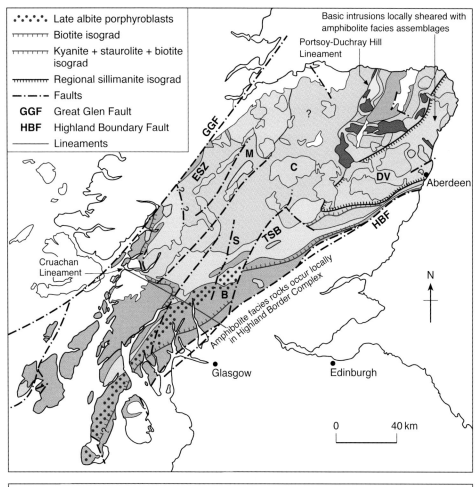

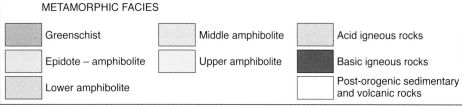

Fig. 4.31. Metamorphic facies within the Grampian Highlands (from Stephenson & Gould with permission of the British Geological Survey). B, Balquidder; C, Cairngorms; DV, Dee Valley; ESZ, Eilrig Shear Zone; M, Monadliath; S, Schiehallion; TSB, Tummel

Southwest Region. This region encompasses the area southwest of the Cruachan Lineament (Fig. 4.31; Graham 1986b). This lineament separates a higher density block to the southwest dominated by the thick mafic successions of the Tayvallich Volcanic Formation from a lower density block to the northeast with a markedly lower abundance of mafic intrusives. The lineament also marks the southwest limit of granitic plutons. The region is characterized by greenschist-facies metamorphism with a thin spine of garnet bearing epidote–amphibolite-facies rocks running through the centre of the region. The isogradic surface swings through 90° across the Cruachan Lineament from a NW trend to the north to a SW trend to the south (Fig. 4.31). The metamorphism of the region is characteristically of low temperature–high pressure type compared to the rest of the Central Highlands. Graham & Harte (1985) report temperatures ranging from 410 to 530°C (in garnet bearing rocks) and pressures in the range 8–10 kbar. They also document a later retrogressive phase associated with lower greenschist-facies conditions and pressures at *c.* 6 kbar. Graham (1986b) notes that the peak of metamorphism in the region was closely associated with the early deformation and thus relatively earlier than in the other regions. Graham (1986b) attributes this

distinctive style of metamorphism, particularly the absence of high temperature assemblages to the relatively low conductivity and low heat production character of the mafic-rich rocks.

South Perthshire Region. This area lies between the Cruachan and Portsoy lineaments and extends from the Highland Boundary Fault northwards to the Tummel Steep Belt. This area encompasses the Highland Boundary Steep Belt and the Flat Belt to the north. The metamorphism shows classical Barrovian zones reflecting an increase in grade to the north. The main porphyroblast growth took place after the main nappe forming movements, mainly post-D2 to post-D3 (Bradbury 1979; Watkins 1985). Dempster (1985) studied the cooling ages recorded by a number of mineral species along a N–S transect of the region. He noted differential and spasmodic uplift. Over most of the transect the rocks showed an initial slow cooling phase from the peak metamorphic conditions followed by a period of rapid uplift and cooling. Dempster (1985) contrasts the presence of chloritoid + biotite assemblages in Perthshire with their absence in the Angus glens (SE Region), indicating slightly higher pressures of metamorphism in the latter. It should be noted that chloritoid + biotite assemblages reappear in the east of Angus both transitional to, and within the area of Stonehavian metamorphism (Harte & Hudson 1979, fig. 2). In the Balquidder area, Elles & Tilley (1930) noted inverted metamorphic zones with garnet zone rocks overlying biotite zone strata. Watkins (1985) noted that the porphyroblast growth post-dated the major nappe-forming movements and, in consequence, the inversion could not be tectonic. He suggested that the inversion represented a negative thermal gradient, which he attributed to the emplacement of relatively hot rocks during the nappe formation. Another possibility, however, is that the garnet crystallization was either inhibited in the biotite zone or subsequently retrograded by late-stage fluid movement, although Watkins (1985) argued that retrogression was not a significant factor. The zone of late-stage albite porphyroblast growth extends from this area to the SW Highlands. Watkins (1983) noted that the porphyroblasts occurred in the crests of regional D3 folds. He attributed their origin to a late-stage metamorphic phase driven by dehydration fluids trapped in the fold crests. However, Dymoke (1989) suggested that the albite was a product of a prograde phase initiated by D3 movements in rocks still at temperatures close to the maximum.

Southeast Region. This region encompasses the SE Highlands, east of the Portsoy Lineament and extends from the Highland Boundary Fault northwards to the Dee Valley. This is the classical area of Barrovian metamorphism. The isogradic surfaces trend broadly parallel to the Highland Boundary Fault and steepen markedly against it. Chinner (1978) suggested that the cause of the steepening was underthrusting by cold material. Harte & Hudson (1979) ascribed the steepening, in part, to late folding but also to the presence of a tectonic boundary to the south, roughly coincident with the Highland Boundary Fault. South of this boundary, a subsiding basin brought cold rocks into juxtaposition with the northern sequences at the time of metamorphism. Harte & Johnson (1969) showed that the main porphyroblast growth of kyanite and staurolite occurred between D2 and D3. A later phase of sillimanite growth occurred post-D3. Dempster (1985) studied the distribution of mineral cooling ages along a N–S transect of the region. He deduced that the area had suffered differential uplift in both space and time with, for example, the northern-most or structurally deepest rocks recording the oldest cooling ages, indicating relatively rapid uplift. In contrast, rocks rotated into the Highland Boundary Steep Belt by late folds showed evidence of very slow cooling. Dempster (1985) noted that the rapid uplift of hot rocks from depth might have resulted in heat transfer to adjacent blocks and prolonged or promoted metamorphism in these blocks.

North Perthshire Region. This region encompasses the Tummel Steep Belt northwards to the Boundary Slide. The rocks in this region are steeply dipping in contrast to the flat-lying aspect of those to the south. Dempster & Harte (1986) noted that the Barrovian zones, which showed a progressive increase in metamorphic grade across the Flat Belt, were poorly developed within the Steep Belt. This they attributed to continued porphyroblast growth in the northern region. In the Flat Belt, the main porphyroblast growth took place between D2 and D3 and syn-D3, whereas in the Steep Belt growth continued post-D3. They further calculated that there was a significant increase in pressure during this later phase: rising from 7 kbar at 550°C in the first phase to 9 kbar at 550°C in the latter. They suggested that this pressure increase was related to rotation and burial of originally flat-lying strata by late folding, promoting continued porphyroblast growth. Dempster (1985)

suggested that the region had cooled rapidly to c. 300°C in the period 460–440 Ma. The fact that the rocks in the steep belt do not record a temperature rise consequent upon their burial suggests that the rocks were uplifted shortly afterwards.

Buchan Region. This is essentially the area of Buchan metamorphism, lying east of the Portsoy Lineament and north of the Dee Valley. The Buchan region is structurally and metamorphically distinct from the rest of the Central Highlands. The region also contains the Newer Gabbro complexes (see above), a unique occurrence in the Scottish Dalradian. Structurally the area is relatively simple; D1 has not given rise to the major nappe structures, zones of inversion and crustal thickening seen in the other regions. Also the only other deformational phase identified in the region is evidenced by a late crenulation cleavage demonstrably post the main porphyroblast growth (Fig. 4.32d). Metamorphically, the area is characterized by the high-temperature–low-pressure conditions characteristic of Buchan metamorphism. Hudson (1985) estimated temperatures of c. 430°C, 490°C and 510°C for, respectively, the cordierite, andalusite and staurolite isograds; pressure estimates are uncertain but are reported by Hudson as 2–3.5 kbar in the staurolite zone.

The Newer Gabbro complexes were intruded after the early deformation and are broadly associated with peak metamorphic conditions (Fettes 1970; Pankhurst 1970). In general, the main regional porphyroblast growth is difficult to separate from the thermal effects. However, the intrusives undoubtedly boosted the ambient regional temperatures and gave rise, for example, to the upper amphibolite-facies sillimanite gneisses around the Huntly–Knock mass (Ashworth 1975). Droop & Charnley (1985) estimate the inner aureole conditions of 700–850°C and 4–5 kbar, indicating an emplacement depth of c. 15–18 km. Harte & Hudson (1979) suggested that there are two generations of sillimanite crystallization. The first was of regional metamorphic origin, and the second was related to the gabbroic complexes. On this basis they defined a regional sillimanite isograd (Harte & Hudson 1979, fig. 1).

Subsequent to the main blastesis, considerable movements occurred on the regional shear zone system (Ashcroft *et al.* 1984). These movements locally sheared both the igneous rocks and their aureoles (Figs. 4.32e, f). Kneller & Leslie (1984) demonstrated that the shearing occurred in rocks at or close to their peak metamorphic conditions and in one case led to the crystallization of sillimanite (fibrolite) in rocks previously with andalusite + cordierite assemblages. Kneller & Leslie suggested that this crystallization was probably facilitated by the percolation of hot fluids along the shear zones. The current position of the kyanite/andalusite isograd is close to the Portsoy Lineament. West of this, however, there is a zone up to 10 km wide where andalusite has inverted to kyanite (Chinner & Heseltine 1979; Baker 1985; Beddoe-Stephens 1990), indicative of a pressure increase. Beddoe-Stephens noted that pressure did not exceed 4.5 kbar east of the Portsoy Lineament but that the rocks to the west recorded significantly higher pressure with pressure values of 8–9 kbar inferred for the lower strata. He calculated that there had been a pressure increase during blastesis of c. 2 kbar across the lineament and it was this increase that had led to the inversion of the regional andalusite to kyanite. He attributed the pressure increase to overthrusting on the Portsoy lineament. Subsequently, Dempster *et al.* (1995) noted the lack of stratigraphical evidence for overthrusting, and suggested the pressure increase was caused by magmatic loading induced by intrusion of the basic complexes. Although this is an intriguing possibility, the question arises as to whether the intrusives have sufficient mass to produce the necessary overpressures.

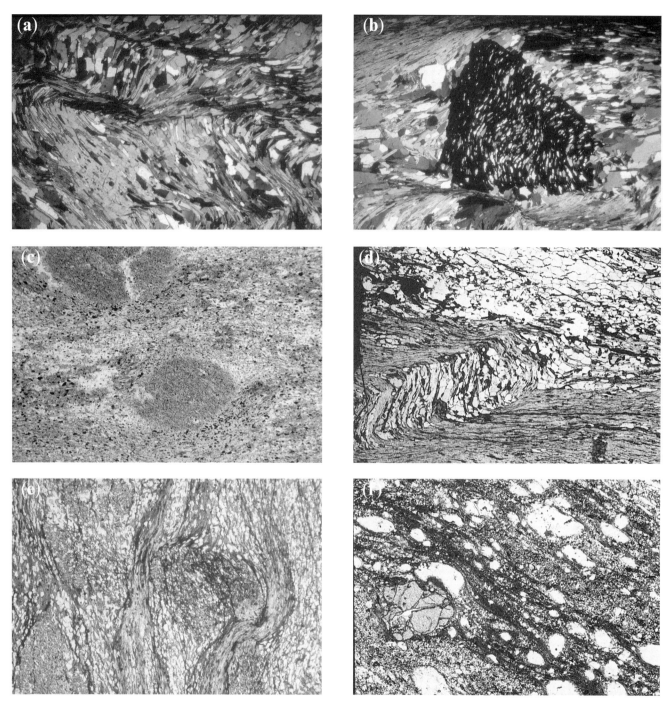

Fig. 4.32. Examples of textures seen in metamorphic rocks in the Grampian Highlands: (**a**) microcline schist with crenulations preserved within the microcline crystals (Inverlair Formation, Grampian Group, Glen Roy, Inverness-shire, XPL, BGS photograph P104092); (**b**) garnet schist with crenulations preserved within the garnet (Leven Schist Formation, Appin Group, Glen Roy, Inverness-shire, XPL, BGS photograph P104081); (**c**) rotated 'knot' from Southern Highland Group rocks (Collieston, Aberdeenshire, PPL, BGS photograph P509292); (**d**) quartz segregations defining a relatively low strain area in a crenulation (Culchavie Striped Formation, Easdale Subgroup, Strathdon, Aberdeenshire, PPL, BGS photograph PMS567); (**e**) andalusite schist with the andalusite crystals rotated within a highly sheared fabric associated with movements on the Portsoy–Duchray Hill Lineament; the central andalusite crystal carries a small cordierite overgrowth in its bottom right corner (Macduff Slate Formation, Southern Highland Group, Clashindarroch Forest, Aberdeenshire, PPL, BGS photograph P509294); (**f**) large garnet, feldspar and quartz porphyroclasts in a highly sheared fabric defined, in part, by biotite and fibrolite trails; the fabric is associated with late movements on the Portsoy–Duchray Hill Lineament (Scors Burn Formation, Argyll Group, Glenbuchat, Aberdeenshire, PPL, BGS photograph PMS565). Field of view is 5mm in (a) and (b) and 7mm in the other photomicrographs.

Monadhliath Region. This covers the remainder of the Central Highlands, dominated by the Monadhliath and Cairngorm areas. This area includes strata of the Glen Banchor and Dava successions that are unconformably overlain by rocks of the Grampian and Appin Groups. Structurally the region contains the notable structural features of the Geal Charn–Ossian Steep Belt, the Eilrig Shear Zone and the Grampian Slide as well as a number of other major shear zones. The greater part of the area lies in the amphibolite-facies, the exception being a strip of greenschist-facies rocks lying below the Eilrig Shear Zone (Fig. 4.31; Phillips *et al.* 1993). Phillips *et al.* (1999) reported a coherent metamorphic history in all the stratigraphical groups with growth of biotite during D1 and kyanite early in D2. The general conditions for kyanite growth are given by Phillips *et al.* (1999) as 7–8 kbar and 500–600°C. During the later part of D2, significant decompression resulted from movements on the shear zones with consequent conditions of 5–6 kbar and 585–695°C. This moved the rocks from the kyanite stability field into that of sillimanite. However, in the south of the region where late D2 shearing is absent no pressure decrease occurred and the rocks remained in the kyanite field. Phillips *et al.* (1993) suggested peak temperatures of 250°C for the greenschist-facies rocks below the Eilrig Shear Zone in contrast with 550°C for rocks above, suggesting considerable crustal shortening.

Metamorphic Models

A great variety of models have been proposed to explain the pattern of metamorphism in the Central Highlands. These include the thermal effects of 'older granites' (Barrow 1912), burial (Elles & Tilley 1930), thermal zonation around a mountain root (Kennedy 1948), uprising migmatite domes (Read & Farquhar 1956) and self-generating heat in tectonically heated crust (Richardson & Powell 1976). The latter is broadly seen as a principal cause although it does not explain the very high heat flows in the Buchan region, the area of least crustal thickening. The high heat flow in the Buchan area has been ascribed to deep-seated igneous masses (Harte & Hudson 1979) and to lithospheric stretching (Kneller 1985). The latter concept is consistent with extension necessary for intrusion of the gabbroic complexes and the absence of D2 structures. Therefore although there is a systematic increase in the geothermal gradient across the region it is probable that there is a fundamental change in the tectonic history into the Buchan region. Thus following the initial phases of nappe formation and the development of D1 recumbent folds, the Buchan region became a zone of extension, whereas to the southwest under ongoing compression the nappes continued to develop and the crust to thicken. Following peak metamorphic conditions the area was subject to differential and spasmodic uplift.

The Shetland ophiolite

An allochthonous complex of ultrabasic and basic rocks exposed in northeast Shetland (Fig. 4.33) has long been recognized as a fragment of the Iapetus Ocean or a related marginal basin that was thrust onto underlying Dalradian metasediments during the Caledonian orogeny (Garson & Plant 1973; Flinn *et al.* 1979; Flinn 1985; Prichard 1985; Spray 1988; Spray & Dunning 1991). The complex occurs in two thrust nappes with the most complete succession exposed in the lowermost nappe. This comprises, from base upwards, a metamorphic sole, peridotite, dunite, pyroxenite, gabbro and the lower levels of a possible sheeted dyke unit (Fig. 4.33). Apart from the absence of contiguous pillow lavas, the complex conforms to the commonly accepted definition of an ophiolite. Similar ophiolites have been identified in related parts of the Caledonian orogenic belt, such as Norway and Newfoundland (e.g. Dunning & Krogh 1985; Dunning & Pedersen 1988), and are critical to an understanding of the likely plate tectonic context of early phases of collision such as the Grampian event.

The lowermost nappe is best exposed on Unst and the internal ophiolite stratigraphy dips eastwards (Fig. 4.33). The peridotite unit is up to 2 km thick and heavily serpentinized; occasional unaltered relics indicate an original harzburgite mineralogy. Between the peridotite and dunite layer is a 500 m thick zone of interbanding of the two lithologies, with layers of dunite 0.1–1 m thick becoming progressively more common upwards. The dunite layer is up to 2 km thick, heavily

serpentinized and contains podiform chromite bodies (Prichard 1985; Chapter 16). The boundary between the dunite and gabbro layers is defined by an irregular pyroxenite-rich layer up to 1 km thick, dominated by banded wehrlite. The gabbro layer is several kilometres thick and dominated by fine-grained gabbros that record widespread recrystallization to actinolitic amphibole. On the east side of the main ophiolite unit about 3 km from the base of the gabbro, the gabbro is cut discordantly by dykes of fine-grained basic rocks that show chilled margins. About 1 km further to the east in southeast Unst, gabbros and cross-cutting dykes are overlain by metavolcanic rocks. The second major thrust nappe mainly comprises peridotite essentially identical to that in the lower nappe (Fig. 4.33). A U–Pb zircon age of 492 ± 3 Ma obtained from a plagiogranite within the gabbro unit dates crystallization of the complex (Spray & Dunning 1991).

Mélange zones occur between the nappes, below the lower nappe and above the upper nappe (Fig. 4.33). These incorporate a series of low-grade siltstones and gritty sandstones (the Phyllite Group), metavolcanic rocks and conglomerate layers. The conglomerates include clasts that can be matched with lithologies in the ophiolite, including gabbro, quartz-albite porphyry and albite-granite (trondjhemite), as well as pebbles of metasedimentary material similar to the underlying Dalradian rocks of the East Mainland Succession (Flinn 1958, 1985). Pillow lavas are found in blocks within the middle mélange on Fetlar (Spray 1988). The Funzie conglomerate on Fetlar (Fig. 4.33) is particularly distinctive because it contains quartzite pebbles. The mélanges are believed to have been derived from erosion of the ophiolite nappes as they emerged above sea-level (Flinn 1958). Continued thrusting resulted in these erosion

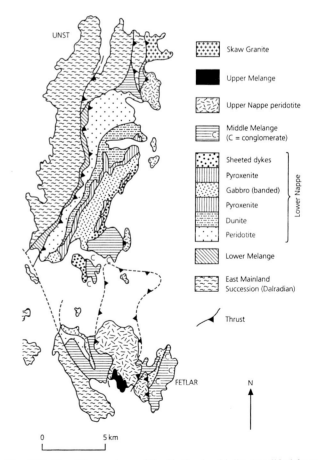

Fig. 4.33. Simplified geology of the Shetland ophiolite (modified from Flinn 1985).

products being overriden, metamorphosed and deformed. The Phyllite Group found in the mélange zone intervening between the nappes was deposited on the eroded upper surface of the lower nappe, prior to emplacement of the upper nappe.

Distinctive schistose sequences of greenschist- to amphibolite-facies metamorphic rocks are discontinuously exposed beneath the basal serpentinites of both thrust sheets, and also occur as detached blocks within the mélange zones (Read 1934). They may represent a 'metamorphic sole' analogous to those recognized beneath other ophiolites (e.g. Newfoundland (Williams & Smyth 1973)) and interpreted as the result of metamorphism and deformation during obduction of hot oceanic lithosphere. The metamorphic sole on Shetland is up to 400 m thick and shows a metamorphic inversion from upper amphibolite-facies in metabasites at the top of the sequence to low greenschist-facies at the base (Spray 1988). The highest grade mineral assemblages formed at $c.750°C$ (at 3 kbar). There is no evidence for high-pressure metamorphism and the maximum overburden may never have exceeded the total thickness of the ophiolite thrust sheets which is $c.10$ km. Obduction was accompanied by widespread greenschist facies metamorphism of the ophiolite as well as ductile shearing, folding and cataclasis. The large-scale synformal folding of the basal thrust of the upper nappe on Fetlar (Fig. 4.32) may reflect the overall structure of the ophiolite. Modelling of gravity and magnetic anomalies associated with the ophiolite shows that it has a synformal disposition and that its base is no deeper than 3 km (Flinn 2000). The overall structure is therefore that of a downfolded klippe, and it might be anticipated that Dalradian metasediments re-emerge on the sea-floor east of Unst and Fetlar.

Timing of the Grampian Event

Constraints on the timing of the Grampian event are provided by: the ages of fossils within the youngest deformed rocks, the isotopic dating of pre-, syn- and late-tectonic intrusions, and mineral 'cooling' ages obtained from metamorphosed Dalradian rocks and detrital micas within Ordovician turbidites in the Southern Uplands (see also Chapter 6).

Constraints on the lower limit of the Grampian event. Maximum ages for the Grampian event are given by dates of 601 ± 4 Ma for the Tayvallich lavas (Dempster et al. 2002) and 590 ± 2 Ma for the Ben Vurich granite (Rogers et al. 1989). However, a post-Early Cambrian age for the event is indicated by the late Early Cambrian age of trilobites from the Leny Limestone (see also Chapter 5). This means that the Grampian event must have occurred after $c.520$ Ma. If the Early Ordovician age proposed for the Macduff Slate Formation on the basis of a single acritarch proves robust, then the Grampian event must have occurred still later, post-485 Ma.

Constraints on deformation and peak metamorphism. In common with many orogenic belts, the dating of prograde metamorphism during the Grampian event is highly problematical. However, the dating of D3 deformation and accompanying low-pressure, high-temperature Buchan metamorphism in Aberdeenshire is constrained by a number of U–Pb mineral ages obtained from syn- to late tectonic plutons (see pp. 112–113) that imply that the Grampian event was well under way by 480–475 Ma and was completed by $c.460$ Ma (Oliver et al. 2000). This is consistent with U–Pb monazite ages of $c.470$–450 Ma obtained from Grampian Group units in the Monadliath area and thought to date peak metamorphism (Barreiro, quoted in Phillips et al. 1999).

Constraints on post-metamorphic cooling. A series of mineral ages obtained from muscovite and biotite using different methods are thought to date uplift and cooling of the metamorphic belt (Dempster 1985; Dempster et al. 1995). Muscovite Rb–Sr ages (with a closing temperature of $c.500°C$) range from 565 to 450 Ma, with clusters around 470, 460 and 450 Ma. The dates older than Mid-Ordovician were obtained from low-grade rocks (chlorite zone) that may not have been entirely reset by Grampian metamorphism (Oliver 2001), or have a very low Rb–Sr ratio and may not be reliable (Evans & Soper 1997). Muscovite K–Ar ages (with a closing temperature of $c.350°C$) range from 480 to 425 Ma, with the majority of analyses between 475 and 440 Ma. Biotite Rb–Sr ages (with a closing temperature of $c.300°C$) range from 505 to 400 Ma. Cooling ages older than 460 Ma again have a very low Rb–Sr ratio and may not be reliable (Evans & Soper 1997; Oliver 2001). A cluster of cooling ages between 415 and 400 Ma is likely to reflect the intrusion of Devonian granites and gabbros. There then remains a cluster of Grampian cooling ages between 450 and 435 Ma. Biotite K–Ar ages (also with a closing temperature of $c.300°C$) range from 475 to 400 Ma.

The present consensus is that the peak of Grampian metamorphism in the Central Highlands occurred at $c.470$ Ma and was followed by cooling and uplift relatively soon thereafter at $c.460$ Ma (Dempster et al. 1995; Soper et al. 1999; Oliver et al. 2000). The mineral ages suggest relatively rapid cooling through 500°C and 350°C between 470 and 440 Ma, and slower cooling through 300°C between 460 and 430 Ma, depending on the location within the orogen, suggesting unroofing of the Grampian metamorphic belt during the Arenig through to the Early Silurian. This is in accord with a date of $c.470$ Ma for peak Grampian metamorphism in Connemara in western Ireland (Friedrich et al. 1999).

Other cooling ages of significance have been obtained from the Shetland and Ballantrae ophiolites. K–Ar hornblende ages obtained from the metamorphic sole of the Shetland ophiolite range between $c.479$ and $c.465$ Ma and are interpreted to broadly date ophiolite obduction and thus the onset of the Grampian event (Spray 1988). An $^{40}Ar/^{39}Ar$ age of 498 ± 2 Ma obtained from hornblende in the metamorphic sole by Flinn et al. (1991) is, however, older than the U–Pb crystallization age for the complex (Spray & Dunning 1991) and therefore of uncertain significance. The Ballantrae ophiolite in the Midland Valley terrane (see Chapter 5) has yielded hornblende K–Ar ages of 478 ± 4 Ma that are similarly interpreted as the age of obduction and thus the start of the Grampian event.

Detrital mineral ages. In the Southern Uplands, Ordovician to Silurian greywacke turbidites contain metamorphic and igneous detritus. K–Ar dating of detrital muscovite grains has yielded ages between 500 and 420 Ma, with a concentration between 490 and 455 Ma and a clear peak at 475 (Kelley & Bluck 1989; Bluck 2001). Provenance work on detrital garnets (Hutchison & Oliver 1998; Oliver 2001) suggests that the source area had been affected by Barrovian-type metamorphism. The ages of the detrital micas are compatible with an Ordovician age for the Grampian event and the source of the sediments in the Southern Uplands could have been the Dalradian. The provenance of the sediments of the Southern Uplands is described further in Chapter 6.

Concluding remarks

There is now a consensus that the Grampian event was well under way by 470 Ma and essentially completed by $c.460$ Ma (Soper et al. 1999; Dewey & Mange 2000; Oliver 2001). The exact duration of the orogenic event remains unclear, mainly because of uncertainty surrounding the age of the Macduff

Slate Formation. If further palaeontological evidence can substantiate the Early Ordovician age proposed for these rocks,
then the Grampian event must have been a relatively short-
lived (10–15 Ma) orogeny during Mid-Ordovician times. On the
other hand, if the Early Ordovician age for the Macduff Slate
Formation does not prove robust, orogenic activity could have
started shortly after *c.* 520 Ma, the age of the Leny Limestone.
In the latter case, orogenic activity could have occurred over a
longer period (*c.* 40–50 Ma).

Grampian structures and metamorphism in the Northern Highlands

Isotopic evidence indicates that parts of the Northern Highlands were also affected by a *c.* 470 Ma tectonothermal event
that has been correlated with the Grampian event. The effects
of this event are most evident in east Sutherland and eastern
Inverness-shire where the effects of later (Scandian) reworking
are apparently restricted.

Sutherland

Regional migmatization of Moine rocks in east Sutherland has
been dated at *c.* 470–460 Ma (U–Pb zircon; Kinny *et al.* 1999).
The migmatites are commonly regularly layered stromatic
types with concordant leucosomes up to 5 cm thick, flanked
by biotite- or quartz-rich selvedges (Fig. 4.34; Burns 1994; Watt
et al. 1996). Evidence for large-scale melt accumulation is
provided by the occurrence of sheets of subconcordant melt up
to a hundred metres wide and several hundreds of metres in
length. Minor 'D2' folds of migmatitic layers are recumbent
and tight-to-isoclinal; fold axes trend parallel to a N–S trending
mineral lineation. These structures are cross-cut locally by late,
discordant layers of melt and must therefore have formed
during the Grampian event. Garnet–pyroxene granulite-facies
assemblages occur within metabasic sheets that intrude Moine
paragneisses of the Naver Nappe (Friend, C. R. L. *et al.* 2000).
Peak metamorphism at 11–12 kbar at 650–700°C is thought
to have occurred during the same Grampian metamorphic
event that resulted in migmatization of the host Moine rocks
(Fig. 4.35).

Inverness-shire

A U–Pb titanite age of 470 ± 2 Ma obtained from the Fort
Augustus granitic gneiss is interpreted to correspond to the age
of Grampian amphibolite facies metamorphism in the rocks of
the 'flat belt' east of the Loch Quoich Line (Rogers *et al.* 2001).
The dominant structures within the flat belt are a series of
recumbent tight to isoclinal folds that have a highly curvilinear
sheath geometry as a result of heterogeneous, low-angle simple
shear parallel to a N–S trending lineation (Fig. 4.36; Holdsworth & Roberts 1984). Microstructures and cm-scale shear
zones indicate a top-to-the-north sense of shear parallel to the
lineation (Strachan, unpublished data). The folds deform rare
isoclinal folds and an earlier bedding-parallel schistosity, and
are therefore assigned to D2 in the local deformation sequence
(Holdsworth & Roberts 1984; Strachan 1985). A Grampian
age for these structures seems probable but remains to be
demonstrated unequivocally (Rogers *et al.* 2001). D2 tectonic
strain within the flat belt varies considerably. Extensive areas
of intensely banded rocks (e.g. Glen Garry) lacking sedimentary structures or fold hinges are thought to reflect the imposi-
tion of large D2 strains that have transposed all planes into
parallelism. In contrast, in areas of apparent low D2 strain,
sedimentation structures and cross-cutting relations between
metabasic sheets and host Moine rocks are commonly preserved (Roberts & Harris 1983).

Fig. 4.34. Kirtomy migmatite, Cnoc Mor, east Sutherland, showing
extensive partial melting. Camera lens cap is 40 mm in diameter.

The D2 structures described above can be traced into the
Northern Highland Steep Belt where they predate intrusion of
the Glen Dessary syenite at 456 ± 5 Ma (Fig. 4.3; van Breemen
et al. 1979b; Roberts *et al.* 1984). Isotopic evidence for Grampian metamorphism comprises concordant U–Pb monazite
ages of 455 ± 3 Ma obtained from the Ardgour granite gneiss
and host psammites at Glenfinnan (Fig. 4.12; Aftalion & van
Breemen 1980). A major concentration of variably deformed
trondjhemitic pegmatites is spatially coincident with the central
belt of high-grade metamorphism in Inverness-shire and Ross-
shire. These pegmatites are thought to have resulted from
localized melting of the Moine, and were once regarded as the
source of the *lit-par-lit* regional migmatites. However, it is now
clear on structural grounds that the migmatites and pegmatites are genetically unrelated: the regional migmatites are
syn-D1 (and arguably Neoproterozoic) and older than the
pegmatites that cut D2 folds and fabrics (van Breemen *et al.*
1974). Two pegmatites near Glenfinnan have yielded ages of
445 ± 10 Ma (Rb–Sr muscovite) and 450 ± 10 Ma (U–Pb monazite, bulk fractions) (van Breemen *et al.* 1974).

Silurian orogenic activity: the Scandian event

It is believed that continued closure of the Iapetus Ocean after
the Grampian orogenic event was achieved by a reversal in
the polarity of oceanic subduction and the development of the
Southern Uplands accretionary prism (Fig. 4.23; Dewey &
Ryan 1990). The final orogenic events recorded in the Scottish
Highlands are the result of the collision of three continental
blocks, Laurentia, Baltica and Avalonia (Soper & Hutton
1984; Pickering *et al.* 1988; Soper *et al.* 1992). In the Early
Silurian, Baltica is thought to have collided with the segment
of the Laurentian margin that incorporated the Northern
Highland terrane, to result in the Scandian orogenic event
(Fig. 4.37; Coward 1990; Dewey & Mange 1999; Dallmeyer
et al. 2001; Kinny *et al.* 2003). Regionally significant ductile
thrusting and folding of the Moine rocks and associated
basement inliers culminated in development of the Moine
Thrust Zone. The Grampian terrane displays no evidence of
regional deformation and metamorphism during the Scandian
event; evidently it must have been located away from, and to
the south of, the main collision (Fig. 4.37). Major sinistral
strike-slip faults developed prior to and during the collision of
Avalonia and Laurentia. Strike-slip faulting associated with
the lateral translation of Baltica and Avalonia along the
Laurentian margin was probably continuous through the Late

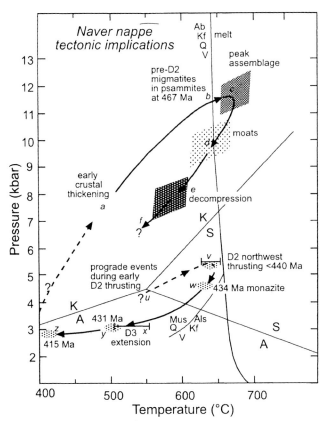

Fig. 4.35. Partial pressure–temperature–time–deformation (*P–T–t–D*) loops for the Grampian and Scandian orogenic events within the Naver nappe, north Sutherland (modified from Friend, C R. L. *et al.* 2000). Trajectory *a–f* is associated with Grampian high pressure metamorphism and melting and is constrained by data presented in Friend *et al.* (2000). Within trajectory *u–v* which is associated with Scandian ductile thrusting, field *v* represents melt-absent, syn-thrusting metamorphism. Bars *v* and *x* represent temperature ranges obtained from garnet–biotite thermometry (Burns 1994). Monazite date at *w* is from Kinny *et al.* (1999). Fields at *y* and *z* represent closure conditions recorded by, respectively, hornblende and muscovite ^{40}Ar/^{39}Ar ages. Ab, albite; Als, Al$_2$SiO$_5$; Kf, K-feldspar; Mus, muscovite; Q, quartz; V, Vapor.

Silurian into the Early Devonian to result in final juxtaposition of the Northern Highland and Grampian terranes.

Scandian deformation and metamorphism of the Moine Supergroup

Field-based structural models have long viewed the Sgurr Beag, Naver and Moine thrusts and associated fold and thrust structures as part of the same kinematically linked system of foreland-propagating deformation (e.g. Soper & Brown 1971; Barr *et al.* 1986; Holdsworth 1989; Alsop *et al.* 1996; Holdsworth *et al.* 2001). However, the prevailing view has been that the Sgurr Beag and Naver thrusts and associated structures and amphibolite-facies assemblages formed during the Grampian event, and were unrelated kinematically to the younger Moine Thrust Zone (e.g. Kelley & Powell 1985; Powell & Phillips 1985; Harris 1995). This interpretation was based mainly on Rb–Sr muscovite ages of *c.*450 Ma obtained from syn- to post-tectonic pegmatites near Glenfinnan (van Breemen *et al.* 1974), a Rb–Sr whole rock age of 467 ± 20 Ma obtained from the Morar Pelite in Knoydart and thought to date amphibolite-facies metamorphism (Brewer *et al.* 1979), and the view of Powell *et al.* (1981) that displacement along the Sgurr Beag Thrust occurred

during the same metamorphic event. More recently, however, U–Pb zircon ages of *c.*435–420 Ma have been obtained from penetratively deformed meta-granites in central Sutherland, and demonstrate unequivocally widespread Late Silurian deformation within the Moine Supergroup (Kinny *et al.* 2003). This has resulted in a reappraisal of the ages of various structures. It is now considered that the major ductile thrusts and widespread associated recumbent folds and fabrics in the Moine Nappe, as well as the upright folds that form the Northern Highland steep belt, are all likely to have formed during the Scandian event (Fig. 4.38; Kinny *et al.* 2003). The intensity of the Scandian event appears to diminish eastwards, because the East Sutherland migmatites and the Loch Eil Group rocks of the 'flat belt' in Inverness-shire are apparently dominated by largely unmodified Grampian structures (Fig. 4.38). Further isotopic dating will test this new view of the Caledonian structural development of the Northern Highland terrane.

Scandian ductile thrusting and folding in Sutherland

The best place to study Scandian thrust-related deformation is Sutherland where the effects of later upright folding are minimal. The most significant regional structure is the Naver Thrust (Fig. 4.38). The structurally lowest part of the overlying Naver Nappe is internally imbricated by a series of thrusts which branch off the Naver Thrust, the most significant of which are the Torrisdale and Swordly thrusts (Burns 1994; British Geological Survey 1997*a*; Strachan, unpublished data; Fig. 4.38). The underlying Moine Nappe is also internally imbricated by the Dherue and Ben Hope thrusts; the latter branches into a ductile imbricate stack in the Talmine area (Fig. 4.38; Holdsworth 1989). Ductile thrusting was accompanied in the Morar Group rocks by widespread deformation that has been traditionally referred to as 'D2' (e.g. Soper & Brown 1971; Soper & Wilkinson 1975; Holdsworth 1989; Strachan & Holdsworth 1988; Alsop *et al.* 1996; Holdsworth *et al.* 2001). It is evident, however, that there can be no correlation between these Silurian structures and the Grampian-age D2 folds referred to earlier in the overlying Sgurr Beag-Naver Nappe.

Within the Morar Group of west and central Sutherland, D2 deformation resulted in ubiquitous development of a composite S0/S1/S2 foliation that dips gently ESE where unaffected by later folding. The foliation intensifies into broad zones of high strain platy blastomylonites associated with the ductile thrusts. An L2 mineral lineation is developed throughout the Moine Nappe. It is thought to lie sub-parallel to the D2 thrust transport direction and shows a well defined swing in orientation from gently ESE-plunging in the west adjacent to the Moine Thrust to SSE-plunging adjacent to the Naver Thrust (Fig. 4.38; Soper & Brown 1971; Barr *et al.* 1986; Strachan & Holdsworth 1988). Microstructures indicate a general top-to-the-NW sense of shear parallel to L2. Tight to isoclinal D2 folds are developed on all scales (Fig. 4.39); they commonly display sheath fold geometries due to intense ductile strains so that the majority of D2 hinges now plunge sub-parallel to L2 (Holdsworth 1989; Alsop & Holdsworth 1999). D2 folds are locally polyphase as a result of differential displacements along ductile thrusts (Holdsworth 1990; Alsop & Holdsworth 1993; Alsop *et al.* 1996). The folding of the Naver and Ben Hope thrusts by D2 structures developed in their footwalls demonstrates that D2 deformation propagated towards the foreland. D2 deformation was responsible for the major interleaving of Moine rocks with Lewisian-type basement in Sutherland (Fig. 4.40). Within the Morar Group, many inliers occupy the cores of D2 sheath folds (e.g. Naver, Borgie). Thin allochthonous slices of highly strained basement lie along the Ben Hope, Naver and Swordly thrusts. Other inliers (e.g. Ribigill) occupy the cores of

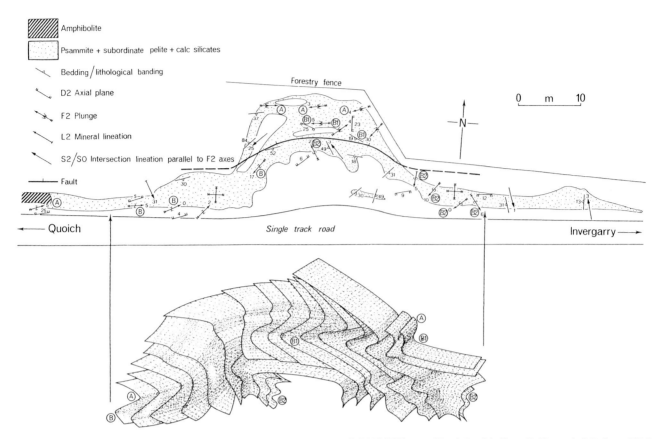

Legend:
- Amphibolite
- Psammite + subordinate pelite + calc silicates
- Bedding / lithological banding
- D2 Axial plane
- F2 Plunge
- L2 Mineral lineation
- S2/S0 Intersection lineation parallel to F2 axes
- Fault

Forestry fence

0   m   10

— N —

← Quoich   Single track road   Invergarry →

Fig. 4.36. Complex curvilinear D2 sheath fold geometries in Glen Garry quarry [NH 196023] east of Loch Quoich (from Holdsworth & Roberts 1984).

isoclinal folds, the lower limbs of which have been replaced by ductile thrusts (Fig. 4.40).

Lines of evidence that indicate that D2 was accompanied by regional amphibolite-facies metamorphism at temperatures of >550–600°C include: (1) the presence of syn-D2 garnet and

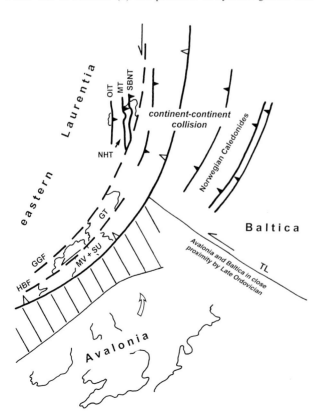

Fig. 4.37. Schematic plate tectonic framework for the Early Silurian (*c.* 435 Ma) showing how regional thrusting in the Northern Highland terrane resulted from Laurentia–Baltica collision (the Scandian orogeny). The dashed lines represent the major strike-slip faults that developed subsequently, prior to, and during, Avalonia–Laurentia collision between the Late Silurian and Early Devonian. OIT, Outer Isles Thrust; MT, Moine Thrust; SBNT, Sgurr Beag–Naver Thrust; GGF, Great Glen Fault; HBF, Highland Boundary Fault; TL, Tornquist Line; NHT, Northern Highland terrane; GT, Grampian terrane; MV, Midland Valley; SU, Southern Uplands.

staurolite within Morar Group pelites; (2) the widespread parallelism of hornblende with L2 in metabasic rocks; and (3) the identification of post-D2 kyanite within basement metasedimentary rocks of the Meadie inlier (Strachan & Holdsworth 1988; Holdsworth 1989; Burns 1994; Holdsworth *et al.* 2001; Strachan, unpublished data). Numerous sheets of deformed meta-granite intrude the Moine rocks in the vicinity of the Naver Thrust in central Sutherland. The granites cut D2 folds but carry the regional L2 lineation, suggesting syn-tectonic emplacement (Barr 1985; Holdsworth & Strachan 1988). U–Pb zircon ages of *c.* 435–420 Ma are interpreted to date emplacement, and hence constrain the regional ductile thrusting event to the Silurian (Kinny *et al.* 2003). $^{40}Ar/^{39}Ar$ hornblende ages and Rb–Sr and $^{40}Ar/^{39}Ar$ muscovite ages obtained from the thrust nappes in Sutherland generally range between *c.* 440 Ma and *c.* 410 Ma (Dallmeyer *et al.* 2001). These ages are interpreted to date cooling during and following Scandian thrusting and folding.

Scandian ductile thrusting and D2 folding in Ross-shire and Inverness-shire

Extensive tracts of the Morar Group in Ross-shire are dominated by NW-trending lineations and associated tight-to-isoclinal, reclined D2 folds (Fig. 4.38; Wilson & Shepherd

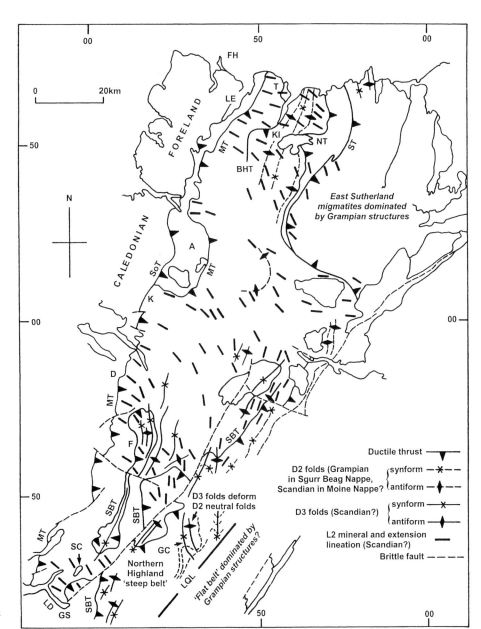

Fig. 4.38. Caledonian structures within the Moine rocks of Ross-shire and Sutherland (compiled from Sutton & Watson 1953, 1954; Clifford 1960; Tobisch *et al.* 1970; Wilson 1975; Strachan & Holdsworth 1988; Peacock *et al.* 1992; May *et al.* 1993; British Geological Survey 1997*a*, and the unpublished data of RAS). KI, Kinloch Valley; T, Talmine; A, Assynt; K, Knockan; D, Dundonnell; F, Fannich; FH, Faraid Head; GC, Glen Cannich; GS, Glen Shiel; LD, Loch Duich; SC, Sguman Cointich; MT, Moine Thrust; SBT, Sgurr Beag Thrust; NT, Naver Thrust; BHT, Ben Hope Thrust; ST, Swordly Thrust, LQL, Loch Quoich Line.

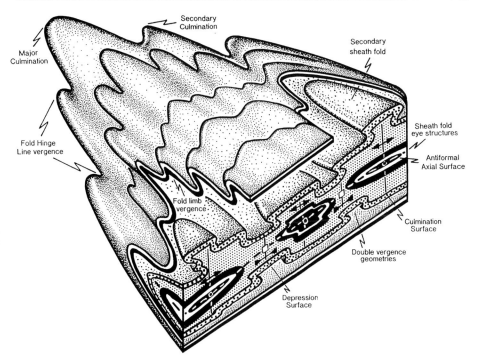

Fig. 4.39. Schematic three-dimensional sketch illustrating the geometry of the type of Scandian 'D2' sheath fold that is responsible for the interleaving of Moine rocks and Lewisianoid basement inliers in the Sleitell area, north Sutherland (from Alsop & Holdsworth 1999 with permission of Elsevier Science). Note that cross-sectional views across culmination and depression surfaces display double vergence and elliptical eye structures that are characteristic of curvilinear hinge geometries.

1979; Kelley & Powell 1985) identical to those described from Sutherland. The prominent linear fabric within the Carn Chuinneag–Inchbae granite also formed during this D2 event (Shepherd 1973; Wilson & Shepherd 1979). These D2 structures are thought to have developed during NW-directed displacement along the Sgurr Beag Thrust. Given that the Naver Thrust is thought to be the northern extension of the Sgurr Beag Thrust (e.g. Strachan & Holdsworth 1988), it seems reasonable to correlate the D2 structures in the Morar Group of Ross-shire and Sutherland. Geometrically similar structures are also present within the Morar Group around Loch Duich (Fig. 4.38) where May et al. (1993) have documented widespread tight-to-isoclinal D2 folding during NW-directed ductile thrusting. Major D2 folds developed further south along the western seaboard include the reclined Beinn a' Chapuill fold in Glenelg (Ramsay 1958), and the downward-facing Arnipol synform in southeast Morar (Powell 1966). In Morar, Ardnamurchan and Mull, highly curvilinear, tight-to-isoclinal D2 folds are associated with generally westerly-facing, semi-penetrative cleavages (Holdsworth et al. 1987; A. L. Harris, unpublished data).

The trace of the Sgurr Beag Thrust through Ross-shire and northern Inverness-shire to Loch Hourn is commonly marked by allochthonous slices of basement (Tanner et al. 1970). These may have been derived from a rift shoulder within the Moine sedimentary basin (Tanner et al. 1970; Soper et al. 1998). Many of the inliers are characterized by remarkable lateral persistence over distances of kilometres as thin, parallel-sided sheets only a metre or so in thickness. This reflects the high tectonic strains characteristic of the ductile thrust zones into which they were emplaced. These high strains are also manifest by the extreme parallelism of the foliation-banding in the adjacent Moine rocks which as a consequence lack sedimentary structures and folds (Rathbone & Harris 1979; Rathbone et al. 1983). The Sgurr Beag Thrust is not associated with basement slices south of Loch Hourn. Identification of its southward course depends largely upon recognition of the highly strained contact between unmigmatized Morar Group and migmatitic Glenfinnan Group units (Powell et al. 1981; Barr et al. 1986) across which local structural discordances have been recorded (Baird 1982). The total displacement along the thrust is uncertain, but likely to be at least tens of kilometres and conceivably >100 km (Powell et al. 1981).

Outliers of the Sgurr Beag Thrust lie in the cores of tight synforms to the west of the main outcrop (e.g. Fannich, Sguman Cointich; Fig. 4.38). Successive trails of basement inliers have been mapped around and within both outliers, suggesting that the Sgurr Beag Thrust passes westwards, at least in Ross-shire, into a ductile duplex marked by numerous discrete thrusts. The recognition of such a duplex structure may explain the nature and origin of other much more complex areas in which basement inliers occur. These include the Coire nan Gall 'series' in Kintail (Clifford 1957) and the Bealach a' Chassim Complex at the foot of Glen Shiel (Fig. 4.38; Simony 1973). The latter comprises numerous basement slices, occurring on all scales of thickness from millimetres to tens or hundreds of metres, interspersed with quartzo-feldspathic rocks that resemble Moine psammites but could be comminuted and recrystallized basement acid gneisses.

D3 upright folding
Widespread upright folding that is commonly referred to as 'D3' resulted in the formation of the Northern Highland Steep Belt (Fig. 4.41). Westwards from the Loch Quoich Line to the western seaboard, much of the Moine is steeply-dipping, mainly as a result of D3 and later structures overprinting D1

and D2 folds and related fabrics. As with the D1 and D2 episodes, strains imposed by D3 appear to be heterogeneous on all scales, and some zones in west Ardnamurchan and Knoydart appear to have escaped the strongest D3 deformation. A large part of the steep belt is occupied by the Glenfinnan Group. D3 folds are represented by N–S to NNE-trending, tight folds developed on all scales. These are accompanied by crenulation cleavage and have hinges that are strongly curvilinear through the horizontal, as shown by abundant closed outcrop patterns. The latter are commonly complicated by interference with earlier D1 and D2 folds (Fig. 4.42; Plate 7) especially where the contrasting siliceous psammite and pelitic units of the Glenfinnan Group clearly define outcrop patterns. Outliers of Loch Eil Group occur within the steep belt (Figs 4.3, 4.41), along the axial trace of a major composite synform characterized by periodic plunge reversals (Roberts et al. 1984, 1987). The stability of garnet, biotite and hornblende within D3 crenulations suggests that deformation occurred at temperatures equivalent to the amphibolite facies (c. 500 °C or higher). Within the steep belt, D3 folding was postdated by the emplacement of ramifying networks of pegmatite (Plate 8).

There is clear evidence in a number of areas that the Sgurr Beag Thrust is folded by D3 folds. Thus a gently-plunging D3 fold pair deforms the thrust east of Lochailort (Fig. 4.3; Powell et al. 1981). Folding of the thrust during D3 also accounts for its repetition, together with overlying Glenfinnan Group gneisses, as a major outlier in the Fannich area (Fig. 4.3). The closed outcrop pattern of the thrust and the Glenfinnan Group rocks reflects their location in the core of a slightly curvilinear D3 synform. A similar synformal outlier of the thrust is present at Sguman Cointich (Fig. 4.3), but here the D3 hinge is strongly curvilinear and sheath-like. The elongate outcrop form of the Carn Chuineag granite also reflects its location in the core of a slightly curvilinear D3 synform. The intensity of D3 deformation diminishes northwards, and D3 folds are absent in most of Sutherland. D3 folds similarly diminish in intensity westwards: the D3 Morar Antiform and an analogous antiform on the Ardnamurchan peninsula are major open folds. The southernmost D3 structures are those exposed on the Ross of Mull where the major, SSW-plunging Assapol synform is cored by the Glenfinnan Group (Holdsworth et al. 1987).

The eastern limit of the Northern Highland Steep Belt is defined by the Loch Quoich Line (Fig. 4.3; Clifford 1957; Roberts & Harris 1983). In its type area this is defined as the axial trace of an open, asymmetric, SSW-plunging D3 synform; the fold has a subvertical western limb and a shallowly dipping eastern limb. In the region between Glen Garry and Invermoriston, there is a marked contrast between the uniformly steep to subvertical, highly strained rocks of the steep belt, and the Loch Eil psammites of the flat belt to the east that remained largely unaffected by F3 folds. However, the Loch Quoich Line is more difficult to define south of Glen Garry because the Loch Eil Group rocks are also commonly steeply-inclined (Stoker 1983; Strachan 1985). Upright (D3?) folding is probably responsible for the emergence of Glenfinnan Group rocks at the east end of Loch Arkaig from beneath the Loch Eil Group (Figs 4.3, 4.41).

Moine Thrust Zone
The Moine Thrust Zone is the westernmost and youngest of the system of Scandian thrusts on the mainland of Northern Scotland. It is conventionally taken to define the northwest edge of the Caledonian orogenic belt, although localized Caledonian displacements may also have occurred along the Outer Isles Fault Zone further to the west. The Moine Thrust Zone dips gently towards the ESE. It has an on-land strike length of

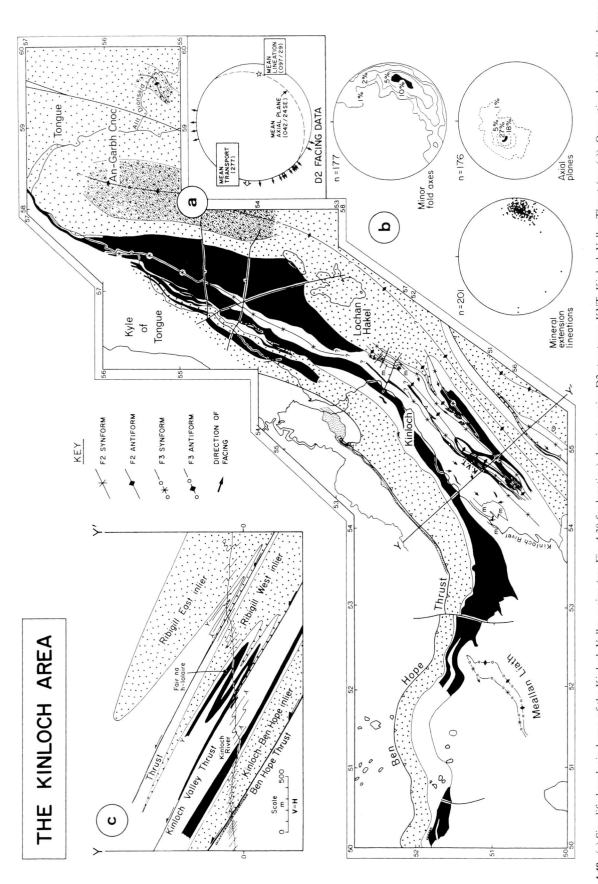

Fig. 4.40. (a) Simplified geological map of the Kinloch Valley region (see Fig. 4.38 for location) showing major D2 structures; KVT, Kinloch Valley Thrust (see **(c)**). Open stipple as well as denser stipple around An-Garbh Cnoc represents Lewisianoid basement; black is the Ben Hope Sill. Moine rocks are unornamented apart from the thin strip of stipple below the Ben Hope Thrust which is a Moine pelite. Stereonet of facing data is shown in box; **(b)** stereonets of D2 structural data in the Kinloch area; **(c)** interpretative NW-SE cross-section (position Y-Y' shown in (a)). From Holdsworth (1989).

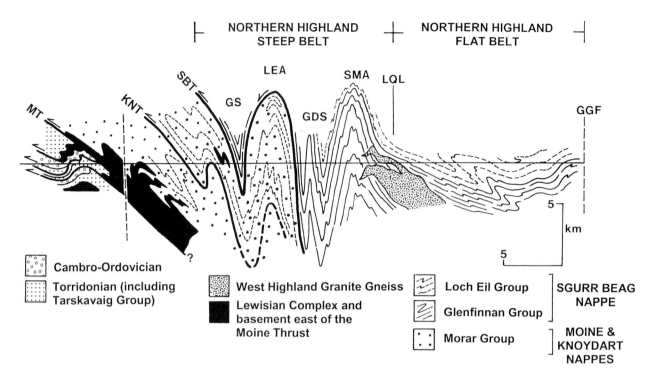

Fig. 4.41. Geological cross-section across the SW Moine drawn approximately along line XY in Figure 4.3 (modified from Powell & Glendinning 1988). MT, Moine Thrust; KNT, Knoydart Thrust; SBT, Sgurr Beag Thrust; GS, Glenshian Synform; LEA, Loch Eilt Antiform; GDS, Glen Dessary Synform; SMA, Spidean Mialach Antiform; LQL, Loch Quoich Line; GGF, Great Glen Fault. Note: (a) the infold of Loch Eil Group in the core of the Glen Dessary Synform; (b) the local emergence of Glenfinnan Group rocks adjacent to the Great Glen Fault.

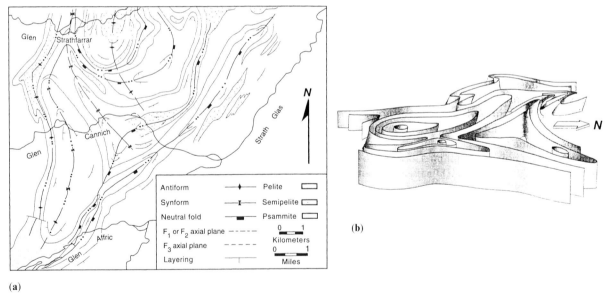

Fig. 4.42. (a) Tectonic sketch map of the Glen Cannich and adjacent areas in the Northern Highland steep belt, showing major dome and basin interference patterns that resulted from the refolding of D1/D2 folds by upright D3 folds during the Scandian event; (b) simplified three-dimensional diagram of the interference patterns in the Glen Cannich area (from Tobisch 1966 with permission of the Geological Society of America).

c. 200 km between Loch Eriboll and Skye (Fig. 4.3), and probably extends northeastwards towards Shetland (Ritchie *et al.* 1987) and southwestwards beyond Mull, to make a total distance of *c.* 500 km. Although in some places the Moine Thrust Zone is a simple structure, with Moine rocks resting more or less directly on the Foreland, elsewhere a complex array of thrust sheets separates the Moine rocks from undeformed Foreland.

Regional structure. Within the Moine Thrust Zone there are a number of major, separate thrust planes (Fig. 4.43), although it is likely that none can be traced for the entire length of the thrust belt. In detail, individual thrusts may be folded, locally discontinuous and coalesce (Fig. 4.44). The most significant structure is the Moine Thrust itself, which has traditionally been identified as the thrust that directly underlies the Moine rocks. However, even this simple definition presents problems because this structure is clearly of different ages within various parts of the thrust zone. Thus the Moine rocks in some areas (e.g. Loch Eriboll) are underlain by an early ductile thrust which occurs within a thick mylonite belt, whereas in other areas (e.g. Knockan) they are underlain by a brittle, low-angle fault that formed at a late stage in the development of the thrust belt (Soper & Wilkinson 1975; Coward 1985).

The structurally highest part of the thrust zone is an extensive belt (hundreds of metres thick) of mylonites, best exposed in the Loch Eriboll area (Soper & Wilkinson 1975; Evans & White 1984). The mylonites are fine-grained and strongly banded schistose rocks formed from the intense ductile shear and recrystallization of Moine metasedimentary rocks, associated slices of Lewisian basement, and Cambrian quartzites. The mylonites are characterized by widespread recrystallization of quartz and the growth of new muscovite and chlorite within the greenschist-facies (Evans & White 1984). Formation of the mylonites is thus thought to record early WNW-directed thrusting onto the Hebridean foreland at mid-crustal levels. The mylonites commonly show evidence for multiple phases of small-scale folding (Soper & Wilkinson 1975); however, these complexities have no regional significance as they are probably the result of complex and localized ductile flow patterns (e.g. Holdsworth 1990; Alsop & Holdsworth 1993). In west Sutherland, the regional Scandian L2 lineation within the Morar Group rocks (Fig. 4.38) is parallel with the main mineral and stretching lineation within the mylonite belt (Soper & Brown 1971). This suggests that internal ductile thrusting and folding of the Morar Group is linked kinematically with development of the mylonite belt during the same Scandian event. The progressive decrease apparent in syn-thrusting metamorphic grade from east to west across Sutherland (Soper & Brown 1971) suggests that the thrust sheets were partially exhumed by erosion and/or extensional faulting as they formed (Barr et al. 1986).

Beneath the Moine Thrust lies what was termed by the original surveyors (Peach et al. 1907) a 'Zone of Complication' within which a number of thrust-bounded nappes are stacked on top of each other (Fig. 4.44). This is the Moine Thrust Zone sensu stricto. The zone comprises complexely thrust-faulted and folded Cambro-Ordovician and Torridonian sedimentary rocks and Lewisian basement (Fig. 4.45). The thrusts are

Fig. 4.43. The Glencoul Thrust, northeast slopes of Loch Glencoul, Assynt. The hummocky ground on the far left is underlain by Archaean orthogneisses of the Lewisian Complex. These are overlain unconformably by Cambrian quartzites of the Eriboll Sandstone Formation which form the steep faces; bedding dips gently to the right. The Glencoul Thrust is located in the poorly exposed ground above the quartzites; the hangingwall comprises Lewisan gneisses.

mostly sharp, brittle features, lacking much mylonite. This part of the thrust belt clearly developed at higher crustal levels than the mylonite belt, and the Cambrian-Ordovician rocks record peak temperatures of only about 275°C, in the upper anchizone (Johnson et al. 1985). The major lower thrusts in the northern part of the zone are mainly localized in the Cambrian Fucoid Beds and underlying quartzites to form complex imbricate thrust zones (Fig. 4.46), whereas south of Assynt, where Torridonian rocks are present, many thrusts are localized along shale horizons within the Diabaig Formation. Inversions of stratigraphical order are common because older rocks typically have been transported to higher structural levels to rest on younger rocks. Overturned and recumbent folds are also developed within parts of the thrust zone, notable examples including the Sgonnan Mor syncline developed within the Ben More thrust sheet in the Assynt region, and the Lochalsh syncline between Loch Carron and Skye. The latter has an upper limb measuring some 10 km across strike, consisting of inverted Lewisian and Torridonian rocks. Both folds can be interpreted as footwall synclines that formed during displacement on overlying thrusts.

Detailed analysis has shown that the thrusts generally developed in a foreland-propagating sequence, with successively younger and lower thrusts transporting older and higher thrusts to the WNW in 'piggyback' fashion (Elliott & Johnson 1980; McClay & Coward 1981; Butler 1982a). The youngest and structurally lowest thrust in this sequence is the basal or Sole Thrust. This lies within Cambrian quartzites around Loch Eriboll but climbs laterally southwards to lie within the Fucoid Beds in Assynt. South of Assynt, the Sole Thrust mainly lies within the Diabaig Formation. Early-formed thrusts within the foreland-propagating sequence are commonly folded as a result of the accretion of underlying thrust sheets. A well-known small-scale example of this occurs near Dundonnell where the Moine Thrust was progressively folded into a broad antiform during accretion of underlying thrust sheets composed of Cambrian strata (Fig. 4.47). A much larger-scale example is apparent in the Assynt region where the development of the Ben More and Glencoul thrust sheets, both carrying Lewisian gneisses, resulted in a large-scale upwarp or culmination in the overlying Moine Thrust (Figs 4.44, 4.45; Elliott & Johnson 1980).

The simple pattern outlined above of foreland-propagating thrusting is complicated in some areas by later, low-angle 'out-of-sequence' faults that cut through previously thrust and folded strata. Such structures may either be late thrusts or extensional faults that developed due to gravitational instability of the evolving thrust zone. Coward (1985) has shown the Moine Thrust in south Assynt is such a late structure because it clearly cuts across underlying thrust imbricates developed within Cambro-Ordovician rocks. Whether or not this late fault is a contractional or extensional structure is uncertain (Fig. 4.48). Clear evidence for extensional movements within the thrust zone have, however, been documented elsewhere within the north Assynt area where 'surge zones' showing 1–2 km displacement affected the already emplaced Glencoul thrust sheet (Coward 1982).

Age of thrusting. Rb–Sr and K–Ar dating of recrystallized micas within Moine mylonites suggests that emplacement of the Moine rocks onto the foreland stratigraphy occurred at c. 435–430 Ma (Johnson et al. 1985; Kelley 1988; Freeman et al. 1998). This is consistent with the U–Pb zircon age of 430 ± 4 Ma obtained from the syn-tectonic Loch Borralan Complex within the Moine Thrust Zone in the Assynt area (van Breemen et al. 1979a). However, isotopic ages as young as c. 408 Ma have been obtained from mylonites in the Dundonell

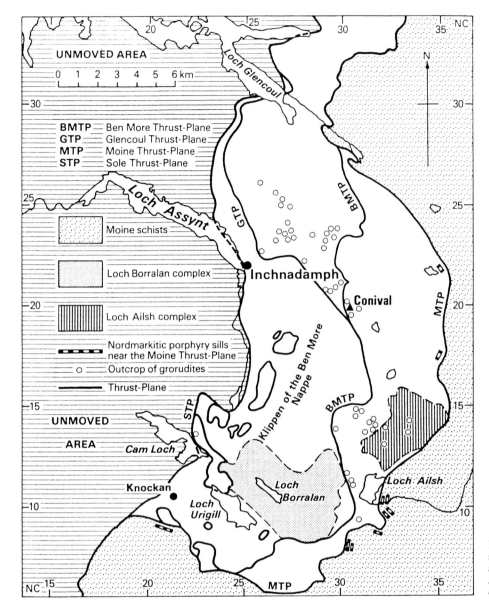

Fig. 4.44. Map showing the major structural units in the Assynt area as well as the major alkaline intrusions (from Johnson & Parsons 1979 with permission of the Edinburgh Geological Society).

area, suggesting that at least locally thrusting may have continued into the Early Devonian (Freeman *et al.* 1998).

Direction and amount of displacement. Various minor structures indicate the direction of regional thrusting. These include: (1) the orientations of deformed pebbles within sheared Torridonian and Cambrian rocks; (2) stretching lineations within the mylonite belt; (3) the sense of shear shown by distorted *Skolithos* burrows within the Lower Cambrian Pipe Rock, and (4) the trends of thrusts and lateral ramps (McClay & Coward 1981). These indicate an overall direction of thrusting towards 290°. A variety of displacement estimates have been proposed for different levels and segments of the thrust belt. The occurrence of a fault-bounded block of Moine mylonites on the foreland at Faraid Head (Fig. 4.3) indicates a minimum displacement on the Moine Thrust of 11 km. Clough (in Peach *et al.* 1907) and Bailey (1934) both showed that a minimum displacement of 20 km has occurred along the Glencoul Thrust in Assynt. The construction of balanced sections drawn parallel to the direction of thrusting has shown that rather larger minimum displacements are likely. Thus Elliott & Johnson (1980) demonstrated a minimum slip across the whole Moine

Thrust Zone of 77 km. Furthermore, Butler & Coward (1984) showed that the Cambrian shelf sequence can be restored for *c.* 54 km to the ESE. It is difficult to estimate the displacement on the Moine Thrust itself, but its association with a very thick belt of mylonites suggests that it is a major displacement zone with a minimum offset of several tens of kilometres. A total minimum displacement for the Moine Thrust Zone of around 100 km is therefore commonly accepted.

Deep structure of the thrust belt. Deep seismic reflection profiling carried out in the Pentland Firth and summarized by Brewer & Smythe (1984) was designed to determine the subsurface profile of the Moine and Outer Isles Thrusts (hence the acronym MOIST). A prominent reflector corresponds to the Outer Isles Fault Zone (Outer Isles Thrust, Fig. 4.49a) along which limited Caledonian thrust displacement may have occurred (Kelley *et al.* 1994; see Chapter 3). The Moine Thrust may be represented by one of several mid-crustal, east-dipping reflectors located further to the east (Figs 4.49b, c; Brewer & Smythe 1984). It is difficult, however, to reconcile either solution with Butler & Coward's (1984) interpretation that the Cambro-Ordovician foreland sequence originally extended

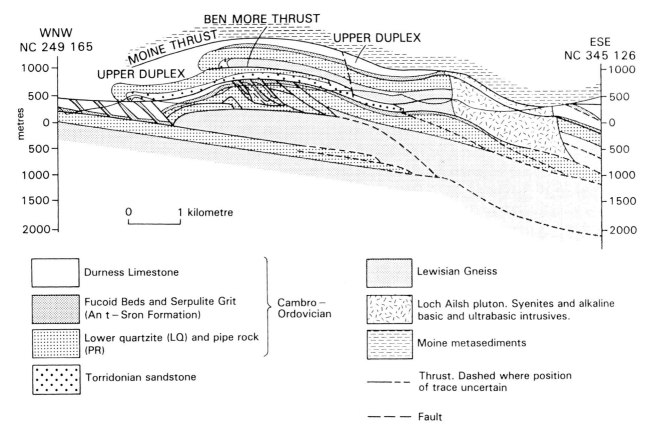

Fig. 4.45. Balanced cross-section across the southern part of the Assynt area, showing the Ben More and Moine thrusts (from Stephenson & Gould, with permission of the British Geological Survey, modified from Elliott & Johnson 1980). Note the recumbently folded Lewisian gneiss and Torridonian sandstone in the upper thrust sheets.

c. 54 km to the ESE. If correct, this means that the Moine Thrust must follow a shallow trajectory (*c.* 3°) within the upper crust over this distance before any steep ramp occurs. A shallow trajectory is consistent with the observation that the Moine rocks in the immediate hangingwall of the thrust never exceed garnet grade metamorphism (Barr *et al.* 1986). Butler & Coward (1984) prefer to interpret the dipping mid-crustal reflectors within the eastern part of the MOIST profile as representing a major duplex developed within the footwall to a shallowly dipping to flat-lying Moine Thrust (Fig. 4.49d). The geometry and deep structure of the margin of the Caledonian orogen is thus still problematic.

Strike-slip faulting in the Northern Highland and Grampian terranes

The main phase of Scandian ductile thrusting and folding was followed by sinistral strike-slip displacements along an array of NE-trending structures that dissect the Northern Highland and Grampian terranes (Fig. 4.50; Johnson & Frost 1977; Watson 1984). The most prominant are the Great Glen–Walls Boundary and Highland Boundary faults along which hundreds of kilometres of displacement may have occurred. Related minor faults include the Strathconon Fault, and possibly also the Strath Glass and Helmsdale faults in the Northern Highland terrane, and a group of faults in the Grampian terrane (Fig. 4.50). The faults are referred to collectively here as the 'Great Glen set' and most developed prior to the onset of post-Caledonian Old Red Sandstone (Devonian) deposition (Watson 1984; Mykura 1991). In the Northern

Highland terrane, a subsidiary set of NW-trending faults (Fig. 4.50) probably developed during the Mesozoic as a series of transfer faults associated with extensional reactivation of the Great Glen set (Roberts & Holdsworth 1999).

Great Glen Fault

The Great Glen Fault (e.g. Kennedy 1946; Holgate 1969; Smith & Watson 1983; Harris 1995) has been linked to the north with the Walls Boundary Fault in Shetland (Flinn 1961; McBride 1994), and to the southwest with the Loch Gruinart–Leannan Fault in Islay and Ireland (Pitcher *et al.* 1964; Alsop 1992). Seismic reflection studies show that the Great Glen Fault is coincident with a subvertical structure that extends to at least 40 km depth (Hall *et al.* 1984). Mantle-derived, late-Caledonian lamprophyre dykes appear to have different isotopic signatures either side of the fault, suggesting that it has some expression in the upper mantle (Canning *et al.* 1996, 1998). On the Scottish mainland, the fault comprises a *c.* 3 km wide belt of fracturing and intense cataclasis of Moine and Dalradian protoliths. Fault rocks range from rare mylonite and quartz blastomylonite to common cataclasite, hydrated cataclasite and phyllonite (Stewart, M. 1997; Stewart *et al.* 1997, 1999, 2000). Kinematic indicators demonstrate a consistent sinistral sense of displacement with a minor southeasterly component of downthrow. Fault-bounded blastomylonites in the core of the fault zone (Fig. 4.51) developed in the region of the frictional–viscous transition zone (*c.* 8–15 km; Stewart *et al.* 2000). The location of these blastomylonitic rocks in the core of the fault zone may reflect the presence of an exhumed positive flower structure formed during sinistral transpression (Stewart *et al.* 1999).

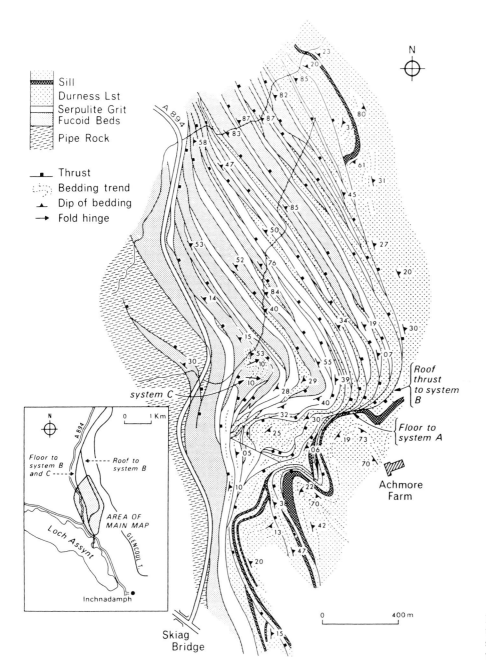

Fig. 4.46. Detailed map of the imbricate thrust belt NE of Loch Assynt; location shown in inset map (from Coward 1984*b* with permission of Elsevier Science).

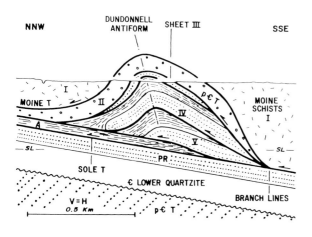

Fig. 4.47. Balanced cross-section through the Dundonnell antiformal thrust stack, perpendicular to its axis and oblique to the direction of thrusting (from Elliott & Johnson 1980 with permission of the American Association of Petroleum Geologists). Pebble pattern (p∈T) is Torridonian; stippled pattern (PR) is the Cambrian Pipe Rock quartzite; dashed pattern A is the Cambrian An t-Sron Formation. The thrust sheets are labelled I to V in order of formation. This structure is of historical importance because it was here that field geologists first recognized the piggyback sequence of thrusting (Cadell & Horne in Peach *et al.* 1907).

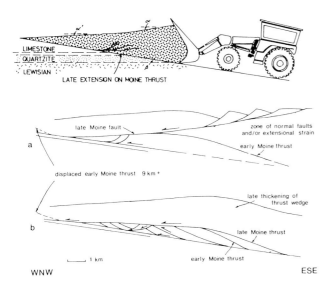

Fig. 4.48. Top diagram shows the development of extensional structures by the collapse of a thrust wedge with a weak basal shear strength; lower diagrams show the 'late' Moine Thrust south of Knockan as either an extensional structure (**a**) or an out-of-sequence thrust. (**b**) From Coward (1985) with permission of Elsevier Science.

Relationships between fault zone structures, dated igneous intrusions and post-orogenic sedimentary rocks constrain the main Caledonian sinistral displacement along the Great Glen Fault to the period between c. 430 Ma and c. 400 Ma (Stewart et al. 1999). A component of Silurian displacement is indicated by the U–Pb zircon age of 428 ± 2 Ma of the Clunes Tonalite (Fig. 4.52) which is thought to have been emplaced during sinistral shear (Stewart et al. 2001). A lower age limit of c. 400 Ma is indicated by the low strain nature of Old Red Sandstone (latest Emsian?) sedimentary rocks within the fault zone. These are relatively undeformed compared with the metamorphic basement and the deformation fabrics described above predate Old Red Sandstone deposition (Stewart et al. 1999; see also Mykura 1982; Stoker 1982). Post-Old Red Sandstone structures along the fault zone are invariably brittle in style, and fault products are typically incohesive, comprising clay fault gouge and poorly consolidated fault breccia (May & Highton 1997; Stewart et al. 1999).

Although the timing of sinistral motion is relatively well constrained, the magnitude of early displacement along the Great Glen Fault is less certain because there is no unambiguous correlation of pre-Devonian features across the fault. Kennedy (1946) proposed a sinistral movement of c. 104 km; this was based on various lines of evidence, including the notion that the Strontian and Foyers granites were once part of a single pluton that was cut into halves and displaced by the fault. However, although the two granite complexes are broadly similar, differences in their internal structure (Marston 1971; Munro 1973), trace-element content (Pankhurst 1979) and zircon distribution patterns (Pidgeon & Aftalion 1978) suggest that they were never joined. Winchester (1974) proposed a sinistral offset of 160 km on the basis of the apparent offset of regional metamorphic zones north and south of the fault, and Piasecki et al. (1981) argued for a similar displacement based on correlation of the Glenfinnan Group with the Central Highland Division gneisses. Both correlations were questioned in the light of debate concerning the timing and relative intensities of Precambrian versus Palaeozoic metamorphic events and the relative ages of major rock units in the Scottish Highlands (Tanner in discussion of Winchester 1974; Harris et al. 1983).

Latterly, the general consensus has been that sinistral displacements are unlikely to have exceeded 200–300 km. This is consistent with palaeomagnetic evidence (Briden et al. (1984) and the inferred offset of reflectors within the mantle lithosphere (Snyder & Flack 1990. A rather larger displacement of at least 500 km is implied, however, by tectonic reconstructions that place the Northern Highland terrane opposite Baltica during the Scandian collision (Fig. 4.37).

Walls Boundary Fault, Shetland
The fault is a steeply dipping structure that may truncate the northern extension of the Moine Thrust Zone just to the north of Shetland (Flinn 1961; cf. Ritchie et al. 1987). In common with the Great Glen Fault, there is no match in pre-Devonian geology across the structure. The fault is associated locally with mylonites that formed at an early stage in its history, and is everywhere accompanied by late fault gouge (Flinn 1977). There is evidence for a polyphase faulting history during the Palaeozoic and Mesozoic. A variety of displacement estimates have been proposed, based mainly upon apparent offsets of various offshore geological features: such correlations are often ambiguous and thus the history has been controversial (e.g. Flinn 1961, 1969, 1977, 1985, 1992, 1993; Bacon & Chesher 1975; Ritchie et al. 1987; Ritchie & Hitchen 1993; Underhill 1993). Importantly, from a Caledonian perspective, the great differences in the Caledonian geology of Shetland either side of the fault indicate an early sinistral offset of at least 100 km (Flinn 1961), which is clearly compatible with linkage of the structure with the Great Glen Fault. Mylonites along the fault plane have given Carboniferous $^{40}Ar/^{39}Ar$ ages (Roddom et al. 1989) and are therefore likely to have formed during a younger reactivation phase.

Faults of the Great Glen set in the Northern Highland terrane
Hutton & McErlean (1991) showed that sinistral shear along the Strathconon Fault (Fig. 4.50) accompanied emplacement of the adjacent Ratagain granite in the Late Silurian (U–Pb zircon 425 ± 2 Ma, Rogers & Dunning 1991) and was followed by later sinistral movement during the Devonian. Caledonian sinistral displacements along the Strathconon and Great Glen faults were thus contemporaneous. The extent of Caledonian displacements, if any, along the Helmsdale and Strathglass faults (Fig. 4.50) are uncertain. There is clear evidence for Mesozoic extension along the Helmsdale Fault (e.g. Pickering 1984; Underhill & Brodie 1993). However, the observation that the older rocks in the footwall of the fault (Moines and Helmsdale granite) are significantly more shattered and cemented than the Mesozoic sediments in the hangingwall is consistent with an earlier, possibly Caledonian history (e.g. Flinn 1993).

Faults of the Great Glen set in the Grampian terrane
In the Grampian Highlands (Fig. 4.50), sinistral offsets of geological markers can be demonstrated across the Loch Mhor, Sronlairig, Markie, Ericht–Laidon, Tyndrum, Garabal, Killin and Loch Tay faults (e.g. Johnson & Frost 1977; Watson 1984; May & Highton 1997). Treagus (1991) studied in detail the Ericht–Laidon, Tyndrum, Garabal, Killin and Loch Tay faults and demonstrated an early phase of dip-slip movement with a cumulative downthrow to the east of c. 7 km, followed by sinistral strike-slip with a cumulative displacement of c. 23 km. Various lines of direct and indirect evidence suggest a Late Silurian to Early Devonian age for these movements, although limited dip-slip reactivation during the Mesozoic cannot be precluded. The Tyndrum and Garabal faults are thought to have controlled the emplacement of the c. 430 Ma Garabal Hill–Glen Fyne appinite complex (U–Pb zircon, Rogers & Dunning 1991). Later, Early Devonian displacement along the

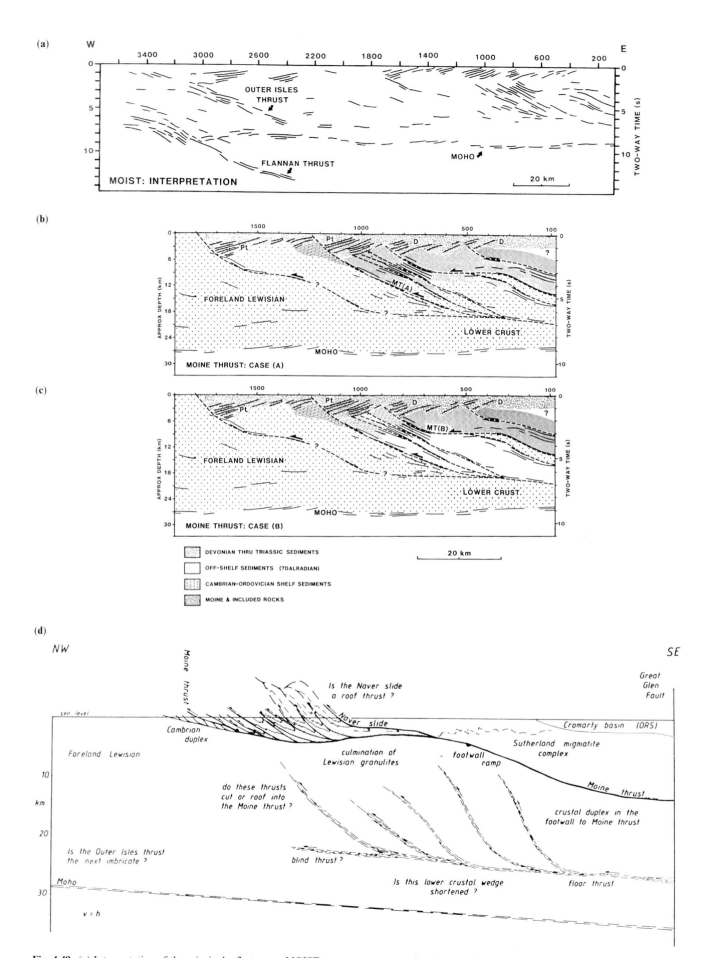

Fig. 4.49. (a) Interpretation of the principal reflectors on MOIST; to correct two-way time in seconds to approximate depth in kilometres, multiply by three (from Brewer & Smythe 1984). Shot-points are numbered along the top; (**b, c**) alternative locations (MT(A) and MT(B)) of the Moine Thrust based on the reflectors in (a). D, Devonian, Pt, Permo-Triassic. From Brewer & Smythe (1984); (**d**) Hypothetical cross-section across northern Scotland, showing the Moine Thrust as a shallow structure (from Butler & Coward 1984 with permission of the American Geophysical Union).

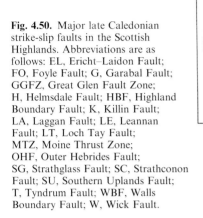

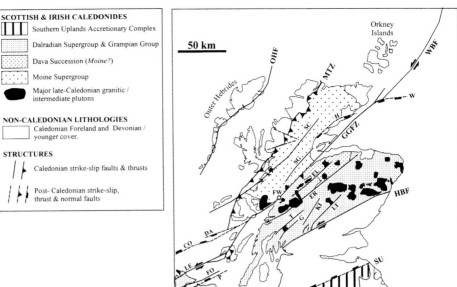

Fig. 4.50. Major late Caledonian strike-slip faults in the Scottish Highlands. Abbreviations are as follows: EL, Ericht–Laidon Fault; FO, Foyle Fault; G, Garabal Fault; GGFZ, Great Glen Fault Zone; H, Helmsdale Fault; HBF, Highland Boundary Fault; K, Killin Fault; LA, Laggan Fault; LE, Leannan Fault; LT, Loch Tay Fault; MTZ, Moine Thrust Zone; OHF, Outer Hebrides Fault; SG, Strathglass Fault; SC, Strathconon Fault; SU, Southern Uplands Fault; T, Tyndrum Fault; WBF, Walls Boundary Fault; W, Wick Fault.

Tyndrum fault is indicated by an ^{40}Ar/^{39}Ar age of *c.* 410 Ma for hydrothermal feldspars that date mineralization during sinistral transtension (Treagus *et al.* 1999). However, a post-tectonic microdiorite dyke which intrudes and seals the Ben Oss fault, a subsidiary of the Tyndrum fault, has yielded a K–Ar age of 412 ± 3 Ma, indicating that faulting cannot have continued later than the Early Devonian (Clayburn *et al.* 1983). The close temporal relationship between Caledonian magmatism and late faulting was emphasized by Morris & Hutton (1993)

who showed that the Early Devonian Etive dyke swarm was intruded during sinistral strike-slip movements. Sinistral movement along the Ericht–Laidon fault occurred prior to eruption of the Late Silurian to Early Devonian Lorne lavas that overlie the fault zone unconformably (Treagus 1991).

Highland Boundary Fault
The present fault is a high-angle reverse fault that emplaced Dalradian rocks onto the Highland Border Complex and Old

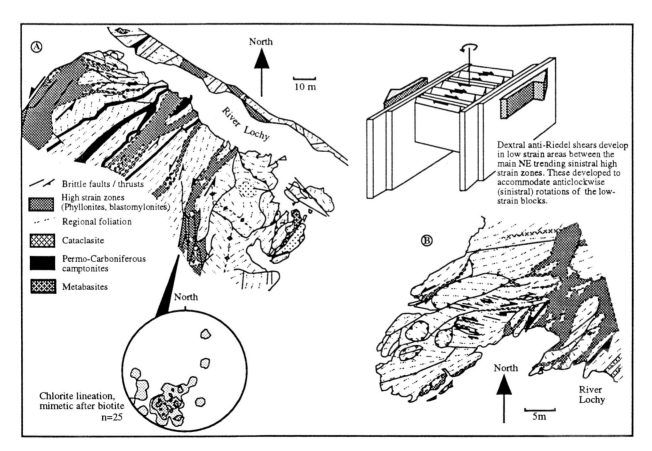

Fig. 4.51. Detailed maps of mylonites in the core of the Great Glen Fault at Torcastle, near Fort William, showing distribution and kinematics of major high-strain zones and representative linear data (lower hemisphere equal area projection) (from Stewart *et al.* 1997).

Red Sandstone rocks of the Midland Valley (Barrow 1901;
Jehu & Campbell 1917; Allan 1928, 1940; Anderson 1946;
Bluck 1984). Geophysical studies have shown that the fault is
broadly coincident with a change in lower crustal structure
(Bamford *et al.* 1978; Barton 1992; Rollin 1994). This implies
that the present late reverse fault may have reactivated an
older and more fundamental structure, and various workers
have speculated that this may correspond to the edge of the
Laurentian craton (e.g. Soper & Hutton 1984). Although Late
Silurian to Early Devonian sinistral displacements comparable with the Great Glen Fault have been assumed commonly
(e.g. Harte *et al.* 1984, Soper & Hutton 1984; Hutton 1987;
Soper *et al.* 1992), other workers have argued against major
displacements (e.g. Hutchison & Oliver 1998) and thus the
regional tectonic significance of the fault is uncertain (see also
Chapters 5 and 8).

Silurian to Early Devonian plutonism

In Silurian to Early Devonian times (c. 430–400 Ma), subduction-related magmatism occurred throughout the Scottish
Highlands (Fig. 4.52; Thirlwall 1981*b*, 1982, 1988; Stephens
& Halliday 1984; Brown, G. C. *et al.* 1985; Soper 1986; Brown,
P. E. 1991; Stephenson *et al.* 1999). The emplacement mechanisms of many intrusions were structurally controlled: the
earliest were emplaced during Scandian thrusting, but the main
phase of plutonism accompanied regional strike-slip faulting.
A first-order petrological division of these igneous rocks
recognizes two main groups. The first is represented by a
series of small alkaline intrusions that occur in the northwest of
Scotland, mainly in the Assynt area. The second is volumetrically more important and commonly referred to as the
'Newer Granites' (Read 1961) although it includes a wide range
of related rock types, including diorite, tonalite and granodiorite. Members of this group are present on both sides of the
Great Glen Fault, but are particularly common in the Grampian terrane where some of the early Devonian plutons acted
as feeders to the volcanic sequences described in Chapter 8.
The group is dominated by I-type, calc-alkaline granites that
are very different to the Ordovician S-type granites described
earlier from the Grampian terrane (Fig. 4.53).

Alkaline intrusions of northwest Scotland

In approximate order of emplacement these comprise: (1) the
deformed Glen Dessary syenite that occurs within the Northern
Highland Steep Belt in Inverness-shire; (2) a suite of alkaline
intrusions that occur within and close to the Moine Thrust
Zone in the Assynt area and cut rocks of the foreland as well as
the various thrust nappes; and (3) the Loch Loyal Syenite
Complex that was emplaced into uppermost structural levels of
the Moine Nappe c. 40 km northeast of Assynt (Fig. 4.52).

Glen Dessary syenite
The deformed Glen Dessary syenite intrudes Moine rocks
assigned to the Loch Eil Group within the Northern Highland
steep belt (Fig. 4.54; Roberts *et al.* 1984). A U–Pb zircon age of
456 ± 5 Ma dates crystallization of the syenite (van Breemen
et al. 1979*b*) that is therefore conspicuously older than all other
members of the alkaline and 'Newer Granite' suites. The intrusion comprises an early, outer mafic syenite and a younger,
inner felsic syenite (Richardson 1968; Fowler 1992). Both are
dominated by alkali feldspar, varying from 50–70% in the
mafic syenite, but comprising up to 85% of the felsic syenite.
The mafic phases comprise pyroxene, hornblende, biotite and

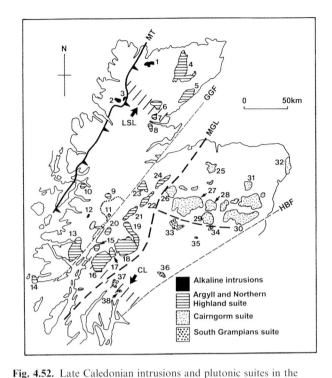

Fig. 4.52. Late Caledonian intrusions and plutonic suites in the
Northern and Grampian Highlands. MT, Moine Thrust; GGF, Great
Glen Fault; MGL, Mid-Grampian Line; HBF, Highland Boundary
Fault. Diagonal hatching corresponds to major transverse lineaments:
LSL, Loch Shin Line; CL, Cruachan Line. Intrusions are numbered as
follows: 1, Loch Loyal; 2, Loch Borralan; 3, Loch Ailsh; 4, Strath
Halladale; 5, Helmsdale; 6, Rogart; 7, Migdale; 8, Fearn; 9, Cluanie;
10, Ratagain; 11, Clunes; 12, Glen Dessary; 13, Strontian; 14, Ross of
Mull; 15, Ballachulish; 16, Etive; 17, Glencoe fault intrusion;
18, Rannoch Moor; 19, Strath Ossian; 20, Ben Nevis; 21, Corrieyairick;
22, Allt Crom; 23, Foyers; 24, Findhorn; 25, Ben Rinnes;
26, Monadhliath; 27, Cairngorm; 28, Glen Gairn; 29, Lochnagar;
30, Mount Battock; 31, Bennachie; 32, Peterhead; 33, Glen Tilt; 34, Glen
Doll; 35, Glen Shee; 36, Comrie; 37, Garabal Hill; 38, Arrochar. Dotted
areas between Cluanie and Strontian intrusions correspond to the
approximate limits of granite vein complexes.

magnetite. The intrusion was strongly deformed and metamorphosed during regional D3 folding and the hornblende and
biotite are therefore unlikely to be of primary magmatic origin
(Roberts *et al.* 1984). Kyanite- and sillimanite-bearing xenoliths within the syenite were probably derived from the
Glenfinnan Group units that underlie the Loch Eil Group
host rocks. Three coarse-grained calcite marble bodies that
crop out at or near the original base of the intrusion (Fig. 4.54)
are, however, absent from the present country rocks. They may
have been derived from a stratigraphic unit present at one time
above the Loch Eil Group rocks. The elongate outcrop of the
syenite reflects its location in the core of a tight, upright, highly
curvilinear D3 synform (Fig. 4.54; Roberts *et al.* 1984). The
syenite is thought to have been emplaced into host Loch Eil
Group rocks while the latter were flat-lying following D2
recumbent folding during the Grampian event. Xenoliths of
Moine rocks enclosed within the syenite contain pre-syenite
D2 isoclinal folds (Roberts *et al.* 1984). Subsequent D3 deformation then rotated the Moine-syenite contacts into their
present orientation.

Alkaline magmatism in the Moine Thrust Zone of the
Assynt area
Loch Borralan complex. This intrusion lies in the Moine
Thrust Zone between the Sole Thrust and the Ben More Thrust

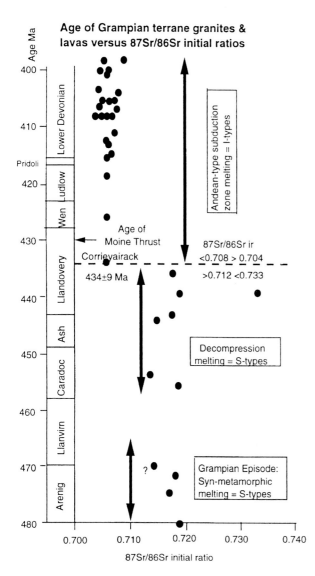

Fig. 4.53. Compilation of age of Grampian terrane granites and lavas versus their $^{87}Sr/^{86}Sr$ initial ratios (from Oliver 2001 with permission of Elsevier Science). Note the significant change at 434 ± 9 Ma from high (S-type ratios, average 0.716) to low (I-type ratios, average 0.706) ratios; this is likely to correspond to the change from post-Grampian decompression melting to subduction zone melting.

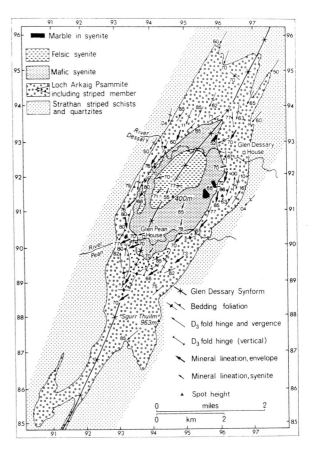

Fig. 4.54. Structural map of the Glen Dessary syenite and its Moine envelope (from Roberts *et al.* 1984).

(Fig. 4.52). It is important petrologically because it is the only plutonic complex composed largely of silica-undersaturated igneous rocks in the British Isles. Some rock types are highly potassic with K_2O contents of up to 15% (Wooley 1973). The intrusion was thought originally to be a stratified laccolith in which mafic nepheline syenites graded upwards into leucocratic syenite and quartz syenites (Shand 1910, 1939). However, it was later shown that the intrusion comprises two separate suites. An early suite of mafic to ultramafic syenite was intruded as a sheeted complex into Durness Group limestones (Wooley 1970, 1973; Matthews & Wooley 1977). This was intruded by a later suite which comprises a group of syenites that differentiated gravitationally *in situ*, with perthosites at low levels and quartz syenites at upper levels. A small carbonatite body associated with the pluton intrudes Durness Limestone on the shore of Loch Urigill (Young *et al.* 1994). A U–Pb zircon age of 430 ± 4 Ma dates crystallization of the intrusion (van Breemen *et al.* 1979*a*).

Loch Ailsh complex. This crops out in the hangingwall of the Ben More Thrust and beneath the Moine Thrust (Fig. 4.52). This intrusion was also interpreted as a stratified laccolith, gravity-differentiated to give an ultramafic base (Phemister 1926). Parsons (1965*a, b*, 1968, 1972, 1979) has shown that the main rocks of the intrusion are sodic, saturated or slightly oversaturated leucosyenites that were intruded as three units, S1 to S3. They form a regular chemical series with decreasing sodium and calcium in feldspars and increasingly sodic pyroxenes. Pyroxenites and other ultramafic rocks do not form a lower zone as envisaged by Phemister (1926), but on the eastern margin of the intrusion occur as a vertical sheet between syenite and limestone. Pyroxene syenites that occur as xenoliths in S2 leucosyenite are now interpreted as remnants of a roof zone formed originally by contact alteration of limestones. Crystallization of the intrusion is dated by a U–Pb zircon age of 439 ± 4 Ma (Halliday *et al.* 1987).

Minor intrusions. The rocks of the foreland, Moine Thrust Zone and the Moine Nappe are intruded by a series of variably deformed and altered dykes and sills. This is one of the few areas in northwest Scotland where Caledonian igneous rocks intrude rocks of the foreland. Sabine (1953) recognized aegerine felsites (grorudites), three types of quartz micro-syenite (Canisp porphyry, hornblende porphyries and nordmarkites), hornblende lamprophyres (vogesites) and nepheline syenites (ledmorites and borolanites).

Relationship between alkaline magmatism and displacement within the Moine Thrust Zone. The alkaline rocks of the Assynt area are important because they provide potential time

markers for structural events within the thrust belt. Peach *et al.*
(1907) noted that many of the minor intrusions are deformed by
thrust-related deformation (folding and cataclasis) and concluded that alkaline magmatism pre-dated regional thrusting.
The restriction of the Canisp pophyry intrusions to the foreland, and the grorudite dykes to the Ben More and Glencoul
nappes (Fig. 4.44; Sabine 1953) further implies that these
components of the alkaline suite were originally emplaced over
a large area which was later telescoped by thrusting (Elliott &
Johnson 1980). Because the grorudite dyke suite cuts the Loch
Ailsh complex, this indicates that the latter was also intruded
prior to displacement along the Ben More Thrust (Halliday
et al. 1987). In contrast, the Loch Borralan complex appears to
postdate movement along the Ben More Thrust. The eastern
part of the complex lies in the footwall of the Ben More Thrust,
but the western margin intrudes quartzites of the Cam Loch
Klippe that rests on the Ben More Thrust (Parsons & McKirdy
1983). In the southeast part of the complex, the early syenite
suite contains a high-temperature fabric defined by flattened
pseudoleucites that are elongate in a WNW direction, broadly
parallel to the direction of regional thrust transport (Elliott &
Johnson 1980). This fabric is thought to have been formed by
high-temperature deformation of the cooling magma during
movement along the structurally overlying Moine Thrust
(Halliday *et al.* 1987). Importantly, the fabric is cut by undeformed veins of the later syenite suite (Bailey & McCallien
1934), thus establishing a syn-tectonic setting for the complex.

Loch Loyal syenite complex
The Loch Loyal syenite complex comprises the Ben Loyal, Ben
Stumanadh and Cnoc nan Cuilean bodies (Fig. 4.55; King
1942; Robertson & Parsons 1974; Holdsworth *et al.* 1999).
They were emplaced into Moine and Lewisian rocks of the
Moine and Naver nappes after Scandian ductile thrusting and
related folding. Most of the syenites carry a high-temperature
foliation defined by aligned feldspar, mafic grains and elongate
aggregates of mafic and accessory minerals. Crystallization of
the complex is dated by a U–Pb zircon age of 426 ± 9 Ma
obtained from the Ben Loyal body (Halliday *et al.* 1987). The
intrusions lie mainly within a zone of large-scale NW-trending
D3 cross folds (Holdsworth *et al.* 1999). The zone of cross
folding is underlain by an ESE-dipping high strain zone, the
Ben Blandy Shear Zone. The northwest basal contact of the
Ben Loyal intrusion dips southeast and strikes sub-parallel to
the foliation within the shear zone. The higher parts of this
syenite, together with those of the Ben Stumanadh and Cnoc
nan Cuilean intrusions, form a series of variably coalesced
dykes trending NW–SE, sub-parallel to the foliation in the pre-
existing zone of cross folds. Minor top-to-the-SE extension
occurred along the northwest boundary of the Ben Loyal body,
while minor dextral shearing is associated with emplacement of
the NW-trending vertical sheets that form the southeast part
of this intrusion and the two other syenite bodies. The high
temperature fabrics within the syenites are thought to result
from internal deformation of the intrusions during and immediately after emplacement. The geometry of these fabrics and
the syenite complex as a whole appears to have been controlled
directly by the pre-existing structure of the country rocks. The
siting and emplacement of the syenites may have been facilitated initially by late Caledonian gravity-driven extension of
the Moine thrust nappes (Fig. 4.56; Holdsworth *et al.* 1999).

Fenites
Sodic and ultrasodic rocks that are probably metasomatic in
origin crop out in the Loch Hourn–Glen Cannich area (Tanner
& Tobisch 1972; Peacock 1973). They occur in Moine metasedimentary rocks and post-date regional deformation and

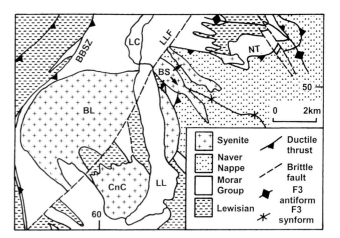

Fig. 4.55. Geological map of the Loch Loyal syenites and surrounding
rocks, showing the axial traces of major F3 cross-folds (modified from
Holdsworth *et al.* 1999). The steeply dipping sheets that comprise the
Conc nan Cuilean (CnC) and Ben Stumanadh (BS) bodies are
interpreted to have formerly been the structurally highest parts of the
intrusive complex, now juxtaposed against the Ben Loyal body (BL) as
a result of SE-side-down movement on the Loch Loyal Fault (LLF).
Other abbreviations: NT, Naver Thrust; BBSZ, Ben Blandy Shear
Zone; LC, Loch Craggie; LL, Loch Loyal.

metamorphism. Most of the sodic rocks appear to have resulted
from the passage of albite-rich hydrous fluids along fractures.
The metasomatism was associated with addition of Na and
Al and loss of K, Ca, Mg and Fe to form albitites with sodic
pyroxenes and amphiboles. Similar rocks were described
from the margin of the Cnoc nan Cuilean syenite (King 1942)
and their presence in the Loch Hourn–Glen Cannich area may
therefore indicate the presence of unexposed syenite bodies at
depth. Fenite-type metasomatism has also been described in the
vicinity of the Great Glen Fault Zone, around Abraichan,
Rosemarkie and Foyers (Deans *et al.* 1971; Garson *et al.* 1984).

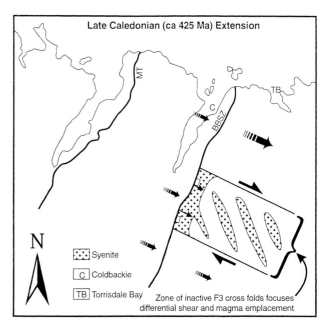

Fig. 4.56. Schematic diagram showing how the pre-existing zone of
F3 cross-folds may have focused differential dextral shear during late
regional extension leading to initial emplacement of the Loch Loyal
syenites as a series of en echelon dykes above an extensionally
reactivated Ben Blandy Shear Zone (from Holdsworth *et al.* 1999).

'Newer Granite' magmatism in the Northern Highland and Grampian terranes

The term 'Newer Granites' was applied by Read (1961) to a wide range of undeformed granitic plutons and associated minor intrusions within the Northern Highland and Grampian terranes. In detail, many plutons are zoned and incorporate a number of different rock types. Emplacement levels of the plutons vary from mid-crustal (e.g. Strontian, Rogart, Find-horn, Foyers, Ballachulish) to subvolcanic (e.g. Etive, Ben Nevis). Contemporaneous plutonic and volcanic activity is evident at Glen Coe and Ben Nevis which are classic examples of cauldron subsidence (see also Chapter 8). The oldest reliable crystallization ages so far obtained from any plutons indicate intrusion during the Mid to Late Silurian at c. 430–425 Ma (Rogers & Dunning 1991; Stewart et al. 2001). It is clear, however, that in Lochaber and Lorne magmatism continued into the Early Devonian, perhaps until c. 400 Ma. Brown (1979) showed that the suite has the geochemical characteristics of modern continental arcs, such as high Rb/Sr and K/Na, low K/Rb and relatively low Sr initial ratios. They are calc-alkaline, I-type granites (Fig. 4.57; Halliday et al. 1985; Stephens 1988; Thirlwall 1988). Further analysis of the chemistry and isotopes of the Newer Granite plutons of the Scottish mainland has led to subdivision into three suites: the Argyll and Northern Highland, the Cairngorm, and the South Grampians (Fig. 4.52; Stephens & Halliday 1984; Plant 1986; Stephenson & Gould 1995). The granites of Shetland remain poorly documented.

Watson (1984) and Leake (1990) both drew attention to the alignment of plutons in gross NE-trending linear arrays along major strike-slip faults or lineaments. They speculated that the faults had acted as ascent pathways for melts derived from the underlying mantle lithosphere. Watson also pointed out the importance of a NW-trending set of lineaments such as the Loch Shin and Cruachan lines (Fig. 4.52) in controlling early Caledonian magmatism. Recent research has largely substantiated this hypothesis (Hutton 1988a; Hutton & Reavy 1992; Jacques & Reavy 1994; Stewart et al. 2001).

Argyll and Northern Highland suite

The plutons of the Argyll and Northern Highland suite define an unusual granitic province with characteristically high values of Ba and Sr (Halliday 1984; Stephens & Halliday 1984; Halliday et al. 1985; Thirlwall 1988; Tarney & Jones 1994; Fowler et al. 2001). The suite mainly comprises hornblende–biotite granodiorite and biotite granodiorite plutons with minor diorite and monzo-granitic components. In the west part of the belt, the Ratagain intrusion has very high Ba and Sr and appears transitional between metaluminous calc-alkaline rocks and the alkaline suite described above. Detailed descriptions of the various plutons can be found elsewhere (Johnstone & Mykura 1989; Stephenson & Gould 1995; Stephenson et al. 1999) and space permits comment on only a limited number of intrusions with particular emphasis on the role of tectonic controls on the style of pluton emplacement.

Intrusions emplaced during Scandian thrusting. These intrusions are typically concordant with the regional foliation in the country rocks. In Sutherland, the deformed Strath Vagastie, and Strathnaver granite sheets were emplaced during Scandian thrusting. The granites cut F2 folds, but are foliated and lineated, and were therefore intruded at a late stage in D2 (Holdsworth & Strachan 1988). The undeformed Strath Halla-dale sheeted granite complex (Fig. 4.52) was also intruded during the late stages of westerly-directed thrusting at a higher structural level in east Sutherland (H. Kocks pers. comm.). The Rogart pluton located in the footwall of the Naver Thrust

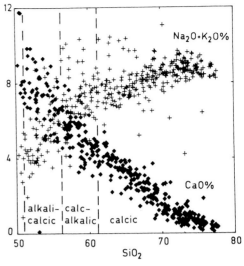

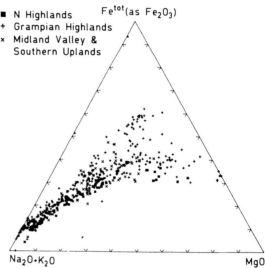

Fig. 4.57. Plot of total alkali oxides and CaO versus SiO$_2$ (top) and an AFM plot showing calc-alkaline nature of the late Caledonian granitoid suites (below). Note that the lower figure also incorporates data from the Midland Valley and the Southern Uplands (from Halliday et al. 1985).

(Fig. 4.52) is bordered by contact migmatites developed from melting of host Morar Group rocks during intrusion (Soper 1963). The pluton comprises an outer quartz-monzodiorite, a middle hornblende–biotite granodiorite and an inner adamel-lite and biotite granite. All three facies are locally associated with large enclaves of coeval mafic appinite (Fig. 4.58; Read et al. 1925; Fowler et al. 2001). The quartz-monzodiorite car-ries a prominent pre-full crystallization fabric (*sensu* Hutton 1988a), the planar and linear components of which are parallel with D2 fabrics in the Moine country rocks (Soper 1963; H. Kocks pers. comm.), suggesting that this part of the pluton was emplaced as a gently-dipping sheet during the late stages of regional ductile thrusting. Later lateral expansion of the pluton, probably during emplacement of the granodiorite, was associated with steepening of the foliation in the quartz-monzodiorite and the Moine country rocks to result in the funnel-shaped geometry of the pluton. The undeformed and post-tectonic inner biotite granite cuts across the junctions of the earlier components.

Fig. 4.58. Xenoliths of appinitic rock in quartz-monzodiorite of the Rogart pluton, SE Sutherland (courtesy of N. J. Soper). Dark biotite-rich selvages are visible at the margin of the xenolith above the compass.

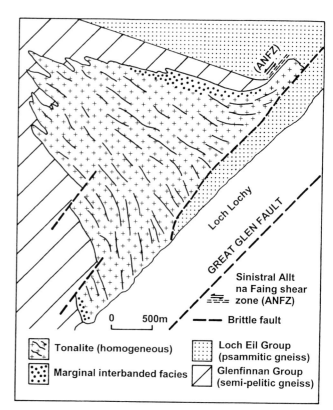

Fig. 4.59. Map of the Clunes Tonalite (modified from Stewart *et al.* 2001). The lines within the homogenous tonalite represent the trend of the pre-full crystallization fabric: the planar component dips steeply, and the linear component is mainly sub-horizontal.

Strike-slip faulting and pluton emplacement. There is a clear temporal and spatial relationship between strike-slip faulting and pluton emplacement. The Clunes tonalite (Fig. 4.59) and the Foyers and Strontian granite complexes crop out adjacent to the Great Glen Fault that appears to have acted as a magma conduit. The Clunes tonalite was emplaced at *c.* 428 Ma by flow of magma into a zone of dilation that developed at high angles to the fault during sinistral shear (Fig. 4.60; Stewart *et al.* 2001). Such an emplacement mechanism may also explain the geometry of the Foyers granite complex (Fig. 4.52) which comprises passively emplaced granodiorite, quartz monzonite, and quartz diorite bodies that are oriented at a high angle to the fault zone (British Geological Survey 1996; Carey & Platten 2000). The Strontian complex (Fig. 4.61) comprises an outer hornblende-biotite granodiorite facies, and an inner biotite granodiorite (Sabine 1963; Munro 1973; Stephenson *et al.* 1999). Mafic enclaves are common in both facies. The hornblende granodiorite and biotite granodiorite have yielded, respectively, U–Pb ages of 425 ± 3 Ma (zircon) and 418 ± 1 Ma (monazite) (Rogers & Dunning 1991; Paterson *et al.* 1993). A 3 km-wide sillimanite-bearing thermal aureole surrounds the pluton and indicates that the complex was emplaced at a pressure of 4 kbar (Ashworth & Tyler 1982). The hornblende-biotite granodiorite is characterized by pre-full crystallization fabrics. These are concordant with the steep contacts with the Moine host rocks and define a S-plunging synform in the core of which is the biotite granodiorite (Fig. 4.61). Hutton (1988*b*) suggested that the biotite granodiorite was intruded into an extensional shear zone developed as a result of *dextral* movement along the Great Glen Fault (Fig. 4.62). Taking into account the evidence from the Clunes tonalite, it therefore seems likely that early sinistral displacement along the Great Glen Fault at *c.* 428 Ma was followed by a dextral displacement associated with emplacement of the Strontian biotite granodiorite at *c.* 418 Ma.

To the northwest, the Ratagain pluton lies adjacent to the Strathconon Fault (Fig. 4.63). The intrusion comprises, in

order of emplacement, small appinite bodies, diorite, and a monzonitic unit (Hutton *et al.* 1993). The nature and sigmoidal orientation of high-temperature deformation fabrics within the intrusion show that it was deformed by sinistral shear along the Strathconon Fault prior to complete crystallization (Fig. 4.64; Hutton & McErlean 1991). The U–Pb zircon age of 425 ± 3 Ma for the intrusion (Rogers & Dunning 1991) overlaps within error the age of the Clunes tonalite, and therefore shows that sinistral displacements along the Great Glen and Strathconon faults were essentially synchronous.

East of the Great Glen Fault, similar tectonic controls have been demonstrated for the emplacement of the Argyll suite. A comparable sequence of intrusive phases is applicable to the major multiphase complexes of Etive, Glen Coe, Rannoch Moor, Strath Ossian, Ballachulish and Ben Nevis (Fig. 4.65; Jacques & Reavy 1994). The earliest activity is represented by appinites, high concentrations of which are found around the margins of the Ballachulish and Etive plutons. The first main phase of the plutons is a quartz diorite (G1) that may contain numerous country rock xenoliths and occasional microdiorite/appinite enclaves. This is followed by G2, a more heterogeneous phase that ranges from monzodiorite through tonalite/granodiorite to monzogranite and contains abundant microgranitoid enclaves. G3 is a minor phase of pink microgranitic dykes and sheets that cross-cut the earlier phases. G4 is a porphyritic monzogranite that is cross-cut by the final G5 phase represented by a non-porphyritic leucocratic monzogranite. To the northeast, the Corrieyairick and Allt Crom plutons are dominated by granodiorites that probably correlate with G2. Contact metamorphic assemblages indicate depths of emplacement for the Ballachulish pluton (9–10 km, Pattison & Harte 1989; Weiss & Troll 1989) and the Etive

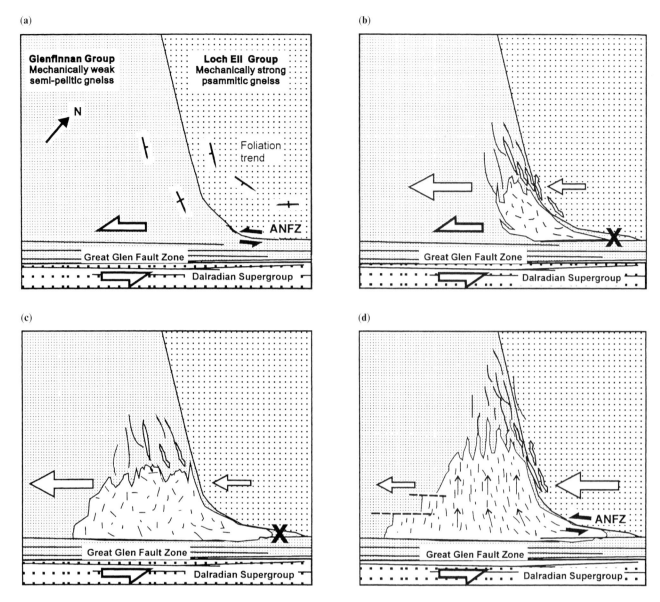

Fig. 4.60. Proposed emplacement model for the Clunes Tonalite (from Stewart *et al.* 2001). (**a**) Early sinistral movement along the Great Glen Fault Zone (GGFZ) is associated with ductile rotation of the regional, north-northwest trending Moine foliation and initial development of the Allt na Faing shear zone (ANFZ). (**b, c**) A stick-point (cross) develops at the Glenfinnan Group–Loch Eil Group boundary, possibly due to rheological contrast. A site of extension initiates as movement of rocks northeast of the stick-point is stalled. Tonalite migrates upwards along the GGFZ and flows laterally into the developing extensional void to form, at least in part, the subhorizontal linear fabric within the intrusion. (**d**) Release of the stick point leads to NE–SW directed contraction across the pluton to form a pre-full crystallization planar deformation fabric; lateral extrusion of melt into the pelitic country rocks (small arrows) may have accentuated the intial subhorizontal linear fabric within the tonalite.

complex (4–6 km, Droop & Treloar 1981). The Glen Coe and Ben Nevis complexes are excellent examples of cauldron subsidence (Bailey 1960). At Glen Coe, a cylindrical block of Devonian lavas and Dalradian rocks were downfaulted into the underlying plutonic complex as a result of subsidence on encircling ring faults (Bailey 1960; Taubeneck 1967; Hardie 1968; Roberts 1974; Moore & Kokelaar 1997). Different episodes of subsidence and escape of magma up the ring faults can be correlated with surface eruptions of ignimbrites. Devonian lavas and underlying Dalradian rocks are similarly preserved by subsidence within the central ring complex of Ben Nevis (Bailey 1960).

Jacques & Reavy (1994) proposed that the intersection of Caledonian shear zones and faults with an earlier set of pre-Caledonian lineaments acted as a fundamental control on magmatism. NE-trending Caledonian structures such as the

Etive–Laggan and Ericht–Laidon shear zones are sub-parallel with linear arrays of plutons as defined by the Ballachulish–Ben Nevis–Corrieyairick–Allt Crom group and the Etive–Rannoch Moor–Strathspey group (Fig. 4.65). An approximately orthogonal set of NW-trending structures is defined by the alignment of the Ballachulish, Etive and Garabal Hill intrusions (the Cruachan line) and the orientation of the Strath Ossian pluton (Strath Ossian line) (Fig. 4.65). The existence of the Cruachan and Strath Ossian lines had been proposed previously on the basis of petrological, geochemical, stratigraphical and geophysical evidence and it is widely believed that they are pre-Caledonian basement structures (Fettes *et al.* 1986). The intrusive complexes are all characterized by complex patterns of curvi-planar, pre-full crystallization fabrics (Fig. 4.66; Jacques & Reavy 1994). Within individual complexes, the various intrusive phases are characterized by differently

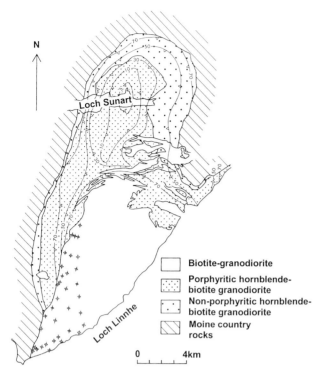

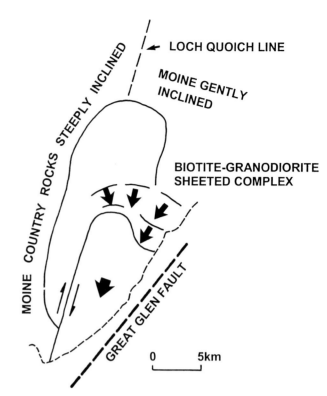

Fig. 4.61. Basic structure of the Strontian pluton. Trends and dips of the pre-full crystallization fabrics within the hornblende-biotite granodiorite facies are shown; single double barbed symbols are foliations in the biotite-grandiorite (modified from Hutton 1988*a*).

Fig. 4.62. Model for emplacement of the Strontian biotite-granodiorite at *c.* 418 Ma in a dextral shear zone termination related to the Great Glen Fault (modified from Hutton 1988*b*).

oriented fabrics, consistent with the emplacement of successive batches of magma during strike-slip movements. Jacques & Reavy (1994) have hypothesized that the plutons are all sited above shear zone or lineament intersections in the lower crust. The development at these intersections of transtensional zones allowed and facilitated ascent of magma as a series of steep sheets; assembly of plutons in the upper crust resulted from rotational ballooning during active strike-slip movements (Fig. 4.67).

Granite vein complexes. Numerous plutons in the Argyll and Northern Highland suite are associated with marginal vein complexes developed within their country rocks. A series of granite vein complexes that are not associated with exposed plutons intrude the Moine rocks of western Inverness-shire (Fig. 4.52). The intrusions range from quartz-diorite to leucogranite in composition, and granitic to aplitic and pegmatitic in texture. Individual veins and sheets have sharp contacts with their country rocks, and range from a few centimetres in width

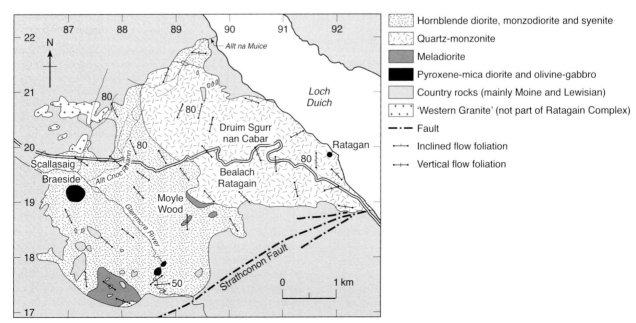

Fig. 4.63. Map of the Ratagain pluton (from Stephenson *et al.* 1999, with permission of the Joint Nature Conservation Committee).

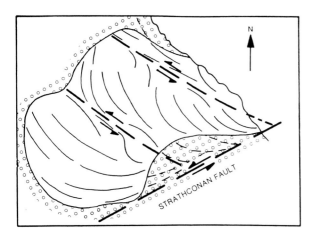

Fig. 4.64. Summary and interpretation of early deformation within the Ratagain pluton (from Hutton & McErlean 1991). Circle ornament indicates country rocks around pluton. Solid lines indicate the trajectories of pre-full crystallization fabrics that were deformed by sinistral shear associated with the Strathconon Fault. Thin dashed lines in the south show interpolated swing of fabrics beneath the gently-inclined roof contact.

to bodies of several hundred metres in extent. The intrusions are undeformed and mostly have no preferred orientation. The density of veining and sheeting is very variable, ranging up to intense ramifying networks that occupy up to 60% of total rock. Areas where they form up to 30% or more of total rock define individual vein complexes (Fettes & MacDonald 1978). The Loch Eil, Loch Arkaig and Banavie complexes consist of granite, aplite and pegmatite, whereas the Glen Garry complex is dominated by granodiorite. The complexes are clearly unrelated to the host Moine rocks and may represent the result of fractionation from a quartz-dioritic magma located below the current erosion level (Fettes & MacDonald 1978).

Cairngorm suite. The Cairngorm suite consists of a series of granitic plutons that occur mainly in the northern Grampian Highlands (Fig. 4.52). Most of the plutons comprise coarse biotite-monzogranite, although there are local textural variations from microgranite to megacrystic K-feldspar bearing types. Significant magnetic anomalies are associated with some intrusions (e.g. Monadhliath, Cairngorm, Lochnagar, Mount Battock, Hill of Fare). In some cases, these can be related to differences in magnetite content of the different granite types, but in other cases basic rocks at depth or pelitic hornfelses around the pluton maybe the source of the anomaly. The gross E–W alignment of the suite may indicate a deep crustal control on its location. An E–W trending gravity low between the Monadhliath and Mount Battock bodies suggests the presence at depth of a large batholith, so the granites at surface may represent cupolas that are connected at depth (Plant *et al.* 1990). However, the detailed emplacement history is not as well documented as for the Argyll and Northern Highland suite. Some of the plutons show evidence for ballooning, whereas others appear to have been emplaced by a combination of stoping and/or cauldron subsidence (Harrison & Hutchison 1987). A high level of emplacement (*c.* 5–8 km) is implied by widespread hydrothermal alteration, common aplitic and pegmatitic phases, and abundant vuggy cavities (Harrison & Hutchison 1987).

South Grampians suite. The South Grampians suite comprises a series of relatively small, composite intrusions mostly dominated by granodiorite and monzogranites, but with important

gabbroic and pyroxene meladiorite (appinitic) facies rocks (Fig. 4.52). All lack an inherited zircon component. The intrusions, like those of the Argyll and Northern Highlands suite, have close spatial associations with major NE-trending faults. The U–Pb zircon age of 429 ± 2 Ma for the Garabal Hill complex (Rogers & Dunning 1991) has therefore been used to argue that the adjacent Tyndrum and Garabal Hill faults were active as strike-slip structures at the same time as the Great Glen and Strathconon faults to the northwest. The depths and exact modes of emplacement of most of the intrusions are poorly known at present. A notable exception is the Comrie pluton that is associated with pyroxene-, cordierite-, corundum- and spinel-hornfelses from which emplacement conditions of *c.* 750°C and 2.5 kbar have been calculated (Pattison & Tracey 1991).

Minor intrusions
A variety of late Caledonian, mainly calc-alkaline minor intrusions is present in both the Northern Highland and Grampian terranes. Emplacement is clearly episodic, with several syn- to late-orogenic regional suites. Many are spatially and genetically related to individual plutons or acted as feeders to extrusive rocks, whereas others may simply reflect the regional 'background' magmatism. The intrusions occur as plugs, sheets and dykes and vary from isolated examples to swarms that comprise a high percentage of total outcrop. Two main suites can be identified: (1) microdiorites, and (2) appinites and calc-alkaline lamprophyres.

Microdiorites. In the Northern Highland terrane, members of the suite are abundant in western Inverness-shire where they comprise two main types, microdiorites and felsic porphyrites (Fig. 4.68; Smith 1979). Both show evidence for variable degrees of deformation and metamorphic recrystallization. The earliest microdiorites are folded by upright (probably D3) structures and show axial planar metamorphic fabrics. Examples have been documented near Glenfinnan and Loch Sunart (Talbot 1983). These intrusions appear to have been emplaced prior to the final increments of deformation associated with development of the Northern Highland Steep Belt. Most are probably slightly younger because they are not folded and occur as narrow, planar sheets that dip gently to the southeast (dominant) or to the northwest at 35–40° (Fig. 4.68; Plate 8). The undeformed central parts of these microdiorites contain zoned andesine and hornblende as well as subordinate quartz and K-feldspar. The margins were, however, foliated and recrystallized under waning amphibolite- to greenschist-facies metamorphic conditions (Johnson & Dalziel 1963; Dearnley 1967; Smith 1979). The felsic porphyrites similarly occur as mainly southeast-dipping sheets (Smith 1979). Where undeformed, they are porphyritic microgranites with phenocrysts of plagioclase, biotite and/or hornblende set in a groundmass of quartz, K-feldspar and plagioclase. Like the microdiorites, they are commonly schistose, having been deformed and recrystallized within the amphibolite- or greenschist-facies (Smith 1979). Emplacement of the microdiorite suite appears to have overlapped intrusion of the granite vein complexes. Microdiorites cut members of the Loch Eil, Loch Arkaig and Mallie vein complexes, whereas members of the Glen Garry vein complex cut microdiorites but are themselves cut by felsic porphyrites.

In the Grampian terrane, microdiorites form sheets and dykes of intermediate composition ranging from quartz microdiorite to microgranodiorite. Several suites have been identified. Some microdiorites are foliated and recrystallized and may have been intruded during the Grampian orogenic event (Stephenson & Gould 1995). Younger, essentially undeformed microdiorites are widespread throughout the Grampian terrane

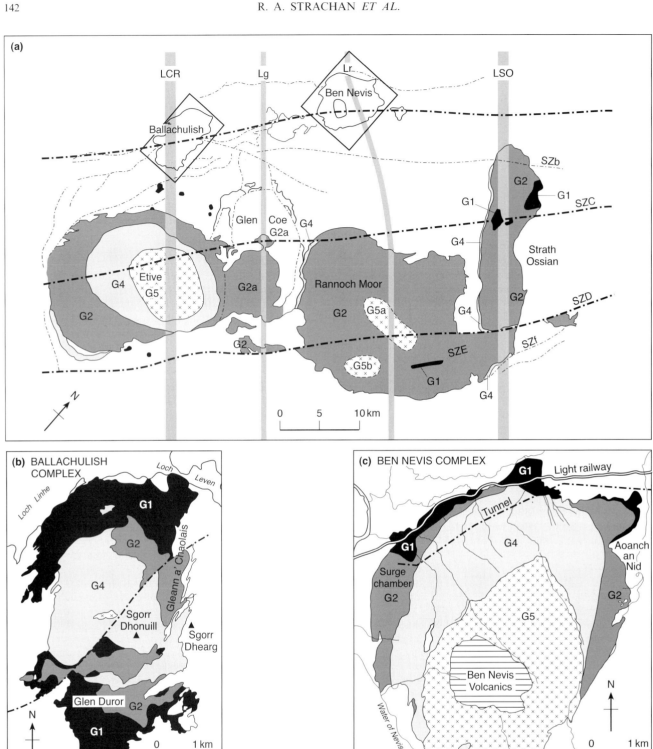

(a)

LCR   Lg   Lr   LSO

Ben Nevis

Ballachulish

SZb
G2
G1 — G1
SZC
G1
G4
Strath
Ossian

Glen Coe
G2a   G4

G4
Etive
G5
G2a   Rannoch Moor   G2   SZD
G2   G2
G4   SZf

G2   G5a

N   G2   G5b   SZE   G4

G1

0   5   10 km

(b) BALLACHULISH COMPLEX

Loch Leven
Loch Linhe

G1
G2
Gleann a' Chaolais
G4

Sgorr Dhonuill ▲   ▲ Sgorr Dhearg

Glen Duror   G2

G1

N   0   1 km

(c) BEN NEVIS COMPLEX

G1   Light railway

Tunnel

G1   G4
Surge chamber   Aoanch an Nid
G2
G5   G2

Ben Nevis Volcanics

Water of Nevis   N   0   1 km

Shear zone (SZ)/fault

A Ballachulish – Corrieyairack
b Allt Buidhe/Laggan Dam Fault
C Etive – Laggan
D Ericht – Laidon
E (Gleann Duibhe – previous position of SZD
f Gleann Chomraidh

Lineaments

LCR Cruachan Lineament
Lg   Glencoe Line
Lr   Rannoch Moor Line
LSO Strath Ossian Lineament

Intrusive phases

G1 Quartz Diorite
G2 Granodiorite
G3 Granitic sheets and dykes (omitted for clarity)
G4 Megacrystic K-feldspar granite
G5 Granite

Fig. 4.65. Sketch map of the SW Grampians showing the major structural features and late Caledonian plutons including the intrusive phases G1–G5, together with more detailed maps of the Ballachulish and Ben Nevis plutons (from Jacques & Reavy 1994).

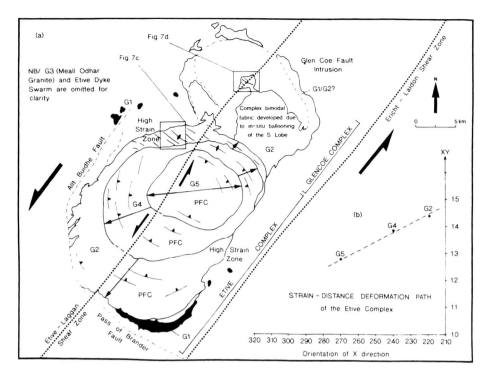

Fig. 4.66. (**a**) Generalized model for emplacement of the intrusive phases of the Etive complex and the Glencoe complex; (**b**) A plot which shows the X/Y ratios for the intrusive phases G2, G4 and G5 against the orientation of the X direction (from Jacques & Reavy 1994).

and appear to be coeval with the 'Newer Granites'. The major granitic plutons in the Lorne and Lochaber districts are spatially associated with extensive, dense swarms of NE-trending dykes of intermediate to acid composition, ranging from microdiorite to felsite. The Etive dyke swarm cuts the Devonian volcanics in the Lorne district and Glen Coe, and also the Rannoch Moor granite. Successive members of the Etive granite complex (apart from the central granite) are cut by dykes associated with later phases of the complex (Stephenson & Gould 1995). Separate microdiorite suites are associated with other intrusions such as the Glen Tilt complex and the Foyers pluton.

Appinites and calc-alkaline lamprophyres. Many small intrusions of appinite and lamprophyre occur throughout the Scottish Highlands: they are, respectively, the coarse- and fine-grained products of the regional 'background' calc-alkaline magmatism within the orogen. The term 'appinite' was used by Bailey & Maufe (1916) to refer to a medium- to coarse-grained rock with essential prismatic hornblende in a groundmass of sodic plagioclase, K-feldspar and quartz. However, the term has been extended to incorporate a range of ultramafic, melanocratic basic and intermediate dioritic and granodioritic rocks, including the Ach'uaine hybrid intrusions of Sutherland (Read *et al.* 1925). Most are shoshonitic in affinity and of mantle derivation (Fowler 1988*a*; Henney 1991; Fowler & Henney 1996), with elevated Sr, Ba, Ni, Cr and light rare earth elements. They occur as plugs and irregular intrusions, many of which are located along major Caledonian faults and/or NW-trending lineaments (Rogers & Dunning 1991). Some appinites have a close spatial relationship with late Caledonian granitic plutons where they invariably pre-date or are partly contemporaneous with granitic magmas. They may occasionally form significant parts of the xenolith population in some plutons (e.g. Corrieyairick, Ratagain, Rogart). Many of the appinite intrusions, notably those in the Appin and Glen Roy areas, are associated with pipes infilled with breccias composed of country rock fragments (Bowes & Wright 1967; Platten & Money 1987). These are likely to represent feeders within subvolcanic systems.

The lamprophyres typically occur as dykes and sheets. In the Northern Highlands terrane, they are mainly minettes. These usually occur as steep-sided, east-west trending dykes with sharp, chilled margins against granites and Moine country rocks. The minettes have all of the high Ba–Sr elemental characteristics of the Argyll and Northern Highlands suite, and Sm–Nd isotope ratios indicate that they were generated in an incompatible-element enriched source (Canning *et al.* 1996), similar to that of the appinites (Fowler & Henney 1996). The suite extends beyond the Moine Thrust and cuts Torridonian and Lewisian rocks of the Caledonian foreland. In the Grampian terrane, the lamprophyres are mainly spessartites; small numbers of vogesites (hornblende with orthoclase) are present in both terranes.

Petrogenesis and geotectonic setting of the late Caledonian magmas

The overall calc-alkaline nature of the Newer Granites has led to the consensus that they formed above an Andean-style subduction zone that dipped beneath the Laurentian continental margin (Fig. 4.23; e.g. Dewey 1971; Soper 1986; Thirlwall 1988; Oliver 2001). The presence of the apparently contemporaneous alkaline suite in the NW Highlands was previously regarded as a major problem, because such magmas were thought to be restricted to zones of crustal extension (van Breemen *et al.* 1979*b*). However, it is now widely accepted that such magmas can result from crystal fractionation from basic, mantle-derived magmas in a subduction setting, thus accounting for their temporal coexistence with the Newer Granites (Thompson & Fowler 1986; Halliday *et al.* 1987; Fowler 1988*a, b,* 1992; Thirlwall & Burnard 1990; Fowler *et al.* 2001).

In recent years there has been considerable debate concerned with the detailed petrogenesis of these late Caledonian magmas. This is because the Newer Granites do not in detail display the spatial variation in chemistry that is characteristic of magmas derived directly from the melting of subducted oceanic crust, such as increase in potassium with distance from the trench. Certain features of the Newer Granites are uncommon in typical subduction-related melts, including the high Ba and Sr of the

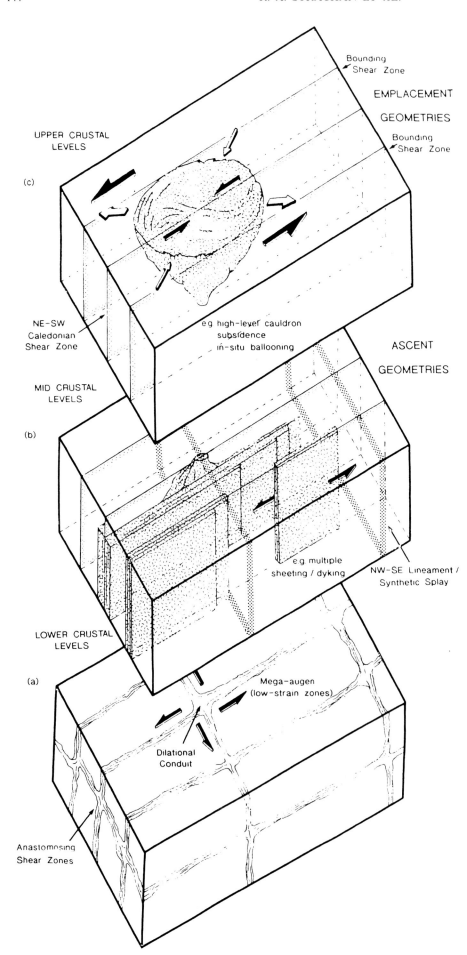

Fig. 4.67. Model for the ascent and emplacement of the Newer Granites in the Grampian Highlands (from Jacques & Reavy 1994) (**a**) Inferred lower crustal structure showing a series of low strain zones bounded by anastomosing shear zones; (**b**) Ascent pathways within the mid-crust for granitoid magma by a process of sheeting within shear zones or at transtensional voids at shear zone intersections; (**c**) Emplacement geometry of a granitoid complex within the upper crust undergoing rotational ballooning within a shear zone system.

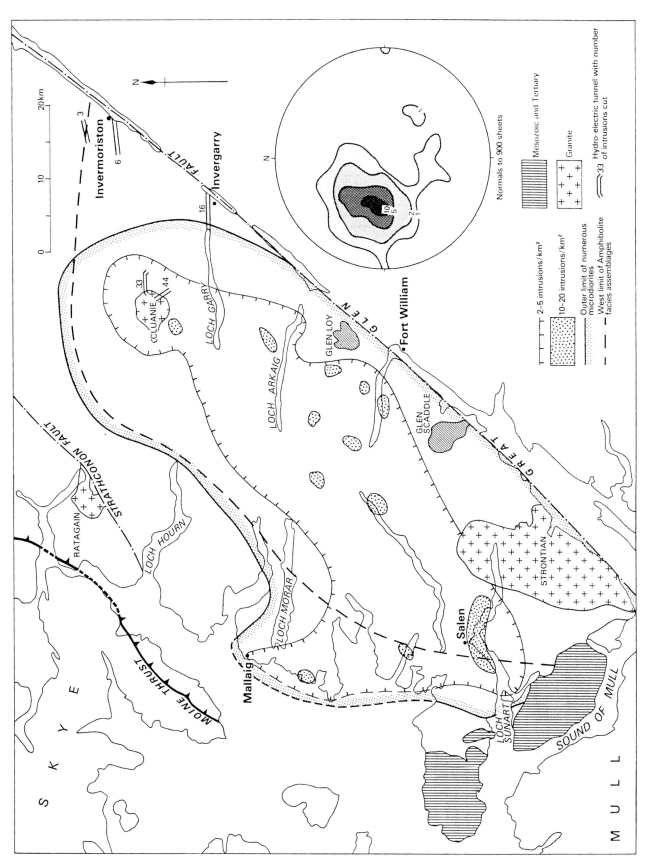

Fig. 4.68. Distribution, orientation and metamorphic grade of microdiorite intrusions in the southern part of the Northern Highland terrane (from Smith 1979).

Northern Highland suite, and the characteristic association of the Newer Granite melts with mantle-derived mafic enclaves, appinites and calc-alkaline lamprophyres. The chemistry of these latter intrusions is consistent with the melting of a hydrated K-rich mantle (Canning *et al.* 1996; Fowler & Henney 1996) modified by mixing, both in the source region and during ascent, with melts derived from the lower continental crust or subducted oceanic crust (Thirlwall 1982, 1983, 1986). Many of the Newer Granite plutons contain 1800–1200 Ma zircons, indicating that there must have been a certain amount of lower crust added to these melts (Halliday *et al.* (1979). The present consensus is therefore that the Newer Granites were derived mainly from the melting of lithospheric mantle and lower crustal sources (Stephens & Halliday 1984; Halliday *et al.* 1985; Tarney & Jones 1994; Fowler *et al.* 2001). Melting was probably initiated by the introduction of fluids derived from the subducting oceanic slab into the overlying mantle wedge.

The variations in the geochemistry and isotope characteristics of the three Newer Granite suites is thought to indicate differences in the composition and age of the lithospheric mantle and lower crust both orthogonal and parallel to the regional tectonic trend within the Scottish Highlands (Halliday 1984; Stephens & Halliday 1984). The Mid-Grampian Line (Fig. 4.52) appears to represent an important boundary in the deep basement (Halliday 1984). Because the chemical differences between the granite suites partly reflect variations in the proportion and composition of the mantle contribution to the melts, it follows that this lineament must have some expression in the mantle. Independent isotopic evidence that it also defines a boundary within the underlying continental crust is provided by studies of zircons within the late Caledonian granites. To the north of the lineament, granites contain inherited zircons with a marked isotopic memory of old radiogenic Pb, whereas to the south, granites contain negligible memory of older zircon (Halliday 1984, see also Pidgeon & Aftalion 1978). Since these zircons have to be derived from continental crust, this indicates a change in the age of the basement through which the magmas traversed. The granites in the north incorporated zircons of *c.* 1600 Ma age, whereas those from the south were derived from younger (Grenville?) crust.

It is thought that NW-directed subduction beneath the Laurentian margin commenced in the Llanvirn at *c.* 460 Ma, following the Grampian event (Fig. 4.23; Oliver 2001). This gives rise to an interesting question: why was there such a long

Table 4.1. *Summary of the main geological events recorded in the Northern Highland and Grampian terranes between c. 1000 Ma and the deposition of the post-Caledonian Old Red Sandstone sedimentary sequences*

Northern Highland terrane	Grampian terrane
Strike-slip faulting along the Great Glen, Highland Boundary and related faults; emplacement of the 'Newer Granite' suite and the syenites of NW Scotland (*c.* 425–400 Ma); continued regional cooling, uplift and erosion prior to the deposition of Old Red Sandstone sequences.	
Scandian orogeny (*c.* 435–425 Ma) NW–WNW-directed thrusting (Sgurr Beag, Naver, Moine thrusts), isoclinal folding and amphibolite-facies metamorphism of Morar Group; followed by tight upright folding, and formation of the North Highland Steep Belt. Pegmatites and early members of the microdiorite suite emplaced during waning stages of deformation.	Cooling and unroofing of the Grampian metamorphic belt (*c.* 460–425 Ma).
Intrusion of the Glen Dessary syenite (*c.* 456 Ma).	
Grampian orogeny (*c.* 470–460 Ma) Isoclinal folding and amphibolite-facies metamorphism of the Glenfinnan and Loch Eil groups. Regional migmatization in east Sutherland.	Grampian orogeny (*c.* 475–460 Ma) Nappe-scale folding and regional metamorphism of the Dalradian Supergroup, accompanied in later stages by the emplacement of the 'Newer Gabbro' suite and late-tectonic granites of the northern Grampians.
	Deposition of the Macduff Slate Formation (= top of the Dalradian Supergroup?) by *c.* 490–480 Ma.
	Deposition of the Southern Highland Group and the Leny Limestone (*c.* 600–520 Ma).
Emplacement of Carn Chuinneag–Inchbae and east Sutherland augen granites at *c.* 600 Ma, rift related magmatism?	Loch na Cille Boulder Bed = Varanger glaciation? Tayvallich Volcanic Formation (*c.* 600 Ma) and emplacement of rift-related 'Older Granite' suite.
	Deposition of Argyll Group
	Port Askaig glaciation (*c.* 720 Ma?)
	Deposition of Grampian and Appin groups (*c.* 800 Ma onwards?)
	Rifting and intitiation of the break-up of Rodinia
Post-metamorphic cooling to *c.* 750 Ma?	Post-metamorphic cooling – duration uncertain.
Knoydartian event (*c.* 820–790 Ma) Isoclinal folding, garnet-grade metamorphism and pegmatite generation (= crustal thickening?).	Grampian Shear Zone (*c.* 806 Ma).
	Kyanite-grade metamorphism and migmatisation of the Dava Succession at *c.* 840 Ma (= Knoydartian event?).
Emplacement of the igneous protoliths of the West Highland Granitic Gneiss and the regional metabasic suite. Tectonic setting (orogeny or rift-related) uncertain.	
Deposition of the Moine Supergroup (Morar, Glenfinnan and Loch Eil groups) (*c.* 1000–870 Ma).	Deposition of the Dava and Glen Banchor successions (<1000 Ma).

time (30 Ma) between initiation of subduction and emplacement of the Newer Granites? Oliver (2001) suggests some solutions: it is possible that the Iapetus subduction zone either did not reach below the Grampian terrane until mid-Llandovery times or it was too shallow-dipping to initiate granite formation. It is interesting to note that the onset of plutonism in the Late Llandovery at *c.*430 Ma coincided with the time in the Southern Uplands when the tectonics changed from orthogonal underthrusting to sinistrally oblique underthrusting (Stone 1995). It is this change in plate kinematics that is likely to have resulted in the development of the crustal-scale, trench parallel, sinistral strike-slip faults in the Laurentian crust that overlay the subduction zone (Fig. 4.37). The strike-slip faults then acted as the fundamental controls on where the granites were emplaced (Hutton & Reavy 1992; Jacques & Reavy 1994) as well as probably locating volcanism and sedimentary basins at higher crustal levels. A similar inter-relationship between the onset of oblique subduction, strike-slip faulting and plutonism has been proposed for the Mesozoic convergent plate margin of the Canadian Cordillera (Glazner 1991). The batholithic scale of Newer Granite magmatism in the Grampian terrane is thought to have induced crustal thickening, regional isostatic uplift and erosion during the Early Devonian (Oliver 2001).

Summary

The main geological events that are recorded within the Northern Highland and Grampian terranes are summarized in Table 4.1. The major advances that have occurred in the understanding of these complex segments of crust since the previous edition of this book was published in 1991 are as follows:

(1) Modern isotopic studies have shown that the Moine Supergroup is younger than *c.* 1 Ga and therefore post-dates the Grenvillian orogeny.

(2) There is clear isotopic evidence that the Moine rocks and their possible equivalents in the Grampian terrane, the Dava and Glen Banchor successions, were affected by an important Knoydartian tectonothermal event at *c.* 800 Ma.

Although the nature of this event remains highly controversial, the balance of evidence indicates that it is related to orogeny and crustal thickening.

(3) The results of detailed mapping in the Central Highlands by the British Geological Survey broadly substantiate the original proposals of Piasecki and coworkers, in that a tectonized unconformity appears to separate the Dava and Glen Banchor successions from the younger Dalradian Supergroup that was not affected by Precambrian orogenic activity.

(4) Further stratigraphical and sedimentological investigations in the Dalradian rocks continue to underpin the seminal models and interpretations of Anderton (1985) and Harris *et al.* (1978). Thickness and lateral facies variations and local basin architecture are better understood and accord with the progressive stretching, and ultimately rifting, of a broad continental shelf during the mid- to late Neoproterozoic breakup of Rodinia.

(5) It has been confirmed that the uppermost parts of the Dalradian Supergroup lie in stratigraphical and structural continuity with strata along the Highland Border that contain a Laurentian fauna. The Dalradian rocks are therefore tied firmly to Laurentia and cannot therefore be interpreted as an exotic terrane derived from another continental block (e.g. Gondwana).

(6) The Grampian orogenic event was a relatively short-lived, arc-continent collision that occurred during the Mid Ordovician at *c.* 475–460 Ma.

(7) The Great Glen Fault does not appear to separate crustal blocks with fundamentally differing histories: this is implied by the proposed correlation of the Moine Supergroup with the Dava and Glen Banchor successions, as well as recognition that the Northern Highland and Grampian terranes both record evidence for Knoydartian and Grampian tectonothermal activity. The apparent restriction of the Silurian Scandian orogenic event to the Northern Highland terrane, does, however, argue for a rather larger strike-slip displacement along the fault (at least 500 km) than has been commonly proposed.

5 The Midland Valley terrane

B. J. BLUCK

Two seminal papers, one from a worker who had insight into tectonics and sedimentation (Kennedy 1958), the other from a classical stratigrapher who had an eye for detail and great experience in synthesizing data (George 1960), present quite different views of the Midland Valley. This difference of opinion, although now in a different form, still exists over both the nature and role of the Midland Valley in Caledonian geology and the nature and significance of its boundaries.

The Midland Valley spans the gap between the deeper parts of the Caledonian orogen to the north, where the Dalradian block underwent Cambro-Ordovician burial, metamorphism and cooling and the more superficial but more clearly subduction-related region to the south. Research over the past three decades has assumed that in the south we have the preserved sedimentary record that can be directly related to a mechanism (subduction) that may have provided the required scale and intensity of heat and pressure required to metamorphose and deform the rocks to the north.

Establishing the nature of the link between these two regions is critical to an understanding of the Caledonides in the UK,

and the Midland Valley of Scotland, being the ground between, is clearly of some significance. However, Lower Palaeozoic rocks of the Midland Valley are poorly exposed being mostly covered by Upper. They are found mainly along its northern and southern margins (Fig. 5.1). This paucity of exposure within the Midland Valley has left much room for speculation about its history in relation to the adjacent blocks.

The Midland Valley, topographically lower than the flanking blocks, is bounded by the Southern Upland Fault to the south and the Highland Boundary Fault to the north (although the exact positioning of each of these structures is open to interpretation). A great deal of its Palaeozoic history is determined not so much from outcrop, but from the rocks that flank it on either side. However, with the possibility of tectonic displacement, strike-slip and thrusting, there is a measure of caution needed in this approach: flanking blocks may record a history that is not directly related to the Midland Valley itself but possibly to some extension of it along strike.

Both Kennedy and George had recognized that the Midland Valley resembles a rift valley in its general appearance. Whilst most of the rocks exposed are Late Palaeozoic in age, it is flanked mainly by Late Neoproterozoic rocks in the north and by mainly Early Palaeozoic rocks to the south (Fig. 5.1). The present Midland Valley is dominated both by Lower Old Red Sandstone rocks which were deposited in two basins, the axes of which run parallel with the Highland Boundary and Southern Uplands Faults (Bluck 1984), and by a series of Carboniferous basins which have axes that are somewhat oblique to these bounding structures (Francis 1991a).

This chapter deals almost totally with the Lower Palaeozoic history of the Midland Valley and relies on outcrops flanking the Highland Boundary Fault to the north and those intermittently found near to the Southern Upland Fault to the south. The oldest known rocks in the Midland Valley are Cambrian in age, being an amphibolite exposed at Bute, and one school of thought also includes the Leny Limestone, near Callander, and of late Lower Cambrian age, into the Midland Valley sequence (Bluck *et al.* 1984).

An examination of its history, stretching back into the Late Neoproterozoic and earlier times, clearly shows that whilst it may now have a rift-like form, the Midland Valley is very far from being a simple rift structure and much of this chapter addresses these complications on the basis of sometimes quite scant evidence. It is appropriate to begin with a study of the bounding faults and their associated rocks since they define the Midland Valley.

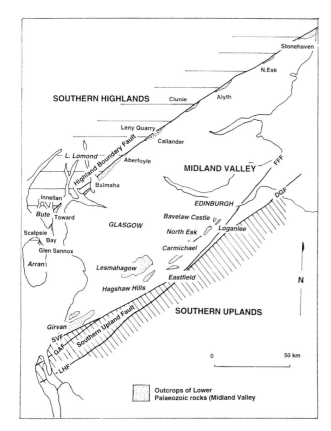

Fig. 5.1. Outline map of the Midland Valley with outcrops of Lower Palaeozoic rocks, (including main inliers), place names and main faults. SVF, Stinchar Valley Fault; GAF, Glen App Fault; LHF, Leadhills Fault; FFF, Firth of Forth Fault; DGF, Dunbar–Gifford Fault (for additional faults see Floyd 1994).

The northern margin: the Highland Border and the Highland Boundary Fault

The Highland Border Complex comprises a group of steeply dipping, often sheared rocks that lie between the Dalradian block to the north and the unconformably overlying Lower Old Red Sandstone rocks of the Midland Valley to the south. It is a narrow, laterally extensive outcrop striking parallel to the

Highland Boundary Fault, and intermittently exposed from the coast north of Stonehaven (Plate 9) to Arran (Fig. 5.1).

Rocks of similar aspect are present intermittently along the southern edge of the Dalradian block in Ireland, extending west to Galway, where they are better exposed than in Scotland. In the Midland Valley, the Complex, although laterally extensive, has an outcrop that is usually less than 1 km wide. Whilst its southern margin is clearly defined by the unconformable (and, in places, faulted) Lower Old Red Sandstone, the position and nature of its northern margin is debated. Some (e.g. Bluck et al. 1984) would have it faulted against the Dalradian whilst others see it as resting conformably on that sequence (e.g. Tanner 1995). As the Complex is seen to underlie the Old Red Sandstone along the northern margin of the Midland Valley then, in this latter view a part, or possibly all of the Midland Valley, could be interpreted as being floored by a southerly extension of the Dalradian block.

History of research

Research on the rocks at the Highland Border has had a long history, suggesting that, despite their limited outcrop, workers in Scottish geology have attached some significance to their interpretation. Anderson (1946) has pointed out that many of those who we now know to have established some of the basic tenets of geology have been intrigued both by these rocks at the Highland Border and their relationships to what we now know to be the Dalradian block to the north.

Although references had been made to the rocks along the Highland Border from the time of Hutton and Lyell the identification of a fault in this region was first clearly indicated by Sedgwick & Murchison (1835) in a paper on Arran. Harkness (1861) recognized the extent of the fault and placed it between the Dalradian block and the Highland Border Complex as we now know them. Both Macculloch (1824) and Lyell (1825) were amongst the first to record serpentinite within this zone. Nicol (1855) and Peach & Horne (1899) drew a comparison between the rocks exposed along the Highland Border and those in the southern Midland Valley at Girvan and in the Southern Uplands. In so doing they raised the possibility that the Upper Palaeozoic rocks of the Midland Valley were underlain by the Highland Border or related rocks.

On the basis of these comparisons came the view that the rocks were Lower Palaeozoic in age, and Barrow (1901) regarded them as a unit which was separated from the Dalradian by a NW-dipping thrust. He then introduced the idea of a major structural dislocation in this zone referring to it as the Great Highland Fault, dividing the Old Red Sandstone from the Highland Border Complex.

Gregory (1910) repeated his view that there was a major fracture between the Dalradian and Highland Border Complex, but an acute observer in the form of Clough (in Geikie 1897) could find no break between the Highland Border rocks and the Dalradian in the region around Callendar. This latter observation was subsequently taken a step further by Johnson & Harris (1967) who demonstrated a striking similarity between the structures in the Dalradian and those in the Highland Border Complex and concluded that the Complex was part of the Dalradian sequence. This view was followed by Henderson & Robertson (1982) who provided much new and valuable data on the Complex, and was again reaffirmed by Tanner (1995), and see Figure 5.2. Partly on the basis of this evidence all these authors regard the Highland Border rocks as part of the Dalradian sequence, and therefore had little to do with the history of the Midland Valley. Recently, however, Harris et al. (1998)

implied that the Cambrian part of the Highland Border Comdplex alone may rest conformably on the Dalradian.

In contrast, Curry et al. (1982), Bluck et al. (1984) and Bluck & Ingham (1997), on the basis of the re-discovery of Arenig trilobites and other fossils (see Ingham et al. 1985) at Dounans Quarry, Aberfoyle, concluded that the sequence could not overlie the Dalradian at this time. Their argument rested partly of the cooling ages determined by Giletti et al. (1961), Fitch et al. (1964), Harper (1967) and Dempster (1985), all of whom, using a variety of isotopic systems had determined that this block was a rising orogenic, metamorphic complex at the time the Ordovician limestones were laid down (but see Evans & Soper 1997). On this basis, the Highland Boundary Fault is located at the junction between the Dalradian block and the Highland Border Complex: the one being uplifted and the other, in a coeval state of subsidence, receiving no recognizable sediment from the uplift. The structure, now dividing rocks with histories incompatible with being adjacent to each other, was raised to the status of a terrane boundary.

Pillow lava and related sediments comprise a good deal of the sequence as does serpentinite. In addition there are slivers of gabbro and dolerite together with cobbles and boulders of trondhjemite and diorite found in some conglomerates. Serpentinite and serpentinite-bearing conglomerates are relatively common (Henderson & Fortey 1982), and at two localities along the outcrop, Bute and Aberfoyle, there are amphibolites, one of which is associated with serpentinite. This combination of rock types has suggested to Henderson & Robertson (1982) and Bluck et al. (1984) that part of the Highland Border Complex comprises a remnant of a fragmented ophiolite.

Description of the Highland Border Complex

On the basis of faunal evidence, unconformable relationships, association and petrography (i.e. identifying clasts of older lithologies in younger deposits), Bluck et al. (1984) suggested that the Highland Border Complex be divided into four assemblages. Firm ages were assigned on the basis of macrofaunas, and tentative ages were assigned for some on the basis of chitinozoa (Burton & Curry 1984). The assemblages, although groupings of rocks with similar characteristics, because of their structural complexity and possible repetition of lithologies, may not always contain rocks of the same age. The assemblages are summarized in Figure 5.3, and are described below.

Assemblage 1 (Bute amphibolite–Leny Limestone)

On the Island of Bute, a serpentinite is associated with an amphibolite resembling those found at the bases of ophiolites (Henderson & Robertson 1982; Dempster & Bluck 1991a). The age of this association which includes gabbro, dolerite and pillow lavas is bracketed by the age of the Bute amphibolite (Sm–Nd age of 546 ± 42 Ma, and a K–Ar age of 537 ± 11 Ma (Dempster & Bluck 1991a)) and the earliest dated sediments containing serpentinite and associated rocks (i.e. The Dounans Limestone, Mid-Arenig, c. 470 Ma (Ingham et al. 1985)). This oldest assemblage is therefore thought to be of either Early Cambrian or Late Neoproterozoic age (the base of the Cambrian being 543 Ma: Davidek et al. 1998; Landing et al. 1998). This ophiolitic mass was uplifted by at least Mid-Arenig times.

At Leny, near Callendar, a limestone has yielded a Lower Cambrian fauna (Pringle 1940; Cowie et al. 1972) and this is included in the oldest assemblage (Fig. 5.3). The fauna, which includes *Pagetides*, brachiopods and other fossils, is thought to belong to the Laurentian province and inhabited the outer shelf (Conway Morris & Rushton 1988). With the boundary between Middle and Early Cambrian now set at c. 509 Ma (Davidek

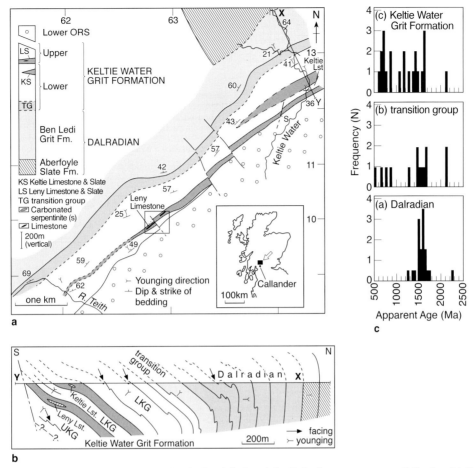

Fig. 5.2. The relationships between the Leny Limestone (Early Cambrian) and the Dalradian sequence near Callendar. (**a**) General map of the outcrop between the river Teith and Keltie Water, together with a stratigraphic section through the Dalradian–Highland Border sequence. (**b**) A true scale, cross-section (X–Y see (**a**), at Keltie Water): LKG, Lower Keltie Water Grits; UKG, Upper Keltie Water Grits. For other abreviations see (**a**). (**c**) ^{40}Ar–^{39}Ar laser fusion age spectra for detrital white micas from the three units figured in (**a**) and (**b**). (Modified from Tanner & Pringle 1999.)

et al. 1998; Landing et al. 1998), then this limestone, being at the top of the Lower Cambrian, is thought to be a little older than that age. If the age determinations from the Bute amphibolite record an obduction event and given that the rocks there are part of the Highland Border Complex, then ophiolite obduction preceded the deposition of the Leny Limestone.

The presence of a Cambrian limestone and a possible ophiolite sole along the same Dalradian margin does not necessarily imply that both events took place in similar positions at this margin. There is obvious considerable structural complexity in the Highland Border rocks and there is the implication of a profound structural break between these two Cambrian units which emphasizes the immense structural discontinuities which clearly exist in this zone. Recent work by Tanner (1995), Tanner & Pringle (1999) and Harris et al. (1998) has re-affirmed the view that the Cambrian Leny Limestone is part of the Dalradian sequence. If it is to be regarded as part of the Dalradian then the position of the older, ophiolitic part of the Complex has to be reassessed and a decision made whether to also include it with the Dalradian block.

Assemblage 2 (Dounans Limestone and conglomerates)

Limestones and associated conglomerates and breccias with a carbonate matrix occur immediately above the ophiolitic rocks as well as elsewhere, higher in the stratigraphy of the Complex (Fig. 5.3). The limestones, which in one locality at Lime Craig Quarry, Aberfoyle, have yielded a fauna including brachiopods,

bryozoans, crinoids, trilobites, conodonts and ostracods, also contain abundant ophiolitic debris (Henderson & Fortey 1982). Thirteen trilobite species are present, but most individuals belong to the species Ischyrotoma stubblefieldi and have Laurentian affinities (Ingham et al. 1985). Both trilobites and conodonts indicate a Mid-Arenig age (Ingham et al. 1985; Ethington & Austin 1991). The associated conglomerates are seen to be relatively thin, although generally fault-bounded. In view of the wide variety of mafic and ultra-mafic (ophiolitic) clasts they contain, it is clear that their deposition was preceded by tectonic activity of sufficient magnitude to bring to the surface groups of rocks that originally formed at totally different temperatures and pressures (Henderson & Fortey 1982).

In addition to the mafic and ultra-mafic clasts, in the Aberfoyle–Balmaha area this conglomerate contains metamorphic clasts, up to boulder size, that have cooling ages of 1817 ± 31 Ma and 1799 ± 26 Ma (Dempster & Bluck 1989). These clasts are therefore not derived from the Dalradian block and have not been reset by any subsequent thermal event.

Assemblage 3 (Black shales and pillow lavas)

In the Balmaha–Aberfoyle region, rocks of assemblage 2 are overlain unconformably by a thin breccia and a thicker sequence of black shale and cherts (Fig. 5.3). Black shale sequences elsewhere in the Complex contain or are associated with pillow lavas, tuffs and breccias. Although this assemblage is found intermittently from Arran in the southwest to Stonehaven

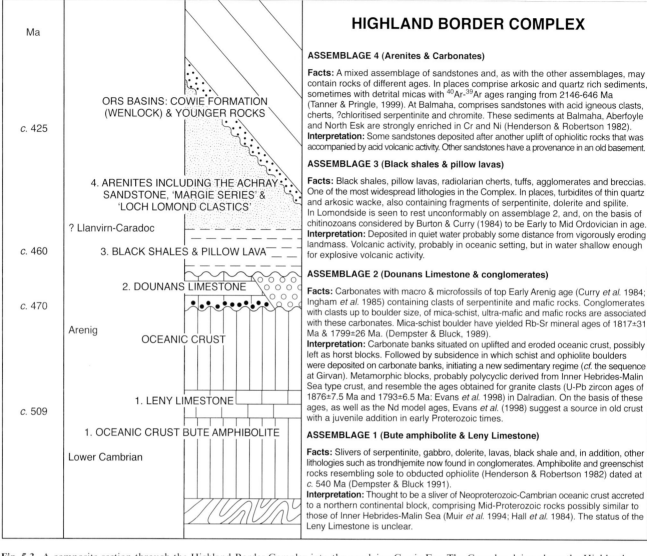

HIGHLAND BORDER COMPLEX

ASSEMBLAGE 4 (Arenites & Carbonates)

Facts: A mixed assemblage of sandstones and, as with the other assemblages, may contain rocks of different ages. In places comprise arkosic and quartz rich sediments, sometimes with detrital micas with [40]Ar-[39]Ar ages ranging from 2146-646 Ma (Tanner & Pringle, 1999). At Balmaha, comprises sandstones with acid igneous clasts, cherts, ?chloritised serpentinite and chromite. These sediments at Balmaha, Aberfoyle and North Esk are strongly enriched in Cr and Ni (Henderson & Robertson 1982).
Interpretation: Some sandstones deposited after another uplift of ophiolitic rocks that was accompanied by acid volcanic activity. Other sandstones have a provenance in an old basement.

ASSEMBLAGE 3 (Black shales & pillow lavas)

Facts: Black shales, pillow lavas, radiolarian cherts, tuffs, agglomerates and breccias. One of the most widespread lithologies in the Complex. In places, turbidites of thin quartz and arkosic wacke, also containing fragments of serpentinite, dolerite and spilite. In Lomondside is seen to rest unconformably on assemblage 2, and, on the basis of chitinozoans considered by Burton & Curry (1984) to be Early to Mid Ordovician in age.
Interpretation: Deposited in quiet water probably some distance from vigorously eroding landmass. Volcanic activity, probably in oceanic setting, but in water shallow enough for explosive volcanic activity.

ASSEMBLAGE 2 (Dounans Limestone & conglomerates)

Facts: Carbonates with macro & microfossils of top Early Arenig age (Curry et al. 1984; Ingham et al. 1985) containing clasts of serpentinite and mafic rocks. Conglomerates with clasts up to boulder size, of mica-schist, ultra-mafic and mafic rocks are associated with these carbonates. Mica-schist boulder have yielded Rb-Sr mineral ages of 1817±31 Ma & 1799±26 Ma. (Dempster & Bluck, 1989).
Interpretation: Carbonate banks situated on uplifted and eroded oceanic crust, possibly left as horst blocks. Followed by subsidence in which schist and ophiolite boulders were deposited on carbonate banks, initiating a new sedimentary regime (cf. the sequence at Girvan). Metamorphic blocks, probably polycyclic derived from Inner Hebrides-Malin Sea type crust, and resemble the ages obtained for granite clasts (U-Pb zircon ages of 1876±7.5 Ma and 1793±6.5 Ma: Evans et al. 1998) in Dalradian. On the basis of these ages, as well as the Nd model ages, Evans et al. (1998) suggest a source in old crust with a juvenile addition in early Proterozoic times.

ASSEMBLAGE 1 (Bute amphibolite & Leny Limestone)

Facts: Slivers of serpentinite, gabbro, dolerite, lavas, black shale and, in addition, other lithologies such as trondhjemite now found in conglomerates. Amphibolite and greenschist rocks resembling sole to obducted ophiolite (Henderson & Robertson 1982) dated at c. 540 Ma (Dempster & Bluck 1991).
Interpretation: Thought to be a sliver of Neoproterozoic-Cambrian oceanic crust accreted to a northern continental block, comprising Mid-Proterozoic rocks possibly similar to those of Inner Hebrides-Malin Sea (Muir et al. 1994; Hall et al. 1984). The status of the Leny Limestone is unclear.

Fig. 5.3. A composite section through the Highland Border Complex into the overlying Cowie Fm. The Complex, lying along the Highland Boundary Fault, comprises tectonic slivers of rocks with quite different histories, and possibly in-faulted from disconnected basins and blocks. The assemblages, discussed in the text, are therefore loose rock associations. The ages of some are known but others are poorly constrained. The relative ages are based on unconformable relationships, old lithologies reworked into younger and rare stratigraphical order. The sequence begins with the obduction of an ophiolite recorded in the Bute amphibolite and is unconformably overlain by the Cowie Fm., considered here to belong to the succeeding Old Red Sandstone basins.

in the northeast it is particularly well exposed on the coast north of Stonehaven (Craigeven Bay, Plate 9) and on Arran (North Glen Sannox). Graded beds composed mainly of quartz grains, and arkosic wackes, are associated with these black shales at Aberfoyle where Jehu & Cambell (1917) recorded a shelly and probably displaced fauna of supposed Ordovician age.

A conglomerate with rounded clasts of ophiolitic debris occurs on the northern margin of the outcrop at the North Esk and Balmaha, and may be a second conglomerate in the sequence. The age of this assemblage is not well founded, but the total fauna, including acritarchs, chitinozoans and inarticulate brachiopods was taken to be Llanvirn–Llandeilo by Burton & Curry (1984).

Assemblage 4 (Arenites and carbonates)

These rocks (Fig. 5.3) comprise arenites with a range of degrees of deformation and petrographic composition. Some are relatively quartz-rich at present but are at a metamorphic grade where most of the more labile grains would have broken down. Rocks of this assemblage are well exposed in the river North Esk and in the Aberfoyle–Balmaha areas. One group, the Loch Lomond Clastics (Henderson & Robertson 1982) have locally escaped penetrative deformation and are relatively well preserved, lithic arenites, that contain a range of rock fragments which include various ophiolitic fragments, chert, metamorphic fragments and acid volcanic and plutonic rocks.

These beds are often found on the very north side of the outcrop, adjacent to the Dalradian. Distinguishing them from Dalradian rocks is difficult and Tanner & Pringle (1999) include beds resembling these in the Dalradian sequence. On the basis of the acritarchs, chitinozoa and that the local presence of clasts of older rocks in the sequence, these beds have been tentatively assigned to the Caradoc–Ashgill by Burton & Curry (1984). From rocks included here in this assemblage, Tanner & Pringle (1999) record detrital mica ranging in age from 2146 to 646 Ma (see Fig. 5.2). A source in old crust that underwent Proterozoic cooling is implied, although the position of this source relative to the Complex is uncertain.

Some general considerations

There are a number of points to emerge from the descriptions of the Complex when it is seen in its regional setting. The Highland Border Complex was largely assembled and probably eroded to a peneplain by the time the beds of the Lower Old Red Sandstone (Cowie Fm.) were laid down (which provides an upper age limit to the Complex). These beds, assigned to the Upper Wenlock–Lower Ludlow (Marshall 1991; Wellman 1993), rest unconformably on the Highland Border Complex north of Stonehaven (Hutchinson 1928). Younger Old Red Sandstone strata also unconformably overlie the Complex in several places SW along the outcrop (Bluck 2000).

Within this thin Highland Border outcrop, younger stratigraphical formations are often found NW of older, although at any one locality there may be evidence for local changes in this direction of younging. At Stonehaven evidence from pillows and sedimentary structures shows younging to the NW. In the North Esk the sequence is duplicated, but near its contact with the Dalradian, in a sequence considered to young NW into the Dalradian block there is a conglomerate with clasts of the underlying basic lavas (Barrow 1901; Shackleton 1958). At Lomondside and Aberfoyle conglomerates with clasts of underlying basic and ultra basic rocks are succeeded by arenites and black shales to the NW. In the vicinity of Leny Quarry the sedimentary structures suggested to Tanner (1995) that the beds get younger to the SE and Johnson & Harris (1967) suggest a SE younging for the Complex in Arran.

As the Old Red Sandstone (Cowie Fm. and younger rocks) is seen to rest unconformably on the southern margin of the Highland Border Complex, then the later must have, partly at least, formed the basin floor to the former. During the post- or syn-depositional folding of the Lower Old Red Sandstone parts of, if not all of the Highland Border Complex, was also folded (Fig. 5.4). The attitude of the Highland Border Complex, when it was the floor to the Old Red Sandstone basin, can be approximated by unfolding the Complex around the dip of the unconformably overlying Old Red Sandstone. When this is done, for some localities, the Highland Border Complex was inverted at the time it was a basement to the Lower Old Red Sandstone basin (Bluck et al. 1984; Bluck 1992a; Bluck & Ingham 1997; Fig. 5.4).

The nature and association of the Highland Border Complex

Any explanation of the nature, association and role of the Highland Border Complex has to address the following three points:

1. In marked contrast to the adjacent Dalradian, the Highland Border Complex has a very wide range of rock types concentrated into a narrow outcrop. It is clearly a structurally dismembered grouping of disparate rock types representing a very wide range of tectonic regimes. Shears sometimes bring into juxtaposition rocks with radically different histories: at Aberfoyle, for example, amphibolites are found to be in contact with black shales and lithic arenites (Henderson & Fortey 1982); amphibolite lies adjacent to epidote bearing rock and serpentinite conglomerates and breccias in Bute. This juxtapositioning is clear evidence for substantial throws on the faults which brought them together.

2. In spite of this, some lithologies such as breccias, conglomerates and sometimes even sandstones have clasts resembling lithologies now exposed in the Complex. This suggests that, in addition to the structural complexity,

there is a degree of continuity in stratigraphy within the complex, although there was clearly much uplift and recycling of older blocks into younger sediments. The presence of unconformities within the sequence confirms the presence of recycling events.

3. Those rocks in the Complex which were formed in oceanic basins would have originally been far more extensive than the present outcrop width (Fig. 5.5). It is therefore a highly compressed assemblage which had a long history of deposition, uplift and erosion, probably acted out some distance from the Dalradian block. In one interpretation the Highland Border rocks extended over the Dalradian block (Henderson & Robertson 1982; Tanner 1995; Soper et al. 1999); in the other they extend beneath the Midland Valley and the Southern Highlands (Bluck et al. 1984; Dempster & Bluck 1991b; Dentith et al. 1992).

The Silurian rocks

Some of the rocks referred to as Old Red Sandstone could, on the basis of the presently fixed timescale (Gradstein & Ogg 1996; Tucker et al. 1998) and the absolute dating of the lavas (Thirlwall 1988), belong to the Silurian. At the NE end of the Midland Valley, the rocks of the Cowie Formation are ascribed to the Wenlock or lowest Ludlow (Marshall 1991; Wellman 1993). These Silurian rocks at Cowie, in resting unconformably on the Highland Border Complex, form the first beds that initiated the new structural regime which typified the Old Red Sandstone sedimentation (Haughton & Bluck 1988; Bluck 2000).

The Highland Boundary Fault

There is evidently an exposed fracture along the northern margin of the Midland Valley, even though its history and exact location is disputed (see Fig. 5.4). The main role of the Highland Boundary Fault is the juxtapositioning of two blocks with incompatible histories. The Dalradian basement to the north was undergoing cooling and uplift during most of Ordovician time (Dempster 1985; Dempster et al. 1995), and at the same time the Highland Border Complex, now lying adjacent to it, was a basin receiving sediment unrelated to this uplift (Bluck 1984). The lithologies within the Complex, which include black shales and limestones, are incompatible with a position beside a cooling and uplifting Dalradian metamorphic block. There is a little metamorphic detritus found in the Highland Border Complex. Quartz-mica schist boulders have cooling ages far older than found in the Dalradian and rocks ascribed to this complex by Tanner & Pringle (1999) also have detrital micas with ages far older than the Dalradian cooling ages (Figs 5.2, 5.3, 5.5). This degree of incompatibility requires the Highland Boundary Fault to be a major, terrane-scale dislocation, and the Fault to be located in the contact between the Highland Border Complex and the Dalradian block.

As with many large faults of this kind throughout the world, the Highland Boundary Fault has been subjected to much reactivation. The last phase of movement, appears to have been relatively trivial compared with the earlier phases. In places, therefore, the existing fault may bear deceptively little sign of its previous, more vigorous history (Fig. 5.5). Dentith et al. (1992) and Dempster & Bluck (1991b), for example, pointed out that there was a possible late stage (possibly Mid-Devonian, Bluck 2001) SE directed thrusting associated with this fault. In addition, evidence from Cowal and Bute, where Carboniferous

a. FACTS: generalised section along the Highland Border

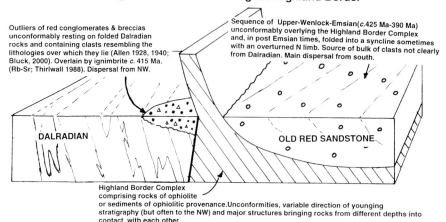

Outliers of red conglomerates & breccias
unconformably resting on folded Dalradian
rocks and containing clasts resembling the
lithologies over which they lie (Allen 1928, 1940;
Bluck, 2000). Overlain by ignimbrite c. 415 Ma.
(Rb-Sr; Thirlwall 1988). Dispersal from NW.

Sequence of Upper-Wenlock-Emsian(c.425 Ma-390 Ma)
unconformably overlying the Highland Border Complex
and, in post Emsian times, folded into a syncline sometimes
with an overturned N limb. Source of bulk of clasts not clearly
from Dalradian. Main dispersal from south.

DALRADIAN

OLD RED SANDSTONE

Highland Border Complex
comprising rocks of ophiolite
or sediments of ophiolitic provenance.Unconformities, variable direction of younging
stratigraphy (but often to the NW) and major structures bringing rocks from different depths into
contact with each other.

b. INTERPRETATION 1: Highland Border Complex not part of Dalradian

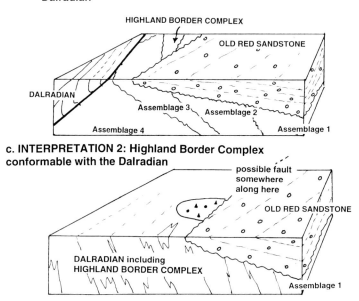

HIGHLAND BORDER COMPLEX

OLD RED SANDSTONE

DALRADIAN

Assemblage 3   Assemblage 2

Assemblage 4   Assemblage 1

c. INTERPRETATION 2: Highland Border Complex conformable with the Dalradian

possible fault
somewhere
along here

OLD RED SANDSTONE

DALRADIAN including
HIGHLAND BORDER COMPLEX

Assemblage 1

Fig. 5.4. (**a**) A generalized section through the Highland Border outlining some of the key facts which help constrain the role of Highland Boundary Fault, the history of the blocks on either side of it and the associations of the Highland Border Complex. The outliers of often gently dipping Lower Old Red Sandstone sited on the Dalradian block imply that there has been little post Devonian rotation of this block (in marked contrast to the rocks of the Strathmore Syncline to the south). (**b**) The interpretation of the Highland Border on the assumption that the Highland Border Complex is not part of the Dalradian block. In this diagram the sequences of assemblages (see text for description), prior to the folding of the Strathmore Syncline are younging towards the Dalradian block. This is a generalization: there are folds within the sequence reversing this order. The Highland Boundary Fault divides the Dalradian from the Highland Border Complex. (**c**) The Highland Border Complex is seen to be part of the Dalradian sequence. In this interpretation, the oldest assemblage is thought to be in contact with the Dalradian and, as there is an unconformity between the Old Red Sandstone and the Highland Border Complex, there is no reason for a great throw on the Highland Boundary Fault in this general area.

rocks are truncated by the Fault, confirms a post Early Carboniferous movement for its westerly extension at least. This later movement may have over-ridden some of the intensive shearing associated with its earlier history. On Arran and Bute there are mylonites in this zone and elsewhere evidence of extreme shearing. However, in other localities (e.g. Aberfoyle, Leny, North Esk) the boundary between the Highland Border Complex and the Dalradian blocks is often difficult to locate.

A reconstruction of the history of the movements along the Fault, together with the evidence for them, is given in Figure 5.5. Whilst separation between the Dalradian and Highland Border Complex is evident, the timing and history of juxtapositioning of them is less clear. In western Ireland, where an extensive outcrop of Ordovician rock lies adjacent to the

Dalradian basements of Conemarra and north Mayo, Graham *et al.* (1991) and Dewey & Mange (1999) have identified detritus in rocks of Llanvirn age (*c.* 465 Ma) which they believe to have a provenance in the adjacent Dalradian block. This suggests to them that the Mayo trough, the possible lateral extension of the Highland Border Complex, was situated sufficiently near to the Dalradian to receive some of the detritus eroded off it. Hutcheson & Oliver (1998), on the basis the geochemistry of garnet populations from the Highland Border Complex and Southern Uplands in Scotland, come to a similar conclusion. Williams, D. M. *et al.* (1994, 1996), however, conclude that there was no contact between Highland Border equivalent rocks in Western Ireland and the Dalradian block until Late Ordovician or Mid-Silurian times.

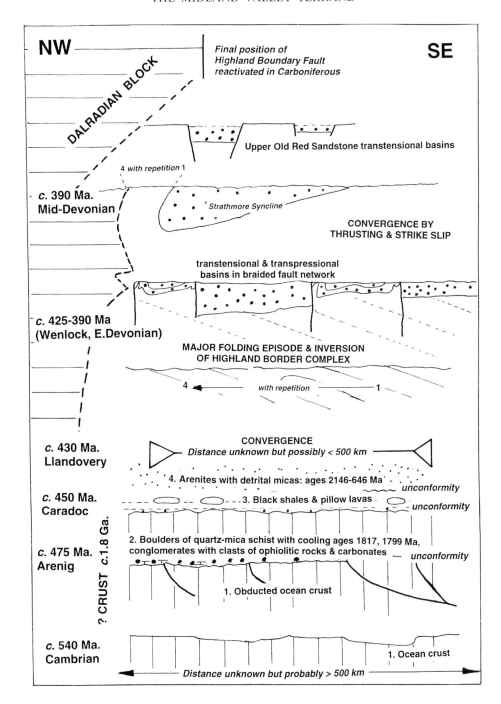

Fig. 5.5. History of the Highland Border and the Highland Boundary Fault. During the Cambrian–Llandovery, rocks of the Highland Border Complex underwent a sequence of uplift, possibly the result of strike-slip fault movements during periods of collision between small plates (see van Staal *et al.* 1998). The Midland Valley is thought to have had an Early Proterozoic block on its northern margin until Llandovery time, when it was replaced by the Dalradian block (Bluck 2001) but the incoming of the Dalradian block may have been earlier in Ireland and is equated with the inversion and over-turning of the Highland Border Complex. Wenlock–Devonian times are characterized by the thrust and strike-slip convergence of the Dalradian onto the Midland Valley.

Care has to be exercised in ascribing undated and sometimes dated metamorphic mineral assemblages to sources. This is particularly so in zones where there are clearly very large faults with probable terrane-scaled movements, potentially cryptic source blocks, and where regional metamorphic blocks with roughly similar cooling ages as the Dalradian block extend the whole length of the Appalachians.

It is difficult to be certain when sediment derived from the Dalradian crossed the Highland Boundary Fault to enter the basins to the south of it. But, despite the great thickness of Old Red Sandstone sediment present in these basins south

of the fault, there is little scope for large volumes of sediment to be contributed from the Dalradian basement in post-Wenlock times. Prior to *c.* 420 Ma, the age of the Lorne Plateau lavas (Thirlwall 1988), it is evident that parts of the Dalradian block in Scotland and possibly in Ireland were significantly eroded. These lavas, overlying a substantial sedimentary basin, over-step the sediments to rest with spectacular unconformity on folded and truncated Dalradian rocks. Similar, relationships are seen along the Highland Border where, for example, sediments below the Lintrathen ignimbrite (*c.* 415 ± 6 Ma; Thirlwall 1988) unconformably overlie folded Dalradian rocks. These

Lower Old Red Sandstone basins, south of the fault, are thought to have been deposited in a strike-slip regime (Haughton 1988; Haughton & Bluck 1988; Bluck 2000) and that would almost certainly have involved movement on the Highland Boundary Fault at that time (Fig. 5.5).

Sediment contributions directly from the Dalradian basement are possible in the Late Wenlock sandstones of the Cowie Formation (Phillips *et al.* 1997), which contains abundant metamorphic rock fragments and detrital micas. Rounded clasts, with Dalradian characteristics, appear locally in conglomerates deposited above these strata in the sections south of Stonehaven, but towards the top of the Old Red Sandstone sequence, fanglomerates, dispersed from the north, have a dominant Dalradian signature. Further evidence of the proximity of the Dalradian block to the Midland Valley comes from the Lintrathen ignimbrite which is found both in the Old Red Sandstone of the Midland Valley as well as on the Dalradian block (Bluck 1984).

Most of the NW–SE shortening that is required along the Highland Border is thought to have taken place before the development of the Lower Old Red Sandstone basins. However, further convergence of the Dalradian onto the Midland Valley is thought to have occurred in Mid-Devonian times with the development of the asymmetrical Strathmore Syncline (Bluck 2000, 2001). There is also evidence for a major downthrow to the north where young Upper Old Red Sandstone and Carboniferous rocks, resting on Dalradian, are brought into contact with, or are topographically lower than, older Lower Old Red Sandstone rocks (as seen at Kintyre (George 1960) and Balmaha (Bluck 1984, 1992*a*)).

The Southern Margin and the Southern Upland Faults

Lower Palaeozoic rocks, although not common, are far better exposed on the southern margin of the Midland Valley than on the north (Fig. 5.1) and unlike the northern margin there is far less controversy over the bounding fault, the Southern Upland Fault. Unlike its northern equivalent, the Southern Upland Fault is not a well marked structure traversing the country but is now seen as a series of structures united by a common alignment in the Caledonian strike (see review by Floyd 1994).

Ordovician

There are quite extensive exposures of Lower Palaeozoic rocks to the north of the Southern Upland Fault that have a considerable role to play in the interpretation of both the Fault as well as the block to the south of it. Apart from the Ballantrae Complex (see Chapter 6), the largest outcrop of Ordovician rock is found the vicinity of Girvan.

The Ordovician rocks at Girvan have been the subject of rigorous refinement and re-interpretation since the time of Lapworth. It is one of the classical areas of British stratigraphy and a huge step forward in its significance was made by Williams (1962) who, amongst many other things, demonstrated that the bulk of the sedimentation was controlled by active faulting.

The post-Arenig Ordovician sequence at Girvan rests on eroded Ballantrae Complex which had been obducted prior to the development of this continent-derived, clastic-dominated sequence (Fig. 5.6). It ranges in age from Late Llanvirn to Ashgill and consists of well-rounded, boulder-bearing conglomerates which fine towards the SE where they are replaced by thick sequences of greywacke. The conglomerates terminate towards the NW against contemporaneous faults that bring the Ballantrae basement to the surface.

Limestones and other shelf-type deposits rest on or just above the basement blocks suggesting that they accumulated on fault controlled topographic highs which were marginal to the basins (Williams 1962; Ingham 1978; Ince 1984; see Fig. 5.6). The limestones are richly fossiliferous with corals and the abundant calcareous alga *Girvanella*. At Craighead, the northernmost limestone exposed, massive reefoidal limestones, built on slight topographic rises in the underlying Ballantrae Complex basement, are enclosed in bedded inter-reef limestone and shales with abundant crinoids, brachiopods and trilobites.

Three basins have been identified, each with progressively younger fill when traced towards the NW (Williams 1962; Ingham 2000). The early, southerly basins, away from the conglomeratic margins are filled mainly by immature turbidite sandstones with faunas, some of which are derived. These faunas, in places abundant and diverse, include the fairly shallow water assemblages of the illaenid–cheirurid association. However, in some localities, the abundance of the trilobites *Lonchodomas* and *Dimeropyge* (Ingham & Tripp 1991) and cyclopygid biofacies, which include pelagic trilobites (e.g. *Cyclopyge* and *Symphysops*) and blind benthic species (e.g. *Dionide* and *Novaspis*) (Ingham 1992), indicate episodes of deeper water conditions where sedimentation failed to keep pace with subsidence.

The youngest and most northerly basin exposed, the Craighead Basin, has a fill which includes a high proportion of shelf deposits with sheets of storm-generated sediment. However, contemporaneous tectonic activity is also evident in the mass-flow deposits that characterize parts of the sequence (Ingham 1992). The sediments, which include the world famous Lady Burn Starfish Bed, have a rich, varied fauna that has been repeatedly collected for more than a century. Trilobites, brachiopods, graptolites, echinoderms, conodonts and ostracodes (Harper 1982; Donovan & Paul 1985; Floyd *et al.* 1999) are amongst the most important Ordovician assemblages in the world (Owen & Rushton 1999). Whilst the assemblages are of shallow water origin, they are in many, if not most cases, clearly displaced into deeper water deposits. Ingham (1978) and Harper (1982) consider some to have been emplaced by slumping from the shelf edge, partly accounting for their fine preservation and lack of reworking.

The Craighead Basin marks a significant change in sedimentation pattern of the finer fill of the distal parts of the basin. The deep water turbidites, infilling the more southerly basins, being less abundant to the north. This may be explained by the Craighead area being near to the southerly margin of a widespread, intermittently developed shelf that continues to the north further into the Midland Valley.

The faunal assemblages at Girvan were amongst the first to be recognized as having affinities with those of the Appalachians and in this sense are of considerable historical interest (see Reed 1935). Their Laurentian affinities are now well documented (Williams 1962; Ingham 1978; Ingham & Tripp 1991) but as the sequence gets younger so the faunas become more cosmopolitan. This change is held to be a response to the convergence of Avalonia–Baltica onto the Laurentian margin with the breakdown of provinciality and marking a stage in the build-up of Pangea.

Clasts, up to 3 m in diameter, of ophiolitic and acid-intermediate igneous rocks, dominate the conglomerates proximal to the fault blocks. The composition of these clasts suggests the unroofing of a major igneous complex which was situated a short distance to the north (Bluck 1983). In a study of the absolute ages of the granite clasts (most of which were boulder size), Longman *et al.* (1979) showed that the clasts had a cooling age near to the ages of the sediment from which they were recovered. The ages of the youngest granite clasts young

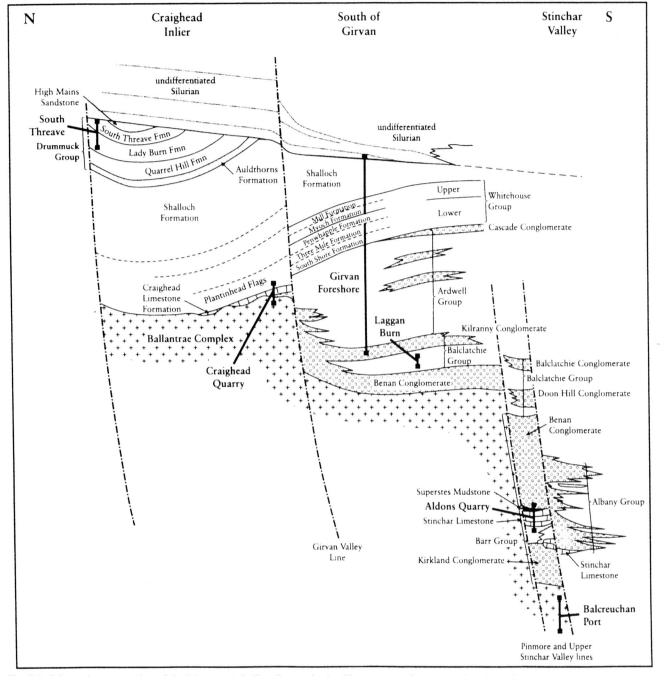

Fig. 5.6. Schematic cross section of the Llanvirn–Ashgill sediments in the Girvan area with some key locations (from Rushton *et al.* (1999), after Ingham (1992, fig. 30.5). Note the conglomerates, which young to the north are also less abundant in that direction. Longman *et al.* (1979) and Bluck (1983) demonstrated that the youngest granite clasts in these conglomerates get younger up the sequence.

upwards in the sequence from 481–451 Ma implying a continuous cooling of intrusions for possibly 30 Ma or more (Bluck 1983). Metamorphic clasts are present in only minor numbers, but slates, mica-schists, detrital micas, and garnets are present in the sandstones (El Fegi 1989; Oliver *et al.* 2000). Rushton & Tripp (1979) record the presence of clasts of Tremadoc age in the Benan Conglomerate.

From these data Bluck (1983) deduced that there was a volcanic-plutonic arc complex within the present Midland Valley which contributed debris to a proximal fore-arc to the immediate south of it. Haughton & Halliday (1991) recorded in the Early Devonian rocks of the NE Midland Valley, granite boulders ranging in age from *c.* 414 to 443 Ma which were

derived from the south (Fig. 5.7). With the bulk of these granite ages being *c.* 420 Ma and with the presence of ash beds with rhyo-dacitic composition of Late Llandovery–Wenlock age (*c.* 430 Ma) in the Pentland Hills (Batchelor & Clarkson 1993; Batchelor 1998), a volcanic–plutonic complex is thought to have existed in the central Midland Valley from Early Silurian times. However, the northerly dispersed granite clasts with ages of *c.* 443 Ma found in the Lower Old Red Sandstone together with the southerly dispersed clasts found in the Ordovician and Silurian rocks of Girvan (with ages of 456 Ma and younger) may demonstrate the continuity of this igneous region from Late Ordovician through Mid-Silurian. Bluck (1983, 1984) suggested that Old Red Sandstone lavas of the Ochil–Sidlaw chain

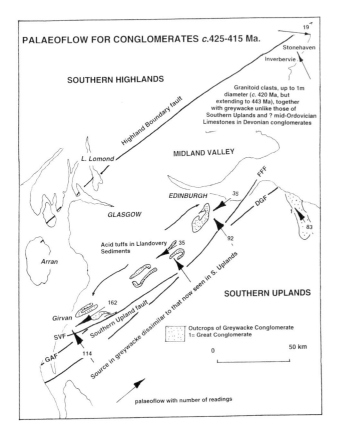

Fig. 5.7. Diagram showing the distribution of the greywacke conglomerate, the palaeoflow and the contrasting compositions of the clasts in this conglomerate and those of the Southern Uplands. Palaeoflow data from Gillen & Trewin (1987b); Syba (1989); Phillips *et al.* (1997); and Bluck (2000) are based on cross strata and clast imbrication. Data on tuff occurrences and compositions from Batchelor (1998) and for the clasts in the Crawton Group (Early Devonian) at Inverbervie from Haughton (1988) and Haughton & Halliday (1991).

and elsewhere, dated at 423–411 Ma, are a continuation of this Ordovician volcanic belt.

The presence of a major volcanic province somewhere to the north of the Ordovician outcrops of the southern Midland Valley is also suggested by the extensive boulder-bearing conglomerates in other outcrops in south Ayrshire, the Rhinns of Galloway and Southern Uplands. The composition of the sandstones in the Girvan area and Southern Uplands also suggests the unroofing of an arc-ophiolitic to the north (Bluck 2001).

Silurian

The Silurian outcrops of the Southern Midland Valley are far more abundant and widespread than those of the Ordovician. They stretch from Girvan in the SW to the Pentland Hills to the NE (Figs 5.1, 5.7). The revised ages for the base of the Devonian are 417 and 418 Ma (Gradstein & Ogg 1996; Tucker *et al.* 1998 respectively). Age determinations of *c.* 412 Ma are obtained for Old Red Sandstone lavas which are well up in the Old Red Sandstone sequence in these southern areas (Thirlwall 1988). In addition, both the Tinto and Distinkhorn intrusions, *c.* 412–413 Ma, cut Old Red Sandstone sediments. Care has therefore to be taken as rocks formerly regarded as Devonian could now fall into the Silurian (see also Chapter 8).

Silurian rocks are seen to rest unconformably on Ordovician in the SW Midland Valley and are unconformably overlain by Old Red Sandstone rocks in both the Pentland Hills and Girvan

areas. Elsewhere there is no evidence of a major structural break between Silurian and Old Red Sandstone rocks (the Old Red Sandstone has long been recognized in these exposures, as a facies which, in places, began in the Wenlock). These Silurian inliers are particularly well known for their fine assemblages of well preserved arthropods and fish. There are five main inliers and all show, near to the Llandovery–Wenlock boundary, an upward transition from marine to continental sedimentation (Rolfe 1960, 1961, 1992; Fig. 5.8). In this respect they share in a marine regression which is common to large areas of Laurentia, Baltica and Avalonia at this time (Clarkson *et al.* 1998).

Llandovery–Early Wenlock rocks: the dominantly marine sequences

Transgressive marine deposits dominate the lower part of the sequence and include abundant storm layers together with, in some inliers, deeper water turbidites (Fig. 5.8). They have an abundance of both shelly and graptolitic faunas that allow for some along strike correlation between inliers. The oldest strata (Lower Llandovery) and the most complete Llandovery sequences, are found in the region around Girvan where the total Silurian sequence, dominated by graptolite bearing rocks, reaches 2837 m in thickness according to Cocks & Toghill (1973); but see Smith (1995). Here the Llandovery successions are dominated by clastic sediment which, with the exception of the Girvan deposits, are derived from the south. Sequences of rock show repeated gradations between fine grained, sediment starved, graptolitic shales through to conglomerates. Cocks & Toghill (1973) have correlated these vertical lithological changes with faunal changes and related both to water depth fluctuations. In particular, they extended the use of animal communities, established in the Silurian rocks of Wales and which are thought to be water depth related. *Lingula*, *Eocoelia*, *Pentamerus* and *Clorinda* communities representing deepening water assemblages, have been identified. There are fine examples of overstep, non-sequences and lateral change in sediment thickness, all of which suggests deposition in relatively small basins where changes in water depth and sediment supply were dominant influences.

The Girvan sequence terminates in rocks of Wenlock age which, after an initial marine transgression and the development of deep water graptolitic shales (the Blair Formation; Late Llandovery), shallowed enough to develop sediments thought to have accumulated at or near sea-level with the development of the *Howellella–Protochonetes* community in the Wenlock Knockgardner Formation. Rocks of this formation, which include pro-delta-intertidal deposits continue into fresh water bivalve and ostracod faunas of the succeeding Straiton Grits (Cocks & Toghill 1973; Clarkson *et al.* 1998). Whilst the composition of the sandstones has not been studied in great detail, the conglomerates, which are inter-dispersed within the Llandovery sequence at Girvan, show a prominent upward gradation from strongly polymict conglomerates at the base to quartz rich conglomerates at the top of the sequence. The lowest conglomerates in the sequence have a composition dominated by clasts of igneous rocks, including granite, along with clasts of hypabyssal and volcanic rock ranging from acid to basic in composition. These conglomerates are replaced upwards by quartz and jasper bearing rocks, all of which suggest an upward maturing in the provenance.

Other inliers are characterized by the same upward change from turbidites and possible storm deposits, dominant in the Llandovery, to littoral and finally into terrestrial deposits in the Wenlock and younger sediments. However marine conditions intermittently persisted well into the Wenlock where they

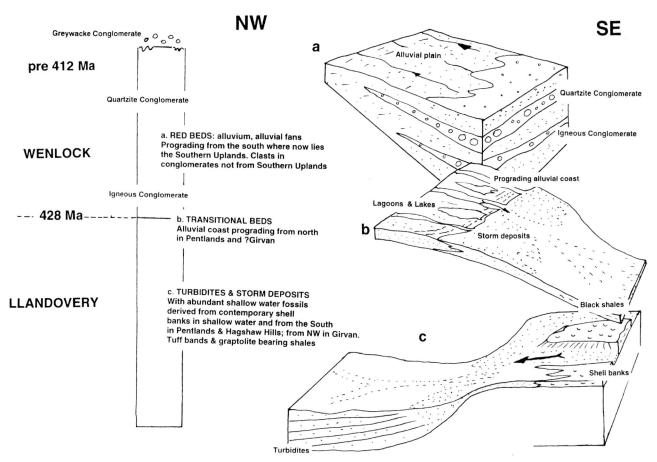

Fig. 5.8. Generalized stratigraphical section for the Silurian Inliers of the Midland Valley (see Figs 5.1, 5.7 for location). The nature of the turbidite sequence differs in the various inliers (see text), and note the change in direction of progradation for the transitional beds. The palaeoflow for the red-bed sequence (which does not appear at the same horizon in all inliers) is from the southwest (McGiven 1967; Smith 1995).

alternate with red beds of fluvial aspect. The sequence in the Hagshaw Hills, for example, begins with turbidites with graptolites in the interleaved shales, and is also of Llandovery age. Faunas within the turbidites, as with much of the Ordovician at Girvan, are displaced from shallow water. They include the brachiopods *Atrypa, Leptaena* and *Howellella*, trilobites, *Calymene* and *Phacops* as well as conoidal fossils and branchiopoda (see Rolfe 1992). These sediments are followed by shelf sediments and intertidal deposits and in this transition from open marine to continental sedimentation there was much opportunity for the development of lagoons and lakes. Faunas are often very well preserved in these finely laminated lagoonal to lacustrine sediments and include not only fish but also eurypterids, pod-shrimps and aquatic scorpions. Fish include *Lanarkia, Logania* and *Jamoytius* and eurypterids include *Lanarkopteris* and *Erettopterus* (Rolfe 1992).

In the Pentland Hills only Llandovery sediments of the *crenulata* Biozone are present. In the general sense of them being deep water, albeit finer than some of the other sediments of this age, they are similar to the Llandovery in other inliers. The sequence also has a fairly abundant fauna, much of which appears to have been derived from shallower, productive shelves (Tipper 1976; Robertson 1989). Close study of the environmental change at the Llandovery–Wenlock boundary has demonstrated a similar transitional lithofacies change from deep-water graptolitic shales into intertidal sediments as seen in Girvan (Robertson 1989).

The Llandovery–Early Wenlock sedimentation is, in some senses, a continuation of the regime that characterized the

Ordovician of Girvan. Carbonate generating platforms supplied bioclastic sediment to turbidites and storm deposits which were deposited in the deeper water regimes of fault bounded basins (which were probably quite restricted in size). There are, however, some considerable differences. The sedimentary sequences are far thinner and, although there are exceptions, the conglomerates are much finer grained, suggesting a source with lower slopes or increased distance between source and basin. The pulses of deepening and shallowing in the Llandovery–Early Wenlock rocks may have been the result of fault activity in small sedimentary basins but the effects of sea-level changes would have to be unravelled to determine faulting as a principal cause (Williams & Harper 1988, 1991).

Whilst the abundance of volcanic and plutonic clasts, typical of the Ordovician sediments, diminished overall in the Silurian, significantly, there are a number of bentonites of intermediate–mafic and rhyodacitic compositions, recovered from the Llandovery rocks of almost all inliers (Batchelor 1998). The presence of lithic arenites with degraded ash fragments attest to far more widespread volcanic activity that occurred in Llandovery and later times. The tuff beds may record only that fraction of ash fall deposited in favourable environments which were free of reworking. It is probably no coincidence that Batchelor (1998) identified many ash beds from the deeper water Llandovery, and that thin ash-like layers are found in some of the fish beds. Ash falling elsewhere may have been reworked and mixed with other sediment (Fortey *et al.* 1995) so that the preserved bentonites may underestimate the total volume of ash that was deposited.

Wenlock and younger sediments: the mainly terrestrial beds

Marine sedimentation persisted into the Early Wenlock in the Girvan area, but in most of the other inliers there was a change to mainly terrestrial sedimentation about the Llandovery–Wenlock boundary (Fig. 5.8). Fluvial, red bed, sequences of sandstone and shales and intermittent coarse conglomerates dominate the sequences that continue up into known Devonian sediments and lavas. However, the presence of fish beds, and strata with crinoids and sponges in the Pentland Hills (Robertson 1989) indicate undoubted marine influence at this time.

There are three significant conglomerates in these Wenlock and younger parts of the sequences, each of which is characterized by a particular clast type. The lowest conglomerate, marking the boundary between Llandovery and Wenlock, is characterized by abundant clasts of igneous rock and is referred to as the Igneous Conglomerate. This conglomerate thins to the NW in the Hagshaw Hills and associated sandstones have cross strata dipping to the NW (McGiven 1967).

Although fine-grained igneous clasts dominate, there are granites, greywacke, cherts and mica schists. The fine-grained igneous clasts have a chemistry which suggests a provenance in an intra plate, peralkaline rhyolitic complex and a calc-alkaline to high K arc-type complex (Heinz & Loeschke 1988). As they could not match many of the clasts which they analysed with rocks in the present Southern Uplands, Heinz & Loeschke (1988) concluded that there was a source to the south which is no longer exposed.

The succeeding quartzite conglomerate is Wenlock in age (Wellman & Richardson 1993). It has a palaeoflow towards the NNW and a thickness and grain size decline which radiates outward from a point near Tinto (Bluck 1983). It is an upward fining wedge of sediment with isopachs defining a lithosome, thickest in the ESE at c. 100 m where there are also the coarsest clasts c. 1.5 m. The conglomerate is dominated by well-rounded quartzite clasts in the coarse sizes but in the range 16–32 mm has >30% fine-grained igneous clasts (predominantly rhyolites) and up to 70% vein quartz.

McGiven (1967) and Bluck (1983) regarded the quartzite conglomerate as an alluvial fan that possibly built into a coastal environment as some of the enclosing sediments are lagoonal–lacustrine with abundant fish and eurypterids. Alluvial fans, with estimated radii exceeding 35 km and with clasts >150 mm require some relief in order to form. This raised the possibility of there being a contemporary uplifted source block to the south and again it is difficult to see the present Southern Uplands as a source for these clasts.

The final conglomerate in this sequence, with the dominant clasts being greywacke, is referred to as the Greywacke Conglomerate. This conglomerate, up to 500 m thick is the most extensive and best exposed of the three conglomerate units. Its age is not known but it rests conformably on dated Silurian rocks, occurs well below lava dated at c. 412 Ma, and is therefore possibly Late Silurian–Lochkovian in age.

The apparent simplicity in lithosome form and palaeoflow orientation that characterized the Igneous and Quartzite conglomerates is contrasted by the complexity of lithosome geometry which is found in the greywacke conglomerate. In the Hagshaw Hills, McGiven (1967) has demonstrated a wedge of greywacke conglomerate thinning and fining to the NW, and less convincingly for the area near Tinto and in the Pentland Hills.

Whilst these data, in conjunction with palaeoflow orientations, make a convincing case for a southerly source for the greywacke conglomerate, data collected from elsewhere in this conglomerate clearly indicates an additional palaeoflow towards the SW (Syba 1989; Smith 1995; Fig. 5.7). This combination of palaeoflow orientations cannot easily be considered as a lateral-axial system as the SW palaeoflow system carries clasts at least as coarse as those transported to the NW. Moreover there is no decline in clast size as the sediment is traced towards the SW although this could be the consequence of continuous input from the SE into a SW, axially flowing fluvial system.

Partly from these observations Syba (1989) and Smith (1995) concluded that there were sources for these clasts within the Midland Valley and its continuation beneath the present

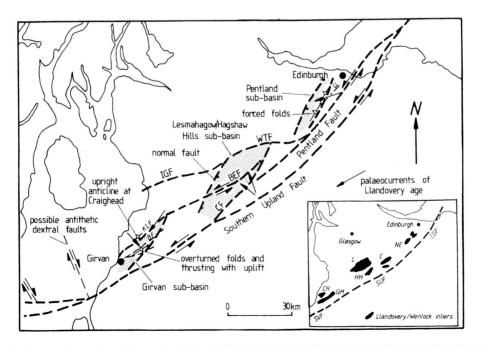

Fig. 5.9. Suggested faults controlling sedimentation if the Silurian Inliers which are thought to be isolated basins developed in a transentional regime (after Phillips *et al.* 1997). LL, Loganlee Fault; WTF, Wilsontown Fault; IGF, Inchgotrick Fault; BEF, Bankend Fault; KLF, Kerse Loch Fault; BF, Bargany Fault; CF, Carmacoup Fault; SVF, Stinchar Valley Fault; CGF, Crossgatehall Fault. Inset shows the location of the Silurian Inliers: SUF, Southern Upland Fault. CH, Craighead; GM, Girvan Main group; L, Lesmahagow; HH, Hagshaw Hills; C, Carmichael; NE, North Esk.

North Sea and postulated uplifted blocks of consolidated grey-wacke which dispersed sediment into adjacent small basins. Phillips *et al.* (1997) have suggested a strike-slip control on the basins, linking their development to the timing of strike-slip activity within the Southern Uplands (Fig. 5.9).

The composition of the greywacke clasts within the conglomerate is of some relevance to these conclusions. McGiven (1967), Bluck (1983) and Syba (1989) concluded that the range of composition of the greywacke clasts in all the conglomerates, including the greywacke conglomerate, was inconsistent with a source in the Southern Uplands. The greywacke clasts in these Silurian conglomerates have a far more restricted range of composition than seen in the present Southern Uplands (Fig. 5.7). Ordovician limestone clasts, with a conodont colour index suggesting thermal alteration at up to 610°C, are also found in the Pentland exposures (Armstrong & Owen 2000*a*).

With outliers of Early Devonian sedimentary rocks unconformably overlying the vertical greywacke of the Southern Uplands it would appear unlikely (although possible) that this block could have been a substantial source at the time. The Great Conglomerate and some of the lavas at St Abbs Head are pre-400 Ma in age (Rock & Rundle 1986) and rest on folded and planed Silurian greywackes, as do the lavas of the Cheviots (*c.* 396 Ma, Thirlwall 1988). In addition the clasts of greywacke in all three conglomerates are similar in composition and all are generally richer in quartz and acid rock fragments than those of either the Silurian or Ordovician rocks of the Southern Uplands. On the basis of these observations both Bluck (1983) and Syba (1989) concluded there was an alternative source for the greywacke clasts and Syba (1989) postulated a source within the Midland Valley and its extension to the NE.

Williams & Harper (1988), Syba (1989) and Smith (1995), citing a range of criteria, including their individual stratigraphies and tectonic histories, interpreted these basins to have formed in a strike-slip regime (Fig. 5.9). Smith (1995) and Phillips *et al.* (1997) identified some of the controlling faults in the development of the basins.

Taking the complete sequence from Llandovery through to the Ludlovian-Lochkovian, Greywacke Conglomerate, there are a number of points to emerge:

1. There is an overall vertical change from marine to fluvial domination in the sequence and this may be the consequence of worldwide sea-level change (Williams & Harper 1988). Whilst there is no clear, independent evidence for a phase of regional uplift in the Midland Valley at this time, there is much evidence for tectonic activity and to separate sea-level change from tectonics would be difficult.

2. In spite of the broad similarity in sequences for each of the inliers, each has a fairly distinctive succession (Fig. 5.8) and there is the possibility that the inliers were to some measure detached from each other and formed separate basins. If this were to be the case then the general similarity in the compositional trends of the conglomerates, with an igneous provenance at the base, followed by a quartzite provenance and finally a greywacke provenance is not a measure of unity in the basin so much as a regional and unifying change in a common source block. This unity is particularly important in the Greywacke Conglomerate which, from observations made so far, had a source block that persisted throughout the whole time of conglomerate deposition and finally became a dominant source which unified all the basins.

3. The dispersal and composition of the clasts provides a prob-lem in locating the source. Many of the clasts in the Igneous Conglomerate appear to be first cycle: it has the least rounded clast population of all the conglomerates

(McGiven 1967). Despite being near to the Southern Uplands it has a dispersal from the SE and contains <10% greywacke clasts, the composition of which, in any case, does not easily match that of the Southern Uplands. Bluck (1983) and Loeschke (1985) concluded that the Southern Upland block was not the source of any of the clasts in this conglomerate.

Both the Quartzite and the Greywacke conglomerates share this problem of provenance. Although the quartzite clasts are very well-rounded and probably polycyclic, there is no obvious source for them in the Southern Uplands; and the greywacke clasts, in both this and the Greywacke Conglomerate, do not have a Southern Upland signature. Again, a source block to the south of the present outcrops is required in the position of the present Southern Uplands.

4. The presence of igneous detritus in conglomerates, bentonites amongst the sandstones and the occurrences of volcanogenic fragments within some sandstone units all point to the presence of much volcanic activity in Llandovery times. Later environments of sedimentation, being nearshore and fluvial are not conducive to the preservation of bentonites as they would be subject to re-erosion, dispersal and mixing. The volcanic activity may therefore have continued into the succeeding Wenlock and then into the Early Devonian where there are abundant lava flows. This view is strengthened by the occurrences of southerly derived granite clasts, the bulk of which are dated at *c.* 420 Ma, in the Lower Devonian conglomerates at Inverbervie (Haughton & Halliday 1991; see Fig. 5.7).

5. Geophysical evidence suggests that the Southern Uplands forms a relatively thin sheet of greywacke resting on a crystalline basement. Hall *et al.* (1983), Davidson *et al.* (1984) and Kalaliddin (1991) all demonstrate a greywacke thickness which is at maximum 5 km in the SW Southern Uplands and, in places, <3 km in the NE. Oliver & McKerrow (1984) suggested that the discontinuity should be interpreted differently: it is a transition in metamorphic grade within the greywacke pile and therefore does not reflect a discontinuity between basement and cover.

6. Xenoliths recovered from lamprophyre dykes (Floyd & Phillips 1998; Anderson & Oliver 1996) are of sheared granodiortes, mylonites and andesites indicating that by *c.* 415 ± 12 Ma, the probable age of the lamprophyres (*see* Floyd & Phillips 1998; Anderson & Oliver 1996), the Southern Uplands was ensconced on continental basement. If this terrane is indeed an accretionary prism then a minimum age of emplacement onto Laurentian crust is given by these dykes. An alternative view taken by Anderson & Oliver (1996) is that the crust beneath the Southern Uplands is Avalonian, being part of the underthrust, Lake District plate (see also Leggett *et al.* 1983).

7. At the time when Llandovery and Wenlock sedimentation was taking place within the Midland Valley of Scotland, with a dispersal to the north or NW, turbidites were accumulating in the Southern Uplands with a dispersal to the south and SE. There was therefore a major source block between the two areas of sedimentation and so Cockburnland of Walton (1983), Morris (1987) and Murphy & Hutton (1986) is resurrected (see also Armstrong & Owen 2000).

The Southern Upland Fault

Floyd (1994) has recently re-evaluated the boundary between the Southern Uplands and the Midland Valley. As a result, the roles of the various faults lying along the trend of, and within the general region of, the Southern Upland Fault have been

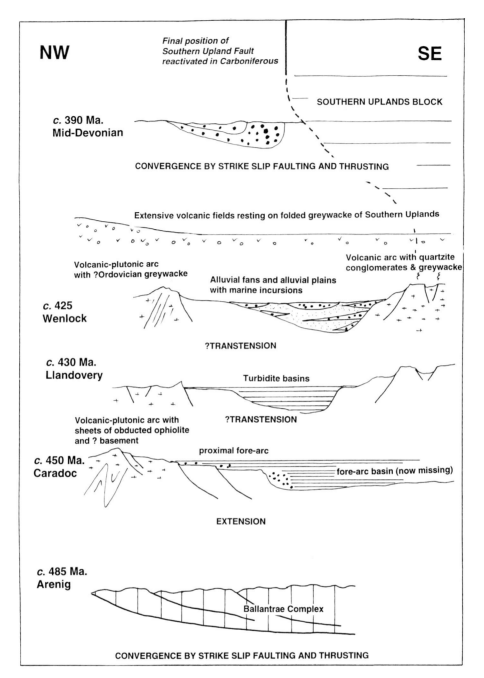

Fig. 5.10. Diagram showing the history of the southern Midland Valley and the Southern Upland Fault. From Arenig to Wenlock times there is no clear indication of the presence of the Southern Uplands in the sediments of the Midland Valley. Some degree of proximity is suggested by the presence of Devonian lavas on both the Southern Uplands and Midland Valley blocks. The deposition of lavas and sediments of the Lower Old Red Sandstone was followed by asymmetrical folding in these sediments, probably of Mid Devonian age, suggesting a convergence from the southeast. At this time the Southern Uplands was probably in place, but underwent subsequent movement as demonstrated by the truncations of the Carboniferous outcrops. In this later, convergent history, it behaved very much like the Highland Boundary Fault, as envisaged by Kennedy (1958), but had clearly been overstepped as envisaged by George (1960).

clarified. As with the Highland Boundary Fault, the Southern Upland Fault has evidence for much convergence onto the Midland Valley with ground missing in the area now occupied by the fracture and the ground to the south of it (Needham & Knipe 1986; Fig. 5.10).

At *c.* 425–430 Ma there was a source block, which included ophiolitic rocks, greywacke and conglomerates and contemporary volcanic rocks, in the region which is now the northern part of the Southern Uplands. This source was activated at least three times to yield coarse sediment into the basins forming in the Midland Valley. Some of the activation was probably the result of stress transmitted from a transpressive

convergence at the plate boundary to the south. At least by *c.* 415 Ma, this involved the northerly or northeasterly transfer of an accretionary prism onto possibly Laurentian continental crust (Floyd & Phillips 1998), whilst the southern margin of the accretionary complex continued to accumulate sediment (Kemp 1987).

By Late Silurian–Early Devonian times (420–415 Ma) the Southern Uplands block was still not close enough to the basins of that age in the Midland Valley to supply clasts, (although the possibility of the sediments of the accretionary prism being unconsolidated at this time, and therefore incapable of forming durable clasts, cannot be ignored). If there were to have been oblique sinistral convergence then, with the over-riding of the source blocks initially from the SW, there would have been a wider and possibly greater uplift to the NE. During the deposition of the greywacke conglomerate this is envisaged to be the case with a dominant source in the NE.

At this Late Silurian–Early Devonian stage at least, the northern margin of the Southern Uplands was planed and the NE source spread gravel of the greywacke conglomerate over both the Midland Valley and probably the northerly regions of the Southern Uplands. Further convergence and overthrusting of the source took place possibly into Carboniferous times perhaps during dextral shearing (Stedman 1988) with the truncations of the Sanquhar and other basins together with intusions, such as the Spango granite, along this fault. These views are consistent with the evidence presented by Hall *et al.* (1983) who demonstrated that crust of continental type underlies the Southern Uplands and Davidson *et al.* (1984) and Kalaliddin (1991) who showed that reflectors were traceable from the Midland Valley into the Southern Uplands.

The development of the Southern Upland Fault is remarkably similar to that of the Highland Boundary Fault. It involves much convergence and loss of ground and in this sense its early behaviour is much as predicted by Kennedy, although he might not have been aware of the lateral displacements involved. However, in its later role, with clear evidence of Old Red Sandstone and Carboniferous overstep onto the Southern Uplands, it has a type evolution envisaged by George, so what both postulated approximated to the truth but referred to different times in the evolution of the structures.

The nature of the basement

The nature of the basement to the Midland Valley assumes some significance in the context of the location of this block between the Dalradian, Moine and related blocks to the north, which was deeply buried in Ordovician times, and the coeval, higher level rocks to the south. The nature of the basement

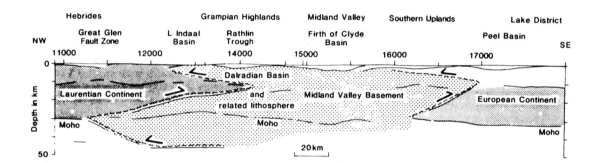

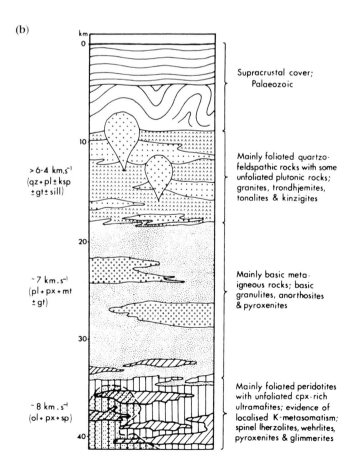

Fig. 5.11. Deep structure of the Midland Valley, (**a**) From seismic experiments (from Hall *et al.* 1984) and (**b**) Based on the xenoliths recovered from Carboniferous volcanic pipes (from Upton *et al.* 1984). It is possible that part of the zone between 10–20 km could be the remnants of the Ordovician–Devonian volcanic–plutonic arc.

has been deduced from four main sources: geophysical profiles, the composition of xenoliths which occur in Carboniferous–Permian pipes within the Midland Valley, the composition of conglomerates within and fringing the Midland Valley and the general context of the earliest rocks.

Geophysical profiles over the Midland Valley show little evidence for crustal thickening: the present depth to Moho is c. 30 km (Brewer et al. 1983; Hall et al. 1984) and is only slightly deflected in the region of the Midland Valley (Fig. 5.11). Accidental xenoliths found in Upper Palaeozoic or younger vents and dykes are thought to have come from most of the crustal and some of the lithospheric section through the Midland Valley (Upton et al. 1983, 1984; Fig. 5.11). Whilst it is difficult and possibly irrelevant to establish the cooling ages for minerals in these xenoliths, Halliday et al. (1993) have established Tdm model ages independently for mafic and felsic rock-types. The whole population is polymodal and as anticipated, felsic rocks, for reasons of magma contamination are 'older' than mafic with a lower variability in 'ages'. In spite of these shortcomings it is significant that one xenolith has a Tdm age which is older than any basement age so far recorded from Scotland. Moreover the bulk of the model ages are relatively young, and of those the xenoliths of lithosphere origin may indicate a young basement interaction with a young underplating event. However, the fact that the mixture ended up with a 'Grenville age' is absolutely no indication of the presence of Grenville crust in the Midland Valley as suggested by Hutcheson & Oliver (1998).

However, the evidence from the Ordovician rocks at Girvan indicated a prominent volcanic and plutonic source to the north in the position of the present Midland Valley. In addition, as there were southerly derived conglomerates in the Devonian section near Inverbervie containing granite clasts c. 420 Ma. (Haughton & Halliday 1991) then, in the intervening ground, there was an igneous complex of unknown scale but certainly one that provided a good deal of sediment to the flanking basins, only remnants of which remain. This source was to continue well into the Devonian along much of the Midland Valley (Bluck 2000; and see Chapter 8). Bluck (1983) concluded that in Ordovician times there was a continental arc in the Midland Valley and in consideration of the great volumes of volcanogenic sediment which entered the Southern Uplands basin (or its strike extension), then there was likely to have been substantial uplift of this putative arc system in Ordovician times (Fig. 5.12).

On the assumption that there was much crustal thickening associated with this arc system, and there would be isostatic uplift associated with the thickening, then the question arises: when was relief removed and the present-day isostatic balance in the Midland Valley crust achieved? Within the Southern Uplands, within the sequence at Girvan (El Fegi 1993) and within the Midland Valley inliers (McGiven 1967; Syba 1989), both sandstones and conglomerates show a general, and albeit hesitant, increase in compositional maturity with decreasing time which might imply that the arc-system was in decline. By Silurian times any crustal thickening, and the attendant isostatic uplift that accompanied the Ordovician arc would have, in a general sense, either greatly diminished or moved away. Phases of activation, such as seen in the igneous and associated conglomerates persisted, but these had little effect

MAIN CONSIDERATIONS

- 470–450 Ma granitoid and abundant intrusive and effusive boulders
- boulders of ophiolite and metamorphic clasts derived from NW
- block faulting at Girvan with NW overlap onto source
- boulders of 2.0–1.8 Ga metamorphic clasts in Highland Border Complex along with detrital micas 2140–507 Ma
- carbonates, black shales and pillow lavas in Highland Border Complex
- Ophiolite obducted at c. 530 Ma: eroded at c. 475 Ma at Highland Border

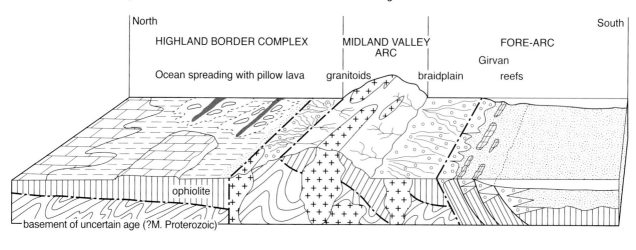

MAIN INFERENCES

- Arc complex on continental crust to north of Girvan
- Fore-arc sequence in Girvan
- Mid-Proterozoic block north of Highland Border Complex
- Highland Border Complex Basin, largely devoid of coarse detritus, developing on ophiolite

major dislocation boundaries
— · — · —

Fig. 5.12. A diagrammatic view of the Midland Valley in Ordovician times (after Bluck 2001).

on the overall composition of the sandstones so could be regarded as of local significance only.

In addition, the Silurian rocks of the Midland Valley up to Wenlock times were marine, showing that at least parts of the region were at sea level. Plutonic activity persisted in the central regions but was no longer the dominant influence it was in the Ordovician. With the Devonian came a period of extensive volcanic activity located in the central areas of the Midland Valley. This was seen as the site of earlier arc-style vulcanicity. These lavas have a chemistry that characterizes post-subduction lavas elsewhere in the world (Saunders *et al.* 1987; Thirlwall 1982). However, in Devonian times there was evidence of large-scale river systems running axially through the Midland Valley and Bluck (2000) believes these to have had a source outside of Scotland (see Chapter 8).

Any attempt to link model ages to mixing events has to take into account that there are many potential times for 'underplating' during and before the Carboniferous. During arc growth in the Ordovician (Halliday *et al.* 1993) but before the xenoliths reached the surface after 360 Ma there were substantial magmatic events in the Devonian (*c.* 415 Ma) and in the Carboniferous. Each or either of these events could have contributed to the final model ages of the xenoliths.

The oldest rocks in the Midland Valley are those of the Highland Border Complex to the north and the Ballantrae Complex to the south. The Highland Border Complex underlies at least part of the Strathmore Syncline, so it provides at least some of the foundation upon which the Old Red Sandstone was laid. Whilst it is not clear what persisted to the north of the Ballantrae Complex at the time, at Tyrone, Ireland, Hutton *et al.* (1985) have demonstrated that an ophiolite of roughly the same age as the Ballantrae Complex is thrust onto a gneiss basement. This is probably an extension of the basement to the Scottish Midland Valley. In this respect the xenoliths of serpentinite in the Carboniferous vent at the Heads of Ayr (Whyte 1964) may indicate the former extent of the ophiolites, as would be anticipated from their presence (i.e. they tend to occur in laterally extensive sheets, see Fig. 5.13).

The Palaeozoic history of the Midland Valley

There are two groups of interpretations of the Midland Valley that, when taken to their logical conclusion, extend into the Caledonides generally. On the one hand there is the view that the Dalradian sequence is the southern region of a passive margin, the northern part of which is to be found in the Neoproterozoic to Cambrian succession of the Hebridean block (see Chapter 3). In this view the Midland Valley would have been oceanic crust in Neoproterozoic to Cambrian times (Dewey 1969; Dewey & Mange 1999; Anderton 1985). The other view sees the Dalradian and Moine blocks as terranes displaced relative to the Foreland sequence which have successively accreted to the Laurentian margin. In this interpretation there is scope for oceanic crust to be in the Midland Valley but it would not be related to passive margin development but rather destructive or strike-slip type margin development (Bluck 2001).

Lower Palaeozoic history of the Midland Valley is to be seen in the context of the evolution of the metamorphic blocks to the north and the basins, thought to be evolving in a subduction-related zone to the south. With the exception of clasts, the

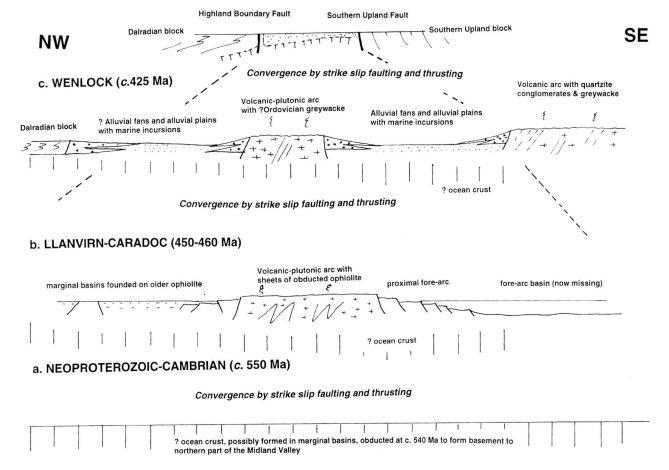

Fig. 5.13. Series of cross sections through the Midland Valley, demonstrating the great contraction in width and the complexity of its history.

oldest rocks exposed in the Midland Valley are Neoproterozoic to Early Cambrian in age and are preserved in the cooling ages of $c.$ 540 Ma for the amphibolite at Bute. If this is the sole to an ophiolite, then the pre-Early Arenig serpentinites and associated mafic rocks are likely to be the ophiolite itself, which would have originally covered a far wider area than the present thin linear outcrop (Fig. 5.12).

The framework in which these rocks are to be interpreted has the following constraints:

Iapetus had opened by $c.$ 616 Ma (Bingen *et al.* 1998) so that by the time the Highland Border ophiolitic complex had been obducted there had been $c.$ 75 Ma of ocean spreading. Given ocean opening rates (i.e. $2 \times$ spreading rate) of between $c.$ 10–150 mm a^{-1}, and given that this ophiolite was part of that spreading event, then between $c.$ 750 to $c.$ 11 250 km of ocean crust had been created by the time the ophiolite at Bute was obducted. The possibility of the ocean basin at the Highland Border being a different, but possibly related ocean spreading phase is clearly quite high. It is evident that the place now occupied by the Midland Valley at this time was within an ocean regime. The position of the Highland Border Complex with respect to Iapetus is uncertain. If the Leny Limestone is part of the Highland Border Complex (but see Tanner (1995)) then it is likely to be a tectonic sliver. However, its fauna belongs to the Laurentian province as does the Arenig Dounans limestone at Lime Craig Quarry. On this evidence, weak as it is, the Highland Border Complex is thought to have formed on the southern margin of Laurentia.

In Scotland, the northern margin to this oceanic basin would not have been the Dalradian block since its interaction with the Highland Border Complex did not take place until possibly Wenlock times. The only evidence for a continental margin, probably, northern, is from the dated boulders in the Complex which yielded ages of $c.$ 1.8 Ga (Dempster & Bluck 1989) and the detrital micas, with ages in the range 2146–646 Ma (Tanner & Pringle 1999; Fig. 5.4). A Palaeoproterozoic crust of the type seen in the Ketelidian of SE Greenland, Makkovik of Labrador and the Rhinns–Rockall areas of Scotland (Muir *et al.* 1994) seems the probable northern margin to this basin (Figs 5.4, 5.12) and, wherever it was at the time, may also have supplied clasts of similar Paleoproterozoic age to the tillites of the Dalradian block (Evans *et al.* 1998).

The next important event in the accretion history was the obduction of the Ballantrae Complex, which had already undergone a varied history before it was added to the Midland Valley. We can only speculate on the nature of the crust which was beneath the $c.$ 490–480 Ma obducted ophiolite. Early post-obduction dykes imply that the Complex was in an oceanic realm and a later, pre-Llanvirn dyke phase suggests the Complex to be on continental crust (Holub *et al.* 1984). On this evidence continental crust is thought to be in the Midland Valley sometime in the Arenig at least. This continental crust was either beneath the Highland Border Complex or was a new addition accreted during the interval between obduction of the Highland Border Complex ($c.$ 540 Ma) and the Ballantrae Complex ($c.$ 500 Ma). A possible clue to the nature of this crust comes from the Tyrone Inlier in Ireland where ophiolitic rocks of a similar age to the Ballantrae Complex rest on gneissose rocks (Hutton *et al.* 1985) which appear not to have affinities with the adjacent Dalradian.

Beginning at $c.$ 470 Ma and following the accretion of the Ballantrae Complex to the Midland Valley block, arc-like activity was established and persisted in the Midland Valley to the end of the Early Devonian. There is now good evidence for there being continental crust in the Midland Valley and, during this time interval, there was ample opportunity for underplating and upper crustal growth through granitic and related igneous activity. Abundant, high level, granitoid clasts with clear continental signatures occur within the sequences at Girvan and also in the Southern Uplands. In addition there are both andesitic and acidic rock fragments in the greywackes of the Southern Uplands indicating that there was constant erosion of an arc-like region to the north, in the Midland Valley or, more probably, its strike extension.

Associated with these clasts are clasts up to boulder size of mica schists with cooling ages $c.$ 463 ± 5 Ma (Kelley & Bluck 1989). In addition, Haughton (1988) identified in the southerly derived conglomerates of the Early Devonian in the NE Midland Valley, a suite of slightly metamorphosed greywacke clasts, enriched in Cr and Ni and acid igneous rock fragments. The greywacke, associated with limestone clasts of Mid-Ordovician age (Armstrong & Owen 2000a), has an unknown provenance, but is thought to be older than the high level, $c.$ 420 Ma granite clasts with which it is associated as some of these clasts have greywacke xenoliths with a similar composition (Haughton 1988).

Ordovician limestone clasts also occur in Old Red Sandstone conglomerates near Ayr (Armstrong & Owen 2000a). All these data together suggest that the block within the Midland Valley or its extension which existed during part of Lower Palaeozoic time was a complex mixture of basement, which possibly yielded sediment to the Southern Uplands (Bluck 2001); a plutonic-volcanic arc, which yielded abundant igneous rocks and sediments, variably metamorphosed. Foliated granites of both Ordovician as well as Llandovery ages might indicate some fault activity contemporaneous with igneous activity.

This continental arc continued through the Silurian (although its extent and location may have changed; see Armstrong & Owen 2000), when it contributed sediments to the conglomerates of the Silurian inliers and to younger sediments in the Strathmore Syncline. An important accretion event in the history of the Midland Valley was the addition of the Highland Border Complex to the Dalradian–Moine block. The timing of this accretion is uncertain. Evidence from West Ireland led Graham *et al.* (1991) and Dewey & Ryan (1993) to suggest that the Dalradian and Highland Border equivalent rocks were in contact by Late Ordovician. Williams *et al.* (1994) present evidence for a Wenlock age docking of Dalradian and possible Highland Border equivalents. Whilst the timing of this accretion event is clearly uncertain, it is probable that the accretion involved not only the Highland Border Complex but also the Midland Valley block.

At 430–420 Ma, the whole of the Caledonian terranes, including the Midland Valley, but with the exception of the Southern Uplands, had joined the Hebridean Craton. The addition of the Southern Uplands to this northern block, which now comprised the Midland Valley and basements to the north of it, may have taken place in Late Silurian. But firm evidence, in the form of greywacke clasts with certain Southern Upland signatures, is seen in the Upper Old Red Sandstone, which in the southern Midland Valley, may be Carboniferous in age.

The nature of this continental block, its relevance to the understanding of the evolution of the Midland Valley and its provenance are all unclear and the many models presented to address these issues are to a greater or lesser extent inadequate. The difficulty lies not only in the paucity of evidence but also in the ambivalence of the evidence available. But that fact, the highly varied nature of its rocks, the presence of cryptic source blocks and ocean crust, the abundance of volcanic activity stretching from Ordovician or earlier times into the Carboniferous and beyond and the clear evidence of massive contraction in the bounding faults may all indicate that the Midland Valley was a zone of massive strike-slip activity during the Palaeozoic (Fig. 5.13).

6 The Ballantrae Complex and Southern Uplands terrane

G. J. H. OLIVER, P. STONE & B. J. BLUCK

The Lower Palaeozoic accretionary thrust belt forming the Southern Uplands terrane lies to the northwest of the Iapetus Suture and to the southeast of the Southern Upland Fault (Fig. 6.1). The former structure marks the line of closure of the Iapetus Ocean and of collision between the continental blocks of Laurentia and Avalonia; it underlies the Solway Firth and approximates to the line of the Anglo-Scottish border. The latter structure separates the Southern Uplands terrane from the mainly Upper Palaeozoic rocks of the Midland Valley terrane and in particular the Ballantrae Complex. The following sections have been contributed by B. J. Bluck (Ballantrae), P. Stone (Southern Uplands stratigraphy, and provenance) and G. J. H. Oliver (Southern Uplands structure, metamorphism, and geodynamics).

The Ballantrae Complex

Interest in the unusual rocks exposed at Ballantrae has been active for some 150 years. Early workers were particularly attracted by the diversity and rarity of the igneous lithologies at Ballantrae. In contrast, Bailey & McCallien (1957) sought to see the rocks in the wider context of tectonic evolution and subsequent work has concentrated on this aspect of the Complex. After the initial discoveries that the Ballantrae Complex had many of the characteristics of ocean crust (Church & Gayer 1973), research concentrated on either modifying and refining this interpretation (Bluck et al. 1980; Stone & Smellie 1990), or evaluating its implications for the whole tectonic evolution of Scotland (Dewey 1974).

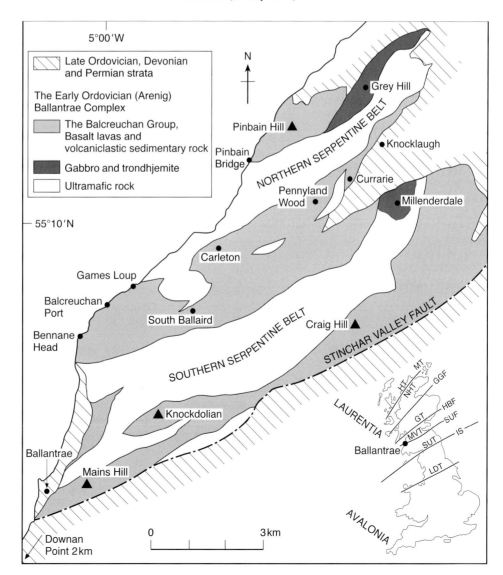

Fig. 6.1. Location in Scotland (inset) and simplified map of the Ballantrae Complex: HT, Hebridean terrane; MT, Moine Thrust; NHT, Northern Highlands terrane; GGF, Great Glen Fault; GT, Grampian terrane; HBF, Highland Boundary Fault; MVT, Midland Valley terrane; SUF, Southern Upland Fault; SUT, Southern Uplands terrane; IS, Iapetus Suture; LDT, Lake District terrane. (Modified from Stone & Smellie 1988; Kimbell & Stone 1995.)

In comparison with most other ophiolites the one at Ballantrae is remarkably small yet has probably had more words written about it per square metre of outcrop than any other ophiolite in the world. Short wavelength magnetic variations strongly suggest an eastward continuation of the Complex beneath rocks of the Ordovician Barr Group (Kimbell & Stone 1995). Ophiolitic debris, widespread in the nearby younger rocks within the Southern Uplands or within the Midland Valley, suggests that it had a large former extent. In this respect, ophiolitic rocks near Tyrone, Ireland, have similar ages to those at Ballantrae and Hutton *et al.* (1985) have suggested that these rocks are a correlative of the ophiolite at Ballantrae which formerly extended up to the southern margin of the Dalradian block. Dunning & Krogh (1985) have shown that ophiolite obduction was widespread along both the Laurentian and Baltic margins at this time so the Ballantrae complex may be seen as part of a widespread phase of ophiolite genesis.

The Ballantrae Complex, situated in the SW margin of the Midland Valley of Scotland (Fig. 6.1), is bounded on its southern margin by the Stinchar Valley Fault (Floyd 1996) and on the north by the unconformable cover of Palaeozoic sedimentary rocks of the Girvan sequence. The age of the overlying sedimentary sequence, which rests unconformable on rocks ranging from pillow lavas to serpentinite, indicates that the ophiolite at Ballantrae was both emplaced and eroded by Late Llanvirn times.

Description of the rocks

Although all of the *components* of an ophiolite are present, the *sequence* of lithologies that characterizes most ophiolites is not found at Ballantrae. It is certainly structurally fragmented. Most units in the ophiolite stratigraphy are structurally bounded so that complete transitions between key parts of it are not present. Of the crustal units that make up an ideal ophiolite, the sheeted dyke complex is the least represented at Ballantrae. Church & Gayer (1973) found the sheeted dyke complex to be present only as shear-bounded blocks within either serpentinite mélanges or black shales and cherts. However, Oliver & McAlpine (1998) have located a *c.* 500 m² block near Knockdolian consisting entirely of sheeted dolerite dykes enclosed within sheared serpentinite.

Sedimentary rocks (excluding those associated with the lavas). Sedimentary rocks occur in a number of localities, and most have fault contacts with other rocks of the ophiolite, the exception being the cherts and associated rocks at Bennane Head. Their relationship to other members of the ophiolite and the significance of the association is therefore not always clear. All of the sedimentary units so far dated by their graptolite faunas range from Early to Late Arenig (Stone & Strachan 1981; Stone & Rushton 1983; Rushton *et al.* 1986). Sedimentary rocks are well exposed at Bennane Head, Pinbain, and on the hillside near North Ballaird where, in addition, there are borehole records (Stone 1982; Stone & Strachan 1981). All sequences of black shale and cherts are found in association with, and sometimes inter-finger with, coarse clastic strata locally including boulder conglomerate.

The cherts at Bennane Head are Mid-Arenig in age (Stone & Rushton 1983), contain fairly well preserved radiolaria (Aitchison 1998), are well bedded, sometimes graded, and the original sediments are thought to have been re-deposited, possibly by turbidity currents. As with many other chert sequences of this type found throughout the world, they are typified by spectacular slumping. There are also zones of detachment and boudinage which cut out parts of the chert succession and imply extension, and possibly represent the areas from which slumped blocks were detached.

Cherts are interstratified with clastic strata with grains ranging from sand to boulder size. The sandstone beds are mainly lithic arenites with abundant volcanic debris, quartz and feldspar, and were sourced from acid to basic volcanic rocks. The conglomerates and breccias are interstratified and intertongue with the cherts, and carry clasts of volcanic rock, chert and sheared carbonate-bearing serpentinite (Bailey & McCallien 1957). At Bennane Head a chert sequence in the raised beach cliff is almost entirely replaced in about 100 m along strike by a conglomerate-chert sequence on the foreshore, and a dominantly conglomerate sequence appears to characterize the offshore. This suggests a westward transition from a chert dominated to a conglomerate dominated sequence in <150 m.

This sequence at Bennane Head was deposited on slopes steep enough to induce both slumping and to transport clasts up to boulder size. The continual generation of conglomerates implies proximity to a block that was topographically high, maintained elevation by continual uplift, and was partly subaerially exposed in order to yield clasts, some of which are well rounded. This block was composed mainly of volcanic rocks, some of which were acid. At least some of this volcanicity was contemporaneous with sedimentation as tuffaceous material also entered the basin, sometimes deposited as discrete tuff beds and also as dispersed fragments within the chert.

This source block included serpentinite as well as abundant spilites, carbonates and coarse-grained intermediate plutonic rocks. Judging by the fairly abundant clasts of deformed rock in the sequence, a good deal of fault activity either accompanied its emplacement or characterized the rocks upon which the volcanic edifice was built. The rapid transitions from conglomerates and breccias to cherts suggest deposition near an area typified by a sudden change in relief, which in turn suggests the presence of a fault-controlled basin margin.

Similar associations can be seen at Pinbain (Fig. 6.2) and at South Ballaird, where black shales and some minor cherts with tuff beds grade rapidly into boulder bearing conglomerates. The conglomerates contain amphibolite, granulite, epidote schist, blueschist, trondhjemite, diorite, serpentinite, dolerite, spilite, limestone and greywacke (Balsillie 1937a, b). As at Bennane Head, many clasts were fractured before being deposited, and the black shales, rather unusually, contain blocks of deformed black shale; an association similar to that seen in the cherts at Bennane Head. These rocks at Bennane Head, Pinbain and probably at South Ballaird were deposited proximal to an active volcanic edifice, in a basin which was probably fault controlled and far enough from a major landmass to exclude normal, recycled cratonic sediment.

Other frequently encountered sedimentary rocks comprise black shales and cherts containing randomly distributed blocks of up to 30 m in diameter. These are almost invariably fault bounded, are associated with a variety of rock types within this Complex, and are sufficiently unlike breccias and conglomerates to be classed as olistostromes (Church & Gayer 1973; Bluck 1992b). The lateral extent of these olistostrome units is far greater than had previously been supposed, and amongst the most extensive is the one that appears beneath the high grade metamorphic sole to the ophiolite. The ages of the olistostromes are not known. Stone & Rushton (1983) point out that there are no firm dates for any of these rocks. However, on the assumption that the clasts within them have been derived from the adjacent ophiolite, and since rocks there carry absolute ages of between 505 ± 12 Ma (Sm/Nd isochon, Thirlwall & Bluck 1984) to 478 ± 8 Ma (hornblende K–Ar, Bluck *et al.* 1980), an Arenig age is highly likely.

The olistostromes, which sometimes grade into conglomerates and breccias, carry a wide variety of clasts (Balsillie 1932, 1937a, b) and to date there has been no attempt to distinguish

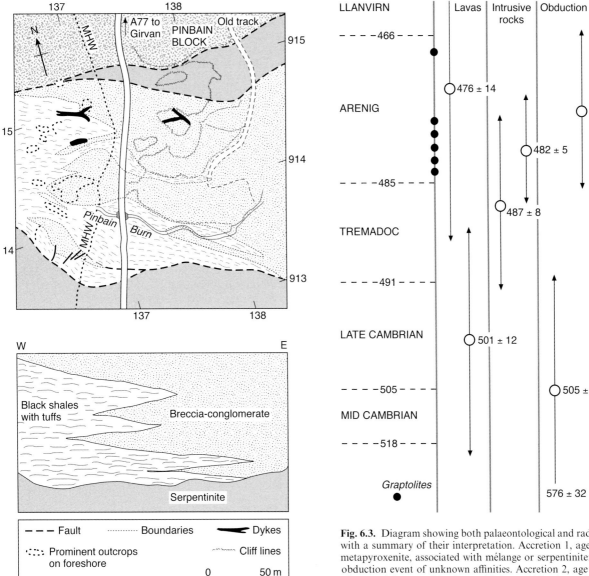

Fig. 6.2. Map and cross-section of the cliffs and foreshore at Pinbain Bridge (see Fig. 6.1 for location), showing the abrupt transitions of shale into conglomerates. (Unpublished map by B. J. Bluck.)

Fig. 6.3. Diagram showing both palaeontological and radiometric ages with a summary of their interpretation. Accretion 1, age of garnet metapyroxenite, associated with mélange or serpentinite: subduction–obduction event of unknown affinities. Accretion 2, age of obduction of serpentinite, possibly along with lava of island arc affinities. Accretion 3, age of lavas of MORB, island arc and intraplate affinities. (Data summarized in Bluck (1992b), timescale after Tucker & McKerrow (1995)).

lithosomic units on the basis of clast composition. Typical igneous clasts are granitoids, including trondhjemite, mainly basic-intermediate rocks, and a great deal of basic lava and serpentinite; metamorphic clasts include greenschist, amphibolite and blueschist. Sedimentary clasts are dominated by cherts, carbonates and some lithic arenites with a strong volcanogenic signature.

The olistostromes are known, in places, to grade down stratigraphically into relatively undeformed black shales and occasionally into sequences of turbidites. In sections like these there is a suggestion that the olistostromes form the top to a sequence that coarsens upward (Fig. 6.2).

There are two important features of these rocks:

(a) many of the clasts were deformed before being deposited as they carry a wide variety of veins and fractures, and

(b) they were derived from a wide variety of rocks, most of which can be identified in the present ophiolite.

The implications of the foregoing are that the source was the higher levels of an already structurally disrupted ophiolite. Deep as well as shallow crustal and deeper lithospheric levels were at the surface, being eroded, and yielding sediment during Arenig and Llanvirn times (Fig. 6.3).

The lava sequence. The lava sequence at Ballantrae is divided into three main blocks: the Pinbain block to the north, the central Bennane Head block, and a block to the south which includes Mains Hill, Knockdolian and Craig Hill. There has been some debate about the inclusion of the Downan Point Lava Formation (Fig. 6.1; Plate 10) into the Ballantrae Complex. It is now placed in the Southern Uplands on the basis of field relationships (Walton 1961), different geochemistries (Lewis & Bloxam 1977), and its situation on the south side of the Stinchar Fault (Leggett *et al.* 1979; Floyd 1996).

The lava sequences included in the Ballantrae Complex, on the timescale of Tucker & McKerrow (1995) and Davidek *et al.* (1998) range in age from Cambrian or Early Tremadoc (501 ± 12 Ma) to Mid to Late Arenig (476 ± 14 Ma); graptolites obtained from sedimentary beds interstratified with lavas have yielded ages which range from Early to Late Arenig (*c.* 480–470 Ma). The oldest lavas occur at Mains Hill in the southern block (Thirlwall & Bluck 1984) and the youngest (Middle Arenig) in the central, Bennane Head block. The greatest age range for the lavas (Early–Mid Arenig) is seen in the central block (Stone & Rushton 1983) whilst the Pinbain block has so far yielded only Early Arenig graptolites (Rushton *et al.* 1986). The Late Arenig faunas only occur in clastic rocks (Stone & Strachan 1981) which may have formed during obduction.

The main lava types fall into the basalt field and include island–arc tholeiites, boninites, ocean–island tholeiites, alkali basalts and possibly MORB-type basalts (Wilkinson & Cann 1974; Thirlwall & Bluck 1984; Smellie & Stone 1992; Smellie *et al.* 1995; Fig. 6.4). Inter-element plots and spider diagrams have been used to evaluate plate tectonic regimes and the bulk of the lavas sampled fall into either Island Arc tholeiite (IAT) or Ocean Island tholeiite (OIT) fields. The southern block has IAT, although the samples are few; the central, OIT and IAT and the northern block OIT but with sandstones at the base of the succession whose composition and chemistry carry an IAT signature (Smellie & Stone 1992). Whilst samples taken from

within a general locality share a common geochemistry, those from elsewhere within a block clearly may not. If the geochemical signatures properly reflect source, then the conclusion has to be that there is much structural or other juxtapositioning of disparate lava-types within blocks.

Apart from the geochemistry, the structure and sequence of the lavas and their relationships with associated sediments are significant to the interpretation of the regime of their formation. The lava–sediment sequences in all blocks are variable. The lavas are often pillowed or massive and individual flow units can be recognized with ease and, when they are distinctively porphyritc, can be traced for hundreds of metres along strike. The most significant feature of the lava sequence is that it contains abundant volcanogenic sediments (Bluck 1982) accounting for as much as 70% of the exposed record in some blocks.

Tuffs, lithic arenites, cherts, black shales, conglomerates and breccias are all found interstratified with the lavas. Some conglomerates contain very well rounded clasts, all of which are volcanogenic and at some stratigraphic positions hyalotuff deltas are interstratified with the lava. One well developed hyalotuff delta sequence is recorded at Pinbain (Bluck 1982), where

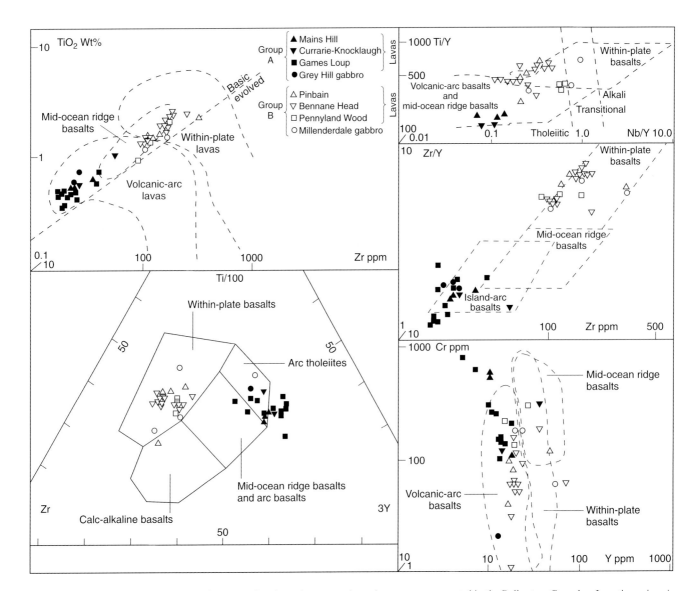

Fig. 6.4. Comparative geochemical plots demonstrating the various tectonic environments represented in the Ballantrae Complex. Locations given in Figure 6.1. (Adapted from Stone & Smellie 1990.)

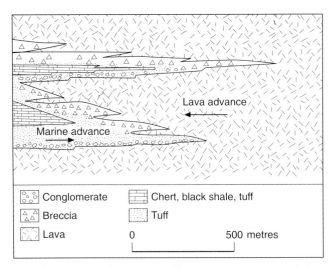

Fig. 6.5. Summary of the regimes of lava and sediment accumulations at Ballantrae, based on field relationships at Pinbain and Bennane Head. (Adapted from Bluck 1992*b*.)

a distinctive porphyritic lava flow has advanced over a large scale, cross-stratified hyalotuff deposit. The lava is followed by another hyalotuff sequence deposited during regression.

Smellie (1984) recorded accretionary lapilli from a tuff within the Pinbain block and there are similar occurrences elsewhere in the sequence, notably in the Bennane Head block. The presence of red tops to some of the lava flows at Pinbain also suggested to him that there were times of subaerial exposure. Thin conglomerates with well rounded clasts, which sometimes truncate underlying lavas, contain a high proportion of reddened clasts, and suggest transgressive sequences across lava surfaces (Bluck 1992*b*). An interpretation of the various lava forms and the interrelated volcanogenic rocks is given in Figure 6.5.

The presence of abundant volcanogenic sediments, clasts which probably acquired their rounding above local wave-base, and prograding hyalotuff deltas all demonstrate that much of the lava sequence was deposited in shallow water. Since the thickness of lava sequences in individual blocks may exceed 2 km, accumulation by subsidence rather than the rise of a volcanic edifice is indicated.

Sheeted dykes. Many dykes at Ballantrae have been ascribed to the sheeted dyke complex. Church & Gayer (1973) considered the pyroxene granulite dykes, which cut the foliated gabbros at Millenderdale as possible candidates and large blocks of pillow lava within some of the olistostromes have many dykes intruded into them. Oliver & McAlpine (1998) have recorded part of a sheeted dyke complex, forming a large tectonic inclusion in serpentinite from the north side of Knockdolian.

Gabbros and trondhjemite. This part of the complex is well exposed on Byne Hill, Mains Hill and at Millenderdale although in all three cases the geological relationships are far from clear. The gabbros at Millenderdale have yielded a K–Ar age of 487 ± 8 Ma (Harris *et al.* 1965). The gabbro at Byne Hill–Grey Hill has an associated trondhjemite with a U–Pb age of 482 ± 5 Ma (Bluck *et al.* 1980). These ages are within error limits of each other.

The gabbro at Byne Hill–Mains Hill is unfoliated and grades through a diorite up into a trondhjemite in a sequence which has been assigned to progressive fractionation (Bloxam 1968;

Jelinek *et al.* 1984). It has a chilled sub-vertical wall of doleritic rock at its contact with the northern serpentinite (Bloxam 1968) which was therefore cool at the time of intrusion but which is itself underlain by the metamorphic zones produced during its obduction when hot.

The foliated gabbros at Millenderdale have uncertain relationships with the adjacent rocks. They lie in a zone typified by much shearing and which, along strike, contains disparate blocks in a highly sheared matrix: the kind of context characterizing a mélange. The gabbros have been retrogressed to amphibolites, as have the granulite dykes that cut them. However, residual pyroxene textures are present in both. The age 487 ± 8 Ma refers to the time of retrogression and hornblende growth in the amphibolites, although this is probably close to the crystallization age. A gabbro pegmatite, 'Bonney's Dyke', is seen to cut the northern serpentinite and, as with the Byne Hill–Mains Hill mass, has distinctive finer-grained chilled margins. The rock, in contrast to the serpentinite, and in common with the main gabbro masses, is unfoliated although very altered.

Unlike many other ophiolites, and quite unlike what would be anticipated from the simple ocean crust profile, the gabbro–trondhemite complex of Byne Hill–Mains Hill, along with the gabbro pegmatite, was intruded into mantle rocks. Jelinek *et al.* (1984) have calculated a crystallization depth of >60 km for the northern serpentinite, which can be assumed to have been brought up from depth along the metamorphic sole which underlies it. The Sm–Nd cooling age of 505 ± 11 Ma (Hamilton *et al.* 1984) for the highest grade rocks is also the oldest age in this metamorphic zone and is taken as the time of uplift. On this basis, the gabbro–trondhjemite mass is post-obduction in age and was intruded into elevated and presumably partly uncovered mantle. As there is no continental crust signature in these gabbro–trondhjemite masses (Jelinek *et al.* 1984), the initial obduction and subsequent gabbro intrusion all took place within an intra-oceanic setting.

The serpentinites. The serpentinites are divided into a northern and a southern belt (Peach & Horne 1899; Balsillie 1932, 1937*a, b*). The northerly serpentinite is essentially a harzburgite with some lherzolite, ortho- and clino-pyroxenite and websterite (Jelinek *et al.* 1984; Stone & Smellie 1990). This northern belt is characterized by a tectonic fabric which is strong in places, and is in contrast to the southern belt which is relatively free of penetrative fabrics. The chemistry of these rocks is similar to those of other ophiolites and suggests that they are residues after the extraction of *c.* 20–30% tholeiite (Jelinek *et al.* 1984).

The southern belt has a wide range of rock types dominated by harzburgite and these are somewhat coarser grained than that in the north. In addition there are dunites, wherlites and troctolites. The penetrative fabrics that characterize the northern serpentinite are not recorded and the serpentinites of the southern belt have been interpreted as forming at higher crustal levels (Church & Gayer 1973; Dewey 1974; Stone & Smellie 1990).

Stone & Smellie (1988, 1990) point out that the detailed chemistry of both the harzburgites and spinels suggest that the serpentinites may not represent typical oceanic mantle. A possible alternative is that they formed above a subduction zone and this will be examined in the light of other evidence below.

The metamorphic aureole. The northern serpentinite, in common with many other ophiolitic complexes is in contact with a very condensed (40–100 m thick) metamorphic sequence. At Ballantrae this is exposed in a number of localities between Knocklaugh and Carleton Hill near the shore (Fig. 6.6). Below

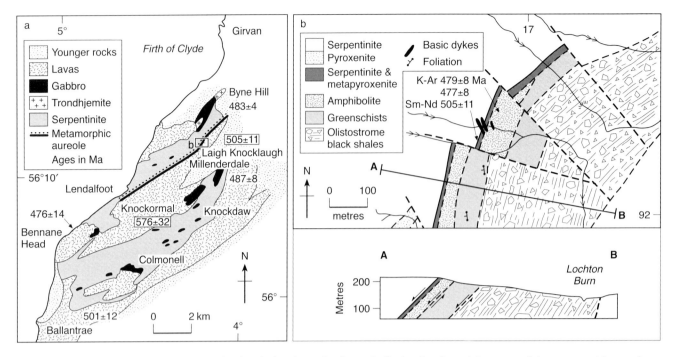

Fig. 6.6. (a) Map of the Ballantrae Complex showing the locations of radiometrically dated rocks and the extent of the metamorphic aureole.
(b) Map and cross-sections of the metamorphic aureole at Laigh Knocklaugh. (Adapted from Hamilton *et al.* 1984.)

the aureole there is an olistostrome of black shale and lava; above the olistostrome there are ultramafic rocks consisting of mylonitic rock in greenschist facies followed by amphibolites and, in places, garnet metapyroxenite, which may be interleaved with serpentinite. Sections through the aureole are fairly continuous, strongly sheared in all instances, and in some the greenschist is well developed with interleaved beds of amphibolite; in other exposures the amphibolite is well developed, with interleaved greenschist at its base.

A Sm–Nd age of 505 ± 11 Ma has been obtained from the garnet metapyroxenite (Hamilton *et al.* 1984) and a resolvably younger K–Ar age of 478 ± 8 Ma for the amphibolite (Bluck *et al.* 1980). The garnet metapyroxenite crystallized at *c.* 900°C and at pressures of least 10–11 kb (Treloar *et al.* 1980); estimates for another hornblende–garnet–pyroxene rock have minima of 850°C and 7 kb (Spray & Williams 1980).

In view of the pressure, temperature and time differences between the metamorphic lithologies in the sole, Treloar *et al.* (1980) and Hamilton *et al.* (1984) suggested that, during the overthrusting of the mantle, the metapyroxenite accreted to the mantle first and that progressively and sequentially, the lower pressure rocks accreted later, during its rise. Spray & Williams (1980) deduced a transport direction towards the NW. The age of the olistostrome is poorly assigned to be within the Arenig, and so the Late Cambrian–Tremadoc obduction date of 505 ± 11 Ma suggests that the olistostrome had not formed by the time this obduction took place. The metamorphic aureole may therefore have been finally emplaced sometime in the Arenig, well after its cooling.

Late stage dykes. The Complex has a range of dykes associated with it, but their significance is far from clear. Rodingite (Ca-metasomatised) dykes are fairly common in the serpentinite and beerbachites (metapyroxenites) are found both in serpentinite and in gabbros. Whatever the country rock, the beerbachites can show chilled margins.

In addition there are at least two suites of roughly NE–SW oriented dolerite dykes (Holub *et al.* 1984) which can be distin-

guished on chemistry, mineralogy and texture. One group has the chemistry of primitive tholeites and is at low amphibolite–greenschist metamorphic grade; the other group, with prominent chilled margins, has ophitic textures and a composition suggesting derivation from a more evolved magma. Both groups are known to cut rocks of the metamorphic aureole, the serpentinite, and the gabbro, and are therefore post-obduction, however both are thought to have been emplaced before serpentinization was complete (Holub *et al.* 1984). As the dykes are not known to cut the cover rocks, their age is therefore bracketed between 478 ± 8 Ma (youngest age determined for obduction) and *c.* 465 Ma (the age of the youngest sediments in the cover).

The two dyke suites are thought to have been intruded during a time when a parent magma source was evolving and the ophiolite was cooling. It would appear from the chemistry that neither dyke suite was derived from magma that was in contact with continental crust, confirming the observations on the gabbros and trondhjemite and demonstrating that the Ballantrae Complex remained in an intra-oceanic setting between *c.* 479 and 465 Ma.

Blueschist, granitoid and metapyroxenite. There are a number of other outcrops at Ballantrae which are of some significance. Blueschists occur at some localities where they are either associated with olistostromes or mélanges. Blocks which occur at Knockormal are less than 3×3 m in size and are poorly exposed, but are within a belt which has abundant blocks with disparate composition, and are surrounded by a matrix that is often highly sheared (Fig. 6.6).

Other blocks included in this sheared ground include granitoids, masses of deformed shale, gabbros and garnet metapyroxenite. The garnet metapyroxenite yielded a Sm–Nd age of 576 ± 32 Ma (Hamilton *et al.* 1984) and Smellie & Stone (1984) obtained an estimated pressure of 10–13 kb and a temperature of 900–950°C. Smellie & Stone (1984) found the chemistry of the garnet metapyroxenite to have affinities more with Alpine-type ultramafic eclogitic rocks rather than those eclogites associated with blueschists. Whatever the association, it is clear that a late Proterozoic event of some significance is recorded by these blocks, although the regional context of this event is unclear.

Timing of events

Age determinations, both palaeontological and radiometric, have provided a much needed framework within which to interpret the Complex, and recent modifications to the absolute age determinations of Ordovician biostratigraphy have necessitated a revision of the relative timing of events. However, in situations where geological events occur at a rapid rate and where the age determinations are not precise, critical levels of interpretation are not possible, and misinterpretations are easily made.

The northern serpentinite was obducted between 505 ± 11 Ma and 478 ± 8 Ma at which time, given the pressures and temperatures in the aureole at its base, this body was clearly hot and part of a very thick (>30 km) sequence. However, by Late Arenig times ($c. 470$ Ma) it was probably exposed, at least partly serpentinized and undergoing erosion, as clasts of serpentinite with algal encrustations are found in fossiliferous strata at North Ballaird (Stone & Strachan 1981). If the chert sequence at Bennane Head is Middle Arenig (Stone & Rushton 1983) then clasts of serpentinite were already available for erosion. During this Middle to Late Arenig interval two known phases of dyke and trondhjemite intrusion occurred.

The intrusion of the trondhjemite into the serpentinite has quite profound implications. If the pressure estimates of Jelinek *et al.* (1980) are taken for the northern serpentinite, and the trondhjemite is regarded as a fairly high level intrusion, then some 60 km of cover was removed prior to the intrusion of the mass at 483 ± 4 Ma, and by 505 ± 11 Ma the overriding block was 30–40 km thick. The location of the sediment which was derived from this uplift and/or the detached plates which formerly may have overlain it is not known.

The only lavas old enough to have been part of the sequence which included the northern serpentinite are at Mains Hill (501 ± 12 Ma; Thirlwall & Bluck 1984). The Pinbain and Bennane Head blocks, being Early–Mid-Arenig and post-480 Ma, were laid down after obduction. They might therefore belong to a different event and were possibly accreted to the Ballantrae Complex by a separate method. It could also be argued that the ultramafic and extrusive rocks developed separately and were brought together by final obduction.

In the time span of the Arenig ($c. 15$ Ma) lavas accumulated with chemistries suggesting eruption in regimes ranging from Island Arc to Ocean Islands. The abundant lava clasts in the sedimentary sequences could have a provenance in either pre-obduction or post-obduction lavas.

The significance of the early age of 576 Ma is not clear. If, as suggested by Stone & Smellie (1984), the dated rock is part of a serpentinite then it dates the cooling of that rock as Neoproterozoic. The other possibility is that it is a block within a mélange (Hamilton *et al.* 1984). Whatever its association, and discounting major strike-slip movements, then there is clearly a record of deep burial and uplift on a margin which, at the time, appears to have been passive.

Other sedimentary units have not been well dated. However, they contain a wide variety of clast types, indicating quite clearly that most lithologies of an ophiolite were being eroded at the time of deposition. The olistostrome unit at Pinbain, with its wide variety of clasts, must therefore post-date the uplift of a major ophiolitic terrane which included blueschist, amphibolite, trondhjemite, serpentines, pillow lavas and dolerite.

The origin of the Complex

Evaluation of the origin of the Complex hinges on some critical points.

(a) Although occupying only 75 km², the Ballantrae Complex has a huge diversity of rock types. In addition, the Complex comprises disparate blocks, many of which were formed at totally different levels within crust and mantle, and which are in outcrops always <3 km wide. There is often great disparity within outcrops: serpentinite is seen thrust over lavas and cherts and rocks from some considerable depth within the crust are seen to have yielded clasts to conglomerates that differ little in age from that of the cooling blocks. Single blocks contain lavas with contrasting chemistries suggesting quite different eruptive regimes (Stone 1984), and have within them evidence of structural repetition (Stone & Rushton 1983).

Given the dimensions of most tectonic regimes, it is fairly clear that the Ballantrae Complex comprises only slivers of each of them (Stone 1984). The Complex is a structural amalgamation of fragments brought together as a series of NE–SW-trending slices. Moreover, fragments of former larger tectonic entities must originally have been separated by large tracts of ground that have also been lost. However, although the complex comprises a series of slivers and the lithologies in each block may not be related to each other, they all have broadly oceanic affinities.

Structural amalgamation of this kind can occur by the telescoping of blocks in a wholly compressive regime but might be better accomplished by strike-slip. The wide areas of mélange or sheared olistostrome that permeate the complex, together with the demonstrated clockwise rotation of the Pinbain block (Trench *et al.* 1988) provides support for such a view.

(b) The abundant sediments intercalated with the lavas display the characteristic features of shallow water deposition, supplementing the clear indications of lava accumulation in shallow water. This, together with the thickness of the lava–sediment succession, indicates accumulation in a regime of subsidence. However it is also clear that most of the lava sequences accumulated in regions remote from uplifted cratonic areas, so that there is little or no influx of terrestrially derived sediment.

On the other hand, there is much evidence of sediment derived from igneous rocks. These sediments, with their range of acid to basic clasts, have a provenance in active subaerial and reasonably mature volcanic regimes, and possibly in older lava piles. In addition the presence of clasts with deep crustal affinities suggests much structural complexity in the source regions at the time of deposition.

The interfingering of boulder-bearing breccias and conglomerates with the slumped black shales and cherts, and the rapid lateral change from coarse to fine sediment imply deposition in regimes characterized by steep accretionary slopes in the basin and high relief in the source. These facies are the products of sedimentation at the margin of basins and bear little resemblance to the layer 1 of normal oceanic crust.

(c) The Ballantrae Complex provides evidence for three phases of accretion and associated uplift. An event $c. 576$ Ma, in the Neoproterozoic; another $c. 505$ Ma, in the Late Cambrian, and a third post Middle–Late Arenig but pre-Late Llanvirn (Fig. 6.3). Thus it is highly probable that major unconformities exist within the sequence so that rocks with quite different histories have been juxtaposed. Igneous and metamorphic rocks formed at depth have been intruded by other rocks at much higher crustal levels, suggesting intervals of substantial intervening uplift. All of this evidence points to genesis in a regime subject to repeated tectonism.

In view of these points the Ballantrae Complex is seen as an assemblage of slivers (Fig. 6.7), partly or wholly brought together by strike-slip faulting (Stone 1984). The slivers are

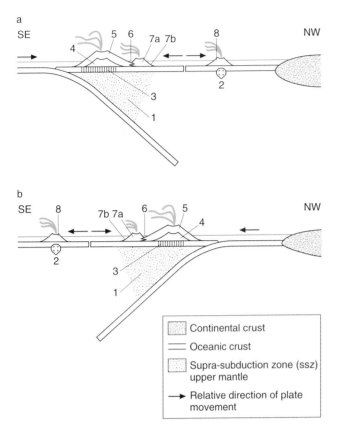

Fig. 6.7. Cartoon cross sections showing the evolution of the Ballantrae Complex in a marginal basin setting: (1) area of melt generation in supra subduction zone (SSZ) upper mantle (N and S sepentinite belts); (2) Millenderdale gabbro; (3) new SSZ oceanic crust (including boninites?); (4) primitive island-arc tholeiite sequence (Games Loup); (5) mature island-arc tholeiite sequence (Mains Hill, Currarie-Knocklaugh); (6) arc-derived sandstones (Kilranny Formation) interbedded with ocean-island sequence; (7) supra-subduction zone ocean-island sequence (Pinbain, 7a; Bennane, 7b); (8) ocean-island tholeiite sequence (Pennyland Wood). (Adapted from Stone & Smellie 1990.)

most plausibly interpreted as components of a disrupted marginal basin with associated arcs, such as can be seen today in the western Pacific (Bluck 1985, 1992). Such a setting displays a great diversity in lava type including MORB, small ocean islands and arcs. Collapse of, and subsequent obduction of, such a marginal basin has the potential to greatly thicken the crust and erosion can then yield rocks carrying evidence of high pressure rocks derived from different depths of the lithosphere, as seen in the two serpentinites.

Lower Palaeozoic cover to the Ballantrae Complex

The fossiliferous sedimentary cover to the Ballantrae Complex is at a very low metamorphic grade (Oliver 1988) and not pervasively deformed (although there is much faulting and some folding). The stratigraphy has been well studied, especially by Tripp (1954), Williams (1962), Cocks & Toghill (1973) and Ingham (1978). This account is based on the summary given by Bluck & Ingham (1992).

As noted there is a good fossil record which not only dates the stratigraphy rather well but also shows strong North American (Appalachian) faunal provincialism. The Late Caradoc shelly fauna has little in common with contemporary Anglo-Welsh faunas; this has been taken as evidence for a 'significantly' wide Iapetus Ocean separating the Anglo-Welsh parts of Avalonia from Laurentia (Cocks & Fortey 1982).

The Ballantrae Complex was obducted on to the south side of the Midland Valley terrane during the Arenig (see above). Soon after, Lower Llanvirn conglomerate-dominated facies transgressed northwards over the Complex, starting first with the Kirkland Conglomerate in the Stincher Valley, then the Middle Llanvirn Bennan Conglomerate between the Stinchar and the Girvan foreshore and then the Lower Caradoc Kilranny Conglomerate near Girvan itself. Lastly, by Middle Caradoc times, the Ballantrae basement at Craighead, 5 km northwest of Girvan, had been transgressed. The full stratigraphic succession is summarized in Chapter 5, Figure 5.7. It is notable that there appear to be cycles of initially shallow water sediments (limestones and conglomerates) that are followed by an abruptly deepening sandstone and shale facies which is in turn capped by conglomerate, often channeled into the underlying sediment. In detail there are large local differences in thickness and provenance between successive conglomerates as indicated by their clast contents. Clasts are dominated by locally derived spilite and serpentinite set in a basic volcaniclastic matrix but large granite boulders indicate a not-too-distant magmatic arc source somewhere to the north. Minor amounts of metamorphic detritus are also reported. Bluck (1983) gives Rb–Sr whole-rock/mineral age dates for some of the granite boulders that are only slightly older than the conglomerates that contain them. Bluck (1992) considers the Ordovician Ballantrae cover sequence is the proximal fore-arc succession to an eroded/buried Midland Valley volcanic/plutonic arc. Oliver (2001) has analysed the heavy mineral content of the matrix to these conglomerates and associated sandstones and found abundant detrital garnet whose chemistry matches those formed in Barrovian metamorphic sequences typical of the Dalradian of the Grampian terrane. He also reported different garnets that would have been sourced from S-type granites and another set that would have come from a high-pressure, low-temperature blueschist–eclogite facies subduction zone. Thus, on the inception of sedimentation in the Early Llanvirn, high-grade metamorphic sand-size detritus was available to mix with ophiolite plus volcanic arc boulders. The fact that no boulders of garnet-mica schist have been reported from the Ballantrae Complex cover suggests that such a source was not local.

Williams (1962) and Ince (1984), proposed that the sedimentation here was controlled by active normal faulting on the southern margin of the Midland Valley. Armstrong *et al.* (1996) have expanded on this by suggesting that following the obduction of the Ballantrae Complex, local Caradocian fan complexes prograded southeastwards across a narrow fault-bounded collapsing shelf into the deep basin of the Northern Belt of the Southern Uplands. However, Hutchison & Oliver (1998) contend that these fans might have been fed by large river systems that originated from within the mountainous Grampian (metamorphic/plutonic) terrane. These rivers then flowed across the Midland Valley (plutonic–volcanic arc) terrane, through and over the obducted Ballantrae Complex (ophiolite) and thence into the Southern Uplands accretionary prism terrane, see Chapter 7.

Llandovery conglomerates, with quartzose clasts dominant, rest with low angle (*c.* 8°) unconformity on eroded Ashgillian sandstones and shales. These conglomerates and associated shallow marine sandstones and shales (see Chapter 5 for details of stratigraphy) contain abundant detrital high grade Barrovian metamorphic garnet (Oliver 2001). The extreme variability of the Llandovery sedimentary lithologies and thicknesses over

Fig. 6.8. Outline geology of the Southern Uplands: note the principal tract-bounding faults. (Adapted from Floyd 1996, 2001.)

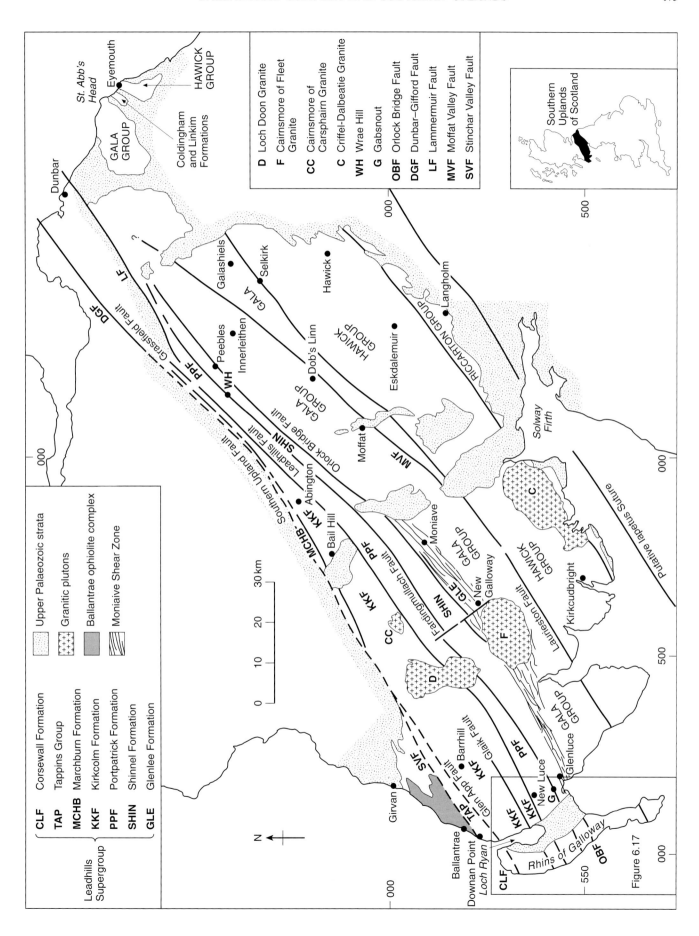

Figure 6.17

short distances is attributed to local fault movements, presumably reactivating the Ordovician normal faults described above. Late Llandovery red beds terminate the Ballantrae cover sequence. End Silurian earth movements folded the rocks into asymmetric folds with northwesterly vergence: several major northwesterly directed thrusts replace the northwesterly facing limbs of these folds. These folds generally verge towards the NW in contrast to the SE vergence shown by early folds in the Southern Uplands. Continentally deposited Lower Old Red Sandstone conglomerates and sandstones lie with strong unconformity on the Ballantrae cover.

The Southern Uplands terrane

A regional overview

The Southern Uplands terrane is made up of Ordovician and Silurian strata, mainly turbiditic greywackes and siltstones, divided into structural tracts by major NE–SW strike-parallel faults (Fig. 6.8). Caradoc and Ashgill greywackes are the dominant lithology in the nothwest of the terrane, Llandovery greywackes form most of the central part, and Wenlock greywackes comprise the southeastern margin. This tripartite division was recognized long ago by Peach & Horne (1899), who referred to the three stratigraphical divisions as the Northern, Central and Southern belts. Dip is generally steep with vertical beds present over wide areas. Abundant sedimentological

evidence shows that the younging direction of the steeply inclined or vertical greywacke beds is dominantly towards the NW. Conversely, biostratigraphical evidence, largely based on graptolite faunas, shows that the overall age of the strata decreases towards the SE. This fundamental paradox has formed the basis for much controversy in the geological interpretation of the terrane.

The stratigraphical framework

When individual fault-bounded tracts are considered in the Northern Belt and northern part of the Central Belt, the turbidite greywacke beds, mostly with steep dips and younging towards the NW, overlie a thin and condensed, basal assemblage of black shale and chert with local occurrences of basaltic lava and volcaniclastic beds. The strike faults are preferentially located within the fissile shales that crop out as lenticular inliers extended NE–SW along the length of the faults. The SE margin of each inlier is faulted, in contrast to the NW margin, which normally passes up conformably into the greywacke sequence. Graptolite faunas are widespread in the shale and establish an age range that generally increases southwards across the Southern Uplands. In the NW of the Southern Uplands the shale is restricted to the Late Ordovician (Caradoc) *gracilis* Biozone, although conodont evidence indicates that the underlying cherts may extend down into the Llanvirn (Lamont & Lindstrom 1957; Armstrong *et al.* 1996). Further SE, the shale

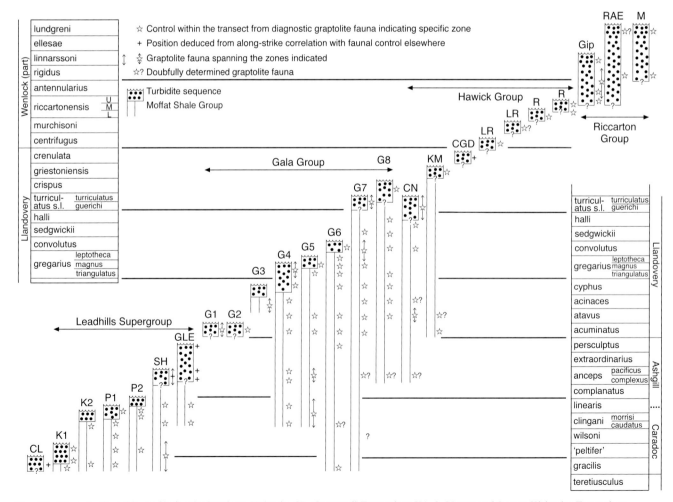

Fig. 6.9. Time-stratigraphic profile for the Southern Uplands: CL, Corsewall Formation; K1, 2, Upper and Lower Kirkcolm Formation; P1, 2, Upper and Lower Portpatrick Formation; SH, Shinnel Formation; GLE, Glenlee Formation; G1-8, Gala Group tectonostratigraphic units; CN, Cairnharrow Formation; KM, Kirkmaiden Formation; CGD, Carghidown Formation; LR, Long Robin unit; R, Ross Formation; Gip, Gipsy Point Formation; RAE, Raeberry Castle Formation; M, Mulloch Bay Formation. (Adapted from Rushton *et al.* 1996.)

ranges from Caradoc up to the Early Silurian (Llandovery) *turriculatus* or *crispus* biozones. Thus the commencement of turbidite sedimentation above the basal shale and chert assemblage was diachronously later towards the SE of the terrane (Figs 6.8 & 6.9).

This combination of features is most readily explicable in terms of an imbricate thrust belt in which the fissile black shales have provided the décollement plane. As the thrust system evolved it incorporated successively younger strata while greywacke deposition ahead of the thrust front overlapped a progressively more extended stratigraphical range of shale. The oldest rocks incorporated in the thrust stack are the Arenig basalts and cherts of the Crawford Group, which are seen very sporadically in the north of the terrane; (Ordovician and Silurian lithostratigraphy is summarized in Fig. 6.9). They are overlain by the black shale, chert, hyaloclastite and meta-bentonite of the Moffat Shale Group; as described above, this unit is restricted to the Caradoc in the north of the Southern Uplands, but ranges up through the Ashgill and Llandovery farther south. Above the Moffat Shale Group, the turbidite greywacke sequence in any one structural tract is generally restricted to one or two graptolite biozones.

The Northern, Central and Southern belts are separated and internally divided by components of the strike fault system, interpreted as the original thrusts now rotated to the near-vertical. Such strike faults within the Ordovician Leadhills Supergroup (Floyd 1996) separate established lithostratigraphical formations which are defined by variations in the composition of the detrital clast assemblage within the greywackes (e.g. Walton 1955; Kelling 1961; Floyd 1982; Floyd & Trench 1989). This is also partially true for the most northerly units of the Gala Group within the Silurian Central Belt but, farther south, the Gala Group formations become compositionally similar. Thus, Gala Group units do not always carry formal lithostratigraphic status and are commonly distinguished partly on biostratigraphical age and partly on their tectonic position within the imbricate thrust structure. Some locally significant lithostratigraphical formations have been defined, but the different structural units of the Gala Group are generally identified by numbers in the range Gala 1 to Gala 8. The lowest numbers indicate the oldest strata, which were the first to be incorporated in the imbricate thrust system, and the highest numbers indicate the younger strata which were incorporated subsequently: this is essentially a tectonostratigraphical scheme. When and if new criteria become available the Gala Group can be properly divided into formations. The younger Llandovery Hawick Group and the Wenlock Riccarton Group are both amenable to lithostratigraphical division and formations within each are defined on a combination of lithological and facies-related criteria.

The biostratigraphical positions of the various structural tracts, some coincident with lithostratigraphy and some defined on other criteria, are illustrated in Figures 6.8 and 6.9, based on the situation in Galloway in the SW of the terrane where the maximum and most orderly development of the imbricated stratigraphy is seen. Along the strike to the northeast there is a tendency for the Ordovician tracts of the Northern Belt to be eliminated by the merging of strike faults, whilst a greater degree of structural repetition occurs within the Llandovery of the Central Belt (Rushton *et al.* 1996*a,b*). The combination of these two effects maintains the overall width of the thrust belt along the length of the Southern Uplands.

The geotectonic setting for sedimentation

The application of plate tectonic theory to the British Caledonides (e.g. Dewey 1971) led to a general interpretation of the

Southern Uplands' sequence as the oceanic and trench deposits formed at a continental margin beneath which an oceanic plate (the Iapetus Ocean) was being subducted northwestwards. This was refined by Mitchell & McKerrow (1975), McKerrow *et al.* (1977) and Leggett *et al.* (1979) into an accretionary prism model in which the imbricate thrust system built up above the subduction zone as slices of cover sediment were sheared from the descending oceanic plate and thrust beneath the previously accreted stack of similar slices (Fig. 6.10). Successively younger material would thus be sequentially incorporated at the sole of the developing thrust stack but the dominant NW-directed younging would be maintained. Continued underthrusting at the trench was thought likely to cause rotation towards the vertical in the older, higher portions of the thrust stack and thus to produce the characteristic Southern Uplands tectono-stratigraphic pattern. In such a situation, all of the thrust tracts within the Southern Uplands should be underlain by oceanic crust, and its apparent absence from the tracts in the Central and Southern belts led Leggett *et al.* (1983) to modify the accretionary prism model; suggesting that continental crust from the southern side of the Iapetus Ocean was thrust beneath the Southern Uplands during the final closure of the ocean. In an alternative interpretation Bluck (1983, 1984) regarded the Southern Uplands as allochthonous, having itself been over-thrust towards the NW onto the northern continental margin.

The accretionary prism hypothesis, although an elegant and popular explanation for the general regional tectonostratigraphic pattern, has not gained universal acceptance. Based on work in Longford–Down (the along strike extension of the Southern Uplands in Ireland), Murphy & Hutton (1986) suggested that only the oldest part of the terrane, the late Ordovician Northern Belt, could be considered an accretionary prism. They suggested that the Silurian part of the Southern Uplands represented a post-collision successor basin disrupted by a southwards propagating thrust stack. Complexity also became apparent from sedimentological and petrographical analyses which, to Morris (1987) and Stone *et al.* (1987), required andesitic material to be derived from the south (the oceanward side) during the latest Ordovician and earliest Silurian. These authors developed a model initiated in a back-arc basin. Morris restricted this phase to the Ordovician Northern Belt, with the subsequent development of an Early Silurian accretionary prism. Stone *et al.* envisaged that collision of the southern continental margin of the Iapetus Ocean with a volcanic arc (Fig. 6.11) caused compression within the back-arc basin so that the resulting thrust system eventually over-rode the arc remnants, propagated across the sutured arc–continental basement, and developed thereafter as a foreland basin fold and thrust complex.

More recently a back-arc interpretation of the Ordovician component of the terrane has been revised by Armstrong *et al.* (1990, 1996, 1999) and Armstrong & Owen (2001) utilizing chert geochemistry and high-resolution biostratigraphy derived from both graptolite and conodont faunas. The latter show a remarkable uniformity of age for the chert immediately underlying the Moffat Shale Group across the whole width of the Northern Belt, and further demonstrated that the older Arenig basalt unit was restricted to the southern part of the belt. In its simplest form the accretionary prism interpretation would predict that the oldest components would occur in the north and that all stratigraphical boundaries would become diachronously younger southwards. Inevitably, out-of-sequence and back-thrusting complicate the pattern and may be responsible for the apparently anomalous relationships in the Northern Belt, although examples of these phenomena have only been documented widely in the Central Belt (Rushton *et al.* 1996*a,b*).

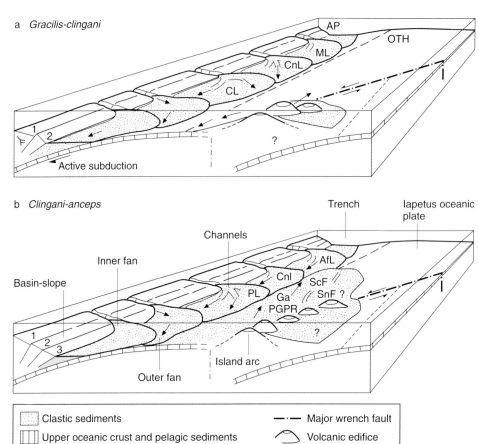

Fig. 6.10. Accretionary prism model for the Southern Uplands. (**a**) Trench and fan palaeogeography and tectonic evolution during Upper Ordovician *gracilis–clingani* times. CL, Corsewall lobe; CnL, Carsphairn lobe; ML, Marchburn lobe. (**b**) Note island arc in *clingani–anceps* times which is shedding volcaniclastic debris towards a back-arc. AfL, Afton lobe; CnL, Carsphairn Lobe; Ga, Galdenoch Formation; PG, Portpatrick Formation; PL, Portslogan Lobe (Kirkcolm Formation); ScF, Scar Formation; ShF, Shinnel Formation. 1, 2, 3, mark earlier accreted tracts. (Adapted from Kelling *et al.* 1987.)

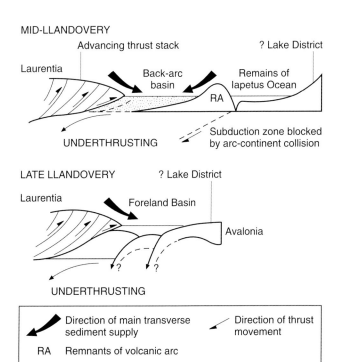

Fig. 6.11. Sequential evolution of the Southern Uplands as a thrust belt from a back-arc to a foreland basin. RA, remnant arc. (Adapted from Stone 1995.)

Despite the continuing debate, a considerable weight of opinion still favours the accretionary prism interpretation of the Southern Uplands terrane, albeit with some modifications (e.g. Anderson & Oliver 1986; Leggett 1987; McCurry & Anderson 1989). There is also a growing acceptance that late in the development of the terrane the Iapetus Ocean was eliminated and the Southern Uplands thrust complex, accretionary prism or back-arc thrust stack migrated onto the margin of the Avalonian continent. Ahead of the thrust front a foreland basin developed and part of its fill is now preserved as the upper Windermere Supergroup in the English Lake District (Kneller 1991; Kneller *et al.* 1993). At what point the transition from back-arc to fore-arc occurred within the Southern Uplands turbidite succession is still a matter of controversy but has important implications for timing of the final closure of the Iapetus Ocean.

The volcanic rocks

Lithology, age and distribution. The majority of the volcanic rocks associated with the Southern Uplands succession are of Ordovician age, but within the Moffat Shale Group, meta-bentonite interbeds range up into the Late Llandovery, becoming most voluminous around the *sedgwickii* Biozone. The whole suite will be considered here although there is considerable stratigraphical and geographical range amongst its components.

The oldest volcanic rocks are the Arenig basalt lavas of the Raven Gill Formation (Crawford Group). They have a restricted outcrop in the Abington area, adjacent to the Lead-hills Fault, and form the base of a succession which continues upwards through the Moffat Shale Group and into Caradoc greywackes of the Kirkcolm Formation. The Arenig lavas are closely associated with blue-grey radiolarian chert and brown mudstone. Some sheet-like doleritic bodies could be related intrusions rather than extrusive lavas. The Arenig age was originally assigned by Peach & Horne (1899) on the basis of a graptolite fauna in the mudstone and a general similarity with the established Arenig volcanic rocks at Ballantrae. Their faunal evidence has subsequently been discounted with the graptolites now regarded as indeterminable, but the Arenig age has been confirmed by the discovery of conodonts (Lamont & Lindstrom 1957; Armstrong et al. 1990). A poorly constrained Sm–Nd age of 490 ± 14 Ma (Thirlwall in McKerrow et al. 1985) is broadly compatible with the biostratigraphical age.

Elsewhere, basaltic lavas form the base of the succession in several of the northern Ordovician tectonic slices in the Northern Belt. Some of these occurrences are overlain by mudstone of the Caradoc gracilis Biozone and there has been a traditional assumption that these lavas might also be of Arenig age, correlating with those at Raven Gill, near Abington. However, at several localities, basaltic lavas are seen interbedded with the lowermost part of the greywacke succession and these must clearly be of a younger, Caradoc, age; for example, Floyd (1982) described two lava units interbedded with the Marchburn Formation.

Recent work by Armstrong et al. (1996) on conodont faunas from chert and mudstone intimately associated with the lavas has shown that most can be assigned to the anserinus conodont Biozone, which spans the Llanvirn–Early Caradoc interval. This association of anserinus conodonts immediately overlain by gracilis Biozone graptolites supports a common, earliest Caradoc age for the volcanic rocks preserved in several successive thrust slices within the Northern Belt. Some are subjacent to the Marchburn Formation (the Noblehouse Lava Member) and others either underlie or are interbedded with the basal greywackes of the Kirkcolm Formation (Kelling 1961; Stone 1995). A different relationship is possible farther south, at Gabsnout Burn near Glenluce, where volcanic rocks are seen close beneath the base of the Portpatrick Formation. These basalt and dolerite bodies have been described by Phillips et al. (1995) as allochthonous blocks within gracilis Biozone Moffat Shale Group mudstone. Their age, their source and the mechanism of their emplacement are not clear.

Stratigraphical uncertainty also surrounds the Downan Point Lava Formation in the northwest of the terrane, south of Ballantrae, and adjacent to the Stinchar Valley Fault. This unit of tholeiitic basalt lava, in which spectacular arrays of pillow forms are preserved (Plate 8), was originally thought to be part of the Arenig Ballantrae Complex (Stone & Smellie 1988, and references therein). However, Walton (1961) had already drawn attention to the apparent interbedding of similar pillow lavas with the structurally adjacent Tappins Group of Llanvirn to Caradoc age. This raised the possibility that the Downan Point lavas are significantly younger than those of the Ballantrae Complex. A poorly constrained Sm–Nd age of 468 ± 22 Ma (Thirlwall & Bluck 1984) did not resolve the issue, which is further complicated by differences in their REE geochemistry between the Downan Point lavas and those interbedded with the sedimentary sequence farther south (Lewis & Bloxam 1977). It has now become common practice to include the Downan Point Formation as one of the oldest (?Llanvirn–Caradoc) tectonostratigraphic tracts in the Southern Uplands terrane (Barrett et al. 1982; Leggett 1987; Floyd 1994).

The largest coherent volcanic assemblage unequivocally within the Southern Uplands terrane is the Bail Hill Volcanic Group which crops out over about 4 km^2 in the central part of the Northern Belt. It comprises a heterogeneous sequence of submarine lavas and volcaniclastic lithologies, ranging from alkali basalt to trachyandesite (Fig. 6.12) and cut by a vent breccia and several minor intrusions, together forming a sequence up to 2 km thick (Hepworth et al. 1982; Phillips et al. 1999). The oldest part of the volcanic assemblage rests on Moffat Shale Group mudstone of gracilis Biozone age; younger parts of the complex laterally interdigitate with and overlie turbidite greywacke beds of the Kirkcolm Formation (Table 6.1) also of gracilis age. Biotite from the Bail Hill lavas has been dated at 453 ± 10 Ma (K–Ar, Harris et al. 1985), compatible with the biostratigraphical indications of eruption in the early Caradoc.

Another likely manifestation of the Caradoc volcanic episode is seen within the eastern part of the terrane as the Tweedale Member of the Shinnel Formation. The member is a heterogeneous assemblage of limestone blocks (the Wrae Limestone) and peralkaline rhyolitic lavas (the Tweedale lavas) regarded by Leggett (1980) as a submarine slide deposit. The host Shinnel Formation contains an anceps Biozone graptolite fauna and overlies Moffat Shale Group strata ranging up to the linearis Biozone (Floyd & Rushton 1993). A largely Ashgill age is therefore likely. However, the exotic limestone blocks contain conodonts of the anserinus Biozone (Armstrong et al. 1996), which gives a strong indication that the original volcanicity might also have been of Caradoc age. In that case the Tweedale Member lavas could be coeval with the other Caradoc volcanic units within the Northern Belt of the Southern Uplands.

Two important aspects of the Southern Uplands volcanism have been established and reinforced by the recent work. Firstly, there were two distinct episodes of eruption, one in the Arenig and the other in the early Caradoc; there is no evidence for diachroneity in the latter (Armstrong et al. 1996). Secondly, in places, the Caradoc lavas are interbedded with the greywacke succession, showing that eruption and turbidite deposition overlapped in time; the lavas do not everywhere form a discrete basement to the sedimentary rocks.

Metabentonites make up an important component of the Moffat Shale Group. Their chemical compositions indicate an acid volcanic arc source (Batchelor & Weir 1988; Merriman & Roberts 1990).

Geotectonic setting of eruption. Basalt trace element geochemistry is widely believed to provide a reliable indication of the tectonic setting of the lava eruption. In view of the controversy surrounding the origin of the Southern Uplands terrane this aspect is clearly of considerable importance. Lambert et al. (1981), using XRF analysis, described the most northwesterly occurring lavas as alkali basalts, succeeded towards the southeast by a mixture of ocean-floor tholeiites and mildly alkaline basalts. This trend was regarded as an older to younger age sequence compatible with initial rifting developing into seafloor spreading with generation of oceanic crust. The Tweedale lavas were studied by Thirlwall (1981a) who described them as peralkaline rhyolites of likely oceanic-island origin. The Bail Hill volcanic rocks were described by Hepworth et al. (1982) as a mildly alkaline, oceanic seamount assemblage.

More recent investigations of the volcanic rocks have produced somewhat different interpretations. A comprehensive computer-based statistical reassessment of the data of Lambert et al. (1981) by Armstrong et al. (1996) was coupled with their biostratigraphical work that demonstrated a widespread Caradoc volcanic episode. Lavas of this age were mostly considered to show attenuated, within-plate characteristics indicating eruption in an extensional regime; minor amounts of continental volcanic arc and oceanic volcanic arc rocks were also

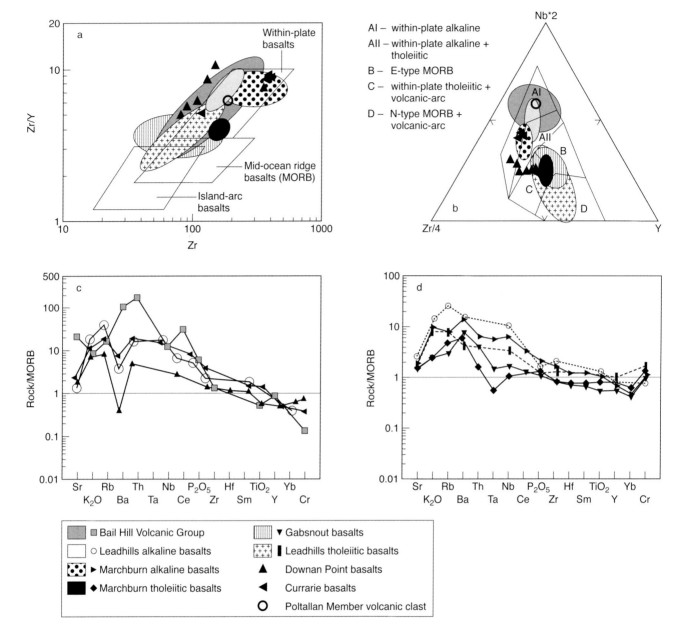

Fig. 6.12. Geochemistry of basalts from the Southern Uplands: (**a**) and (**b**) suggest a mix of MORB and within plate volcanism; (**c**) and (**d**) averaged rock/MORB normalized spidergram data suggest mainly within plate volcanism. (Adapted from Phillips *et al.* 1995, 1999.)

detected. None of the lavas were regarded as true ocean floor basalts. At about the same time new XRF and INA analyses were reported by Phillips *et al.* (1995) which also showed a dominance of within-plate and ocean-island types amongst the Caradoc suite. The more restricted Arenig lavas were shown to be a mixture of within-plate types and tholeiitic basalts of possible MORB affinity. Both Phillips *et al.* (1995) and Barnes *et al.* (1995) presented data for the allochthonous basaltic blocks at Gabsnout, showing them to be most akin to volcanic arc basalts and/or island arc tholeiites. Most recently, Phillips *et al.* (1999) have confirmed the Bail Hill Group as the result of alkaline, oceanic within-plate volcanism. Selected geochemical data for the Southern Uplands volcanic rocks are summarized in Figure 6.12.

The recent work has produced a consensus that the Arenig volcanic rocks, the substrate to the Moffat Shale Group adjacent to the Leadhills Fault, comprise both alkaline within-plate

basalts and possible MORB-like tholeiitic basalts. The *in situ* Caradoc volcanic rocks are all within-plate or ocean-island types associated with cherts of the *anserinus* conodont Biozone and/or mudstones of the *gracilis* graptolite Biozone. This overlap defines a well constrained Early Caradoc age. These lavas are also interbedded locally with the greywacke sequences of the Marchburn and Kirkcolm formations establishing that eruption occurred within the main depositional basin and over an area wide enough to span turbidite fan systems derived contemporaneously from contrasting provenances. In this respect the REE chemistry of the associated cherts is interesting in that Owen *et al.* (1999) reported close similarities with recent deposits from continental margin settings and discounted the origin in a deep open ocean, which had been previously assumed and incorporated within the accretionary prism interpretation.

The Bail Hill Group and the allochthonous Tweedale Lavas formed as part of the widespread Caradoc volcanic episode, but

Table 6.1. *Stratigraphy of the Southern Uplands Ordovician successions, with sedimentological and provenance characteristics (adapted from Floyd 2001)*

Unit	Lithology	Bedding in sandstones	Setting	Provenance character	Dominant current directions toward
Crawford Group	bedded chert red mudstone pillow basalt		ocean floor ooze pelagic silt oceanic within-plate		
Moffat Shale Group	black hemipelagite grey shale		ocean floor		
Tappins Group	greywacke sandstone conglomerate pillow basalt	thin-med thick	mid-fan channels on inner fan submarine lava	acid to intermediate plutonic basement, with metabasics, basalt (intermediate to basic), ophiolite, older sedimentary rocks and Barrovian high grade metamorphic terrane	SE
Kirkcolm Formation Barrhill Group	greywacke sandstone conglomerate thick siltstone	thin-med	mid-outer fan sheets channels on mid-fan	Barrovian and blueschist metamorphic terranes including basalts and minor intrusions. Sedimentary cover of limestones/calcareous sandstone	SW
Galdenoch Formation Barrhill Group	greywacke sandstone	medium	inner to mid-fan lobes	Tholeiitic to calc-alkaline island arc founded on continental crust. Barrovian and blueschist metamorphic terranes	NW, SE?
Blackcraig Formation Barrhill Group	greywacke sandstone conglomerate	med-thick	inner to mid-fan channels on inner-fan	metasomatised acidic, intermediate and basic plutonic basement with areas of basalt (intermediate to basic) and older sedimentary rocks, all cut by shear zones	SE
Bail Hill Group	lava		alkaline oceanic within-plate seamount		
Portpatrick Formation Scour Group	greywacke sandstone	med-v thick	inner to mid-fan lobes	Evolved calc-alkaline island arc founded on continental crust. Barrovian metamorphic and blueschist terranes.	NE, N
Glenwhargen Formation Scour Group	greywacke sandstone conglomerate	med-thick	inner to mid-fan lobes, channels on mid fan	acid plutonics, Barrovian metamorphic terrane	SE, E
Shinnel Formation	greywacke sandstone	med-thick	mid-to outer fan sheets and lobes channels overbank on mid-fan, outer fan debris flows	Barrovian metamorphic terrane including basalts and minor intrusions, with cover of older Caradoc limestone	SE
Glenlee Formation	greywacke sandstone thick siltstone	med-thick	mid-to outer fan sheets and lobes outer fan	Calc-alkaline and transitional (to tholeiitic) island arc founded on continental crust. Barrovian metamorphic terrane.	SE, SW

the allochthonous arc-like volcanic rocks from Gabsnout, near Glenluce, at the base of the Portpatrick Formation, are more enigmatic. They could have been derived from a contemporary arc but equally could have been eroded from an exposed 'basement' mass of significantly older age than the Moffat Shales in which they are now enclosed. They are geochemically distinct from the Arenig Raven Gill Formation, subjacent to the Moffat Shales elsewhere, but have some similarities with Arenig arc tholeiites from the Ballantrae Complex.

The Arenig volcanic rocks seem likely to have diverse origins with possible MORB, within-plate/ocean island lavas and perhaps arc-related rocks all represented. Such an assemblage offers no definitive discrimination between the competing interpretations of the terrane. The uniformity of age seen across the Caradoc volcanic rocks, their likely eruption in an extensional environment, and their relationship with the turbidite sequences was thought by Armstrong *et al.* (1996) to 'confound' the accretionary prism model of Leggett *et al.* (1979). However, the contrasting back-arc interpretation of the Ordovician Northern Belt (Morris 1987; Stone *et al.* 1987) suggests a greater subduction influence would be expected than is in fact present. Instead, Armstrong *et al.* (1996) preferred an extensional environment developed within a narrow continental shelf for the volcanicity and turbidite deposition. In support of this model they cited other, sedimentological and stratigraphic evidence (which is discussed below) but alternative interpretations may be possible and the geotectonic argument remains unresolved.

The sedimentary rocks

A formal lithostratigraphy for the Ordovician strata of the Southern Uplands has been proposed by Floyd (2001) (Table 6.1). Most of the sedimentary formations defined either coincide with structural tracts or combine into groups which so coincide. The Raven Gill and Downan Point formations and the Bail Hill Volcanic Group are separated and have been described above. Other volcanic units and some distinctive but localized sedimentary lithologies are defined as members. The biostratigraphical framework has been reviewed by Rushton *et al.* (1996*a,b*).

The Moffat Shale Group forms a distinctive and widespread stratigraphical datum recognized by Lapworth (1878) and Peach & Horne (1899). It was formalized by Floyd (1996) to include only the *gracilis* Biozone and later sequence dominated by black mudstone. Previous usage had included within this group the basal Arenig–Llanvirn basalt-chert-mudstone assemblage (e.g. Stone 1995) but these were separated by Floyd into a new underlying unit, the Crawford Group, comprising the volcanic Raven Gill Formation described above and the Kirkton Formation of chert and mudstone. The Moffat Shale Group is diachronously overlain by the turbiditic greywacke sequences of the Southern Uplands and all of these north of the Orlock Bridge Fault, together with the sparse associated volcanic rocks, were defined by Floyd within a framework of formations and groups aggregated within the Leadhills Supergroup. This also includes the Tappins Group, the turbidite-dominated sequence between the Stinchar Valley and Glen App faults which is itself believed to be largely of *gracilis* age and has no underlying Moffat Shale, and a greywacke interval within the Ordovician part of the Moffat Shale Group further south at Ettrickbridge.

Southwards, the Moffat Shale Group extends to progressively higher Llandovery stratigraphical levels beneath the Gala Group tracts. The youngest Moffat Shale seen, within the *turriculatus* (or possibly *crispus*) Biozone, underlies the southernmost two Gala Group tracts and a similar level appears to underlie the most northerly parts of the Hawick Group. Further south there is no sign of Moffat Shale beneath the younger, late Llandovery to early Wenlock parts of the Hawick Group or beneath the even younger, but still Wenlock, Riccarton Group. It is unclear whether this means that the thrust front had advanced beyond the southern limit of Moffat Shale deposition or whether the basal décollement rose into the turbidite sequence. In either case it introduces uncertainty as to the maximum age of the southern turbidite tracts. The biostratigraphical control of the late Llandovery and Wenlock turbidite sequences has been reviewed by White *et al.* (1991).

Crawford Group. The oldest strata, the Arenig basalt lavas of the Raven Gill Formation, are succeeded by red and grey chert interbedded with red and green siliceous mudstone containing chert nodules. These cherts and mudstones form the Kirkton Formation. They crop out in the Abington area on the north side of the Leadhills Fault where, despite structural complication, they appear to intervene between the Arenig lavas of the Raven Gill Formation and the basal, Caradoc black mudstone of the Moffat Shale Group. Armstrong *et al.* (1996) determined an age equivalent to the *anserinus* conodont Biozone spanning the latest Llanvirn to the earliest Caradoc. The Crawford Group is only seen in fragmentary and isolated outcrops in which the preserved strata seem unlikely to exceed 200 m in thickness.

Moffat Shale Group. The Moffat Shale Group is a condensed sequence about 100 m thick dominated by graptolitic, carbonaceous, black shale (locally pyritous) and siliceous mudstone. It ranges in age from a base within the Ordovician *gracilis* Biozone upwards into the Silurian, Late Llandovery *turriculatus* and/or *crispus* Biozone. The fauna is dominated by graptolites, on which the biostratigraphy is based, but inarticulate brachiopods also occur sporadically and blind, dalmanatid trilobites have been recovered from a horizon just below the top of the Ordovician (Lésperance 1988). It has been proposed by Batchelor & Weir (1988) that repeated, local extinctions of the graptolite fauna were caused by intermittent falls of volcanic ash, now preserved in the sequence as metabentonites. Conversely, Rigby & Davis (2001) have argued that the input of 'nutritional' volcanic ash sparked increased planktonic activity after the ashfall. The overall sedimentological variation across the Ordovician–Silurian boundary has been interpreted by Armstrong & Coe (1997) in terms of the Late Ordovician glaciation. Stages recognized included pre-glacial cooling of the deep ocean in the Early Ashgill, and initiation of intense thermohaline circulation from the end of the Ashgill into the Early Llandovery.

A complete succession through the Moffat Shale Group is nowhere preserved with the most extensive uninterrupted sequence, the type section at Dob's Linn, Moffatdale (Webb *et al.* 1993), ranging upwards from the '*peltifer*' Biozone to the *halli* Biozone. Thin interbedded chert and metabentonite layers occur throughout. The metabentonites are produced by the diagenesis of silicic vitric volcanic ash and, apart from the discrete horizons, many of the black shales also contain a significant proportion of dispersed ash (Merriman & Roberts 1990). The Moffat Shale Group has been widely described as of pelagic, open-ocean origin (e.g. Leggett 1987) although the large quantities of interbedded ash, the common presence of detrital mica from a terrigenous source (Merriman & Roberts 1990) and the rare interbedded sandstone horizons (Rushton & Stone 1991) cast some doubt on this interpretation. The thickest of the sandstone intercalations occurs at Ettrickbridge where about 50 m of quartzose greywackes intervene between *anceps* Biozone and possible Early Llandovery Moffat Shales (Peach & Horne 1899; Rushton & Stone 1991). This unit has been formally defined as the Ettrickbridge Formation by Floyd (1996) and assigned to the Leadhills Supergroup (see below).

Stratigraphically the Moffat Shale Group can be subdivided into three lithologically distinct shale units (Lapworth 1878; Peach & Horne 1899) now accorded formational status. At the base of the Group the lowest shale division (Glenkiln Shale Formation) includes two units of black, cherty graptolitic mudstone, referred respectively to the Caradoc *gracilis* and '*peltifer*' biozones, separated and succeeded by grey mudstone and siltstone. The middle shale division (Hartfell Shale Formation) consists, in its lower part, mainly of black graptolitic shale with sporadic chert interbeds, whereas the upper part consists of grey 'barren' mudstones with a few thin black shale horizons. The Hartfell Shale ranges up from the Caradoc *wilsoni* Biozone to the Ashgill *anceps* Biozone, above which a very thin horizon is characterized by *Climacograptus? extraordinarius* (Williams 1983; Clarkson & Taylor 1993). The upper shale unit (Birkhill Shale Formation) consists of black shale or pale grey shale with black graptolitic beds and abundant metabentonite horizons. It continues upwards from the Ashgill *persculptus* Biozone into the Llandovery (Early Silurian) *halli* Biozone. It should be stressed that the complete Moffat Shale Group succession is rarely preserved and may indeed only have existed as a single entity very locally. Its outcrop is always associated with major strike faults at the base of successive structural tracts where it is commonly seen as disrupted tectonic lenses.

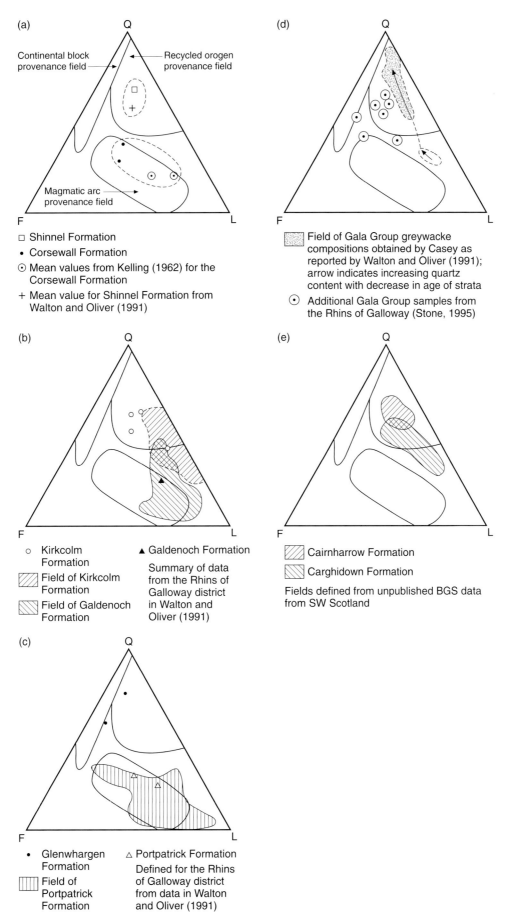

Fig. 6.13. Compositional range of Southern Upland greywacke turbidites. Q, quartz; F, feldspars; L, lithics. Provenance fields after Dickinson & Suczek (1979). (Adapted from Stone 1995.)

Table 6.2. *Stratigraphy of the Southern Uplands Silurian successions, with sedimentological and provenance characteristics (adapted from Floyd 2000)*

Unit Local name	Lithology	Bedding in sandstones	Setting	Provenance character	Dominant current directions towards
Gala 1 Kilfillan Fm	greywacke sandstone laminated siltstone sedimentary breccia	med-v thick	inner to mid-fan channelized slump	Acidic to intermediate plutonics with sedimentary cover. Barrovian metamorphic terrane	SW
Gala 2 Mindork Fm	greywacke sandstone laminated siltstone	med-v thick	inner to mid-fan channelized	Acidic plutonics. Calc-alkaline and transitional (to tholeiitic) island are founded on continental crust. Barrovian metamorphic terrane	SW
Gala 3 Money Head Fm	greywacke sandstone	thick-v thick	inner to mid-fan channel to channel margin	Acidic plutonics and felsic minor intrusions, quartzite, vein quartz, minor spilite. Older sedimentary rocks. Barrovian metamorphic terrane	SW to W
Gala 4 Float Bay Fm Sinniness Fm	greywacke sandstone silty mudstone	med-v thick	mid-fan sheets and lobes interlobe deposits	Acidic plutonics and felsic minor intrusions, quartzite, vein quartz, minor spilite. Older sedimentary rocks. Barrovian metamorphic terrane	S to W
Gala 5 Stinking Bight Beds Garheugh Fm	greywacke sandstone laminated siltstone conglomerate	thin-v thick	mid-fan sheet flows; overbank to outer fan; channel-fill	Acidic plutonics and felsic minor intrusions, quartzite, vein quartz, minor spilite. Older sedimentary rocks. Barrovian metamorphic terrane	SE to SW
Gala 6 Grennan Point Fm	greywacke sandstone	thin-thick	mid-fan sheet flows with minor channels	Acidic plutonics and felsic minor intrusions, quartzite, vein quartz, minor spilite. Older sedimentary rocks. Barrovian metamorphic terrane	SW to W
Gala 7 Mull of Logan Fm Corwall Fm	greywacke sandstone conglomerate intraclast breccia	thin-med	mid-fan lobes and channels; slump deposits	Acidic plutonics and felsic minor intrusions, quartzite, vein quartz, minor spilite. Older sedimentary rocks. Barrovian metamorphic terrane	SW to W
Gala 8 Port Logan Fm	greywacke sandstone	thin-med	mid- to outer fan, channelized	Acidic plutonics and felsic minor intrusions, quartzite, vein quartz, minor spilite. Older sedimentary rocks. Barrovian metamorphic terrane	SW
Hawick Group Cairnharrow Fm	calcareous greywacke sandstone	med	mid- to outer fan	Acidic plutonics and felsic minor intrusions, quartzite, vein quartz, minor spilite. Older sedimentary rocks. Carbonate sand/mud	NW
Hawick Group Kirkmaiden Fm	calcareous greywacke sandstone	thin-med	mid- to outer fan	Acidic plutonics and felsic minor intrusions, quartzite, vein quartz, minor spilite. Older sedimentary rocks. Carbonate sand/mud	SW to NW
Hawick Group Carghidown Fm	calcareous greywacke sandstone red mudstones syn-sedimentary soft sediment disrupted zones	thin-med	channelized mid- to outer fan with slump deposits	Acidic plutonics and felsic minor intrusions, quartzite, vein quartz, minor spilite. Older sedimentary rocks. Carbonate sand/mud	SW to NW
Hawick Group Ross Fm	calcareous greywacke sandstone syn-sedimentary soft sediment disrupted zones laminated carbonaceous siltstone (hemipelagite)	thin-med	sheet fan with channel/levee complexes and slump deposits	Acidic plutonics and felsic minor intrusions, quartzite, vein quartz, minor spilite. Older sedimentary rocks. Carbonate sand/mud	SW
Riccarton Group Raeberry Castle Fm	calcareous greywacke sandstone; conglomerate silty mudstone hemipelagite	thin-med	depositional lobe, channel and overbank deposits; slump deposits; basin plain (hemipelagite)	Older sedimentary rocks. Intermediate minor intrusions. Carbonate sand/mud	NE
Coldingham Fm	Calcareous greywacke sandstone, shale, yellow-weathering calcareous siltstone	thin	upper slope/trench wall deposits	Older sedimentary rocks. Intermediate minor intrusions. Carbonate sand/mud	?
Linkim Fm	Red-brown calcareous greywacke sandstone and siltstone	thin-med	upper slope/trench wall deposits	Older sedimentary rocks. Intermediate minor intrusions. Carbonate sand/mud	?

The Leadhills Supergroup: a Caradoc to Ashgill turbidite succession. Turbidite sandstones form the bulk of the succession but significant differences in their petrography have allowed the fully lithostratigraphical scheme to be erected (Fig. 6.13). Differences in sedimentological characteristics such as bed thickness, grain-size range and variation in development of internal Bouma sequences and external sedimentary structures, occur both within and between formations but are never sufficiently distinctive or consistent to be of stratigraphical value. Typically, the sequences are well bedded on a scale of centimetres to several metres. Grading is widespread, ripple cross-lamination is locally common, and external sedimentary structures at the bases of many beds include flute casts, groove casts and load structures, the latter producing flames in cross-section. A comprehensive lithofacies analysis by Kelling *et al.* (1987) recognized depositional environments associated with prograding submarine fans; strata were variously assigned to channel fills, proximal to distal depositional lobes, sheet flows and interchannel sectors. Typical sedimentary sections are illustrated by Stone (1995). The sedimentological and provenance characteristics are summarized in Table 6.2.

The principal differences between the Ordovician greywacke formations lie in their compositions, with contrasting clast contents imparting different physical properties to the rocks. Magnetic susceptibility has proved particularly significant in that respect, and has been used as one method of tracking the boundary between adjacent formations (Floyd & Trench 1989; Floyd & Kimbell 1995). In the following description of the individual stratigraphical units the tract sequence is followed from NW to SE in order of decreasing age.

Tappins Group. This assemblage lies between the Stinchar Valley and Glen App–Carcow faults (Fig. 6.8). At its northern margin it includes the Downan Point Lava Formation described above. Uniquely amongst the turbidite units of the Leadhills Supergroup, the constituent sedimentary formations of the Tappins Group do not overlie the Moffat Shale Group. Instead, limited graptolite and conodont evidence suggests an age range within the *gracilis* to '*peltifer*' biozones, chronologically equivalent to the lowest part of the Moffat Shales. Tappins Group greywackes are relatively immature with a high proportion of mafic, ophiolitic detritus and significant detrital magnetite. The latter feature is particularly apparent in the most northerly of the sedimentary tectonostratigraphic tracts where the Traboyack Formation (*c.* 1000 m of mainly red and purple mudstone and sandstone) has a distinctive magnetic signature (Floyd & Kimbell 1995).

South of the Downan Point Lava Formation in the coastal section is the Currarie Formation olistostrome (90–300 m) (Ogawa 1998), a complex association of red and green mudstone and chert with interbedded masses of pillow lava and lava breccia. Inland, the Traboyack Formation is tectonostratigraphically succeeded southwards by the Dalreoch Formation (*c.* 1000 m), which consists largely of grey-green turbiditic sandstones. Red mudstones and lavas are poorly exposed along the southern margin of its outcrop and may possibly correlate with the Currarie Formation.

Towards the southwest, the Dalreoch Formation is faulted against coarse, boulder conglomerates which interdigitate with thin-bedded flaggy greywackes to form the Corsewall Formation (*c.* 1700 m). Three main conglomeratic members are recognized; from northeast to southwest these are the Glen App, Finnarts and Corsewall Point conglomerates. The sedimentology of the background greywacke sequence was interpreted by Kelling *et al.* (1987) to indicate turbidite fan deposition in a basin-plain environment (Fig. 6.10). The greywackes are immature, with less than 20% detrital quartz and a high

Fig. 6.14. Corsewall Point Conglomerate Member of the Corsewall Formation. Rounded coarse-grained granite boulders at centre and right, sub-rounded fine-grained spilite at left, all in a coarse, sandy matrix. Corsewall Point, Well Isle, NW 9825 7276. BGS photograph.

proportion of lithic fragments, most commonly acid igneous lithologies ranging from granodiorite to felsite; abundant spilitic grains, some andesite clasts, various schistose grains (some of which contain glaucophane) and rare fragments of serpentinite (Kelling 1961, 1962). The channel-fill conglomerates appear abruptly in the upper part of the formation and in places are spectacularly coarse with boulders up to 1.5 m in diameter; they may be clast- or matrix-supported and many of the boulders are well rounded. The conglomerates form stacked, lenticular bodies and have been interpreted by Kelling *et al.* (1987) as proximal or inner fan sediments deposited in a laterally migrating channel with a minimum width of 2–3 km. A wide range of lithologies is present in the boulder suite (Fig. 6.14) including various granitic and granodioritic types (some with an apparently tectonic foliation), felsite, spilite, greywacke, chert and polymict conglomerate (Kelling 1961, 1962). The provenance of the conglomerates is a contentious issue and is discussed later in this chapter as part of the broader, regional assessment. Palaeocurrent evidence shows that the conglomerates were derived from the NW, whereas data from the greywacke beds is equivocal showing current flow from the northeast and southwest.

In the northeastern part of the Southern Uplands terrane the Marchburn Formation (*c.* 1300 m) is the lateral equivalent of the Corsewall Formation. The Marchburn Formation lies between the Southern Upland and Carcow faults and is structurally and geographically removed from the rest of the Tappins Group. Dark grey, thinly bedded greywackes and laminated siltstones dominate the sequence but are interbedded with sporadic beds of shale and red chert; a microconglomerate, the 'Haggis Rock', is a distinctive component (Ritchie & Eckford 1936) and interbedded basalt lavas form the Noblehouse Lava Member (Floyd 1982). The clast assemblage is similar to that of the Corsewall Formation with an additional, significant proportion of clinopyroxene and hornblende grains (Floyd 1982). A remarkably high magnetic susceptibility suggests the presence of abundant detrital magnetite (Floyd & Trench 1989). Palaeocurrent flow from the NW to NE quadrants is shown by Leggett (1980, Fig. 2) in his Coulter/Noblehouse tract.

Barrhill Group. Southwards from the Tappins Group outcrop as far as the Leadhills–Killantringan fault line (Fig. 6.8). The Barrhill Group comprises three turbidite formations of differing character. The Kirkcolm Formation (3000 m) is dominant and consists of quartzo-feldspathic greywacke and siltstone (Plate 11). Quartz grains range up to about 45% with abundant detrital feldspar (Floyd 1982; Evans *et al.* 1991; Stone 1995);

Fig. 6.15. Kirkcolm Formation, looking towards the north at the slightly overturned base of a greywacke turbidite bed with an array of elongate flute casts. Correction for dip gives current flow from the southeast. Finnarts Bay, Loch Ryan, NX 0520 7204. BGS photograph.

accessory lithic fragments include spilite, quartzite and schist whilst garnet is an important accessory mineral (Hutchison & Oliver 1998). The majority of the formation lies within the *gracilis* and '*peltifer*' biozones and Moffat Shale Group strata of *gracilis* age underlies the turbidite sequence. However, along the southern margin of the outcrop, between the Glaik and Killantringan/Leadhills faults, Kirkcolm-type greywackes overlie Moffat Shale ranging up to the *clingani* Biozone (Floyd 1982; Stone 1995). Both parts consist of pale grey, turbidite greywacke beds generally ranging in thickness from a few centimetres to 1.5 m, but with the sporadic thicker bed (Fig. 6.15). Alternating with the greywacke-dominated sequences are thicknesses from a few centimetres to about 20 m of very thinly bedded, fine-grained greywacke and laminated siltstone. Palaeocurrent data (Fig. 6.16) show a very variable pattern with much flow towards the south and southwest quadrant but with the reverse situation, current flow towards the north and northeast, important locally (Kelling 1962; Leggett 1980; Stone 1995).

Very different greywackes, rich in detrital andesitic material, interfinger and in places alternate bed by bed with the older, mainly *gracilis*, part of the Kirkcolm Formation. The Galdenoch Formation (*c.* 500 m) occurs in three main members where dark grey greywacke beds range up to 2 m in thickness. The characteristic andesitic detrital component consists of both clinopyroxene and hornblende mineral grains and lithoclasts of pyroxene and/or hornblende andesite. This may exceed 25% whereas the quartz content is less than 20% (Evans *et al.* 1991). Mineral chemistry suggests a tholeiitic source (Styles *et al.* 1989, 1995) and sparse palaeocurrent data show opposed directions; current flow from the south in the northern part of the outcrop but from the north in the southern part (Stone *et al.* 1987; Floyd 1996,1999). The Blackcraig Formation (*c.* 1500 m) has a restricted, lenticular outcrop centred in the Afton Water area. At the southern margin of the outcrop it conformably overlies Kirkcolm Formation strata but its northern margin is faulted. It consists of coarse boulder conglomerate and massive, coarse-grained sandstone with a greenish colour imparted by the high concentration of epidote, clino-

pyroxene and hornblende (Floyd 1982); quartz does not exceed 33%. The boulders in the conglomerates are generally well rounded and range up to 1.5 m in diameter. Acid igneous rocks, including granite, granodiorite and felsite, form the largest proportion of the clast population with some gabbro, spilite and dolerite also present; vein quartz, quartzite, sandstone, shale and chert clasts are also common (Floyd 1982). Sediment transport direction was towards the southeast (Holroyd 1978).

Scaur Group. Between the Killantringan/Leadhills and Morroch Bay/Fardingmullach faults two starkly contrasting turbidite greywacke formations again interfinger. They jointly comprise the Scaur Group (Floyd 1996). The dominant Portpatrick Formation (*c.* 2000 m) is composed of medium to thick bedded, dark bluish-grey sandstone with sporadic laminated siltstone intervals up to about 1 m thick. Andesitic detritus is very abundant, up to 25%, and includes fresh clinopyroxene and hornblende grains. The andesitic component is broadly sub-alkaline to calc-alkaline in character (Styles *et al.* 1989, 1995). Palaeocurrent data (Fig. 6.16) show consistent current flow from the southwest quadrant (Kelling *et al.* 1987; Stone 1995).

Interbedded with the Portpatrick Formation are markedly dissimilar, pale grey quartz-arenite and quartz-greywacke sequences included together as the Glenwhargen Formation (up to 500 m). The thickest and most continuous development is seen to the north of Newton Stewart, whence the formation thins to the northwest and southeast. Fine-grained quartz arenite is the dominant lithology but, in the thickest sequence, coarse quartzose sandstones form thick beds alternating with quartz-pebble conglomerates. Overall, the quartz content of the Glenwhargen Formation approaches 70%; accessory detrital components include feldspar, quartzite, chert, mica schist and rare spilite (Evans *et al.* 1991; Stone 1995).

On the west coast of the Rhins of Galloway the basal Portpatrick Formation greywackes are interbedded with Moffat Shales of the *clingani* Biozone at Morroch Bay, whilst more than 1000 m higher in the succession, at Killantringan Bay, laminated siltstones within the Portpatrick Formation contain a *linearis* Biozone fauna (Stone 1995). However, the base of the sequence is diachronous both along strike and southwards with records of the basal greywackes overlying *linearis* Biozone Moffat Shales (Stone 1995; Rushton *et al.* 1996*a, b*).

Shinnel and Glenlee formations. In the Floyd (1996) lithostratigraphic scheme these two formations were not included in a formal group. They are the youngest units within the Leadhills Supergroup and form the southernmost part of its outcrop. The Shinnel Formation has the most extensive outcrop. It lies to the south of the Morroch Bay/Fardingmullach faults and to the north of the Orlock Bridge Fault, except in the central Southern Uplands where the Glenlee Formation intervenes. In that area the two formations are separated by the Glen Fumart Fault.

The Shinnel Formation (*c.* 2000 m) consists dominantly of quartzose greywackes, coarsening into pebble conglomerate locally, but throughout the succession thick intervals of grey laminated siltstone (the Lowther Shales) are characteristic. The greywackes are generally thinly bedded but sporadic thicker beds range up to 1.5 m. The detrital quartz content is about 55% (Floyd 1982) with some feldspar grains and accessory lithoclasts of granodiorite, granophyre, rhyolite and spilite. Interbedded with the greywackes and siltstones are rare, massive conglomeratic units which may be as much as 300 m thick and contain clasts up to 30 cm in diameter. Some conglomeratic beds are monomict, consisting almost exclusively of intrabasinal greywacke, siltstone and shale; others have a more

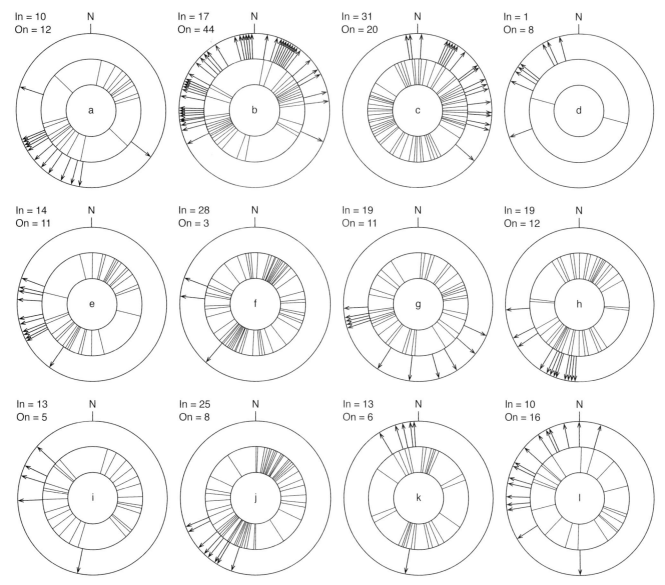

Fig. 6.16. Palaeocurrent data from the Southern Uplands. Rhins of Galloway greywacke/turbidites. Inner circle (In) groove casts; outer circle (On) flute casts. Tectonostratigraphic units: (**a**) to (**d**), Leadhills Group; (**e**) to (**j**), Gala Group; (**k**) to (**l**), Hawick Group. (**a**), Kirkcolm Formation south of Galdenoch on the Rhins of Galloway; (**b**), Kirkcolm Formation north of Galdenoch on the Rhins and east of Loch Ryan; (**c**), Portpatrick Formation, main part of outcrop; (**d**), Portpatrick Formation, Port of Spittal Bay; (**e**) to (**j**), Gala 3 to 8 inclusive; (**k**), Cainharrow Formation; (**l**), Carghidown Formation. For locations, see Figure 6.19. (Adapted from Stone 1995.)

variable composition with clasts of acid igneous lithologies in the majority. The conglomerates have a derivation broadly from the northeast but palaeocurrent evidence from the greywacke beds is much more variable (Evans *et al.* 1991; Stone 1995). The Tweedale Member has been defined by Floyd (1996) to include the likely olistostrome of limestone and lava discussed previously. An *anceps* Biozone fauna has been recorded from the formation (Floyd 1987; Rushton 1993), which overlies Moffat Shale of the *linearis* Biozone.

The Glenlee Formation (*c.* 2000 m) crops out between the Glen Fumart and Orlock Bridge faults in the central Southern Uplands. Greywackes alternate with laminated siltstone that may form continuous successions up to several hundred metres thick. The greywackes are variably quartzose and andesitic, with the latter containing both andesite and dacite litho-clasts and detrital grains of fresh clinopyroxene and hornblende. The mineral chemistry shows a sub-alkaline composition (Styles *et al.* 1995). Graptolitic bands within the siltstone units indicate the highest part of the *anceps* and the succeeding *persculp-*

tus biozones (Floyd & Rushton 1993; Floyd 1996). Sparse palaeocurrent data show that the quartzose beds were derived from the north.

The Gala Group: a Llandovery turbidite succession. The sedimentological and provenance characteristics of the Silurian succession in the Southern Uplands are summarized in Table 6.2. The Gala Group, jointly with the Hawick Group, comprises the Central Belt of the Southern Uplands (Peach & Horne 1899). The Gala Group extends southwards from the Orlock Bridge Fault in a series of tectonostratigraphic tracts in which a greywacke sequence overlies sequentially higher Llandovery levels of the Moffat Shales (Fig. 6.9). Although informal lithostratigraphical names have been applied to several geographically separate parts of the group, a comprehensive formal scheme has not been adopted since there is little systematic sedimentological or compositional difference between most tracts and their immediately adjacent neighbours. Instead, a tectonostratigraphic tract numbering scheme has been generally adopted (e.g. Stone 1995) wherein Gala 1 is the presumed oldest tract at the northern margin of the outcrop, adjacent to the Orlock Bridge Fault, and Gala 8 is the youngest tract at the southern margin of the outcrop, structurally juxtaposed against the Hawick Group. Few of the tectonostratigraphic tracts are continuous across the full strike length of the terrane. In the southwest, on the west coast of the Rhins of Galloway, Gala 3 is the northernmost tract preserved but is not seen elsewhere (Stone 1995). Further northeast, tracts 2 and 1 successively appear immediately south of the Orlock Bridge Fault but Gala 1 is subsequently lost so that in the Peebles area Gala 2 is the most northerly tract seen. At the southern margin of the group a similar effect is seen with an additional unit appearing east of Moffat and thence broadening towards the northeast by multiple imbrication. This is the Buckholm Formation of Kassi & Weir (1993), originally the Garnetiferous Group of Walton (1955).

In the central and western parts of the Southern Uplands, graptolites recovered from shale laminae within the Gala Group greywacke sequences are either of the same biozone, or one biozone younger than the youngest faunas seen in the underlying Moffat Shale Group. A regional exception to this rule is the Gala 7 succession in the northeast of the terrane where the succession in several imbricate repetitions spans up to five graptolite biozones (Rushton *et al.* 1996*a, b*) ranging as high as the *crenulata* Biozone. Gala 7 thus overlaps with the Gala 8 tract of the southwest part of the terrane and with the Buckholm Formation, which is itself repeated in several tectonic imbricates. A range of turbidite lithofacies styles are present but variations in lithological proportions, bed thickness and overall sedimentological characteristics are as apparent within tracts as they are between tracts. A comprehensive lithofacies analysis by Kelling *et al.* (1987) established a variety of fan-type depositional systems and the likely existence of several structurally separated sub-basins (cf. Fig. 6.10). Locally, a well-developed ichnofauna (Benton 1982; Benton & Trewin 1980) forms at least five distinct assemblages that are believed to reflect the differences in the nature and frequency of the turbidite flows, and the oxygen content of the sea-bottom sediment.

In compositional terms there is an overall southward decline of the detrital andesitic component into the younger rocks and a trend towards increasing maturity. The Gala 2 greywackes, containing up to 15% andesitic detritus, are sufficiently distinctive (Fig. 6.13) to warrant lithostratigraphical definition as the Mindork Formation (e.g. Kassi & Weir 1993; Barnes in press; cf. the Pyroxenous Group of Walton 1955). An *acuminatus* Biozone graptolite fauna is present locally (Rushton *et al.* 1996*a, b*) but no underlying Moffat Shale Group stratum is anywhere preserved to provide a maximum age. The Formation is present across almost the complete strike length of the Southern Uplands but is structurally eliminated in the extreme west, on the Rhins of Galloway, against the Orlock Bridge Fault (Stone 1995). The andesitic material is calc-alkaline in character (Styles *et al.* 1995). Detrital glaucophane has been analysed (Kassi & Wier 1993), indicating that a high-pressure–low-temperature metamorphic terrane was exposed nearby. Palaeocurrent evidence is sparse and variable but generally suggests a NE or SW axial flow (e.g. Kassi & Weir 1993).

The quartzose Gala Group units show a range of lithofacies styles with thinly to thickly bedded greywackes alternating with up to 2 m thicknesses of laminated siltstone. Sporadic black shale laminae and massive sandstone beds up to about 3 m thick also occur. In the Gala 7 tract there is an intraformational slump conglomerate about 550 m thick with exceptionally large clasts up to 10 m across (McCurry 1990, Stone 1995). This inner trench slope intraformational slump conglomerate (Duniehinnie Member) has been recognized for 20 km along strike eastwards from the Rhins of Galloway.

Quartz content ranges up to about 55% in some examples from Gala 8 but the overall trend of increasing quartz content into the younger strata reported from the eastern Southern Uplands by Casey (cited in Walton & Oliver 1991) is less apparent in the Rhins of Galloway (Stone 1995) (Fig. 6.13). Detrital plagioclase and K-feldspar each contribute about 10–15% to the detrital assemblage in the Gala 1 to Gala 6 greywackes but K-feldspar is a less significant component in Gala 7 or Gala 8, where plagioclase may contribute up to 20%. The decrease in K-feldspar is balanced by an increase in detrital muscovite from minor accessory levels to form several per cent of the detrital content in Gala 5 and 6, 5–10% in Gala 7 and up to 15% in some Gala 8 samples (Stone 1995). Strained quartz, quartzite and schist grains seem to show a southward increase matching muscovite but at much lower levels. Accessory acid plutonic and spilitic grains occur throughout the group. Detrital garnet grains are a characteristic feature of the Gala Group in general and the Buckholm Formation in particular (Walton 1955; Kassi & Weir 1993; Oliver 2001).

Palaeocurrent data are abundant. Bottom structures, flute and groove casts, show a dominant axial flow towards the west and southwest across the whole terrane (Fig. 6.16, cf. Greig 1988; Kelling *et al.* 1987; Kassi & Weir 1993; Stone 1995). Ripple cross-lamination from the upper parts of the turbidite beds commonly gives an orthogonal flow direction to that obtained from bottom structures, suggesting reworking by transverse currents.

Hawick Group: a Llandovery–Wenlock turbidite succession. The Hawick Group is separated from the Gala Group by major strike faults, the Laurieston Fault in the west and the Ettrick Valley Fault in the east. However, in the Wigtown promontory a lateral transition between the two groups has been recognized (British Geological Survey 1992*b*), implying that there was physical overlap in the deposition of the Hawick and Gala groups and not simply contemporaneous deposition in two discrete basins. This situation was presaged by Webb *et al.* (1993, fig. 6.10) using evidence from Moffatdale.

Lithologically the Hawick Group is characterized by uniform sequences of metre- to centimetre-bedded, medium- to fine-grained, greenish grey greywacke typically with replacive diagenetic calcite. These thinner greywacke sequences alternate with sporadic thick and massive greywacke beds and units of laminated siltstone containing thin interbeds of both fine-grained greywacke and mudstone. The mudstone-dominated units may show intense soft sediment deformation and have acted as the focus for subsequent faulting (Knipe & Needham 1986; Kemp 1987; Knipe *et al.* 1988). Trace fossils are relatively abundant in the laminated siltstone. Overall, all of the Hawick Group originated through deposition in a mid-fan environment but there is sufficient facies and lithological variation to allow formal lithostratigraphical division into four formations. These crop out as tectonostratigraphic tracts continuing the regional pattern for the Southern Uplands terrane. From north to south, the lithostratigraphical units are the Cairnharrow, Kirkmaiden, Carghidown (characterized by interbeds of red mudstone and detrital grains of reddened mica) and Ross formations.

The Ross Formation is of Wenlock age and was traditionally included within the Southern Belt (Peach & Horne 1899) of the terrane and so assigned to the Riccarton Group (described below), most recently by Kemp (1986, 1987). However, Barnes *et al.* (1989) cited lithological, sedimentological and structural grounds for transfer of the Ross Formation to the Hawick Group and this has been adopted subsequently in some cases (e.g. White *et al.* 1991; Lintern & Floyd 2000). In this account the Ross Formation is included within the Hawick Group. It is characterized by interbeds of dark grey, laminated siltstones, each consisting of a silt-clay couplet and interpreted as hemipelagite (Kemp 1986). The Ross Formation is restricted in outcrop to the Solway Firth coast and scattered inliers further NE around Langholm. There is an important lateral variation between these two areas with many more thick and coarser grained sandstone beds appearing in the Langholm succession. Kemp (1987) has calculated a commensurate thickness variation for the formation of 500 to 2000 m. There is also a difference in the predominant palaeocurrent pattern with flow towards the southeast in the Langholm area and towards the southwest on the Solway coast. Kemp combined this information into a depositional model wherein high density, sand-rich turbidites were introduced into the Langholm area from the northwest and were then diverted axially along the depositional basin so that their more distal deposits were introduced into the coastal section from the northeast.

The distinctness of the Hawick Group was recognized early in the geological investigation of the Southern Uplands. Lapworth & Wilson (1871) differentiated the 'Hawick Rocks' as the oldest, possibly Cambrian, part of the Southern Uplands succession and the general paucity of biostratigraphical control that permitted this interpretation continued until the first graptolite fauna was reported by Rust (1965). The history of Hawick Group chronostratigraphy, which during the past century has ranged across the entire Silurian, has been reviewed by White et al. (1991). Currently, the best available evidence suggests a range from the Llandovery turriculatus Biozone in the Cairnharrow Formation to the Wenlock riccartonensis Biozone in the Ross Formation.

Compositionally, the greywackes from each of the four formations of the Hawick Group are very similar (Fig. 6.13). The constituent detrital mineral grains are predominantly of quartz, which ranges from 30% to over 50%, feldspar, which commonly forms about 10% with plagioclase dominant over K-feldspar, and mica (mainly muscovite), which rises to 15% in some fine-grained greywackes. Accessory minerals include tourmaline, zircon and garnet but the latter becomes rare to non-existent in the youngest Hawick rocks (Oliver 2001). Lithic clasts generally make up about 15% but may exceptionally reach 50% in some of the coarse-grained sandstones; lithologies represented include granitic types, highly weathered basic and acid volcanic rocks, quartzite, sandstone and siltstone. A particular feature is the presence of detrital 'red mica' that, although only present in accessory amounts, is clearly visible to the eye as coarse flakes lying parallel to bedding. The red colour is caused by a coating of haematite and since there is no sign of haematization of the matrix surrounding these grains it seems that they were oxidized in the source area prior to deposition. Palaeocurrent indications from bottom structures show axial flow towards both the northeast and southwest with transverse flow towards the northwest (Barnes 1989; Stone 1995; Lintern & Floyd 2000) and, in the Langholm area, towards the southeast (Kemp 1987).

The characteristic high carbonate content in the matrix of the Hawick Group greywackes derives largely from recrystallized grains. Some grains are still recognizably bioclastic and Kemp & White (1985) concluded that they were derived from reefs in a shallow marine environment. The proportion of carbonate present is particularly variable in the Cairnharrow Formation and parts of the Kirkmaiden Formation where it may be low in some beds within an overall carbonate-rich sequence. This alternation is compatible with the proposed lithological transition between the Gala and Hawick groups.

The Wenlock turbidite successions, including the Riccarton Group. The Southern Belt of the Southern Uplands as origin-

ally applied by Peach & Horne (1899) included all of the known Wenlock strata. The Ross Formation described above was part of this and accordingly was subsequently incorporated in the Riccarton Group. As discussed previously, the current stratigraphical status of the Ross Formation is contentious but the remaining formation of the Riccarton Group, the Raeberry Castle Formation, and along-strike equivalents in the Langholm area are distinctive. Two minor stratigraphical components from the extreme east of the terrane, the Coldingham and Linkim formations, are also thought to be Wenlock in age.

The Raeberry Castle Formation has a restricted outcrop along the southern, Solway Firth coast of the Southern Uplands between Kirkcudbright Bay and Rough Firth. It has a likely equivalent in the Caddroun Burn Beds (Warren 1964) of the Langholm–Hawick area where Wenlock strata are poorly exposed in a number of small inliers (cf. Lumsden et al. 1967). It is also likely to correlate with strata forming inliers in the Cheviot area, for example on Greyhound Law (Barron 1989). Kemp (1986, 1987) recognized three tectonostratigraphic units in the Raeberry Castle Formation, each internally coherent and younging to the north but following the regional pattern and becoming biostratigraphically younger towards the south (Fig. 6.9). Graptolite faunas allow close stratigraphical control between the riccartonensis and lundgreni biozones (Kemp & White 1985). Each of the three tracts comprises between about 500 and 700 m of interbedded turbidite and hemipelagite strata with sporadic channel sandstone and slumped beds. Rare bioclasts with bryozoa, brachiopods and corals have been found in channel bodies (Kemp & White 1985). At Gypsy Point, one slump sheet is particularly impressive, being about 30 m thick, internally chaotic, and overlain by a bed carrying large and well-preserved sand volcanoes. The latter were originally recognized by Lovell (1974) as arising from dewatering of the slump sheet. Palaeocurrent indicators show axial flow to have been dominant, mainly towards the northeast but sporadically towards the southwest, with some transverse input from the northwest. Kemp (1987) interpreted the formation in terms of meandering and laterally-migrating, channel-levée complexes on a submarine fan together with fan fringe and channel mouth deposits. The quartzo-feldspathic grain assemblage contains much sedimentary and felsic igneous material. Detrital garnet is absent indicating that metamorphic sources had been cut off (Oliver 2001).

The Coldingham and Linkim formations crop out in the extreme east of the Southern Uplands, on the North Sea coast between St Abbs and Eyemouth; these two formations form a small inlier surrounded by Devonian volcanic rocks (Fig. 6.8). Although still composed of turbiditic strata they have unique characteristics that set them apart from the rest of the terrane. The Coldingham Formation (Greig 1988) forms the northern part of the inlier. It is a sequence of sandstone and siltstone, thinly bedded in the range 10 to 25 cm and very rarely up to 1 m. The detrital grains in the sandstone are largely quartzose with only an accessory accompaniment of feldspar, muscovite and lithic fragments. A high proportion of carbonate is common in the matrix and the rocks have a characteristic yellow, ochreous weathering and are intensely veined by both quartz and carbonate. The strata have been pervasively and chaotically deformed by slumping (Casey 1983). The slump folds were at one time thought to be tectonic and of such greater complexity than seen elsewhere in the terrane that a Cambrian or earlier age was considered for the strata (Shiells & Dearman 1963, 1966). There is no biostratigraphical control on the age of the formation but the high matrix carbonate invites comparison with the Hawick Group, of Llandovery age, whilst association with the adjacent Linkim Formation (see below) suggests a Wenlock age.

The Linkim Formation (Greig 1988) occupies the southern part of the inlier. It is a succession of turbiditic greywacke, siltstone and shale and is pervasively reddened. Beds generally range from 10 to 60 cm in thickness. The detrital clast assemblage is dominantly quartzose with only a very small proportion of feldspar and lithic grains. Sedimentary structures, including cross-bedding and bottom structures are well preserved. The approximately 200 m of strata are relatively coherent compared to the neighbouring Coldingham Formation but, despite generally low dips, the sequence is inverted. A sparse and low-diversity acritarch assemblage is indicative of an Early Wenlock age (Molyneux 1987).

Despite the extreme disruption of the Coldingham Formation and the inversion of the Linkim Formation neither unit has a well-developed tectonic cleavage. Further, the metamorphic grade in both is reported by Casey & Oliver (in Oliver *et al.* 1984) to be amongst the lowest found in the Southern Uplands, precluding any interpretation of the complex structure in terms of a lengthy history of tectonism. Instead, these authors envisage deposition of both formations in trench-slope basins perched on the top of the Southern Uplands accretionary thrust stack. Deformation (and inversion) was caused by gravity-induced sliding soon after deposition. Hence the Coldingham and Linkim formations are approximately coeval with the Ross Formation but were deposited on top of the thrust hinterland whilst the latter was deposited and incorporated at the thrust front. Thereafter the Coldingham and Linkim formations were down-faulted into the body of the thrust belt and now occupy a position between the Gala and Hawick groups.

Provenance variation through time

The Southern Uplands thrust belt may be regarded as a continuum of sedimentation and deformation driven by subduction of Iapetus Ocean crust and convergence of Laurentia and Avalonia. The compositional changes seen in the greywackes through time reflect this dynamic environment and record the variations in provenance that accompanied the wider geotectonic changes.

Amongst the oldest, mainly Caradoc greywackes, many of those in the Tappins Group (notably the Traboyack and Marchburn formations) contain a high proportion of detrital ophiolitic material. A mixing model utilizing Sm–Nd isotope ratios suggests that the juvenile ophiolitic component is as much as 90% (Stone & Evans 1995). It is tempting to relate this to a provenance in the Tremadoc–Arenig Ballantrae Complex ophiolite immediately to the north but, since ophiolites of that age were widely obducted onto the Laurentian continental margin during the same early Llanvirn interval (Colman-Sadd *et al.* 1992) the full potential provenance is extensive. In the same group, the provenance of the Corsewall Formation conglomerates, also derived from the north, have been investigated by Elders (1987). Granitic boulder suites were used to obtain Rb–Sr mineral/whole rock age dates which clustered around 1200 Ma, between 600 and 700 Ma, and at 470–490 Ma. These ages were correlated by Elders with a possible provenance terrane in Newfoundland from which intrusive rocks of similar age and lithology were known. This implied extensive post-Caradoc sinistral strike-slip movement of about 1500 km. Contrary to this interpretation, Kelley & Bluck (1989) found no metamorphic mica ages in excess of about 500 Ma using the ^{40}Ar–^{39}Ar fusion dating method. Further, derived shelly faunas in the Kirkcolm Formation bear a close resemblance to *in situ* Caradoc faunas in the Girvan succession and, from this association, Clarkson *et al.* (1992) deduced that movement could not have exceeded a few hundred kilometres.

The metamorphic mica ages obtained by Kelley & Bluck (1989) were permissive of the micas being derived from the Dalradian Supergroup, although the authors argued against such a conclusion on palaeogeographical grounds. More credence was given to a Dalradian source for the micas by Hutchison & Oliver (1998) based on comparisons of *in situ* Dalradian metamorphic garnets with their detrital counterparts in the Southern Uplands. From this comparison, Hutchison & Oliver proposed a relatively local, northern source for the Corsewall and Kirkcolm formations within the Dalradian Supergroup. Some contrary Nd isotope evidence to this association had previously been presented by O'Nions *et al.* (1983) and discussed by Evans *et al.* (1991) and Stone & Evans (1995), but the Dalradian data available to these authors was probably inadequate for any firm conclusion (Stone & Evans 2001). The available Nd isotope data was more usefully utilised within the Southern Uplands terrane to illustrate the remarkable duality of provenance that existed for much of the Late Ordovician and earliest Silurian. As discussed by Stone & Evans (1995), relatively high εNd values of about −2.5 characterize the andesitic-rich greywackes of the Galdenoch, Portpatrick and Mindork formations, signifying a major juvenile component. The freshness of the detrital andesitic mineral grains, and their systematic association with palaeocurrent flow from the south to southwest, led Morris (1987) and Stone *et al.* (1987) to propose a volcanic arc provenance in that direction, thus instigating the back-arc model for the Northern Belt. Work on mineral chemistry of the detrital pyroxenes (Styles *et al.* 1989, 1995) suggested two distinct igneous sources. The most important was a volcanic arc founded on continental crust which appeared to have evolved from tholeiitic to calc-alkaline between deposition of the Galdenoch Formation (Early Caradoc) and the Portpatrick Formation (Late Caradoc to earliest Ashgill). A contemporaneous relationship between volcanism, erosion and sedimentation would thus seem to be supported, but Ar–Ar fusion ages obtained by Kelley & Bluck (1989) from detrital volcanic clasts were in the 560–530 Ma range, Early Cambrian rather than Late Ordovician. More recently, the correlation by Hutchison & Oliver (1998) of detrital garnets from the Galdenoch and Portpatrick formations with a metamorphic provenance in the Dalradian Supergroup requires that the volcanic arc provenance area was also to the north. Hutchison & Oliver reconcile this with the palaeocurrent evidence by adopting proposals by Leggett (1987) for meandering and axially deflected depositional systems.

The Nd isotope data presented by Stone & Evans (1995) shows a second Ordovician provenance supplying the Kirkcolm and Glenwhargen formations and characterized by low εNd values of about −10. These are close to the theoretical values for Proterozoic crust. There is a general consensus that this provenance area lay to the north of the Southern Uplands depositional basin but less agreement as to whether the Highland terranes occupied that position at that time (see discussion in Hutchison & Oliver 1998). From the Nd data it seems likely that this Proterozoic provenance continued to be available at least until late in the Llandovery.

Whole rock geochemistry has been used to define the geotectonic environment of the Leadhills Supergroup by Duller & Floyd (1995), based on comparisons with provenance characteristics of modern analogues. Their results showed a range of possible settings, including both fore-arc and back-arc situations, but perhaps more importantly established a distinctive geochemical stratigraphy derived from provenance-related mineralogical differences. The lithostratigraphy was assessed in terms of variable mixtures of ophiolitic, calc-alkaline, acid-igneous and low-grade metamorphic detritus.

A similar geochemical approach to provenance assessment has used the regional, stream sediment, geochemical database (British Geological Survey 1993) as a surrogate for whole rock data (Stone *et al.* 1991, 1993, 1997*a*). This has proved particularly useful in revealing cryptic variations across the Gala and Hawick groups where most of the tectonostratigraphic tracts are compositionally similar. Particularly noteworthy are high regional levels of the ultrabasic and basic elements, such as Cr (contained in detrital chrome spinel), not only across the ophiolite-derived Tappins Group but also over the whole terrane. The maximum Cr values (and hence the maximum likely ophiolitic influx) within the central part of the Southern Uplands are coincident with a Gala Group greywacke sequence spanning an interval in the Early Llandovery defined by the *acuminatus* to *gregarius* graptolite biozones (Stone *et al.* 1991, 1997*a*; British Geological Survey 1993). Palaeocurrent data indicate that the Gala Group was consistently derived from the northeast and, in that direction, the Scandian Orogen was initiated in Llandovery times (Gee & Roberts 1983). Erosion there of ophiolites would provide a possible source of the Cr-rich detritus carried southwestwards into the Southern Uplands depositional basin (Stone *et al.* 1999*a*), but detailed mineralogical work is still required to test this hypothesis.

Within the regional geochemical dataset the feldspar elements, Rb, K, Sr and Ba were shown by Stone *et al.* (1993, 1999*a*) to define two stratigraphical populations. The Rb and K levels are relatively low over a zone corresponding to the Ordovician sequence north of the Orlock Bridge Fault; conversely, a relatively high-level zone corresponds to the Silurian sequence south of that structure. The Sr distribution shows an abrupt change across the Moffat Valley Fault with relatively high values to the north and relatively low values to the south. Barium distribution is apparently controlled by both of these major structures with a marked zone of high Ba bounded to the north by the Orlock Bridge Fault and to the south by the Moffat Valley Fault. The combination of low Rb, K and Ba with high Sr over the Ordovician greywacke sequence suggests a plagioclase feldspar provenance within rocks of a dioritic or granodioritic composition. The converse relationships south of the Moffat Valley indicate a more granitic provenance largely within moderately evolved continental crust. The discrepant correlations across the Gala Group, between the Orlock Bridge Fault and the Moffat Valley–Laurieston faults, suggests the interaction of different provenance areas rather than the geochemical evolution of a single source.

A major provenance adjustment within the Gala Group is also indicated by whole rock rare earth element (REE) variation (Williams, T. M. *et al.* 1996). Their results for the older Gala Group tracts (1, 2 and 4) show REE ratio characteristics plotting on a straight line from an andesitic arc end-member, through to a moderately evolved, continental metamorphic end-member; this continues the Ordovician pattern. The younger Gala Group tracts (5, 6 and 7) fall on a trend-line indicating mixing between an evolved granitic provenance and a possibly sedimentary source enriched in the heavy and middle REE; this trend is then continued into the younger Hawick Group.

The accumulated evidence suggests that the maximum rate of change in Gala Group provenance occurred in the Early Llandovery, soon after the *gregarius* Biozone. It may be significant that this timing is very similar to that established by Rushton *et al.* (1996) for an interruption of the regular, forward-breaking thrust development in the accretionary complex. Thereafter, the Hawick and Riccarton groups, the former notable for the presence of much detrital, shelf-derived carbonate material, have been linked with deposition subsequent to closure of the Iapetus Ocean, as the Avalonian continental margin was overthrust by Laurentia (Stone *et al.* 1987) which then advanced, preceded by a foreland fold and thrust belt, towards the Avalonian hinterland. There, the tectonostratigraphic successor to the Southern Uplands terrane is the foreland basin sequence described from the upper part of the Windermere Supergroup (Kneller 1991; Kneller *et al.* 1993).

Structure

Terrane boundaries

The Southern Uplands terrane is the geological region between the putative Iapetus Suture (the southern boundary with the Lake District terrane) and the Southern Upland Fault (the NW boundary with the Midland Valley terrane) (Fig. 6.8).

Faulting

Faulting is discussed before folding because it plays the more important role in determining rock distribution. Individual important faults will be described first and then a more general outcrop scale fault classification will be summarized.

Iapetus Suture. The Iapetus Suture is arguably the most important fault in Britain in that it forms the boundary between the Avalonian and Laurentian terranes along the Solway Line (Fig. 6.8). However, it lies buried under the Carboniferous Northumberland Basin and is defined by contrasts in faunal provinces, geophysical properties and granite geochemistry (see below).

North American faunas in the Girvan succession and European faunas in the Lake District have long been cited as evidence to propose a wide Ordovician Iapetus Ocean (Wilson 1966; Williams 1973; Cocks & Fortey 1982). Ultimate closure took place along the Solway Line forming the so-called Iapetus Suture (Phillips *et al.* 1976), thus bringing the provincial faunas together.

The suture has been identified on several deep seismic reflection profiles and in magnetotelluric surveys (Brewer *et al.* 1983; Beamish & Smythe 1986; Freeman *et al.* 1988; Klemperer *et al.* 1991). The contact between seismically reflective hanging wall and a non-reflective footwall dips north at about 45°. Soper *et al.* (1992*a*) interpreted this feature as the leading edge of Avalonia (the Lake District terrane) dipping under the Southern Uplands. Support for this model was given by Anderson & Oliver (1996), who found xenoliths of mylonitized basaltic andesite in lamprophyre dykes from Co. Down. One xenolith has major and trace element chemistry very similar to basaltic andesites of the Borrowdale Volcanic Group now exposed in the Lake District. As an alternative, Armstrong & Owen (2001) propose that this xenolith was derived from 'Novantia', a now-hidden Gondwana derived volcanic arc terrane that collided with the Midland Valley terrane in Arenig times.

A 400 Ma Rb–Sr isochron diagram clearly separates granites from Leinster and the Lake District from those north of the Solway Line in Longford Down and the Southern Uplands. Todd *et al.* (1991) consider this to be the result of different granite protoliths on either side of the suture and, by inference, different kinds of continental crust and lithosphere. Other work (e.g. Thirlwall 1989; Stone *et al.* 1997*b*) suggest that the principal dividing line lies under the Southern Uplands terrane.

Southern Upland Fault. The Southern Upland Fault (SUF) forms the boundary with the Midland Valley; up to now it has not been subjected to modern structural analysis. Floyd (1994) has reviewed the contributions of Peach & Horne (1899), Peach *et al.* (1910a), Kennedy (1958), George (1960), Williams (1959) and Bluck (1983) on the derivation and definition of the Southern Upland Fault and concluded that the Stinchar Valley Fault–SUF (*sensu stricto*)–Crossgatehall–Firth of Forth Fault line represents the original terrane boundary although the zone of the SUF is now a complex of associated sub-parallel faults (Fig. 6.8). In the central region of the SUF (*sensu stricto*), downthrow appears to be predominantly northwards with the Upper Palaeozoic rocks in the Midland Valley lying against Ordovician strata to the south. In the southwest the Stinchar, Dove Cove and Glen App faults split from the Southern Upland Fault and run sub-parallel to each other to the coast. The Pyet Thrust is caught up between the first two of these faults.

The Pyet Thrust of Williams (1959, 1962), separates Midland Valley terrane Ballantrae Complex serpentinites from Southern Uplands terrane Traboyack Formation arenites and is recognized to be the terrane bounding fault in the Girvan area (Floyd 1994). Williams (1959) and Bluck (1983) propose that the Pyet Thrust is the thrust front to the Southern Uplands terrane.

Floyd (1994) estimated 12 km of post-Ordovician, pre-Carboniferous sinistral movement on the Stinchar Valley Fault (Fig. 6.8) based on the offset of the correlated Tappins/Marchburn formations, whilst Anderson & Oliver in Walton & Oliver (1991) proposed a 4.5 km upthrow to the south based on contrasting metamorphic grade estimated from graptolite reflectance results. The cumulative offset of the Stinchar Fault is therefore oblique.

The Glen App Fault forms a *c.* 300 m wide zone on the east coast of Loch Ryan (Fig. 6.8). Two sets of strike-slip shear planes occur, a later dextral set cutting an earlier sinistral set. The dextral set is parallel to the spaced fracture cleavage in a felsite dyke within the fault zone. To the south, just outside the fault zone, another dyke is uncleaved whereas the surrounding greywackes and shales display the main Southern Uplands first cleavage. Taking the dykes as coeval with the *c.* 400 Ma granites of the Southern Uplands and elsewhere, or maybe as part of the widespread suite of lamprophyres in the Southern Uplands K–Ar dated in the range 395–418 Ma by Rock *et al.* (1986) gives the following chronology (Anderson & Oliver in Walton & Oliver 1991). Firstly, regional first (S1) cleavage in the Northern Belt, pre-400 Ma, possibly end-Ordovician (since cleaved black shales with *Dicellograptus* occur as detritus in Silurian conglomerates at Pinstane Hill); secondly, sinistral shear planes formed in the fault zone later than S1 and earlier than the dykes; thirdly, intrusion of the dykes at about 400 Ma; fourthly, dextral strike-slip movement off-setting the sinistral planes and foliating the dyke in the fault-zone. The inference is that dyke intrusion at *c.* 400 Ma spanned the dextral movement.

Considerations of metamorphic grade using graptolite reflectance and illite crystallinity suggest a pre-Carboniferous (Early Devonian?) downthrow of some 6 km on the southeast side of the Glen App Fault. In contrast the Carboniferous rocks of Loch Ryan have been thrown up to the NW along this fault. Between the Glen App Fault and the central portion (Southern Upland Fault *sensu stricto*) the Carboniferous rocks at Cumnock overstep the line of the fault without any marked displacement but at Sanquhar they have been thrown down to the SE. In many places along the length of the SUF (*sensu lato*) slickenfibres on fault planes are predominantly horizontal and small-scale fractures have lateral offsets. The fault zone was temporarily exposed near Abington in 1990 during road excavations: clay gouge in the fault plane dips southeast at 70–80° and separates little-deformed Ordovician greywacke from 3 m of intensely crushed (?)Devonian lavas (Floyd & Stiven 1991). Map patterns show that large dip-slip movements took place about Mid Devonian times (George 1960). Movement affecting Carboniferous sequences seems to have been variable both in amount and direction of downthrow.

The northeastern segment of the SUF zone is made up of a combination of the Lammermuir, Dunbar–Gifford, Crossgatehall, Pentland and Firth of Forth faults all running sub-parallel and trending NNE to SW (see Fig. 6.8). Floyd (1994) has proposed a model in which the Dunbar–Gifford and the Crossgatehall/Firth of Forth Faults acted as thrusts and/or sinistral strike-slip faults during the Ordovician and Silurian, with possible repeated (?)Mid-Devonian strike-slip movement. During the Carboniferous, the Forth Approaches Graben developed between the Lammermuir Fault to the SE and the Firth of Forth Fault to the NW, Southern Uplands terrane rocks form the basement to this graben. It is the Lammermuir Fault that forms the present-day prominent scarp south of Edinburgh. Carboniferous strata are faulted against Ordovician strata: downthrow is *c.* 250 m on the north side (Davies *et al.* 1986).

Orlock Bridge Fault. The boundary between the Silurian and Ordovician part of the terrane is locally known as the Kingledores Fault near Edinburgh (Leggett *et al.* 1979) and the Cairngarroch Fault (Anderson & Oliver 1986) in the Rhins of Galloway. It is best exposed in Ireland as the Orlock Bridge Fault (OBF) and the Slieve Glah Shear Zone (Anderson & Oliver 1986). The boundary in Ireland was given the name Orlock Bridge Fault by the Geological Survey of Great Britain (1959). This name for the boundary is now accepted in Scotland (Fig. 6.8). Anderson & Oliver (1986) analysed the effects of the ductile fault kinematics in Ireland and Scotland. The fault zone is characterized by numerous shear zones slicing arenites at low angles to the bedding. Phyllonites and quartz segregations parallel the foliation and highlight the schistosity. The fault fabric is folded into minor folds with sinistral vergence and sinistral strike-slip, C-S mylonites occur in the zone of greatest deformation. Five uppermost Ordovician graptolite zones are missing in Ireland and are presumably cut out by the fault. The metamorphic grade on either side of the fault in the Rhins of Galloway precludes a large vertical component of displacement (Stone 1995). Greywacke successions cannot be correlated across the fault along the whole of its 400 km trace. Furthermore it is cut by lamprophyre and felsite dykes thought to be associated with the 400 Ma granitic activity in the Southern Uplands and Ireland. Originally, Anderson & Oliver (1986) suggested that either two accretionary prisms were amalgamated around Early Devonian/Late Silurian times or that one large prism was dissected by the fault at this time (but see Floyd *et al.* 1987 for counter-opinions). Floyd & Rushton (1993) have subsequently reduced the stratigraphic break in Scotland to one Ordovician graptolite zone and Barnes *et al.* (1995) have emphasized the integrity of the Southern Uplands as a single terrane. Thus in Ireland, the OBF appears to increase in importance towards the southwest. In Scotland the maximum effect is in the middle around Moniaive and apparently decreases to both NE and SW.

Kimbell & Stone (1995) and Stone *et al.* (1997b) observed that the OBF coincides with deep crustal magnetic, magnetotelluric, and gravity boundaries and Thirlwall (1989) noted that the Early Devonian granites on either side of the OBF have very contrasting geochemical characteristics. The OBF and the related Moniaive Shear Zone may therefore be more significant than any of the other tract-bounding faults reflecting the reactivation of a deep basement structure (see also Chapter 1).

Moniaive Shear Zone. Phillips *et al.* (1995) traced a major ductile shear zone for 100 km between Newton Stewart and

Stanhope (Fig. 6.8). The northern boundary of this, the Moniaive Shear Zone (MSZ), is the Orlock Bridge Fault. The similarities with the Slieve Glah Shear Zone (SGSZ) in Ireland (Anderson & Oliver 1986) are noteworthy: in both areas the shear zone is almost entirely located to the south of the OBF; the MSZ is 5 km wide at its maximum width compared to the 1 km wide SGSZ; high strain zones are truncated against the OBF; low strain zones are surrounded by high strain zones with pervasive linear and planar fabrics with consistent sinistral strike-slip sense of shear. The age of shearing is very similar: the SGSZ is cut by cleaved but not veined or sheared microgranite thought to be related to the ?c. 400 Ma Cross-doney Granite: therefore these dykes post-date the main phase of shearing. The MSZ is cut by the 392 ± 2 Ma (Rb–Sr biotite method; Halliday et al. 1980) Fleet Granite which has deformed cordierite porphyroblasts in its aureole whilst contact metamorphic biotite has overgrown the fabric mimetically: therefore the MSZ was broadly coeval with the intrusion of the Fleet Granite. Late Silurian lamprophyre dykes in the MSZ and at Orlock Bridge are deformed by the shear fabric.

Illite crystallinity results show no appreciable differences across the SGSZ/OBF in Ireland (Oliver et al. 1984) or the Rhins of Galloway (Stone 1995) suggesting that the vertical component of throw is minimal. Illite results from the MSZ indicate a gradational transition from anchizone to epizone northwards across the southern boundary of the MSZ and a sharp transition from epizone to low anchizone/diagenetic zone across the northern boundary (i.e. the OBF), indicating some 3 km of uplift to the south (Merriman pers. comm. to Phillips et al. 1995). Phillips et al. (1995) discuss the possibility that an early OBF acted as a focus for the MSZ as at Slieve Glah. Since the OBF truncates the MSZ (and the SGSZ), it must have been reactivated as a dip-slip fault. The variation in width of the MSZ might be related to erosion level over a compound Permian horst where the widest sector of the shear zone also has the highest grade of regional metamorphism (Stone et al. 1995).

Outcrop scale fault classification

In the Rhins of Galloway, where coastal exposure is excellent, it is possible to classify faults on the outcrop scale (Stone 1995). Poor inland exposures do not lend themselves to this type of classification but its regional application seems likely, particularly in view of the similarities with the Ards Peninsula in Northern Ireland (Anderson 1987).

Group 1 tract-bounding faults. The vast majority of the beds in the Southern Uplands strike NE–SW and dip steeply or are overturned. Younging is directed predominantly towards the NW except for a zone of Silurian rocks. Overall, Ordovician rocks are found to the NW of the Silurian; i.e. the tectono-stratigraphy becomes older towards the apparent 'top' of the pile. This paradox is the result of strike faults which divide the area into blocks or tracts, typically 2–5 km wide, which consistently throw down to the SE. These tract-bounding faults are best seen in the coastal exposure of the Rhins of Galloway (Fig. 6.17). The Orlock Bridge Fault is exceptional in the Northern and Central Belts in not having graptolitic shales marking the trace of the tract bounding faults. The Leadhills Fault and the other major tract-bounding faults, for example those in the central Moffat area, are all characterized by a zone of imbricated slices of Moffat Shales. In the Northern Belt, Ordovician shales are accompanied by cherts and sometimes basalts; in the Central Belt Ordovician and Silurian shale occurs but basalts are absent. Fyfe & Weir (1976) mapped a section at Craigmichan Scaurs across the Ettrick Valley

Thrust, showing that imbricate slices of shale and greywacke are bounded by (inferred listric) faults with the Ettrick Valley Thrust forming a floor fault. The Leadhills Fault in the type area also has a very wide imbricate zone some 1.7 km across. Here the floor fault is vertical and associated imbricate faults have a variety of inclinations. Tracts in the Southern Belt are difficult to pick out because they lack the imbricate zones of graptolitic shales. Careful mapping and fossil collecting by Kemp & White (1985) and Kemp (1986) allowed the recognition of repeated zones in Wenlock strata along with their boundary faults.

All of the Northern and Southern Belt and most of the Central Belt tract-bounding faults are top to the south directed thrusts. This geometry is well illustrated in the almost continuously exposed Rhins of Galloway (Fig. 6.17) where Stone (1995) has constructed a regional structural profile (Fig. 6.18). This profile shows that some of the thrusts in the Central Belt are essentially vertical or dipping steeply south, with the south side moved up to the north; i.e. opposite to the majority of tract-bounding faults.

Folding is often most intense in the imbricate zones of the major faults. Associated features of the zones are belts of intense disruption and brecciation. These belts have been ascribed to deformation before lithification and cleavage formation or alternatively to later deformation during continued thrust movements after folds have locked (Knipe & Needham 1986; McCurry 1987). The faulting is relatively brittle compared with the mylonitization found in the Orlock Bridge Fault. Changes in younging direction commonly occur across bedding-parallel or subparallel faults (thrusts) that have moved along fold hinges: thus faulting and folding are presumed to be contemporaneous D1 structures.

The major tract-bounding faults in the Southern Uplands terrane are the principal imbricate faults within the thrust system; they show at the surface as near vertical reverse faults down-throwing on the south side, typically with Moffat Shales in the hangingwall. Stone (1995) has classed these faults as Group 1 'probably originating as hangingwall detachments during D1 thrust generation' (Fig. 6.19).

Group 2 minor thrust faults. Minor strike or near strike-parallel faults, trending between NE–SW and E–W, occur in most sizeable exposures in the Southern Uplands. D1 fold structures and cleavage are cut. Dips are generally low and vary between 5° and 45° to the north and south. The higher angle faults may show normal or reverse throws but in view of the probable rotation of the blocks these designations may not be significant. Following the theory of thrust tectonics (Butler 1982b), the northerly directed thrust faults are a consequence of out of sequence back thrusting within the hinterland (Rushton et al. 1996) producing a pop-up structure (Stone 1995). Alternatively, McCurry & Anderson (1989) argued that north-directed thrusting in the Hawick Group could be caused by a period of obduction (i.e. northward overthrusting) at the thrust front. The 'late thrusts' described by Knipe and Needham (1986) would fit this class (Fig. 6.18). According to Stone (1995), these faults are presumed to be accommodation structures formed during a D2 deformation episode 'in response to compression within the thrust hinterland'.

Group 3 and 4 strike-slip faults. Strike-slip faults may form topographic features where they have generated zones of brecciation, susceptible to subsequent erosion. Slickenlines and slickenfibers are subhorizontal on steep to vertical fault planes. The faults form a conjugate set, with sinistrals, generally the more abundant, oriented approximately N–S and dextrals, WNW–ESE (i.e. 018–306° and 126–306° in the Rhins of

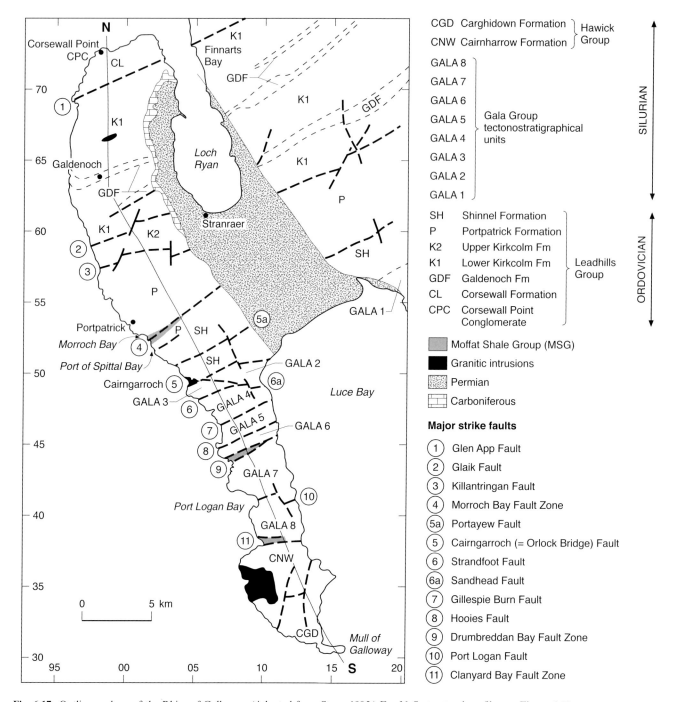

Fig. 6.17. Outline geology of the Rhins of Galloway. (Adapted from Stone 1995.) For N–S structural profile, see Figure 6.18.

Galloway (Stone 1995)). The net effect suggests NNW–SSE directed compression and ENE–WSW extension. Sinistral faults in the Langholm area have been called shatter belts. One, the Cue Sike Fault, with a horizontal displacement of 1 km, has disrupted strata for up to 500 m on either side (Lumsden *et al.* 1967). The wrench system displaces major strike faults and folds.

The strike-slip fault system was shown to be penecontemporaneous with the intrusion of a lamprophyre dyke swarm in Co Down (Anderson & Cameron 1979) and subsequently dated at 395 to 418 ± 10 Ma in the Southern Uplands (K–Ar hornblende and biotite; Rock *et al.* 1986): some strike-slip faults contain or are cross-cut by uncleaved dykes, others contain foliated dykes, still other dykes are displaced by the faults. Stone (1995) has classed the sinistral strike-slip faults as

Group 3 and the dextrals as Group 4. Subsequently, Permian basin boundary faults formed by reactivation of both sets of the Caledonian wrenches.

Group 5 sinistral strike-parallel faults. The D1 tract-boundary thrust faults commonly show later reactivation as sinistral shears. However, the Orlock Bridge Fault at Cairngarroch (Fig. 6.17) does not involve Moffat Shales, post-dates D1 structures and predates (i.e. is cut by) *c.* 400 Ma acid intrusions (Anderson & Oliver 1986) and originated as a major strike parallel strike-slip fault later than the Group 1 tract bounding faults. It cuts obliquely across the high strain zones of the Moniaive Shear Zone with sinistral shear sense (Lintern *et al.* 1992). The relationship between this and the Group 3 and 4 wrench faults is unclear although they appear to have about

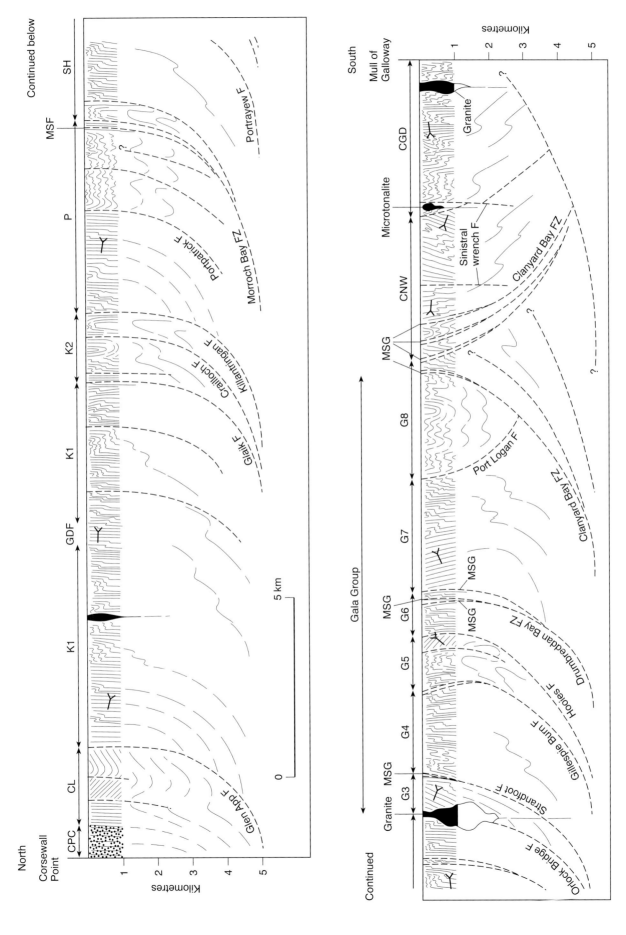

Fig. 6.18. Structural profile along the Rhins of Galloway. For key to abbreviations and location of N-S- line of section, see Figure 6.17. (Adapted from Stone 1995.)

the same ages (?Early Devonian) relative to *c.* 400 Ma intrusions. The Glen App Fault in Finnarts Bay also shows brittle post-D1 sinistral kinematics. Sinistral transpression and the oblique closure of Iapetus during the Silurian has been discussed by Soper *et al.* (1992*b*)

Folding

The inclination of the axial surfaces of the main fold-phase had a profound effect on early interpretations of the general structure of the region. Observations suggested that axial surfaces had a fan arrangement around two 'lines' running NE–SW; respectively the Leadhills line in the north and the Hawick line in the south. The general structure was therefore interpreted as an anticlinorium with the Leadhills line as the axial trace and a synclinorium with the Hawick line as its axial trace (Lapworth 1889). The recognition of the dominance of tract bounding faults (Craig & Walton 1959; Kelling 1961; McKerrow *et al.* 1977) has negated the structural fan model. The variation in axial-surface dip would seem to be determined by the amount of rotation experienced by individual imbricate slices during thrusting.

Understanding of the fold patterns in the Southern Uplands has been greatly improved following the publication of a regional structural profile drawn down the length of the Rhins of Galloway (Fig. 6.18) by the British Geological Survey (1992*b*) and described by Stone (1995). Stone has recognized four structural styles based on fold vergence: a fold pair 'verges' in the direction of a major anticline as illustrated on Figure 6.19 where north, south and neutral verging folds can be defined.

Type 1 has 'uniform, usually steeply inclined or vertical bedding younging consistently northward. The regular pattern of strike and dip is locally interrupted by sporadic south-verging fold pairs'. Type 2 has 'continuous sequences of south-verging, small- to medium-scale folds separated by minor shears and/or narrow unfolded units of steeply inclined bedding younging northwards. Most of the folds are tight or close with axial planes steeply inclined and fold hinges which generally plunge gently; some folds are periclinal'. Type 3 has 'continuous sequences of close to open folds, ranging considerably in wavelength and amplitude but geometrically neutral'; i.e. with no preferred sense of vergence. Axial planes are upright or steeply inclined and fold hinges plunge gently. Type 4 are 'continuous sequences of north-verging, small- to medium-scale folds separated by minor shears and/or unfolded

units of steeply inclined bedding younging southward. Most of the folds are tight with axial planes steeply inclined and fold hinges which generally plunge gently but which are locally highly variable.' Types 1 and 2 merge locally; Type 3 neutral folding could form in short flat-lying limbs of major south-verging folds (Fig. 6.19). The consistent association of folds and reverse faults suggest that Types 1, 2 and 3 may be re-lated to southward directed thrusting whilst Type 4 is the opposite: i.e. related to northward back-thrusting. The structural geometry is compatible with an imbricate thrust stack that propagated southwards.

The intensity and frequency of folding and (domainal) cleavage is greatly enhanced in the Late Llandovery and Early Wenlock strata of the southern part of the Hawick Group (Fig. 6.20). Folds affecting older strata in the Northern and Central Belts have cleavage that is widely axial planar but cleavage in the southern Hawick Group commonly transects gently plunging upright folds in a clockwise manner; the angle is usually smaller than 10° in mudstones and up to 25° in greywackes (Stringer & Treagus 1980; Cameron 1981; Anderson 1987). Stringer & Treagus demonstrate that this is not a cross-cutting, later cleavage. This arrangement could arise by folding and cleavage development in beds already inclined at an angle to the maximum direction of shortening (Stringer & Treagus 1980) or by the cleavage developing on folds initiated with axes already slightly oblique to maximum shortening but within the XZ-plane in a transpressive regime (Knipe & Needham 1986). Cleavage is usually domainal in that it refracts through mudstone and silt interbeds but is rare in the more massive, coarser-grained greywackes. In the southern Hawick Group greywackes, steeply plunging and downward-facing folds have a strong pervasive clockwise transecting cleavage and a sinistral sense of vergence (Anderson 1987; Barnes 1989). These features are absent in the relatively undeformed but sub-vertical, Mid to Late Wenlock Raeberry Castle Formation of the Riccarton Group immediately to the south (Kemp *et al.* 1985; Kemp 1987). The age of the fault junction between the Ross and Raeberry Castle formations is precisely dated within the upper *riccartonensis* graptolite Biozone (White *et al.* 1991); this Wenlock age is the time when penetrative deformation ended in the Southern Uplands.

The folds illustrated in Figure 6.19 are designated D1, arising from diachronous deformation as the thrust front propagated southwards. D2 minor folding (Fig. 6.21) and crenulation phases are regarded by Stone (1995) as accommodation structures: these formed in the thrust hinterland at the same time as the D1 structures at the thrust front. D2 could also be diachronous and could form anywhere in the hinterland during the entire D1 range. By Stone's (1995) interpretations, D1 folds would be related to Group 1 thrust faults in time and space whilst D2 folds would be related to Group 2 minor thrust faults. Figures 6.18, 6.19 and 6.22 summarize these relationships. The subsequent sinistral strike-slip Group 5 faults post-date D2 and thus constitute part of D3 (Plate 12).

In contrast to diachronous D1 and D2, initiation of D3 appears to have been relatively synchronous throughout the Southern Uplands. According to Barnes *et al.* (1989) 'an increasing element of sinistral shear is seen during D1 in the youngest (Wenlock) two tracts of the Hawick Group where it formed steeply plunging sinistral folds'. Locally these are downward facing and very rarely the D2 and D3 effects have been reversed. Through the Northern and most of the Central Belts, D3 is in the form of new sinistral shear zones and sinistral reactivation of old tract-defining thrusts.

The Hawick Group is intruded by a lamprophyre dyke swarm. Early dykes are cleaved by D1 and deformed by D2 and D3; others are undeformed and post-tectonic (Barnes *et al.*

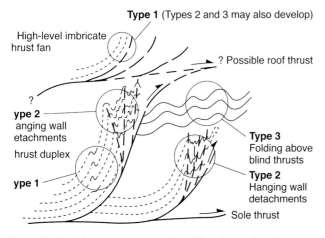

Fig. 6.19. Variation in structural style within a developing thrust stack. (Adapted from Stone 1995.) Compare with Figure 6.18.

Fig. 6.20. Carghidown Formation, Hawick Group, looking towards the northeast at inverted thin bedded turbidites, dipping steeply to the southeast and younging north. Bedding is cut by a near vertical, downward facing, S1 slaty cleavage. S1 transects bedding clockwise by about 10°. Brighouse Bay, Kirkcudbright. NX 6325 4531. BGS photograph.

Fig. 6.21. Kirkmaiden Formation, Hawick Group: looking towards the north at thinly bedded turbidites, with a minor F2 fold on the limb of a F1 anticline. The F2 axial plane has a shallow dip to the northwest, F1 axial plane is upright. Isle Mouth, Borgue, Kirkcudbright. NX 5768 4988. BGS photograph.

1986; Anderson & Cameron 1979). As already noted, the post-tectonic dykes have been K–Ar (biotite, hornblende) dated at 400–418 Ma (Rock *et al.* 1986). Therefore D1–D3 occurred prior to end Silurian times (Fig. 6.22).

The 408–392 ± 2 Ma Early Devonian granite plutons of the Southern Uplands are not tectonized and therefore also post-date D1–D3 (Fig. 6.22). However, Phillips *et al.* (1995) have shown that the Moniaive Shear Zone deforms the metamorphic aureole of the Fleet Granite but has contact metamorphic biotite overgrowing its shear fabric: thus the Moniaive shear Zone was coeval with the intrusion of the 392 ± 2 Ma Fleet Granite (Stephens & Halliday 1979).

Late kink-bands are widespread. These small angular folds with long and short limbs and steeply plunging axes correspond to sinistral or dextral wrenches (Anderson 1968). The folds are particularly associated with thin-bedded flags. Although both sinistral and dextral kink-bands occur, the latter are much more abundant.

Metamorphism

Because of a general lack of deformational-metamorphic fabrics, the Southern Uplands terrane was traditionally considered as part of the non-metamorphic Caledonides (e.g.

Dewey 1969). However, Oliver (1978) identified prehnite–pumpellyite facies metamorphic assemblages, initially in the County Cavan and Portpatrick areas and then subsequently over much of the Southern Upland region (Oliver & Leggett 1980; Oliver *et al.* 1984). There has been much progress in the study of metamorphism of the Southern Uplands since the review given by Oliver (1988). The British Geological Survey (1992b) and Merriman & Frey (1999) have refined the picture, especially in the southwest. Metamorphism in the terrane has been studied using index mineralogy, clay mineralogy and illite crystallinity, conodont alteration indexing (CAI), graptolite reflectance and K–Ar age dating.

Index mineralogy. Oliver & Leggett (1980) showed that the various lava occurrences in the Northern Belt are spilites metamorphosed to prehnite–pumpellyite grade. Original clinopyroxene and opaques are largely preserved with an igneous texture but all other minerals have been metamorphosed to form albite + chlorite + prehnite + pumpellyite + phengite + sphene + quartz ± calcite ± hematite. Vein and vesicle assemblages are similar. Bail Hill Volcanic Group lavas contain prehnite + pumpellyite + chlorite + thomsonite + analcite indicating zeolite facies metamorphism (Hepworth *et al.* 1982). Volcaniclastic greywackes, both in the Northern and Central Belts, were

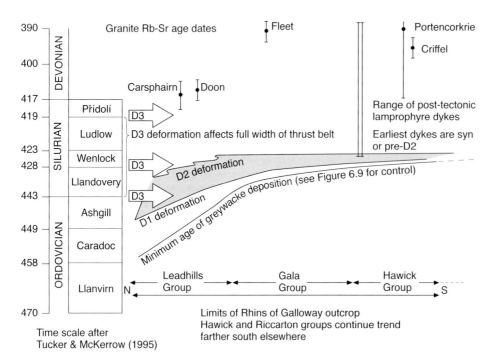

Fig. 6.22. Time of deformation in the Southern Uplands. (Adapted from Barnes *et al.* 1989.)

originally rich in detrital plagioclase, clinopyroxene and hornblende, but now have groundmass and vein assemblages containing albite + prehnite + pumpellyite + chlorite + white mica + quartz + calcite indicating prehnite–pumpellyite facies metamorphism. Sedimentary textures are usually preserved. Oliver & Leggett (1980) used the experimental *P–T* curves of these index minerals to estimate maximum metamorphic conditions of *c.* 340°C and 10 km depth of burial. Southern Belt lithologies are not basic enough in composition to have grown index minerals.

Clay mineralogy and illite crystallinity. Hepworth *et al.* (1982) noted kaolinite as a significant component in volcaniclastic sedimentary rocks associated with the Bail Hill Volcanic Group. Kaolinite is typical of diagenetic zone (zeolite facies, *c.* 150–200°C), as is thomsonite and analcite in the associated lavas (Kisch 1987). Illite plus chlorite (with kaolinite absent) is typical of pelites from the rest of the Southern Uplands. Illite (white mica) and chlorite crystallized from the originally saponitic clay size fraction in pelites (Merriman *et al.* 1995). Phyllosilicate crystallites grow progressively thicker with increasing metamorphism and this crystallinity can be measured in illite by X-ray diffraction (XRD) in terms of the illite (001) peak width. Thus illite crystallinity defines the diagenetic, anchizone and epizones corresponding quite closely to the zeolite, prehnite–pumpellyite and greenschist facies respectively (Kübler 1968; Weber 1972; Merriman & Roberts 1985; Frey & Merriman 1999). This method is particularly useful in the southern Central and Southern belts where other metamorphic indicators are rare. Oliver & Leggett (1980), Hepworth *et al.* (1982), Oliver *et al.* (1984) and Kemp *et al.* (1985) used this method for reconnaissance studies and noted diagenetic grades in the Southern Belt and anchizone grades in the Central and Northern Belts.

The British Geological Survey (1992); Stone (1995) and Merriman *et al.* (1995), using XRD, scanning and transmitted electron microscopy, and electron probe analysis, carried out detailed surveys of chlorite and white mica–illite crystallinity in the Rhins of Galloway, and noted diagenetic grades north of the Glen App Fault in the Northern Belt and within the back thrust Hawick Group tracts; elsewhere anchizone grades dominate, with occasional areas of epizone, agreeing with the index mineralogy (Merriman *et al.* 1995). They concluded that progressive metamorphism of the ductile clay matrix in mudrocks occurred in the deforming thrust stack with a field gradient of less than 25°C km^{-1} over a temperature range of 150–320°C and burial depths of no more than 6 km in some places, to at least 13 km in others. The contoured illite crystallinity map of the Rhins shows that away from the influence of contact metamorphism such as seen around the Cairngarroch and Portencorkrie intrusions, the isocrysts are both sub-parallel to, and are cut by, the Group 1 tract bounding faults. This suggests that regional metamorphism was penecontemporaneous with D1 faulting (and folding). Since sedimentation and deformation were diachronously younger towards the south, then so too would be the metamorphism. However, along strike variation in metamorphic grade, e.g. across the Loch Ryan Fault, suggests that burial grades were imposed on vertical strata.

Casey & Oliver in Oliver *et al.* (1984) used illite crystallinity (and acritarch colour) to show that the chaotically folded and disrupted Coldingham Beds and inverted and thrusted (Wenlock) Linkim Beds in Berwickshire are of significantly lower metamorphic grade (<200°C) compared to the nearby prehnite–pumpellyite facies (i.e. *c.* 350°C) (Llandovery) greywacke/shale turbidites of the Central Belt. This relationship fits the hypothesis that the Coldingham Bay inlier represents younger Wenlock slope deposits deformed by gravity slumps that came to rest on previously metamorphosed Llandovery turbidites. The Cambro-Ordovician polyphase deformation theory of Shiells & Dearman (1966) is now regarded as untenable.

Conodont alteration indexing (CAI) and graptolite reflectance. Conodonts irreversibly change colour with progressive metamorphism and this has been experimentally calibrated and indexed by Epstein *et al.* (1977). Three localities in the Northern Belt (Fig. 6.8) indicate maximum temperatures between 300 and 400°C, compatible with prehnite–pumpellyite facies metamorphism.

Graptolite reflectance increases with progressive metamorphism, and is a near-mimic of vitrinite reflectance. Watson (1976) first applied this technique as an indicator of contact and regional metamorphism. Reflectance data from the Southern

Uplands shows a general decrease in metamorphic grade from north to south (Oliver 1988; Kemp et al. 1985). Significantly, there is a jump in reflectance within the Southern Belt at the junction between the Long Robin and Ross tectonic units, where Barnes et al. (1989) map a deformation front. To the immediate north, metasediments have penetrative cleavage and numerous folds with illite crystallinity indicating anchizone prehnite–pumpellyite metamorphism; to the south, sediments lack a penetrative cleavage and illite crystallinity and grapto-lite reflectance values are correlated with diagenetic to zeolite facies grades.

Walton & Oliver (1991) correlated graptolite reflectance data with metamorphic temperature estimates given by Oliver (1988) to propose a pre-Carboniferous (Early Devonian?) downthrow of some 6 km on the north side of the Glen App Fault (i.e. metamorphic grade jumps from upper prehnite–pumpellyite to upper zeolite facies) and a 4.5 km upward throw on the south of the Stinchar Fault (i.e. metamorphic grade jumps from low zeolite facies to upper zeolite facies). These results are in agreement with illite crystallinity data from the northern Rhins of Galloway (Stone 1995).

Dating of K-bentonites. These occur as obvious cm-thick pale clay bands within the black Moffat Shales and as less obvious bands in greywackes and are interpreted as subduction-related explosively erupted ashes of acid to intermediate composition (Cameron & Anderson 1980; Batchelor & Weir 1988; Huff et al. 1988, 1991; Merriman & Roberts 1990). They are impor-tant for the Early Palaeozoic stratigraphic timescale of Tucker & McKerrow (1995) who utilized precisely dated zircons extracted from Ashgillian (445.7 ± 2.4 Ma) and from Llando-verian (438.7 ± 2.1 Ma) bentonites from Dob's Linn using the U–Pb isotope dilution method.

The bentonite mineralogy is now dominantly mixed layered illite/smectite (I/S) containing 90–95% illite with minor chlor-ite formed from glassy ash during low grade metamorphism (Huff et al. 1991). Low $K+$ activity during alteration at Dob's Linn slowed down illitisation reactions such that I/S expand-ability is anomalously high compared to elsewhere in the Southern Uplands (Pearce et al. 1991; Pearce & Clayton 1995).

Huff et al. (1991) have carried out K–Ar dating on $<0.5\,\mu m$ illite/smectite, separated from uncleaved, Central Belt, Llan-dovery, K-bentonites from Dob's Linn in Scotland and equiva-lents in Co Down. The mean of nine ages is 390 ± 6 Ma with a range from 379 ± 10 Ma to 406 ± 10 Ma: there is no strati-graphical correlation with these ages. Halliday (1977), esti-mated that the blocking temperature for argon diffusion in fine-grained illite (i.e. $<0.1\,\mu m$) should be c. 200°C. Since peak metamorphic temperatures in the Central Belt reached c. 340°C during D1 and D2 (Oliver & Leggett 1980), these rocks would have been open to argon diffusion throughout Wenlock and Ludlow times until Early Devonian exhumation and cooling through c. 200°C occurred at around 390 Ma. The earliest known post-tectonic Old Red Sandstone conglomerates cover-ing the Southern Uplands are Early Devonian (Lochkovian) (Rock & Rundle 1986). The Lochkovian is dated at 412–417 Ma (Tucker & McKerrow 1995) coincident with the oldest ex-humation age (406 ± 10 Ma) and coincident with the intra-Old Red Sandstone unconformity in the Midland Valley (Mykura 1991). This Lochkovian age is of significance when mica age dates from south of the Iapetus Suture are considered (see Chapter 7).

Discussion of geodynamic models

The place of the Ballantrae Complex and the Southern Uplands terrane in the regional geodynamics of Scotland will be discussed in the next chapter. The Ballantrae Complex is undoubtedly an ophiolite. The origin of the Southern Uplands is still controversial: is it an accretionary prism or is it a back-arc plus fore-arc thrust stack?

Accretionary prism: missing volcanic arc to the north?

Points in favour. Slivers of gabbro plus MORB-like volca-nics, deep water facies cherts and black shales at the base of turbidite sequences, sea mount volcanics inter-bedded with turbidites; turbidites containing abundant volcanic, plutonic arc, ophiolite and Barrovian metamorphic detritus mostly derived from the northern quadrant, all suggest an accre-tionary prism model (see Fig. 6.10). Ophiolites, arc and conti-nental basement need to be located in the Midland Valley area. Ophiolite, including arc rocks, are present in the Ballantrae Complex; Barrovian metamorphic sources are not far away in the Grampian terrane. Generally, younging directions within turbidite tracts are towards the north whilst tracts become younger towards the south: this is predicted by an accretionary prism model. Patterns of regional metamorphism are as in an accretionary prism model. K-bentonites within the Moffat Shales are subduction related ash falls. If the Iapetus Ocean between Avalonia and Laurentia was subducted under the Iapetus margins during the Later Ordovician and Early Silurian then surely an accretionary prism would have been formed between the colliding plates? A modern analogue for this model is the Aleutian arc–trench system, Alaska (Kven-volen & von Heune 1985).

Points against. There is no apparent *in situ* source for the acid and intermediate volcanic /plutonic detritus in the Midland Valley (presumably this is now eroded and/or buried?). How-ever, suitable sources might be correlated with the Tyrone Igneous Complex in Ireland (Hutton et al. 1985). A significant amount of volcanic arc detritus (e.g. the Northern Member of the Galdenoch Formation and the Portpatrick Formation) has come from the SE, as well as the NW, suggesting that an arc lay to the SE. Moffat Shale facies (including cherts) have significant terrigenous (clay) content so that this could not be a mid-ocean environment (Armstrong et al. 1999). The struc-tural style is not unique to an accretionary prism: theoretically, identical structures can form in any thrust belt.

Back-arc plus fore-arc in thrust stack: missing volcanic arcs to north and south

Points in favour. MORB chemistry is not widespread, and where seen is most like that of a ridge in a back-arc basin (see Fig. 6.11); actually, within-plate (oceanic island) basalt chem-istry is more common. The oldest strata are not found in the most northerly part of the Northern Belt; in fact conodont ages stay constant in the northern Northern Belt: this is not the geometry of a typical accretionary prism. Generally however, over the rest of the Southern Uplands Central and Southern Belts, younging directions within tracts are towards the north whilst successive tracts become younger towards the south as predicted by a fore-arc thrust stack model. Structural style is similar if not identical to that which is found in thrust belts. Palaeocurrent directions indicate that volcanic arc material was derived from the north and south. The missing volcanic arc to the south has either been excised by the Orlock Bridge Fault or over-run by the advancing thrust belt. An arc to the north in the Midland Valley has been eroded or buried. Recent analogues for this model can be found in the New Guinea/Banda Arcs area (van Staal et al. 1998) and in the Australian continental edge versus Indonesian arc collision zone (Stauffer 1985).

Points against. The basal detachment for the Southern Uplands accretionary prism may lie mostly above the MORB layer of the Iapetus ocean floor and therefore has not sampled much typical MORB: more elevated volcanic oceanic islands have been sliced off. The structural style is not unique to a thrust belt: theoretically it is the same as in an accretionary prism. The thrust stack model predicts that metamorphic isograds would lie parallel to the buried stratigraphy and that metamorphic packages would be repeated by the tract-bounding faults. Metamorphism in each thrust slice would be expected to increase down section. Kemp *et al.* (1985) showed that metamorphic grade in the youngest (lowest) Southern Belt thrust sheet decreases downwards with increased tectonic burial: i.e. it does the opposite to what might be expected in a fore-arc thrust-stack. Oliver & Leggett (1980) and Merriman & Frey (1999) predicted that isograds would lie sub-parallel to the palaeo-surface and would cross-cut the tract boundaries. Merriman & Frey (1999) compared contrasting metamorphic patterns in accretionary prisms and thrust-stacks and proposed that there would be sharp contrasts in metamophic grade across the tract-bounding faults in a fore-arc thrust stack. There would be a sharp increase in grade across the faults in the direction of propagation. Actually, they demonstated that illite crystallinity isocrysts in the Southern Uplands are not cut by these faults (where they have not been reactivated), consistent with burial in an accretionary prism.

The volcanic arc to the south has been excised without trace: this might need special pleading. If an island arc was positioned south of the Northern Belt during Mid and Late Ordovician times then volcaniclastic turbidites would be deposited both north and south of the arc: where are the southerly directed volcaniclastic turbidite deposits of Late Ordovician age, lying south of the Orlock Bridge Fault? Palaeocurrent information may be misleading. Leggett (1987) noted that turbidite currents in the Nankai Trough have in places been diverted by the trench topography to make it appear that volcanic arc detritus originated from the west; i.e. opposite to the direction of the present-day arc. The bathymetric map of New Zealand (CANZ 1996) also shows how arc-derived volcaniclastic turbidites originating from the mainland could cross the Cambell Plateau and neighbouring shelf in an easterly direction and enter the Hikuangi Trench travelling westwards.

Conclusions

The Ballantrae Complex is a repeatedly tectonized assembly of slivers of a disrupted, mostly Arenig, marginal basin complete with MORB-like seafloor, deep-sea pelagic sediments, volcanic arcs and seamounts. There is good correlation with the Arenig ophiolites in Newfoundland. Much of the former mantle peridotite is now represented by serpentinite mélanges. Modern analogues are found in the western Pacific marginal basins.

The Llanvirn to Wenlock sedimentary cover to the Ballantrae Complex and the Southern Uplands turbidites are a mixture of locally derived ophiolite and volcanic/plutonic arc material plus more distally derived Barrovian metamorphic detritus. A modern analogue is in the Bismark Sea along the northern margin of New Guinea (van Staal *et al.* 1998).

Arguments concerning the origin of the Southern Uplands terrane have not been resolved since the publication of the third edition of this book (Craig 1991); either the terrane is an accretionary prism that developed in front of an open Iapetus ocean, which was closed when Avalonia collided with Laurentia, or it initially developed in a back arc basin that was subsequently thrust over a foreland as Avalonia collided with the Laurentian margin. Many key elements of the Southern Uplands geology fit both models. In any case, the Southern Uplands terrane and all its constituents were accreted against the margin of Laurentia during the Ordovician and Silurian.

7 Chronology and terrane assembly, new and old controversies

G. J. H. OLIVER

The original aim of this chapter was to present a synthesis of the geological evolution of the terranes of Scotland prior to their assembly into the current geography of the region. Given the differing hypotheses presented in the preceding four chapters, this chapter could as well concentrate on what is *not* known about Scotland's geological evolution. There are too many unresolved big issues to be complacent about the progress that has been made since the third edition of this book was published in 1991. So, in attempting to synthesize the geology, pre-370 Ma, perhaps the aim should also be to deconstruct the currently held views (as summarized in Chapter 1) in an attempt for better understanding. Chapters 3 to 6 were largely completed in 2001, but some important age dating papers have subsequently been published and these data are considered below.

Scottish geochronology

The reason that differing hypotheses are now possible is because of the application of U–Pb single-zircon geochronology, in particular by using Thermal Ionization Mass Spectrometry (TIMS) and Sensitive High Resolution Ion Microprobe (SHRIMP) technology. With these methods, single zircon grains are selected for analysis after careful study of core and overgrowth textures using cathode luminescence (CL). In the case of the SHRIMP, individual rims and cores can be directly dated.

Before continuing, it is worth reviewing the various radiometric age dating techniques that have been applied to Scottish rocks. TIMS zircon dating using bulk-fractions that combined inherited and newly grown crystals usually gives geologically meaningless discordant ages. Similarly, TIMS dating of zoned zircon grains can give meaningless ages, mixed between old cores and younger rims. Finally, grains that have not been abraded can give spurious discordant TIMS ages since most zircon rims have experienced recent lead loss.

There is a consensus that whole rock Rb–Sr and Sm–Nd isochrons, even with excellent statistics (i.e. mean squares of weighted deviates: MSWDs) cannot always be relied upon to give accurate igneous protolith or metamorphic ages. Rb–Sr and Sm–Nd isotopic dating does not always give the same age as U–Pb dating of zircons from the same suite. Discrepancies can often be explained by either the samples not having the same initial Sr or Nd isotope ratios, that they were never fully isotopically homogenized, or that their isotopic ratios were partially reset by external interferences. Thus it often requires independent single-zircon dating to confirm the validity of whole rock Rb–Sr and Sm–Nd isochrons, (for further discussion see Daly 2000).

K–Ar mineral and Rb–Sr mineral ages in metamorphic rocks date the cooling from the *last time* the mineral was at a temperature above the isotope blocking temperature. Therefore, in high grade gneisses like those of the Hebridean and Northern Highland terranes, these mineral ages are unlikely to be related directly to the age of the peak of metamorphism. On the other hand, radiogenic Nd is thought to be retained in garnet at high temperature (>700–750°C, Hensen & Zhou 1995). Therefore, Sm–Nd garnet dating should date the peak of amphibolite facies metamorphism. Modern practice is to acid-leach out 'inherited' inclusions in garnet prior to isotopic analysis (e.g. Oliver *et al.* 2000). As yet, few leached garnet Sm–Nd dates have been obtained from Scotland.

There is some irony in that Scotland was one of the first places where isotopic dating was successfully and routinely applied to distinguish orogenic events, yet the methods used then are now thought not to be precise enough for discriminating the details. We now have conflicts between qualitative (structural) and quantitative (geochronological) evidence: e.g. the same main phase structures in the Moine are currently assigned to either the Knoydartian, Grampian or Scandian in different places depending on what age dates are available. The problem is now to discriminate between 'good dates on misinterpreted rocks, . . . and misleading numbers on well understood rocks . . .' (N. J. Soper pers. comm.).

The Hebridean terrane

Lewisian

According to Rogers (1996) and Rogers & Santosh (2002) by 2.5 Ga cratonic North America, Greenland (including NW Scotland) and Siberia formed a continental configuration called Arctica (Fig. 7.1). Before 1.5 Ga, Artica was joined by Baltica such that Northern Europe and North America formed Nena (Fig. 7.1). In the meantime, Ur and Atlantica had formed separate continents. After 1.5 Ga, Nena, Ur and Atlantica were combined into the supercontinent called Columbia (Fig. 7.2). Thus during the Archean–Proterozoic, Scotland occupied a marginal situation to these supercontinents.

The Lewisian Gneiss Complex has been conventionally been regarded as a contiguous mid-Archaean crustal block, reworked by major crustal scale shear zones (Park & Tarney 1987). Recently, Friend & Kinny (2001) have used SHRIMP U–Pb single-zircon geochronology to test the correlation of so-called Lewisian events between the mainland and the Outer Hebrides. It now appears that there is little correlation between these areas during the Archean and Palaeoproterozoic. The Minch Fault and regionally important Laxford and Langavat shear zones separate terranes with different protolith and inheritance ages (Chapter 3). Even the Scourie dykes from

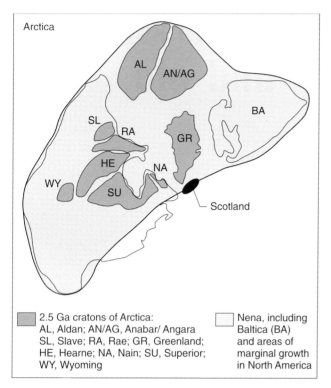

Fig. 7.1. Configuration of the supercontinent Arctica at ~2.5 Ga, showing the position of Scotland. After Rogers & Santosh (2002).

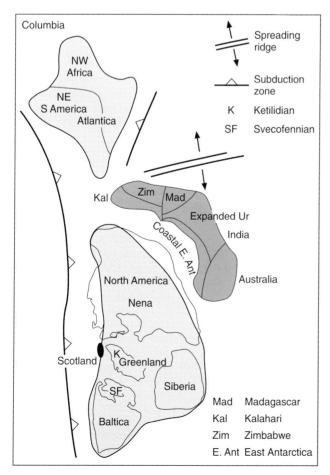

Fig. 7.2. Configuration of the supercontinent Columbia at ~1.5 Ga, showing the position of Scotland. After Rogers & Santosh (2002).

the type area have proved to have a 430 Ma range in ages (Heaman & Tarney 1989), a range equivalent in time from the present back to the Silurian. Mafic dykes in the other terranes are undated and cannot be assumed to be contemporary. Granite sheets, formally considered to be contemporary and thus to link Laxfordian events between the mainland and the Outer Isles, have a 182 Ma difference in ages (i.e. 1854 ± 13 and 1672 ± 8 Ma respectively (Friend & Kinny 2001)).

In South Harris, the Palaeoproterozoic 1880 Ma Roineabhal terrane oceanic/island arc granulite facies complex is accreted against the 3.1–2.9 Ga Tarbert terrane along the post-1670 Ma Langavat Shear Zone. These have no correlatives on the mainland. Indeed, Friend & Kinny (2001) speculate that the Lewisian of the Outer Isles is more akin to terranes found in East Greenland. Thus, there is the potential paradox that the Lewisian of Lewis belongs more to Greenland than to mainland Scotland.

The Loch Maree Group of ~2000 Ma oceanic crust, delta sediments and ~1900 Ma calc-alkaline arc intrusives form an ill-defined subduction zone boundary between the Southern and Central Assynt Zone (Park & Tarney 1987). However, the Loch Maree Group does not have protolith or detrital zircon ages that can be matched to the Outer Isles or East Greenland (Whitehouse *et al.* 1997). The Minch–Outer Hebridean Fault Zone is therefore an important terrane boundary.

Compared to the studies that have been carried out in the Archaean of the North American continent, it would have to be said that the number of reliable age dates from the Lewisian is small. With such large time spans available in the Archaean and the Proterozoic, it would not be surprising if further detailed SHRIMP and TIMS studies did not reveal even more complicated histories.

Rhinns Complex

U–Pb zircon, Sm–Nd whole rock and $^{40}Ar–^{39}Ar$ mineral isotope data indicate that the complex represents addition of juvenile subduction-related material to the crust at 1790 ± 3 Ma (Marcantonio *et al.* 1998; Daly *et al.* 1991a; Muir *et al.* 1994b) and amphibolite facies metamorphism at 1710 Ma (Roddick & Max 1983). These ages allow correlations between the Ketilidian province of South Greenland and the Svecofennian of Scandinavia (Fig. 7.2). The formation of the Rhinns Complex is coincidental with early Laxfordian deformation and metamorphism between 1690–1670 Ma (Corfu *et al.* 1994) and 1729 ± 36 Ma (Kinney & Friend 1997) in the Assynt–Rhiconich terranes. These Rhinns protolith ages are similar to metamorphic and granite injection ages from South Harris (Cliff *et al.* 1998). Lack of Archaean inheritance in Rhinns crust might indicate an absence of Archaean basement south of a line along the Great Glen Fault (Marcantonio *et al.* 1998). The question remains as to how much of the Grampian Highland terrane is underlain by Rhinns-like Proterozoic basement. On the basis of Sm–Nd isotope data from Caledonian granites Dikin & Bowes (1991) suggested that an early Proterozoic basement block (~100 km wide and 600 km long) lies on the south side of the Great Glen Fault. Colonsay Group sediments that lie unconformably on the Rhinns Complex are undated: detrital zircon provenance studies would throw light on the nature of the neighbouring terranes at the time of Colonsay Group deposition.

Perhaps the best that can be proposed is that by the end of the Palaeoproterozoic, enough terranes had been accreted such that NW Scotland occupied the crust that connected Laurentian and Baltica in the supercontinent called Nena (Northern Europe and North America). Figure 7.2 shows the configuration of a supercontinent called Columbia at ~1.5 Ga and the position of Scotland at that time.

Clearly the Hebridean terrane is not a contiguous mid-Archaean crustal block, simply reworked by major crustal scale shear zones; rather, exotic terranes that grew on the margins of Arctica and Nena, had been amalgamated together by the Palaeoproterozoic and have then been partially reworked along suture zones.

Grenvillian

Biotite Rb–Sr ages of ~1100–1000 Ma from the Tarbert terrane in Lewis, NW of the South Harris Shear Zone, indi-

cate Grenvillian cooling below 350°C in at least part of the Hebridean terrane (Cliff & Rex 1989). Presumably this involved Grenvillian exhumation, uplift and erosion; alternatively this might indicate heating associated with thrusting along the South Harris Shear Zone (Cliff & Rex 1989).

Storey *et al.* (2002) have confirmed Grenvillian tectono-metamorphic events with U–Pb zircon dates from the Glenelg–Attadale Inlier, within the Northwest Highland terrane. The Western Unit (WU) is separated from an Eastern Unit (EU) by an amphibolite facies, ~1 km thick, compressional, ductile

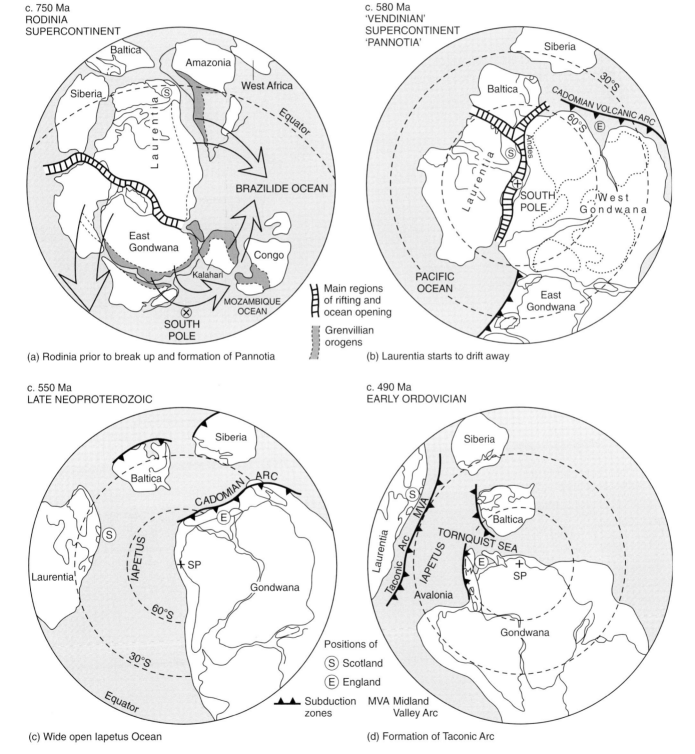

Fig. 7.3. Global continental plate reconstructions from the Neoproterozoic to Late Carboniferous as modified from a compilation by Holdsworth *et al.* (2000). Note the position of Scotland.

shear zone. The WU has a history comparable to the Lewisian. Eastern Unit acid gneisses were formed in the late Archaean but metamorphosed at 1.45 Ga; basic EU rocks were metamorphosed to eclogite facies during the Grenville orogeny at *c.* 1100 Ma. Both the EU and WU show zircon disturbances at 0.9–1.0 Ga caused by Grenvillian amphibolite facies metamorphism. Grenville Sm–Nd garnet ages have been obtained from garnet granulite xenoliths from Carboniferous vents in the Midland Valley (van Breemen & Hawkesworth 1980). Another granulite facies xenolith has a 1180 ± 55 Ma chondrite uniform

reservoir (CHUR) model age which may be a Grenvillian time of separation of magma from the mantle. However, *in situ* Grenvillian magmatic protolith ages are absent in Scotland, although ~1000 Ma granites, migmatites and pegmatites do occur in the Annagh Gneiss Complex of Co. Mayo in Ireland (see below).

Thus there seems to be evidence for Grenvillian events within 'basement' to link the Hebridean, Northwest Highland, Grampian Highland, and Midland Valley terranes at ~1000 Ma. The Grenvillian orogeny in North America is linked

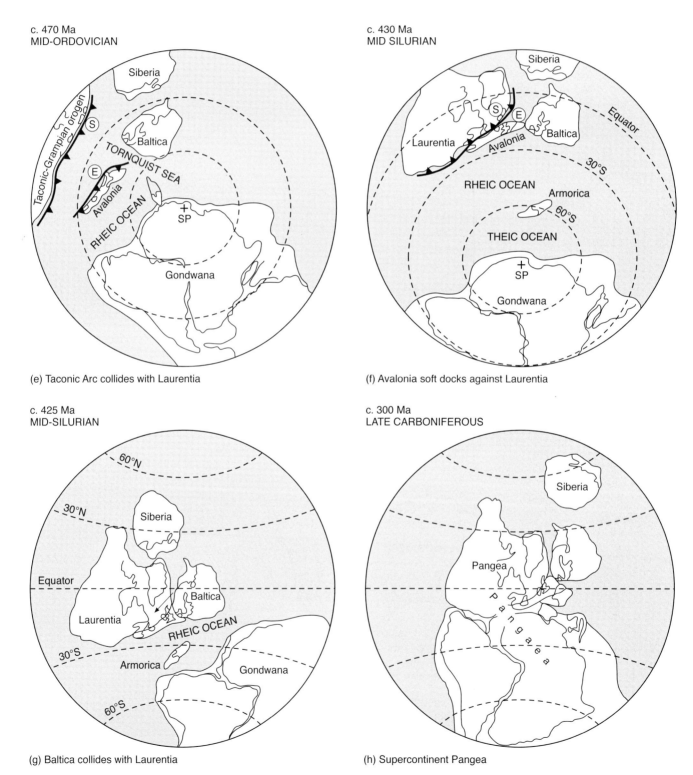

(e) Taconic Arc collides with Laurentia

(f) Avalonia soft docks against Laurentia

(g) Baltica collides with Laurentia

(h) Supercontinent Pangea

Fig. 3. (*continued*)

to many other continents that amalgamated into the supercontinent called Rodinia (Fig. 7.3a). Dalziel (1997) used similarities of provincial faunas between Argentina and northeastern America, palaeomagnetics, and the linking of Grenville-aged orogenic belts to propose that Scotland formed part of a Laurentian promontory that was once fitted into the Arequipa embayment of coastal Peru. Previously, Wilson (1969) had proposed that Laurentian faunas in Scotland should be linked with North America via a Proto-Atlantic ocean which had opened and closed during the Early Palaeozoic. Scotese & McKerrow (1990) using geological correlations and much of the same palaeomagnetic evidence as Dalziel (1997), proposed the same Wilson Cycle for an Iapetus Ocean. New Argentinian palaeomagnetic data and a reassessment of geological correlations suggested to Thomas et al. (2002) that the Laurentian faunas in Argentina are located on a far travelled microcontinent that had split off from Laurentia and later collided with South America. Hence, Dalziel's (1997) preferred Rodinia fit (Fig. 7.3a) is not confirmed and other reconstructions are possible (e.g. Scotese & McKerrow 1990).

Torridonian

Stewart (1969) has long maintained that the Torridonian represents Neoproterozoic easterly pro-grading alluvial fan deposition in local syn-rift basins developed on Lewisian basement (see Chapter 3). Soper (1994b) and Williams (2001) have re-iterated this hypothesis linking basin development with incipient break up of Rodinia. Nicholson (1993) and Rainbird et al. (2001) agreed that the Sleat and Stoer Groups were deposited in local rifts. However, they proposed that the upper part of the Torridonian was deposited as a broad alluvial braidplain apron, by rivers several hundred kilometres long that originated in the Grenville orogenic belt in Canada. Prave et al. (2001) have gone further; using detrital 1088 Ma U–Pb zircon (Rogers et al. 1990) and detrital 997 Ma ^{40}Ar–^{39}Ar muscovite ages (Demster in Bluck et al. 1997), plus more unpublished ages, they proposed that the Torridon Group is the molasse to the Grenville Orogeny. Indeed, they suggested that the distal marine equivalent of a proximal fluvial Torridon Group is represented by the Morar Group of the Moine Series in the Northern Highland terrane. This latter correlation was first proposed by Peach et al. (1907) on lithological grounds. Thus there is a potential link between the Hebridean and Northern Highland terranes during the Neoproterozoic.

Cambro-Ordovician

The Durness Cambro-Ordovician transgressive quarzite to limestone sequence, with its Laurentian fauna, is understood to be the inshore passive margin shelf sequence to the developing Iapetus Ocean (Chapter 3). Dewey (1969) summarized the view that the shelf would have extended across the Moines of the Northern Highland terrane and into the deeper water facies of the Cambrian upper Dalradian of the Grampian Highland terrane. Thus the Moine thrust sheet is 'moderately' allochthonous.

Bluck et al. (1997) preferred not to make any spatial correlations between the Cambrian Durness and Dalradian sequences and therefore invoked a passive margin plus its attendant oceanic crust to have extended hundreds of km to the south and east of the Hebridean terrane. They appealed to major post-Llanvirn strike-slip movements to bring the far-travelled Northern Highland and Hebridean terranes together and to displace the evidence for the missing ocean. Therefore, the Hebridean and Northern Highland terranes were not linked during the Neoproterozoic. They relegated the Silurian Moine Thrust movements to a 'comparatively trivial final convergence'.

Northern Highland terrane

Moine

The age of the Moine basement is controversial: the original mappers (e.g. Peach et al. 1907) treated all inliers of deformed gneiss within the Moine as Lewisian on the basis of lithological comparison with the Hebridean foreland. U–Pb zircon dating by Friend et al. (2002a) confirms Archean ages in northern inliers (e.g. 2.8–2.9 Ga protolith ages from the Ribigill, Borgie and Farr inliers, and 2.7 and 1.7 Ga ages from the Loch Duich inliers. However, the 2.9 Ga ages are too old for comparison with the Rhiconnich or Gruinard terranes and there is no zircon record of the 2.49 Ga granulite facies event from the Assynt terrane. Furthermore there is no record in these inliers of new Caledonian, Knoydartian or Grenvillian zircon growth. Therefore, there is no requirement to match Archaean gneiss inliers in the Moine Supergroup with the Archean in the Hebridean terrane. Considering the westward sense of Caledonian thrusting along the north coast, they may have once been positioned far to the south and east. This supports the contention that the Northwest Highland and Hebridean terranes are very exotic to each other (Bluck et al. 1997).

Moine sedimentation may have spanned 110 Ma. This is constrained by the age of the youngest detrital zircon (980 ± 4 Ma, Peters et al. 2001) and the age of the intrusive West Highlands Granitic Gneiss at 870 Ma (Friend et al. 1997). The Upper Morar Psammite Formation has yielded U–Pb detrital zircon age clusters at 980–1100, 1400–1500, 1650–1850 and very rare 2800 Ma grains (Peters et al. 2001). Perhaps the Upper Morar was once connected to the ~1700 Ma Rhinns terrane. As noted above, the ~1000 Ma ages suggested to Prave et al. (2001) that the Morar and Torridon groups were connected to a common Grenvillian source. This goes against the idea that the Hebridean and Northwest Highland terranes were strongly separated from each other at this time (Bluck et al. 1997).

The lack of significant Archaean detrital zircon has led to the speculation that the bulk of the Moine was not derived from the Hebridean terrane (Friend et al. 2002a). SHRIMP analyses of zircon cores from the Fort Augustus granitic gneiss (which intrudes the Loch Eil Group) vary from 1626 ± 9 to 947 ± 59 Ma, with the bulk indicating a Grenvillian source for the Moine sediments that were later melted to form the granite protolith (Rogers et al. 2001). Likewise the Ardgour Granitic Gneiss (which intrudes the apparently older Glenfinnan and Loch Eil Groups) also includes Grenvillian inherited zircon cores (Friend et al. 1997).

Soper et al. (1998) have proposed that the Moine Supergroup was deposited in successive half-graben basins formed on the rifted margin of NE Laurentia (Fig. 7.3a) following the break up of Rodinia. In contrast, Prave et al. (2001) (see above) have proposed that the Morar Group is the distal marine equivalent of the Torridon Group, both being primarily derived from the Grenvillian orogenic belt.

Knoydartian orogeny

Ever since Gilletti et al. (1961) measured ~740 Ma Rb–Sr muscovite ages from pegmatites in Moine metasediments from the Knoydart region, there has been controversy over the significance of a Knoydartian orogeny. Zircon and monazite U–Pb ages now date these pegmatites at 827–784 Ma (Rogers *et al.* 1998). Sm–Nd garnet ages from Morar pelites give 823 ± 5 and 788 ± 4 Ma. Results of geothermobarometry of the dated garnets show the effects of progressively higher pressure regional amphibolite facies metamorphism consistent with compressive orogeny (Vance *et al.* 1998).

Ryan & Soper (2001) have proposed an extensional model for the origin of the Ardgour granite gneisses (zircon TIMS, 873 ± 7 Ma (Friend *et al.* 1997)) and contemporaneous gabbros/ basic dyke swarms (zircon TIMS, 873 ± 6 Ma (Millar 1999)). They proposed a lower crustal stretching and heating model that formed extensional basins for the accumulation of Moine sediments, and enough heat to give amphibolite facies metamorphism and partial melting. As in the rift model for the Torridonian, Moine extension is related to the break-up of Rodinia and the formation of the new Iapetus Ocean. It is worth noting that there is a 50 Ma gap between the 873 Ma Ardgour granite plus gabbro/basic dyke intrusions, and the 823 Ma Morar pro-grade garnet-growing episode, giving ample time for the tectonic regime to change from extensional into compressional. The Knoydartian orogeny needs to be defined more precisely.

Prave *et al.* (2001) noted that modern rift basins are much shorter lived than 110 Ma, have proximal fault related sedimentary facies plus significant bimodal volcanism; features that the Moine Supergroup lacks. Rather, Prave *et al.* (2001) speculated that the Torridon/Morar arkosic sandstones are a more distal Grenvillian molassic apron, separated from the rest of the Moine Glenfinnan and Loch Eil Groups by the Sgurr Beag slide. The Glenfinnan and Loch Eil Groups then become the debris of the Knoydartian orogeny and the Sgurr Beag thrust becomes a reactivated foreland thrust.

There is no equivalent to the Knoydartian so far reported from Northeast USA, Canada or Greenland. However, 804 ± 19 Ma granites (Daly *et al.* 1991*b*, U–Pb zircon) cross-cut folded gneisses on Sørøy with *c.* 1.2 Ga model ages that define the Porsanger orogeny of northernmost Norway. Daly *et al.* (1991*b*) hypothesized that the Porsanger may be related to the Knoydartian orogeny. Greiling & Smith (2000) have a reconstruction of Gondwana, Laurentia and Baltica at Varangerian ice age times (~590 Ma) with the Grampian Highlands of Scotland adjacent to northern Norway which supports such a correlation. However, Daly *et al.* (1991*b*) did not rule out a Grenvillian age for the Sørøy gneisses, and Reginiussen & Elvevold (pers. comm.) would concur on the basis of PT and deformation studies.

Grampian Highland terrane

Central Highlands

Migmatites from the Central Highlands have 840 ± 11 Ma metamorphic zircon (Highton *et al.* 1999). Pegmatites formed in the Grampian Shear Zone have 806 Ma monazite ages (Noble *et al.* 1996). These ages show that perhaps there are Neoproterozoic links with the Knoydartian events across the Great Glen Fault. Furthermore, the Beinnn Mheadhoin Pebbly Psammite Formation from the area of the 840 Ma migmatites has yielded detrital zircon ages between *c.* 1675 and 1010 Ma (Peters *et al.* 2001). Cawood *et al.* (in press) date the youngest zircon detritus at 900 ± 17 Ma (U–Pb). Therefore, the Central Highlands has a post-Grenville, pre-Caledonian sedimentary sequence as in the Moine of the Northern Highlands. The 1675 Ma zircon may be related to the Rhinns terrane. Thus the Great Glen Fault need not be a terrane boundary between the Grampian Highland and the Northern Highland terranes after ~1700 Ma.

Dalradian

Basement. As noted above, Dikin & Bowes (1991) suggested that an early Proterozoic ~1700 Ma Rhinns-like basement block (~100 km wide and 600 km long) lies on the south side of the Great Glen Fault. Granites and migmatites in the ~1000 Ma Annagh Gneiss Complex of Co Mayo, Ireland, are in tectonic contact with overlying Dalradian rocks (Daly 1996). Thus ~1000 Ma Grenville rocks form basement to part of the Grampian Highland terrane. The Strichen Granite, which intruded the Dalradian at 470 ± 5 Ma, has 850 Ma zircons inherited from an acid plutonic source (Oliver *et al.* 2000). In the region of Slochd Summit, in the Central Highlands, Piasekie & van Breemen (1983) and Piasecki & Temperley (1988*b*) have mapped a tectonic boundary between the 840 Ma Central Highland migmatites and the Dalradian Grampian Group as the Grampian Slide (Fig. 7.4). Thus Rhinns, Grenville and Knoydartian basement underlies Grampian Highland terrane (Fig. 7.5a).

Dalradian Supergroup. Piasecki & van Breemen (1983) maintained that coarse foliated segregations, i.e. pegmatites, dated at 808^{+11}_{-9} Ma by U–Pb monazite by Noble *et al.* (1996), were segregated during mylonitization of Grampian Group metasediments along the Grampian Shear Zone at Lochindorb: thus the Grampian Group must pre-date this by an unknown amount. Furthermore, syn-mylonitic monazite is dated at 804^{+13}_{-12} Ma (Noble *et al.* 1996) and the mylonite fabric cuts 'early fabrics' in the Grampian Group. Consequently, Noble *et al.* (1996) imply a pre-804 Ma tectonometamorphic history

Fig. 7.4. The Grampian Shear Zone at Slochd Summit A9 road cuts (map reference NH850239). View is looking east with Grampian Group to the north (left) and Central Highland Group to the south (right). See Piasecki & Temperley (1988*b*) for details.

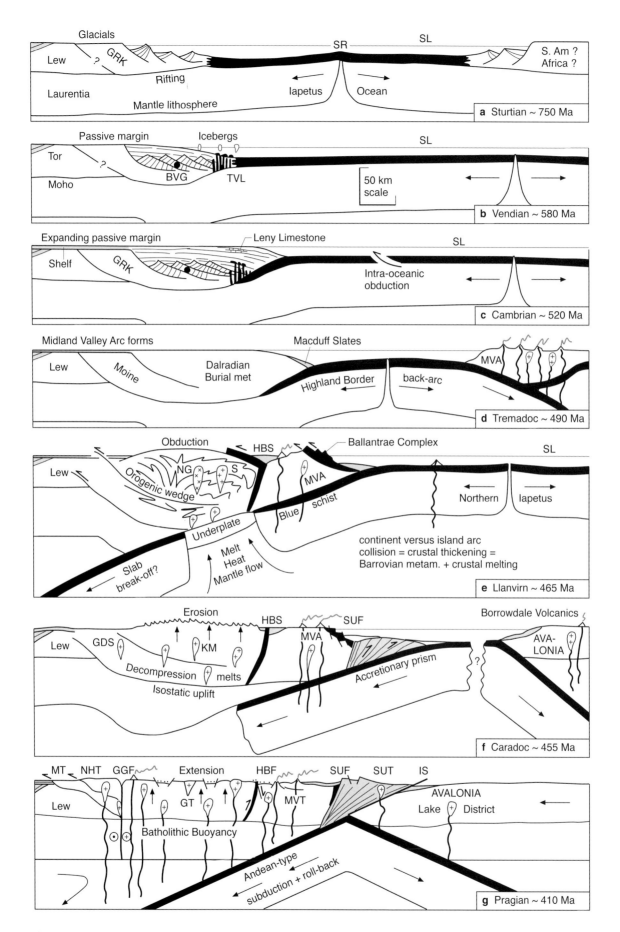

Fig. 7.5. Plate tectonic evolution of Scotland from ~750 to 410 Ma based on compilations in Oliver (2001) and Atherton & Ghani (2002), see text for discussion. BVG, Ben Vuirich Granite; GDS, Glen Dessary Syenite; G, Grenvillian; GT, Grampian Highlands terrane, HBF, Highland Boundary Fault; HBS, Highland Border Series; HT, Hebridean terrane; IS, Iapetus Suture; KM, Kennethmont granite; K, Knoydartian; Lew, Lewisian; MVA, Midland Valley Arc; MVT, Midland Valley terrane; NG, Newer Gabbro; NHT, Northern Highlands terrane; R, Rhinns; S, Strichen granite; SL, sea level; SUF, Southern Upland Fault; SUT, Southern Uplands terrane; TVL, Tayvallich Lavas; Tor, Torridonian.

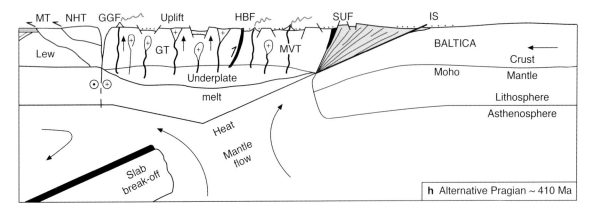

Fig. 5. (*continued*)

for this part of the Dalradian. Smith *et al.* (1999) used stratigraphic and sedimentological evidence to infer an unconformity between the Grampian Group and the underlying rocks. Thomas (pers. comm.) has measured $^{87}Sr/^{86}Sr$ ratios on a number of Grampian and Appin Group meta-limestones and by comparison with $^{87}Sr/^{86}Sr$ ratios of limestones from other dated Neoproterozoic sequences, has interpreted the data to indicate that the Dalradian, as a whole, is younger than 800 Ma. Therefore there is no agreement on the maximum age of the ~20 km thick Dalradian Supergroup although Cawood *et al.* (in press) date the youngest zircon detritus in the Grampian Group at 900 ± 17 Ma (U–Pb).

There are two glacial horizons, the middle Dalradian Port Askaig Tillite (Fig. 7.5a) and the upper Dalradian Loch na Cille Boulder Bed (Fig. 7.5b) that are correlated with the Sturtian (~720) and the Varangerian (~590 Ma) respectively (Prave 1999; Brazier & Shields 2000). The Loch na Cille Boulder Bed is in close association with the 601 ± 4 Ma (TIMS U–Pb zircon, Dempster *et al.* 2002) tuffs from the Tayvallich Lavas. The fossiliferous Leny Limestone from near the top of the succession is Early Cambrian (~520 Ma) (Fig. 7.5c). The upper age is constrained by the Early Ordovician Strichen Granite which intrudes the Upper Dalradian at 476 ± 5 Ma age. Thus there is the potential for 20 km of sediment and volcanics to have been deposited in ~330 Ma, apparently without breaks. According to Glover *et al.* (1995) and Soper & England (1995) this was accomplished during episodic extension of the lithosphere as Rodinia broke apart to form the Iapetus Ocean (Fig. 7.5a, b) during the Sturtian and Vendian.

Prave (1999) did not accept that continuous sedimentation could carry on for more than 300 Ma of extension, especially since the preceding ~300 Ma of Moine and Torridonian sedimentation were also supposed to be dominated by extensional tectonics. Rather, he proposed that the lower Dalradian (Grampian plus Appin Groups) could represent the flysch and molasse of the Knoydatian orogeny, and that only the Argyll plus Southern Highland Groups represent Iapitean rifting.

Cawood *et al.* (in press) have U–Pb SHRIMP dated detrital zircons from the Dalradian Supergroup. The presence of Archean grains with 1.8 Ga overgrowths together with detrital age peaks of around 1.8 Ga, 1.75–1.7 Ga, 1.65–1.6 Ga, 1.55–1.5 Ga, the paucity of mid-Mesoproterozoic detritus (1.4–1.2 Ga), and the evidence for a tectothermal overprinting event in the source region between 1.0–0.9 Ga, is the geological history of the Labrador–Greenland (Superior–Grenville) region of Laurentia. This Laurentian Archaean detrital signature can be interpreted to mean that the Dalradian (Grampian terrane) was autochthonous in relation to the Laurentian margin, contrary to the allochthonous theory (Bluck 2001).

There is no definitive evidence for 0.9–0.8 Ga detritus, particularly in the Lower Dalradian: this throws doubt on the theory that the Grampian and Appin Groups are the molasse and flysch of the Knoydartian orogeny (Prave 1999).

Dempster *et al.* (2002) considered that the Ben Vuirich Granite was intruded at 590 ± 2 Ma into a rifting Lower Dalradian Laurentian margin sequence that had already been thickened and somewhat regionally metamorphosed (Fig. 7.5b). The reason for this proposed post-720 Ma–pre-590 Ma crustal thickening event is not known and the lack of any reported field evidence (e.g. unconformities, re-worked fabrics and structures) makes this hypothesis difficult to sustain. However, Prave & Alsop (1998) suspected that there are significant discontinuities in the Dalradian succession (e.g. the Scarba Conglomerate could be a 650–600 Ma break-up unconformity, (Fig. 7.5a)). Alsop *et al.* (2000) have reported cleaved clasts in conglomerates in the Argyll and Southern Highland Groups which they tentatively assigned to a post-Grenvillian–pre-Caledonian, perhaps Knoydartian provenance.

Grampian event. The Grampian event is relatively well understood in Western Ireland (Dewey & Mange 1999) but less well so in Scotland (Oliver 2001). A peri-Laurentian Taconic island arc, partly exposed in the Ballantrae Complex but mostly presumed buried in the Midland Valley terrane, collided with the Laurentian margin causing regional deformation, crustal thickening and Barrovian metamorphism (Figs 7.3e, 7.5d, e). Collision probably started with the obduction of the Ballantrae Ophiolite at 478 ± 8 Ma (K–Ar hornblende age of the metamorphic sole, Bluck *et al.* (1980)). Post-nappe deformation is dated by the syn-D2 Newer Gabbros (470 ± 9 Ma TIMS zircon age (Dempster *et al.* 2002); 471 ± 1.7 Ma TIMS zircon age (Carty *et al.* 2002); 471.9 ± 2.4 Ma TIMS zircon age (Oliver *et al.* 2002)) whilst peak metamorphism is dated at 467 ± 2.5 Ma (Sm–Nd garnet whole rock (Oliver *et al.* 2000)).

Grampian Newer Gabbros. The Newer Gabbros may represent the plutonic arc formed as the Highland Border back-arc was subducted (Fig. 7.5d, e). Alternatively, slab break-off at the time that the Midland Valley arc collided may have initiated the plutonism (Oliver *et al.* 2002). Whatever the cause, the extra heat brought into the NE Grampian Highlands contributed to the high temperature, low pressure Buchan metamorphism (Dempster *et al.* 1995).

Grampian granites. Another unresolved issue of Grampian Highland geology is the origin of the voluminous granites. Oliver (2001) noted that few granite intrusions have been accurately dated or analysed for REE and Sm–Nd isotopes.

Nevertheless, he speculated that Arenig foliated granites with high strontium initial ratios might represent S-type syn-metamorphic melting of Grampian crust thickened during collision with the Midland Valley Arc, or maybe formed as a consequence of slab break-off (Oliver *et al.* 2002) (Fig. 7.5d, e). Caradoc to Llandovery post-tectonic, high strontium initial ratio S-type granites might have formed by decompression melting of the Grampian crust during exhumation driven by isostacy (Fig. 7.5f). A change to low strontium initial ratio I-type granites occurred in the Llandovery (~435 Ma), possibly when subducting Iapetian crust reached under the Grampian Highland terrane (van Breemen & Bluck 1981). This ceased in the Early Devonian when Avalonia (the Lake District terrane) docked against the Southern Uplands (Fig. 7.5g). Another hypothesis (Fig. 7.5h) is that the Newer Granites are mostly Early Devonian in age (rather than spread through the Silurian and Early Devonian) and that they are related to the break off of a subducting Iapetian slab, synchronous with the Scandian orogeny which involved collision with Baltica (Atherton & Ghani 2002). There is now the possibility that the Newer Granites involved the oblique collision of both Avalonia and Baltica with Laurentia starting at *c.* 435 Ma (Fig. 7.3f, g) and ending at the collision with Armorica at *c.* 410 Ma (Soper *et al.* 1987). At least 35 Ma of subduction is required if the Southern Uplands terrane is indeed a Caradoc (460 Ma) to Wenlock (425 Ma) accretionary prism (see below) and unless the subduction zone remained at a shallow angle during this time, Andean I-type plutonism might have been expected. As noted above, the precise age of the majority of Scottish granites is unknown and until the dating is done, there can only be speculation.

Midland Valley terrane

Basement

Precambrian basement is not exposed in the Midland Valley. However, undated conglomerate in the Highland Border Complex has 1800 Ma quartz mica-schist boulders of unknown provenance (Dempster & Bluck 1989). As noted above, Midland Valley Carboniferous vents include Grenvillian lower crustal granulite facies xenoliths (van Breemen & Hawkesworth 1980).

Highland Border Complex

Fragments of Highland Border Complex ophiolite outcrop along the Highland Boundary Fault. Garnet amphibolite from a possible metamorphic sole on Bute has yielded 546 ± 42 Ma (Sm–Nd garnet) and 537 ± 11 Ma (K–Ar hornblende, Dempster & Bluck 1991*a*). Bluck (2001) interprets this as the age of oceanic obduction onto middle Proterozoic basement (Fig. 7.6a). Because the Leny Limestone (with Laurentian fauna) near the top of the Dalradian Supergroup (but see discussions by Tanner (1995), and Bluck & Ingham (1997)) is possibly younger (at ~520 Ma), it might be that the garnet amphibolite dates Cambrian intra-oceanic obduction rather than Arenig obduction onto the Grampian Highland terrane (Fig. 7.5c). Slivers of Arenig limestones with Laurentian fossils in tectonic contact with both spilite and younger conglomerate (containing ophiolite debris) and arenites (of possible Caradoc age with Barrovian-type garnet detritus) make a possible link with the Llanvirn Grampian orogenic episode (Hutcheson & Oliver 1998; Oliver 2001) (Fig. 7.5e). In this scenario the Highland Border ophiolite is the Cambrian to Early Ordovician back-arc basin to the Midland Valley arc terrane (Fig 7.5d). The ophiolite was dismembered when the arc collided with the Grampian

terrane (Fig. 7.5e). Thus it is possible that the pre-Llanvirn parts of the Highland Border Complex could have shared the same tectonic history as the neighbouring Southern Highland Group in the Grampian terrane (Johnson & Harris 1967).

On the other hand, the lack of extensive Llanvirn and Caradoc syn-orogenic Highland Border deposits eroded from the Grampian terrane has led Bluck (2001) to propose that during the Ordovician, the Highland Border and the Grampian Highland terrane were at some distance from each other. They were brought together just prior to post-Wenlock Lower Old Red Sandstone sedimentation (Fig. 7.6d). Thus the similarities in structures on either side of the Highland Boundary Fault are artefacts of repeated deformation along the fault zone.

Ballantrae Complex

There is general agreement concerning the Ballantrae Complex (Bluck 2001) (Chapter 6). It is a highly tectonized and foreshortened assemblage of intra-oceanic blocks containing a Cambrian to Lower Ordovician island arc, marginal back-arc ocean floor, seamounts, serpentinite, deep sea sediments, olistostromes and mélanges (Figs 7.5d, 7.6b). The complex was accreted onto Midland Valley basement at the same time that the Grampian Highland terrane was regionally deformed and metamorphosed in the Llanvirn (Figs 7.5e, 7.6b). Less well understood is the nature of this basement and the position of an Ordovician Midland Valley arc which is only recorded in conglomerates overlying the complex. In addition, the latter have ophiolite, blueschist-eclogite and Barrovian-type metamorphic detritus. Hutcheson & Oliver (1998) consider that the Barrovian detritus originated from the Grampian Highlands terrane, and therefore link the two terranes from the Llanvirn onwards (Fig. 7.5f). Bluck (2001) prefers a local Midland Valley basement source for this detritus and therefore sees no reason to link the terranes until the Early Silurian (Fig. 7.6c), although Barrovian-type xenoliths have not been found in Carboniferous vents in the Midland Valley. The blueschist-eclogite detritus is of unknown provenance but is presumed to be derived from an (Ordovician?) subduction zone perhaps once situated along the Highland Boundary or within the Ballantrae Complex (Fig. 7.5e).

Southern Uplands terrane

Basement

Opinions about the type of basement under the Southern Uplands differ. Leggett *et al.* (1983) proposed that the leading edge of the Lake District had under-thrust the Southern Uplands at a moderate angle, a view supported by Soper *et al.* (1992*b*) based on seismic data, and Anderson & Oliver (1996) based on the evidence of mylonite xenoliths in lamprophyre dykes in Co. Down (Fig. 7.5g). Hall *et al.* (1983) interpreted seismic velocities to predict a shallow crystalline basement which had been overthrust northwards by an allochthonous Southern Uplands (Fig. 7.6e). Oliver & McKerrow (1984) used the same seismic data to suggest a change with depth from low to medium grade regional metamorphism without the need for an exotic basement.

Origin

Opinions on the origin of the Southern Uplands terrane have been divided since Leggett *et al.* (1979) proposed an accretionary prism model (Fig.7.5f). Morris (1987) and Stone *et al.* (1987) preferred a combined model of fore-arc and back-arc deposition, Armstrong & Owen (2000*b*) proposed a back-arc

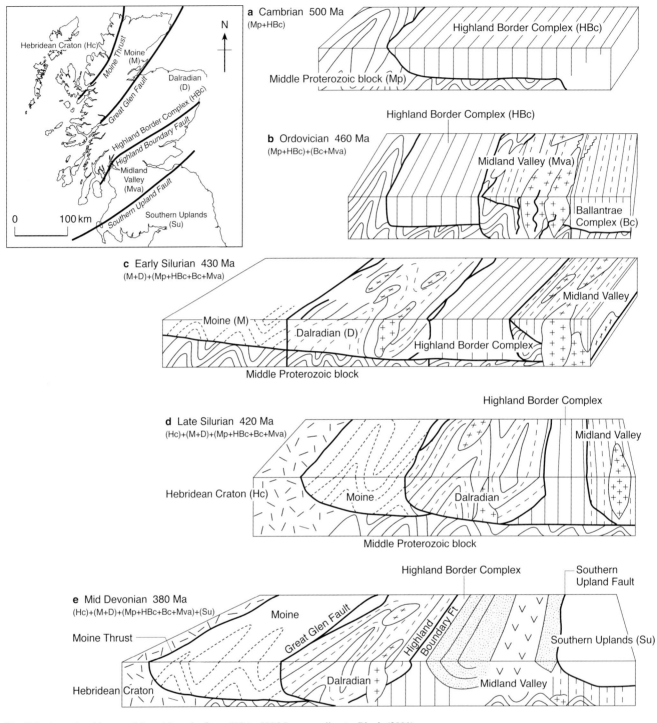

Fig. 7.6. Accretion history of Scottish rocks from 500 to 380 Ma, according to Bluck (2001).

basin model whilst Bluck (2001) speculated again on a fore-arc basin model. The relative abundance of volcanic arc, metamorphic and ophiolite detritus in the Southern Uplands, with variable turbidite palaeo-flow directions allows all these models. A problem with arc models is that the arc has not been preserved.

Links with neighbouring terranes

Oliver (2001) supported the accretionary prism model (Fig. 7.5f, g) pointing out that the age of metamorphic detritus in the Southern Uplands terrane (470 Ma garnet Sm–Nd, and muscovite ^{40}Ar–^{39}Ar ages) corresponds with Grampian High-

land terrane metamorphic ages (470 Ma garnet Sm–Nd, and muscovite K–Ar). Thus the two terranes have been linked since the Caradoc. Bluck (2001), despite the identical garnet ages, argued that the mean of muscovite ages from the Grampian Highland terrane are 25 Ma younger than the mean of Southern Upland detrital muscovite ages and therefore the two terranes can not be linked. However this difference in ages is what would be expected if the first metamorphosed Dalradian to be uplifted (i.e. with the oldest K–Ar dates) was first to be eroded away and deposited in the Southern Uplands.

In Bluck's (2001) view there is no need to amalgamate the Grampian, Midland Valley and Southern Uplands terranes until the Early Devonian, when Dalradian and Southern

Uplands detritus is allegedly first seen in the Midland Valley (Fig. 7.6e). Bluck (2001) maintains that Grampian Highland metamorphic detritus could not have survived travelling ~100 km across the Midland Valley from the Grampian to the Southern Uplands terrane and that a different metamorphic source is buried in the Midland Valley. However, Bluck (2000) proposes that first cycle metamorphic detritus can travel 1000 km from the Scandian orogenic front in Norway, to be deposited in the Lower Old Red Sandstone basins in the Midland Valley.

Nevertheless, the problem still remains that there are no records of Ordovician or Silurian river systems connecting the Grampian and Southern Uplands terranes. This is exacerbated by the fact that quartz-mica schist boulders in the supposed Arenigian part of the Highland Border Complex gave Proterozoic (~1800 Ma Rb–Sr muscovite ages (Dempster & Bluck 1989)) rather than Grampian ages. Fig. 7.5e–g is based on the assumption that the Ordovician and Silurian rivers by-passed the Highland Border Complex on their way south. If the Southern Uplands is full of Grampian terrane detritus then large-scale strike-slips of many hundreds of km along the Highland Boundary and Southern Upland faults are unnecessary (cf. Bluck 2001).

Despite the differences in opinions described above, there is general consensus that Avalonia drifted away from Gondwana during the Mid Ordovician until its leading edge (the English Lake District) under-thrust the Laurentian margin (the Southern Uplands) starting in the Wenlock (Torsvik et al. 1996)

(Fig. 7.3d–f). The putative Iapetus Suture is now buried under the Northumbrian Carboniferous Basin (Fig. 7.5g). Wenlock strata in the south of the Southern Uplands are uncleaved, suggesting a soft collision. K–Ar and ^{40}Ar–^{39}Ar white mica Early Devonian cooling ages in the Southern Uplands (390 ± 6 Ma, Huff et al. 1991) are similar to those in the Lake District (397 ± 7, 418 ± 3 Ma, Merriman et al. 1995) and Wales (399 ± 9 Ma, Dong et al. 1997). This is the age of the end of Lower Old Red Sandstone sedimentation (Emsian) in the Midland Valley. These events are presumably expressions of the Acadian orogeny when Armorica collided with the southern margin of Avalonia (Fig. 7.3g).

Future research

At the start of the new Millennium, Scottish pre-Devonian geology is in flux. In the past ten years, as more and more accurate and precise age dates have become available the picture has become more complicated and some would say, more confused. The consensus is that there is no concensus and that it will require at least another decade of dedicated research to clarify matters. More, not less ground mapping is necessary. More radiometric dating and geochemistry is essential. Could these Scottish 'big' issues be better resolved by looking at the bigger scale: i.e. by making comparisons with Greenland, Labrador, Canada, and Scandinavia? Systematic, not piece-meal research is required.

8 Old Red Sandstone

N. H. TREWIN & M. F. THIRLWALL

The account of the Old Red Sandstone (ORS) given by Wally Mykura (1991) in the third edition of this book remains an authoritative account containing many details which will not be repeated here. Wally Mykura wrote at a time of active controversy concerning the relation of the Grampian Block to Devonian successions south of the Highland Boundary Fault. His untimely death robbed him of the opportunity to discuss problems which have been reconciled to some extent by recent work and revision of absolute ages for the Devonian (Tucker *et al.* 1998).

The chapter title follows tradition, recognizing that both the base and the top of the Devonian cannot generally be defined in Scotland. The Stonehaven Group of ORS facies is now thought to be as old as the Mid-Silurian (Marshall 1991) and the top of the Upper ORS passes conformably up into Carboniferous strata. The term Old Red Sandstone (discussion in Waterston 1965) was originally derived from the 'Oelter rother Sandstein' of Werner, and was applied to the Permian red sandstones of Germany. Phillips (1818) used ORS in its present sense, and Murchison (1839) considered it should be regarded as a system. However, it was Sedgwick & Murchison (1839) who established the Devonian system for marine strata in SW England and included the ORS within the Devonian. Old Red Sandstone is now used as a facies term and, whilst the rocks are mostly of Devonian age, there are notable exceptions.

The distribution of ORS strata (Fig. 8.1) shows two major preserved areas of deposition: the Orcadian Basin area and the Midland Valley. Remnants occur to the south of the Southern Upland Fault (SUF) and north of the Highland Boundary Fault (HBF) in the Lorne–Ben Nevis area. Outliers at Rhynie and Tomintoul occur between the major areas, but drainage here was northwards into the Orcadian area. To the north, the rocks of Shetland can also be considered part of the Orcadian area on the basis of fish faunas.

The ORS is traditionally divided into Upper, Middle and Lower divisions following Murchison (1859*d*) who correctly recognized that the Middle division was confined to the Orcadian area, but erroneously thought the Lower division was only present south of the HBF. In the Midland Valley an erosional unconformity separates Lower and Upper ORS. In the Orcadian area unconformities can be locally demonstrated between Lower/Middle and Middle/Upper. However, detailed stratigraphic work by Rogers, D. A. *et al.* (1989) has shown that the Middle and Upper ORS are generally conformable, and that with few exceptions, the whole of the ORS in the Orcadian area is contained within the Emsian–Frasnian (Fig. 8.2). Hence the Upper ORS is considered to extend significantly into the Middle Devonian. At the time of writing two significant publications are in preparation; Marshall & Hewitt (2003) on the offshore Devonian and its connections to the onshore, and Browne *et al.* (in press) on lithostratigraphy south of the Orcadian area.

Timescales and stages of the Devonian and Late Silurian

Several timescales (Fig. 8.3) have been used in recent years for the Silurian and Devonian that emphasize different isotopic age determination methods. For example, the timescale prior to the mid-1980s was dominated by Rb–Sr whole-rock ages on acid volcanic rocks, but these are now known to be commonly too young because of post-eruptive fluid interactions. More recent schemes use U–Pb zircon ages extensively, but even then there are discrepancies between ion probe and conventional determinations (e.g. Tucker & McKerrow 1995). Tucker *et al.* (1998) have revised the Devonian timescale based on precise U–Pb zircon ages, yielding significant differences with previous timescales such as a 418 Ma age for the base of the Devonian and a short duration of only 1 Ma of the Přídolí stage. Further revision by Compston (2000) discussed by Williams *et al.* (2000) makes radical changes reducing the combined Lochkovian and Pragian to only 3.1 Ma, expanding the Přídolí to 7.2 Ma, and putting the base of the Devonian at 411.6 Ma. Hence it is not possible to assign age dates to Devonian or Silurian time in the region of 410–420 Ma. In the timescale of Tucker & McKerrow (1995) both the base of the Přídolí and the base of the Pragian are defined by age determinations of palynologically dated Scottish ORS igneous rocks: these are fully consistent with the revisions of Tucker *et al.* (1998).

General position of Scotland in Devonian times

Scotland was part of Euramerica or the 'Old Red Sandstone Continent' in the Devonian. The continent consisted of most of North America, Greenland, and northern Europe to the north of the Rhenoherycnian suture as far east as the Caucasus. To the south in Cornwall and Devon, and east into Europe lay marine conditions of the Rhenohercynian basin and the Variscan orogen, which owed its existence to continental collision from the relative northward movement of the African/South American plate (North Gondwana). Reconstructions (e.g. Ziegler 1988*b*) suggest that throughout the Devonian the ORS Continent was surrounded by active foldbelts. Details of the subduction history in most areas are rather sketchy and there is little agreement on the number or direction of subduction features in the British area. However, the volcanism associated with the Lower ORS of Scotland has been regarded as subduction-related (Thirlwall 1981*b*); so it may be that the ORS Continent was not fully assembled until the Early or Mid-Devonian.

ORS sedimentation in Scotland is clearly related to 'Caledonian' uplift, cooling and basin formation. The Caledonian fold belt resulting from closure of the Iapetus Ocean formed a strong feature across the continent and became the site of limited strike-slip movement with the formation of both extensional and compressional features. Much discussion has centred on the timing of the closure of the Iapetus Ocean and the final docking of the various terranes. This subject is considered elsewhere in this volume since it is now considered that the various terranes that supplied sediment to the ORS were essentially in place at the start of the Devonian, and any post-Silurian strike-slip motion has been of a modest nature both in the Highland Border and in the Great Glen (Thirlwall

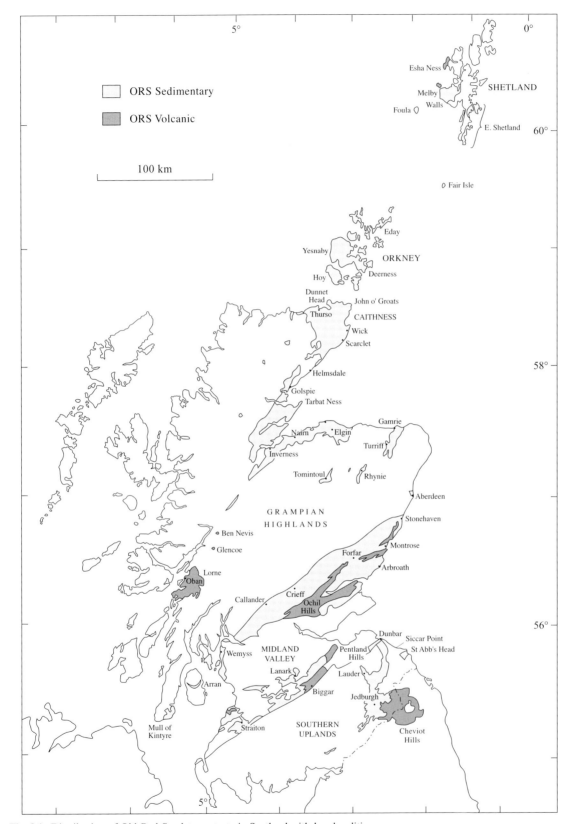

Fig. 8.1. Distribution of Old Red Sandstone strata in Scotland with key localities.

1989; Bluck 1995). The very large post-Silurian displacements postulated by Van der Voo & Scotese (1981) on the basis of palaeomagnetic data are not generally accepted.

In a palaeogeographic context Scotland lay about 30° south of the equator in the Early Devonian, moving to 20° south at the end of the period (Witzke & Heckel 1988). The climatic indicators such as marine carbonates and evaporites, and the general nature of ORS sediments are taken to indicate that Scotland lay in a dominantly arid belt. However, the Devonian sequences in Scotland record considerable climatic variation. The extensive calcrete development in the Upper ORS is indicative of semi-arid conditions, but the mud-rich, grey-green,

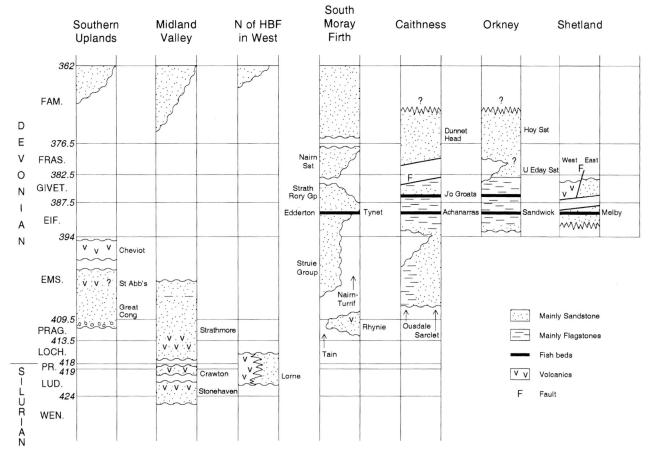

Fig. 8.2. General age distribution of strata, and presence of volcanics in the main outcrop areas of the Old Red Sandstone. Based on timescale of Tucker *et al.* (1998).

fluvial and lacustrine rocks of the Lower ORS Arbuthnott Group of the Midland Valley, and similar facies at Rhynie and in the Moray Firth indicate a much wetter and/or cooler climate at times. In the Middle ORS of the Orcadian area the

cyclic lacustrine flagstones have been shown to reflect a Milankovitch cyclicity in climatic change (Hamilton & Trewin 1988; Astin 1990; Kelly 1992), but the absolute time periods to be assigned to the sedimentary cycles are still a matter for debate.

			HARLAND *et al.* 1989	GRADSTEIN & OGG 1996 TUCKER & McKERROW 1995	TUCKER *et al.* 1998
D E V O N I A N	L A T E	FAMENNIAN Inc. STRUNIAN	362.5	354	362
			367	364	376.5
		FRASNIAN			
			377.4	370	382.5
	M I D	GIVETIAN			
			380.8	380	387.5
		EIFELIAN			
			386	391	394.0
	E A R L Y	EMSIAN			
			390.4	400	409.5
		PRAGIAN			
			396.3	412	413.5
		LOCHKOVIAN			
			408.5	417	418
S I L U R I A N		PRIDOLI			
			410.7	419	419
		LUDLOW			
			415.1	423	424
		WENLOCK			
			424	428	

Fig. 8.3. Published timescales for the Devonian and part Silurian relevant to Old Red Sandstone deposition.

Fauna and flora

The fauna of the Scottish ORS has been of world renown since the time of Miller (1841) and Agassiz (1844), and is dominated by fish, arthropods and early land plants. Details of individual occurrences are discussed at the appropriate points in this chapter but a brief overview is appropriate as an introduction.

The oldest fauna of note is that found in the Cowie Harbour Fish Bed of the Stonehaven Group which includes the arthropods *Archidesmus*, *Kampecaris*, *Ceratiocaris*, *Dictyocaris*, *Hughmilleria* and *Pterygotus*, and the fish *Hemiteleaspis* and *Traquairaspis*. The age of the fauna is now regarded as Late Wenlock to Early Ludlow on the basis of spores (Marshall 1991; Wellman 1993).

Lower ORS fish faunas are virtually confined to the Midland Valley where spectacular acanthodian and cephalaspid assemblages were collected in the late 19th century when quarries were active in the Strathmore area. The fish fauna has been summarized by Dineley & Metcalf (1999) and is dominated by acanthodians. *Mesacanthus*, *Ischnacanthus*, *Euthacanthus*, *Parexus*, *Climatius*, *Vernicomacanthus* and *Brachyacanthus* occur in lacustrine laminated shales and constitute the most diverse and earliest articulated fauna of these fish in the world. The cephalaspids also occur in lake shales but are more frequently associated with fluvial sandstones. Lower ORS arthropods in the same area include millipedes (*Archidesmus*) and eurypterids, of which the large predatory (to 1.5 m) *Pterygotus* is the most notable. Other arthropods were present as indicated by trace fossils originally described by Smith (1909) and revised by Walker (1985). Plants are also abundant and include *Zosterophyllum, Cooksonia* and *Parka*. The flora has been summarized by Cleal & Thomas (1995).

To the north of the Midland Valley the Lower ORS outlier at Rhynie includes the Rhynie chert containing a biota silicified by hot spring activity (Trewin 1994), and includes the plants *Rhynia, Aglaophyton, Nothia, Asteroxylon, Horneophyton* and *Trichopherophyton* together with algae, fungi, and cyanobacteria. Arthropods include a trigonotarbid (*Palaeocharinus*) the earliest insect, a springtail (*Rhyniella*), and the freshwater crustacean *Lepidocaris*. The Windyfield chert (Trewin & Rice 1992) discovered 700 m from the original Rhynie chert site, contains the zosterophyll plant *Ventarura* (Powell *et al.* 2000*a*), and a number of new arthropods including centipedes, crustaceans, and examples of *Heterocrania,* now considered to be a euthycarcinoid (Anderson & Trewin in press). The chert deposits are of world renown, the plants form the cornerstone of Devonian palaeobotany, and the arthropods represent the most diverse associated terrestrial/freshwater fauna of the Silurian/Early Devonian anywhere in the world. An ichnofauna dominated by arthropod trackways and burrows is locally present in the Lower ORS of the Turriff Basin (Carrol 1991) and in the Ousdale Mudstones of Caithness (Trewin 1993*a*).

In the Middle ORS the fish of the Orcadian basin are spectacularly preserved in organic-rich laminated lacustrine siltstones in the cyclic sequences of the Caithness Flagstones. The Eifelian Achanarras horizon (Trewin 1986) yields the greatest variety with some 15 genera from localities as far apart as Gamrie (Banffshire) and Melby (Shetland). Orcadian Basin Middle ORS fish include dipnoans, crossopterygians, actinopterygians, arthrodires, antiarchs and acanthodians plus a variety of enigmatic forms. The high diversity implies a connection to the sea, probably by rivers, which allowed the fish to invade the dominantly freshwater area (Trewin 1986). Marshall *et al.* (1996) have recovered scolecodonts from a level in the Givetian Eday Group that implies a brief connection to a marine area to the east. In the present North Sea marine Devonian limestones have been recorded in the Auk and Argyll oilfield area (Pennington 1975; Marshall *et al.* 1996).

The Middle ORS is remarkably devoid of invertebrate body fossils; apart from the abundance of the conchostracan *Asmussia* at some levels in the Rousay Flagstones, the only records are of eurypterid fragments, a possible limuloid, and a chasmataspid (Anderson *et al.* 2000). Plants are represented by sparse drifted material. Trace fossils are scarce in Middle ORS deposits, being generally confined to basin margin situations, and including arthropod trackways and burrows (Trewin 1976*a, b*; Carroll 1991).

The Upper ORS is generally poorly fossiliferous, but contains a few classic palaeontological sites. The most celebrated is that of Dura Den (Anderson 1859; Waterston 1965) where a great concentration of *Holoptychius*, with rarer *Glyptopomus, Eusthenopteron, Phyllolepis, Phaneropleuron* and *Bothriolepis* was discovered in sandstones. The fish are partially preserved in 3D and may have been preserved when a sand dune migrated over a pool in which they were trapped. Another important Upper ORS locality is that of Scaat Graig near Elgin from where Ahlberg (1991) has described the earliest Scottish tetrapod on the basis of fragmentary material from fluvial sandstones. Evidence of tetrapods is also provided by a trackway in the Upper ORS at Castlehaven, Easter Ross (Rogers 1990).

Perhaps the greatest progress has been in palynology, where significant new dates have been assigned to many sequences to produce valuable stratigraphic revisions, (Rogers, D. A. *et al.* 1989; Marshall 1988, 1991, 2000).

Terrestrial conditions in the Devonian

Before describing the deposits of the Old Red Sandstone it is worth briefly considering the controls on erosion, transport and deposition that were of major importance in Devonian times. The greatest influence on sediment generation was probably relief. Closure of biotite Rb–Sr and K–Ar systems (*c*. 300°C) following Grampian metamorphism in the southern part of the Dalradian tract took place at about 440 ± 10 Ma (Dempster 1985), while further north in the Central and Northern Highlands younger (400–410 Ma) biotite ages are dominant This has been used to infer rapid uplift in the central Highlands in the Late Silurian and Early Devonian, perhaps associated with granitoid emplacement. In the Dalradian areas Bluck (2000) suggests that up to 20 km of overburden must have been removed by about 430 Ma. Similarly the Highlands and Southern Uplands had been deeply eroded by Late Silurian times. The present location of a lot of this material is unknown, and much must be buried in offshore areas or recycled into more recent sediments. It is also unclear where exactly the mountains were: in the SW Grampian Highlands the ORS/ Dalradian unconformity surface does not have much relief, while in the northern Midland Valley the dominant ORS sediment dispersal direction is from the south, and clasts derived from the Grampian area are localized.

Uplift giving strong relief favoured erosion, and water was probably supplied by orographic rainfall over the Caledonian mountains (Witzke & Heckel 1988). Much of the fluvial sedimentology (Bluck 2000) of the ORS implies rivers, some very large, with continuous flow. Lakes existed for periods of thousands of years in Lochkovian (Lake Forfar, Trewin & Davidson 1996), probable Emsian (Moray Firth, Richards 1985*a*) and Eifelian–Givetian times (Orcadian Lake). These lakes were frequently hydrologically open, but in the case of the Orcadian Lake became closed and evaporitic at times (Duncan & Buxton 1995).

Seasonality, as indicated by lacustrine laminites in the Lower ORS (Trewin & Davidson 1996) and the Middle ORS Orcadian Lake (Rayner 1963; Donovan 1980; Trewin 1986) probably also gave seasonal discharge to rivers, and seasonal fluctuation of lake levels. On a larger scale Milankovitch cyclicity probably resulted in relatively wetter or cooler and drier or hotter periods. Drier periods favoured aeolian deposition and evidence for dune deposition is seen in the spectacular cross-beds of the Yesnaby Sandstone, Orkney (Lower ORS) and to a lesser extent some Middle ORS Orcadian deposits such as the Lower Eday Sandstone (Astin 1985). The Upper ORS Hoy and Dunnet Sandstones display mixed fluvial and aeolian deposition (McAlpine 1977), as also do Upper ORS sandstones in the Midland Valley (Hall & Chisholm 1987). Given the poor plant cover, sandy alluvial systems were probably generally prone to aeolian reworking, but the aeolian deposits themselves were generally reworked by water before final deposition.

Vegetational control of erosion was probably virtually absent and sediment yield would have been high. Only the lowland areas with surface water would have been vegetated with small primitive plants (e.g. Rhyniophytes, Zosterophylls) and with the absence of true rooting structures they would have provided little resistance to erosion, and not exerted a significant control on river channel morphology.

Semi-arid conditions are evidenced by carbonate-rich palaeosols at several levels, most notably in the Lower ORS of the South Moray Firth (New Aberdour, Gamrie, Rhynie) and at the top of the Upper ORS in most areas. Such profiles are scarce in the Middle ORS.

Igneous activity

The Old Red Sandstone is associated with the most extensive igneous episode in Scottish history, stretching from Shetland to northern England, although there are no *in situ* representatives in the Northern Highlands. A comprehensive chemical study of the volcanic rocks by Thirlwall (1979, 1981*b*) showed that, with the exception of the minor Hoy lavas in Orkney, the rocks belong to a broadly calc-alkaline suite dominated by basaltic andesites and andesites and their higher potash equivalents (potassic basaltic trachy-andesite and latite). Basalts and rhyolites are relatively rare, and dacites and potassic trachytes only common in some areas (Fig. 8.4). The volcanic sequences are characteristically shallow-dipping lava piles up to 2000 m in thickness, with volcaniclastic rocks being very subordinate, in contrast to similar rock suites at the present day (continental margin magmatic arcs) and elsewhere in the Caledonides (e.g. the English Lake District). This may reflect fluvial erosion of the softer parts of the original sequences, as volcanogenic detritus is abundant in the Lower ORS sedimentary record. There is little evidence for the former existence of stratovolcanoes, with caldera subsidence features only present at Glencoe and Ben Nevis (Bailey & Maufe 1916; Moore & Kokelaar 1998). Anastamosing crevices containing laminated sand and silt are common in many of the volcanic units: these may reflect sediment washed into lava flows, as seen at St Cyrus, near Montrose (Trewin 1987*b*) and at Dunure, Ayrshire (Smith 1909). However, in some cases the presence of vesiculation in the overlying sediments and occasional discordance at the upper surface demonstrates that wet sediment has been mobilized by emplacement of shallow sills (Kokelaar 1982; Moore & Kokelaar 1998). Most lavas are of aa type, with common autobrecciated tops and reddening implying subaerial

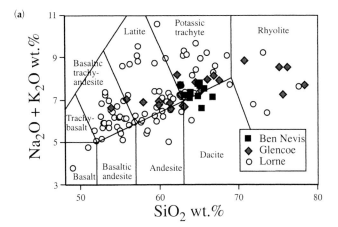

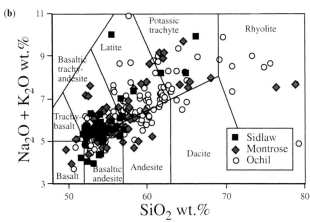

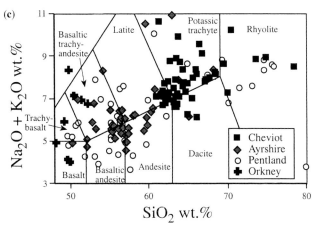

Fig. 8.4. Total alkali–silica diagrams for volcanic rocks and associated minor intrusions of the ORS; data from Thirlwall (1979). (**a**) western Grampian Highlands; (**b**) north Midland Valley; (**c**) South Midland valley, the Cheviot Hills and Orkney. Note the rarity of basaltic and rhyolitic compositions, the siliceous nature of the Cheviot and Ben Nevis sequences, and the largely basaltic nature of Orkney lavas. Some of the scatter in alkali content reflects alteration; e.g. the lower alkalis of two Cheviot lavas is due to K-loss from their glassy groundmass.

(a)

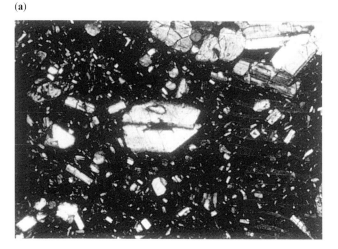

(b)

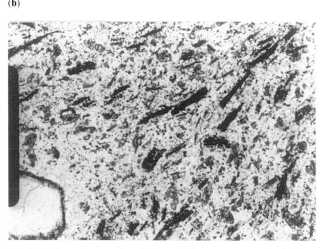

Fig. 8.5. Photomicrographs of (**a**) a typical two-pyroxene, plagioclase-phyric dacite with a fresh glassy groundmass, Cheviot Hills (C54, crossed polars). (**b**) A shoshonitic andesite. The black streaky crystals are (largely) resorbed phlogopite phenocrysts, small phencrysts are augite. Euhedral crystal at lower left is quartz ?xenocryst with reaction rim, Lorne. (L113, plane polarized light). Scale bar at left is 140 mm.

eruption. Vesicle content is very variable within and between flows: these are frequently infilled with calcite, agate and some quartz and zeolites.

Hydrothermal alteration is pervasive in these lava piles, with relic olivine being preserved in only five samples of some 630 studied by Thirlwall (1979). Bronzite–hypersthene orthopyroxene (largely altered to pale green chlorite), augitic clinopyroxene (frequently altered to carbonate) and labradorite–oligoclase plagioclase (commonly partly sericitized) are the common phenocrysts in addition to olivine in basalts and basic andesites, although plagioclase is absent from rocks with <59% SiO_2 in the SW Highlands. Olivine (pseudomorphed by iddingsite, serpentine or haematite) is less frequent in andesites than more basic rocks. Hydrous minerals are relatively rare, with pargasitic amphibole being restricted to occasional andesites and dacites, and mica being restricted to dacites and rhyolites (biotite, often replaced by green chlorite or haematite) and some potassic basic rocks (phlogopite, Fig. 8.5b). Magnetite and apatite are common phenocrysts in andesites and more evolved rocks, although phenocryst apatite also occurs in some highly potassic basic rocks. Quartz and alkali feldspar phenocrysts are restricted to acid compositions, although augite-rimmed quartz crystals in many Highland basic andesites might represent high-pressure phenocrysts rather than crustal xenocrysts (Fig. 8.5b). Groundmass textures range from coarse doleritic to petrographically fresh glass in some samples from the Ochil and Cheviot Hills (Fig. 8.5a).

The hydrothermal alteration has affected the chemistry of many lavas, though pervasive addition of H_2O and CO_2 (loss on ignition rarely under 1%) can be simply corrected by using analytical data on a volatile-free basis. Alkali and alkaline earth elements can be shown to be mobile in several samples, particularly those with fresh matrix glass. However, careful sampling of fresher holocrystalline material and comparison between this and more altered samples allows fairly ambiguous interpretation of even alkali element chemistry (Thirlwall 1979). Chemical features vary significantly between different locations, and are discussed along with outcrop details below, and synthesized at the end of this chapter.

The volcanic activity is intimately associated with several intrusive suites discussed in previous chapters: the Newer Granite suite of dominantly granodioritic plutons extending from Shetland to the English Lake District, the appinite suite (hornblende-bearing minor intrusions ranging from pyroxenite to diorite), lamprophyric dyke swarms and even the alkaline plutons of NW Scotland either bear chemical similarities to the volcanics or have close field relationships. Although the calc-alkaline volcanic sequences show a relatively limited age range of 420–390 Ma on the Scottish mainland (Thirlwall 1988), granitic clasts in Midland Valley ORS conglomerates extend the record back to 443 Ma (Haughton & Halliday 1991). Since Midland Valley Ordovician conglomerates contain clasts ranging in age from 450 to 475 Ma (Longman *et al.* 1979), there may well have been near-continuous calc-alkaline activity in Scotland extending back to the Early Ordovician.

Lower Old Red Sandstone

The Midland Valley and adjacent areas

The 'southern area' outcrops of Lower ORS (Fig. 8.6) form a broad area south of the Highland Boundary Fault along the northern margin of the Midland Valley from Stonehaven in the NE to Loch Lomond and Arran in the SW. Important outcrops of Lower ORS also occur north of the HBF in

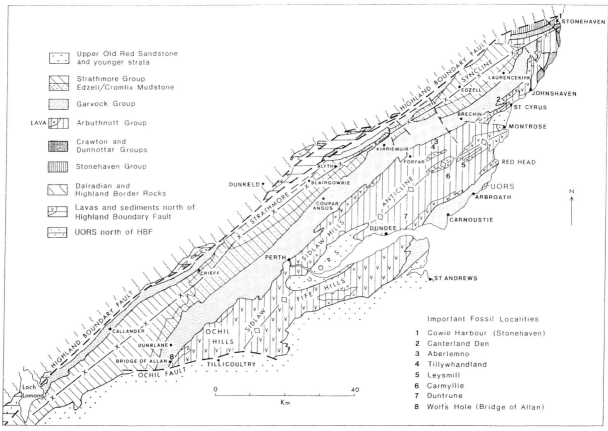

Fig. 8.6. Sketch map of the Lower ORS in the northern part of the Midland Valley. Adapted from Mykura (1991).

the Lintrathen and Glen Turret outliers, and on Kintyre. To the north of the Midland Valley area are the extensive volcanic areas of Lorne and Glencoe. Outcrop areas are more fragmented in the south of the Midland Valley, extending from the Pentland Hills in the NE to the Lanark Basin, and to Ayrshire in the SW. Lower ORS also exists south of the Southern Upland Fault in the Dunbar and Lauderdale areas and further south between Eyemouth and St Abbs. Part of the Cheviot Volcanic Formation also lies within Scotland.

The general picture of the Lower ORS of the southern area is of alluvial fan and fluvial valley sedimentation with sediment derived from both north and south of the present Midland Valley as defined by the HBF and SUF. Sources, now buried, within the Midland Valley also supplied detritus, particularly through the reworking of contemporaneous volcanics. Palaeo-drainage was to the SW through the Midland Valley with lateral input of more locally derived alluvial material. The axial rivers were large and possibly sourced in Scandinavia (Bluck 2000). Lakes periodically developed in the valley (Arbuthnott Group) due to interruption of drainage by volcanic or fault activity, and more arid phases are evidenced by the presence of caliche (Garvock Group), hence a variable climate is considered probable.

Evidence for widespread volcanism is provided by lava sequences in the Cheviots; the volcanic centres between the Pentland Hills and Ayrshire to the north of the Southern Uplands Fault; the broad band of volcanics which extends from the Montrose area through the Sidlaw and Ochil Hills, and the extensive outcrops of the Lorne–Glen Coe area. Extrusive activity was clearly more widespread than the present outcrop areas suggest with volcanic debris sourced from the SW of the Southern Uplands area, from the the Grampian area (with a vent and lava flow at Rhynie), in the Caithness–Sutherland area of the Highlands, and offshore in the present Moray Firth. The time range of the volcanism extends from Late Wenlock–Early Ludlow (Cowie Formation, Stonehaven Group) (c. 425 Ma?) through to Early Pragian (412 ± 3 Ma, Thirlwall 1988) in the N Midland Valley (Arbuthnott Group) to Late Emsian in the Cheviot Hills (396 ± 3 Ma, Thirlwall 1988). Middle ORS volcanics occur further north in the Orcadian Basin and will be considered later.

Northern Midland Valley

The classic Lower ORS geology of the Strathmore Syncline that extends parallel to the Highland Boundary Fault (Fig. 8.6) has been re-interpreted by several authors in recent years. Bluck (1983, 1984) questioned earlier palaeogeographic reconstructions and from examination of clast types postulated that there was no connection between the sediments south of the HBF and the Grampian Block until deposition of the Upper ORS, and considered that a 'missing' terrane of metamorphic rocks lay between the Grampian Block and the HBF. This view was questioned by Gillen & Trewin (1987a) who noted clasts of Dalradian derivation in the Dunnottar Group, (Early Devonian) south of Stonehaven, and confirmed by Haughton et al. (1990) in a detailed geochronological and geochemical study of clasts from northerly-derived conglomerates which closely matched Ordovician to Silurian magmatic rocks from part of the Grampian Block.

However, it can be demonstrated that pre-existing conglomerates were also being reworked from the surface of the Grampian Block that was already deeply eroded, and these rocks may have been sourced from areas no longer exposed. Exposures north of the HBF (Glen Turret and Lintrathan outliers, Bluck 2000) contain Dalradian material derived from the NW but immediately south of the HBF derivation is from a southerly source within the Midland Valley. Bluck (2000) con-

siders that a number of basins existed in the area, controlled by strike-slip faulting, and some basins certainly extended to the north of the present position of the HBF. Palaeomagnetic constraints (Trench et al. 1989) indicate that the Grampian, Midland Valley and Southern Upland terranes had docked to within the limits of the palaeomagnetic determinations by Late Silurian–Early Devonian time.

A distinctive rhyolitic ignimbrite traditionally known as the 'Lintrathen porphyry' occurs to the north of the HBF in the Lintrathen outlier of the Blairgowrie area. It is rich in crystal clasts of quartz, plagioclase, biotite, muscovite and apatite. It rests unconformably on the Highland Border Complex in the North Esk near Edzell, and is correlated with a similar development in the Crawton Group at Glenbervie to the south of the fault (Trench & Haughton 1990). The 415 ± 6 Ma date of this flow (Thirlwall 1988) places it within the Lochkovian on the timescale of Tucker et al. 1998). This dating is now consistent with the Lochkovian date of the Arbuthnott Group spore assemblage (Richardson et al. 1984), and clearly shows that the Grampian block, Highland Border Complex and Midland Valley were in very close proximity.

A further complication is the apparent 9 km measured thickness of the Lower ORS succession (Armstrong & Paterson 1970) which was certainly never present as a blanket cover over the area as demonstrated by the burial history based on vitrinite reflectivity and clay mineralogy (Marshall et al. 1994). These authors propose that the Stonehaven Group (Cowie Formation) is a separate basin fill of Late Wenlock to Early Ludlow age, resting on the Highland Border Complex and displaced along the Cowie/Carron formations boundary. The Carron Formation together with the Dunnottar and Crawton Groups accumulated in a separate narrow, fault-bounded basin (Haughton & Bluck 1988), and the rest of the succession accumulated in an elongate trough extending along the northern Midland Valley, and overstepping the earlier basins. By this means Marshall et al. (1994) demonstrate that the maximum burial of 3–5 km probably took place in the Late Carboniferous.

The Strathmore region.   The general problems relating to interpretation in this area have been summarized above and outcrop features will be described in this section. Selected successions are illustrated in Figure 8.7.

The *Stonehaven Group* was defined by Armstrong & Paterson (1970) to include both the Cowie and Carron Formations. However, Campbell (1913) includes only the Cowie Formation in his 'Stonehaven Beds'. It appears from the geological evolution viewpoint that there is a major break (unexposed) between the two formations. The distinctive sedimentology, petrography (Armstrong et al. 1978b), palaeomagnetism (Sallomey & Piper 1973) and the Late Wenlock to Early Ludlow age (Marshall 1991; Wellman 1993), combined with the burial history (Marshall et al. 1994) indicate that the Cowie Formation is a distinct unit, and that the Carron Formation is best considered with the overlying Dunnottar Group. However, for mapping purposes, the base of the Dunnottar Conglomerate is clearly a significant horizon.

The Cowie Formation (730 m) is exposed on the shore from Cowie Harbour north to the unconformity with the Highland Border Series close to the HBF. The outcrop extends 13 km to the west along the NW limb of the Strathmore Syncline (Fig. 8.6) but is poorly exposed. The unconformity is now steeply dipping (70–80°) and structurally disturbed, but a thin locally derived breccia is present resting on reddened and weathered slaty rocks of the Highland Border Series. A few metres above the unconformity sandstones and mudstones are thin-bedded with desiccation cracks and small-scale planar and

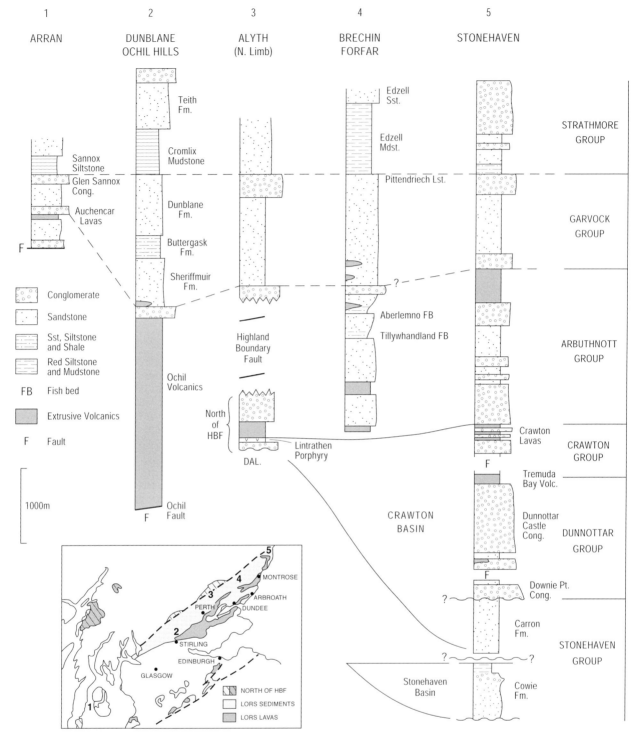

Fig. 8.7. Selected sections of the Lower ORS in the northern Midland Valley. Part adapted from Mykura (1991).

trough cross-bedding in sets less than 0.3 m thick, with current directions locally from the WNW (Gillen & Trewin 1987*a*). A thin andesitic lava is present close to the unconformity. Clearly the local relief was low and slopes were gentle, giving low-energy deposits close to the unconformity. Higher in the sequence a series of fining-up fluvial packages, with each package seldom exceeding 4 m in thickness, was deposited by streams of moderate sinuosity and flowing to the SW. The top of the Formation includes sandstones of fluvial origin together with a conglomerate with clasts of andesite and rhyolite, a few of boulder size, and derived from a contemporaneous local volcanic source. Great interest lies in a series of grey sandstones

and shales which include the Cowie Harbour Fish Bed. A fauna with the arthropods *Archidesmus*, *Kampecaris*, *Ceratiocaris*, *Dictyocaris slimoni*, *Hughmilleria norvegica* and *Pterygotus* and including the very rare fish *Hemiteleaspis heintzi*, *Traquairaspis campbelli* and *?Pterolepis* (Westoll 1977) is sparsely distributed in shaly rocks and rarely enclosed in concretions. Given the recently revised age of these rocks on the basis of spores, the millipeds are possibly the earliest known British terrestrial animals.

The Carron Formation (*c.* 820 m) comprises medium-coarse grained sandstones with abundant volcanic debris, including an agglomerate of andesite fragments in a matrix of altered volcanic glass. Tabular and trough cross-bedding is present with sets to 1 m thick, containing common dewatering structures. Pebbles are concentrated in troughs and also occur scattered in cross-bedded sandstone. The sandstones appear to have been deposited rapidly in sandy channels, and undergone liquefaction.

The *Dunnottar Group* is exposed on the coast south of Stonehaven and extends for 13 km along the northern limb of the Strathmore Syncline (Fig. 8.6). The succession given by Armstrong & Paterson (1970) is:

Tremuda Bay Volcanic Formation	60 m+
Dunnottar Castle Conglomerate	1035 m
Strathlethen Formation	350 m
Downie Point Conglomerate	170 m

The Downie Point Conglomerate rests erosively on the Carron Formation and contains rounded boulders up to 1 m in diameter. Clasts of quartzite, and contemporaneous lavas together with a variety of granitic and microgranitic/microdioritic lithologies are most frequent, but altered lava and jasper of the Highland Border Series is also present. This sudden influx of coarse material must coincide with significant uplift, probably to the NE, since the transport direction is to the SW and dominated by a large braided river system (Haughton & Bluck 1988). The Strathlethen Formation is a cross-bedded sandstone with an agglomerate at the base. A major slide is present with disruption structures in a zone 100 m wide with blocks of undeformed sandstone, some over 10 m across, in a matrix of disrupted sand. Disruption features die out up section away from the main slide plane at the base. The movement may have occurred on a slope in partly lithified sands triggered by earthquakes of structural or volcanic origin (Gillen & Trewin 1987a).

The Dunnottar Castle Conglomerate has clasts of boulder size but is dominated by pebbles of quartzite with subordinate lithologies typical of the Highland Border Complex; some units are rich in volcanic pebbles attesting to periodic, localized extrusive activity. Individual conglomerate units display pebble sorting and imbrication and lenses of cross-bedded and laminated sandstone are present. Deposition took place from large braided rivers in which sand was deposited as bar-edge sand wedges at the margins of large gravelly braid bars (Haughton & Bluck 1988). It needs to be stressed that these conglomerates are not the deposits of 'alluvial fans' derived from the NW. The Tremuda Bay Volcanic Formation contains several flows of olivine basalt, but the top is faulted out in the coastal section and the continuity of the measured succession depends on a correlation with a lava at Todhead, although this correlation is not substantiated by their chemistries (Thirlwall 1979).

The *Crawton Group* is dominated by conglomerates and pebbly sandstones with quartzite, schist and volcanic pebbles. Thickness is difficult to determine due to faulting but is estimated at 670 m by Armstrong & Paterson (1970). The Crawton Volcanic Formation at the top of the group contains four basic lava flows (c. 52% SiO₂) including a distinctive plagioclase–phyric basaltic trachyandesite that is unusual in showing Fe–Ti enrichment similar to tholeiitic magmas, and very high incompatible trace element concentrations (e.g. 80 ppm La; Thirlwall 1979). The lavas are interbedded with conglomerates which, on the basis of pebble imbrication, were transported both from the SE to SW as well as from the NE. A great variety of clast types is present including quartzites, granitic rocks, metagreywackes, jasper and 'greenstone'. The jasper and 'greenstone' are derived from the Highland Border Series and the metagreywackes are typical of Dalradian lithologies seen north of the HBF near Stonehaven (Trewin 1987c).

Haughton & Bluck (1988) showed that there is a marked change in clast types in the Crawton Group and this is accompanied by a sedimentological change to conglomeratic cross-bedded deposits of confined low sinuosity streams which cut into volcanogenic pebbly sandstones. The streams were sourced from the south and east, and the immaturity of the sediments suggests the source was only a few tens of kilometres distant, in the east central Midland Valley. The volcanogenic material includes laterally extensive tuff breccia sheets and parallel bedded tuffaceous sandstones. The igneous material is mainly a distinctive hornblende andesite suggesting a source in a single volcano, and there are also boulder-sized clasts with SE derivation and ages of c. 420 Ma (Haughton & Halliday 1991). Haughton & Bluck (1988) suggest that the inclusion of first cycle metamorphic clasts in the predominently volcanic debris may indicate that thermal uplift induced by volcanism may have resulted in exposure of basement.

The *Arbuthnott Group* as defined by Armstrong & Paterson is dominated by c. 2000 m of conglomerates and sandstones in the north (Stonehaven area); passing south into sandstones and shales of the Dundee Formation in the Forfar–Dundee area with generally subordinate volcanics, but including the Montrose volcanic centre. To the south of Dundee the Group passes into the thick Ochil Volcanic Formation in the Ochil and Sidlaw Hills. On the NW limb of the Strathmore Syncline supposed equivalents of the Arbuthnott Group are dominated by conglomerates and lavas, but there is no direct age information available. They are found both north and south of the HBF. The conglomerates are dominantly composed of volcanic clasts, among which evolved compositions (latite and potassic trachyte) seem common, perhaps because more basic ones are more prone to weathering. Lavas are found intermittently from Glenisla in the NE to Aberfoyle in the SW; they span the range from basalt to trachydacite and have distinctly higher initial Sr isotope ratios than other Midland Valley lavas (Thirlwall 1982, 1986).

Conglomerates in the north of the region were deposited by braided rivers flowing to the SW; drainage was probably interrupted by the Montrose volcanic centre from which volcanic debris was being locally shed, as seen at St Cyrus (Trewin 1987b). Lavas were subaerially exposed and weathered and fine-grained, probably wind-blown, sand is trapped in flow surfaces. Lavas were also extruded into soft sediment producing complex deformation, and fine grained sediments deposited in hollows and fissures within the lavas after they cooled contain arthropod trackways and burrows (Walker 1985).

The Montrose Volcanic Formation has been divided into six members by Armstrong & Paterson (1970), intercalated with sandstones of the Dundee Formation. The Ferryden Member (c. 400 m thick) is the oldest exposed unit in the core of the Sidlaw anticline on the coast, and is broadly equivalent to the St Cyrus Member (650 m) further NE. Both thin westward where they are replaced by the East Hills and Dunnichen members (c. 150 m each). The top of the Arbuthnott Group is marked by the Ethie Haven Member (c. 320 m) on the southern flank of the anticline, and the Morphie/Bruxie Hill members in the NE. Each member has characteristic petrography and chemistry, although the southwestern, inland outcrops (Dunnichen, East Hills, inland parts of the Ferryden member) are almost exclusively weakly olivine–plagioclase-phyric basaltic trachyandesites and potassic trachytes with high alumina and very low Ni and Cr (<10 ppm). In contrast, outcrops near the coast, and the northeastern members, are basaltic andesites and andesites with common phenocryst bronzite in addition to olivine, and sometimes augite and plagioclase, with low alumina and very high Ni and Cr (>100 ppm).

The Dundee Formation of the Arbuthnott Group in the Dundee–Forfar area is dominated by plane- and cross-bedded fluvial sandstones, probably deposited as braid bars and in

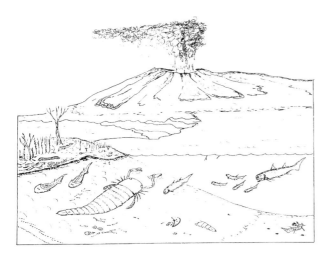

Fig. 8.8. Diagrammatic reconstruction (not to scale) of the margins of Lake Forfar at the time of deposition of the Tillywhandland fish bed. Plants, millipedes and other arthropods known only from trace fossils occupied the terrestrial environment. Cephalaspids and *Pterygotus* co-existed in sandy shallow areas of lake and river, and a variety of acanthodian fishes inhabited open water. An *Ischnacanthus* attacks a shoal of *Mesacanthus*, and a solitary *Euthacanthus* searches for food. After death the carcasses float and decay before sinking and becoming incorporated in the deeper lake laminites. Modified from Trewin & Davidson (1996).

channels, but drainage was periodically blocked to produce lacustrine conditions and deposition of clastic/carbonate/organic laminites in a seasonal climate (Trewin & Davidson 1996). The organic-rich laminites grade up into greenish siltstones and drab to yellow sandstones which rapidly filled the lake and enabled fluvial conditions to be re-established. The lake area, termed Lake Forfar by Trewin & Davidson (1996) was created and filled several times. The faunas of the Arbuthnott Group (Fig. 8.8) occur mainly in the laminated lake shales and are dominated by acanthodian fish of which *Mesacanthus* and *Ischnacanthus* are the most common of eight genera present. Cephalaspids are also present and arthropods include the large eurypterid *Pterygotus* and the milliped *Archidesmus*.

To the south of Dundee the whole of the Arbuthnott group is represented by the Ochil Volcanic Formation. A rhyolite from the base of the sequence, and a diorite intrusion into the upper part of the volcanics in North Fife have both yielded Rb–Sr biotite ages of 411 ± 6 Ma (Thirlwall 1988). The volcanics were possibly responsible for periodically blocking the southwesterly drainage of the axial river and creating Lake Forfar. Near the Bridge of Allan conglomerate lenses fill deep valleys cut in the lavas (Armstrong in Francis *et al.* 1970) which might indicate overflow from the lake area. The Ochil Volcanic Formation thickens rapidly southwestward on both flanks of the Sidlaw anticline. Around Dundee, some 500 m of volcanics form the upper units of the Arbuthnott Group, with the core of the anticline being occupied by Dundee Formation sandstones, thin intercalated lavas, and some 30 minor intrusive bodies, possibly stocks, of similar composition to the lavas. Some 1500 m of volcanics form the Sidlaw Hills around Perth, and there are *c.* 2400 m further southwest in the core of the anticline in the Ochil Hills, which is the only location where volcaniclastic rocks are common. A wide range of lava types is shown on the Geological Survey maps of these areas, including several basaltic types, but these are largely field terms and bear little relation to modern chemical classifications of rocks from the same areas. In all three areas (Sidlaw Hills, Ochil Hills, and the hills of North Fife), chemical compositions straddle the boundary on the total alkali-silica diagram (Fig. 8.4) between

the lineages basaltic andesite–andesite–dacite and potassic basaltic trachyandesite–latite–potassic trachyte. There are very few true basalts (<52% SiO_2), with some units mapped as basalt having >60% SiO_2. Rhyolitic lavas are also very rare. Mean SiO_2 content increases westward, and dacites and potassic trachytes are only reasonably common in the Ochil Hills, while in the Sidlaw Hills the vast majority of lavas are basaltic (trachy-)andesites (Fig. 8.4). The Geological Survey maps commonly identify 'trachyandesites' as mapping units: these are characterized by being close to aphyric, but chemically they are indistinguishable from strongly porphyritic trachyandesites that are not identified on the maps. In all areas, both high- and low-Cr (and Ni and MgO) lavas are found over the range $SiO_2 = 51$–62%, and low-Cr lavas tend to be richer in alkalis and alumina. A detailed chemical and isotopic study of the lavas of North Fife (Thirlwall 1983) showed that the low-Cr lavas were probably the result of localized fractional crystallization of associated high-Cr lavas, while chemical and isotopic variation in the high-Cr lavas reflected variable contributions of sediment, probably subducted, to the magmas. Very similar relationships to those reported by Thirlwall (1983) are present in all the Arbuthnott Group volcanics (Thirlwall 1982, 1986, unpubl.).

The *Garvock Group* is conglomeratic (*c.* 1 km thick) in the north of the Strathmore area and on the NW limb of the syncline, but sand dominated (*c.* 2 km thick) on the southern limb, with intercalations of shale to the SW from Auchterarder to Dunblane. Thin poorly exposed volcanic rocks include an unusual olivine-basalt (with <50% SiO_2) that is transitional to tholeiitic composition. The group is red in colour, with sandstones deposited by a major river system from the NE (Scandanavia) with channels as much as 15–20 m deep (Bluck 1986, 2000). The sandstones contain intraformational conglomerates with limestone pebbles representing reworking of caliche soil profiles of the alluvial plain. At the top of the Garvock Group a thin persistent calcrete is present (Pittendrich Limestone and equivalents,). This palaeosol is indicative of slower sedimentation, and increased aridity in the area. There is, however, some interdigitation of the Garvock and Arbuthnott Groups and the lithological variations are likely to be facies related, maybe depending on depositional position with regard to elevation in the alluvial plain and water availability.

The *Strathmore Group* occupies the axis of the syncline from Loch Lomond for 150 km NE to Auchenblae. The group as a whole fines to the SE with conglomerates and pebbly sandstones on the NW limb, and thick (to 1200 m) red and green mottled calcareous mudstones on the SE limb (e.g. Edzell Mudstones). The conglomerates are derived from the NW and include much first cycle metamorphic and volcanogenic material. Two notable thick alluvial fan deposits occur in the Comrie area (1645 m) and on Strathfinella Hill (1200 m) (Haughton & Bluck 1988). These fans pass laterally into sandstones and mudstones and record the entry points to the basin of river systems draining the Grampian area, and providing lateral supply to the Strathmore Basin. The metamorphic grade of clasts in these fans is consistent with derivation from the currently adjacent Dalradian. The mudstones are poorly bedded, blocky, and poorly sorted with scattered sand grains. Since they contain channel sandstones they possibly represent alluvial plain deposits with incipient soil profiles. Possibly the massive nature is due to repeated wetting and drying of the muds. Some flaggy sandstones have yielded plant remains such as *Psilophyton* and *Arthrostigma*; the spore assemblage suggests an Early to Mid-Emsian age (Westoll 1977).

Loch Lomond to Arran. Lower ORS in the Loch Lomond area has been estimated to be 1500 to 1800 m thick on the basis of gravity data (Qureshi 1970) and is correlated with the Garvock and Strathmore Groups (Morton 1979). In Arran the Lower ORS is possibly 1500 m thick and the Arbuthnott, Garvock and Strathmore Groups are recognized. The Arbuthnott Group basal breccias contain quartz, volcanogenic (largely trachytic) and metasedimentary clasts but most of the section is sandstone and the thin Auchencar lava occurs at the top. The latter is an olivine-basalt which bears many chemical similarities to basic lavas from Lorne. The Garvock Group overlaps the Arbuthnott Group in Glen Rosa and has a basal breccia of Dalradian-derived clasts. The Strathmore Group contains red to brown mudstones with sandstone and conglomerate intercalations in Glen Sannox. Deposition in the area was by braided rivers flowing to the SW with lateral input of alluvial material at the basin margin.

Southern Midland Valley

A series of fault-dissected outcrops of Lower ORS conglomerates, sandstones and volcanics extends from the Ayrshire coast in the SW to the Pentland Hills in the NE. The succession has been summarized by Mykura (1991) to comprise a series of conglomerates and lithic sandstones which contain variable thicknesses of volcanic rocks derived from three main volcanic centres in the Pentland Hills, The Upper Clyde area, and the Carrick and Dalmellington hills of Ayrshire. These volcanic centres have only been inferred by having the greatest preserved thickness of volcanic rocks. There are no clear eruptive centres preserved, and chemical differences suggest that in Ayrshire alone, the volcanic rocks of the Carrick Hills, of Straiton/Dalmellington, and those found near Distinkhorn were probably derived from different eruptive centres. Further, gaps in volcanic rock outcrop between the Biggar and Dalmellington areas are largely a function of pre-Carboniferous erosion.

Beneath the volcanics, the conglomerates (locally to 700 m) contain abundant clasts of greywackes, mudstones, cherts and silicified lavas derived from the Southern Uplands. They rest unconformably on Wenlock and Llandovery strata in the Pentland Hills, and on Llandovery to Ordovician rocks in Ayrshire. The conglomerates become thinner with sandstone increasing to the NW, and the sediments were probably derived as coarse alluvial outwash fans from the Southern Uplands which fed SW flowing rivers within the Midland Valley. Conglomerates above the lavas have pebbles dominated by igneous clasts derived from the contemporaneous volcanic centres. The sandstones throughout the succession contain abundant igneous lithic clasts, indicating that more distant sources of volcanic material were available prior to the inception of the local volcanic centres.

In Ayrshire, a sequence of 1200 m of alluvial sandstones with thin conglomerates occurs in the Maybole area and includes volcanic debris towards the top of the sequence which may be derived from a volcanic vent 3 km west of Maybole. The overlying igneous rocks form the Carrick Hills, and comprise up to 450 m of lavas and sills intruded into soft sediment (Kokelaar 1982), with intervening debris flow deposits and conglomerates of lava clasts and tuffs near the top of the lava pile. The sills usually have lower and upper vesicular pillowed zones with pockets of intervening sediment, and massive centres in which joints are commonly filled with sediment. The tops often show irregular protrusions of igneous rock into the sediment together with detached pillows, while the overlying sediment is usually structureless and may be vesicular (Kokelaar 1982). Smith (1909) discovered a variety of arthropod-produced traces (revised by Walker 1985) in thin-bedded sandstones occuring as patches within the igneous rocks at Dunure, and considered that the terrestrial arthropod fauna possibly took advantage of the shelter provided by an irregular lava topography. How-ever, he noted that trackways were cut by lava contacts. The sediment patches are now considered to be relics of more extensive deposits, the majority having been removed by a process of fluidization by the magma (discussion by Durant in Stephenson et al. 1999).

Chemically, the igneous rocks are mostly basic andesites and andesites lying close to or below the dividing line to trachyandesitic compositions on the total alkali–silica diagram (Fig. 8.4). No basalts are found, and only one dacite. The rocks are all plagioclase-phyric, and most have phenocryst bronzite (even in the dacite) and/or augite and some olivine. Many samples are rich in Ni and Cr, with even 150 ppm Cr in the dacite (Thirlwall 1982, 1986). Isotopic compositions are similar to those of ORS lavas from the north Midland Valley.

Closer to the Southern Upland Fault in the Dalmellington–Straiton area a 200 m basal conglomerate dominated by greywacke clasts is present below some 600 m of volcanic rocks, which include olivine-basalts in addition to the more common plagioclase–pyroxene–olivine-phyric basic andesites and andesites. Orthopyroxene at Straiton is hypersthene, unusually for the ORS, and augites are also more Fe-rich than usual, and contain pseudomorphs after exsolved pigeonite (Thirlwall 1979). Further north near Distinkhorn 650 m of ORS conglomerates and sandstones that have yielded cephalaspid fish are overlain by plagioclase-phyric volcanics ranging from a hornblende-bearing trachyte to an olivine-phyric basalt. These rocks are intruded and metamorphosed by the Distinkhorn granodioritic pluton which has been dated by Rb–Sr biotite at 412.8 ± 5.5 Ma (Thirlwall 1988). The Straiton lavas tend to have lower La/Y and lower Sr, and the Distinkhorn lavas higher La/Y, than the majority of rocks in the Carrick Hills.

In the Lanark Basin Smith (1995) and Phillips et al. (1997) subdivided the ORS into four formations. The base of the northeasterly derived Greywacke Conglomerate Formation is taken as the base of the ORS, and it rests with apparent conformity on Mid-Silurian rocks in the Hagshaw and Lesmahagow inliers. This is in contrast to the situation in Ayrshire and the Pentland Hills where there is a marked angular basal unconformity. The succeeding Swanshaw, Duneaton and Achtitench formations contain conglomerates dominated by igneous clasts and were derived from the south. Interbedded sandstones have a general palaeoflow to the SW with cross-bed sets to 6 m, indicating substantial channels (Bluck 2000). The Greywacke Conglomerate was deposited in a series of strike-slip basins generally filled from the NE (Smith 1995; Phillips et al. 1997).

The interbedded lavas in the sequence include plagioclase–pyroxene-phyric basic andesites and basaltic trachy-andesites, some highly altered olivine basalts and basic andesites, hornblende-phyric trachyandesites and weakly plagioclase-phyric andesites, trachytes and rhyolites that are usually depicted on Geological Survey maps as trachytes. At Tinto Hill there is a 1 km thick biotite-rhyolite laccolith that in one locality contains garnet yielding a Sm–Nd age of 411.9 ± 1.9 Ma, concordant with Rb–Sr on biotite from the same body of 407.2 ± 6.7 Ma (Thirlwall 1988).

A similar succession in the Pentland Hills contains 600 m of sandstones, pebbly sandstones and thin greywacke conglomerates. These sediments interdigitate with the Pentland Hills volcanics (Mykura 1960b) which are over 1800 m thick and commence with a cumulo-dome of felsite resting directly on Silurian, and continue with ten groups of lavas including olivine– and olivine–plagioclase–phyric basalts, trachybasalts and basaltic andesites, a trachyte and rhyolites (Fig. 8.4). Acidic tuffs and thin volcaniclastic sediments are intercalated with the lavas. Lavas in the SW Pentland Hills are more incompatible-element enriched than those in the NE and may derive from a different centre. A rhyolite in the NE Pentland Hills has yielded a Rb–Sr biotite age of 412.6 ± 5.7 Ma (Thirlwall 1988). Volcanics are present to the north of the Pentland Fault at Carlops and to the SW of the North Esk Silurian inlier, where they thin northeastwards and are clearly not part of the Pentland volcanic sequence. At Carlops there are some unusual Cr-rich andesites with large fresh bronzite phenocrysts.

Lower ORS north of the HBF in western Scotland

Kintyre

Lower ORS on Kintyre is considered to lie to the north of the HBF and comprises 1440 m of breccias, conglomerates and sandstones (Friend & MacDonald 1968). At the base, the Glenrainsgill Formation displays 150 m of basal breccia with Dalradian clasts, passing up into red sandstones with volcanogenic debris at the top, and followed by 100 m of quartzitic conglomerate and 200 m of purple sandstone and siltstone. The overlying New Orleans Conglomerate (890 m) is coarse, with lava boulders, and the succession is capped by 100 m of the Bastard Sandstone which is parallel to cross-bedded purple sandstone and red siltstone. The sediments appear to have been derived from the north with quartzite pebbles possibly from the Islay–Jura area, and the volcanic clasts from a source material similar to the Lorne Plateau Lavas, but probably situated close by in North Kintyre. Friend & MacDonald (1968) note three vents, only one of which contains lava, the other two being gas vents or cryptovents.

Oban, Glencoe and Ben Nevis

In the Oban area there are outcrops of fossiliferous Lower ORS on Kerrera, and the extensive outcrops of the Lorne Plateau Lavas. Lower ORS volcanics and some sediments are preserved in the cauldron subsidences of Glen Coe and on Ben Nevis.

On Kerrera a local basal breccia rests on a slightly irregular topography of Dalradian slates. Overlying the breccia are 300 m of conglomerates, sandstones, shales and siltstones. In the lower part of the sequence in the southeast of the island a fauna with cephalaspids, an anaspid and *Kampecaris* together with

plants has been obtained from flaggy shale (Lee & Bailey 1925; Waterston 1965). The age of this fauna is considered to be latest Silurian to earliest Devonian (probably earliest Lochkovian) in age on the basis of palynology (Marshall 1991; Wellman 1991). This is consistent with Rb–Sr phlogopite–apatite ages of c. 415 to 424 ± 5 Ma (Thirlwall 1988). In the Oban area 30 m of sandstone is overlain by volcanic-derived conglomerate and by grey shales interbedded with basaltic lava. The shales have produced the fish *Cephalaspis*, *Mesacanthus* and *Thelodus* as well as the arthropods *Pterygotus* and *Kampecaris* (Lee & Bailey 1925; Johnstone 1972). This fauna is closely similar to that of the Arbuthnott Group of the Forfar area as noted by Morton (1979).

The Lorne volcanic succession which overlies and is partly interbedded with the sediments of Kerrera and Oban covers some 300 km^2 and is over 800 m thick. Apart from on the west coast, the volcanic rocks rest directly on Dalradian metasediments, which must have had subdued topography by this time. The volcanic rocks form a shallow SW-trending syncline, and are cut by a SW–NE porphyritic microdiorite dyke swarm, and form a screen between the earliest plutonic rocks of the Etive Complex. The lower and largest part of the sequence is dominantly composed of potassic basaltic andesites with some latites (potassic trachyandesites) and rare basalts (Fig. 8.4). These lack phenocryst plagioclase, and are usually olivine– or olivine–augite-phyric (basaltic andesites) or orthopyroxene–augite-phyric (latites). The latter frequently contain augite-rimmed quartz ?xenocrysts. In the west, there are a few phlogopite–augite–apatite-phyric flows (Fig 8.5b), and minor intrusions that can be described chemically as shoshonitic basaltic andesites and shoshonitic andesites. The central parts of the sequence include some highly altered hornblende-andesites and a few rhyolitic to K-trachytic lavas and ignimbrites, while two-pyroxene–plagioclase-phyric latites and trachytes mark the upper part of the sequence. The Lorne volcanic rocks are particularly rich in Sr, Ba, P and LREE compared with other Scottish ORS lavas (Thirlwall 1981b), with generally higher concentrations in western Lorne. The volcanic rocks have Sr–Nd–Pb isotopic compositions indicating derivation from a mantle source with mild long-term enrichment in

Fig. 8.9. West face of Aonach Dubh and An't Sron (right), Glen Coe. Aonach Dubh is composed of gently inclined andesitic lavas (lower two-thirds), overlain by thick rhyolitic ignimbrites, forming the paler upper cliffs. The gully on the left edge of An't Sron marks the line of the Glen Coe Ring Fault, the rest of An't Sron is granite of the ring intrusion. (BGS photograph D01927).

incompatible elements (Thirlwall 1982, 1986), with crustal contamination being involved in the generation of the latites and trachytes.

The well-exposed ORS volcanic sequence of Glen Coe (Fig. 8.9) has been described by many workers including Clough *et al.* (1909), Bailey (1960), Roberts (1974) and Moore & Kokelaar (1998). The ORS sequence is preserved by subsidence along an arcuate fault interpreted as a caldera-bounding fault, and rests unconformably on Dalradian metasediments (Fig. 8.10). Sediments have yielded carbonized sporomorphs interpreted as Mid-Lochkovian in age (Wellman 1991), somewhat younger than the 421 ± 4 Ma Ar–Ar age of phenocryst amphibole in the lavas (Thirlwall 1988). The volcanics are cut by the Cruachan Granite and a major NE-trending dyke swarm, one of which has been dated by Rb–Sr biotite at 412 ± 5 Ma (Thirlwall 1988). The lowest part of the sequence is a *c.* 500 m thick sequence of latites and potassic basic andesites (Fig. 8.4), with intercalated conglomerates and sandstones. The igneous rocks were originally interpreted as lava flows, but Moore & Kokelaar (1998) have proposed that they represent sills that were emplaced into wet sediment, deposited in a graben or half-graben system prior to the development of the Glen Coe caldera. It is possible that both flows and sills are present. This sequence has been correlated with the Lorne volcanics, but the Glen Coe sequence is more evolved, with higher SiO_2, and lower Ni and Cr for a given SiO_2. In terms of their high Sr, Ba and LREE content, and isotopic compositions, the whole Glen Coe sequence is very similar to Lorne. A subaerial unconformity with alluvial fan deposits reflecting local fault activity indicates extensive erosion prior to caldera collapse and the deposition of three rhyolitic sheets, the Etive Rhyolites, with intercalated and underlying phreatomagmatic tuff (Moore & Kokelaar 1998). These rhyolitic sheets are up to 100 m thick and strongly flowbanded, and were originally interpreted as lava flows, but their low aspect ratios and the presence of stratified eutaxitic tuffs within them led Moore & Kokelaar

(1998) to interpret them as lava-like ignimbrites formed proximally to pyroclastic fountains. They are overlain by two ignimbrites, both up to 150 m thick, which range in bulk composition from rhyolitic to potassic trachyte, with intervening and overlying alluvial deposits (Fig. 8.10). Overlying *c.* 300 m thick hornblende–pyroxene-phyric andesites/trachyandesites and two ignimbrites (100–200 m thick, Moore & Kokelaar 1997) are preserved in the highest peaks in southern Glen Coe, and are cut by the Cruachan Granite intrusion.

At Ben Nevis, some 600 m of ORS volcanic rocks are preserved, again by subsidence on a probable caldera-bounding fault. The sequence is mostly composed of rather homogeneous potassic trachytic lavas (Fig. 8.4), with phenocrysts of hornblende, plagioclase, magnetite, apatite and pyroxene pseudomorphs, with some dacites probably reflecting K-loss during alteration. A thin basal conglomerate rests on Dalradian metasediments and thin siltstones and tuffs also occur in the volcanic sequence. The sequence is metamorphosed by the Ben Nevis granitoid complex. The lavas share the high Sr and Ba contents of other ORS volcanic rocks and late Caledonian granitoids in this part of Scotland, though they have rather lower concentrations of light rare earth elements, Zr and Nb than similar rocks in Glen Coe, and are thus unlikely to be part of the same eruptive sequence (Thirlwall 1979).

Southern Uplands

Three outcrop areas of poorly sorted Lower ORS greywacke-conglomerates occur at the NE end of the Southern Uplands. One trends NNW–SSE in Lauderdale with a small outlier on the Lammermuir Hills near the Southern Upland Fault; the second extends for 25 km south from near Dunbar; and the third trends NE–SW inland from Eyemouth before being overlain by Carboniferous. In the first two regions conglomerates dominate and comprise locally derived material, particularly of greywacke, chert and jasper. The Eyemouth sequence of red feldspathic sandstones and conglomerates (the

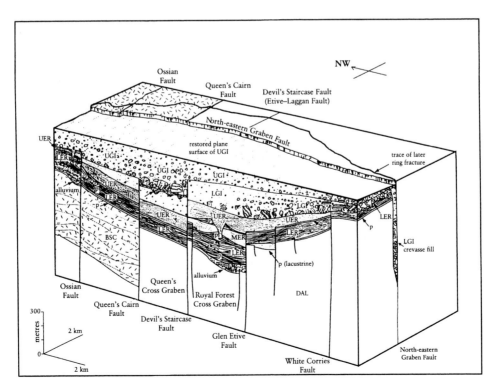

Fig 8.10. Block diagram of the Glen Coe caldera restored to a horizontal plane at the top of the Upper Glen Coe Ignimbrite. The long axis of the diagram coincides with the axis of the Glen Coe Graben. DAL, Dalradian metesediments; BSC, Basal Sill Complex; LER, MER and UER, Lower, Middle and Upper Etive rhyolites; LGI and UGI, Lower and Upper Glen Coe ignimbrites; p, Phreatomagmatic tuff. After Moore & Kokelaar (1997).

'Great Conglomerate') includes minor thin cornstones (caliche) and red marl (Greig 1971). The age of the Great Conglomerate is poorly constrained by a K–Ar biotite age of 400 ± 9 Ma on a lamprophyre dyke (Rock & Rundle 1986). At St Abbs Head a well-exposed $c.\,600$ m thick sequence of basaltic andesites and intercalated volcaniclastic deposits is present, which are distinct from ORS volcanics in the Midland Valley in only having olivine and orthopyroxene phenocrysts. These basaltic andesites are accompanied by plagioclase–hornblende-phyric andesites, dacites and one rhyolite in the poorly exposed areas around Eyemouth. Incompatible element concentrations and Sr–Nd isotope ratios are similar to ORS volcanics of the Midland Valley. The volcanics were probably erupted from vents filled with andesitic agglomerate, exposed on the shore near Eyemouth and St Abbs.

In the Cheviot Hills some of the Cheviot Volcanic Group lies within Scotland. The volcanics are subhorizontal and rest unconformably on Wenlock marine sediments. Over the Border in England the Cheviot 'Granite' and associated dykes and minor stocks intrude the volcanic sequence, and coarse breccias are present in volcanic vents. Thirlwall (1988) has reported Rb–Sr biotite ages of 394–398 Ma on three quartz-monzonites from the Cheviot 'Granite' and a biotite–trachyte lava, substantially younger than biotite ages from the Midland Valley ORS. Compared with ORS volcanics further north, the lavas are remarkably homogeneous, with >90% being latites and potassic trachytes (Fig. 8.4) with phenocrysts of plagioclase, hypersthene, augite, ilmenite and apatite. There are also many chemical differences: Cheviot is the only large-scale ORS volcanic suite to lack basic andesites (Fig. 8.4); it is much more potassic, with $K_2O/Na_2O \sim 1$, than other ORS suites; and despite having strong LREE-enrichment, it is relatively poor in Sr. The 'mica-felsites' reported by Carruthers et al. (1932) are rare flows of biotite–feldspar-phyric trachytes that are somewhat more fractionated than the majority of the latites and trachytes. Rhyolitic compositions are confined to a single flow, and clasts in coarse volcaniclastic deposits produced in a short-lived initial explosive stage. The Cheviot 'Granite' is, in the main, chemically and mineralogically similar to the K-trachytic lavas, although there is a small true granite component.

Deformation and denudation of the Midland Valley and adjacent areas

From the above discussion it can be concluded that the Lower ORS basins that make up the 'Midland Valley' had a complex history involving strike-slip deformation in the Late Silurian and Early Devonian. Basins also extended north of the HBF and into the Southern Uplands and have been severely fragmented. Detailed examination of clasts and transport directions reveals only part of the history (Bluck 2000). Basins generally filled axially from the NE following the establishment of a major river system from Scandinavia. In Emsian times basins in the Midland Valley were folded, uplifted and eroded to give a subdued topography as illustrated in Fig. 8.11.

Lower ORS, the Orcadian Basin

The northern areas of Lower ORS (Fig. 8.1) to the north of the Grampian divide can be considered to belong to the Orcadian Basin s.l.

The Rhynie Basin

The Rhynie Outlier forms a narrow NNE trending outcrop some 21 km long and fault bounded in the western side. The outlier is of international palaeontological importance on account of the presence of the Rhynie cherts. The succession determined by Wilson & Hinxman (1890) and Read (1923b) in the south of the outlier comprises a basal breccia and conglomerate of local derivation which is succeeded by red and grey shales (Lower Shales) which contain carbonate-cemented sandstones and carbonate concretions of caliche origin. The overlying Tillybrachty Sandstone contains conglomeratic lenses, and is immature, poorly sorted, and was possibly deposited by flashy local discharge on outwash fans. The succeeding Quarry Hill Sandstone is more mature, and contains channel forms with cross bedding and concentrations of rip-up clasts and drifted plant debris. Palaeocurrents were to the north indicating drainage into the Orcadian Basin.

The northern part of the outlier has a synclinal structure and the stratigraphy is complicated by contemporaneous extrusive volcanic activity producing a widespread lava, together with tuffs and hot-spring activity (Fig. 8.12, and see Chapter 16) in the vicinity of Rhynie (Rice & Trewin 1988; Rice et al. 1995, 2000). Recent drilling has shown that the Dryden Flags and Shales which contain the Rhynie and Windyfield fossiliferous cherts, rest on sandstones above a low angle easterly-dipping fault. Hydrothermal fluids were channelled up the fault plane, which contains a cherty breccia. The reinterpretation of the basement contact as a low angle fault rather than an unconformity allows the Dryden Flags and Shales to be interpreted

OLD RED SANDSTONE OF MIDLAND VALLEY

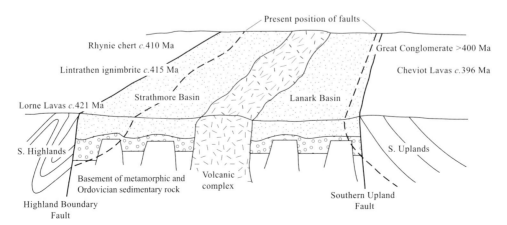

Fig 8.11. Block diagram showing the evidence for the planation of the blocks flanking the Midland Valley and the probable Mid-Devonian shortening of the Midland Valley as a result of covergence and the thrusting of the flanking blocks. Modified from Bluck (2000).

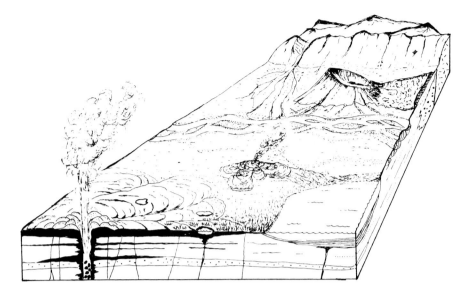

Fig 8.12. Diagrammatic reconstruction of the depositional environment of the Rhynie chert. Geyser activity produces siliceous sinters that engulf plants growing on an alluvial plain with lakes, marginal to an axial river system. Local lateral sediment supply comes from the basin margin, and from erosion of contemporaneous volcanic rocks. After Trewin (2001).

as the topmost unit of the Rhynie succession, rather than an equivalent of the Lower Shales in the south of the outlier as interpreted by Trewin & Rice (1992).

The Dryden Flags and Shales comprise grey-green shales and thin sandstones with current ripples, fine lamination with graded laminae, desiccation cracks and soft-sediment deformation features. They represent a dominantly lacustrine and alluvial plain environment, possibly partly equivalent to the fluvial sandstones of the Quarry Hill Sandstone, which is much reduced in the northern part of the outlier.

Volcanic activity at Rhynie includes a vesicular andesitic lava and locally, at Windyfield, a series of tuffs at least 50 m thick which probably derived from reworking of a cinder cone. Volcanic clasts occur in locally derived sandstones and are sporadically associated with the Rhynie and Windyfield cherts. The cherts were deposited as hot-spring sinters (Rice & Trewin 1988) and display textures typical of surficial sinters deposited in close proximity to geyser vents (Trewin 1994, 1996; Powell et al. 2000b). The cherts were discovered by Mackie (1913), and were found to contain early land plants with the cellular structure superbly silicified (Fig. 8.13). Classic work on the plants by Kidston & Lang (1917–1921) resulted in the description of the spore-bearing plants *Rhynia, Aglaophyton, Horneophyton, Asteroxlyon* and *Nothia* as well as fungi, algae and cyanobacteria. Numerous palaeobotanical papers have been published on the chert flora of which the more recent highlights are the recognition of gametophytes of some plants (Remy et al. 1993), the Zosterophyll plants *Trichopherophyton* (Lyon & Edwards 1991) and *Ventarura* (Powell et al. 2000a), a parasitic relationship between fungi and a green alga (Taylor et al. 1992), and the earliest known lichen (Taylor et al. 1997). The flora has been summarized by Cleal & Thomas (1995).

The arthropod fauna of the Rhynie chert is an important early terrestrial assemblage (Rolfe 1980) including trigonotarbid arachnids (*Palaeocharinus*), the mite *Protacarus*, the earliest insect (*Rhyniella*) which is a springtail, and *Heterocrania*, now recognized as a euthycarcinoid (Anderson & Trewin in press). An aquatic crustacean *Lepidocaris* is also present. The Windyfield chert locality has yielded *Palaeocharinus, Heterocrania*, centipede material, *Lepidocaris* and several other arthropods of uncertain affinities (Anderson & Trewin in press).

The presence of book lungs in *Palaeocharinus* and stomata on the plants show this to be a true terrestrial community. The ecosystem was preserved due to flooding of the land surface, with silica-rich waters from the hot springs, and permeation of the shallow subsurface by hot mineral-rich water (Trewin

1994). Arthropod trackways (*Diplichnites*) up to 100 mm wide occur in the Quarry Hill Sandstone together with arthropod burrows, hence larger arthropods, possibly arthropleurids, also inhabited the area. The spore assemblage suggests a late Pragian age, and an Ar–Ar date on the chert gives 396 ± 12 Ma (Rice et al. 1995).

(a)

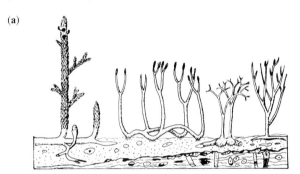

(b)

Fig 8.13. (a) Reconstructions of some of the Rhynie plants growing on a sandy substrate and siliceous sinter. From left to right, *Asteroxylon, Aglaophyton, Horneophyton* and *Rhynia*. Plants are about 100–250 mm high. (b) Block of Rhynie chert with upright axes of *Rhynia* encased in silicified sinter. After Trewin (2001).

Tomintoul and Cabrach outliers

The outliers of Tomintoul and the Cabrach serve to illustrate how close the present Grampian surface lies to the sub-ORS surface. The Cabrach outlier is, like Rhynie, fault-bounded to the west. It contains 200 m of conglomerate, sandstone and an andesitic lava (Johnstone 1966) with lithologies resembling the Tillybrachty Sandstone of Rhynie. The Tomintoul outlier is dominated by alluvial fan conglomerates up to 150 m thick which pass northward into sandstone.

The Turriff Basin

The Turriff Basin extends about 30 km inland from the Moray Firth coast and is generally fault-bounded to the west. There is a gap of less than 20 km between the Rhynie and Turriff outcrop areas and the two may have been linked. The Turriff Basin contains both Lower and Middle ORS, separated by an angular unconformity as seen at Pennan (Trewin 1987a), and above which there is a radical change in clast type from quartzite and granitic debris in the Lower ORS, to locally derived Dalradian metasediments in the Middle ORS. The Lower ORS constitutes the Crovie Group of Read (1923b), which on the basis of spores from the Gamrie area (Westoll 1977) is probably Pragian–Emsian in age.

The main outcrop areas are at New Aberdour and Gamrie Bay. The Crovie Group consists of at least 600 m of breccia, conglomerates, sandstones and mudstones, which are laterally highly variable in facies, derivation and thickness (Sweet 1985; Trewin & Kneller 1987a, b). At New Aberdour a coarse basal breccia of local derivation overlies irregular Dalradian topography and is rapidly succeeded by 100–200 m of poorly sorted conglomeratic sandstones of alluvial fan origin, and deposited by flash floods. The fan deposits fine upwards through 10 m of sheet sandstones representing the fan toe, to mudstones with abundant caliche of the alluvial plain. *Beaconites* burrows are common in some mudstones and thin channel sandstones, and concentrations of locally derived felsite boulders, apparently facetted by wind action, are present. The conglomeratic sandstones contain abundant granitic wash derived by erosion of the Strichen Granite now exposed only 5 km to the south.

The other major outcrop area of the Crovie Group at Gamrie is extensively faulted and several differing interpretations of the stratigraphy exist (Read 1923b; Archer in Donovan et al. 1978; Trewin & Kneller 1987a). Correlation of strata between fault blocks is tentative at best, and the presence of caliche pebbles in some units indicates reworking of mature alluvial plain sediments maybe implying local fault activity. The main feature of the succession is a 150 m coarsening-up sequence commencing with grey-green lake margin deposits with wave ripples, desiccation cracks and minor calcrete. This passes up into interbedded sandstones and mudstones, the sandstones with parallel and current ripple lamination, rip-up mud clasts and a variety of arthropod produced trace fossils (*Diplichnites*, *Beaconites*, *Isopodichnus*, *Diplocraterion* and *Rusophycus*). The succession continues to coarsen-up into cross-bedded sandstones with channel forms up to 2 m deep. (Trewin & Kneller 1987a). These sandstones were deposited by a northward-flowing river system prograding into an impermanent lake. In the Moray Firth the lacustrine deposits of Well 12/27-1 (Richards 1985a) may represent more central lake facies but if Lower ORS sedimentation in the Moray Firth was fault controlled as suggested by Marshall (1998) it is not likely that the river fed the region of 12/27-1. The sandstones compare with the Quarry Hill Sandstone of the Rhynie area in showing channel features, and contrast with the Crovie Group sandstones of New Aberdour in lacking coarse, locally derived granitic debris. Possibly the northward flowing river system was channelled at the faulted western margin of the basin.

Great Glen, Inverness and Black Isle region

Since the publication of the third edition of this volume there have been major changes in interpretation of the Old Red Sandstone succession and its depositional and structural history. Rogers et al. (1989) proposed that the whole of the Old Red Sandstone sequence is virtually conformable, and that unconformable relations between the divisions cannot be generally demonstrated or are only of local significance. Furthermore, Underhill & Brodie (1993) interpret seismic data in Easter Ross associated with the drilling of onshore exploration Well Tain-1 as indicating a conformable succession, and find no evidence for strong intra-Devonian structural events. Thus both Rogers et al. (1989) and Underhill & Brodie (1993) assign the folding and thrusting of the Struie Group which resulted in the Struie Hill thrust to Permo-Carboniferous inversion rather than activity prior to Middle ORS deposition (Mykura 1991).

In the Great Glen between Loch Lochy and Fort Augustus, three outcrop areas to the SE of the Great Glen Fault consist of conglomerates and sandstones with minor shales. On the NW side of Loch Ness, the Meallfuarvonie fault-bounded outcrops extend for 16 km SW from Glen Urquhart and contain ten lenses of breccia-conglomerates 50 to 400 m thick interbedded with at least 1800 m of red planar-bedded fine sandstones (Mykura & Owens 1983). To the northeast purple and green shales are present and have yielded a miospore assemblage of late Emsian to earliest Eifelian age (Mykura & Owens 1983). When 25–29 km of post-Devonian dextral movement is removed from the Great Glen Fault those outcrops to the SE and NW of the fault form part of a single basin. This reconstruction is strengthened by the presence of granitic clasts in the SW of the Meallfuarvonie outcrops, which were derived from

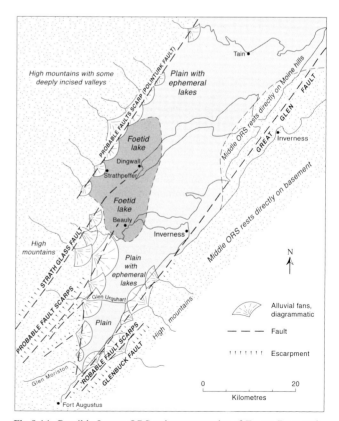

Fig 8.14. Possible Lower ORS palaeogeography of Easter Ross and the northern part of the Great Glen. Assumes 27 km post-Devonian dextral movement on Great Glen Fault. Modified from Mykura & Owens (1983).

the SE side of the fault, and likely sources are granite outcrops on the SE side of the Great Glen between Loch Lochy and Loch Oich. The general picture (Fig. 8.14) is of alluvial fans fed from deeply incised valleys at active fault scarps oriented between N–S and NE–SW and fed from the NW Highlands and from the Grampian area to the SE. The fan toes rapidly grade into sandstone, which is dominantly planar-bedded and may have been deposited by sheet floods which fed ephemeral lakes where mud deposition took place.

The Lower ORS outcrop continues northwards to the Dingwall–Strathpeffer area and follows the Polinturk Fault NE to Struie Hill. Basal conglomerates and breccias rest on an irregular topography of Moine, and formed as fans along active fault scarps. In an area some 25 km from north to south and centred on the Dingwall–Strathpeffer area, a succession of some 400 m of olive to black bituminous shales and shaly limestones is present. The organic-rich lithologies are described as 'foetid' on account of the hydrogen sulphide smell given off when they are broken. They are the source of the 'sulphur waters' of the Strathpeffer Spa. This fine-grained succession was deposited in a lake with high organic productivity, of bacterial and algal origin. Probable algal stromatolitic lamination is present, and pseudomorphs after gypsum (Parnell 1985) record evaporative concentration in this internal drainage basin. The age of the lake deposits was considered to be Siegenian or Emsian (Richardson 1967), but Rogers et al. (1989) place the Lower ORS of this area in the late Emsian. North of the Strathpeffer lake area the organic-rich facies is replaced by grey to greenish siltstones and calcareous mudstones, possibly the deposits of ephemeral lakes on an alluvial plain.

Golspie and Badbea basins to the northern coast

In the Golspie and Badbea basins (Dec 1992) situated south and north of the Helmsdale Granite outcrop there is, in places, a marked angular unconformity between Lower and Middle ORS. The Golspie Basin (Brora outlier of Mykura 1991) is considered by Dec (1992) to have been an individual basin at least partly isolated from the main Orcadian Basin. However, it is likely that the whole of the 'Orcadian Basin' was made up of many sub-basins.

The Golspie Basin is 28 km long and up to 5.5 km wide forming a general synclinal structure cut by numerous NE–SW faults. The Lower ORS succession comprises a basal series of conglomeratic units (Beinn Lunndaidh Formation) which range from 40 m up to a maximum of 400 m in thickness in the area of Mound Rock. The conglomerates on the NW basin margin were deposited by debris-flow dominated fans composed of material recycled from pre-existing gravels and sands to the NW of the basin. The eroding Helmsdale Granite supplied first cycle debris to sheetflood dominated fans which entered the northerly part of the basin from the NE. The overlying Glen Loth Formation is up to 530 m thick in the south of the basin and dominated by fluvial sandstones (Beinn a' Bhragaigh Member). To the north up to 450 m of lacustrine mudstones (Beinn Dharain Member) and 400 m of fluvial sandstones (Ben Uarie Member) overlie the conglomerates.

The Badbea Basin exposures of the Ousdale–Badbea area provide a sequence similar to that in the north of the Golspie Basin with a basal arkosic conglomerate (Ousdale Arkose) derived from the Helmsdale Granite, overlain by fine-grained mudstones (Ousdale Mudstones) of alluvial plain and impermanent lacustrine environments. Middle ORS is again unconformable on Lower. The Lower Devonian (Early Emsian) age is based on spores obtained from the Ousdale Mudstones (Collins & Donovan 1977). The Helmsdale Granite was apparently deeply weathered to a 'grus' and supplied products of granular disintegration to the Ousdale Arkose (Trewin

1993a). Derived angular pink feldspar phenocrysts to 3 cm are abundant, but pebbles of granite scarce. The arkose was mainly deposited by sheet floods on alluvial fans (Dec 1992). The Ousdale Mudstone (Ceann Ousdale Fm., Dec 1992) is dominated by red alluvial plain to impermanent lacustrine mudstones, siltstones and fine sandstones. Sub-aerial desiccation cracks and current ripples are common, and thin beds of arkose deposited by sheet floods are present (Trewin 1993a). Thin channel sandstones contain a greater variety of clasts than the arkose, mainly derived from Moine basement indicating a more distant supply. An assemblage of non-marine trace fossils including *Diplocraterion, Beaconichnus, Tasmanadia, Merostomichnites, Rusophycus* and *Cruziana* was produced by a varied arthropod fauna (Trewin 1993a). Plant debris is associated with channel sandstones and a relatively wet environment is envisaged for deposition of the Ousdale Mudstone.

The northern Lower ORS in the area from Ousdale to the north coast in the Reay and Strathy area is poorly known. Basal conglomerates tend to be of local derivation and contain pebbles of andesites, probably representing contemporaneous volcanism. Fine-grained sandstones, mudstones and siltstones (Braemore Mudstones) frequently rest directly on basement and indicate a northward continuation of the fine-grained alluvial plain to lacustrine facies of the Ousdale Mudstone. At the northern end of the outcrop small outliers appear to fill N–S trending valleys in the pre-existing topography.

Further west along the coast in the Strathy outlier possible Lower ORS conglomerate and arkose underlies the Middle ORS. Minor outliers described by Blackbourn (1981) are recognized as Lower ORS on lithological grounds only. The wide distribution of the outliers west of the main outcrop at Crask, Ben Griams, Tongue, The Roan Islands and Kirtomy serves to illustrate how close much of the Highland area topography is to the Devonian erosion surface.

Sarclet, Caithness

The Sarclet inlier on the coast 3 to 6 km south of Wick displays 434 m of strata considered to belong to the Lower ORS. This sequence is overlain, apparently conformably, by the quartzitic Ellen's Goe Conglomerate at the base of the Middle ORS. At the base 70 m of the Sarclet Conglomerate contains rounded clasts of granites, schists, gneisses and abundant volcanic clasts indicative of contemporaneous volcanism. The conglomerates and the overlying Sarclet Sandstone (85 m) are fluvial deposits of rivers flowing from the SE, indicating that a narrow basin may have existed in this area in the Early Devonian. Above the fluvial sandstones the Ulbster/Riera Geo Mudstones (172 m), and Ulbster/Ires Geo Sandstone (107 m) comprise a sequence dominated by green mudstone with some calcareous marls passing up into two thick fluvial sandstones with grey mudstones from which miospores of probable Late Emsian age have been obtained (Collins & Donovan 1977). The overall impression is of coarse fluvial deposits grading up into an impermanent shallow lacustrine environment that was periodically invaded by fluvial conditions.

Moray Firth

Offshore in the Moray Firth Well 12/27-1 contains a thick (c. 1 km) sequence of green-grey claystones and siltstones, which are variably dolomitic (Richards 1985a). Similar sequences have been encountered in Wells 12/27-2, 12/28-2 and 13/19-1, and an Early Devonian age confirmed on the basis of miospores (Andrews et al. 1990). Deposition is thought to have taken place in shallow lakes, and sedimentation was probably fault controlled in several small basins. For further details of the offshore successions see Marshall & Hewett (2003).

Orkney

On Orkney, the Yesnaby Sandstone Group forms spectacular cliff outcrops some 7 km NW of Stromness (Fannin 1970; Mykura 1976). To the south of the Garthna Geo Fault which is intruded by a later dyke, the Harra Ebb Formation can be seen banked against a palaeo-hillside of Moine basement which forms the modern cliff. Up to 100 m of sandstones and silt-stones are present with tongues of breccia and conglomerate near the base; deposition was from currents flowing down the hillside and out onto a flatter plain. There is some doubt as to the age of these beds and they may be Mid rather than Early Devonian (see notes in Mykura 1976). Cliffs at Yesnaby (Plate 13) to the north of the Garthna Geo Fault display a superb sequence of aeolian sandstones with large scale cross-bedding indicating wind direction from the W to NW (Fig. 8.15). The aeolian sandstones pass up into waterlain sandstones with occasional pebbles, desiccation cracks and ripples. It appears that the top of the dune sequence was reworked by fluvial or lake-margin processes. The top of this sequence is marked by a 10° angular discordance with a pebble lag beneath the Middle ORS but there is little evidence for a major unconformity. A borehole at Warbeth, 2 km west of Stromness encountered 50 m of purple siltstone and fine grained sandstone beneath the sub-Middle ORS unconformity and overlying 11 m of breccia resting on metamorphic base-ment (Mykura 1976). This fine-grained development resembles parts of the Lower ORS of Caithness. Mykura (1976) suggests that there were strong local facies changes in the Lower ORS of the area related to the topography of the basement surface. No palaeontological confirmation of the age of the Yesnaby sequence is available.

Depositional conditions in the Orcadian Area

The most striking features found in separate basin areas of the Lower ORS successions in the northern area are: (1) basal conglomerates/breccias of local derivation forming fans domi-nated by debris flows and sheet floods: (2) rapid upward transition from basal conglomerates to fine-grained mud-dominated facies of alluvial plain or lacustrine association; and (3) incoming of fluvial channel deposits of wider derivation in the top of the sequence.

Where a date has been obtained, usually on the basis of spores in the fine-grained facies it is usually quoted as Emsian (Gamrie, Ousdale, Sarclet), or Pragian to Emsian (Rhynie, Strathpeffer).Thus, it is important to stress that there is only a small overlap between the youngest Lower ORS sediments of the Midland Valley (Strathmore Group – Early to Mid-

Emsian, Westoll 1977) and the oldest Lower ORS (Pragian, Rhynie) of the northern area. It seems possible that the com-pression that resulted in Midland Valley uplift and formation of the Strathmore Syncline was coeval with subsidence, exten-sional faulting and the start of sedimentation in the Orcadian area. The generally NE–SW, fault-bounded basins could have been initiated by the same forces. It can also be shown that contemporaneous volcanic activity took place at Rhynie, and activity is inferred in the Caithness area and offshore from Sarclet on the basis of volcanic clasts in the Lower ORS.

Deposition apparently took place in small faulted basins in which initial conglomerate deposition was succeeded by low-energy conditions and fine-grained deposition, with sediments frequently of grey-green colouration. In some areas (e.g. Gol-spie) older sediments were apparently reworked, but generally coarse clastic supply was low, suggesting generally low and local relief. Apart from some sections in the Turriff Basin, caliche is only of sparse occurrence suggesting a cooler/wetter climate for this period. Organic content of the fine-grained rocks is locally high (Strathpeffer and Block 12) giving potential hydrocarbon source rocks (Trewin 1989; Marshall 1998). Generation of oil has taken place in the Palaeozoic and again during Mesozoic burial (Marshall 1998) and, thus, the Devonian (including Middle ORS Caithness Flagstones) is a strong candidate as the source of oil in the Beatrice Field (Duncan & Hamilton 1988; Peters et al. 1989; Bailey et al. 1990).

The entirely local nature of sedimentation in the basal conglomerates was replaced by a wider derivation for fluvial sandstones, which show well-developed channel and cross-bedding features indicative of sustained flow. The river systems may have been channelled north and northeast along active faults into the Orcadian Basin from the Grampian area, as illustrated by fluvial drainage in the Rhynie and Turriff basins. Where conditions were suitably damp, terrestrial plants flour-ished as demonstrated by the contents of the Rhynie chert, and a fauna of arthropods left abundant trace fossils at a few local-ities in marginal lacustrine deposits (e.g. Gamrie, Ousdale).

Lower Old Red Sandstone palaeogeography

General features of Late Silurian–Early Devonian palaeogeo-graphy are illustrated in Fig. 8.16. The main features are south-westerly directed drainage through the Midland Valley of a large river system originating in Scandanavia (Bluck 2000). Lateral supply came both from sources now hidden, and, particularly in the latter part of the Early Devonian, from the Southern Uplands and South Highlands. A watershed sepa-rated the Midland Valley from the Orcadian area where deposition did not generally start until Emsian time when extensional basins were initiated following cessation of trans-tensional sinistral strike-slip in the Late Silurian to Early Devonian (Tregus et al. 1999). The abundance of fine-grained sediment, plant debris and grey-green shales points to the existence of temperate rather than semi-arid conditions for considerable periods of time.

Middle Old Red Sandstone

The Middle Old Red Sandstone forms disconnected outcrops which border the Moray Firth, occupy most of Caithness and Orkney, and occur in three fault bounded blocks in Shetland that have suffered differing structural histories and have been brought together by transcurrent fault movement. Broadly speaking, the outcrops of Caithness and Orkney are dominated by flagstones deposited in cyclic lacustrine sequences within the Orcadian lake. The more southerly outcrops in Tarbet Ness, the Black Isle, and from Inverness along the southern margin of

Fig. 8.15. Aeolian cross-bedding in Lower ORS Yesnaby Sandstone. Yesnaby, Orkney.

LOWER OLD RED SANDSTONE

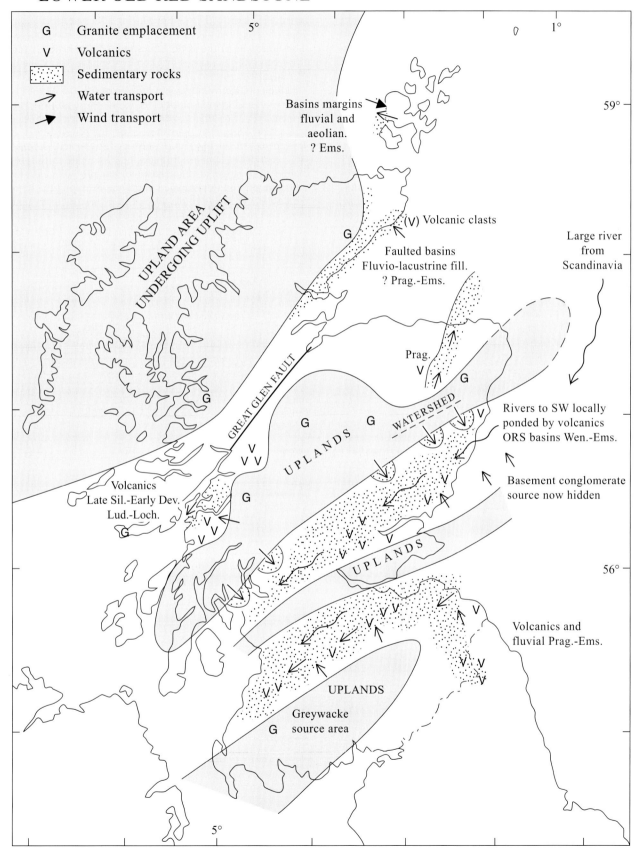

Fig 8.16. Suggested palaeogeography of Lower ORS based on present geography of Scotland. Areas of preserved sedimentary and volcanic rocks are generalized. Granite emplacement indicated dated as Late Silurian to Early Devonian.

the Moray Firth show fluvial domination with only thin, but extensive, lacustrine units representing southward extensions of the Orcadian lake.

The Midland Valley is devoid of Middle ORS and Upper ORS rests unconformably on folded Lower ORS rocks of the Strathmore Syncline. The Strathmore Syncline formed in post-Emsian to ?pre-Frasnian times as a consequence of NW–SE compression and reverse faulting on the HBF which dips northwestwards, sometimes by as much as 60° (Cope *et al.* 1992). It is significant that the period of folding and compression in the Midland Valley coincides with the start of widespread deposition in the Orcadian Basin. The uplift involved probably being responsible for the northerly directed fluvial outwash in the southern Moray Firth region.

Offshore, marine Middle Devonian limestone was recognized by Pennington (1975) in the Argyll Oilfield. Marshall *et al.* (1996) have reassessed the available material and noted

crinoids, calcareous algae and shell fragments together with probable tabulate corals and bryozoa. Marine Devonian limestone has now been reported from several wells in the central North Sea, with Well 38/3-1 producing a fauna of brachiopods, corals and crinoids from a section of over 100 m of limestone. The limestone is the Kyle Limestone of the Kyle Group of Cameron (1993), which is overlain by the Kyle Mudstone unit. Marshall *et al.* (1996) discuss the dating of this sequence and conclude that a Givetian age is most likely. In the Auk Field in 30/24-3 two limestones appear to be present separated by red-brown anhydritic mudstone (Trewin & Bramwell 1991). The lower limestone rests unconformably on slate-grade Lower Palaeozoic in 30/24-3 with only a thin breccia separating basement from laminated limestone. No undoubted marine faunas were noted in this limestone, but probable calcareous algae are present in laminated limestone overlying the breccia. Energy conditions were clearly low and the contact resembles

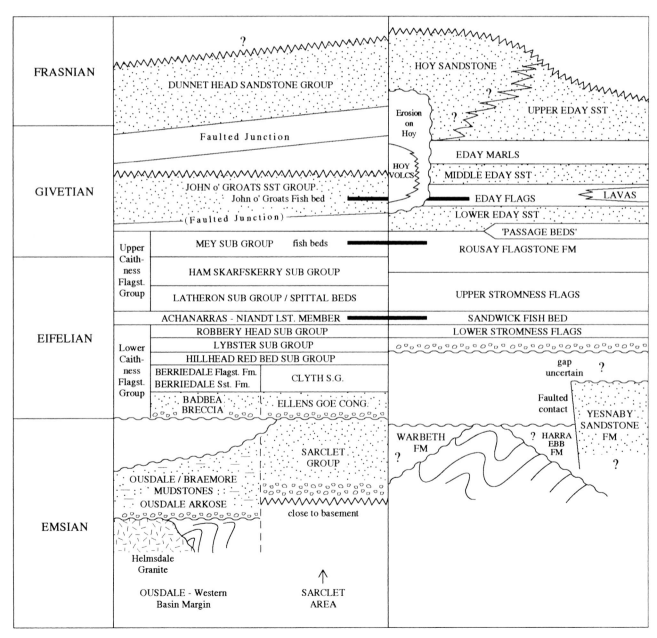

Fig 8.17. Middle and Lower ORS successions in Caithness and Orkney.

that of coincident lake margins in the Orcadian area (Bessa 1991). Marshall *et al.* (1996) consider both limestones are likely to represent marine transgressions, the earliest probably of Givetian age. For further details of the offshore Devonian see Marshall & Hewitt (2003).

Recognition of Mid to Late Givetian marine influence based on the presence of scolecodonts in the Eday beds of Orkney and in Well 14/6-1 (Marshall *et al.* 1996) is considered to represent incursions from a marine area. Marshall *et al.* (1996) argue that the sea lay to the east and entered the area along the Tornquist Zone, rather than along a narrow seaway to the south as is frequently represented.

Penetrations of proven Middle ORS in the Moray Firth reported by Andrews *et al.* (1990) and in more detail in Marshall & Hewett (2003) reveal granite (South Halibut Granite) 100 km NE of Peterhead which was being eroded to supply Middle ORS sandstone and conglomerate in 13/24-1. Well 13/22-1 contains a 267 m sequence of dominantly fine-grained sandstones, siltstones and mudstones, but only minor mudstones occur in 13/24-1; hence the Orcadian lake margin lay in this region. To the east in 14/19-10 and 11, over 870 m of sandstones, siltstones and mudstones are considered to belong to the Middle ORS.

Well 12/13-1, about 30 km east of Wick penetrated over 500 m of cyclic fine-grained deposits with high gamma-ray peaks interpreted as fish-bed lithologies (Kelly 1992). No palae-ontological conformation of the age is given by Kelly, who makes lithological comparisons with onshore deposits and those of 12/28-1 which are dated to Middle ORS.

To the NE, on the margin of the East Shetland Platform adjacent to the Beryl Embayment Well 9/16-3 encountered lacustrine Middle ORS, in which Duncan & Buxton (1995) tentatively identify the Achanarras horizon within an Eifelian–Givetian sequence. A hundred metres higher in the sequence an evaporitic development comprises three anhydrite beds to 6.1 m interbedded with claystone and sandstone. The age is considered equivalent to the Eday/John o'Groats Groups of the onshore exposure, and the sequence might represent part of an evaporitic centre to the lacustrine area, as predicted by Duncan & Hamilton (1988), or an evaporative marine mar-ginal area connected to marine conditions to the east as in the palaeogeographic reconstruction of Marshall *et al.* (1996).

Middle Old Red Sandstone outcrop areas

The outcrop areas can be conveniently divided for discussion into: (1) the Caithness and Orkney region where deposition is dominated by lacustrine deposits which overstep Lower ORS to rest on basement, and generally show a lack of coarse grained clastic supply; (2) the southern Moray Firth area from the Brora area around to the Turriff Basin where fluvial conditions dominate with considerable quantities of sandstone and conglomerate and only thin lacustrine intervals; and (3) the Shetland area sequences, together with the Clair Field of the West Shetland Basin.

Caithness and Orkney

The Flagstone Groups. The flagstone sequences of Caithness and Orkney (Fig. 8.17) show marked variations in thickness that reflect progressive overstep onto the basin margins. The distinctive fish fauna of the Achanarras horizon enables widespread correlation between Caithness and Orkney, and further afield to the Southern Moray Firth and north to Shet-land. In eastern Caithness the Flagstone Groups appear to succeed the Lower ORS conformably (at Sarclet) and the Achanarras horizon is possibly some 2.5 km above the base of

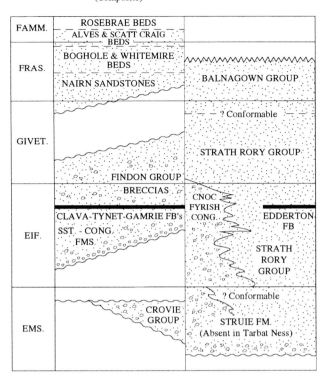

Fig 8.18. Middle and Lower ORS successions in the Tain–Elgin area.

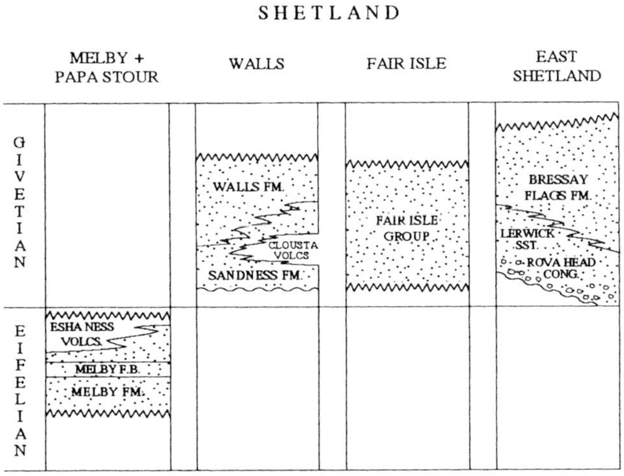

the sequence, whilst in Orkney it is about 200 m above the basal unconformity in the Stromness area. Some of this variation represents extension of the depositional areas through time, and part the drowning of an irregular topography (Plate 14). It has been suggested that the Middle ORS was deposited in a basin sag following Lower ORS rifting. However, active fault-ing controls sedimentation in the Eday Group in Orkney (Astin 1985), so part of the variation may be due to drowning of areas of footwall uplift.

The aggregate flagstone sequence in Caithness reaches 4 km, but given the faulted nature of the sections in Caithness some of the apparent thickness may be due to unrecognized facies variations. In Orkney, work by Fannin (1970) and Astin (1990) gives a thickness of only 900 m for the flagstone groups rather

Fig. 8.19. Middle ORS successions in the Shetland area.

Fig. 8.20. Lacustrine shoreline clastics with gravel ridge at top, overlying small clinoforms of flagstones with gravel lenses possibly representing beach cusps, and resting on deeper water lacustrine flagstones. Red Point, Reay, Caithness. Exposed section *c.* 3 m thick.

than the 3 km suggested by Wilson *et al.* (1935). The most useful horizon for correlation is that of the Achanarras fish bed (Fig. 8.17) with a distinctive fauna that has been recognized in Shetland, Orkney, Caithness and in 'nodule-bed' localities from Easter Ross to Gamrie (Figs. 8.18, 8.19). The John o'Groats fish bed is also distinctive and aids correlation between Caithness and Orkney. These horizons can also be utilized in offshore well correlation due to distinctive gamma-ray log signatures (Marshall & Hewett 2003).

The unconformable base of the Middle ORS in Caithness and Orkney is characterized by lacustrine deposits resting directly on basement, generally reflecting a lack of coarse sediment input from rivers in the area. However, it should be recognized that several of the exposures are undoubtedly exhumed topographic highs where such sediments might not be expected. At Dirlot Castle in Caithness (Donovan 1973) Moine basement is mantled by a thin breccia in which pebbles are coated with algal stromatolite and tufa-lined fissures extend into the basement. This appears to be a Devonian hill drowned by the lacustrine deposits. At Red Point, near Reay (Donovan 1975, 1978; Janaway & Parnell 1989) lacustrine deposits comprising local shoreline clastics (Fig 8.20), and lacustrine limestones drape a topography with a demonstrable local relief in excess of 30 m. Lacustrine limestones grade from massive to laminated downslope illustrating increasing water depth, and soft sediment deformation is due to sliding of sediments on the slope. Variation in water depth is illustrated by gravelly lithic beach deposits overlain by laminated limestones deposited when the topography was drowned by rising lake waters. Lake level fall subsequently resulted in reworking of lithified limestone as clasts. Similar basal Middle ORS deposits are also seen in Orkney at Stromness and on Graemsay.

The flagstone sequence is justly famed for the remarkable cyclicity of sedimentation initially described by Crampton & Carruthers (1914). The cyclicity varies in detail between different formations and in different areas, but the basic scheme of Donovan (1980) summarizes the main features seen in the flagstone groups (Fig. 8.21). A fully developed cycle commences with dark, organic rich, finely laminated silty flags, frequently fish bearing and comprising the 'fish beds' (Plate 15).

CAITHNESS FLAGSTONE CYCLICITY

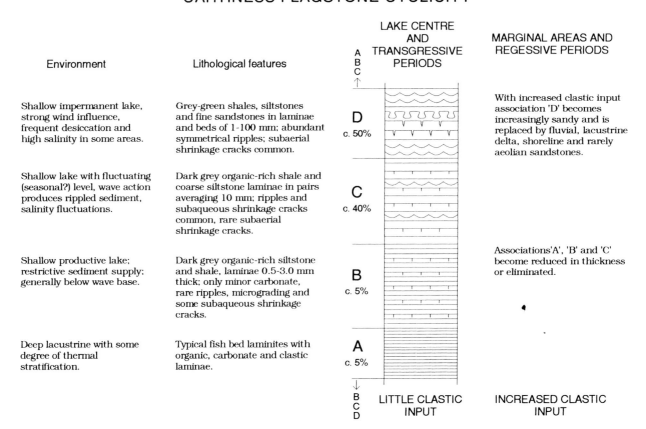

Fig. 8.21. Summary of the characteristics of lithological associations A–D of Donovan (1980) that form the cyclic lacustrine deposits of the Middle ORS of Caithness and Orkney.

Such deposits are interpreted as the deposits of a permanent thermally stratified eutrophic lake, with laminite deposition controlled by a seasonal climate giving deposition of annual clastic/carbonate/organic triplets on a sub-mm scale (Rayner 1963; Donovan 1980). Clastic laminae represent input from rivers in a rainy season, carbonate laminae were deposited in a dry, warm season due to photosynthetic activity of phytoplankton in the lake, and the organic laminae represent the annual decay of the phytoplankton. Clastic laminae were also introduced by other mechanisms such as dust storms passing over the lake (Trewin 1986) but in general the lamination is interpreted as annual. Water depth during fish bed deposition might have been as much as 80 m in central lake areas at the time of deposition of the Achannaras fish bed (Hamilton & Trewin 1988) but was considerably less during deposition of fish beds containing disarticulated fish material. The Achanarras fish bed (Trewin 1986), was deposited over a period of about 4000 years and contains many surfaces with abundant well-preserved fish that perished in mass-mortalities. The mortalities may have been caused by deoxygenation events due to algal blooms; storms mixing anoxic water from the deep lake with the oxygenated surface waters, or salinity fluctuations due to evaporative concentration. The events responsible for the transport of carcasses of fish from shallow lake areas to the deep lake laminites are illustrated in Fig. 8.22.

The 'fish beds' of Association A of Donovan (1980) are succeeded by Associations B, C and D (Fig. 8.21) which record progressive shallowing, culminating in an impermanent playa lake. Surface exposure and repeated drying produced polygonal mudcracks in closely spaced beds (Fig. 8.23). A characteristic feature of Associations B, C and D is the presence of lenticular shrinkage cracks interpreted to be of subaqueous origin by Donovan & Foster (1972). More recently Astin & Rogers (1991) and Rogers & Astin (1991) have suggested that many of these cracks were initiated on evaporite (frequently gypsum) crystals and are subaerial in origin. If they are correct much more of the flagstone sequence is of subaerial origin than previously thought. Trewin (1992) still prefers most of the lenticular cracks to be of subaqueous origin, particularly in Associations B and C of Donovan (1980).

The thickness of the cycles averages about 6.5 m in the Upper Flagstone Group at Brims Ness (Donovan 1980), and around 12 m in the Upper Stromness and Rousay flagstones of

Orkney (Astin 1990). The Achanarras cycle is some 60 m thick with more than one fish bed near the base within a continuous permanent lacustrine sequence. In this deep-water phase the fish bed is succeeded by turbidites both in Orkney (Astin 1990) and Caithness (Trewin 1986).

The control on the cycles is considered to be due to climatic variations with Milankovitch periodicities reflecting orbital variation. Hamilton & Trewin (1988) calculated periodicities of around 20 ka (precession) and 90 ka (eccentricity) for the Brims Ness and Murkle Bay sections in Caithness. Astin (1990) favoured a precession cycle control estimated at 25 ka for the Devonian, and therefore calculated that 70 cycles comprising the Flagstone Groups in Orkney were deposited in 1.75 Ma; he also tentatively recognized 100 and 400 ka cycles, the latter being reflected by drier and wetter periods. Kelly (1992) interpreted the gamma ray log of ORS cyclic sediments in Well 12/13-1 to represent precession and eccentricity controlled cycles.

The interval from the Sandwick fish bed to the John o'Groats fish bed equivalent in Orkney contains 45 cycles plus the Lower Eday Sandstone cycle (Astin 1990). The time equivalent using a 25 ka cycle duration is only 1.15 Ma indicating that these fish beds might be much more closely spaced on the Devonian timescale (Fig. 8.3) than is generally indicated. Alternatively, there is a time gap in the succession or the wrong cycle periodicity has been picked. A basic 90–100 ka periodicity may be more reasonable figure, but more detailed studies are required.

Whilst Figure 8.21 gives a general impression of the cyclicity, the lithological components vary both stratigraphically and regionally. The Achanarras cycle represents the most extensive and probably the deepest lacustrine phase, hence more of the cycle comprises Associations A and B and turbidites are present. In contrast, the Clyth and Mey subgroups of Caithness are dominated by Associations C and D and are more sandy, with fluvial and minor aeolian sandstones present as at the top of the Mey Beds sequence at Thurso (Trewin 1993b). Fish beds in the Upper Flagstone Group are generally thin, and disarticulated fish material is more common, as seen in the Holborn Head fish bed (Hamilton & Trewin 1994).

Sandstones are frequently dominated by laterally extensive laminated beds representing sheetflood deposits, and current-rippled beds up to 30 cm thick and tens of metres in lateral extent, which were deposited in shallow unconfined channels. Desiccation cracks indicate periods of exposure and wave ripples formed during times of shallow lake formation. The timing of such wet and dry 'events' is uncertain and may just represent infrequent water drainage to the lake from distant

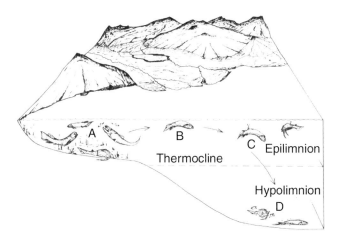

Fig. 8.22. Origin of fossil fish carcasses in deep lake laminite facies. Fish lived in rivers and shallow lake areas (A) where waters were oxygenated. Following periodic mortalities carcasses (B) drifted out into the lake where they eventually decayed (C), and sank through the thermocline to be preserved in the anoxic laminites of the deep lake. Modified from Trewin (1986).

Fig. 8.23. Desiccation cracks in ephemeral lake deposits. Middle ORS, Upper Flagstone Group, Thurso foreshore. Scale bar 10 cm.

sources giving flooding events every 10 or 100 years as documented today at Lake Eyre in central Australia. Thus extreme weather events rather than local climate change may be responsible. Towards the basin margins greater fluvial influence is apparent, with lenticular cross bedded channel sandstones in the Clyth and Mey Groups, and thicker sequences of sheet-flood sandstones as represented by the Berriedale Sandstone in southern Caithness.

Fauna and flora of the flagstone groups. The flagstone sequences of Caithness and Orkney are famed for the fish faunas which are abundant and superbly preserved in some of the fish beds notably at the Achanarras/Sandwick horizon. Fish are very rare in lithologies other than typical organic-rich laminated fish beds and thus the zonal schemes based on fish (Donovan *et al.* 1974) depend on the recognition of specific beds. The arthrodires are of most stratigraphic value with *Coccosteus cuspidatus* characteristic of the Late Eifelian Achanarras level, and the top of the Lower Flagstone Group. *Dickosteus* ranges through the Ham–Scarfskerry Subgroup and *Millerosteus* is characteristic of the Mey Subgroup. The sequence is continued with *Watsonosteus* in the Givetian John o'Groats–Eday Groups. Crossopterygian and acanthodian fish have good potential for correlation, and will prove useful when taxonomic revisions have been completed.

It is possible that each fish fauna represents a separate invasion of the basin from marine areas via rivers at times of lake overflow. The Achanarras level invasion being the richest in terms of genera (15) and the most widespread. The sequence of fish within the Achanarras fish bed at Achanarras has been investigated by Trewin (1986) who demonstrated that the lungfish *Dipterus* has the longest range and was presumably most tolerant to adverse conditions. The greatest diversity of genera is associated with the more calcitic laminites of the central part of the fish bed. There are marked similarities between the faunal sequence in the fish bed at Achanarras and at Sandwick in Orkney, but abundances of individual genera are variable between the localities. *Osteolepis* and *Gyroptychius* are abundant in Orkney but *Osteolepis* is rare, and *Gyroptychius* absent at Achanarras. Conversely, *Palaeospondylus* is abundant at Achanarras, but very rare in Orkney. Recent finds from Achanarras include the jawless vertebrate *Cornovichthys* (Newman & Trewin 2001) and a chasmataspid (Anderson *et al.* 2000). The variability of faunas between localities may represent distribution of suitable habitats in the adjacent shallow lake living areas of the fish.

The conchostracan *Asmussia* occurs sporadically in the Upper Flagstone Group of Caithness and the Rousay Flags of Orkney, but cannot be relied on for correlation purposes. Evidence of other arthropods is provided by rather scarce trace fossils, particularly *Isopodichnus* (Trewin 1976), which seems to have favoured areas close to the lake margin. Algal stromatolites occur at several levels, most notably in the Lower Stromness Flags at Stromness and Yesnaby (Fannin 1969). The algae colonised mudflats and formed sheets and mounds of digitate stromatolites. Ripped-up stromatolites and oriented runnels with stromatolite debris provide evidence of shallow lake-margin environments with minor wave action.

John o'Groats and Eday Sandstone Groups. Above the flagstone groups there is a marked change to a cyclic sandstone dominated sequence of the John o'Groats and Eday Groups in which lacustrine laminite deposition is only represented in the Eday Flagstones. The distinctive fish fauna of *Tristichopterus alatus, Pentlandia macroptera, Microbrachius dicki* and *Watsonosteus fletti* permits correlation of the Eday Flagstones with the John o'Groats fish bed in Caithness. The replacement of all

fish genera of the flagstone sequence at this level implies a new colonization of the basin following deposition of the Lower Eday Sandstone and equivalents in Caithness.

The sandstones are dominantly yellow to red in colour, medium grained with occasional conglomeratic units, and display trough and planar cross bedding, parallel and ripple lamination, dewatering structures and desiccation features. Deposition was dominantly by fluvial processes, but aeolian dune sandstones and beach deposits are locally important as demonstrated by Astin (1985) in the Lower Eday Sandstone.

There is marked facies variation within the outcrop area which extends from John o'Groats on the mainland to Eday and Sanday in the north. The Lower Eday Sandstone has a transitional base with an upward increase in sand content from the Rousay Flagstones. The main, upper, amalgamated sandstones of the Lower Eday Sandstone have a diachronous base and the top is defined by lacustrine deposits of the Eday Flagstones. Astin (1985) has clearly shown that these sandstones resulted from deposition by two river systems. The northern system, seen in Eday, Sanday, Stronsay and Shapinsay is markedly conglomeratic and flowed to the SE, and the southern system seen in the outcrops of John o'Groats Sandstone in Caithness flowed NE to interdigitate with the northern system in mainland Orkney. Both systems were dominated by shallow sand-rich braided streams. Interaction with lacustrine facies is seen in the development of low-angle laminated beach deposits. Using values for alluvial gradients Astin calculated that the lake seldom exceeded 20 m in depth during Lower Eday Sandstone deposition. Astin (1985) demonstrates that the alluvial surfaces were reworked by wind from the S to SE to form a dune field which thickens to over 60 m in the NW of the outcrop area in Eday, and developed on the western side of the northern alluvial system.

The preservation of the dune field, and thickness changes of sandstones relating to the present synclinal areas of Eday and Deerness, led Astin (1985) to the conclusion that deposition was controlled by contemporaneous extensional faulting. He suggested that the Rack Wick/Shapinsay Fault and North Scapa Fault defined the margin of the Eday basin, and that western Orkney may have undergone erosion at this time.

The cyclic Eday Flagstones with their distinctive fish fauna record the brief return of deeper lake conditions, but the presence of fluvial sandstones in the cycles shows that the clastic source was still available. The thinning of the flagstones from 150 m in SE Orkney to 10 m in north Eday also reflects continuation of the northern clastic source.

The Eday Flagstones contain a few thin flows of olivine–plagioclase-phyric basalt and hawaiite (Fig. 8.4) with chemically similar minor intrusions and volcaniclastic lithologies. Because of groundmass analcite, Kellock (1969) compared these with Carboniferous alkali basalts of the Midland Valley, but the analcite may be secondary and the least altered samples lack normative nepheline (Thirlwall 1979). Apart from one intrusion, the three samples analysed by Thirlwall (1979) have low incompatible element concentrations similar to Shetland basic rocks, though La/Nb is *c.* 1.0 suggesting an extensional origin for the magmatism.

The succeeding Middle Eday Sandstone is characterized by volcanic debris representing contemporaneous erosion of volcanics. The volcanics on Hoy that occur at the base of the Upper ORS rest on an eroded surface of flagstones and Lower Eday Sandstone (Wilson *et al.* 1935) and are themselves erosively overlain by the Hoy Sandstone. Whilst they might be broadly contemporaneous with the Eday Group volcanics they have markedly different chemistries suggesting different sources of magma.

The Eday Marls are red and green calcareous mudstones and siltstones with thin channel and sheet sandstones of fluvial origin (Marshall *et al.* 1996). The mudstones are frequently apparently structureless, or brecciated due to repeated desiccation events. Incipient caliche soil profiles are also developed. Evaporitic conditions are indicated by dolosparite pseudomorphs after gypsum (Parnell 1985) and calcitic, sparite-filled vugs, probably representing moulds of evaporite nodules (Marshall *et al.* 1996). Trace fossils occur at several levels and include *Diplocraterion*, *Rusophycus* and *Cornulatichnus* (Carroll 1991; Carroll & Trewin 1995). *Thalassinoides* is recorded by Marshall *et al.* (1996) who have recognized marine influence in a grey-green unit within the Eday Marls on the basis of the presence of scolecodonts (jaws of polychaete worms). Marine conditions lay to the east at this time and the lacustrine phase of the Middle Old Red Sandstone had come to an end.

The Upper Eday Sandstone succeeds the Eday Marls conformable and is largely of fluvial facies. It is possible that the Upper Eday sandstone is part equivalent to the Hoy Sandstone (Fig. 8.18, and see Rogers, D. A. *et al.* 1989, and Marshall & Hewett 2003) and the traditional view of the separation of the Upper and Lower ORS successions requires revision (see below under Upper ORS).

The Southern Moray Firth

To the south and immediately to the north of the Scaraben Ridge which is marked by the position of the Scaraben Quartzite to the north of the Helmsdale granite, the Middle ORS outcrops are dominated by fluvial sandstones and alluvial fan conglomerates with only minor lacustrine intervals. Donovan (1993) interprets the basal Middle ORS sequence at Berriedale in terms of fan aprons bordering basement outcrop, and passing east into an alluvial plain of braided streams of the Berriedale Sandstone, however, extensive plane-bedded sandstones with evidence of rapid deposition may also be the result of repeated sheet-flood events. The overlying fluvio-lacustrine deposits with occasional evaporite relics that comprise the Berriedale Flagstones were deposited in an embayment on the SW margin of the basin (Fig. 8.24). It is possible that flagstone deposition extended further south than Berriedale since clasts of flagstones dominate the northerly outcrops of the Upper Jurassic Helmsdale Boulder Beds adjacent to the Helmsdale Fault to a point 1 km SW of Portgower. Marshall (1998) records Givetian spores from a clast at Helmsdale, and the presence of *Coccosteus cuspidatus* in a clast from the boulder bed (NHT pers. obs.) indicates a stratigraphic level at, or just below, the Achanarras horizon and a Late Eifelian age.

However, the presence of flagstone clasts in the boulder beds could be used as evidence for post-Devonian dextral movement on the Helmsdale Fault.

In the Golspie Basin the Middle Old Red Sandstone rests with angular unconformity on both Lower ORS and basement (Dec 1992). The basal deposits (Beinn Smeorail Formation) comprise five conglomeratic units distinguished on the basis of clast type and dispersal directions. These coarse alluvial fan deposits are up to 360 m in thickness and are succeeded by up to 260 m of fluvial sandstones of the Col-bheinn Formation. This sequence is similar to the Badbea Formation Breccia and overlying Berriedale Sandstone to the north of the ridge where the Middle ORS again rests unconformably on both Lower ORS and basement.

The Middle ORS of the area from Tain south to the Black Isle and Inverness and eastwards towards Nairn provides a record of abundant sand supply to a dominantly braided fluvial plain (Mykura 1983). Active NE–SW fault scarps controlled the NW margin of the basin and shed material to alluvial fans building to the SE. Conglomerates (e.g. Knock Farril and Cnoc Fyrish) are up to 500 m thick, and although the majority of clasts are of Moine derivation, Peach *et al.* (1912) noted clasts of Torridonian and Cambrian rocks from west of the Moine Thrust. Alluvial fans also occur on the SE side of the outcrop, and were deposited by rivers draining the Grampian area. Contemporaneous fault control of sedimentation took place on the Gleann Liath Fault in the Foyers area. Alluvial fans of conglomeratic material are present to the south of Nairn with detritus derived from the south. The region between the alluvial fans is occupied by the sandstones of the Strath Rory Group (Armstrong 1977), and Millbuie Sandstone of the Black Isle area (Horne & Hinxman 1914). Thickness is certainly variable but the 2.8 km quoted by Armstrong (1977) is not in agreement with the *c.* 1 km interpreted from geophysics and study of an exploration well drilled near Tain (Underhill & Brodie 1993).

The Middle ORS sandstones are generally of fluvial origin and rivers drained NE along the axis of a basin that was probably controlled by extensional faulting. Clasts of andesitic lavas are common in the sandstones, but it is uncertain whether they represent contemporaneous activity or erosion of earlier (Lower ORS) volcanics to the west. The sequence displays marked cyclicity that is controlled by transgression of the alluvial plains by the Orcadian lake. Fluvial cycles commencing with erosively based red channel sandstones and conglomerates fine upwards into planar bedded and rippled sandstones of

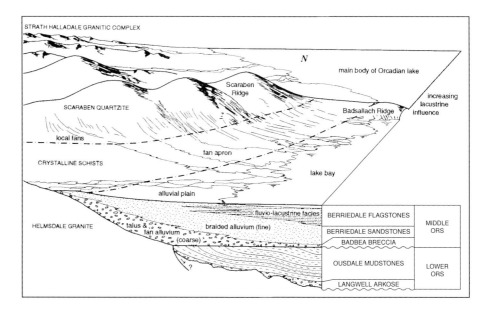

Fig. 8.24. Diagrammatic reconstruction of Middle ORS deposition in the Berriedale area. The vertical section is about 950 m thick. Modified from Donovan (1993).

lacustrine shorelines, and lacustrine grey shales with carbonate concretions, or laminated limestone representing lacustrine transgression. Regressive, coarsening up sequences record progradation of alluvial deposits into the lake.

Several lake incursions took place as shown by the cyclic sequence at Hilton of Cadboll, near Balintore, where one limestone bears a fish fauna that can be correlated with the Achanarras fauna of Caithness. This faunal horizon also occurs at Blackpark, Edderton, where *Coccosteus* is abundant and associated with *Osteolepis, Dipterus, Pterichthyodes, Diplacanthus, Cheiracanthus, Cheirolepis* and *Rhamphodopsis* in nodular laminated lacustrine carbonates within a generally fluvial sequence. At Cromarty, the equivalent fauna is found only 100 m above the unconformity with the Moine inliers of the Souters of Cromarty. Achanarras equivalent fish beds also occur at Eathie, and SE of the Great Glen Fault at Clava and Lethan Bar.

In the Elgin area Peacock *et al.* (1968) estimate that 300–600 m of Middle ORS might be present. The sequence is dominated by red sandstones and conglomerates of fluvial origin containing abundant pebbles of Dalradian quartzites, but several lacustrine intervals are also present. The Tynet Burn fish bed contains the typical Achanarras fauna (Trewin & Davidson 1999) preserved in nodules in laminated shale and laminated limestones at the top of a fining-up sequence commencing with conglomeratic deposits of fluvial channels. The fish bed laminites are capped by a shallow water limestone that was subsequently exposed as the lake retreated northwards. The exposed lake bed sediments were extensively fractured and invaded by sands, and reddening of the strata took place by bacterial oxidation giving the Tynet Burn fish fossils their characteristic red and purple colours. Filamentous bacteria are preserved in calcite veins in the fish bed (Trewin & Knoll 1999).

In the Tynet Burn section three lacustrine transgressions can be recognized (Trewin & Davidson 1999) at, or close to, the Achanarras equivalent event. This is consistent with other areas (e.g. Orkney) where several laminite beds with fish occur within the thick Achanarras cycle. The Dipple fish bed from the Elgin area contains *Dickosteus* and osteolepids and thus represents a higher stratigraphic level.

In the Turriff Basin the Findon Group (Read 1923*b*) is recognized as Middle ORS on the basis of the presence of the Achanarras fish fauna in the Gamrie fish bed. The fish bed is a lacustrine laminite with calcareous nodules containing the fish, and is included in 1–2 m of mudstones and shales sandwiched between a conglomerate and overlying breccia. The conglomerate rests unconformably on Lower ORS Crovie Group (Trewin 1987*a*) and contains abundant rounded quartzite clasts probably reworked from the Lower ORS. The conglomerate varies from a few metres thick at Pennan to 50–200 m at Gamrie (Read 1923*b*). The conglomerates were probably deposited on an irregular topography by high energy rivers. The Orcadian lake covered these deposits at the time of the main Achanarras transgression, but the resulting fish bed was possibly only locally preserved due to erosion at the base of the overlying breccia. The breccia is of local derivation and largely comprises clasts of the Dalradian Macduff Slates. Local faulting and uplift, possibly on the lines of the marginal faults of the Turriff Basin is implied.

To sum up, the outcrops around the Moray Firth to the south of the Caithness Ridge display a dominance of alluvial deposits, with fault controlled development of conglomeratic fans at some basin margins. Conglomeratic to sandy deposits formed a broad alluvial plain with rivers draining NE and north into the Orcadian Basin. Lacustrine transgressions from the north invaded the area on several occasions, but the most extensive transgression contains the Achanarras fauna, and

can be correlated with the Achanarras and Sandwick fish beds of Caithness and Orkney. This lake transgression illustrates the generally contiguous nature of the Orcadian Basin despite the presence of smaller, fault controlled, sub-basins.

Shetland area
The Old Red Sandstone outcrops of the Shetland area are divided by N–S transcurrent faults into three distinct areas with differing sedimentary, igneous and structural histories.

The outcrops to the west of the Melby Fault include the Melby Formation on the Walls Peninsula, the volcanics of Papa Stour and Esha Ness, and the sandstone-dominated sequence of Foula. The Melby Formation is about 600 m thick and comprises red to buff sandstones with subordinate pebbly sandstones and sandy siltstones (Mykura 1976). Near the base of the sequence two beds of siltstone and shale contain scattered carbonate concretions. These are the Melby fish beds that yield a typical Achanarras equivalent fish fauna of Late Eifelian age. The sandstones are cross-bedded and are interpreted to be of fluvial origin with currents from the west to WNW and deposited close to the northwestern margin of the basin. Above the level of the fish beds clasts of rhyolite and basalt are present and current directions indicate derivation from ENE. Mykura (1976) speculated that volcanicity altered drainage patterns in the area. At the top of the Melby succession two acidic flows occur within the sedimentary sequence: the sample analysed by Thirlwall (1979) is trachytic, but the level of alteration is such that it is unclear whether these are lavas or ignimbrites. A thin olivine–plagioclase-phyric basalt is present on the Holm of Melby, an island just offshore from the main Melby sequence, and is chemically similar to the basalts of Esha Ness, but very different from the basic rocks of Papa Stour.

On Papa Stour a 200 m sequence commences with at least four lava flows of sparsely olivine–plagioclase–pyroxene-phyric basaltic andesites and andesites. These have high Cr and Ni and low incompatible element abundances and in these respects are quite different from other Shetland basic lavas, including that of nearby Holm of Melby. The eroded top of the lavas is overlain by a sandstone with tuffaceous bands and rare dark shales from which Marshall (1988) has obtained miospores of probably Late Eifelian age, and consistent with the age of the Melby Formation. Sanidine-phyric rhyolite and trachyte lavas and rhyolitic tuffs of air-fall origin make up the rest of the succession: as with the basic rocks, the trachyte is petrographically and chemically different from that at Melby.

The rocks of Esha Ness comprise a series of lavas, volcaniclastic sediments and ignimbrites with only minor sandstone and tuffaceous sandstone. The rocks range from basaltic trachyandesites through latites to potassic trachytes and rhyolites. Many rocks shown as andesites on Geological Survey maps are trachytes and rhyolites. The ignimbrites are sanidine–plagioclase–phyric potassic trachyte in composition. Phenocryst mineralogies range from olivine + plagioclase in the basaltic trachyandesites through plagioclase + orthopyroxene + clinopyroxene + magnetite + apatite in the latites with additional sanidine in the trachytes and rhyolites (Thirlwall 1979). The suite is a high-K calc-alkaline suite like most on the Scottish mainland, but many samples show high Fe/Mg ratios more akin to tholeiites (Thirlwall 1981*b*). Apart from the most basic andesites, all samples have low Ni and Cr, contrasting with ORS suites on the mainland, and suggesting that the high K may be a consequence of more extensive fractionation than elsewhere. No direct evidence of age is present, but the basaltic trachyandesites are chemically similar to the basalt on the Holm of Melby, suggesting that the rocks may be similar in age to the Melby succession.

On Foula a thick (1800 m) sequence of sandstones of fluvial origin was deposited by currents from the WNW. Two inter-bedded thin sequences of siltstone and shale yield plant debris and a spore assemblage of Late Eifelian or Early Givetian age (Donovan et al. 1978).

Between the Melby Fault and the Walls Boundary Fault lies the Walls Group, comprising the Walls and Sandness forma-tions that were considered to be in fault contact with each other along the Sulma Water Fault by Mykura (1976). However, Astin (1982) concluded that the formations are thinner than previously believed and not separated by faulting. The age of the Walls group is Givetian on the basis of spores (Marshall 2000), and the two formations are probably, in part, time equivalents. Astin (1982) considers that the more northerly outcrops of the Sandness Formation represent alluvial fan deposits derived from metamorphic basement to the north and that the Walls Formation was deposited in a shallow lake. The Clousta volcanic rocks are interbedded with the alluvial fan deposits in the north and are mostly olivine–plagioclase ± augite-phyric basalts and basaltic trachyandesites, with a latite, trachyte and rhyolitic ignimbrite reported by Thirlwall (1979). Apart from the basalts, the suite is Cr- and Ni-poor, like Esha Ness, and K_2O and other incompatible element contents increase from calc-alkaline levels in the basalts to shoshonitic values in some basaltic trachyandesites. This is believed to be a function of extensive olivine–plagioclase fractionation from incompatible-element poor parent magmas (Thirlwall 1979, 1981b). Volcaniclastic rocks are common and include cones of acidic agglomerate (Mykura 1976). Felsites appear to have been intruded prior to lithification of the sediments. Other opinions on the depositional environment of the Walls Formation include deep lake deposits (Mykura 1976) and an entirely fluvial origin (Melvin 1985).

Problems of interpretation arise from the intense two-phase folding with development of a slaty cleavage, and a regional metamorphic grade, locally reaching greenschist facies. The Sandsting Plutonic Complex intrudes the Devonian and has a metamorphic aureole up to 1.5 km wide. These features, com-bined with poor outcrop, make interpretation of these rocks problematic.

The Fair Isle succession which has been tentatively linked with Walls by Astin (1982), is over 3 km thick with conglom-erates passing up into fluvial cross-bedded sandstones and units up to 200 m thick of dolomitic mudstone and siltstone of prob-able lacustrine origin (Mykura 1972, 1976). Overlying this sequence is a fluvial sequence interpreted as the deposits of meandering rivers flowing to the NE. The plants Dawsonites, Hostimella and Thursophyton were recorded by Challoner (1972), and the spore assemblage indicates that the succession is of Late Givetian age (Marshall & Allen 1982). The rocks at the south of the island are folded and have a prominent cleavage. Acid and basic dykes are present in fault planes and are associated with scapolite–carbonate veins. Mykura considered it possible that a granite may be present southwest of Fair Isle.

The Old Red Sandstone of Eastern Shetland occupies the eastern coastal strip of Shetland from Sumburgh Head to the Lerwick area, including the islands of Bressay, Noss and Mousa. Considerable lateral variation is in part due to the influence of the Devonian topography of the basement (Mykura 1976). Depositional environments and lithologies have been described by Allen & Marshall (1981). Coarse breccias of local screes rest on basement, and conglomerates of alluvial fans exposed at Rova Head and on Bressay were deposited as gravel sheets by currents flowing dominantly to the NE. The alluvial fan conglomerates grade into sandstones and conglomerates of braided stream origin with trough and planar cross-bedding in channels. The Brindister Flags of Finlay (1926) overlie a

basement high in the Cunningsburgh area, and comprise 1 km thickness of fluvial fine sandstones and siltstones of channels and overbank deposits of high sinuosity rivers which flowed to the SE. The general direction of fluvial transportation in the area is to the east and SE.

Lacustrine deposits include wave-rippled sandstones of lake margins which trended generally N–S, and deeper water deposits of laminated and non-laminated siltstones, calcareous siltstones, and shaly limestones deposited below wave base in depths estimated at greater than five or ten metres. In the south of the area aeolian sandstones with cross-bed sets to 3 m were deposited by transverse to barchanoid dunes driven by wind from the south to southwest. The dune sandstones are inter-bedded with sandstones and siltstones of interdune origin with adhesion ripples.

Several fish beds are present within the succession, and whilst they contain elements in common with Orkney, particularly the Eday Group, there are distinctive differences. Fish beds in the south of the area have yielded the characteristic genera Microbrachius and Tristichopterus of the Eday Group, but instead of the expected Watsonosteus and Pentlandia we find Dipterus and a new 'Coccosteus' together with Asterolepis and Stegotrachelus. A stratigraphically higher fish bed on Bressay contains Glyptolepis, Asterolepis and Holonema that could be considered comparable with Upper ORS faunas. Allen & Marshall (1981) placed the whole sequence as Late Givetian to possible Early Frasnian on palynology, hence the fish faunas might represent a slightly younger age than the Eday Flags of Orkney, and possible equivalence with the Nairn and Boghole Beds of the Moray Firth. It is worth noting that the wind direction conforms with that of the Lower Eday Sandstone rather than the Upper ORS Hoy and Dunnet sandstones. The younger age in comparison to west Shetland is also consistent with the absence of volcanic rocks.

The Clair field of the West Shetland Basin lies only 40 km NW of the Walls Peninsula, on the western side of the fault-bounded West Shetland Platform. The Clair Lower Group (Allen & Mange-Rajetzky 1992) is about 450 m thick and rests on metamorphic basement. It is possibly of Mid-Devonian (Givetian) age on the basis of miospores from near the top of the group. (Marshall, in Allen & Mange-Rajetzky 1992). However the age of the lower part of the sequence is still in doubt, but is likely to be of Mid-Devonian age. The Upper Clair Group is of Late Devonian to Carboniferous age and is considered later.

The Clair Group has been described briefly by Ridd (1981), Blackbourn (1987) and Meadows et al. (1987), and their inter-pretations are discussed by Allen & Mange-Rajetzky (1992) from which the following notes for the Lower Clair Group are condensed. The sequence commences with a 'Rift Lake Stage' (0–118 m) characterized by grey-green and red mudstones with small desiccation cracks; ripple-laminated fine sandstone, and thin fining-up sandstone units with a pebbly base of gran-itic and intraformational mudstone clasts. The unit thickens towards bounding faults in the west and NE. An environment of fluvial input to rift valley lakes is suggested.

The succession continues with two units of sandstones and conglomerates deposited by low-sinuosity fluvial systems, which are separated by deposits with a strong aeolian influence, and include aeolian dune sandstones and sub-horizontal sand-stones with 'crinkly' lamination formed by adhesion of sand to damp interdune areas. Following the second fluvial unit which also has associated aeolian influence and rare thin pedogenic calcretes, the sequence fines and is dominated by laminated very fine to fine sandstone, locally rippled and with concentrations of small mudstone clasts. Wave and current rippled sandstones, thin cross-stratified beds with limestone and mudstone intraformational clasts, and pedogenic mud-stones are also recognized. An environment of playa flats which periodically flooded to give shallow lakes with wave action is envisaged by Allen & Mange-Rajetzky (1992).

The interaction of fluvial and aeolian facies, and a probably conformable junction with undoubted Upper ORS and Carboniferous is reminiscent of both the east Shetland and Eday Group successions.

Middle Old Red Sandstone palaeogeography

Any reconstruction of the Middle ORS palaeogeography of Scotland requires consideration of post or intra-Devonian movements on major faults; particularly the Great Glen, Helmsdale, Walls, Nesting and Melby faults. Strong differences in interpretation exist between the reconstructions of Rogers, D. A. et al. (1989) and Mykura (1991) which take into account various estimates of post-Devonian dextral displacements along the above faults, and that of Bluck et al. (1992) who show progressive sinistral displacement along the Great Glen–Walls Boundary Fault from Wenlock times to Late Devonian. The map (Fig. 8.25) does not take into account transcurrent displacements.

The geological evidence clearly supports the post-Devonian dextral displacement hypothesis and ranges from sedimentological and petrographic matching of alluvial fan deposits across the Great Glen Fault in the Lower ORS of Loch Oich and Mealfuarvonie (Holgate 1969; Mykura & Owens 1983) to the geophysical evidence of Underhill & Brodie (1993) who demonstrated that the whole of the ORS succession is apparently conformable close to the Great Glen Fault. There is no evidence of major intra-Devonian structural features that would be expected if about 100 km of sinistral movement took place from Emsian to Late Frasnian times as interpreted by Bluck et al. (1992).

Whilst sinistral movement might have taken place in pre-Devonian times (c. 425 Ma) on the Great Glen (Rogers & Dunning 1991; Hutton & McErlean 1991), it may not have been large scale as has been pointed out by Bluck (1995). It does, however, appear that a major Devonian valley existed along the Great Glen, and associated faults controlled Devonian sedimentation.

Although there are strong similarities between the reconstructions given by Rogers, D. A. et al. (1989) and Mykura (1991), points of contention remain. There is general agreement that there has been 25–30 km of post-Devonian dextral movement on the Great Glen Fault (Holgate 1969; Donovan et al. 1976; Rogers, D. A. et al. 1989; Mykura 1991). Minor dextral movement has occurred on the Helmsdale Fault (Rogers et al. 1989), but is unlikely to be as much as the 50 km suggested by Flinn (1967, 1977) since the fault does not continue to the SW and joins other faults on which only small displacements can be demonstrated. Problems arise with reconstruction of the Shetland area since the total dextral displacement is much greater than that on the Great Glen. Estimates for the Walls Boundary Fault include 65 km (Flinn 1977), 60–80 km (Mykura 1975) and 95 km (Astin 1982). Dextral movement on the Walls Boundary Fault brings the similar Walls and Fair Isle successions into close proximity. Furthermore, Flinn (1977) estimates 16 km of dextral movement on the Nesting Fault which Rogers et al. (1989) consider to be post-Devonian. Mykura (1976) also favoured 60–80 km of dextral movement on the Melby Fault to explain the juxtaposition of the low grade Melby rocks with the metamorphosed rocks of the Walls Sandstone. However, Rogers, D. A. et al. (1989) prefer to regard the Melby Fault as an inverted syn-depositional normal fault with little or no dextral displacement.

Whichever values are accepted it is clear that there is 'lost' displacement between Shetland and Inverness. It has been suggested (Rogers, D. A. et al. 1989) that post-ORS, pre-Mesozoic dextral faults might run from Shetland down the Minch, or that the Tornquist Line of strike slip extends between Orkney and Shetland and took up some motion and offset the faults in Shetland from their continuations to the south. It is possibly significant that the Wyville–Thomson Ridge fault extensions truncate the south end of the West Shetland Platform and may have had a role in accommodating fault offset (see Allen & Mange-Rejetzky 1992, fig. 1). Thus the traditional continuation of the Walls Boundary Fault with the Great Glen Fault (e.g. Mykura 1991) might be rejected. The Walls Boundary Fault forms the eastern margin of the West Fair Isle Basin, extends south to the Wick Fault, and is downthrown to the east and is not shown extending north of Orkney (PESGB 2000).

There is no evidence for marine influence in the Eifelian of the Orcadian Basin and the lake, or lakes, which reached their maximum extension in the Late Eifelian Achanarras fish bed, were probably hydrologically open and connected to marine areas by overflow via rivers. The diverse fish fauna implies a marine connection to allow fish to migrate into the area (Trewin 1986). The southern margin of the basin received detritus from the Grampian Mountains to the south and a broad alluvial plain extended north into the basin. Active extensional fault control of alluvial fans is recognised south and west of Inverness with drainage from the Grampian and Highland areas respectively. This drainage contributed to the sandy alluvial plains of the Black Isle and Tarbet Ness regions, which were periodically invaded by the Orcadian Lake.

Drainage from major rivers continued north to the Golspie Basin, but to the north of the Scaraben ridge in Southern Caithness and Orkney there was a major change to the dominantly fine-grained lacustrine succession of the Caithness Flagstones which display a cyclicity (Donovan 1980) generally considered to have Milankovitch periodicities (see previous discussion). A lack of coarse clastic input is combined with coincident lake margins where lacustrine limestones may rest directly on irregular Moine topography. To the north in Shetland the Melby and Foula sandstones indicate further fluvial input from the west at the lake margin, and the volcanics of Papa Stour and Esha Ness probably provided striking topographic features.

In Givetian times the evidence is more restricted and the main correlative fish fauna is that of the John o'Groats fish bed and the Eday Flags. Lake conditions were more restricted by this time with water depths possibly not exceeding 20 m. Fluvial sandstones still bordered the Moray Firth, but extended from both the NW and the SE into the central lake area in the form of the Eday and John o'Groats sandstones (Astin 1985), the deposition of which was controlled by extensional faulting in Orkney. Exposed alluvial surfaces were reworked into dunes by winds from the south. The more westerly part of the basin may have been undergoing erosion at this time. Marine conditions lay to the east (Marshall et al. 1996) and briefly reached Orkney during deposition of the Eday Marls on the basis of the presence of scolecodonts.

In Shetland the thick Walls Sandstone of broadly fluvio-lacustrine origin was deposited in association with the Clousta volcanics which produced extensive explosive activity in a rapidly subsiding basin. This basin was deeply buried, partly metamorphosed and intruded by the Sandsting plutonic complex before being rapidly inverted.

The east Shetland succession is of Givetian age, but possibly slightly younger than the Eday Group. A lake margin is again recorded with fluvial drainage dominantly from the west.

MIDDLE OLD RED SANDSTONE

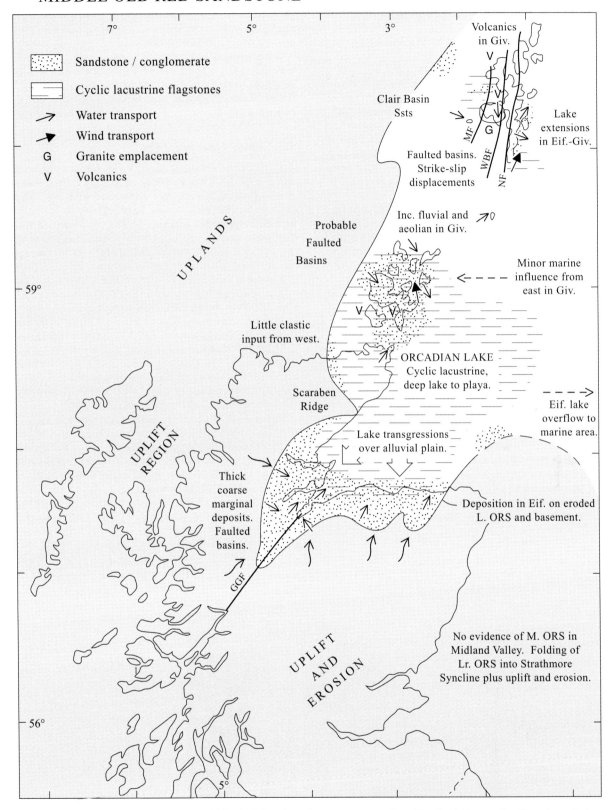

Fig. 8.25. Generalized palaeogeography of the Middle ORS based on the present geography of Scotland. See text for discussion relating to displacements on major faults. GGF, Great Glen Fault; MF, Melby Fault; WBF, Walls Boundary Fault; NF, Nesting Fault.

Strong differences in the fish faunas might indicate that this lake was not in direct connection with the Orkney area. Aeolian deposits amongst the alluvial lake margin deposits indicate wind from the south as recorded at this time in Orkney.

The Clair succession of fluvial and aeolian facies and associated shallow lake and lake margin deposits is comparable with that of east Shetland and possibly of roughly the same age, but appears to have been deposited in a separate rift basin (East

Shetland Basin). Other similar basin fills may be present west and east of Orkney, but stratigraphic proof of age of red sandstones encountered offshore is seldom available.

Upper Old Red Sandstone

The Upper Old Red Sandstone of the Midland Valley and Southern Uplands rests unconformably on folded Lower ORS and older rocks. This sequence passes conformably into the overlying Carboniferous and it is difficult to define the Devonian–Carboniferous boundary. The term Upper ORS is generally applied to fluvial, and locally aeolian, strata that underlie undoubted Carboniferous. In some areas, such as in the Buchan oilfield, fluvial 'Old Red Sandstone' facies is partly of Carboniferous age.

In the Orcadian Basin area there is little evidence of intra-ORS unconformity and Rogers, D. A. *et al.* (1989) consider that Upper ORS is generally conformable with Middle ORS in the Moray Firth, and this view is supported by geophysical evidence from Easter Ross (Underhill & Brodie 1993). Only in Orkney, on Hoy (Fig. 8.26), is a clear unconformity with a significant time gap observed. Here the Hoy Sandstone rests on Upper Stromness Flagstones (or possibly Rousay Flagstones), and Lower Eday Sandstone.

Thus there is a marked difference in the structural histories to the north and south of the Grampians/Southern Highlands area. It is doubtful whether any Middle ORS was deposited in the Midland Valley area, and there is a period of at least 10 Ma available during which compressive forces elevated the Grampian block by reverse faulting on the HBF. At the same time the Lower ORS of the Midland Valley was folded into structures such as the Strathmore Syncline and Sidlaw Anticline. These folds were then eroded prior to deposition of the Upper ORS. However, there is no evidence from clast compositions that the eroded sediment was shed north to the Orcadian area, and a long-lived watershed probably existed between the two areas. Drainage and palaeoslope in the Midland Valley was to the east, in contrast to the westerly drainage of major rivers

of the Lower ORS. The Upper ORS is dominated by fluvial sandstones in shades of red and brown, with localized conglomerates. The sandstones generally have a greater maturity (higher quartz content, fewer lithic grains) than the sandstones of the Lower and Middle ORS.

Outcrop areas of Upper ORS are considered under the following headings: The Midland Valley; the Southern Uplands–Northumbrian Basin; Southern Moray Firth, Elgin to Nairn; Easter Ross; Caithness and Orkney; offshore areas, Clair and Buchan.

The Midland Valley and Arran

The Upper ORS of the Midland Valley forms a broad upward-fining sequence (Bluck 2000). In the lower part sedimentation is fault-controlled, and contains coarse braided stream deposits. In the middle part larger rivers, up to 10 m deep, provided regional drainage, and there is a greater variety in clast type. Aeolian deposits become significant due to reworking of flood plains, and in the upper part of the sequence mature flood plains with caliche soil profiles developed as the depositional area extended and overstepped basement areas.

The outcrops can generally be divided into northern and southern areas. In the northern outcrops the thickest sequences (>1000 m) occur in the west of the area (Bluck 1978), and thin to 600 m in Stirlingshire (Read & Johnstone 1967) and 350–550 m in Fife and Kinross (Chisholm & Dean 1974; Fig. 8.27). Thicknesses in the southern region range from 100–425 m in Ayrshire (Eyles *et al.* 1949), a maximum of 275 m in Lanarkshire and 300 m in the Pentland Hills, but thickens to 640 m in the Edinburgh area (Mitchell & Mykura 1962).

Throughout much of the area, particularly in the southern outcrops, it is not possible to tell whether strata are of Devonian or Carboniferous age, and the scheme of Paterson & Hall (1986) for the Fife and Kinross area can be usefully followed, with the Upper ORS showing generally similar characteristics throughout the Midland Valley (Fig. 8.27). The Stratheden Group is taken to be of Upper Devonian age, and the Kinnesswood Formation, part of the 'Upper Old Red Sandstone'

Fig. 8.26. Old Man of Hoy, Orkney. A sea stack of fluvial Hoy Sandstone of the Upper ORS resting unconformably on the Hoy volcanics, which are unconformable on Upper Stromness Flagstones that form the foreshore (BGS photograph D01541).

of the earlier nomenclature is placed in the Inverclyde Group of the Carboniferous.

The Wemyss Bay Formation of Bluck (1978) is dominated by cross-bedded sandstones and is only seen in the Wemyss area (Fig. 8.27), and was deposited in a restricted basin by fluvial currents from the SSE. The succeeding conglomeratic formations (Skelmorlie, Burnside) were deposited by a combination of alluvial fans and braided rivers. There is considerable local variation in current directions in the west of the area with conglomeratic material derived both from the NW and SSE, but current directions swing round to give a general transport to the east.The conglomeratic facies tends to die out southwards to give a succession of sandstones with cornstones in central and south Ayrshire. Contemporaneous faulting in south Bute and north Ayrshire resulted in alluvial fans forming at the foot of fault scarps oriented NW–SE, roughly perpendicular to the main transport direction.

Sandstones of the Kelly Burn, Stockiemuir Sandstone and Glenvale formations are generally cross-bedded and have numerous intraformational clasts of red mudstone. Cross-bedding again indicates currents from the WSW in the Firth of Clyde, from the north in the Loch Lomond area and generally to the east or ENE in the central part of the basin. Bluck (1980, 1986, 2000) has shown that upward coarsening sandy and conglomeratic units relate to the formation of lateral and medial bars within river channels. The amalgamated bar sequences form the base of larger scale fining-up sequences in which the finer-grained deposits represent sandy floodplain deposits.

Towards the top of the Stratheden Group in the northern outcrops an aeolian influence has been documented by Hall & Chisholm (1987). Dune sandstones with cross-bedding made up of grainflow and grainfall laminae together with interdune sheets of wind-rippled sandstone were deposited by winds dominantly from the E and NE, but significant local components from the NW and SE probably represent small complex dunes formed by winds, possibly seasonal, from more than one direction. Aeolian sandstones were frequently reworked by fluvial processes, and in weathered outcrops distinction between aeolian and fluvial sandstones can be difficult. Hall & Chisholm (1987) recognize widespread aeolian influence including the top part of the Stockiemuir Sandstone west of Stirling, and the Knox Pulpit Formation in Fife. The latter was interpreted as having a marine influence on the basis of bipolar cross-bedding and presence of *Skolithos* burrows (Chisholm & Dean 1974) but the aeolian/fluvial interpretation is now favoured, and *Skolithos* is now frequently recognized in non-marine environments.

The Dura Den Formation was erected by Chisholm & Dean (1974) for about 40 m of strata in Dura Den in Fife which are dominantly fine-grained sandstones with micaceous siltstones. The sandstones are a mix of fluvial and aeolian deposits with opposed current directions, and ripple lamination, mudcracks and clay clasts are also present (Armstrong *et al.* 1985). The Formation marks a transition from dominantly fluvial to dominantly aeolian deposition. Dura Den is famed for spectacular mass preservations of complete fossil fish in sandstone; first described in a classic monograph by Anderson (1859). Several fish-bearing beds have been recorded (Anderson 1859; Chisholm & Dean 1974). In the *Holoptychius* bed fish are preserved in a bed of fine-grained sandstone between two surfaces with desiccation cracks. The fish can be compacted, or partly preserved in three dimensions with the carcass sand-filled. Some 15 m higher in the sequence the *Bothriolepis* bed was a very localized concentration of *Bothriolepis hydrophila* in sandstone.

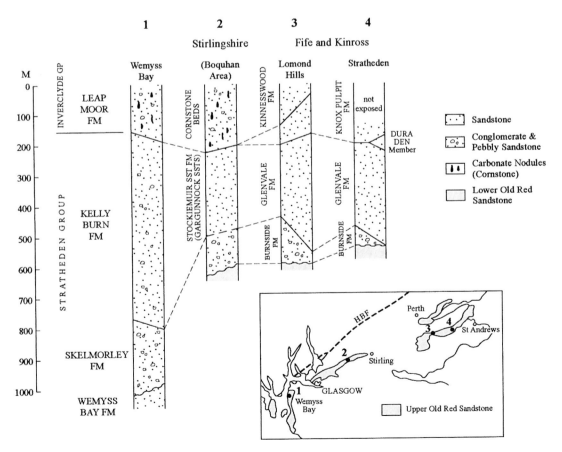

Fig. 8.27. Correlation of the Upper ORS in the northern Midland Valley. The Kinnesswood Formation replaces local names for the 'cornstone'-bearing (caliche) sandstones at the base of the Inverclyde Group. Modified from Mykura (1991).

It seems likely that the fish died through exposure and desiccation, and sand filtered into the dried carcasses. The movement of aeolian dunes may have trapped fish in shallow pools where they were overcome by blown sand. The fish genera recorded are *Bothriolepis*, *Phyllolepis*, *Glyptopomus*, *Eusthenopteron*, *Holoptychius* and *Phaneropleuron* and indicate a Famennian age (Westoll in House *et al.* 1977).

The Kinnesswood Formation (Fig. 8.27) and correlative 'cornstone' bearing strata in the Midland Valley overlie the aeolian sandstones, and form the basal formation of the Carboniferous Inverclyde Group (Paterson & Hall 1986). The change to alluvial deposition by meandering rivers resulting in fining-upwards cycles capped by cornstone representing caliche palaeosol profiles is taken to represent climatic change at about the Devonian–Carboniferous boundary, but good biostratigraphic evidence is generally lacking.

In the NE of the Midland Valley at Arbroath, Upper ORS conglomerates and sandstones rest with marked angular unconformity on Lower ORS, and a local relief of 100 m on the unconformity surface is suggested by Armstrong *et al.* (1985). Breccias with reworked Lower ORS clasts up to 2.5 m in length occur immediately above the unconformity and show current directions relating to local topography; succeeding fluvial sandstones and conglomerates were deposited as bars in rivers flowing to the SE (Armstrong *et al.* 1985). Other outcrops of Upper ORS are present in the Montrose area, where mature caliche profiles with calcrete are seen at the tops of fining-upwards fluvial sequences at Milton Ness (Trewin 1987; Balin 2000). This development is of similar facies to the Kinnesswood Formation and by comparison might be of Carboniferous age.

The southern outcrops of the Midland Valley are generally poorly exposed and bounded by faults. There is little evidence for a Devonian age for sandstones below undoubted Carboniferous and much of the Upper ORS may be of Carboniferous age. The abundance of caliche limestones at the tops of fining upward alluvial cycles led Paterson & Hall (1986) to assign such strata to the Kinnesswood Formation. The Upper ORS is not present everywhere beneath Carboniferous, notably it is absent in the Strathaven to Lanark area, and locally absent in the Pentland Hills. Sedimentation in Late Devonian to Early Carboniferous times gradually drowned an irregular topography and some hills were not covered until Carboniferous times.

Outcrops in the SW between Ayr and Straiton consist of up to 300 m of pink, yellow and white sandstones, frequently cross-bedded and deposited by rivers flowing to the northwest. The sandstones form the base of fining-up cycles capped by red sandstones and mudstones of alluvial plain origin. Mature caliche profiles up to 2 m thick are present indicating periods of thousands of years without significant deposition in a semi-arid climate. Similar soil profiles developed by alteration of Lower ORS strata immediately beneath the unconformity (Mykura 1991), indicate that a mature subdued topography with slow erosion developed prior to the start of Upper ORS deposition. Clast types (e.g. greywacke and cherts) indicate derivation from the Southern Uplands area, and George (1960) considered that the degraded scarp of the Southern Uplands Fault might have been a topographic feature. Within the Midland Valley the Lower ORS lavas of the Carrick Hills and Lower Palaeozoic rocks north of Muirkirk stood up as hills and also contributed sediment.

To the east of Lanark in the Pentland Hills similar facies of red fluvial sandstones with local conglomerates are present. Thickness variations from 300 m in the southern Pentlands to local absence of Upper ORS beneath Carboniferous in the north of the Pentlands may again represent filling of a marked topography as alluvial plains graded to the cyclically rising sea level of the time.

The Southern Uplands and Northumbrian Basin

In the Southern Uplands area scattered outcrops of Upper ORS occur beneath the Carboniferous from the Solway to the North Sea coast with the largest outcrop area in the Jedburgh area of the Borders. In the SW to the north of the Solway, two small inliers of Upper ORS alluvial facies with pedogenic calcretes (dolomitic) occur near Kirkbean below Carboniferous lavas and cementstones (Leeder & Bridges 1978). Sediment was locally derived from Lower Palaeozoic strata and the Criffel pluton. There is a strong possibility that these inliers are of Carboniferous age. Between the Solway and Hawick the Upper ORS sequences described by Leeder (1973) comprise 30–200 m of alluvial sandstones, siltstones and minor conglomerates deposited in a fluviatile environment and sourced in the Galloway uplands. Rivers flowed to the NE and included both high and low sinuosity channel deposits and floodplain deposits. The unconformity surface has a demonstrable relief of over of 100 m in places, and the thickness variations partly represent filling of topography. There is a general trend to upward coarsening of the whole succession accompanied by a change from high to low sinuosity fluvial deposits, a feature considered by Leeder to represent uplift possibly associated with volcanism.

Leeder (1973) considered that the rivers drained to an internal drainage basin in the Jedburgh area to the west of the Cheviots, citing evidence of Smith (1967) that SW directed current directions are present in north Berwickshire. However, Paterson *et al.* (1976) considered that currents are generally to the east and southeast. It is possible that the northeasterly-flowing rivers swung round into a more southerly-directed flow at the NE end of the Southern Uplands.

Outcrops on the North Sea coast include the classic unconformity between subhorizontal Upper ORS conglomeratic sandstones and near vertical Silurian greywackes at Siccar Point used by James Hutton in 1788 to indicate the great antiquity of the Earth (Plate 16). Nearby, in Pease Bay and at Burnmouth, typical fluvial and aeolian Upper ORS with caliche development is seen passing up into Carboniferous.

Palaeontological evidence of Devonian age for at least part of the Upper ORS of the Borders area is provided by scattered finds of *Bothriolepis* and *Holoptychius* with rarer *Phyllolepis* and ?*Remingolepis*. Occasional spectacular finds such as a block from Pease Bay crowded with *Bothriolepis* which probably perished in a drying pool (Clarkson 1986) recall the preservation seen at Dura Den. A Famennian age is assigned to part of the Upper ORS on the basis of the fauna (Westoll 1977; Andrews 1978) which is comparable with that of the Rosebrae Beds of the Elgin area.

The Southern Moray Firth, Elgin to Nairn

The extensive area of Upper ORS which extends for over 60 km along the southern margin of the Moray Firth in the Nairn–Elgin area is very poorly exposed. Stratigraphic interpretations (Fig. 8.28) rely on a few river sections such as the River Findhorn and Muckleburn, and information from old quarry sections, many of which are no longer available for study.

The area is important for the variety of fish faunas that have enabled subdivision of the stratigraphy as summarized by Miles (1968). It must also be remembered that Middle ORS, Permian and Triassic strata occur in similar facies in the area, and even the separation of 'Old' and 'New' red sandstone posed problems in the 19th century; eventually solved by careful palaeontological collection. Classic work by Mackie (1923*a*) showed that Middle and Upper ORS could be distinguished on the basis of heavy minerals.

ELGIN AREA

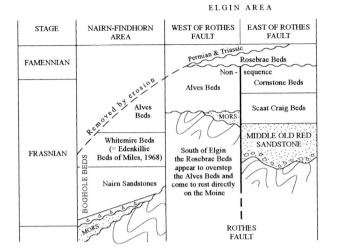

Fig. 8.28. Correlation of the lithostratigraphic divisions of the Upper ORS, and possible relation to the Middle ORS and basement in the Nairn–Elgin area. Modified from Peacock *et al.* (1968).

Stratigraphic nomenclature is informal due to the impossibility of defining formations. Thickness is similarly difficult to estimate with possibly 450 m in the River Findhorn (Westoll 1977) and maybe 1200 m east of the Rothes Fault (Peacock *et al.* 1968). The locally named stratigraphic units are placed in a stratigraphic framework on the basis of fish faunas. Traquair (1896, 1897, 1905) first recognized that a succession of faunas existed and Westoll (1951, 1977), Tarlo (1961) and Miles (1968) have refined the subdivisions. Faunal lists presented by Miles (1968) and reproduced in Mykura (1991) are not repeated here.

There is little sedimentological detail published on the area, but the whole succession is fluvial, with sandstones dominant, and subordinate conglomeratic and fine-grained lithologies. Sandstones and conglomerates generally represent channel deposits and contain mudstone clasts, sometimes associated with fish debris. Transport directions are generally northwards, ranging from NW to NE (Westoll 1977). Alluvial plain deposits have associated caliche profiles, particularly east of the Rothes Fault. Similarity of facies in the various stratigraphic units makes lithological distinction of the units most unreliable given the nature of the exposure.

Peacock *et al.* (1968) recognized variation across the NNW-trending Rothes Fault near Elgin (Fig. 8.28), and considered that a non-sequence, post-dating fault activity, occurs at the base of the Rosebrae Beds. The oldest strata, of Frasnian age, occur in the Nairn area where the Nairn Sandstones contain *Asterolepis maxima*. The terms Boghole Beds (Westoll 1951), Whitemire Beds and Edenkillie Beds (Miles 1968) are only defined on the basis of changes in fish fauna and the incoming of *Bothriolepis*. The Alves Beds contain both *Bothriolepis* and *Holoptychius*, and the Scaat Craig Beds, which are considered to be equivalent to a level low in the Alves Beds contain a varied fish fauna dominated by species of *Bothriolepis* and *Holoptychius*, but also including acanthodians and the porolepiform *Duffichthys* described by Ahlberg (1992). The same author has also recognized the earliest Scottish tetrapod (or near-tetrapod) in material from this site (Ahlberg 1991). The Scaat Craig vertebrate material is fragmentary, preserved uncrushed, and occurs in friable fluvial sandstones, pebbly sandstones and conglomerates. It appears that the phosphatic bone material was protected from destruction by a calcite cement of early diagenetic origin which has been recently leached from the rock.

The Rosebrae Beds are possibly gently unconformable on earlier strata and contain a varied fauna with *Bothriolepis, Holoptychius, Phyllolepis* and *Glyptopomus* which is comparable with that of Dura Den in the Midland Valley, and also with faunas in Belgium and the Baltic (Westoll 1977). As at Dura Den, fish are frequently preserved as articulated remains in the Rosebrae Beds.

The variety, and the large size of some of the fish, imply the existence of a complex food chain in the river systems of the Upper ORS. The similarity of the faunas with those of the Baltic, Spitzbergen and Greenland implies widespread basin connection at the time.

The Elgin–Nairn Upper ORS deposits are clearly oldest in the west of the area, and the Rosebrae Beds only occur in the east, being cut out beneath the sub-Permo-Triassic unconformity. The sandstones and conglomerates are the marginal fluvial-dominated deposits of an extensive depositional area with distant faunal connections.

Easter Ross

The Balnagown Group (Armstrong 1977) crops out on the Tarbet Ness peninsula and to the north of the Dornoch Firth. Underhill & Brodie (1993) consider that the Middle to Upper ORS transition is probably conformable in the area on the basis of seismic interpretation. In the Tarbet Ness to Tain coastal section at least 1050 m is present in mixed fluvial and aeolian facies (Rogers 1987, Marshall *et al.* 1996).

The lower 250 m of trough cross-bedded sandstones with pebbles and mudclasts was deposited by braided streams draining to the NE. The upper 800 m also includes fluvial sandstones but of greater significance are cross-bedded sandstones of barachanoid dunes 2–3 m in height and composite draa forms over 8 m high deposited by winds from the east to southeast. The dune sands are interbedded with sabkha sandstones that are flat-bedded and display wavy, wispy and contorted lamination interpreted by Marshall *et al.* (1996) as having formed by expansion and buckling of salt-cemented crusts that have been affected by aeolian scour. Examples of sand-filled desiccation mud curls are also present. Wave rippled beds record periods of flooding of the sandy sabkha surface. An environmental reconstruction is illustrated in Figure 8.29. Marshall *et al.* (1996) postulate that the sabkha and dune sediments bordered a marine area that lay to the east. Palaeontological information is sparse, but fragments of *Psammosteus, Asterolepis* and *Holoptychius* from the Balnagown River 6 km south of Tain suggest a correlation with the Boghole–Alves beds in the Nairn region and are probably Frasnian in age (Westoll 1977).

Caithness and Orkney

The Hoy Sandstone of Orkney and Dunnet Head Sandstone of Caithness are the remaining parts of a thick (>1000 m) sandstone sheet in which McAlpine (1977) noted nine lithostratigraphic units recognisable in both areas. The evidence for an Upper ORS assignment is the presence of *Holoptychius* scales on Dunnet Head, and the general lithological character.

On Hoy (Fig. 8.26) an irregular angular unconformity is present beneath the Hoy volcanic rocks and Hoy Sandstone which rest on tilted and faulted Middle ORS. Wilson *et al.* (1935), Mykura (1976) and others show Upper ORS resting on Lower Eday Sandstone and Lower Stromness Flags, but Brown (pers. comm.) considers that the underlying flagstones may belong to the Rousay Flagstones, so implying less erosion than previously thought. Astin (1985) and Marshall *et al.* (1996) consider that erosion was due to footwall uplift caused

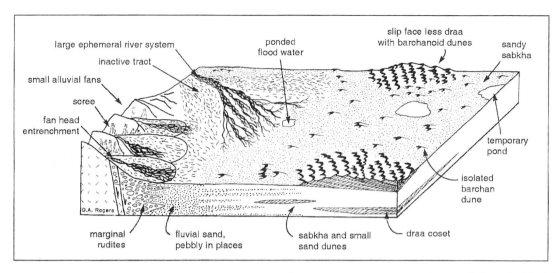

Fig. 8.29. Palaeoenvironmental model for the Upper ORS based on the Tarbat Ness area, Easter Ross. Fault-controlled marginal fluvial facies drain into a sandy sabkha with aeolian dunes. Not to scale. Modified from Marshall *et al.* (1996).

by extensional faulting, possibly at the time of deposition of the Eday Group to the east of the Scapa Fault. If the Hoy Sandstone is part equivalent to the Eday Group as advocated by Marshall & Hewett (2003), the Hoy volcanics and part of the Hoy Sandstone are as old as Givetian (see Rogers, D. A. *et al.* 1989). Possible relationships are shown in Figure 8.17.

The volcanics comprise up to 15 m of volcaniclastic sandstones and tuffs, some of airfall origin, which are draped over an existing topography. Overlying the tuffs are five localized lenticular outcrops of olivine–plagioclase–augite-phyric basalt and hawaiite lavas (Fig. 8.4; Thirlwall 1979). These are fresh, with fresh olivine, a very unusual feature in ORS volcanics, and are nepheline-normative with high Nb and other very incompatible elements and low Zr/Nb. They are clearly an alkali basalt suite, but have lower Ti than typical Scottish Carboniferous alkali basalts. The chemical variability of the lavas indicates that the remnants of several local flows are present, the most impressive example is a maximum of 90 m thick with a columnar portion 60 m thick. At Too of the Head the columnar lava is banked against a hillside of Lower Eday Sandstone (Wilson *et al.* 1935).

The overlying Hoy Sandstone is apparently banked against slopes of the lava, or rests with an erosional contact on the lava. It is thus possible that the volcanics significantly predate the Hoy Sandstone, but are geochemically distinct from the Eday Group volcanics. The Hoy Sandstone later covered an irregular unconformity surface and the eroded relics of the Hoy volcanics.

The Hoy and Dunnet sandstones are red to yellow and dominantly cross-bedded. McAlpine (1977) recognized two major facies which have been summarized by Donovan (1978). The first is a braided fluvial facies (Fig. 8.30) containing trough cross-bed sets up to 1.2 m thick and indicating transport to the NE. Distorted and fluidized cross-bedding, convolute lamination and intraformational mud clasts are common. Extraformational conglomeratic lenses contain pebbles of quartz, schist, gneiss, chert and limestone. Impersistent green marlstones have yielded fish scales and contain salt pseudo-morphs and desiccation cracks and may have been deposited in abandoned channels.

The second facies consists of broad low-angle cross-bed sets up to 2.5 m thick, interpreted as aeolian, and flat-bedded laminated siltstones with current and wave ripples and some bioturbation. Current directions are bipolar, probably due to

dunes being driven up the palaeoslope by winds from the NE. The rivers depositing the Hoy and Dunnet sandstones drained a wide area of the Northern Highlands and flowed consistently NE. There is a possibility that the Hoy and Dunnet sandstones are, in part, the equivalent of the Upper Eday Sandstone, thus the local base of the Upper ORS could be taken at the base of the Upper Eday Sandstone. This correlation is advocated by Marshall & Hewett (2003) on the basis of offshore data that do not support the general presence of an unconformity between Middle and Upper ORS.

Offshore areas, Clair and Buchan

In the Clair field NW of Shetland the Clair Upper Group of Allen & Mange-Rajetzky (1992) is of ORS facies and of Late

Fig. 8.30. Sandstones of fluvial origin with cross-bedding and soft-sediment deformation features. Upper ORS, Dunnet Sandstone, Dunnet, Caithness.

Devonian to Carboniferous age. A major change in heavy mineral compositions at about the base of the group is reminiscent of the change usually observed from Middle to Upper ORS, and the presence of a *Holoptychius* scale is likely to be indicative of a Late Devonian age. The top of the sequence is of Dinantian age on the basis of spores. The base of the group shows diachronous onlap in the Clair field area. The group is up to 439 m thick and above a coarse arkosic basal lag comprises cross-bedded and plane-bedded medium to coarse grained sandstones, with limestone and shale clast conglomerates that tend to form the basal parts of fining-up cycles. The cycles are capped by finer sandstones, frequently rippled, and red and green mudstones. Pedogenic carbonates (calcrete) are common in the basal part of the group, both *in situ* and reworked, but towards the top, carbonaceous material is preserved, and a climatic change to increasing humidity is implied. The topmost unit preserved contains dark grey mudstones and carbonaceous rippled sandstones. Miospores give a Viséan age, and the presence of acritarchs indicates marine influence. It is clearly possible that much, if not all, of the Clair Upper Group is of Carboniferous age.

The Buchan oilfield in the North Sea some 150 km NE of Aberdeen has a reservoir of Upper ORS facies which ranges from Famennian to Viséan in age (Richards 1985). The sequence is over 675 m thick and represents an upward-fining sequence with amalgamated channel deposits of cross-bedded and planar-bedded sandstones at the base. There is an upward increase in fining-up alluvial cycles in which red and green micaceous siltstones overlie sharp-based sandstones with cross bedding and abundant mud clasts. Calcitic nodules representing caliche soil profiles occur near the top of the section. Richards (1985) also recognized sheet-flood deposits within the cycles which contain reworked carbonate from eroded soil profiles. Thus the general features of the succession are comparable with the top of the Upper ORS of the Midland Valley, but appear to lack aeolian influence. The source of the sand for the Upper ORS may have been the granite 75 km WNW of the Buchan Field; an ORS conglomerate with granite clasts in Well 13/24-1 shows that the granite was a sediment source at this time.

Upper Old Red Sandstone palaeogeography

The reconstruction (Fig. 8.31) shows a considerably expanded depositional area in comparison with the Middle ORS (Fig. 8.25). Alluvial systems drained generally eastwards in the Midland Valley, but considerable local variation is present due to effects of remaining upland topography surrounding the area and the irregular sub-Upper ORS erosion surface within the Midland Valley. In the Orcadian area there is apparently continuity between Middle and Upper ORS in some areas, but a widespread lithological change to cleaner quartzitic sandstones is generally observed. Fluvial drainage is to the north in the Grampian area and the NE in the Highland region and Orkney. Wind directions are generally from the east or northeast. Marine transgressions from the east flooded the Midland Valley in the Early Carboniferous, following a period of slow deposition in a semi-arid climatic phase as evidenced by abundant calcretes towards the top of the Upper ORS.

Origin of the Scottish ORS volcanic suite

The genesis of the ORS volcanic suite and related Newer 'Granite' intrusive suite has been controversial for many years. Their broadly calc-alkaline chemistry and wide distribution show many similarities to continental margin magmatic arcs (Thirlwall 1979, 1981b). However, evidence that the Iapetus

Ocean had closed before the Devonian has led many workers to regard them as the result of post-collision processes (e.g. Watson 1984; Zhou 1984; Saunders *et al.* 1987; Smith 1995; Armstrong & Owen 2001). In this section we review some of the evidence that it is critical to this debate.

Closure of Iapetus in the British sector has been assigned to times ranging from Late Ordovician to Mid-Devonian. The presence of ORS continental sedimentation over the entire British region has been taken as strong evidence against any remnant Iapetus marine environment in the Devonian, but continental sedimentation extends back into the Wenlock in the Midland Valley (Stonehaven and Lesmahagow), when there was marine sedimentation in the Southern Uplands. Midland Valley continental sedimentation continues until the early Emsian (Strathmore Group), while the age of Lower ORS sedimentation in the Southern Uplands is essentially unconstrained, apart from that associated with the Late Emsian (394–398 Ma) Cheviot lavas. Laurentian and Avalonian apparent polar wander paths and trilobite and brachiopod faunas are essentially identical from the Late Ordovician onwards, but this simply implies that oceanic separation was less than *c.* 1000 km. Sediment was probably transported from Laurentia to Avalonia in the Mid-Silurian, but this too only requires proximity, not closure. If closure was marked by a widespread tectonic event, the conformable Upper Ordovician to Přídolí and Llandovery to Lower Devonian sedimentary sequences in respectively the Lake District and southern Midland Valley require that closure happened in the Late Ordovician or the Mid-Devonian. Although the Mid-Devonian deformation in the Midland Valley has been ascribed to transpression (Smith 1995), Bluck (2000) has suggested thrust emplacement of the Grampian terrane along the Highland Boundary Fault at this time. There is also strong isotopic and geophysical evidence that the entire Southern Uplands has been underthrust by Lake District lithosphere (Thirlwall 1989; Freeman *et al.* 1988). The termination of calc-alkaline igneous activity cannot be used to date closure (e.g. Phillips *et al.* 1976) if it is possible that calc-alkaline magmatism may postdate subduction.

It is clear, however, that the entire ORS volcanic province cannot be related to Iapetus subduction, as the Cheviot Volcanic Group is subhorizontal and lies across the trace of the suture (Fig. 8.1). Various models have thus been proposed to generate the magmatism in a post-collisional setting, or by inferring a relationship to subduction much further south (Soper 1986). Many authors have proposed that the many small basins in which Lower ORS sediments were deposited were produced by transcurrent fault activity, and have suggested links between major magmatic centres and fault locations (e.g. Watson 1984; Hutton 1987, 1988b; Rogers & Dunning 1991). Apart from the fact that it would be difficult to avoid proximity to a major fault in Scotland, it is difficult to see how the observed magma chemistry can be generated by this mechanism. The mechanism implies that transtension has generated melting in subduction-modified lithosphere to produce calc-alkaline chemistry. Extension generates melt through mantle upwelling, and the extent of melting produced is directly related to the stretching factor β (McKenzie & Bickle 1998). The probably small β-values associated with ORS transtensional basins would be expected to yield small-degree, small volume mantle melts such as basanites or alkali basalts, not the large volumes of silica-oversaturated basaltic andesites characteristic of the ORS and other calc-alkaline provinces. Such alkaline rocks may show a subtle superimposed subduction signature in their incompatible trace elements (e.g. Hole 1988), but their major element characteristics are determined by the low degree of melting induced by extension. Crustal melting cannot be expected to contribute to the production of silica-rich melts

UPPER OLD RED SANDSTONE

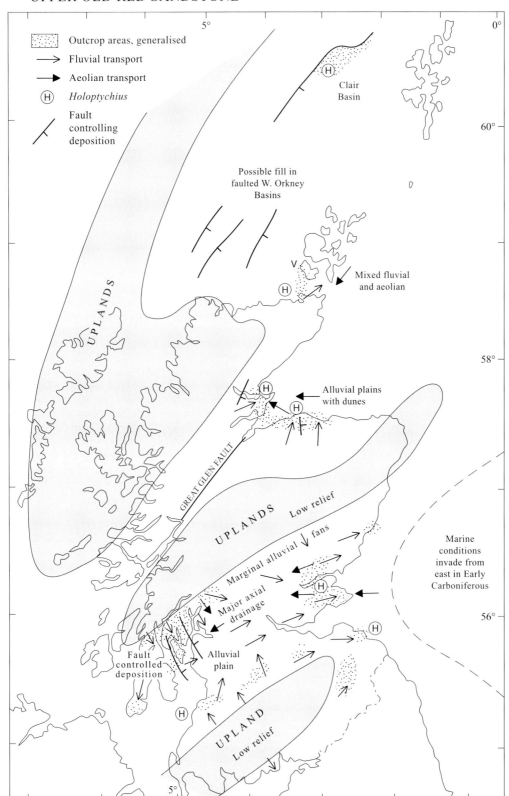

Fig. 8.31. Upper ORS palaeogeography and outcrop areas. Upland areas were generally of low relief.

during this transtensional episode, as at least in the Highlands and Midland Valley the crust was cool, except where heated by mantle-derived magmatism, since major crustal thickening and uplift in the Highlands had terminated in the Ordovician, based on 430–450 Ma biotite cooling ages in the Highlands (Demp-ster 1985). Thus the large granodioritic complexes produced from 425–408 Ma can also not result from extension-induced melting. The Frasnian alkali basaltic lavas of Orkney are the only ORS volcanics that have appropriate chemistries to be generated by post-orogenic extension, and show some evidence

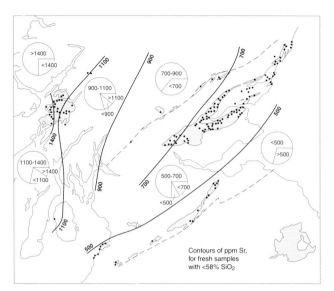

Fig. 8.32. Distribution of Sr content in fresh ORS lavas with <58% SiO₂ in central Scotland. Sample locations shown by spots on outcrop map. Contour lines based on Sr content: pie charts indicate the proportions of of samples between each pair of contours that conform to the contour lines. Data from Thirlwall (1979).

of generation in subduction-modified lithosphere, but these are much younger than the bulk of the ORS volcanic province.

Saunders *et al.* (1987) described the unusual chemistry of post-subduction volcanism in Baja California, where subduction terminates due to ridge subduction. They specifically noted that the Lorne ORS lavas shared features such as high Sr and Ba, depleted heavy REE and high Ni and Cr with the bajaites, which they proposed were produced by eclogite-facies slab melting during ridge subduction. While high-Mg andesites are common in much of the ORS province, and unusual in modern arc settings, they do occur in normal modern arcs (e.g. St Vincent and Grenada, Lesser Antilles, Thirlwall *et al.* 1994, 1996), and indeed occur in Baja California in volcanic suites when subduction was still active (Saunders *et al.* 1987). Their abundance in the ORS is probably the main magma chemical effect of the contemporaneous transcurrent activity in reducing crustal residence times and thus the extent of fractional crystallization. The high Sr and Ba and depleted heavy REE of Lorne lavas are part of a continuum from the otherwise chemically very similar Midland Valley lavas which have concentrations of these elements that are normal for calc-alkaline suites (Fig 8.4; Thirlwall 1981). As these lie closer to the suture than Lorne, and are if anything younger (Thirlwall 1988), it is unacceptable to ascribe a bajaitic origin to the Lorne lavas without also ascribing it to the Midland Valley lavas, which show none of the bajaite chemical features.

Most of the problems with a relationship to Iapetus subduction were resolved by the detailed geochronology of Thirlwall (1988), and Pb isotopic work of Thirlwall (1986, 1989). All ORS volcanic rocks in mainland Scotland north of the Southern Upland Fault, which show closely related chemistries and systematic spatial changes in incompatible element chemistry (Thirlwall 1981; e.g. Fig. 8.32) are older than 408 Ma and are most probably 410–420 Ma. Plutonic rocks from these regions show similar spatial chemical changes, and those with reliable

ages range from contemporaneous with the volcanics (e.g. Distinkhorn, Midland Valley, Thirlwall 1988) back to *c.* 430 Ma (e.g. Garabal Hill, Grampian Highlands, Rogers & Dunning 1991). These ages are Wenlock to Pragian, significantly older than the late Emsian 392–397 Ma ages of the Cheviot volcanics and the plutons in the southern part of the Southern Uplands (Thirlwall 1988; Halliday *et al.* 1980), and of post-tectonic granites in the Lake District. These igneous rocks are chemically rather different (Thirlwall 1981; e.g. they frequently lack basaltic components), and are too close to the trace of the Iapetus suture to be related to subduction there. The older volcanic rocks in the Highlands and Midland Valley all show Pb isotope evidence for a sedimentary component of similar composition to Southern Upland Lower Palaeozoic sediments, incorporated into their mantle source by subduction (Thirlwall 1986). Despite emplacement through these sediments, there is little evidence that the sediments contribute to the Pb isotopic signatures of the Southern Uplands igneous rocks. Instead, these igneous rocks, and especially the younger rocks nearest the suture, display a dominant high-[207]Pb component that can only be matched with sedimentary and igneous rocks in the Lake District, implying that they were generated in response to collisional melting of underthrust Lake District lithosphere (Thirlwall 1989).

There are two main unresolved complications to the above scenario. The ORS volcanics of St Abbs, in the northern Southern Uplands, are undated but have chemical and isotopic affinities to plutons in the northern Southern Uplands dated from 408–414 Ma (Thirlwall 1988; Halliday *et al.* 1980). Despite contemporaneity with and some chemical similarities to ORS lavas in the south Midland Valley, they are probably too close to the suture to be related to the same subduction system as the more northerly lavas, and they also show a Pb component from the Lake District that is absent in the Midland Valley. For these reasons, Thirlwall (1989) supported the view that the Southern Uplands terrane may not have been contiguous with that of the Midland Valley in the early Devonian (e.g. Bluck 2000). An origin through subduction in the Tornquist Sea was rejected by Soper (1986), who preferred a relationship to northward subduction between the London Platform and the Ardennes for all the igneous rocks south of the Highlands. This is not consistent with the age and chemical differences between the three regional groups of igneous rocks, Midland Valley, north Southern Uplands, and Lake District with south Southern Uplands.

The ORS volcanic rocks of Shetland provide a second complication. They have undoubted volcanic arc affinities, but their chemistries indicate closer proximity to a subduction zone than the ORS magmas of mainland Scotland. Thirlwall (1981) interpreted this to result from a swing in the strike of the subduction system from NW-dipping under northern Ireland to west-dipping under NE Scotland. Although this proposal has been criticised as more palynological dates have become available from the Shetland ORS that confirm Mid-Devonian ages (e.g. Astin 1983; Marshall 2000), the swing in strike is supported by the detailed chemical variation in the lavas and plutons in mainland Scotland, with for example highest Sr concentrations in the western Highlands (Fig. 8.32). The persistence of subduction-related magmatism into the Mid-Devonian in Shetland might possibly relate to its position near the triple junction between Laurentia, Avalonia and Baltica.

9 Carboniferous

W. A. READ, M. A. E. BROWNE, D. STEPHENSON
& B. G. J. UPTON

Introduction

Carboniferous rocks are now most extensively preserved in central Scotland, the Borders and the offshore areas east of Scotland. Preservation is patchy and successions are generally thin and incomplete in the offshore areas west of Scotland, the Highlands and Southern Uplands, which all tended to remain positive throughout much of the period. However, Carboniferous cover was formerly much more extensive than at present, as demonstrated by a series of isolated outliers with attenuated successions in the Western Highlands and Islands and the Southern Uplands. Most of the cover in these areas was stripped off during the latest Carboniferous uplift and erosion. The basal junction with the Upper Devonian is arbitrary, because it is drawn at the first appearance of calcareous soil profiles (calcretes) within an unfossiliferous fluvial and aeolian succession, but it is usually conformable and coincides with a widespread change to a slightly wetter climate (Paterson et al. 1990; and Chapter 8). Progressive overlap took place at various horizons including the early Carboniferous, the base of the Namurian and the Early Westphalian. Figure 9.1 shows Scotland and the adjacent offshore areas, with onshore Carboniferous outcrops, major structures and the principal localities mentioned in the text, and Figure 9.2 shows the onshore outcrops in central and southern Scotland in greater detail. Preserved Carboniferous strata tend to be thin in the west and thickest in the east, with thickening in local basins (Browne et al. 1985). Figure 9.3 shows the chrono- and lithostratigraphical divisions into which the Scottish Carboniferous succession is currently classified, plus critical radiometric dates from Scale B of Menning et al. (2000), which gives maximum ages.

Within this chapter the Carboniferous succession has been divided into three stratigraphical slices, following its recent reclassification by Browne et al. (1996). The dividing lines have been drawn at the first really widespread Scottish Carboniferous marine transgression (the Mid-Brigantian Hurlet Limestone) and at the local base of the Scottish Coal Measures (the Early Westphalian Lowstone Marine Band). Within each slice the lithostratigraphy, sedimentary rocks and general geological history have been described regionally from west to east and from north to south. The area of Carboniferous outcrops that lies between the Lower Palaeozoic rocks of the Southern Uplands and the English Border has here, for convenience, been designated the 'Southern Borders'. The Carboniferous geology of this area has more in common with that of Cumbria and Northumberland in northern England than with the rest of Scotland. Regionally based descriptions of igneous activity within each stratigraphical slice follow in separate sections after the corresponding lithostratigraphy.

Following the latest (Acadian) phase of the Caledonian Orogeny during the Early Devonian, Scotland formed part of the Laurussian supercontinent (Cocks 2000; McKerrow et al. 2000). At the beginning of the Carboniferous, Scotland lay in low latitudes south of the contemporary equator on the fringes of the southern arid climatic belt. Within Laurussia, Ziegler (1992) and Friend, P. F. et al. (2000) have suggested that left-lateral strike slip was taking place along a major fracture between Laurentia and Eastern Avalonia plus Baltica. According to Warr (2000) a narrowing belt of thinned and stretched Avalonian and oceanic crust lay, during the earlier part of the Devonian, along the Rhenohercynican zone which ran from extreme southwest England eastwards into France and Germany. During the Late Devonian and Early Carboniferous this belt was affected by early Variscan Bretonian transpressive folding along a destructive boundary between the eastern Avalonian and Armorican microplates, well before the major collision between Laurussia and Gondwana.

Tectonic syntheses by Coward (1993) and Maynard et al. (1997b) suggest the progressive eastward expulsion of a triangular European–Baltica block that was squeezed between Greenland to the northwest and the Variscides to the south. This would have given rise initially to left-lateral strike slip along the northwestern margin of the block, including Scotland, changing later to right-lateral strike slip when the block was pushed back to the west (Fig. 9.4). However, in Scotland right-lateral shear seems to have been dominant over left-lateral shear during most of the Carboniferous.

Folding, accompanied by right-lateral shear, crept progressively northwards during the Carboniferous and eventually gave rise to the major Variscan fold belt which linked with contemporaneous folding in the Appalachians and ran eastwards from southern Ireland through southern England into France, Germany and beyond. The foreland north of this belt was generally in overall N–S tension, which Leeder (1988) has attributed to back-arc stretching of thinned crust. As the Laurussian plate migrated progressively north during the Carboniferous, Scotland crossed the equator and probably lay within the 'everwet' equatorial belt during the Namurian and the Early Westphalian (Scotese & McKerrow 1990). However, as the supercontinent of Pangea progressively assembled, the climate may have become monsoonal with seasonal winds crossing the equator. By the end of the Carboniferous, Scotland lay north of the equator, fringing the northern arid climatic belt, whilst the northern margin of the Variscan fold belt lay in southern Britain, thus retarding any monsoonal circulation and blocking any moisture-bearing winds from the south (Parrish 1982, 1993). The presence of giant insects and the prevalence of wildfires in Carboniferous tropical forests both suggest an atmosphere particularly rich in oxygen at that time (Scott 2001).

The local stress field in Scotland did not stay constant but changed more than once during the Carboniferous, possibly reflecting various stages in the continental-scale tectonic movements outlined above (Rippon et al. 1996). Structures within the Midland Valley that are thought to have been active during, or at the end of, the Carboniferous have been described and grouped into related families by Read (1988) and Francis (1991a). These include E–W (plus WSW–ENE), NE–SW and

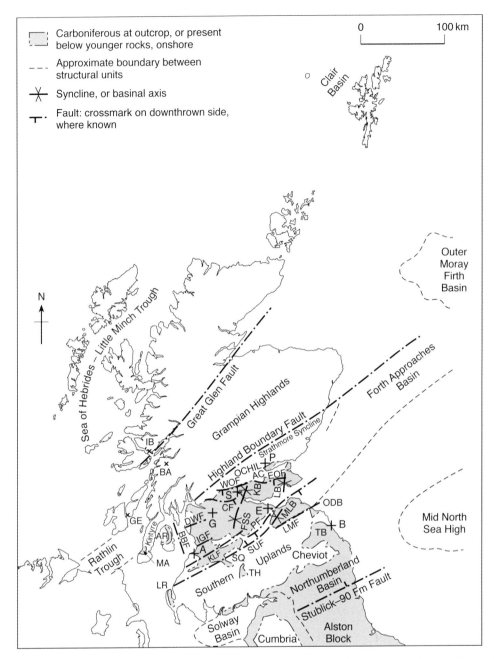

Fig. 9.1. Scotland and adjacent offshore areas, showing onshore Carboniferous outcrops, major structures and some of the principal localities mentioned in the text. A, Ayr; AC, Anticline; AR, Arran outliers; B, Berwick; BA, Bridge of Awe (Pass of Brander) Outlier; BBF, Brodick Bay Fault; CF, Campsie Fault; DWF, Dusk Water Fault; E, Edinburgh; EOF, East Ochil Fault; Fm, Fathom; FSS, Falkirk–Stane Syncline; G, Glasgow; GE, Glas Eilean (Sound of Islay, Permian outlier); IB, Inninmore Bay (Morvern) Outlier; IGF, Inchgotrick Fault; KB, Kincardine Basin; KLF, Kerse Loch Fault; MA, Machrihanish (Kintyre) Outlier; MLB, Midlothian Basin; LB, Leven Basin; LMF, Lammermuir Fault; LR, Loch Ryan Outlier; ODB, Oldhamstocks–Dunbar Outlier; P, Perth; PF, Pentland Fault; S, Stirling; SQ, Sanquhar Outlier; SUF, Southern Upland Fault; TB, Tweed Basin; TH, Thornhill Outlier; WOF, West Ochil Fault.

NW–SE families of faults and N–S (plus NNE–SSW) trending basins, some of which were initiated as half-grabens. The pattern of basins changed during the Carboniferous. Intervening and adjacent highs included contemporaneous and earlier Devonian volcanic piles.

Depositional environments changed dramatically during the Carboniferous, reflecting changes in latitude, climate and stress field. Early Carboniferous meandering rivers and hypersaline lakes and lagoons with only sporadic access to the sea were replaced during the Viséan by a varied suite of fluvio-lacustrine and fluviodeltaic environments subject to periodic marine incursions from the east. In the Midland Valley barriers formed by the widespread outpouring of lavas helped to create

a set of semi-isolated basins, each with its own particular lithostratigraphy, whilst in the Southern Borders thick fluvial sandstones were followed locally by a succession with numerous marine horizons plus coals, the latter suggesting a change to a wetter climate. A somewhat similar succession was laid down in the offshore areas east of Scotland.

In the Late Viséan, cyclical Yoredale-type successions became increasingly more widespread. In these cycles laterally persistent marine limestones are followed in turn by marine claystones and prograding upward-coarsening fluviodeltaic deposits capped by palaeosols and coals. By the Late Brigantian a uniform succession of this type was found in both the Midland Valley and the Southern Borders. The widespread

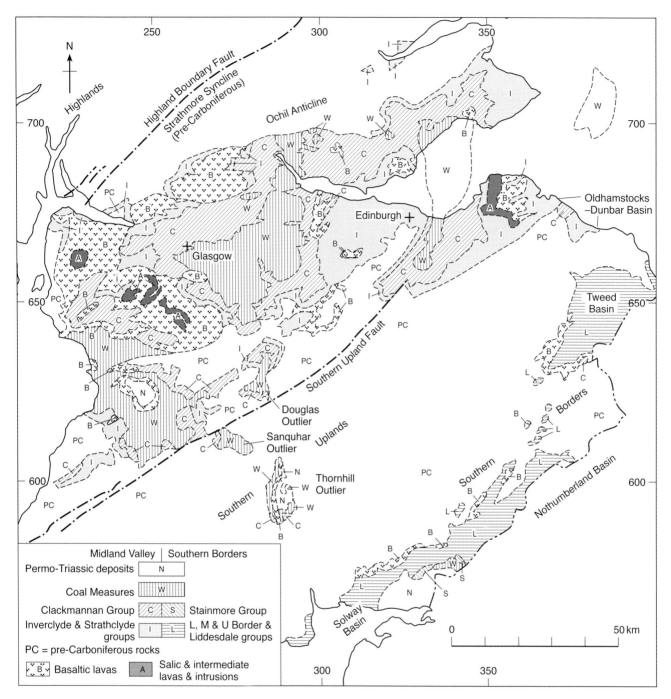

Fig. 9.2. Outcrop distribution of Carboniferous rocks onshore in the Midland Valley, Southern Uplands and Southern Borders. Modified from BGS Geological Survey Ten Mile Map, North Sheet, 3rd Edition (Solid) 1979. PC, Pre-Carboniferous left unornamented.

appearance of this type of cyclicity seems to have followed a change in global climate from a 'greenhouse' to an 'ice-house' phase which allowed a continental-scale south polar ice cap to form. Periodic variations in solar energy made this ice cap fluctuate in size, giving rise to glacioeustatic oscillations in sea level (Smith & Read 2000; Wright & Vanstone 2001).

Yoredale-type cyclical environments continued well into the Namurian in the Southern Borders, whereas in the Midland Valley the Early Namurian succession remained cyclical but became dominantly fluviodeltaic with numerous thick coals but hardly any limestones. Later in the Namurian, Yoredale-type conditions reappeared in central Scotland. Finally, after uplift and erosion in Scandinavia and the Highlands, fluvial environments became dominant in the Midland Valley and also,

somewhat later, in the Northumbrian Basin. Few sedimentary rocks of this age have been preserved in the Southern Borders. During the Early Westphalian fluviodeltaic coal-bearing environments probably spread over the greater part of Scotland and adjacent areas, which thus became part of a vast Coal Measures alluvial plain that stretched far to the west and also eastwards into continental Europe (Rippon 1996; Eagar & van Amerom 1999). This uniform environment disappeared only when, during the Late Westphalian, a semi-arid climate returned to Scotland and spread progressively farther south into England. Deposition was finally curtailed by latest Carboniferous tectonism and subsequent erosion.

Much of the industrial prosperity of Scotland from the late 18th to the mid-20th century depended on the extensive

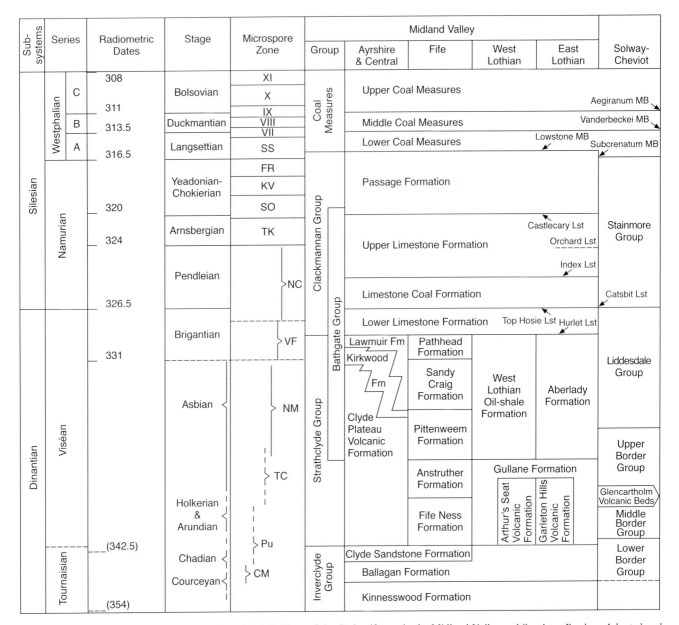

Fig. 9.3. Lithostratigraphical and chronostratigraphical divisions of the Carboniferous in the Midland Valley and Southern Borders. Adapted and updated from Francis (1991a, table 10.3) and Browne et al. (1996, table 1). Key marine bands (MB) and limestones (Lst) used in correlation are noted. For further details on the Dinantian of the Southern Borders see Figure 9.17. No positive evidence for the presence of the Chokierian or Alportian Stages has been found within Scotland, possibly reflecting the Mid-Carboniferous Break (see text). Radiometric dates are from Menning et al. (2001), Scale B, which gives maximal values.

exploitation of Carboniferous coals, sideritic ironstones and refractories. The Longannet project in west Fife, supplied a large thermal generating station with Namurian coal until 2002, but this last deep coal mine is now closed, along with the iron-smelting and refractory brickmaking industries. However coal is still worked at the surface by strip (open-cast) mining (Fig. 9.5; Plate 32; and Chapter 17). Carboniferous sandstones were formerly extensively quarried for high quality building stone. Igneous rocks have long been quarried for aggregate (see Chapter 18), particularly those of the latest Carboniferous tholeiitic Midland Valley Sill-complex.

Most of the Carboniferous outcrop in Scotland is covered by thick Quaternary deposits and good exposures of the sedimentary rocks are rare, especially in the economically important Namurian and Westphalian successions of central Scotland. Our principal sources of information for these are thousands of cored mineral boreholes, many of which were logged in detail

by BGS and British Coal geologists, and former underground workings for coal and refractories. Offshore east of Scotland most of the relevant information comes from seismic surveys and drilling for the oil industry.

Previous work

Like any synthesis, the present account has drawn information from a very large number of maps, memoirs and papers which are far too numerous to list individually. Accordingly, the reader is referred to earlier compilations by Francis (1965, 1983, 1991a, b), Cameron & Stephenson (1985), Read (1988) and Browne & Monro (1989) and the references listed therein. For a more comprehensive list of references to Scottish Carboniferous and Permian igneous activity, particularly the older references see Francis (1965, 1983, 1991b) and Stephenson et al. (in press).

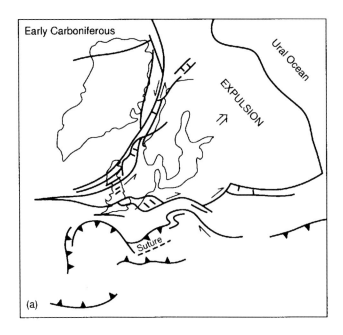

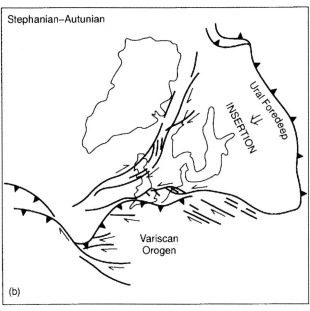

Fig. 9.4. Plate-tectonic reconstructions after Coward (1993, figs. 8 & 11) for Greenland and Europe during (**a**) Early Carboniferous and (**b**) Stephanian–Autunian (Early Permian), suggesting initial squeezing out and later pushing back of European indenter.

Fig. 9.5. The NW corner of the former Westfield Opencast Site, Fife in 1966, showing a NNE-plunging syncline in coals and shales of the Passage Formation. Note upward decrease in fold amplitude. Folding was induced by right-lateral strike-slip along the East Ochil Fault (see Read 1989). British Geological Survey photo D757.

Stratigraphy and its problems

Any attempt to write a systematic account of the Scottish Carboniferous encounters the difficulty that the major pre-Westphalian chronostratigraphical and lithostratigraphical divisions do not correspond very closely with each other (Fig. 9.3). The lithostratigraphical succession in the Midland Valley differs markedly from that in the Southern Borders and within the latter area there are different lithostratigraphical classifications for the west and east. Furthermore, stratigraphical intervals which would now be classed as formations in the Midland Valley are still classed as groups in the Southern Borders and northern England. Recently Midland Valley Carboniferous lithostratigraphy has been extensively updated by Browne *et al.* (1996) whose revised classification has been used in the present account. Figure 9.3 shows this new classification and Figure 9.6 attempts to summarize the Carboniferous geological history of this area. For a summary of Scottish chronostratigraphy and its problems see Francis (1991*a*). The radiometric dates of many Scottish igneous rocks are currently being reassessed.

Particular attention has been focused on four horizons in an attempt to provide 'snapshots' of the contemporary palaeogeography, active structures, volcanicity and depositional environment, of Scotland and adjacent onshore and offshore areas during the Courceyan, Asbian, Early Namurian and Early Westphalian. Within the Midland Valley, where information is most abundant, 'snapshots' have also been provided for each formation above the Hurlet Limestone.

Fauna and Flora

A remarkable number of important Carboniferous fossil localities are concentrated in Scotland. These are notable for both the degree of preservation of the fossils and the evidence of critical evolutionary developments (see below). Critical stem taxa survived a major faunal extinction event that occurred towards the end of the Devonian (McGhee 1990; Hadfield 2002) and these were able to proliferate and diversify during the Carboniferous, especially after Scotland had migrated north into the humid tropics. New environments, some of which were very widespread, became available for colonization leading, for example, to the development of dense two-storey lycopod-dominated lowland rain forests on well watered delta tops and floodplains (Fig. 9.7) and to the colonization of brackish water, and ultimately freshwater, environments by non-marine bivalves. Extensive vegetation provided the basis for a complex food web that included insects and other arthropods and tetrapods (Scott 1980, fig. 1). Scott & Galtier (1984, 1996) have described the rapid evolution of several plant groups during the Dinantian and discussed the problems of 'facies floras'. Summaries of the biostratigraphical frameworks used for correlation have been provided by Wilson (1974, 1989), George *et al.* (1976) and Ramsbottom *et al.* (1978). Unfortunately, with the partial exception of spores, non-marine bivalves and conodonts, few Scottish Carboniferous taxa provide an adequate

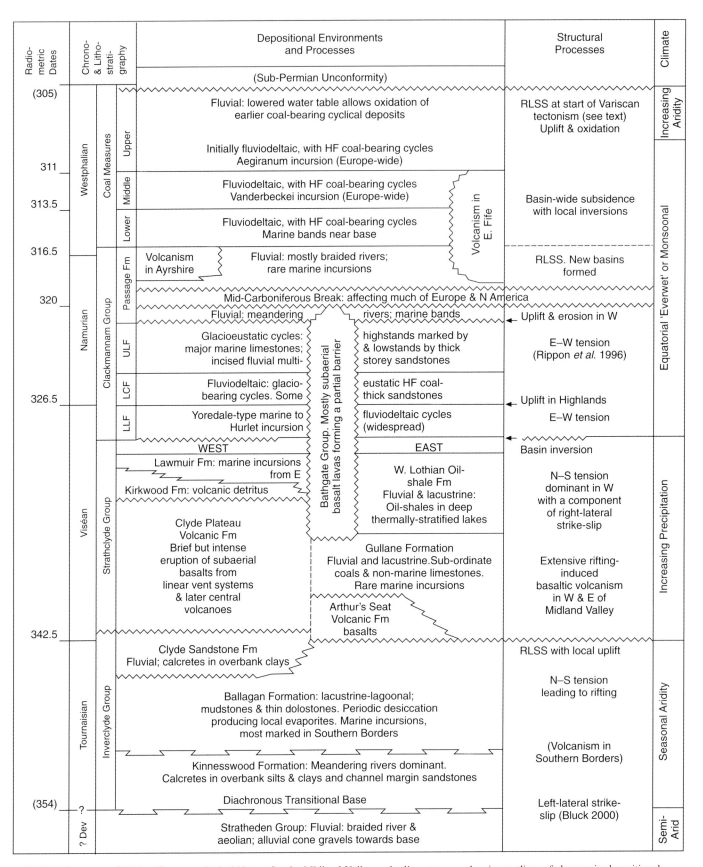

Fig. 9.6. Summary of Carboniferous geological history for the Midland Valley and adjacent areas, showing outlines of changes in depositional environments, structural control and climate. For distribution of volcanic activity, mostly related to rifting, see Figure 9.8. Radiometric dates from Menning *et al.* (2001), Scale B. See also Figure 9.3. Dev, Devonian; Fm, Formation; HF, high frequency; LCF, Limestone Coal Formation; LLF, Lower Limestone Formation; RLSS, right-lateral strike-slip; ULF, Upper Limestone Formation.

Fig. 9.7. Westphalian 'coal-swamp' forest, dominated by arboreal lycopods. (**a**) *Stigmaria*; (**b**) *Lepidodendron*; (**c**) tree fern; (**d**) *Calamites*; (**e**) dragonfly. From Ramsbottom in McKerrow *et al.* (1987, fig. 17). Reproduced by permission of Gerald Duckworth and Co. Ltd.

basis for detailed comprehensive biostratigraphical zonation schemes (Francis 1991*a*).

Highlights and general outlines of faunal and floral developments have been included in the introductory descriptions of the relevant lithostratigraphical groups but space does not permit a more comprehensive coverage of the vast literature. More details may be found in the references listed.

Igneous activity

Most of Scotland experienced over 50 Ma of magmatic quiescence following the cessation of Caledonian igneous activity in the Early Devonian. The start of the Carboniferous period, however, saw a renaissance of magmatism, associated with faulting and basin formation. Tournaisian eruptions were a prelude to more vigorous activity, commencing at the beginning of the Viséan, which affected a wide region but was particularly concentrated in the Midland Valley. Volcanism continued intermittently for approximately 100 Ma into the Mid-Permian (see also Chapter 10), although the post-Dinantian activity was generally on a more subdued scale (see Fig. 9.8). The Carboniferous–Permian volcanism was of typical intraplate type of the kind that was to become common and globally widespread in the Mesozoic and Cenozoic. The volcanism is remarkable in being an unusually early Phanerozoic example of its kind, and also in its longevity. The magmas were of transitional to mildly alkaline to highly alkaline and silica-undersaturated character with the principal exception occurring in the Stephanian when a short-lived event saw widespread intrusion of tholeiitic basalt magmas across a broad zone embracing much of Scotland and northern England.

Basal Carboniferous to Mid-Brigantian lithostratigraphy

The structural controls that were active during the pre-Brigantian period are more difficult to discern than those later in the Carboniferous. This largely reflects a lack of precise and widespread borehole information. Initially, N–S tension, possibly with a component of left-lateral strike-slip, seems to have been dominant. However right-lateral strike-slip, which may have been combined later with a component of E–W compression appeared in the Midland Valley towards the end of the Tournaisian. Gentle folding and fault reactivation followed by erosion then resulted in an unconformity at the base of the Clyde Plateau Volcanic Formation (see below) in the west of the Midland Valley (Fig. 9.6; Paterson *et al.* 1990).

Older NW–SW Caledonian structures, including the Highland Boundary, Southern Upland, Dusk Water, Inchgotrick, Kerse Loch and Pentland faults, together with the Strathmore Syncline and the Ochil Anticline dominantly controlled the synsedimentary tectonic pattern during most of the Dinantian (Fig. 9.1; Browne & Monro 1989; Browne *et al.* 1985). Relatively positive areas included contemporaneous Dinantian and earlier Devonian volcanic piles and intrusions. Figure 9.9 shows the overall palaeogeography of Scotland and adjacent onshore and offshore areas during the Late Courceyan.

In the Midland Valley and adjacent areas the Carboniferous succession before the first really widespread marine transgression at the Hurlet Limestone (see below) has been divided into the Inverclyde Group (Courceyan to early Chadian) below and the Strathclyde Group (late Chadian to mid Brigantian) above (Fig. 9.3; Browne *et al.* 1996). Volcanic activity was largely confined in the Southern Uplands and the Southern Borders during Inverclyde Group deposition but basaltic volcanism became intense in the Midland Valley, especially in the west, during Strathclyde Group deposition. Extensive subaerial lava piles and some tectonic highs, divided the Midland Valley into a series of semi-isolated basins, each with its own local lithostratigraphy. Thus, in contrast to the more uniform successions of the later Carboniferous, the pre-Hurlet deposits of the Midland Valley represent a mosaic of fluvial, fluviodeltaic and lacustrine–lagoonal sedimentary environments and correlation between basins can be difficult. Marine transgressions from the east started to appear in the Strathclyde Group and became progressively more extensive, so that eventually a more uniform environment spread to both the Midland Valley and the basins of the Southern Borders and northern England.

The climate was initially semi-arid with a markedly seasonal rainfall, resulting in the formation in the Inverclyde Group of pedogenic calcretes (cornstones) in fluvial deposits and evaporites in local basins. Later, as Scotland moved nearer the equator, rainfall increased and coals started to appear in the Strathclyde Group.

As the climate became progressively wetter, both flora and fauna became more abundant and diverse. Scottish Dinantian fossil localities are especially important for fish, tetrapods, conodonts and anatomically preserved plant remains. Thus, for example, Bearsden is a world-class shark locality (Dineley & Metcalfe 1999) and Cheese Bay and East Kirkton have yielded the earliest proto-reptiles (Smithson *et al.* 1994; Paton *et al.* 1999). The long sought-for conodont animal, which is now considered to belong with the vertebrates, was found in the Granton Shrimp Bed (Aldridge *et al.* 1993; Aldridge & Purnell 1996). This, together with other Scottish Dinantian 'shrimp' beds has also provided evidence of the adaptive radiation of eumalacostracan crustacea in marginal marine to lacustrine environments (Cater *et al.* 1989). Widespread volcanic activity and associated permineralization facilitated the

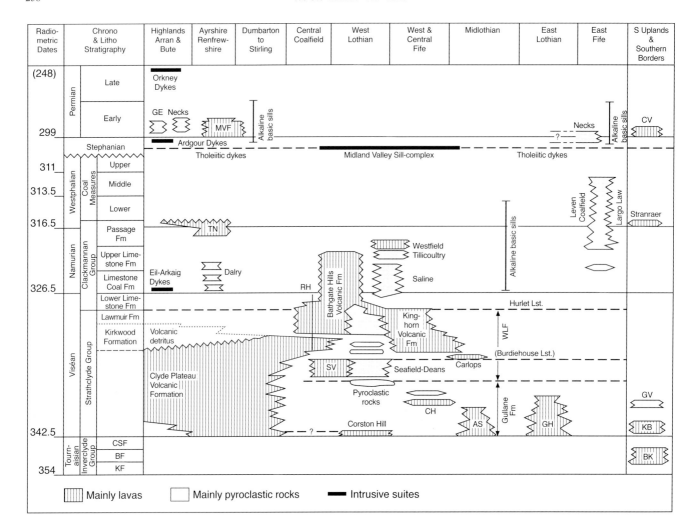

Fig. 9.8. Lithostratigraphical and geographical distribution of Carboniferous and Early Permian volcanic rocks in the Midland Valley and southern Scotland plus approximate age ranges of major intrusive suites. Vertical scale shows stratigraphical range and not thickness of volcanic successions. Radiometric dates from Menning *et al.* (2001), Scale B, but date for latest Permian from Gradstein & Ogg (1996). After Cameron & Stephenson (1985) and Stephenson *et al.* (in press). AS, Arthur's Seat Volcanic Formation; BF, Ballagan Formation; BK, Birrenswark Volcanic Formation and Kelso Lavas; CH, Charles Hill Volcanic Member; CSF, Clyde Sandstone Formation; CV, Carron Volcanic Formation; GE, Glas Eilean Lavas; GH, Garleton Hills Volcanic Formation; GV, Glencartholm Volcanic Beds; KB, Kershopefoot Basalts; KF, Kinnesswood Formation; MVF, Mauchline Volcanic Formation; RH, Rashiehill Borehole; SV, Salsburgh Volcanic Formation; TN, Troon Volcanic Member; WLF, West Lothian Oil-shale Formation. (Fife formation names omitted).

anatomical preservation of the plant remains. These illustrate the evolution of both equatorial 'swamp-forest' (Fig. 9.7) and of desiccation-resistant ovules or protoseeds that allowed drought-resistant upland plants to develop (Scott 1980, 1990; Scott *et al.* 1984; Scott & Rex 1987; Cleal & Thomas 1999).

Offshore west of Scotland, western Highlands and Islands

Most of our offshore information comes from BGS geophysical surveys and shallow boreholes, so the Carboniferous succession is not known in any detail and ages are uncertain. Glennie (2000, fig. 3a) has demonstrated how much of the formerly extensive cover of Carboniferous in the offshore areas west and east of Scotland was removed by latest Carboniferous erosion. He also considered that over much of the offshore Devonian outcrop fluvial sedimentation continued into the Early Carboniferous. A residual outlier of these Early Carboniferous strata has been preserved in the small Clair Basin on the Rona Ridge west of Shetland (Figs 9.1, 9.9). Here a succession of fluvial sandstones and mudstones with pedogenic calcretes containing Tournaisian spores is conformably overlain by 27 m of Viséan marine siltstones and thin sandstones containing acritarchs. Seismic evidence and derived spores suggest that Carboniferous sedimentary rocks may underlie Permo-Triassic rocks in the Sea of the Hebrides–Little Minch Trough and up to 1000 m of Carboniferous strata, some of which are likely to be Viséan, may be present in the NE-trending Rathlin Trough (Fig. 9.1; Stoker *et al.* 1993). The North Channel may have originated as a Devono-Carboniferous basin and Carboniferous rocks may still be present here at depth (Maddox *et al.* 1997).

Onshore, the Highland High and adjacent areas probably functioned intermittently as a source area during much of the Carboniferous. However, outliers, such as at Inninmore Bay, Bridge of Awe and Arran on the west coast (Fig. 9.1), suggest a former thin patchy Carboniferous cover. The attenuated successions in these outliers belong mostly to the later Carboniferous. Early Carboniferous rocks similar to those in the Midland Valley are preserved in southern Kintyre, where fluvial deposits

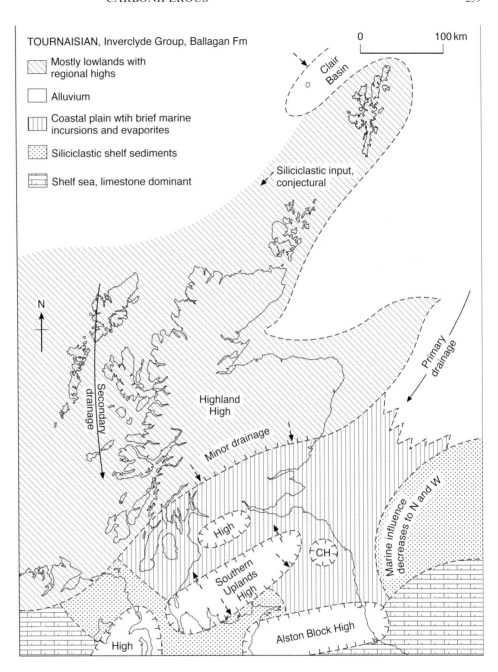

Fig. 9.9. Palaeogeography and palaeoenvironments of Scotland and adjacent onshore and offshore areas during deposition of the Ballagan Formation, Inverclyde Group. CH, Cheviot High.

of the Inverclyde Group are unconformably overlain by basaltic lavas assigned to the Strathclyde Group. The Firth of Clyde can be regarded as a southwestward extension of the Midland Valley with ENE-trending faults continuing those in Ayrshire or replacing them en echelon. Differential subsidence along these faults controlled sedimentation. The NNW-trending Brodick Bay Fault may also have been active during the Carboniferous. This fault bounds the Northeast Arran Trough where 1100 m of Carboniferous sedimentary rocks overlie Strathclyde Group lavas (Fig. 9.1 and McLean & Deegan 1978).

Midland Valley and adjacent areas

Inverclyde Group (Courceyan to earliest Chadian)
The base of the group is transitional and is taken where the sandstone-dominated aeolian and fluvial facies of the underlying Upper Devonian (Famennian) Stratheden Group are succeeded by carbonate-bearing strata. This group, which was

deposited whilst Scotland lay in low latitudes south of the equator, forms the topmost part of an Upper Devonian to Lower Carboniferous fluvial succession onlapping from the Central North Sea Basin onto mainland Scotland. It consists of the Kinnesswood, Ballagan, and Clyde Sandstone formations (Fig. 9.3) and is characterized by the presence of carbonate beds and nodules and by the absence of carbonaceous rocks, especially coal seams and oil-shales. The fluvial, sandstone-dominated Kinnesswood (Fig. 9.10) and Clyde Sandstone formations contain calcareous and dolomitic pedogenic horizons (calcretes or cornstones) formed under a semi-arid climate. The intervening lacustrine–lagoonal Ballagan Formation is characterized by mudstone, ferroan dolostone (cementstones), and evaporites (mainly gypsum).

The Kinnesswood Formation, which locally exceeds 300 m in thickness (Fig. 9.10), consists of upward-fining fluvial cycles, in which purple-red, yellow and white, upward-fining, erosive-based, cross-bedded sandstones deposited in braided or meandering river channels are capped by red and green overbank

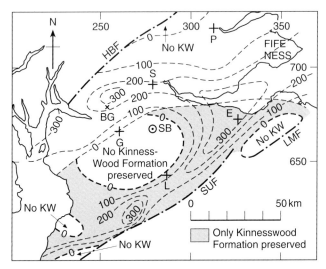

Fig. 9.10. Isopachs, in metres, of the Kinnesswood Formation, Inverclyde Group, in central Scotland. Modified from Browne *et al.* (1985, fig. 17). BG, Ballagan Glen; E, Edinburgh; G, Glasgow; HBF, Highland Boundary Fault; KW, Kinnesswood Formation; L, Lanark ; LMF, Lammermuir Fault; P, Perth; S, Stirling; SB, Salsburgh Borehole; SUF, Southern Upland Fault.

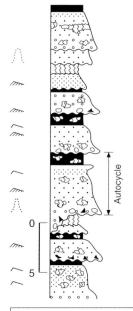

Repeated upward-fining, erosive-based autocycles deposited by meandering rivers under a tropical semi-arid, but seasonally wet, climate. Calcretes (cornstones) formed in soil profiles in clay & silt overbank deposits on stable alluvial plains. These autocycles were formed by purely local fluvial sedimentary processes such as meander migration & channel avulsion. Each autocycle conventionally starts at the sharp erosive base of an upward-fining channel-fill sand which was subsequently capped by overbank silts & clays.

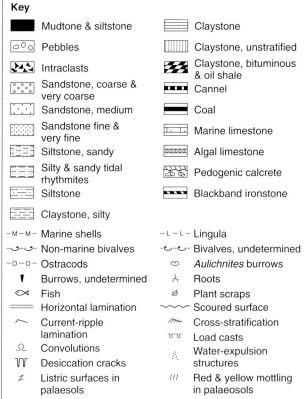

Key

◼	Mudtone & siltstone	☰	Claystone
◦◦◦	Pebbles	⦀	Claystone, unstratified
▰	Intraclasts	▨	Claystone, bituminous & oil shale
▦	Sandstone, coarse & very coarse	▬	Cannel
⋯	Sandstone, medium	▬	Coal
⣿	Sandstone fine & very fine	⊞	Marine limestone
▦	Siltstone, sandy	▤	Algal limestone
▦	Silty & sandy tidal rhythmites	▨	Pedogenic calcrete
▤	Siltstone	▬	Blackband ironstone
▤	Claystone, silty		

–M–M–	Marine shells	–L–L–	Lingula
–∪–∪–	Non-marine bivalves	–∪–∪–	Bivalves, undetermined
–◦–◦–	Ostracods	∞	*Aulichnites* burrows
❚	Burrows, undetermined	⋏	Roots
◁	Fish	∅	Plant scraps
═	Horizontal lamination	∿	Scoured surface
⌒	Current-ripple lamination	⇝	Cross-stratification
Ω	Convolutions	⊽⊽	Load casts
Ⲱ	Desiccation cracks	⋏	Water-expulsion structures
⟋	Listric surfaces in palaesols	///	Red & yellow mottling in palaeosols

Fig. 9.11. Vertical section showing typical, generally upward-fining, fluvial autocycles within the Kinnesswood Formation as exposed in the Gargunnock Burn, Stirlingshire, with outline of the depositional environments. Key also applies to other figures with logs in this chapter, apart from solid black ornament which is here used for mudstone, and in other figures for coal.

siltstones and mudstones (Fig. 9.11). The latter contain nodules and thin beds of pedogenic concretionary carbonate. The carbonates (cornstones) that characterize this formation developed in soil profiles on stable alluvial plains under the influence of a fluctuating water table during a semi-arid but seasonally wet climate. The carbonate may be brecciated or replaced by chert and rhizoliths may be present locally (Browne *et al.* 1996; Balin 2000). Although generally unfossiliferous, palynomorphs assigned to the NI-CM miospore zones at the base of the Tournaisian have been recorded from near the base of the formation at Douglas (Smith 1996).

The overlying Ballagan Formation (Courceyan, CM Zone) is characterized by generally grey mudstones and siltstones, with nodules and beds of argillaceous, ferroan dolostone (cementstone) that are generally less than 0.3 m thick. Gypsum, or locally anhydrite, and pseudomorphs after halite occur. Desiccation cracks are common and the rocks frequently show evidence of brecciation during diagenesis, perhaps reflecting dissolution of salts. Both these features are associated with reddening of the strata during periods of lowered water table and partial oxidation. Thin sandstones are ubiquitous. Sandy alluvial fans are a feature of the Ballagan Formation north of the subdued northern flank of the Southern Uplands. In the Edinburgh area, pedogenic carbonate nodules are common throughout the unit. Where present, the restricted fauna in the Ballagan Formation is characterized by the bivalve *Modiolus latus*, but ostracods are more abundant and belong to the basal Tournaisian. *Lingula* and juvenile marine bivalves occur locally. Raymond (1991, p. 178) recorded the presence of the marine to terrestrial alga *Tasmanites* in this formation near Perth. Andrews *et al.* (1991) and Turner (1991) have interpreted the formation as being laid down in coastal alluvial plains, lakes and marginal marine flats. These were subject to periodic desiccation with episodes of fluctuating salinity, partly as a result of seawater being introduced by storm flooding events.

Figure 9.9 shows the broad palaeogeography of Scotland and adjacent offshore areas during the deposition of the Ballagan Formation. The open sea initially lay to the east, but later it lay more to the south of the Midland Valley (Cope *et al.* 1992), with the more marine faunas in the 'cementstones' being found

in the Solway Basin. Andrews *et al.* (1991) explained the lack of sulphide in the mudstones and the sourcing of the magnesium and calcium ions in the cementstones by limited inundation of alluvial plains and lakes by seawater. Argillaceous limestone is present where lakes were deep enough to avoid diagenetic dolomitization. The inundations in general left no marine faunal record but provided a strong geochemical signal in the sulphate evaporites, ferroan dolostones and strontium isotopes. Because of the dominance of the siliciclastic over the evaporitic components, Andrews *et al.* (1991) concluded that the formation was laid down in a relatively humid rather than a generally arid environment, subject to periods of evaporation.

The Clyde Sandstone Formation consists mainly of white and pale greenish-grey fluvial channel-fill sandstones, commonly pebbly, with beds of red-brown, greenish or grey overbank mudstone. Pedogenic limestones, as nodules or beds, formed on stable alluvial plains in both the river channel and overbank deposits. In more northerly areas of the Midland Valley some of the conglomeratic sandstones contain pebbles of quartz and Dalradian rock types. Elsewhere the clasts are largely of intraformational limestone, cementstone or mudstone. These strata were laid down during a time of active uplift in parts of the basin and in a wide variety of fluviatile environments ranging from braided streams to meandering river floodplains with well-developed overbank deposits. The base of the Clyde Sandstone Formation, like those of the two formations below, is usually transitional but is erosional in some areas. Algal nodules and fish scales have been recorded from this unit.

Lateral variation

Bluck (2000) suggested that the distribution of the oldest Inverclyde Group was controlled by left-lateral movement along Caledonian basement faults and by residual palaeogeographical highs. The succession of Kinnesswood Formation followed by Ballagan Formation is common to the Midland Valley, Southern Uplands and Southern Borders and extensional rifting may have been operating initially in all of these areas. Subsequently the sedimentary and volcanic story of the Midland Valley went its own way with intra-Dinantian uplift and erosion during the deposition of the Clyde Sandstone Formation, probably following a defining change in the tectonic style to right-lateral strike-slip.

Lateral variations in thickness and lithology within the Inverclyde Group in the Midland Valley and adjacent areas have been illustrated by Francis (1991a, fig. 10.2) and Browne *et al.* (1996, fig.1). However, the scattered and incomplete nature of the natural sections and the scarcity of borehole data makes it difficult to trace lateral variations with any degree of precision. Furthermore, boundaries between formations are almost certainly diachronous (Cameron & Stephenson 1985) and facies assemblages commonly interdigitate.

The distribution and isopachs of the Kinnesswood Formation in central Scotland, together with areas where this, but not the two overlying formations, have been preserved are shown in Figure 9.10. The isopachs indicate a major, roughly triangular, depocentre west of Edinburgh embracing parts of what later became the West Lothian Oil-shale Basin and the Midlothian Basin (see below). From this depocentre the isopachs run westwards to a subsidiary depocentre north of the Campsie Fells and southwestwards to another depocentre in what later became the South Ayrshire Trough (see below). In all three of these lows thicknesses exceed 300 m. The Highland Boundary and Southern Upland faults may have been active during deposition of the formation (Browne & Monro 1989).

In the west of the Midland Valley, erosion prior to Strathclyde Group volcanicity has removed all or part of the Kinnesswood Formation in many places (Fig. 9.10). Active fault movements are indicated by variations in thickness across NNE- and ENE-trending faults in Ayrshire. In the north–central part of the Midland Valley the formation is about 400 m thick near Fintry but thins eastwards towards Stirling. It may however be present at depth below the Clackmannan Syncline as it crops out on the eastern flank of that structure.

The formation was either not deposited, or was subsequently eroded over a broad area south and southeast of Glasgow (Fig. 9.10), but it reappears farther south around Douglas.

In the east of the Midland Valley the Kinnesswood Formation reaches its maximum thickness of 640 m in the Edinburgh area (Browne *et al.* 1996) within the major depocentre. In Fife it is reduced to only 30 m in the northern Lomond Hills but it is present in the Tay Graben and on the coast near Montrose.

The overlying Ballagan and Clyde Sandstone formations have been cut out over much of the southern Midland Valley by the widespread erosional unconformity at the base of the Clyde Plateau Volcanic Formation (Fig. 9.10). Fault movements seem to have continued in Ayrshire during deposition of the Ballagan Formation. In the south, between the Kerse Loch and Southern Upland faults (Fig. 9.1), it is 365 m thick, despite an eroded top, foreshadowing the rapid subsidence of the later South Ayrshire Trough (see below). Here it is sandy towards the base and contains sandstone units with pedogenic limestones.

Farther east in the north–central area the formation is about 300 m thick near Fintry but thins eastwards towards Stirling. It is particularly well exposed in Ballagan Glen south of the Campsie Fells (Fig. 9.10; Francis 1991a, fig.10.4), where its base is unfortunately not exposed. The Ballagan Formation crops out on the eastern flank of the Clackmannan Syncline in the Cleish Hills where it contains tuffaceous intercalations and may be traced eastwards to Cupar, and at least 230 m are preserved in the Tay Graben (Browne *et al.* 1996).

In West Lothian the formation is 900 m thick and around Edinburgh its base is sandy. Here the abundant sandstone-dominated members of the formation contain pedogenic calcretes and are difficult to distinguish from the underlying Kinnesswood Formation. In East Lothian, the Ballagan Formation is at least 266 m thick. It includes tuffaceous beds and, unlike the succession in Edinburgh, the whole sequence is typically argillaceous. The reddened and sandy topmost 70 m may belong to the Clyde Sandstone Formation. To the east in the Oldhamstocks–Dunbar Basin (Fig. 9.2) the Ballagan Formation is more than 364 m thick and includes tuffaceous strata. Southeast of Dunbar it thins to 86 m and includes both a bed containing the marine bivalve *Sanguinolites* and a cross-bedded, probably fluvial, sandstone.

Preservation of the Clyde Sandstone Formation has been greatly affected by the erosional unconformity at the base of the succeeeding lavas. It is thickest and best developed in the west of the Midland Valley. Although it is rather intermittently preserved in Ayrshire, it is as much as 450 m thick near Gourock, reflecting contemporaneous fault subsidence and input from alluvial fans from the north (Paterson & Hall 1986; Browne & Monro 1989, fig. 4). At Fintry, where about 100 m of the formation are preserved, the topmost part of the succession contains volcanic detritus, heralding the volcanicity in the overlying Strathclyde Group. The formation thins eastwards from here towards Stirling. South of the Campsie Fells only 12 m are preserved at Ballagan Glen. Intermittent exposures allow the formation to be traced eastwards through northern Fife. It has been overstepped and eroded away in the northern Lomond Hills but reappears farther east near Fife Ness. To the south in the Edinburgh area it becomes difficult to separate from the local sandy facies of the Ballagan Formation.

Strathclyde Group

The Strathclyde Group (late Chadian to mid Brigantian) is a varied succession of sedimentary and volcanic rocks (Fig. 9.3; Browne & Monro 1989, figs 8, 9). It is characterized by the presence of carbonaceous beds, including coal and oil-shale, indicating increased rainfall. Deposits are largely of fluviatile and lacustrine origin, with sporadic marine incursions which are most frequent in the east. The base of the group is taken at the base of the Clyde Plateau Volcanic Formation in the centre and west of the Midland Valley (335 Ma; A. A. Monaghan, pers. comm.), at the base of the somewhat earlier volcanic formations in the Lothians (342 Ma; A. A. Monaghan, pers. comm.) and at the base of the Fife Ness Formation in Fife (see below).

The overall palaeogeographical and palaeoenvironmental setting of Scotland and adjacent areas during the deposition of the Strathclyde Group is shown in Figure 9.12. Isopachs of the group in central Scotland are illustrated in Figure 9.13a, and active structures, low subsidence areas, areas of contemporaneous volcanicity and directions of coarse-grained siliciclastic input in Figure 9.13b.

Low subsidence areas included the Ochil, Pentland and Salsburgh highs, plus a more minor high around the Lomond Hills in Fife. Basinal areas generally trended NE–SW. These included the major West Lothian Basin and the precursors of the Midlothian and Leven basins, with the last-named extending eastwards into a basinal area in East Fife and below the Firth of Forth. (Fig. 9.13; Browne & Monro 1989, fig. 15).

The Clyde Plateau Volcanic Formation dominates the western succession. Eruption during this intense but short-lived event formed a volcanic pile that persisted as a long-lived residual topographic high (see below), which was not fully overtopped until the Mid-Brigantian. Deposition was also affected by the Arthur's Seat and Garleton Hills volcanic piles, by ancient topographical highs such as the Salsburgh High and by pre-existing faults (Figs 9.1, 9.12 & 9.13b). Fault control is thought to reflect right-lateral strike-slip with volcanicity being located in areas of local transtension. A pre-Brigantian unconformity in the Lomond Hills High in Fife may reflect local transpression. Petrological and compositional details of these and other volcanic rocks in the Strathclyde Group are described below in the sections on igneous activity.

Oil-shales and freshwater limestones (Loftus 1985; Loftus & Greensmith 1988; Raymond 1991) are minor but important components of the group. These reflect the development under

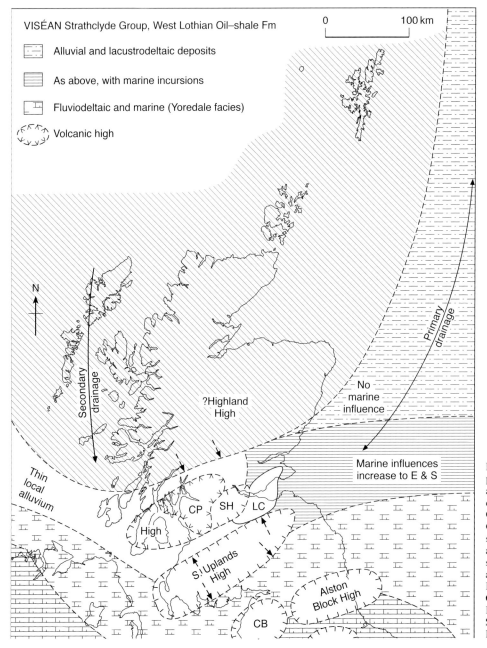

Fig. 9.12. Palaeogeography and palaeoenvironments of Scotland and adjacent onshore and offshore areas during deposition of the West Lothian Oil-shale Formation, Strathclyde Group, showing probably active structures, low subsidence areas (highs) and directions of coarse-grained siliciclastic input. For ornaments and symbols not shown in key see Fig. 9.9. CB, Cumbrian High; CP, Clyde Plateau Volcanic High; LC, 'Lake Cadell' oil-shale lake; SH, Salsburgh High. See also Fig. 9.13b for further details.

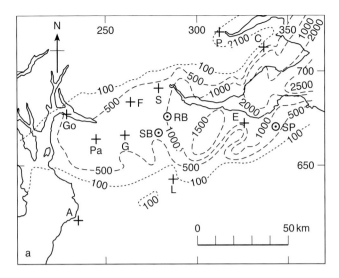

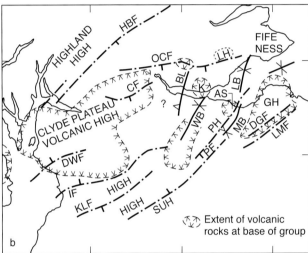

Fig. 9.13. Strathclyde Group: (**a**) Isopachs in metres. (**b**) Summary map showing probably active structures, low subsidence areas ('highs') and extent of thick volcanic rocks at base of Group. AS, Arthur's Seat Volcanic High; BL, Bo'ness Line flexure; C, Cupar; CF, Campsie Fault; DGF, Dunbar–Gifford Fault; DWF, Dusk Water Fault; F, Fintry; GH, Garleton Hills Volcanic High; Go, Gourock; IF, Inchgotrick Fault; K, Kinghorn Volcanic High; KLF, Kerse Loch Fault; LB, Leven Basin; LH, Lomond Hills High; LMF, Lammermuir Fault; MB, Midlothian Basin; Pa, Paisley; PF, Pentland Fault; PH, Pentland High; RB, Rashiehill Borehole; SB, Salsburgh Borehole; SP, Spilmersford Borehole; WB, West Lothian Oil-shale Basin. For abbreviations not listed above see Figures 9.1 and 9.10.

a humid climate of substantial lakes as much as 2000–3000 km^2 in area (Figs 9.12 & 9.14b, c). The former lake sediments are characterized by the accumulation of abundant remains of filamentous, mat-forming, benthonic cyanobacteria (Raymond 1991) with a minor contribution from the non-filamentous planktonic *Botryococcus brauni*. Maddox & Andrews (1987) recognized the value of cryptalgally laminated dolostones in regional correlation as time markers of basin-wide 'regression'. Guirdham (1998) and Raymond (1991) believed these carbonates were deposited in hydrologically closed, shallow, playa-type lakes, whereas the oil-shales formed in hydrologically open, thermally stratified, deep lakes in which shorelines and water levels were stable over long periods (Fig. 9.14b,c). Switches between the two systems were caused either by climate change, *i.e.* increased aridity and seasonality within an overall humid sub-tropical environment, or by local tectonism and volcanicity. Guirdham also recognized a second category

of closed lakes in which microbial tufa carbonates accreted in shallow, volcanigenically supplied, nutrient-rich sub-basins.

The NNE-trending Bo'ness Line and the low subsidence area to its east (Fig. 9.13b; Rippon *et al.*1996, fig. 1) may, together with residual volcanic piles, have determined the lithostratigraphical and sedimentological contrasts between the west and east of the Midland Valley. Such piles functioned as residual topographical barriers to ingress of the sea from the east and as landward margins to the east and west. The Southern Uplands and the Salsburgh High (Fig. 9.12) influenced deposition to the south. Although the palaeoclimate was mainly humid the presence of calcretes in the Aberlady and Sandy Craig formations (Fig. 9.14a; Andrews & Nabi 1998) and 'marls' (calcareous mudstones and limestones) in the West Lothian Oil-shale Formation point to semi-arid climatic periods during the Asbian. Glacioeustatic climatic and sea-level oscillations started to affect deposition from the early Asbian onwards (Wright & Vanstone 2001; and see below).

Western Midland Valley
Minor outcrops of fluvial and lacustrine strata are preserved in northeast Arran and Bute. On the mainland the Clyde Plateau Volcanic Formation, described in detail in the following section on igneous activity, dominates the succession and may be as much as 1000 m thick in the Renfrewshire Hills; the base of the formation is normally sharp, representing a gentle but irregular unconformity.

The Kirkwood Formation consists of dark reddish brown to greenish grey volcanic detritus and 'tuffaceous' mudstones, which erosively and locally unconformably overlie the basaltic lavas of the Clyde Plateau Volcanic Formation. The formation is highly variable in thickness, reaching about 30 m in Paisley, but is locally absent and in places it is known to pass laterally into the succeeding Lawmuir Formation. The Kirkwood Formation was mostly formed by the reworking of materials derived from the underlying volcanic rocks, but also includes some non-tuffaceous sedimentary rocks and even occasional marine horizons (equivalent to those in the Lawmuir and Pathhead formations). The Kirkwood Formation shows extensive subaerial tropical weathering and lateritization.

The Lawmuir Formation at the top of the group consists of a sequence of mudstones, siltstones and sandstones with palaeosols, coals and limestones. North of Glasgow around Milngavie, sandstone with a local quartz conglomerate dominates the lower part of the formation. Around Paisley, sandstone is interbedded with thick, poorly-bedded siltstones and mudstones (including marls). In one small area influenced by strike-slip faulting a few thin coals coalesce locally to form the Quarrelton Thick Coal, up to 30 m thick. The lower part of the formation is essentially fluviatile with channel, floodplain, lake and coal deposits, whereas the upper part of the formation is partly cyclic and includes laterally persistent marine horizons, including limestones. The apparently non-marine Baldernock Limestone, which occurs near the top of the formation (Whyte 1994) is succeeded by the widespread but sulphurous Hurlet Coal.

Eastern Midland Valley
In West Lothian and Midlothian the Strathclyde Group consists of the Arthur's Seat Volcanic Formation, followed by the Gullane Formation and the West Lothian Oil-shale Formation (Figs 9.3, 9.13b). The Arthur's Seat Volcanic Formation is 400–500 m thick and consists of lavas, tuffs and volcaniclastic sedimentary rocks (see below).

The Gullane Formation may be more than 860 m thick south of Edinburgh in the proto-Midlothian Basin. Its lithology is described in the following section on East Lothian.

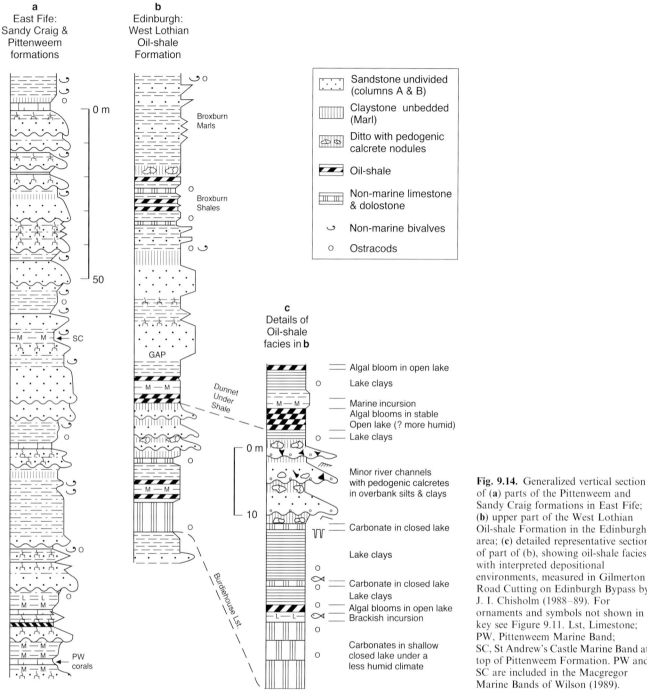

Fig. 9.14. Generalized vertical section of (**a**) parts of the Pittenweem and Sandy Craig formations in East Fife; (**b**) upper part of the West Lothian Oil-shale Formation in the Edinburgh area; (**c**) detailed representative section of part of (b), showing oil-shale facies with interpreted depositional environments, measured in Gilmerton Road Cutting on Edinburgh Bypass by J. I. Chisholm (1988–89). For ornaments and symbols not shown in key see Figure 9.11. Lst, Limestone; PW, Pittenweem Marine Band; SC, St Andrew's Castle Marine Band at top of Pittenweem Formation. PW and SC are included in the Macgregor Marine Bands of Wilson (1989).

The overlying West Lothian Oil-shale Formation reaches its maximum thickness of 1120 m in the depositional axis of the West Lothian Basin (Figs 9.13, 9.14; Chisholm *et al.* 1989) but thins towards the western basin margin. The formation is characterized by thin seams of oil-shale in a sequence of pale coloured sandstones interbedded with grey siltstones and mudstones. A vertical section through the upper part of the formation and a representative detailed section of the oil-shale facies is shown in Figure 9.14. Subordinate lithologies include coals, ostracod-rich non-marine limestones/dolostones such as the laterally persistent Burdiehouse Limestone, sideritic iron-stones and marine beds, including bioclastic limestones with rich and relatively diverse faunas. Thick, massive, pale green-grey or grey argillaceous marls, thought to contain derived volcanic detritus, may have formed on extensive plains. The marl can rest directly on the mud-cracked top of an oil-shale. The environment of deposition of the formation was similar to that of the laterally equivalent Aberlady Formation (see below), but with more oil-shales. These formed in large stratified freshwater lakes or lagoons rich in algae and other organic matter and are particularly abundant in the upper part of the formation (Cameron & McAdam 1978, fig. 2). They were formerly extensively mined and distilled for hydrocarbon products (see Chapter 19). Sandstones (e.g. Hailes), some of which were formerly used extensively for building stone, are more prominent in the lower part of the formation, the base of which is taken at the local equivalent of the lowest of the Macgregor Marine Bands (Fig. 9.14; Wilson 1989). The formation is laterally equivalent to part of the Bathgate Hills Volcanic Formation to the west.

The East Kirkton Limestone occurs locally intercalated with the lower part of the Bathgate Group and is assigned to the upper part of the West Lothian Oil-shale Formation (Smith *et al.* 1994), within the Strathclyde Group. It comprises a complex of laminated spherulitic limestones, cherty limestones, cherts and thin black shales interrupted by tuff bands. It is overlain by a lacustrine shale with fish remains, capped by a coarse-grained tuff. The whole complex is thought to have been deposited in an isolated lake fed by silica-rich hot springs (Rolfe *et al.* 1990). Deltas of volcaniclastic detritus prograded into the lake, which was surrounded initially by an extensive woodland dominated by pteridosperms (seed ferns). Forest fires were common (Fig. 9.15). Later the lake deepened and was subject to algal blooms and oxygen depletion. At this stage it was bordered by vegetation of a drier character, but finally rainfall increased and the flora became dominated by lycopsids (Rolfe *et al.* 1994; Scott *et al.* 1994).

The fauna of the East Kirkton Limestone is of international significance. It is largely terrestrial and includes a scorpion, millipedes, harvestmen, large eurypterids and four groups of amphibians that had adapted to living on land. These include temnospondyls that may have been ancestral to modern frogs and salamanders, plus the protoreptile *Westlothiana lizziae*. Fish, including sharks, acanthodians and actinopteryians have been found in the overlying shale (Rolfe *et al.* 1990; Smithson *et al.* 1994; Dineley & Metcalf 1999). Figure 9.15 shows a reconstruction of the East Kirkton environment.

In East Lothian the Garleton Hills Volcanic Formation is overlain by the Gullane Formation, and in turn by the Aberlady Formation (Fig. 9.3). The Garleton Hills Volcanic Formation (Fig. 9.13) is about 380 m thick and consists of lavas and tuffs with subordinate volcaniclastic sedimentary rocks produced by a single episode of volcanic activity. Both the base and the top of the formation show transitions to sedimentary rocks (see below). Their main outcrop is in the Garleton Hills, and the formation has been proved under younger rocks as far SW as Cousland. The overlying Gullane Formation is 135 m thick in its type section in the Spilmersford Borehole (Fig. 9.13) but is thicker to the west. It consists predominantly of pale coloured sandstone interbedded with grey mudstone and siltstone. Subordinate lithologies include coal, ostracod-rich limestone/dolostone and rare marine beds with restricted faunas. In Edinburgh, the Granton Shrimp Bed with its distinctive fauna displaying some marine influence (see above) lies in the lower part of the formation and somewhat above the Craigleith Sandstone. The depositional environments were predominantly fluvial, deltaic and lacustrine and the sequence includes fluvial cycles. Coals within the Gullane Formation in the Oldhamstocks–Dunbar Basin (Fig. 9.2; Andrews & Nabi 1994) are thought to be equivalent to the Scremerston Coal 'Group' of the Tweed Basin (see below). The succeeding Aberlady Formation is up to 140 m thick and is broadly similar to the Gullane Formation, but contains more marine bands and bioclastic limestones with relatively rich and diverse marine-shelf faunas. Its base is drawn at the lowest of the multiple Macgregor Marine Bands (Wilson 1989).

In Fife, typically in east Fife, the Strathclyde Group comprises the Fife Ness, Anstruther, Pittenweem, Sandy Craig and Pathhead formations (Fig. 9.3); details of lithologies and thicknesses are given by Browne *et al.* (1996). Elements of the top two formations can be identified well beyond the type area

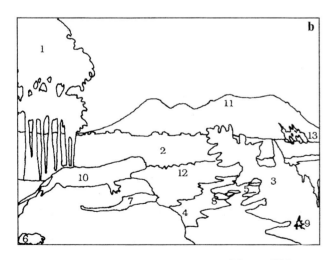

Fig. 9.15. East Kirkton palaeoenvironments and faunas; Viséan, Bathgate Group. (**a**) Reconstruction by Clarkson *et al.* (1994, fig. 1). (**b**) Key to (a): 1, lycopods; 2, dense tropical forest dominated by arborescent gymnosperms and pteridosperms; 3, gymnosperm frond; 4, floating algal and microbial stratiform mats next to shoreline; 5, stromatolites; 6, millipede fragments; 7, disarticulated pincer of *Pulmonoscorpius*; 8, *Hibbertopterus*; 9, opilionid (harvestman); 10, the tetrapod *Westlothiana*; 11, inactive, forest-enveloped basaltic cones; 12, lake shoreline within possible tuff-ring crater; 13, forest fire producing charcoal. Reproduced by permission of the Royal Society of Edinburgh.

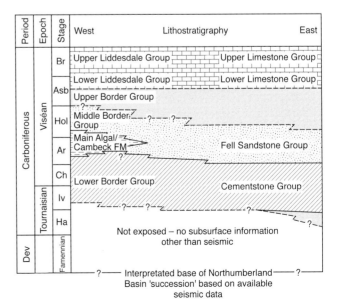

Fig. 9.16. Relationship between the Dinantian lithostratigraphies in the west and east of the Southern Borders (after Turner *et al.* 1997, fig. 2). Reproduced by permission of the Yorkshire Geological Society.

as in the Lawmuir Formation around Glasgow. Broadly similar lithologies and depositional environments are represented in all the top four formations, but the proportions vary. Fluvial, lacustrine and deltaic deposits are dominant, with coals and marine bands in all but the basal formation. Marine horizons become most prominent in the Pathhead Formation which resembles the succeeding Lower Limestone Formation (see below). Palaeocurrent flow was generally from the north throughout this group and Ar–Ar ages of detrital muscovites suggest a persistent source area in Scandinavia (Stuart *et al.* 2001). The Fife Ness Formation is known only in east Fife where it is at least 230 m thick. It is of fluvial and lacustrine origin and consists dominantly of white and red or purple sandstones. Argillaceous beds are commonly poorly bedded, and seatearths are present, but no coal seams. Bedded dolostones are rare and their associated non-marine faunas comprise ostracods, spirorbids and algal nodules.

The overlying Anstruther Formation, which is at least 810 m thick, consists dominantly of mudstone, siltstone and sandstone. Non-marine limestones and dolostones are also present, usually as thin beds, some of which contain oncolites and stromatolites. Minor components include marine mudstone and siltstone, plus a few algal-rich oil-shale beds that were

mined locally. Sandstone is subordinate, but thick, multistorey sandstones are locally developed. Thin beds of coal and ironstone are present. Much of the succession may be interpreted as upward-coarsening lake-delta cycles, capped by thinner erosive-based, upward-fining fluvial units, but parts seem noncyclic. The marine faunas are usually restricted. The abundant but restricted non-marine faunas are dominated by *Naiadites obesus*, with *Paracarbonicola* in the lower part of the formation.

The Pittenweem Formation (*c.* 260 m thick) is generally similar to the Anstruther Formation but is distinguished by its commonly diverse and abundant marine faunas which occur in the thin Macgregor Marine Bands (Fig. 9.14).

The Sandy Craig Formation (Fig. 9.14a), which is up to 670 m thick, is characterized by mudstone and siltstone with a minor proportion of algal-rich oil-shale. Beds of non-marine limestone and dolostone are present, some of which contain oncolites, and stromatolites. These beds are generally thin, but the Burdiehouse Limestone is up to 6 m thick. Variegated sandstones are subordinate, but thick, multistorey sandstones are found locally. Greenish grey clayrock and marl, plus nodular beds of pedogenic limestone and dolostone occur, together with beds of coal (up to 3 m) and ironstone. Most of the succession may be interpreted as a series of upward-coarsening

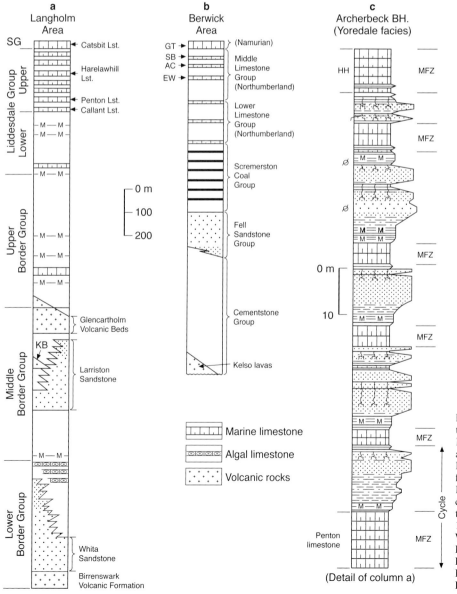

A succession of major limestone-bearing cycles, controlled by low frequency glacioeustatic oscillations in sea level. Conventionally each cycle starts at the base of a Maximal Flooding Zone produced by a rapid post-glacial rise in sea level and marked by a major clear water marine shelf limestone. This is typically followed by marine clays containing a varied and abundant fauna, which becomes attenuated upwards as the clays become silty. This increasing turbidity reflects the progradation of a fluviodeltaic system during a stillstand and gradual fall in sea level with the onset of a renewed glaciation. Peats may colonize the tops of deltas and floodplains only to be overwhelmed by the next postglacial sea-level rise. A superimposed higher frequency oscillation may give rise to minor coal-bearing cycles.

Fig. 9.17. Generalized vertical sections of the Dinantian successions in the Southern Borders. (a) The Langholm area in the west and (b) the Berwick area in the east. (c) Detailed representative section of Yoredale facies cyclical deposits in the Upper Liddesdale Group with interpreted depositional environments. Sections from the Geological Survey Archerbeck Borehole, 1954–55 [NY416 782] after Lumsden and Wilson (1961). AC, Acre Limestone; EW, Eelwel Limestone; GT, Great Limestone; KB, Kersehopefoot Basalts; SB, Sandbanks Limestone; SG, Stainmore Group. For further key see Figure 9.11.

deltaic cycles, capped by thinner upward-fining fluvial units. Marine faunas are rare and are usually restricted, consisting in one case of only *Lingula*. The abundant but restricted non-marine faunas are dominated by *Curvirimula*.

The Pathhead Formation, (up to 220 m thick), consists predominantly of mudstone and siltstone with beds of limestone and dolostone and thin beds of coal and ironstone. Pale coloured sandstone is subordinate to the argillaceous rocks. Most of the succession is composed of upward-coarsening marine-deltaic cycles, capped by thinner upward-fining fluvial units. Marine bands with thin limestones are more common than in the underlying formations and their faunas are usually diverse and abundant. The non-marine faunas are dominated by *Curvirimula*.

Southern Uplands

The Southern Uplands may have remained a high throughout much of the Carboniferous, probably through the buoyancy effect of the low density late-Caledonian granitic intrusions. This high contributed much less erosional detritus to the adjacent lows than did the Highlands, but acted as an incomplete barrier between the Midland Valley and the Carboniferous basins of the Southern Borders and northern England. This barrier was crossed by south- or SSE-trending palaeovalleys, with Late Palaeozoic fills that included attenuated Carboniferous successions, but none of these valleys seems likely to have formed a continuous seaway.

A 10 m-thick succession of interbedded mudstones, siltstones, sandstones, seatclays and thin argillaceous limestones, containing Late Viséan brachiopods and bivalves rests unconformably on Ordovician strata in the east of the Sanquhar Outlier (Davies 1970). At Thornhill a similar Late Viséan succession about 45 m thick contains at least four marine bands and two relatively thick marine limestones. Some of the beds seem to have been reddened. Farther east scattered volcanic necks, plugs and outliers suggest that a formerly more exten-

sive cover of Carboniferous volcanic and sedimentary rocks lay above the fluvial Kinnesswood Formation outliers in the Jedburgh–Earlston lowlands (Grieg 1971).

Southern Borders

A composite depositional trough, comprising the Solway Basin in the west and the Northumberland Basin and the Tweed Basin farther east and northeast overlay the former Iapetus Suture (Fig. 9.1). Here volcanicity was less extensive and marine influences stronger than in the Midland Valley. The main trough is a complex ENE-trending half-graben faulted to the south against the slowly subsiding Alston Block by the major Stublick–Ninety Fathom Fault, and locally faulted also to the north. Here the most complete succession lies in the Northumberland Basin well south of the Border and adjacent to that bounding fault, where the Dinantian succession is locally more than 5000 m thick, i.e. even thicker than in the Midland Valley (Chadwick *et al.* 1995). Unfortunately the successions preserved north of the Border are more attenuated and may contain gaps. At present there are also different lithostratigraphies for the west (Solway–Langholm–Liddesdale–Bewcastle area) and the east (Tweed Basin and northeast Northumberland). The approximate equivalence of the two sets of lithostratigraphical groups is shown in Fig. 9.16, and Fig. 9.17 illustrates generalized vertical sections from the west and the east, plus a detailed representative section of Late Viséan Yoredale facies in the west.

Solway to Cheviot
Early extensional subsidence followed Acadian basin inversion in this area. In the west the northern margin of the Solway Basin was bounded by a series of active faults throwing down to the south. Local alluvial cones fringed by sheet flood deposits carried coarse detritus southwards from the eroding footwalls (Deegan 1973). However, during most of the Dinantian the main siliciclastic input came from a persistent axial river system that flowed southwestwards and prograded into a

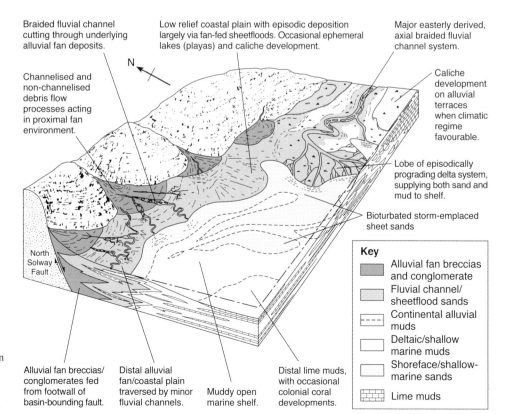

Fig. 9.18. Schematic representation of Dinantian depositional environments along the northern margin of the Solway Basin (after Maguire *et al.* 1996, fig. 18).

Braided fluvial channel cutting through underlying alluvial fan deposits.

Low relief coastal plain with episodic deposition largely via fan-fed sheetfloods. Occasional ephemeral lakes (playas) and caliche development.

Major easterly derived, axial braided fluvial channel system.

Channelised and non-channelised debris flow processes acting in proximal fan environment.

Caliche development on alluvial terraces when climatic regime favourable.

Lobe of episodically prograding delta system, supplying both sand and mud to shelf.

Bioturbated storm-emplaced sheet sands

North Solway Fault

Alluvial fan breccias/conglomerates fed from footwall of basin-bounding fault.

Distal alluvial fan/coastal plain traversed by minor fluvial channels.

Muddy open marine shelf.

Distal lime muds, with occasional colonial coral developments.

Key
- Alluvial fan breccias and conglomerate
- Fluvial channel/sheetflood sands
- Continental alluvial muds
- Deltaic/shallow marine muds
- Shoreface/shallow-marine sands
- Lime muds

marine open-shelf environment (Fig. 9.18; Maguire *et al.* 1996). Pre-Dinantian intrabasinal highs trending NNE affected sedimentation in the west of the Solway Basin.

The Lower Border Group (Courceyan–Arundian) was deposited initially under semi-arid climatic conditions. The Birrenswark Volcanic Formation, formerly taken to mark the base of the Carboniferous, reflects an initial episode of tensional rifting (see below); it is overlain by the Ballagan Formation. Numerous anhydrite beds have been found at about this level only a few kilometres south of the Border (Crowley *et al.* 1997; Ward 1997). The thick fluvial Whita Sandstone Member, which locally overlies the lavas and interdigitates with the Ballagan Formation, was brought into the Langholm area by a local river from the north. A cyclical succession (Lyne Formation), which includes algal limestones, forms the upper part of the group. Marine influences appeared and fluviodeltaic systems started to prograde from the northeast (Fig. 9.18; Leeder 1978). A more varied open marine fauna, including corals, appeared towards the top of the group.

In the overlying Middle Border Group (Arundian–Holkerian) mudstones and limestones, including algal bands containing this open marine fauna, were succeeded by a coarsening-upward siliciclastic succession which passed up into the thick fluvial Larriston Sandstone. This sandstone reflected the increasing influence of the persistent axial (Fell Sandstone) river system from the northeast that fed high-constructive deltas farther west. Local basaltic volcanicity reappeared east of Langholm near the middle of the group. More extensive volcanicity (Glencartholm Volcanic Beds) occurred in the top of the group, and continued into the succeeding Upper Border Group (Early Asbian). In this group marine mudstones and limestones with thin sandstones, reflected a widespread Early Asbian transgression which may have been related to increased extensional subsidence. These marine beds passed up into a more sandy cyclical facies with few limestones and generally thin coals, which may be equivalent to the Scremerston Coal Group to the east. Marine influences became much stronger in the lower part of the Lower Liddesdale Group (Late Asbian) when Yoredale-type cyclicity linked to glacioeustatic oscillations in sea level (Wright & Vanstone 2001) spread over the whole of the southern Borders. Fully developed Yoredale cycles with widespread thick marine limestones (Fig. 9.17c) characterize the Upper Liddesdale Group (Brigantian). Of these, the Harelaw Hill Limestone may represent the widespread Hurlet transgression of the Midland Valley.

Tweed Basin

This is another, smaller, ENE-trending half graben fault-bounded to the south, It was initially separated from the main Northumbrian Basin to the south by the slowly subsiding Cheviot Block (Figs 9.1, 9.3). Overall the facies are more proximal than farther west (Fig. 9.17b), reflecting the stronger influence of the axial river, and more closely resemble the facies in the Midland Valley. The Kelso Lavas mark the same tensional episode as the Birrenswark Volcanic Formation in the west. They are followed by the Ballagan-facies deposits of the Cementstone Group (Courceyan–Chadian), which includes gypsum bands, a few horizons with marine fossils and sporadic fluvial channel sandstones. The evidence suggests a semi-arid coastal plain crossed by intermittently flowing, probably meandering, rivers. The group is best exposed in the coastal section at Burnmouth north of Berwick where the basal beds are Kinnesswood Formation fluvial deposits with calcretes; fluvial sandstones towards the top may be equivalent to those of the Clyde Sandstone Formation.

Increased tectonic instability and runoff from the source area resulted in the appearance of the thick fluvial sandstones

within the Fell Sandstone Group (Chadian–Holkerian), which were mostly deposited by braided rivers and represent the more proximal deposits of the large axial river system from the northeast. Mudstones may however comprise 50% to 60% of the group (Turner *et al.* 1993). The succeeding Scremerston Coal Group (Early Asbian) partially exposed south of Berwick contains formerly worked coals and rare marine limestones. It reflects a period of increased rainfall and resembles the (later) early Namurian Limestone Coal Formation of the Midland Valley (see below) but was subject to stronger marine influences. The succeeding Lower and Middle Limestone groups (Asbian–Brigantian) of Northumberland are both of Yoredale facies but are poorly represented north of the Border. The Cheviot Block ceased to be an effective barrier, the composite Northumberland Trough became more open and the facies became more uniform at this time.

Offshore east of Scotland

Commercial seismic surveys and subsequent drilling have proved that, despite extensive latest Carboniferous erosion, large areas of Carboniferous deposits have been preserved east of the Scottish coast. Deposition of Old Red Sandstone fluvial facies is thought to have continued well into the Viséan in the Buchan Field (Glennie 2000). The Outer Moray Firth Basin (Fig. 9.1) also contains a Holkerian to Mid-Namurian succession some 1500 m thick, which includes both volcanic rocks and thick coals (see below and Leeder & Boldy 1990). Similar deposits have been found in the Forth Approaches Basin, which is a northeastward extension of the Midland Valley Graben. Unlike the Midland Valley, the Carboniferous succession here extends well to the north of the Highland Boundary Fault.

Basal Carboniferous to Mid-Brigantian igneous activity

Outcrops of Dinantian volcanic rocks within the Midland Valley, Southern Uplands and Southern Borders are shown in Figures 9.2 & 9.19. The earliest Carboniferous activity in Scotland took place during the Tournaisian (Fig. 9.8), and occurs in a linear zone roughly coincident with the fault-controlled northern boundaries of the developing Solway and Northumberland basins, and also in the separate Tweed Basin (Fig. 9.1; Leeder 1974; Leeder *et al.* 1989; Chadwick *et al.* 1995). Subaerial lava fields, which may never have been contiguous, were built up across Kinnesswood Formation semi-arid floodplains (Leeder 1974). A discontinuous strip of lavas is traceable for more than 95 km from the northern coast of the Solway Firth ENE towards Langholm (Fig. 9.2). This Birrenswark Volcanic Formation (Figs 9.8, 9.17) comprises transitional basalts and hawaiites up to about 90 m thick, with intercalations of reddened sandstone and siltstone. It rests upon Lower Palaeozoic rocks or Lower Carboniferous Kinnesswood Formation deposits and is overlain conformably by a thick succession of undisputed Tournaisian sedimentary strata (Lumsden *et al.* 1967). Some 50 km farther to the northeast, in the Tweed Basin, a 120 m-thick succession of basaltic to hawaiitic lavas and rare volcaniclastic rocks constitutes the Kelso Lavas (Fig. 9.8), and is believed to have been contemporaneous with the Birrenswark lavas.

There are at least fifty diatremes and intrusive plugs scattered between Langholm, Jedburgh and Greenlaw (Fig. 9.19), which are inferred to mark the conduits through which the Birrenswark and Kelso lavas erupted. However, some of the pipes northeast of Langholm may have acted as feeders for the younger (Viséan) Glencartholm pyroclastic rocks and lavas that were erupted in the same region (Lumsden *et al.* 1967).

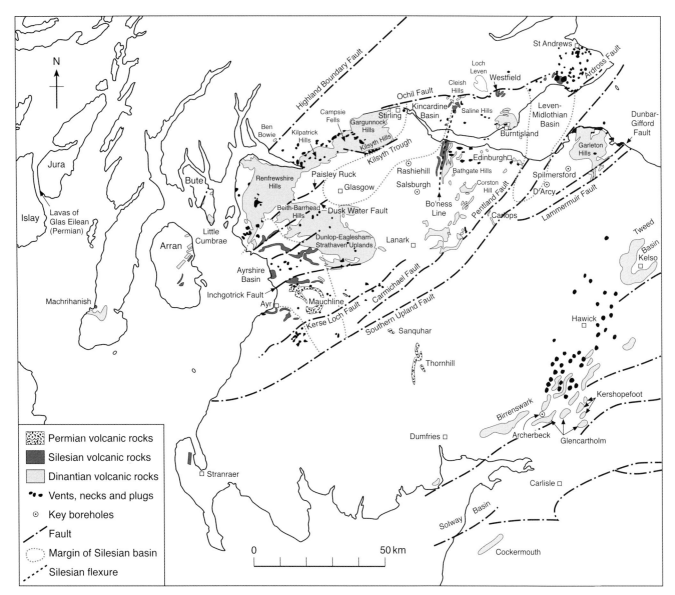

Fig. 9.19. Map of the Midland Valley and southern Scotland showing the outcrops of Dinantian, Silesian and Permian volcanic rocks and major structural components. After Leeder (1974); Cameron & Stephenson (1985) and BGS Tectonic map of Britain, Ireland and adjacent areas (1966).

Volcanism resumed on a much broader scale during the Viséan (Figs 9.8, 9.19). The lavas produced during this episode constitute over 90% by volume of all of the Carboniferous and Permian lavas, originally totalling almost 6000 km³ according to Tomkeieff (1937). Major eruptions were largely concentrated within the Midland Valley and in an area north of the Highland Boundary Fault in southern Kintyre, with minor occurrences in the Southern Borders. Some of the dykes and diatremes in the Northern Highlands that are described elsewhere in this chapter may be Viséan.

Within the Midland Valley the most extensive and most voluminous volcanic successions are those of the Clyde Plateau Volcanic Formation, which forms the near-continuous hills to the north, west and south of Glasgow. In the eastern Midland Valley an extensive volcanic field is centred upon the Garleton Hills of East Lothian with smaller centres in Edinburgh (Figs 9.8, 9.13, 9.20). These Early Viséan volcanic successions are dominated by lavas, although considerable thicknesses of pyroclastic rocks and volcaniclastic sedimentary rocks occur locally. Uniquely within the Carboniferous–Permian igneous province of northern Britain, they are characterized by a wide

range of compositions and, although most successions are dominated by transitional to mildly alkaline basalts, hawaiites and mugearites, many include trachytic rocks and some have rhyolites.

The outcrop of the Clyde Plateau Volcanic Formation is divided by major faults into several discrete 'blocks', each with its own succession in which stratigraphical units have some degree of lateral persistence (Francis *et al.* 1970; Paterson *et al.* 1990; Forsyth *et al.* 1996; Hall *et al.* 1998; Monro 1999). The formation attains its maximum thickness of up to 1000 m in the Renfrewshire Hills but it thins markedly southwards towards Ardrossan. To the NE, across the River Clyde, in the Kilpatrick Hills, the Campsie Fells and Kilsyth Hills, the formation is at least 400–500 m thick, but it thins generally eastwards in the prominent escarpment of the Fintry, Gargunnock and Touch hills (Figs 9.19, 9.21, 9.22). Across the fault-zone of the Paisley Ruck, to the SE, the lava sequence in the Beith–Barrhead Hills is probably less than 300 m thick, but farther to the SE, across the Dusk Water Fault, thickness estimates range from 500 to 900 m (MacPherson *et al.* 2001). Volcanic outcrops terminate abruptly at the Inchgotrick Fault,

(a)

(b)

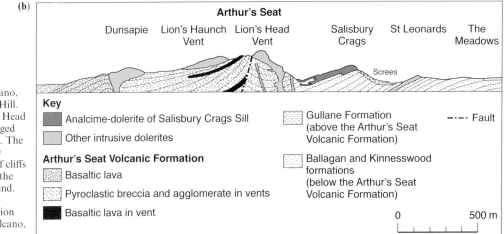

Fig. 9.20. (a) Arthur's Seat Volcano, Edinburgh, viewed from Calton Hill. The volcanic necks of the Lion's Head and Lion's Haunch form the rugged highest ground in the rear centre. The analcime-dolerite sill of Salisbury Crags forms the prominent line of cliffs at right centre. Lava flows form the trap features in the left background. (British Geological Survey photo D4957): (b) Geological cross-section E–W across the Arthur's Seat volcano, after Mitchell & Mykura (1962).

but a neck at Heads of Ayr on the coast may represent a small isolated volcano of similar age.

The original Clyde Plateau lava fields probably never extended far to the NW of the present outcrops (Whyte & MacDonald 1974), although they do spill across the Highland Boundary Fault near Helensburgh (Paterson *et al.* 1990). Outlying lava successions on the islands of Little Cumbrae, Bute and Arran are thin, suggesting that there was dramatic attenuation westwards from the main outcrops in the Midland Valley. However, around Machrihanish in south Kintyre (Fig. 9.1), a volcanic succession up to 400 m thick rests upon Kinnesswood Formation, Lower Old Red Sandstone and Dalradian rocks to the NW of the Highland Boundary Fault. The Machrihanish succession is overlain unconformably by volcaniclastic detritus akin to the Kirkwood Formation and by the Lower Limestone Formation; hence it has been assigned to the Clyde Plateau Volcanic Formation, although it probably formed an entirely separate lava field.

East of Stirling, thin volcanic sequences close to the West Ochil Fault near Dollar (Browne & Thirlwall 1981) and in the Cleish Hills may be contemporaneous with, but separate from, the Clyde Plateau activity. Farther south, below the Central Coalfield, Clyde Plateau lavas are present in the Rashiehill Borehole, near Slamannan (Figs 9.8, 9.19), but seismic evidence suggests that they thin abruptly farther east and are replaced by sedimentary rocks of the West Lothian Oil-shale Formation.

In Edinburgh, the rocks of the Arthur's Seat Volcanic Formation (Fig. 9.8) dominate the landscape (Fig 9.20), together with those of the thinner succession at the Craiglockhart Hills to the SW. Farther east, the Garleton Hills Volcanic Formation

crops out between the projection to the NE of the Southern Upland Fault and a splay of NE-trending faults including the Dunbar–Gifford Fault (Fig. 9.19; McAdam & Tulloch 1985; Davies *et al.* 1986). Here the volcanic rocks are underlain by Lower Palaeozoic rocks at no great depth. An unusual feature of this lava-field is its apparent association with high-level laccoliths and plugs of phonolitic trachytes, such as those that form Traprain Law, North Berwick Law and the Bass Rock.

Within and around the West Lothian Oil-shale Basin, much of the volcanic activity started somewhat later than elsewhere in the Midland Valley and, being entirely basaltic, was less varied in composition. In the Salsburgh 1A oilwell (Fig. 9.13a), supposed Early Devonian igneous rocks are overlain by some 100 m of basaltic tuffs and lavas with interbeds of limestone and mudstone that have been termed the Salsburgh Volcanic Formation (Cameron *et al.* 1998). These are succeeded directly by a freshwater limestone that marks the base of the Hopetoun Member of the West Lothian Oil-shale Formation and hence were contemporaneous with the 100 m-thick Seafield–Deans Ash of the West Calder area. This initial activity may have been contemporaneous with later phases of the Clyde Plateau Volcanic Formation. Other thin but widespread tuff beds occur slightly higher in the Hopetoun Member and above the Houston Marls, thick and widespread pyroclastic rocks mark the base of the Bathgate Hills Volcanic Formation. This major volcanic formation overlaps the Clyde Plateau Volcanic Formation to the west in the Rashiehill Borehole (Anderson 1963; Francis 1991*b*, fig. 11.7), and in the oil-shale basin it is interdigitated with the sedimentary succession throughout the remainder of the Viséan and well into the Namurian (see below).

Fig. 9.21. View across the Touch Hills towards Stirling and the Ochils. Trap features in foreground formed by lavas in the Clyde Plateau Volcanic Formation. In the middle distance are the wooded escarpments of the Midland Valley Sill-complex near Stirling, and in the distance the Ochils formed of Lower Old Red Sandstone lavas, truncated to the south by the West Ochil Fault. British Geological Survey photo D778.

Late Viséan volcanic activity was also centred around the Burntisland area of Fife, where up to 485 m of basaltic lavas with subordinate pyroclastic rocks and volcaniclastic sedimentary rocks constitute the Kinghorn Volcanic Formation (Browne & Woodhall 1999). The formation is well developed offshore beneath the Firth of Forth. The succession is dominantly subaerial, but with periodic submergence beneath freshwater lakes or marine incursions resulting in some pillow lavas and hyaloclastites.

In the Southern Borders, smaller-scale Viséan eruptions took place along much the same zone as the earlier Birrenswark lavas (Fig. 9.8; Lumsden et al. 1967; Day 1970) and basalt to hawaiite lavas formed the Kersehopefoot succession (up to 60 m thick). Slightly younger basaltic and trachytic pyroclastic rocks, with sedimentary units and rare lavas, compose the Glencartholm Volcanic Beds, locally 180 m thick (Fig. 9.19). Felsic intrusions among the plugs and diatremes of the Borders include alkaline and peralkaline compositions such as the trachytes and riebeckite rhyolite of the Eildon Hills laccolith, near Melrose and the quartz-trachyte, riebeckite trachyte and riebeckite-aegirine phonolite of Skelfhill Pen, SSW of Hawick.

Mid-Brigantian to basal Westphalian lithostratigraphy

The widespread marine transgression marked by the Hurlet Limestone initiated the progressive submergence of most of the upstanding Devonian and Strathclyde Group volcanic piles. The semi-isolated basins with different lithostratigraphies that typified the Strathclyde Group of central Scotland were replaced by a much more uniform marine-influenced depositional environment that extended over the Midland Valley and southwards into the Borders and northern England. Figure 9.23 shows the palaeogeography of Scotland and adjacent areas during the earlier part of the Namurian, when Scotland lay within the 'everwet' equatorial climatic belt, possibly with monsoonal interludes.

Offshore west of Scotland, Western Highlands and Islands

The Highlands probably remained an intermittent minor source for siliciclastic sediments during much of this period, but deposits of this age have been preserved in some marginal

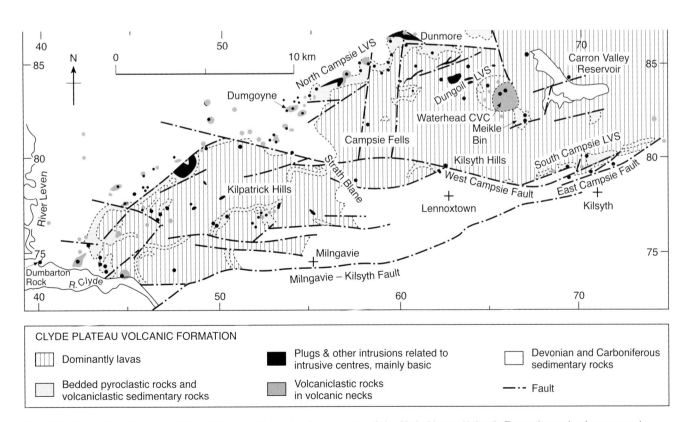

Fig. 9.22. Map of the Kilpatrick Hills and Campsie Fells, showing outcrops of the Clyde Plateau Volcanic Formation and volcano-tectonic lineaments (linear vent systems) defined by plugs, necks and proximal volcaniclastic beds. After Stephenson et al. (in press) and based on the BGS 1:50 000 sheets 30W (Greenock, 1990), 30E (Glasgow, 1993) and 31W (Airdrie, 1992). CVC, Central Volcanic Complex; LVS, Linear Vent System.

areas. In the Malin–Hebrides area, subsidence of the NE–SW Rathlin Trough (Figs 9.1, 9.23) continued to control deposition between Loch Foyle and Islay. The Machrihanish outlier, which extends only a short distance offshore, was formerly connected to the Ballycastle Coalfield in Northern Ireland. The lithological successions here and in Arran are broadly similar to those in Ayrshire but are generally more attenuated. The offshore successions in the Firth of Clyde also resemble those in Ayrshire and were affected by extensions of the major WSW–ENE faults of that area.

Midland Valley

Mid-Brigantian to Early Namurian deposits are best known in the Midland Valley. Here the structural pattern changed, following a change in the regional stress system to one that probably included a strong E–W tensional component (Rippon *et al.* 1996). The former West Lothian Oil-shale Basin and the eastward extension of the Leven Basin into east Fife disappeared, to be replaced by relative highs. New basinal elements also appeared. Figure 9.24 shows structures thought to have been active after the Mid-Brigantian (see also Read 1988, fig. 16.3). The loci of volcanicity shifted and volcanic activity generally declined, apart from late renewals in Ayrshire and east Fife (Fig. 9.8).

Abundant reliable borehole information and the presence of laterally persistent marker horizons, particularly marine bands, generally permit much more accurate correlation and a more detailed lithostratigraphy than in the earlier groups. Thus lateral variations in thickness and facies may be traced at formation level with some degree of confidence and most formation boundaries approximate to time lines.

Bathgate Group (Viséan–Arnsbergian)

This group is almost entirely volcanic and is time-equivalent to parts of Strathclyde and Clackmannan groups (Fig. 9.3).

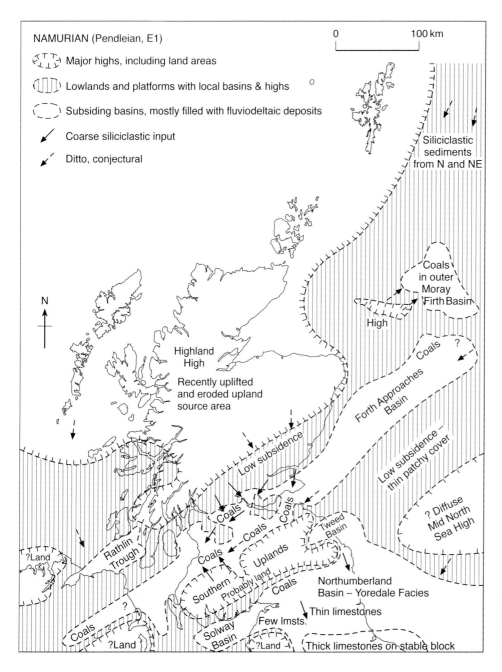

Fig. 9.23. Palaeogeography and palaeoenvironments of Scotland and adjacent onshore and offshore areas during the Early Namurian (Pendleian, E1).

It is geographically restricted to the central and eastern parts of the Midland Valley and was defined by Browne *et al.* (1996) who divided it into three formations, which may represent separate volcanic piles. The group includes lavas with subordinate tuffs and re-sedimented volcanic detritus, and the volcanic piles formed a partial barrier between the west and east of the Midland Valley from Late Dinantian until Mid-Namurian times. The base of the group is generally drawn at a conformable upward transition from the locally underlying sedimentary strata into tuffs and lavas, but is drawn at a conjectural subsurface unconformity between Devonian and Carboniferous volcanic rocks in the Salsburgh A oilwell. In the Rashiehill borehole west of Slamannan (Figs 9.8, 9.19), where the basal lavas of the Bathgate Group overlap with those of the Clyde Plateau Volcanic Formation, the base is drawn at a change to more mafic olivine basalts (Anderson 1951).

The Salsburgh Volcanic Formation is of somewhat uncertain age and chemical composition. It is known only from the Salsburgh A oilwell (Fig. 9.13a) where it consists of tuffs and highly decomposed lavas. The better-known Bathgate Hills Volcanic Formation (Smith *et al.* 1994) is associated with the Bo'ness–Bathgate hinge line (see below). It crops out in the Bathgate Hills, extends westwards in the subsurface and is equivalent in age to the upper part of the Strathclyde Group and the lower part of the Clackmannan Group (Fig. 9.3). The formation, which is 600 m thick in the Bathgate Hills (Cameron *et al.* 1998), includes basaltic lavas, tuffs and volcanic detritus and is described further in the following section on igneous activity. In the Bathgate Hills, many flows are capped by subaerially weathered boles, but to the north around Bo'ness a high proportion seem to have flowed into wet sediment or water, possibly below contemporary sea level. Thin intercalated sedimentary wedges also lie within the Bathgate Hills lava pile. Some intercalations correspond with major marine transgressions because they contain marine limestones that correlate with the Hurlet, Blackhall and Mid- and Main Hosie limestones.

The Kinghorn Volcanic Formation is closely related to the Burntisland anticlinal high (Fig. 9.13). It corresponds in age to the upper part of the Strathclyde Group and consists of subaerial and subaqueous olivine-basaltic lavas with subordinate tuffs. Its base interdigitates with sedimentary rocks of the Sandy Craig and Pathhead formations on the coast between Kinghorn and Kirkcaldy.

Clackmannan Group (Brigantian–Langsettian)
This group, which is recognizable only within the Midland Valley (Fig. 9.3), was defined by the British Geological Survey (1992) as including the Lower Limestone, Limestone Coal, Upper Limestone and Passage formations. The first three of these are basically similar and typically comprise cyclically alternating marine, or quasi-marine, and fluviodeltaic sedimentary rocks. By contrast the Passage Formation represents a more proximal, dominantly fluvial, environment and includes the major Mid-Namurian break, equivalent to the Mississippian–Pennsylvanian hiatus in North America (Read 1989; Riley *et al.* 1994), together with more minor breaks. The Mid-Brigantian Hurlet Limestone marks the base of the group and the early Langsettian Lowstone Marine Band and correlative horizons mark its top. Thus both the top and base of the Namurian lie within the group (Fig. 9.3). The lithostratigraphy and facies geometry of the group are known in considerable detail from thousands of fully cored mineral boreholes and from underground workings.

Following the changes in the regional stress system new structural elements appeared, as shown in Fig. 9.24. The present outcrops of the Clackmannan Group are concentrated in three areas, namely Ayrshire in the west, a central area including much of Lanarkshire and Fife and Midlothian in the east. Only the eastern area was a reasonably straightforward Late Carboniferous depositional basin, as may be seen from the isopach maps of the constituent formations, listed below. In the western and central parts of the Midland Valley deposition was largely controlled by WSW–ENE fault blocks (Fig. 9.24; Richey 1937; Read 1988). These blocks included that below the Dalry Basin, plus the North and Mid Ayrshire

Fig. 9.24. Major structural units that controlled Carboniferous sedimentation after the Mid-Brigantian in the Midland Valley and immediately adjacent areas. Normal faults have crossmarks on side of apparent downthrow and lines of variation in stratal thickness have triangles on the side of increased thickness. Updated from Read (1988, fig. 16.1) BBF, Brodick Bay Fault; CDF, Calder Fault; DGF, Dunbar–Gifford Fault; DMF, Dalmellington Fault; EOF, East Ochil Fault; F, Fault; FAB, Forth Approaches Basin; FSS, Falkirk–Stane Syncline; GAF, Glen App Fault; HBF, Highland Boundary Fault; KXF, Kennox Fault; LB, Littlemill Basin; LOS, Lochore Syncline; LMF, Lammermuir Fault; MB, Mauchline Basin; MF, Murieston Fault; NEAT, North-east Arran Trough; PR, Paisley Ruck; RL, Richey Line; SBA, Salsburgh Anticline; SUF, Southern Upland Fault; UDS, Uddingston Syncline; WB, Westfield Basin; WTF, Wilsontown Fault.

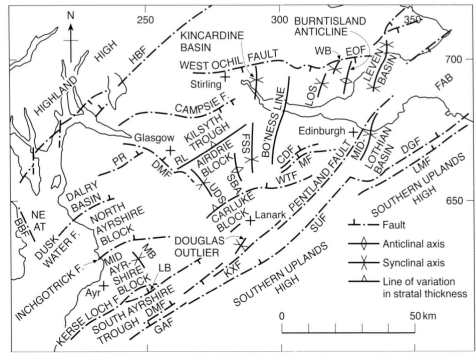

blocks and the South Ayrshire Trough in the west, and by the deep Kilsyth Trough, the Airdrie Block and the slowly subsiding Carluke Block in the central area. Movements along the faults and flexures that bounded these blocks probably reflected the tensional reactivation of pre-Carboniferous fractures in the basement. An area of low subsidence over the incompactable lava-pile of the Renfrewshire Hills lay between Ayrshire and the central area.

By contrast, in the northern and eastern parts of the Midland Valley a system of N–S and NNE–SSW trending, commonly asymmetrical, basins separated by highs were active, probably reflecting the onset of E–W tension (Rippon *et al.* 1996). Of these the Kincardine Basin east of Stirling, the precursor of the Clackmannan Syncline, appeared during the late Brigantian and became the most rapidly subsiding onshore basin in Scotland during the Namurian. During the Mid to Late Namurian and Westphalian the new Uddingston and Falkirk–Stane synclines started to subside in the central area (Fig. 9.24). To the east the Burntisland High and the pre-existing Leven and Midlothian basins continued to be active during the Brigantian and were still prominent during the Westphalian. Volcanic activity tended to be concentrated on structural highs and the hinges between basins and highs.

Repeated widespread major marine transgressions took place during deposition of the first three formations. These transgressions are marked by laterally persistent limestones or major marine bands, many of which can be traced into England. They most probably reflected glacioeustatic rises in sea level which produced the cyclical sedimentation that characterizes most of the group. The best developed cyclical intervals were fundamentally similar to the Late Dinantian and Namurian Yoredale cycles of the Southern Borders, Northumberland and the Pennines (as in Fig. 9.17c) in which marine limestones marked interglacial maximum flooding periods. Major glacial lowstands in sea level were marked by thick erosive-based multistorey fluvial sandstones with stacked channel-fills that were generally incised into the underlying deposits and by subaerial exposure of the interfluves with the formation of mature palaeosols between the incised channels (see below).

Sea-level oscillations of more than one frequency were commonly superimposed (Read 1994*a*) so that higher-frequency (short) cycles and intermediate-frequency (intermediate) cycles were superimposed on lower frequency (long) cycles. In addition to these *allocycles* produced by widespread external changes in sea level, some parts of the succession were affected by purely local sedimentary processes. These included the repeated building out and subsequent abandonment of local delta lobes (delta-switching), the avulsion of fluvial channel belts, and the migration of meander belts. Such local episodic processes produced local *autocycles* (Read & Forsyth 1989) that tended to increase in number towards the axes of subsiding sedimentary basins (Read & Dean 1982). The processes outlined above combined and interacted to produce complex cyclical successions that are commonly difficult to interpret.

As the sea repeatedly advanced and retreated in the Midland Valley the faunas migrated back and forth. Wilson (1967, 1989) considered that the ultimate source of the marine faunas lay far to the east of Scotland, probably in eastern Europe. During the most widespread transgressions the Midland Valley was a continuous marine strait which was sometimes tidal (Read 1992). It was successively colonized from the east by a series of abundant and varied invertebrate shelly marine-shelf faunas. The biofacies represented in particular localities were strongly affected by salinity, proximity to the shoreline, substrate and turbidity, as reflected in a progressive series of faunal phases analogous to those described by Calver (1968) in the

Westphalian. The chitinous brachiopod *Lingula* and the bivalve *Streblopteria* were initial colonizers of marginal reduced-salinity environments, which were succeeded by a muddy nearshore zone with soft substrates supporting a somewhat restricted but fully marine fauna that was generally dominated by bivalves. This zone might be further succeeded by a zone of calcareous muds with a varied shelly fauna, including a wide variety of calcareous brachiopods, zaphrentid corals, bryozoa and crinoids.

Finally, during the maximum flooding periods of the more widespread marine transgressions, the succession culminated in a clearer water limestone belt with firm substrates which supported a dominantly epifaunal assemblage of colonial corals, brachiopods, crinoids and echinoids, as described by Wilson (1967, 1989) and summarized by Cameron & Stephenson (1985). Such faunas reached their acme in the SE of the Midland Valley, particularly in the Lower Limestone Formation, and became progressively more attenuated towards the NW where the water was more turbid and less saline. No deeper water basinal ammonoid-bearing black-shale phase is known in the Scottish Namurian, and the scarcity of thick-shelled ammonoids makes it difficult to correlate the succession in Scotland with that of the Pennines (Ramsbottom *et al.* 1978).

Scottish Namurian *Lingula* bands were commonly succeeded by claystones containing non-marine bivalves such as *Paracarbonicola*, *Naiadites* and *Curvirimula,* which had evolved from marine ancestors, possibly in estuarine settings, and progressively adapted to lower salinities (Eagar 1977; Brand 1998). The basal Namurian Bearsden Fish Bed, which contains complete well preserved sharks, unique bony fish and crustaceans, is associated with somewhat similar marginal environments with varying salinities, degrees of oxidation and alternating marine and non-marine faunas. The sharks include the famous Bearsden Shark *Stenacanthus* with an enigmatic brush organ on top of its head (Dineley & Metcalf 1999, and references therein).

The northward migration of Scotland into the 'everwet' equatorial climatic zone allowed land vegetation to colonize new environments. During the deposition of the Clackmannan Group, Scotland was part of the Euramerican floral province and lay in the 'coal belt' dominated by heterosporous lycopod trees. These formed a primitive type of rain forest (Fig. 9.7; Phillips & Peppers 1984) in which thick domed equatorial peats accumulated, ultimately giving rise to thick coals (Clymo 1987). The peats were generally underlain by marshy water logged palaeosols (gleys) riddled with stigmaria, the roots of lycopods, which ultimately became seatearths. The 'Fossil

Fig. 9.25. Photograph (taken in 1937) of the 'Fossil Grove', Victoria Park, Glasgow. Seatearth (palaeosol) in Limestone Coal Formation (Pendleian), packed with stumps of giant club-mosses (lycopsids). Stumps *c.* 0.4 m high. British Geological Survey photo C3560.

Grove' in Victoria Park Glasgow (Fig. 9.25) provides a good example of this environment. A major floral change occurred early in the Namurian and the Late Namurian floras were similar to those of the Coal Measures. During the Silesian a drier upland flora, distinct from the lowland wetland flora, also appeared (Scott *et al.* 1993; Scott 1999).

The Lower Limestone Formation (Late Brigantian) is the interval with the strongest marine influences during the Scottish Carboniferous. Low frequency, probably glacioeustatic, oscillations in sea level resulted in seven widespread major marine transgressions marked by the Hurlet, Inchinnan, Blackhall, Main-, Mid-, Second- and Top Hosie limestones, of which the first-named marks the base and the last-named

the top of the formation. Wilson (1989) has traced all seven limestone horizons throughout the greater part of the Midland Valley. A generalized vertical section of the formation in west Fife, together with a more detailed log, and an interpretation of the depositional environments, is given in Fig. 9.26. The Hurlet Limestone and the Blackhall Limestone were generally the thickest, but local thickening occurred in several of the others. The Hurlet transgression marked the first period when the sea covered almost the whole of the Midland Valley so that only a few isolated highs escaped flooding (Fig. 9.27). During major transgressions a varied marine fauna entered from the east and between transgressions siliciclastic sediments prograded from the north and northeast.

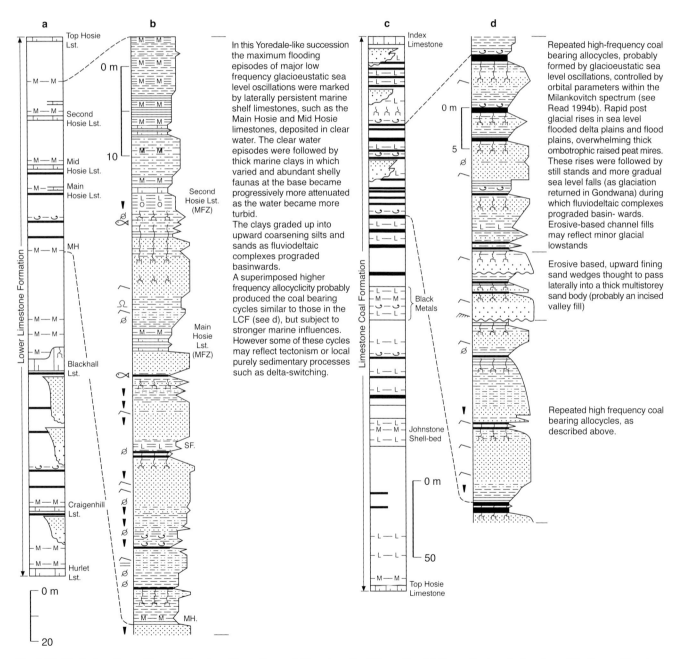

Fig. 9.26. Vertical sections of Lower Limestone Formation and Limestone Coal Formation **(a)** Generalized vertical section of the Lower Limestone Formation in West Fife. **(b)** Detailed representative section from part of (a) with interpretated depositional environments, from IGS Annfield Borehole, 1965 [NT 142 865] (Forsyth 1970). **(c)** Generalized vertical section of the Limestone Coal Formation in the Kilsyth Trough. **(d)** Detailed representative section of high frequency coal-bearing allocycles from part of (c) with interpreted depositional environments, from Gartcosh No. 1 Borehole, 1966 [NS 707 684]. For key see Fig. 9.11. LCF, Limestone Coal Formation; Lst, Limestone; MFZ, Maximum Flooding Zone; MH, Mill Hill Marine Band; SF, Seafield Marine Band.

Major low-frequency Yoredale-type cycles were dominant, but minor higher-frequency cycles were commonly superimposed upon them. Some of these minor cycles may have been autocycles produced by the episodic progradation and subsequent abandonment of successive local deltas. Others may have reflected local tectonism (Fielding *et al.* 1988; Kassi *et al.* in press). Puzzling features include the subaerially weathered, reddened and locally rooty tops of some of the limestones (Paterson *et al.* 1998; Monro 1999) and the comparative rarity of thick erosive-based multistorey sandstones (incised valley fills) cut during major lowstands. The successions in the west were dominantly argillaceous whereas sandstones and coals became progressively thicker and more numerous towards the east. In general limestones were thickest in the SE and thinnest in the central areas. The proportion of limestone in the succession increased in marginal low-subsidence areas remote from the input of siliciclastic sediments (Goodlet 1957; Wilson 1989).

Because the Lower Limestone Formation lies below most of the economically workable Carboniferous coals, borehole information is sparse and our knowledge is more dependent on scattered outcrops. Thus the isopach map and the map summarizing palaeogeography, active structures and volcanicity (Fig. 9.27) are more conjectural than the corresponding maps for the higher formations. The formation is thin in the west and thickest in the Kilsyth Trough, Midlothian and Leven basins. Tectonism was fairly active and a component of E–W stretch became apparent. Tensional movement also took place on WSW–ENE faults in both the west and the east of the Midland Valley.

In Ayrshire the succession is generally less than 50 m thick and is commonly truncated at its base, especially where the formation overlaps eastwards against the Clyde Plateau Volcanic Formation. Deposition was generally controlled by the differential subsidence of fault blocks separated by the ENE-trending Dusk Water, Inchgotrick and Kerse Loch faults. The succession is up to 60 m thick in the Dalry Basin north of the Dusk Water Fault where subsidence was greatest but thins abruptly southwards across that fault onto the North Ayrshire Block. Here it thickens southwards from 20–30 m to about 60 m before thinning abruptly across the Inchgotrick Fault onto the Mid Ayrshire Block. On this block the succession is thin and incomplete in the west and pinches out altogether in the east as well as in the area south of Ayr. South of the Kerse Loch Fault, in what later became the South Ayrshire Trough, the formation thickens modestly to 16–22 m (Cameron & Stephenson 1985).

The influence of fault blocks extended ENE from Ayrshire into the central part of the Midland Valley (Richey 1937). Here too, subsidence was greatest in the Kilsyth Trough in the north, where the succession is more than 200 m thick and thin sandstones and coals appear within a dominantly argillaceous succession (Forsyth & Wilson 1965). Sand from a persistent river north of Glasgow periodically prograded south and southeast into the trough (Wilson 1989). To the south the formation thins abruptly onto the Airdrie Block, in the east of which the basal sedimentary strata start to pinch out against the Bathgate Hills lava pile. The formation thins yet again onto the Carluke Block to the south, where the succession becomes greatly attenuated, but thickens in the Douglas Outlier within a northeastward extension of the South Ayrshire Trough. The N–S Kincardine Basin appeared east of Stirling in the north of the central area. Here the lower part of the formation below the Blackhall Limestone doubles in thickness within only 4 km on the western flank, but there is inadequate information to define the basin axis and its eastern flank. Rippon *et al.* (1996) suggested that this basin may have been initiated by W–E extension across a pre-Brigantian basement

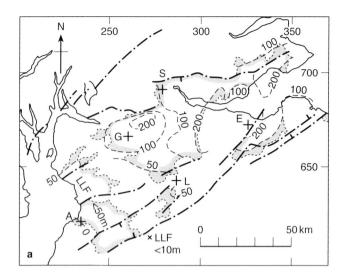

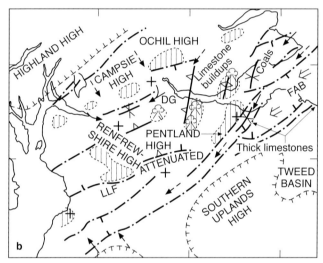

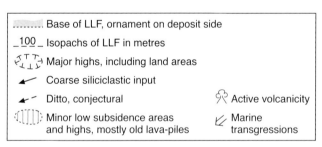

Base of LLF, ornament on deposit side
_100_ Isopachs of LLF in metres
Major highs, including land areas
Coarse siliciclastic input
Ditto, conjectural
Minor low subsidence areas and highs, mostly old lava-piles
Active volcanicity
Marine transgressions

Fig. 9.27. Lower Limestone Formation: (**a**) isopach map; (**b**) summary map, showing probably active structures, low subsidence areas (highs), contemporaneous volcanicity, and directions of coarse-grained siliciclastic input. For names of persistent structural elements and symbols not shown in key see Figure 9.24. DG, Denny Gap; FAB, Forth Approaches Basin; A, Ayr; E, Edinburgh; G, Glasgow; L, Lanark; S, Stirling.

fault that ran along the NNE-trending Saline–Bo'ness flexure line, with the Ochil Fault acting as a sidewall fault. The Bo'ness Line continued southwards along the Bathgate Hills as a line of persistent volcanicity.

A complex high, which included the Bathgate Hills volcanic pile, the Burntisland Anticline, and the Siluro-Devonian lava-pile of the Pentland Hills (Fig. 9.27) separated the central area from the Leven and Midlothian basins to the east. Pickard (1992, 1994) has described buildups in the locally thickened Blackhall (Charlestown Main) Limestone caused by increased carbonate productivity in clear shallow water on the flanks of the slowly subsiding Burntisland Anticline. Root casts at the tops of the buildups indicate local subaerial exposure. The formation thickens east of the complex high to reach about 240 m in the northeast of the Leven Basin in east Fife (Forsyth & Chisholm 1977). Most of the limestones are relatively thin in east Fife, but sandstones and especially coals are thicker and more numerous in this area than in other parts of the Midland Valley, suggesting a major input of sand from the northeast.

To the south the asymmetrical Midlothian Basin, where the formation is more than 200 m thick, is probably controlled by movement on the NE-trending Pentland Fault. The limestones here are thicker than in east Fife, especially on the eastern flank of the basin, and coals are thinner, but sandstones are still prominent. In East Lothian a thin distal succession, which contains unusually thick limestones along with some sandstones, was deposited near Dunbar just south of the Lammermuir Fault. Here the limestones have been extensively quarried for lime and cement.

The Limestone Coal Formation (Early Pendleian) lies between the top of the Top Hosie Limestone (Plate 17) and the base of the Index Limestone and is dominated by fluvio-deltaic high frequency cyclical deposits (Read 1994a) containing coals and sideritic ironstones, both of which were formerly mined. Closely spaced exploratory drilling and underground workings have made this the best known and most closely studied formation within the Scottish Carboniferous. A generalized vertical section of the formation from the Kilsyth

Trough, together with details of cyclicity and depositional environments is illustrated in Fig. 9.26c, d. At the beginning of the Namurian the Highland High sourceland was uplifted and eroded, causing siliciclastic sediments to pour into the Midland Valley from the north and northeast together with distantly-sourced material from Scandinavia. Within the Midland Valley fault blocks continued to dominate subsidence patterns in the west and south, and asymmetrical basins in the north and east (Figs 9.24, 9.28, 9.29). Contemporaneous volcanic activity was concentrated in the Bathgate Hills, with more local activity farther north along the Bo'ness Line, and in north Ayrshire but older volcanic piles also formed highs which continued to influence sedimentation.

Most marine transgressions now came from the west rather than the east, but marine influences were considerably weaker overall. Marine limestones are virtually absent but two composite marine bands, the Johnstone Shell-bed and the Black Metals, both of which mark major low-frequency eustatic transgressions (Read 1994a), allow the formation to be divided into three unequal portions. Of these the lowest is dominantly argillaceous in the west of the Midland Valley and the topmost accounts for about half the total thickness and contains the thickest coals. Traced eastwards the Black Metals passed shorewards into individual coal-bearing cycles (Read 1965). In addition to the two major composite marine bands, more than sixteen *Lingula* bands have been found in the upper part alone of the formation. These quasi-marine bands are most numerous in the Glasgow region and become rarer towards the east

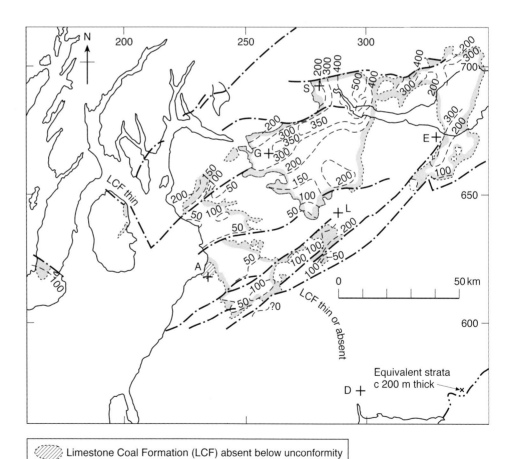

Fig. 9.28. Isopachs of the Limestone Coal Formation in the Midland Valley. Updated from Read (1988, fig.16.7). A, Ayr; E, Edinburgh; G, Glasgow; L, Lanark; S, Stirling.

(Forsyth 1979). Thick, erosive-based multistorey sandstones, thought to mark major eustatic lowstands, also become prominent above the Black Metals (Fig. 9.26c).

The formation is attenuated and coals are generally fewer and thinner in Ayrshire, where the lowest part of the succession is mostly mudstone (Monro 1999). The formation is thickest in the Dalry Basin in the north, thinner on the North Ayrshire Block and is reduced to only 15 m of sandstone on the Mid Ayrshire Block where overstep occurs at the base. The formation may never have been deposited at all around Ayr (Cameron & Stephenson 1985). The thickness increases to more than 100 m in the South Ayrshire Trough where sand and pebbles derived from the Southern Uplands entered locally from the south (Stedman 1988), but most sand entered from the NE (Mykura 1967).

Fault blocks also continued to control deposition in the central Midland Valley, with the greatest subsidence still in the Kilsyth Trough in the north. Here lateral facies changes can be followed in some detail in the upper part of the formation. In the west the 'layer-cake' geometry of the marine-influenced distal facies association (Fig. 9.26d) is dominated by regularly-

spaced, generally upward-coarsening coal-bearing allocycles that are thought to have been formed by high-frequency glacio-eustatic oscillations controlled by orbital parameters within the Milankovitch spectrum (Read & Forsyth 1991; Weedon & Read 1995). However, to the east, tongues of the less regular transitional facies association, which was increasingly affected by episodic fluvial processes, appear and thicken upstream, and some tongues pass into the autocyclic fluvially-dominated proximal facies with its highly irregular 'chickenwire' geometry (Read 1994b, 1995).

The progressive upstream changes in facies geometry are illustrated in Fig. 9.30. Minor erosive-based upward-fining incised channel sandstones that cut through extensive fluvio-deltaic sheet sandstones generally mark minor high-frequency glacial lowstands. On the SE-tilted Airdrie Block south of the Kilsyth Trough the succession thins and becomes less regular and the number of workable coals decreases sharply. On the Carluke Block (Fig. 9.24) the formation becomes even more attenuated but it thickens to more than 200 m in the Douglas Outlier. Here Lumsden (1964) recognized a similarity with the succession in the Midlothian Coalfield, suggesting unimpeded

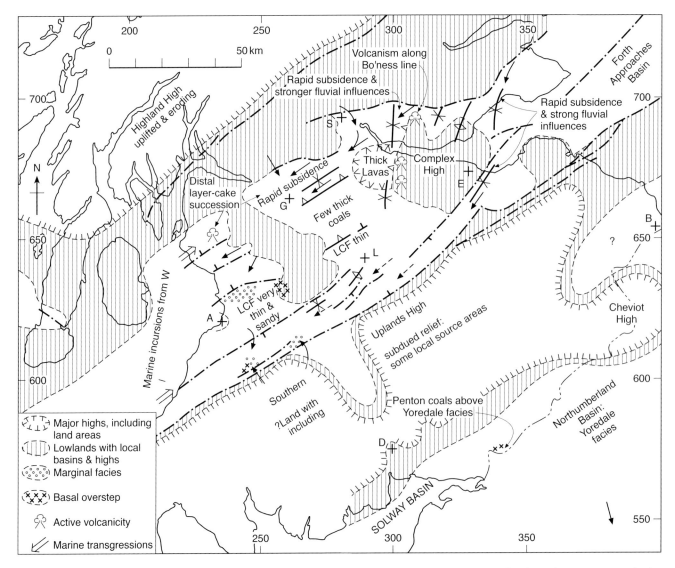

Fig. 9.29. Summary map for the Limestone Coal Formation (LCF) in the Midland Valley and adjacent areas, showing active structures, major low subsidence areas, contemporaneous volcanicity and siliciclastic sediment input. Updated from Read (1988, fig. 16.8). For names of persistent structural elements and explanation of symbols not shown in the key see Figures 9.1 and 9.24. A, Ayr; B, Berwick; E, Edinburgh; G, Glasgow; L, Lanark; S, Stirling.

sediment transport from the NE down a trough between the Pentland and Southern Upland fault systems that continues the line of the offshore Forth Approaches Basin (Fig. 9.24).

The Limestone Coal Formation reaches its maximum onshore thickness of about 550 m in the axis of the Kincardine Basin, which now became clearly defined as an asymmetrical basin with a steep eastern limb. It is bounded to the east by the NNE-trending Bo'ness Line flexure which was the locus of local explosive volcanism. Sand entered the basin from the NW and NE and left the basin to the SW via the Denny Gap constriction (Fig. 9.27) before prograding westwards down the Kilsyth Trough. On the eastern flank of the basin the transitional and proximal facies associations became dominant, suggesting stronger fluvial influences. Farther east the small Lochore Basin and, beyond the Burntisland Anticline, the much larger, rapidly subsiding, Leven and Midlothian basins were fed with sand from the north and northeast. Here the Johnstone Shell-bed and Black Metals become attenuated, *Lingula* bands become sparse and the facies geometry becomes irregular, all suggesting stronger fluvial influences towards the east of the Midland Valley.

In the Upper Limestone Formation (Late Pendleian–Early Arnsbergian), between the Index and Castlecary limestones (Fig. 9.31a), marine influences became stronger and volcanism and tectonism generally became weaker. Subsidence probably slowed, but the pattern of structural controls remained much as before. Rippon (1998) listed evidence that at least one of the

E–W family of tensional faults moved at this time. Marine transgressions entered from both the west and the east and at times the Midland Valley was an open marine strait into which new faunal elements migrated from the east (Wilson 1967).

Three superimposed sets of allocycles, related to low-, intermediate-, and high-frequency sea-level oscillations, can be detected within the formation (Read 1994a). Laterally persistent marine limestones overlain by thick marine mudstones, e.g. the Index, Lyoncross, Orchard and Calmy limestones, the three closely-grouped Plean limestones and the Castlecary Limestone (Fig. 9.31a), are fairly evenly spaced and represent the maximum flooding episodes of the low frequency oscillations. The Orchard limestone near the middle of the formation marks the base of the Arnsbergian. The three relatively thin Plean Limestones and the marine bands between them comprised a composite transgression analogous to those of the Johnstone Shell-bed and Black Metals. Most of the limestones tend to thicken towards the southwest and south, i.e. towards the distal environments most remote from the points where siliciclastic sediments entered the Midland Valley, and some of them die out altogether in the northeast. Unlike the others, the Castlecary Limestone tends to be thickest in the east. It was uplifted, subaerially exposed and widely eroded shortly after deposition.

An intermediate-frequency cyclicity is marked by thinner less persistent marine limestones such as the Huntershill Cement Limestone (Fig. 9.31a) and, more clearly, by thick multistorey sandstones which were deposited during lowstands in sea level. Research currently in progress suggests that some of the thick sandstones are incised valley-fills deposited during glacio-eustatic lowstands and are laterally equivalent to thin interfluve successions with mature subaerially-oxidized palaeosols. As they are more numerous than the major limestones, they cannot be linked to the same low-frequency cyclicity. The thick sandstones are not laterally continuous but each sandstone appears within the same restricted stratigraphical interval in different parts of the Midland Valley. The highest frequency cyclicity is marked by coal-bearing allocycles, closely similar to those in the Limestone Coal Formation (see above) but subject to stronger marine influences. These allocycles constitute much of the succession, especially below the Orchard Limestone and between the Plean limestones. Episodic delta-switching autocycles may also be present. All these superimposed and interfering cyclicities make the Upper Limestone Formation particularly difficult to unravel. Figure 9.31a, b & c shows a generalized vertical section, and more detailed partial sections illustrating typical facies associations with interpreted depositional environments. Isopachs and a palaeogeographical summary are illustrated in Figure 9.32.

In Ayrshire some explosive volcanic activity persisted into the Early Arnsbergian in the Dalry Basin, where the formation is only about 100 m thick. On the North and Mid Ayrshire blocks the succession is further attenuated, especially on the latter block which was uplifted and eroded some time after the Orchard Limestone was deposited (Monro 1985). The formation thickens to 210 m in the South Ayrshire Trough, where the limestones are particularly well developed. The sea is known to have transgressed farther south onto the Southern Uplands than during the preceding formation (Mykura 1967). In the central Midland Valley, thicknesses are greatest in the Kilsyth Trough in the north, where they now exceed 400 m, less on the Airdrie Block and least on the Carluke Block, where uplift and erosion took place sometime after deposition of the Calmy Limestone. Effusive and explosive volcanic activity continued, albeit at a reduced level, in the Bathgate Hills to the east (Fig. 9.8). Thick multistorey sandstones consisting of stacked upward-fining erosive-based fluvial channel fills are prominent

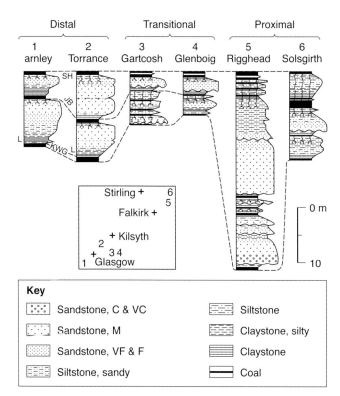

Fig. 9.30. Proximal to distal facies changes in the Limestone Coal Formation. Vertical sections, all through exactly the same stratigraphical interval between the base of the Knightswood Gas Coal (KWG) and the top of the Shale Coal (SH), in the Kilsyth Trough and the Kincardine Basin. These illustrate the eastward passage upstream from the distal facies association, with its high-frequency glacio-eustatic allocycles and regular 'layer-cake' facies geometry, through the more variable transitional facies association into the strongly fluvially influenced, dominantly autocyclic, proximal facies association with its highly variable 'chickenwire' facies geometry. After Read (1995, fig. 3). JB, Jubilee Coal; L, *Lingula* band.

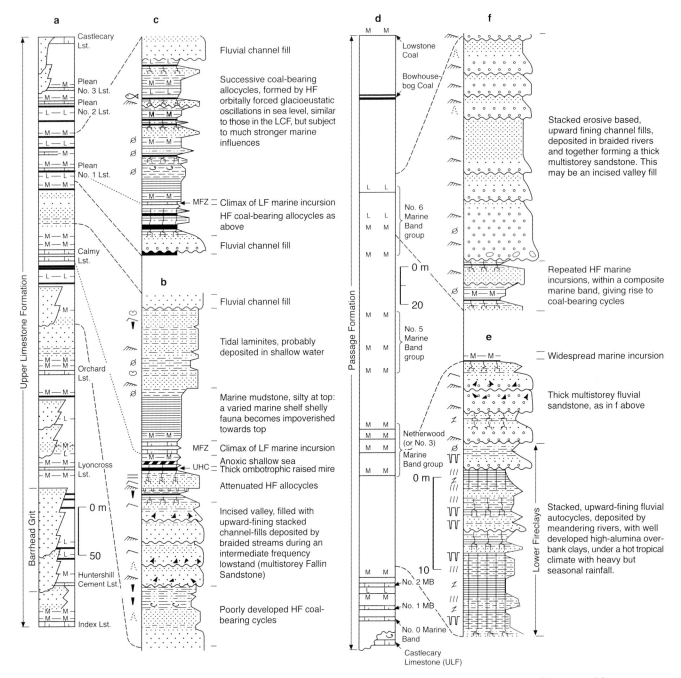

Fig. 9.31. Vertical sections of Upper Limestone Formation and Passage Formation. (**a**) Generalised vertical section of the Upper Limestone Formation, as fully developed in the Kincardine Basin. (**b**) Detailed representative section with interpreted depositional environments of part of (**a**) showing a thick multistorey sandstone, the thick Upper Hirst Coal (UHC) and the laterally persistent Calmy Limestone. From Headswood No. 1 Water Borehole, 1964, [NS 829 825]. (**c**) Detailed section with interpreted depositional environments of a later part of (**a**) showing Plean No. 1 Limestone overlain by high-frequency coal-bearing cycles in NCB Maggie Duncan's Hill Borehole, 1964 [NS 942 905]. (**d**) Generalized vertical section showing the stratigraphical framework of the Passage Formation, as fully developed in the Kincardine Basin, after Read (1989, fig. 1). (**e**) Detailed representative section with interpreted depositional environments of part of (**d**) including part of the Glenboig Lower Fireclays from IGS Arns Farm Borehole, 1970 [NS 871 350]. (**f**) Detailed representative section with interpreted depositional environments of a later part of (**d**) in IGS South Kersie Borehole, 1970 [NS 872 898]. For explanation of symbols and ornaments see Fig. 9.11. HF, High frequency; LCF, Limestone Coal Formation; LF, Low frequency; Lst, Limestone; MFZ, Maximum Flooding Zone; MB, Marine Band; ULF, Upper Limestone Formation.

in the Kilsyth Trough where some of these thick sandstones are themselves stacked to produce even thicker composite beds such as the Barrhead Grit (Fig. 9.31a), which is locally 58 m thick (Forsyth 1982; Hall *et al.* 1998). South of the attenuated succession on the Carluke Block the formation thickens to more than 320 m in the middle of the Douglas Outlier, where the limestones are also unusually thick.

The formation attains its maximum onshore thickness of about 600 m in the Kincardine Basin. The axis of this basin had migrated west so that it now became more symmetrical (Rippon *et al.* 1996) and some synsedimentary faulting may have taken place along roughly E–W lines. Limestones tend to be thicker towards the basin axis but are thin or even absent in the northeast. Tidal couplets (Fig. 9.31b; Read 1992) have

The Colour Plates

This colour section contains photographs illustrative of the geology of Scotland. The photographs are generally arranged in geological sequence, and chapters in which the plates are referenced are indicated. Colour photographs for the Permo–Trias are within Chapter 10.

Plate 1. Typical Scourian banded gneiss showing intrafolial folds refolded by NW–SE-trending Inverian folds. NG 815 705, near Loch Braigh Horrisdale, Gairloch, NW Highlands. Photo R.G. Park (Ch. 3).

Plate 2. Undeformed Scourie dyke, east side of Ben Tarbert, South Uist, Outer Hebrides. Photo B. G. J. Upton. (Ch. 3).

Plate 3. Precambrian gneiss topography exhumed from beneath the Torridon Group in the NW Highlands. View looking north from Slioch, across Loch Garbhaig towards An Teallach (in the far right). The coincidence of Precambrian and present topography is demonstrable from the presence of scattered outliers of breccia on the exhumed surface (see Stewart 1972, figs 4, 5) Photo A. D. Stewart. (Ch. 3).

Plate 4. Stronchrubie cliffs, near Inchnadamph, NC 246 224. Durness Limestone in the imbricate thrust zone, NW Highlands. The lower, flat-lying dark grey beds of the Ghrudaidh Formation are overlain by thrust packages comprising pale grey imbricated beds of the Eilean Dubh Formation. Photo D. T. Wright. (Ch. 3).

Plate 5. Folded dolomite raft in a 40 m thick unit (the 'Great Breccia'), possibly representing a catastrophic platform collapse unit, within glacimarine Dalradian sediments of the Port Askaig Tillite. NW coast of Holy Island, Garvellach Islands. Height of cliff *c*. 60 m. Photo I. J. Fairchild. (Ch. 4).

Plate 6. Macduff Boulder Bed with large glacial dropstone of anorthosite in bedded mudstones of the Southern Highland Group of the Dalradian. Shore at Berrymuir, Macduff, Banffshire. Photo N. H. Trewin. (Ch. 4).

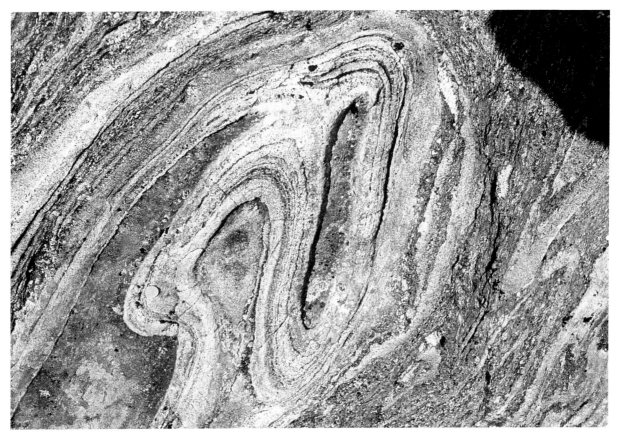

Plate 7. Interbanded psammites and semi-pelitic gneisses of the Moinian Glenfinnan Group within the Northern Highland Steep Belt, showing lithological layering folded by an isoclinal, highly curvilinear, D2 fold that is itself refolded by a D3 fold. Width of view *c.* 1 m. Sgurr a'Mhuide near Glenfinnan, (NM 858 817). Photo B.G. J. Upton. (Ch. 4).

Plate 8. Late Caledonian microdiorite cutting late pegmatites, the latter intruded into Ardgour granitic gneiss and amphibolite. Road section on A830 east of Glenfinnan, NM 916 802. Photo A. L. Harris. (Ch. 4).

Plate 9. Craigeven Bay, Stonehaven. The junction between the Highland Border Complex and the Dalradian block. The boundary, conventionally regarded as the Highland Boundary Fault crosses the bay and juxtaposes the psammitic rocks of the Dalradian block with cooling ages of *c.* 460 Ma against black shales, pillow lavas and tuffs of the Highland Border Complex (Llanvirn, *c.* 455–470 Ma). As no sediment from the former is recognised in the latter, a major displacement on the fault is suggested. Photo B. J. Bluck. (Ch. 5).

Plate 10. Downan Point Formation pillow lavas opposite Sgavoch Rock, near Downan Point, near Ballantrae. NX 075 809. Part of the northernmost tectonic unit within the Southern Uplands terrane. Age uncertain, but most probably Caradoc. View is to the NE, along strike, the lavas are slightly overturned, dipping to the SE and younging NW. BGS photograph. (Ch. 6).

Plate 11. Caradocian Kirkcolm Formation greywackes between Salt Pans Bay and Port Beg, Rhins of Galloway. NW 962 620. View is along strike to the NE. The beds are slightly overturned and dip steeply south; they form cycles with upward-thickening beds. BGS photograph. (Ch. 6).

Plate 12. Steeply-plunging F3 fold hinge in Llandovery Gala Group, unit 5 (Garheugh Formation) at The Hooies, south of Ardwell Bay, Rhins of Galloway. NX 067 445. View is towards the SW. BGS photograph. (Ch. 6).

Plate 13. Cliffs of Lower ORS Yesnaby Sandstone showing large-scale aeolian dune bedding. Yesnaby, Mainland, Orkney. Photo N. H. Trewin. (Ch. 8).

Plate 14. Old Red Sandstone fluvial deposits unconformably onlapping and covering a small hilltop of migmatitic gneiss. Western margin of the Orcadian Basin at Port Skerra, Sutherland. Photo N. H. Trewin. (Ch. 8).

Plate 15. Two well-preserved specimens of *Osteolepis panderi* from a mass-mortality horizon in fish bed laminites of the Middle ORS, Latheron Sub-group, near Thurso, Caithness. Width of view 120 mm. Photo N. H. Trewin. (Ch. 8).

Plate 16. 'Hutton's Unconformity' The historic locality at Siccar Point, Berwickshire with gently dipping Old Red Sandstone unconformably overlying near-vertical Silurian greywackes and shales. Photo N. H. Trewin. (Chs 2, 8, 20).

Plate 17. Aerial view looking north showing a syncline in the Lower Limestone Formation and Limestone Coal Formation of the Carboniferous. The 'Hosie Limestone' separating the formations occurs within the section. Wave-cut platform at St Monance, Fife. Photo R. Garton and J. A. F. Allen. (Ch. 9).

Plate 18. The Rock and Spindle sea-stack near St Andrews, Fife, named from its resemblance to parts of a spinning wheel. The tall Rock is formed from pyroclastic breccia, and the Spindle is basanite with radial columnar jointing. Both intrude bedded tuffs of the ?Late Carboniferous Kinkell Ness Neck. BGS photograph. (Ch. 9).

Plate 19. The base of Salisbury Crags Sill, Holyrood Park, Edinburgh. The analcime-dolerite of the sill has prised up a slab of the underlying sandstone, which has also been baked by the heat of the intrusion. This exposure was cited by James Hutton in the late 18th century as evidence for the forceful intrusion of magma. Photo D. Stephenson. (Ch. 9).

Plate 20. Cross-bedding in lunate tidal bar forms of the Bajocian Druim an Fhuarain Sandstone (Bearreraig Sst. Fm.). NG 514 133 south of Port na Cullaidh, Elgol, Skye. North is to the left as viewed. Photo N. H. Trewin. (Ch. 11).

Plate 21. View of the Cuillin Hills Tertiary Igneous Centre looking NW over Loch Slapin from Elgol, Skye. The cliff in the foreground is formed of the coarsening-upward sequence of sandstones of the deltaic Elgol Sandstone Formation of the Great Estuarine Group (Mid Jurassic). Photo N. H. Trewin. (Chs 11, 14).

Plate 22. Large-scale cross-bedding in shallow marine bar deposits of the Brora Sandstone at Strathsteven cliff, Brora, Sutherland. Photo N. H. Trewin. (Ch. 11).

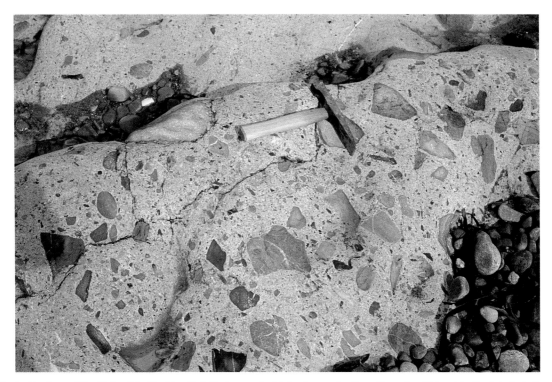

Plate 23. Typical texture of the Helmsdale Boulder Beds that were shed into deep water from the active Helmsdale Fault in Late Jurassic (Kimmeridgian) times. Rounded to angular clasts of Devonian flagstones are set in a matrix of bioclastic, shelf-derived debris. North side of Helmsdale harbour wall, Helmsdale, Sutherland. Photo N. H. Trewin. (Ch. 11).

Plate 24. Columnar jointing in dolerite of the Trotternish Sill Complex, intruding white sandstones and shales of the Valtos Sandstone Formation of the Great Estuarine Group (Mid Jurassic). Kilt Rock viewpoint, Valtos, Trotternish, Skye. Photo I. T. Williamson. (Chs 11, 14).

Plate 25. Typical scenery produced on the Palaeogene lavas of the British Tertiary Igneous Province. Ross of Mull, Mull. Photo I. T. Williamson. (Ch. 14).

Plate 26. The Carsaig Tree, a *c*. 14 m high vertical basalt cast 2.5 m in diameter, embedded within a columnar-jointed basaltic flow of the Staffa Lava Formation, cropping out above Carsaig Arches, south coast of the Ross of Mull, SW Mull. Note the fanning orthogonal attitude of the jointing within the lava in the vicinity of the tree cast. Person for scale near the base of the tree. Photo B. J. Bell. (Ch. 14).

Plate 27. Tertiary lava scarp and head of the landslip at the Quirang, near Staffin, Trotternish, Skye. Photo N. H. Trewin. (Chs 14, 15)

Plate 28. Ice-abraded gabbro at the lip of Coire Lagan in the foreground contrasting with the frost-shattered back wall of the corrie where eroded dykes result in gullies. Cuillin Hills, Skye. Photo N. H. Trewin. (Ch. 15)

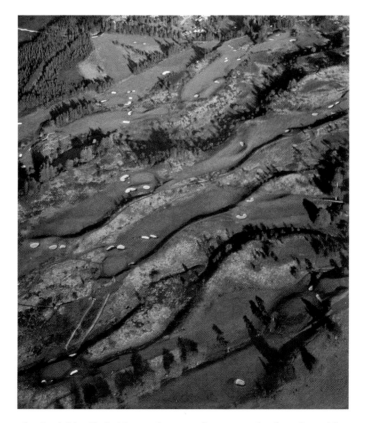

Plate 29. An esker system at Gleneagles, Perthshire. Such ridges as these are often supposed to have formed from streams flowing beneath a glacier. However, these examples probably formed from proglacial outwash beneath which dead ice was buried. The major streams had incised through ice, and when this finally melted, the deposits of the major streams stood up as ridges. Photo Patricia Macdonald. (Ch. 15).

Plate 30. The summit plateau and eastern corries of Braeriach. The Cairngorm mountain-top plateaux are thought to be remnants of Tertiary erosion surfaces. Deep corries on their flanks have been progressively excavated by small glaciers, which have repeatedly occupied these hollows through the Quaternary. Photo Patricia Macdonald. (Ch. 15).

Plate 31. Caledonite (**a**), lanarkite (**b**), and leadhillite (**c**) from the Leadhills–Wanlockhead district. Photograph by permission of the trustees of the National Museum of Scotland. (Ch. 16)

Plate 32. House of Water opencast coal site in Lower Coal Measures, Ayrshire, looking NW to Burnston Cottage. A fault cuts the succession in left centre of the view. Photo Ken McDonald and Scottish Coal. (Chs 9, 17, 20)

Plate 33. Interpretive notice boards at popular tourist locations help visitors to understand key geological features; in this case glacially transported erratics near Rhiconich, Sutherland. Photo L. Gill, Scottish Natural Heritage (Ch. 20).

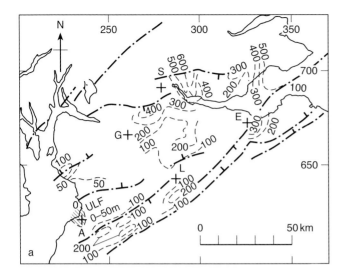

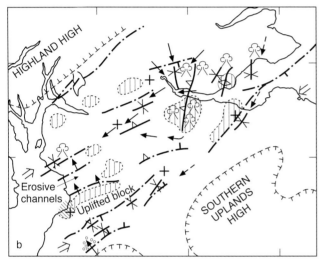

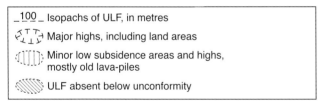

_100_ Isopachs of ULF, in metres

Major highs, including land areas

Minor low subsidence areas and highs, mostly old lava-piles

ULF absent below unconformity

Fig. 9.32. Upper Limestone Formation (ULF) in the Midland Valley: (**a**) isopachs in metres; (**b**) summary map showing active structures, low subsidence areas, contemporaneous volcanicity and siliciclastic sediment input. Updated from Read (1988). For names of other persistent structural elements and symbols not shown in key see Figure 9.24.

been identified in the thick marine mudstones that overlie the Index, Orchard and Calmy limestones. Sand entered the basin from the northwest, north and northeast and at times seems to have passed right over the hitherto-positive Ochil Lower Old Red Sandstone lava pile. Thick multistorey fluvial sandstones are prominent within the basin (Fig. 9.31a, b) and these tend to merge to form even thicker composite beds such as the Barrhead Grit in the southwest where rivers flowed westwards through the constricted Denny Gap into the Kilsyth Trough. Coals were numerous but seldom thick, except for the Upper Hirst Coal below the Calmy Limestone which can locally exceed 2.5 m. Intermittent, largely explosive, volcanic activity continued along the Bo'ness Line flexure that bounded the basin to the east. Apart from within the minor Lochore Basin,

the formation is relatively thin and it is patchily preserved in west and central Fife. Dominantly explosive volcanic activity including necks and Surtseyan tuff-rings (see below) formed in shallow water extended into this area, but basaltic lavas were extruded subaqueously around the small Westfield Basin. Francis & Walker (1987) suggested that in this area alkali basaltic magma spasmodically rose along E–W and NE–SW basement faults as pipes cutting the wet low-density early Namurian sediments and flowed down-dip into local basin axes to form alkali dolerite sills (Francis 1991b, fig. 11.18).

East of the Burntisland High the Leven and Midlothian basins continued to subside rapidly. Siliciclastic sediments continued to be fed in from the north and northeast and thick multistorey sandstones are present. Individual limestones are thin or even absent in the Leven Basin and the north of the Midlothian Basin but are relatively thick in the south of the latter. Dominantly explosive volcanic activity started in the Largo Law area of east Fife and continued until the Westphalian (Fig. 9.8).

The Passage Formation (Arnsbergian–Early Langsettian) lies between the top of the Castlecary Limestone (or at a basal unconformity that cuts out that limestone) and the base of the Lowstone Marine Band (Fig. 9.31d). Unlike the three preceding formations in the group it is dominantly sandy, fluvial and autocyclic. Tectonic instability during deposition created local unconformities and breaks in deposition. The formation also includes the more widespread, possibly eustatic, Mid-Carboniferous break. Extensive volcanism returned to Ayrshire, died out in the Bathgate Hills and continued in east Fife (Fig. 9.8). The climate may have been monsoonal with intense seasonal rainfall and fluctuating river flows and water tables (Read 1989).

A change in structural pattern led to new basins forming in areas where deposition had hitherto been controlled by fault blocks. Local structural reversals took place along some major ENE- and NE-trending faults during a right-lateral transpressive episode with local basin inversion and the superimposition of basins on former highs (Read 1988, 1989). At the very beginning of the period the widespread marine transgression marked by the Castlecary Limestone was abruptly terminated, the limestone was uplifted, subaerially weathered and dolomitized and, in the west and southwest of the Midland Valley, it was completely removed by erosion. At the same time the source area in the Highland High was tectonically uplifted and eroded, sending a surge of sand and pebbles into the Midland Valley (Muir 1963). In most areas the succession is incompletely preserved and interrupted by erosional breaks, as well as being subject to abrupt changes in lithofacies. Thus reasonably complete successions have been preserved in relatively few places, notably the Kincardine Basin. Although the depositional environment was strongly proximal and predominantly fluvial, a stratigraphical framework is provided by sporadic marine bands and clusters (groups) of marine bands. Individual bands may be missing locally, but this overall framework can usually be recognised in the deeper basins. Thin coals closely associated with the marine bands have yielded spores which, together with very rare ammonoids, have enabled the succession to be subdivided at stage level (Neves et al. 1965). Figure 9.31d illustrates a generalized vertical section, based on the Kincardine Basin, with the known marine bands, and Fig. 9.31e, f shows more detailed partial sections from within the lower and upper parts of the formation, together with interpreted depositional environments.

The subaerially weathered and locally rooty top of the Castlecary Limestone (Cameron et al. 1998) is overlain, not by the usual thick marine mudstone, but by a thin carbonaceous mudstone containing only non-marine bivalves. In many localities the limestone was eroded by deeply incised fluvial channels filled with coarse-grained pebbly sandstones. The succession then briefly reverted to an environment similar to that of the Plean limestones, with three persistent Late Arnsbergian marine bands, Nos 0, 1 and 2, (Fig. 9.31d) each containing a limestone and underlain by a thin coal. Each of these bands is locally eroded by the base of the overlying sandstone. Closely above No. 2 Marine Band there is a drastic change to an autocyclic meandering-river environment (Fig. 9.31e). The thick, leached, overbank mudstones with mature soil profiles were formerly extensively worked as high-alumina refractories, and were known as the Lower Fireclays. Above the Lower Fireclays a cluster of four closely-spaced marine bands, underlain by thin coals, and collectively termed the Netherwood or No. 3 Marine Band group, are known to belong to the Kinderscoutian. Thus there is no trace of either the Chokierian or Alportian stages and it seems highly probable that the widespread Mid-Namurian Break (Fig. 9.6), equivalent to the Mississippian–Pennsylvanian break in North America, lies at the base of, or within, the autocyclic fluvial interval (Read 1989).

A further change to a braided river environment took place in the succession above the Netherwood Marine Band group (Fig. 9.31e, f). This dominantly sandstone succession is interrupted by two clusters of rather impersistent marine bands, grouped together as No. 5 and No. 6 Marine Band groups (Fig. 9.31d; Read 1989; Cameron *et al.* 1998). Each marine band generally carries only a sparse attenuated marine fauna or *Lingula* alone, and is underlain by a thin coal. All but the topmost band of No. 6 group probably belong to the Marsdenian, whereas this topmost band may represent the Subcrenatum Marine Band at the base of the Westphalian (Neves *et al.* 1965). Another cluster of clayey palaeosols, formerly worked as refractories and collectively known as the Upper Fireclay, interrupts the sandy basal Langsettian succession between No. 6 Marine Band group and the Lowstone Marine Band. These palaeosols are associated with the thick but impersistent Bowhousebog Coal. Passage Formation isopachs and a summary of the active structural and depositional elements are shown in Fig. 9.33.

Widespread uplift and erosion took place in Ayrshire at the very beginning of the Passage Formation with deep erosion of the Upper Limestone Formation, even in the Dalry Basin. Nowhere has the Castlecary Limestone been preserved. The subsequent sedimentary succession is attenuated and generally lacks identifiable stratigraphical markers, as well as being complicated by extensive contemporaneous volcanicity. The ENE-trending fault blocks continued to control deposition, with the greatest subsidence in the South Ayrshire Trough where Arnsbergian marine bands seem to be present. On the tectonically unstable North and Mid Ayrshire blocks only an attenuated sedimentary succession has been preserved below the great pile of basaltic lavas belonging to the Troon Volcanic Member (Fig. 9.8; Browne *et al.* 1996, fig. 6), and south of Ayr the erosive base of the Passage Formation oversteps onto the Strathclyde Group. Sedimentary intercalations within the lavas have yielded spores thought to indicate a Kinderscoutian to Marsdenian age. Subsequent subaerial weathering and erosion of the lavas, followed by the transportation of some of the resulting volcanic detritus, produced the high-alumina Ayrshire Bauxitic Clay Member worked for the chemical industry (Monro *et al.* 1983; Monro 1999; Browne *et al.* 1996). Namurian lavas also occur at Arran, Machrihanish and Loch Ryan.

In the north of the central part of the Midland Valley subsidence continued in the Kilsyth Trough (Fig. 9.24), where a widely preserved Castlecary Limestone is followed by a succession closely similar to, but thinner than, that in the Kincardine Basin (Forsyth *et al.* 1996). Refractory clays were formerly worked extensively in this area, especially around

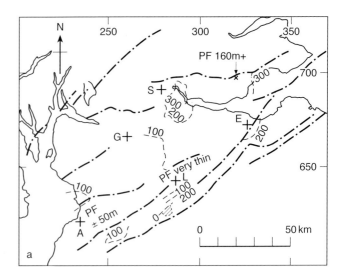

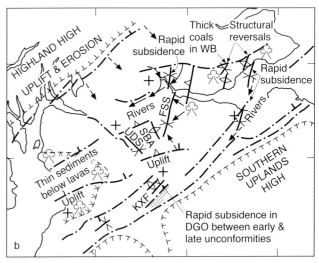

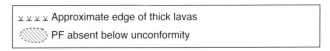

Fig. 9.33. Passage Formation (PF) in the Midland Valley: (**a**) isopachs in metres; (**b**) summary map showing active structures, major low subsidence areas, contemporaneous volcanicity and siliciclastic input. Updated from Read (1988). Abbreviations: DGO, Douglas Outlier; FSS, Falkirk–Stane Syncline; KXF, Kennox Fault; SBA, Salsburgh Anticline; WB, Westfield Basin. For names of other persistent structural elements and symbols not shown in key see Figure 9.24.

Glenboig and Bonnybridge. Further south the Castlecary Limestone and the Arnsbergian marine bands are absent over the western part of the Airdrie Block, probably reflecting early uplift and erosion. Here the subsidence pattern was modified during the deposition of the formation by the initiation of the N–S trending Uddingston and Falkirk–Stane synclines, separated by the Salsburgh Anticline (Fig. 9.24; Read 1989). Tectonic instability continued over the Carluke Block to the south where the top of the Upper Limestone Formation is deeply eroded and the Passage Formation is reduced to a few metres of sandy sediment. Still farther south in the Douglas Outlier Lumsden (1967) has described angular unconformities at the local base and the top of the formation, but the intervening succession is some 200 m thick and closely resembles that in the Kincardine Basin. Apart from the Castlecary

Limestone, most of the main stratigraphical marker horizons are represented. Towards the end of the period the north of the outlier was uplifted and eroded, whilst to the south the formation was entirely eroded southeast of the Kennox Fault where Westphalian sedimentary rocks overstep onto Dinantian strata. In the Bathgate Hills volcanic activity waned and died out during the Late Arnsbergian (Fig. 9.8).

The Kincardine Basin, where the Passage Formation is at least 370 m thick, continued to be the most rapidly subsiding onshore basin in Scotland. Here the marker horizons described earlier are best known and most widely preserved. Two major channel belts entered the basin from the northwest and the northeast, suggesting that the Ochil lava pile had reappeared as an active high. The two channel belts converge and merge in the southwest before passing through the Denny Gap and flowing westwards down the Kilsyth Trough (Read & Dean 1982). Each channel belt carries a different assemblage of heavy minerals derived from different parts of the Highlands (Muir 1963). A minor spasm of basin inversion led to deep incision of the northeastern channel and of the merged channel belt, which eroded the Castlecary Limestone in a belt across the south of the basin.

To the east, in Fife, right-lateral transpressive strike-slip along the eastern part of the Ochil Fault, probably initiated the Westfield Basin as an oblique fold immediately to the south. This small but rapidly subsiding basin, which lay within the broad complex high east of the Kincardine Basin, was superimposed on an earlier local topographical high. The basin fill contrasts sharply with that of the larger basins to west and east as it is dominated by unusually thick but purely local coals (Fig. 9.5; Brand et al. 1980). Adjacent local highs and the vertical stacking of a series of thick domed peats excluded contemporary rivers carrying coarse siliciclastic sediments. Structural reversal also took place somewhat later farther east along the Ochil Fault where the Earl's Seat Anticline was formed by the inversion of an earlier basin (Read 1988, 1989).

The formation reverted to its normal fluvial facies in the Leven and Midlothian basins, both of which continued to subside rapidly. Siliciclastic detritus entered from the north but came from a more easterly Highland source than the detritus that entered the Kincardine Basin. Detritus also came from the east, with a possible contribution from uplifted and eroded earlier Carboniferous strata (Muir 1963). Significantly, the Castlecary Limestone has generally been preserved intact, although it was eroded on the eastern flank of the Midlothian Basin. Most of the other marine bands and marine band groups seem to be represented, but in Midlothian No. 5 group is locally reduced to a single marine band and No. 6 group seems to be missing altogether. In the same area the proportion of overbank clays indicative of meandering rivers is greater in the upper, rather than the lower, part of the formation, in contrast to the situation in the Kincardine Basin. Both in Fife and Midlothian there are thick coal seams near the top of the formation. Some siliciclastic detritus also entered the Midlothian Basin from the northwest towards the end of the period. Largely explosive volcanism continued throughout the deposition of the Passage Formation in the Largo Law area in east Fife (Fig. 9.8).

Southern Uplands

The Southern Uplands High remained an effective barrier between the Midland Valley and the major basins of northern England and some Namurian sandstones derived from this high are found in southern Ayrshire (Fig. 9.23). Nevertheless limited deposition took place in some localities. Attenuated and incomplete successions equivalent in age to parts of the Clackmannan Group have been preserved in the Loch Ryan, San-

quhar and Thornhill outliers, generally above a discordant base (Fig. 9.1; Grieg 1971). The poorly exposed Namurian strata in the Loch Ryan Outlier include a thin basaltic lava. At Sanquhar a thin Late Viséan succession including marine bands rests unconformably on Ordovician, and is itself unconformably overlain by thin, dominantly sandy, Namurian strata containing at least one marine band (Davies 1970). An attenuated succession including marine strata thought to be of Brigantian to Pendleian age is found below the Westphalian deposits of the Thornhill Outlier (McMillan & Brand 1995).

Southern Borders

Conditions were fairly uniform throughout this area and Yoredale-type cyclical sedimentation was dominant, especially at the beginning of the period. The Cheviot High had ceased to be an effective barrier between the Tweed Basin to the north and the Northumberland Basin to the south.

Solway to Cheviot. Thermal sag took place in the Solway and Northumberland basins, albeit interrupted by a spasm of right-lateral transpression during the Mid to Late Namurian. Strata equivalent in age to the Clackmannan Group are present at Canonbie and in Liddesdale. Here the higher part of the Upper Liddesdale Group, known from the Archerbeck Borehole (Lumsden & Wilson 1961), is similar in age and of similar Yoredale facies (Fig. 9.17) to the Lower Limestone Formation of the Midland Valley. This part of the succession includes thick limestones, marine mudstones, sandstones and thin coals. The Yoredale facies continues above the thick Catsbit Limestone close to the base of the Namurian into beds equivalent in age to the Stainmore Group of northeast England (Chadwick et al. 1995), and the Limestone Coal, Upper Limestone and Passage formations of the Midland Valley. This part of the succession is poorly exposed and may include one or more major breaks in deposition, especially one marked by reddening at the top of this interval. However it is known to include marine limestones, coals (including the locally worked Penton coals), palaeosols and thick sandstones (Lumsden 1967).

Tweed Basin. Strata of Yoredale facies in the upper part of the Middle Limestone Group of Northumberland are exposed on the foreshore at Berwick on Tweed (Turner & Scruton 1995). These strata (Fig. 9.17b) include the thick marine Eelwell, Acre and Sandbanks limestones and are thought to be equivalent in age to the Scottish Lower Limestone Formation.

Offshore east of Scotland

The principal palaeogeographical and structural features in the offshore areas north and east of mainland Scotland and Northumberland at the beginning of the Namurian are outlined in Fig. 9.23. A lack of precise dating of some of the coal-bearing Carboniferous deposits discovered by drilling makes it difficult to construct an accurate synthesis. However a coal-bearing succession more than 1500 m thick and thought to be of Asbian to Namurian age has been discovered in the Outer Moray Firth Basin (Andrews et al. 1990; Leeder & Boldy 1990). The succession includes thick coals, mudstones, some of which may contain marine bands, thinly-bedded sandstones and thick coarse-grained erosive-based sandstones up to 30 m thick, plus local volcanic rocks. A similar succession has been found in the Forth Approaches Basin. The Mid-North Sea High remained a positive feature like the Southern Uplands. Coal-bearing

Namurian and Viséan to Westphalian strata have been found south of this high in the vicinity of the Central Graben, suggesting the possibility that the latter structure may already have been in existence during the Carboniferous (Gatliffe *et al.* 1994).

Westphalian and Stephanian

The Subcrenatum Marine Band which marks the base of the Westphalian has not been positively identified in Scotland, but may correspond with the top marine band of No. 6 group in the upper part of the Passage Formation (Fig. 9.31d). Within the Midland Valley an arbitrary local base has been chosen at the Lowstone Marine Band or a closely correlative horizon within the *lenisulcata* Biozone, or at a basal unconformity. The top of the Coal Measures has been drawn at the sub-Permian unconformity. Browne *et al.* (1996) class the Scottish Coal Measures as a lithostratigraphical group. The widespread Van-

derbeckei (Queenslie) and Aegiranum (Skipsey's) marine bands which can be traced over much of Europe allow the group to be divided into three informal formations, namely the Lower, Middle and Upper Coal Measures. These belong respectively to the Langsettian (Westphalian A), Duckmantian (Westphalian B) and Bolsovian (Westphalian C) stages. The topmost Upper Coal Measures may be of Westphalian D age (Fig. 9.3), but there is no firm evidence of onshore Stephanian deposits. In Scotland the base of the Coal Measures has been drawn at a slightly higher horizon and the base of the Upper Coal Measures at a somewhat lower horizon than in England. The Coal Measures are less extensively preserved than the underlying groups and north and south of the Midland Valley they occur only in isolated outliers. The palaeogeography of Scotland and adjacent areas during the early Westphalian is illustrated in Figure 9.34.

Both the Lower and Middle Coal Measures are mostly cyclical 'grey beds' with repeated, generally upward-coarsening,

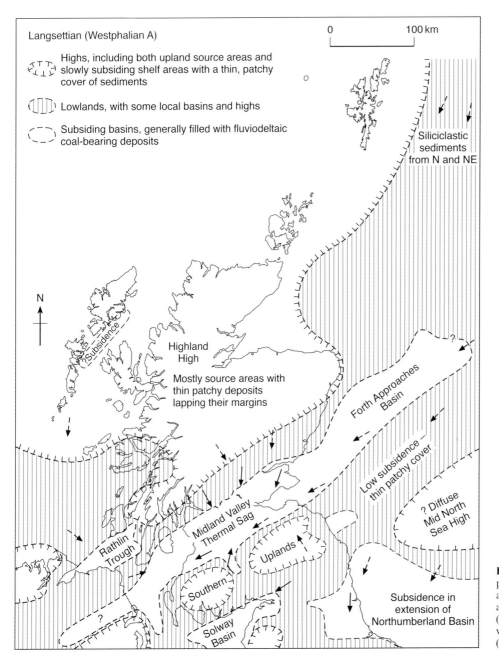

Fig. 9.34. Palaeogeography and palaeoenvironments of Scotland and adjacent onshore and offshore areas during the Langsettian (Westphalian A). Compiled from various sources, including Cope *et al.* (1992) and Rippon (1996).

fluviodeltaic cycles (Fig. 9.35). Coarser-grained upward-fining erosive-based channel sandstones (together with marine incursions) appear in the lower part of the Lower and the upper part of the Middle Coal Measures. The lowest Upper Coal Measures are usually 'grey beds' but these pass upwards into oxidized 'red beds' with thicker sandstones and no surviving coals. Many of the Westphalian coals were extensively worked, as also were sideritic ironstones within the claystones and high-alumina refractory clays from a few palaeosols (seatearths). Generalized vertical sections for the Middle and Upper Coal Measures of the Airdrie district and the Lower Coal Measures of the Falkirk district are shown in Figure 9.35 together with representative details of the lowest part of the Lower Coal Measures, and an interpretation of depositional environments. Figure 9.36 is a summary map of active structures, for the combined Lower and Middle Coal Measures. It is difficult to convey an adequate impression of thickness variations within the three formations by means of isopach maps because of the geographically limited preservation of the Middle and Upper

Coal Measures. However, isopachs of the combined Lower and Middle Coal Measures within restricted parts of the Midland Valley have been illustrated by Read (1988, fig. 16.13).

During the later Westphalian and the succeeding Stephanian, Scotland moved from the 'everwet' equatorial climatic belt into a belt with a markedly seasonal rainfall, and towards the end of the Carboniferous, into a semi-arid belt. These climatic changes were partly due to the Laurussian plate moving away from the contemporary equator. They may also reflect the onset of monsoonal conditions and the creation of a rain shadow in the lee of the Variscan mountains which were rising to the south, following the closure of the mid-world ocean between Laurusssia and Gondwana (Maynard *et al.* 1997; Warr 2000). After late Namurian tectonic movements most of Scotland became tectonically less active. The Highland High and the Southern Uplands High continued, whilst in most of the Midland Valley variations in thickness became less marked and the Namurian structural subsidence pattern was modified. No clear pattern of subsidence is detectable in the

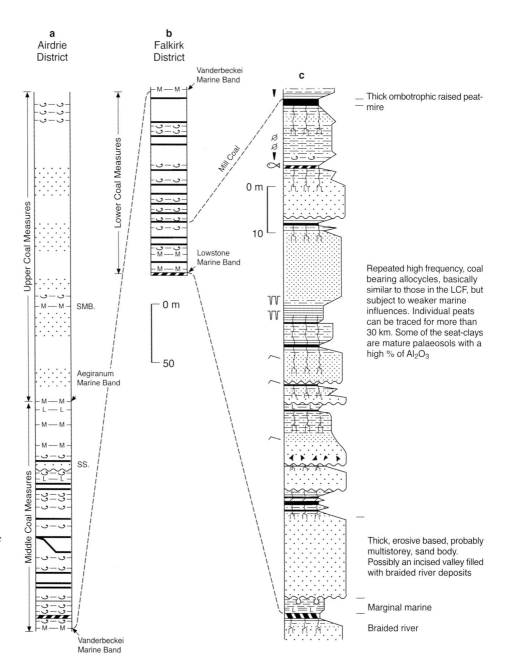

Fig. 9.35. Generalized vertical sections of (**a**) the Middle and Upper Coal Measures of the Airdrie district, and (**b**) the Lower Coal Measures of the Falkirk district. (**c**) Detailed representative section with interpreted depositional environments of part of (b) from NCB Cuttyfield No.1 Borehole, 1978 [NS 889 843]. For key see Figure 9.11. SMB, Shafton Marine Band; SS, Shettlestone Sandstone.

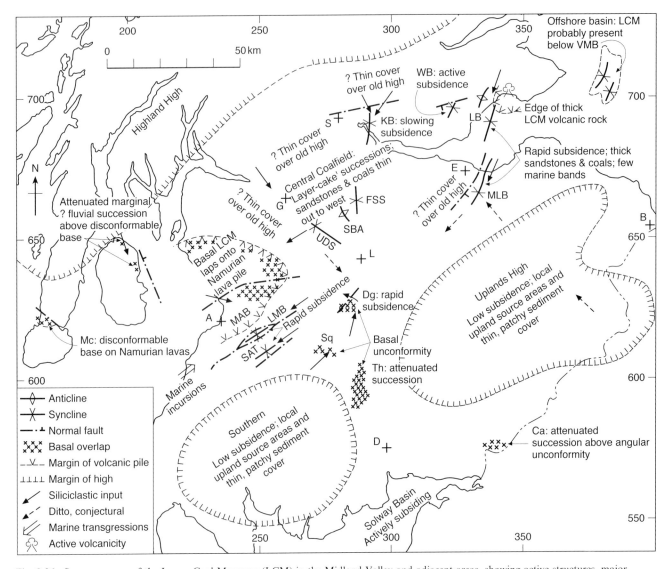

Fig. 9.36. Summary map of the Lower Coal Measures (LCM) in the Midland Valley and adjacent areas, showing active structures, major low-subsidence areas, contemporaneous volcanicity and siliciclastic input. Compiled from various sources, including Read (1988) and Kirk (1983). Ca, Canonbie Coalfield; Dg, Douglas Coalfield; KB, Kincardine Basin; LB, Leven Basin; LMB, Littlemill Basin; MAB Mid Ayrshire Block; Mc, Machrihanish Coalfield; MLB, Midlothian Basin; SAT, South Ayrshire Trough; Sq, Sanquhar Coalfield; Th, Thornhill Outlier; VMB, Vanderbeckei Marine Band; WB, Westfield Basin. For other symbols and abbreviations see Figure 9.24. A, Ayr; B, Berwick; D, Dumfries; E, Edinburgh; G, Glasgow; L, Lanark; S, Stirling.

Northumberland Basin, although the Solway Basin continued as a well defined sub-basin. Tectonic activity greatly intensified during the Late Westphalian and Stephanian and culminated in latest Carboniferous compression, transpression, basin inversion, uplift and erosion (see below). Volcanicity had probably died out in Ayrshire and was now confined to east Fife and the Firth of Forth (Figs 9.8, 9.36).

Depositional environments and processes in the Lower and Middle Coal Measures were basically similar to those of the Limestone Coal Formation, albeit with much weaker marine influences. The principal source areas lay to the northeast and north with some minor contributions from the Southern Uplands High. Scotland lay near the northern edge of a vast, flat, rather uniform, alluvial plain which covered much of northwest Europe and probably extended far to the west (Rippon 1996). Successive fluviodeltaic complexes, in which rivers followed deltas, prograded westwards down the centre of the Midland Valley from Fife and Midlothian towards Glasgow and south Ayrshire (Fig. 9.36; Kirk 1983). Fluvial influences were thus strongest in the east where thick coarse-grained, erosive-based

sandstones, thick coals and complex lithofacies geometries are most common. Attenuated proximal fluvial successions near the margins of the Midland Valley contain channel sandstones and well developed palaeosols but few, if any, coals. Patchy attenuated Westphalian successions may originally have covered much of the slowly subsiding Highlands, Southern Uplands and Mid-North Sea highs.

Marine incursions were rather rare and generally carried only a restricted fauna, although ammonoids appeared in the more basinal areas during the peaks of the widespread Vanderbeckei and Aegiranum transgressions (Brand 1977; Forsyth & Brand 1986). Incursions generally came from the west and some may be correlated with widespread marine bands in England and continental Europe. Most incursions occurred during the Early Langsettian, the Late Duckmantian and the Early Bolsovian (Fig. 9.35).

By the Westphalian, non-marine bivalves were able to colonize progressively less saline environments, and to cope with rapid sedimentation (Eagar 1977). Their rapid proliferation and diversification in such environments formed concentrated 'musselbands', commonly with distinctive faunal assemblages, in the claystone roofs of many coals. Some individual 'musselbands' can be traced from Ireland, through Britain, eastwards to Belgium and the Rhur (Eagar & van Amerom 1999). Westphalian non-marine bivalves belonging to the genera *Carbonicola*, *Anthracosia*, *Anthracosphaerium*, *Naiadites*, *Anthraconaia*, *Curvirimula* and *Anthraconauta* have been used to define a succession of faunal zones, as illustrated by Cameron & Stephenson (1985, fig. 29) and Francis (1991*a*, fig. 10.26), which can be traced throughout Britain. These zones, together with laterally persistent marine bands, reveal that distribution patterns of thick coals and marine bands in Scotland are similar to those in the English coalfields, which suggests some form of widespread external control (Rippon 1996). Within the Midland Valley non-marine faunas become increasingly impoverished and marine bands less common towards the east.

During the Westphalian Scotland lay within the broad Euramerican floral province in which coal-swamp and wetland vegetation was dominated by tree-sized lycopods such as *Lepidodendron* and *Lepidophloios* (Fig. 9.7), but many lycopod taxa died out as the climate became drier towards the end of the Westphalian. The lycopod *Sigillaria* however continued into the Stephanian, together with calamites, ferns and seed ferns. Tree ferns like *Psaronius* appeared in the Westphalian and became abundant in the Stephanian. Cordaites, which were closely related to conifers, grew as trees and shrubs in the Westphalian wetlands and, probably more abundantly, in the drier uplands. They continued into the Stephanian. True conifers appeared in Europe during the Duckmantian (Phillips & Peppers 1984; Cleal & Thomas 1999).

In the Westphalian of Scotland and northern England Scott (1977, 1979) has used both macrofloral and sporal evidence, mostly from the Duckmantian, to identify plant communities linked to specific depositional environments. Peat mires in coal swamps were still dominated by various types of lycopods, especially *Lepidodendron* and *Sigillaria*. Drier environments away from coal swamps were dominated by seed ferns along with cordaites, lycopods, sphenopsids and true ferns (Scott & Galtier 1985). A varied floodplain flora was dominated by seed ferns, with some sphenopsids and lycopods, whilst seed ferns also grew on the better drained channel levees. Calamites, which had creeping rootstocks, were able to colonize unstable environments such as river point bars and lakesides.

Below the sub-Permian unconformity the Westphalian strata were deeply weathered and oxidized. Siliciclastic strata were reddened. Argillaceous strata also lost their fissility and coals were either oxidized to thin ferruginous beds or were replaced by limestone. Most of this oxidation probably took place during the Permo-Triassic and it locally penetrated down Late Carboniferous faults (Mykura 1960*a*).

Offshore west of Scotland and Western Highlands

The Coal Measures are poorly preserved in the offshore area west of Scotland but are known to be present, largely below a Permo-Triassic cover, in the Firth of Clyde. A relatively thin succession, which nevertheless includes both the Vanderbeckei and Aegiranum marine bands and thus all three constituent formations, has been preserved in the Machrihanish Outlier (Fig. 9.1) where it lies disconformably on Passage Formation volcanic rocks. Coals, locally of workable thickness, are present in the cyclical fluviodeltaic Lower and Middle Coal Measures. The Upper Coal Measures are mostly reddened and become more sandy upwards. In Arran attenuated marginal Langsettian and Duckmantian fluvial successions, which lack both coals and marine bands and have been completely oxidized, lie

disconformably on pre-Passage Formation rocks. Here palaeocurrents came mainly from the north (Kirk 1989).

Midland Valley

The thickest and most complete Coal Measures successions in Scotland have been preserved within the Midland Valley (Fig. 9.35). Fault blocks continued to control sedimentation in the west but their influence waned in the central area, where the new Salsburgh Anticline and Falkirk–Stane Syncline developed further. Subsidence was now greatest in the Leven Basin, the Douglas Outlier and southern Ayrshire (Read 1988, fig. 16.13).

Cyclical fluviodeltaic deposits of the Lower Coal Measures succeeded the Early Langsettian sandy braided river deposits of the topmost Passage Formation. The earliest cyclical deposits include sporadic marine incursions and erosively-based fluvial sandstones (Fig. 9.35), whereas later deposits tend to be more argillaceous and contain thick coals but no marine bands. The junction with the Passage Formation is conformable in the north and east, but in the west and south there is a definite break in sedimentation.

In Ayrshire, Passage Formation (Troon Volcanic Member) volcanicity was probably now extinct, but the lava pile it had created remained upstanding. Its northwestern and southeastern flanks were progressively overstepped, but it was not completely covered until late in the Langsettian. The major Caledonian fault blocks continued to be active, with reduced subsidence over the Mid-Ayrshire Block but rapid subsidence in the South Ayrshire Trough and the Littlemill Basin (Fig. 9.36; Mykura 1967; Brand 1983). Rapid subsidence also took place in the Douglas Outlier, where the local base of the Coal Measures is drawn at the Porteous Marine Band. Here the Kennox Fault had recently been active, because the basal Coal Measures overstepped unconformably onto the Upper Limestone Formation on its upthrown southeastern side. In the central area (Central Coalfield) a uniform, initially 'layer-cake,' fluviodeltaic succession, as illustrated in Fig. 9.35, covered the formerly active Kilsyth Trough, Airdrie Block and Carluke Block. Many individual coals may be traced from Glasgow eastwards to Falkirk and westwards into Ayrshire (Forsyth & Brand 1986), suggesting some degree of allocyclic, possibly glacioeustatic, control, as has been suggested for contemporaneous cyclical coal-bearing deposits in the Rhur Coalfield of Germany (Hampson *et al.* 1999). During deposition of the earlier part of the formation cannels and locally oil-shales accumulated in shallow organic-rich water bodies and some of the mature leached palaeosols (seatclays) have been worked as high-alumina refractories.

Subsidence slowed markedly in the Kincardine Basin to the north, which had now ceased to be the most rapidly subsiding onshore basin in Scotland. The succession here thins northwards towards the West Ochil Fault, which must have become inactive because river channels from the northwest, north and northeast flowed right over it. To the east the small Westfield Basin also subsided less rapidly and cyclical Langsettian deposits with relatively thin coals succeeded the anomalously thick coals of the Passage Formation. The Leven Basin now became the most rapidly subsiding basin in Scotland and thicknesses of 220 to 240 m have been recorded in the Lower Coal Measures near its axis below the Firth of Forth. Subsidence was only slightly less rapid in the Midlothian Basin immediately to the south. The successions in both major eastern basins were subject to strong fluvial influences and they include thick coals and thick erosive-based, coarse-grained channel sandstones. Increased explosive volcanicity with some basaltic lavas took place in east Fife and below the Firth of

Forth on the eastern flank of the Leven Basin (Francis & Ewing 1961).

The Middle Coal Measures may originally have spread over a wider area than the Lower Coal Measures, but the complete succession is now preserved largely in synclinal axes. In most areas the extensive marine transgression of the Vanderbeckei Marine Band, that contains a varied fauna, locally including ammonoids, is succeeded by cyclical fluviodeltaic deposits. These are similar to those in the Lower Coal Measures and contain workable coals. Minor marine incursions, which reappeared fairly late in the Duckmantian, culminated in the major transgression of the Aegiranum Marine Band. In some areas the higher deposits have been oxidized.

Major Caledonian faults continued to control subsidence patterns in Ayrshire. The most rapid subsidence continued to be in the south of the South Ayrshire Trough and in the Littlemill Basin where the marine transgressions from the west are also best developed. In late Duckmantian times the Mauchline Basin started to form on the Mid-Ayrshire Block over the site of an earlier high. Sand entered the area of the Mid-Ayrshire Block from the northwest and northeast and then passed southwestwards along the South Ayrshire Trough (Fig. 9.36; Mykura 1967; Read 1988, fig. 16.14). Sandstones became more prominent in the upper part of the formation and the topmost strata have commonly been oxidized (Mykura 1960*a*). Rapid subsidence continued at Douglas where thicknesses of more than 330 m have been recorded (Lumsden & Calver 1958).

The formation is thinner in the central area, where it is best preserved in the southwest and west of the Central Coalfield with only isolated outcrops farther east. The lower part contains thick coals, whereas the upper part contains marine and *Lingula* bands and thick, erosive-based, channel sandstones, including the prominent Shettleston Sandstone (Fig. 9.35a; Forsyth *et al.* 1996). The top of the formation has commonly been oxidized. Many coals can be correlated with those in Ayrshire and the Kincardine Basin (Forsyth & Brand 1986), again suggesting some degree of external control, despite stronger autocyclical fluvial influences than in the Langsettian.

Subsidence continued to slow in the Kincardine Basin, where the succession resembles that in the central area. Here the thick, erosive-based Devon Red Sandstone lies at a similar horizon to the Shettleston Sandstone but is thicker and has been oxidized and reddened. The sandstone is overlain by cyclical fluviodeltaic deposits containing coals and 'musselbands' (Forsyth & Brand 1986). The topmost strata have been oxidized and probably lie not far below the horizon of the Aegiranum Marine Band, which has been eroded away. Moderate subsidence continued in the Westfield Basin, where the Aegiranum horizon seems to have been preserved (Brand *et al.* 1980). More rapid subsidence continued in the Leven Basin, where the formation reaches its maximum thickness of about 350 m, and in the Midlothian Basin. In both of these basins strong fluvial influences continued, thick coals and thick, erosive-based sandstones occur throughout the formation and the upper part of the formation has been oxidized.

The Upper Coal Measures are not widely preserved. The basal Aegiranum Marine Band commonly carries a basinal ammonoid–bivalve fauna and extends over much of Europe. At the beginning of this period Scotland still lay within a low latitude belt of paralic environments that stretched across northern Europe from Ireland to Poland and the Czech Republic (Eagar & van Amerom 1999). However, semi-arid climatic conditions appeared considerably earlier in Scotland than in England and started to encroach southwards as Laurussia moved northwards. Although the Aegiranum transgression may have submerged much of Scotland, only the Shafton

Marine Band (Fig. 9.35a) has been recorded above it within the Midland Valley, where marine influences sharply declined. Cyclical fluviodeltaic 'grey bed' deposits generally followed the Aegiranum transgression but, with the onset of seasonal aridity, coals disappeared, fluvial sedimentation became dominant and the succession passes up into fluvial primary redbeds containing pedogenic calcretes. The top of the formation has been abruptly truncated everywhere by the sub-Permian unconformity. It is particularly difficult to unravel the structural and depositional history because of a lack of marker horizons and reliable borehole sections, plus the subsequent oxidation of fluviodeltaic sediments which were originally laid down as 'grey beds'. Tectonic instability increased progressively and there may be undetected breaks in the preserved successions.

Westphalian D stage deposits may possibly be present in Ayrshire, but the relevant non-marine faunas are difficult to differentiate (Brand 1983). Cyclical fluviodeltaic deposits precede the Shafton (here, formerly the Bogton) Marine Band. They are interspersed with thick, coarse-grained or even pebbly channel sandstones and are succeeded by fluvial deposits including thick, poorly bedded (overbank?) siltstones and mudstones. The topmost deposits included pedogenic calcrete nodules, sand-filled desiccation cracks and angular mudflake breccias, all indicating marked seasonal aridity. To the north of the Kerse Loch Fault all deposits above the Aegiranum Band have been oxidized and reddened, but the lower limit of reddening rises further south.

In the central area the Upper Coal Measures are largely confined to the Uddingston Syncline in the southwest. Some 80 m of cyclical fluviodeltaic deposits with thin coals and thick channel sandstones underlie the Shafton (here, formerly the Bothwell Bridge) Marine Band (Fig. 9.35a). The succeeding strata are mostly oxidised and include cyclical intervals, together with thick erosive-based sandstones and thick, poorly bedded mudstones. To the south, some 270 m of strata have been preserved in the Douglas Outlier where cyclical 'grey-beds' are only locally reddened. The Leven and Midlothian basins initially continued to subside rapidly. Here the horizon of the Aegiranum Marine Band has recently been re-correlated with the Buckhaven Planolites Band that lies some 100 m higher in the succession than the previously accepted horizon (Browne *et al.* 1996). The succession preserved onshore in the Leven Basin is more than 250 m thick. Here massive argillaceous redbeds with impersistent sandstones are overlain by dominantly argillaceous 'grey beds', overlain in turn by 150 m of red sandstone (Francis & Ewing 1961). Basin inversion is known to have taken place here during deposition of the Upper Coal Measures, producing a major intraformational unconformity (Browne & Woodhall 1996). The Upper Coal Measures preserved below the sub-Permian unconformity onshore in the Midlothian Basin are considerably thinner. Seismic reflection surveys indicate that the formation attains its maximum thickness of about 1200 m offshore below the Firth of Forth (Browne *et al.* 1996).

Southern Uplands

Isolated downfaulted outliers preserve relics of what may formerly have been a more extensive, albeit attenuated, Westphalian cover. In the Sanquhar Coalfield almost immediately south of the Southern Upland Fault more than 600 m of Coal Measures, representing depositional environments closely similar to those in the Midland Valley, have been preserved. The discordant base rests disconformably on an attenuated Clackmannan Group and oversteps onto the Ordovician. All three constituent formations are present. Although the major Vanderbeckei transgression is represented by only a *Lingula* band, the Aegiranum transgression carries a varied marine fauna.

More minor transgressions occured during the Early Langsettian, the Late Duckmantian and the Early Bolsovian. Cyclical fluviodeltaic 'grey-beds' characterize the Lower, Middle and basal Upper Coal Measures. Almost all of the workable coals lie in the middle formation, and most of the Upper Coal Measures have been oxidized.

At Thornhill the whole succession is thin and oxidized. It is now known to include Lower, Middle and Upper Coal Measures, but the two lower formations are much thinner than at Sanquhar. The Vanderbeckei transgression is represented by a *Lingula* band and the Aegiranum transgression by foraminifera, *Lingula* and marine trace fossils. Two more Duckmantian *Lingula* bands underlie the Aegiranum horizon but McMillan & Brand (1995) considered it unlikely that an open seaway intermittently crossed the Southern Uplands High. The Lower, Middle and lowest Upper Coal Measures were originally cyclical fluviodeltaic deposits which were subsequently reddened and the coals within them completely oxidized.

Southern Borders

Coal Measures probably originally extended over the Solway and Northumberland basins, but were mostly eroded at the end of the Carboniferous. Only the isolated synclinal Canonbie Outlier at the margin of the Solway Basin has been preserved onshore. Towards the centre of the syncline the Lower Coal Measures may be almost 100 m thick and contain variable coals (Picken 1988), but at outcrop in the north a thin sandy succession overlies an angular basal unconformity. The Vanderbeckei transgression is represented by only a *Lingula* band and the Aegiranum transgression by only a restricted marine fauna. The Middle Coal Measures are about 180 m thick, but the Upper Coal Measures, with a local unconformity at their base (Picken 1988, fig. 2), are no less than 800 m thick, thickening to the south. The former formation consists of normal cyclical fluviodeltaic deposits, including several worked coals. Its top has locally been oxidized. The earliest deposits of the Upper Coal Measures are similar and include no fewer than three marine bands. The last of these has been correlated with the widespread Cambriense Marine Band which represents the last Westphalian marine transgression in Britain. Almost all of the Upper Coal Measures were subsequently oxidized and the formation grades up into red sandstones and poorly bedded silty mudstones with sporadic *Spirorbis* limestones. The *Tenuis* non-marine bivalve zone has been recorded, so Westphalian D strata may have been preserved.

Offshore, east of Scotland

Westphalian sediments probably originally covered a large part of the area between the present east coast of Scotland and the Viking and Central Grabens, with an attenuated succession over the Mid-North Sea High, but most of this cover was eroded before the Permian. All three formations have probably been preserved in a small sub-basin east of Fife Ness (Fig. 9.36), within the larger Forth Approaches Basin. Here the Vanderbeckei transgression is represented by a *Lingula* band (Thomson 1977). To the north a thin Bolsovian black shale has been reported from the Beryl Embayment (Johnson *et al.* 1993) and far to the east a coal-bearing Westphalian succession has been recognized at the southern end of the Central Graben (Gatliffe *et al.* 1994).

Latest Carboniferous Tectonic activity

Most workers have related British latest Carboniferous tectonism to N–S compression which propagated northwards from the Variscides, although Read (1988) suggested an element of right-lateral strike-slip in Scotland. South of the Southern Uplands and the Mid-North Sea High, compressive movements were diachronous from south to north, possibly reflecting the effects of the collapse of the Variscan orogen spreading outwards. Basin inversion took place in Bolsovian and again in Westphalian D to Stephanian times, with NE–SW trending basins being most strongly affected (Corfield *et al.* 1996). However E–W, rather than N–S, compression was dominant in the Northumberland Basin (Chadwick *et al.* 1995) and has also been recognised farther south in England, where Peace & Besley (1997) date it as 'intra-Stephanian.'

In Scotland, which may have been partly shielded from N–S compression by the Southern Uplands and Mid-North Sea highs, E–W compression, associated with right-lateral strike-slip, dominated the first obvious phase of tectonism. Stress systems changed dramatically between the Late Westphalian and the Early Permian and successive tectonic phases overprinted each other, making them difficult to unravel. Basin subsidence and subsequent inversion were both somewhat less in central Scotland than in the Northumberland Trough. Thus Early Namurian sandstones within basinal fills were never buried much deeper than about 2 km in the central Midland Valley and 4 km in the east. A high geothermal gradient related to intermittent Carboniferous igneous activity is known to have existed in the Midland Valley, even before the phase of tholeiitic intrusion described below (Dean, M. T. 1992; Raymond & Murchison 1991).

During the initial phase of E–W compression, N–S and NNE–SSW trending basins, some of which had probably been initiated by E–W tension during the Brigantian or earlier, were formed, including the Clackmannan, Westfield, Leven and Midlothian synclines. This compression was accompanied by right-lateral strike-slip, which was generally most intense along major Caledonian fracture systems thought to be related to deep-seated basement structures, e.g., the Great Glen, Paisley Ruck, Kerse Loch, Dalmellington, Campsie, Kennox–Pentland, East Ochil and Calder–Murieston fault systems (Fig. 9.24). Along the last-named fault, flower structures characteristic of strike-slip movements have been reported by Dentith & Hall (1990). Most of the thin Carboniferous cover on the Highlands, Southern Uplands and Mid-North Sea High was probably stripped off at about this time. The Southern Borders suffered similar compression, also with an element of right-lateral strike-slip. The Solway Basin was folded into a NNE-trending syncline, whilst less intense folding affected the Northumberland Basin.

The second structural phase, which may have followed almost immediately after the first, was marked by basin inversion in response to a brief episode of N–S compression, detectable in the Clackmannan Syncline (Rippon *et al.* 1996, fig. 8a). Some basin inversion also occurred in the first structural phase. The Solway Basin was strongly inverted so that, after subsequent latest Carboniferous erosion, only the Canonbie Outlier and its subsurface extension survived onshore (Chadwick *et al.* 1995). Inversion, followed by intense erosion, also took place in the Northumberland Basin and offshore east of Scotland in the vicinity of the Central Graben (Gatliff *et al.* 1994).

The third structural phase was dominated by N–S tension. This regime created or enhanced the numerous E–W normal faults within the Midland Valley (Read 1988, fig. 16.3), some of which may have been initiated during the Namurian or even earlier (Francis & Walker 1987; Rippon 1998). During, or shortly after the faulting, a brief but intense phase of tholeiitic intrusion affected much of Scotland, northern England, the adjacent offshore areas, and extended as far east as Scandinavia. This produced the Midland Valley Sill-complex (see below), which changed its horizon along dyke-like bodies, some of which followed pre-existing E–W tensional faults (Read 1959).

The fourth and final structural phase, which probably dates from the Early Permian, was marked by a change in the direction of regional tension that gave rise to a series of NNW–SSE aligned extensional basins. These include the Mauchline, Stranraer, Dumfries and Lochmaben basins onshore and the Northeast Arran Trough offshore (Figs 9.1, 9.24). The Permian alkali basaltic lavas of Ayrshire (see below) are related to this fourth structural phase. This new stress system may have reflected southward propagation of the Norwegian–Greenland Sea rift system, as postulated by Ziegler (1990*a*). Contemporaneous rifting and magmatism took place in the Central Graben of the North Sea and the Oslo Graben.

Mid-Brigantian to Westphalian igneous activity

The stratigraphical ranges of Carboniferous volcanic rocks in this part of the succession in various parts of Scotland are illustrated in Fig. 9.8 and their geographical variations are described below from west to east.

Outcrops of Silesian volcanic rocks within the Midland Valley, Southern Uplands and Southern Borders are shown in Fig. 9.19. In the west of the Midland Valley, phreatomagmatic activity from numerous short-lived local volcanic centres is recorded in the early Namurian of north Ayrshire, especially in the area around Dalry. More extensive eruptions, almost exclusively of subaerial basalt lavas, took place in the later Namurian and may have continued into the Early Westphalian (Fig. 9.8). These lavas, within the Passage Formation, belong to the Troon Volcanic Member (see above), which extends beneath the Coal Measures of most of the Ayrshire region. Thinner representatives of these eruptions occur on Arran, in Kintyre, near Stranraer and possibly in Northern Ireland. Their most notable feature throughout the outcrop is their decomposition as a result of deep *in situ* tropical weathering.

In the central Midland Valley volcanic activity was restricted to the vicinity of the Bathgate Hills and Burntisland by the Late Viséan (Fig. 9.8). In the former area it persisted until the Mid-Namurian, accumulating a total thickness of about 600 m of volcanic rocks (Smith *et al.* 1994; Cameron *et al.* 1998). Here, the upper parts of the Bathgate Hills Volcanic Formation consist of dominantly basalt lavas at outcrop, but thick proximal pyroclastic rocks in boreholes to the west suggest the presence of a major eruptive centre. Intercalated marine limestones, coals and seat-rocks of the Lower Limestone, Limestone Coal and Upper Limestone formations indicate that subsidence kept pace with accumulation close to sea-level and that there were episodic marine incursions. The presence of boles indicates subaerial weathering and the volcanoes probably built up islands with fringing reefs (Jameson 1987) and anoxic back-reef lagoons in which synsedimentary Pb–Zn mineralization formed (Stephenson 1983).

To the NNE of the Bathgate Hills, thick tuffs, volcaniclastic sedimentary rocks and rare basalt lavas occur in the Limestone Coal and Upper Limestone formations around the Saline Hills (Francis 1961*a*). This volcanism was centred upon the high east of the Bo'ness Line (Read 1988) where several necks have been recognized (Francis 1957, 1959; Barnett 1985).

Farther east, bedded tuffs provide evidence of phreatomagmatic activity at numerous volcanic centres throughout the

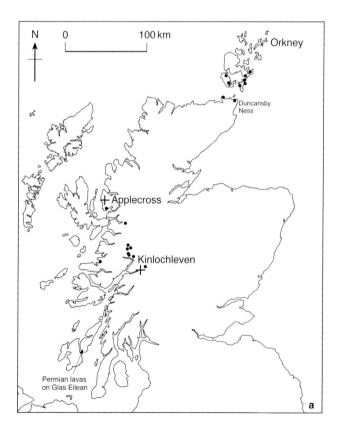

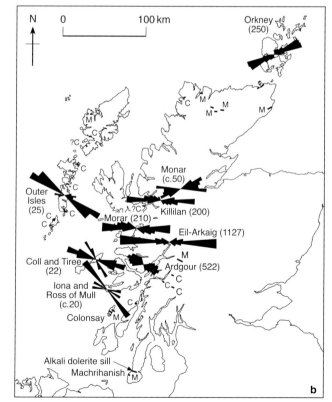

Fig. 9.37. (**a**) Map showing the location of plugs and vents of Carboniferous to Early Permian age in the Highlands. The Permian lavas of Glas Eilean are also indicated. After Rock (1983). (**b**) Map showing the location and azimuth distribution of the main alkaline lamprophyre (camptonite and monchiquite) dyke swarms of the Northern Highlands. Azimuth distributions are presented as total percentage of dykes in each swarm with a particular orientation; thus long arms indicate swarms trending more uniformly than short ones. The number of dykes recorded in each swarm is shown in brackets. Isolated occurrences of monchiquite and camptonite are shown by M and C, respectively. After Rock (1983).

Silesian. Onshore outcrops are restricted to Namurian strata around the former Westfield opencast site in central Fife, where there are basaltic pillow lavas and hyaloclastites, and around large complex necks at Largo Law and Rires in East Fife (Figs 9.8, 9.19). However, offshore boreholes in the Firth of Forth have revealed pyroclastic rocks and rare lavas extending into the Middle Coal Measures (Wellesley Volcanic Member). East Fife is renowned for the presence of over a hundred volcanic necks (Figs 9.19, 9.38; Forsyth & Chisholm 1977), including the Kinkell Ness Neck containing the 'Rock and Spindle' (Plate 18). The necks cut strata ranging from Late Viséan to Duckmantian and radiometric dates suggest a Namurian to Westphalian age for most (Forsyth & Rundle 1978; De Souza 1979; Macintyre *et al.* 1981), although some are within a range of 295–288 Ma, close to the Stephanian–Permian boundary (Fig. 9.8; Wallis 1989).

Permian igneous activity

It is appropriate to consider Permian volcanism here in the context of preceding Carboniferous activity. This is particularly so in view of on-going debate as to the precise date of the Carboniferous–Permian boundary. Dates should be compared with the Carboniferous timescales of Menning *et al.* (2001) in which the top of the Carboniferous is placed at 299 Ma (see Fig. 9.8), considerably older than 290 Ma as in the timescale of Gradstein & Ogg (1996). Some of the magmatism may accordingly be assigned to either a latest Carboniferous or earliest Permian age. Further details of Permian volcanism are given in Chapter 10.

Overall, the Early Permian saw a significant change in the regional stress pattern affecting northern Britain. Although many of the Permo-Triassic basins of offshore Scotland follow possibly inherited Caledonian NE–SW trends (Anderson *et al.* 1995), they are cut by NNW–SSE rifting (see above) that was to provide a major control, not only on sedimentation but also on the distribution of volcanism. The westernmost 'rift', just off the southwest coast of Scotland and tangential to the Ulster coastline, contains 616 m of basaltic lavas and tuffs (Penn *et al.* 1983). Farther east is the Islay–Machrihanish–Stranraer lineament, marked onshore mainly by fault-controlled basins of Permian sedimentary rocks. Between Islay and Jura, one such narrow half-graben that cross-cuts the Dalradian, includes the 120 m-thick Glas Eilean lava succession erupted from an isolated volcano at *c.* 285 Ma (Fig. 9.37a; Upton *et al.* 1987). Farther NNW along the same lineament are small sub-silicic alkaline dykes of Permian age on Colonsay and Mull (Upton *et al.* 1998). Basaltic lavas and thin tuffs on Arran, somewhat to the east of the lineament, appear to be at the base of the Permian succession.

In the next rifted zone to the east, lavas are preserved in the Mauchline, Sanquhar and Thornhill areas. The most extensive outcrop is in the Mauchline Basin, where the volcanic succession is 238 m thick and includes highly silica-undersaturated lavas (basanites and olivine nephelinites). The volcanic rocks rest unconformably upon Upper Coal Measures and are interbedded with characteristic aeolian and fluvial sandstones. Plants, radiometric dates and palaeomagnetism suggest an Early Permian age (Wagner 1983; De Souza 1979, 1982; Harcombe-Smee *et al.* 1996). Over sixty necks are known, mostly within a 20 to 30 km radius of the Mauchline Basin (Fig. 9.19). Many contain wind-rounded sand grains and blocks of sandstones similar to those interbedded in the lava sequence. Also intrusions within the necks are predominantly silica-undersaturated, including olivine analcimite, monchiquite, camptonite and alkali dolerite, with petrological affinities to the lavas. Lava sequences less

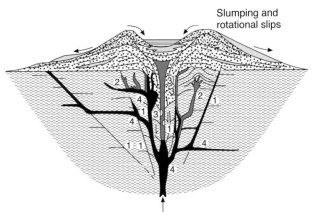

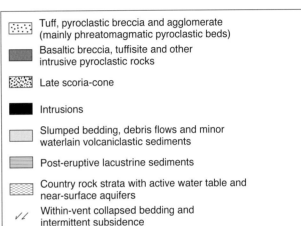

	Tuff, pyroclastic breccia and agglomerate (mainly phreatomagmatic pyroclastic beds)
	Basaltic breccia, tuffisite and other intrusive pyroclastic rocks
	Late scoria-cone
	Intrusions
	Slumped bedding, debris flows and minor waterlain volcaniclastic sediments
	Post-eruptive lacustrine sediments
	Country rock strata with active water table and near-surface aquifers
	Within-vent collapsed bedding and intermittent subsidence

Fig. 9.38. Schematic cross-section through an evolving tuff-ring, illustrating some of the volcanic processes thought to have been involved in the emplacement of the East Fife volcanic necks. From Williamson in Stephenson *et al.* (in press), and based on Francis (1970), Lorenz (1973, 1986) and Godchaux *et al.* (1992).

Features marked on the diagram: (1) Ring faults with marginal tuffisite and breccia, or basaltic dykes (2) Tuffisite within country rock – may develop adjacent to sills or dykes. (3) Large foundered bodies of country rock within vent and entrained within breccias and tuffisite. (4) Minor intrusions emplaced along bedding and fault planes.

than 50 m thick, with petrological affinities to the Mauchline lavas, occur in the Sanquhar and Thornhill basins.

The north-eastern extrapolation of the Southern Upland Fault in East Lothian seems to have controlled Viséan volcanism (Fig. 9.19). A number of analcime-dolerite and basanite sills also occur in the vicinity of this lineament, including those of Fidra and the Isle of May, and several nearby necks are intruded by basanite or various foidites. Equivocal radiometric dates (Wallis 1989) suggest an Early Permian rejuvenation of activity along this zone of weakness.

The principal magmatic foci in the Carboniferous and Permian lay in south and central Scotland (Fig. 9.19). However, there are some small subvolcanic necks in the Highlands and Islands (Figs 9.37a), composed largely of explosion breccia, but characterized by the presence of monchiquitic rocks (Rock 1983). Hence, these diatremes may owe their existence to explosive degassing of the volatile-rich magmas that were also responsible for the Late Carboniferous to Permian lamprophyric dyke swarms of the Northern Highlands and Orkney (Fig. 9.37b), described below. Nine necks define a NW-trending lineament between Kinlochleven and Applecross, and others form a cluster around southeast Orkney. The latter includes the Duncansby Ness Vent, dated by MacIntyre *et al.* (1981) at 270 Ma.

Offshore east of Scotland, subaerial basaltic lavas of Permian age have been reported from the Central North Sea Graben (Dixon *et al.* 1981) and from the edge of the Magnus Trough north of Shetland (Hitchen & Ritchie 1987). Further details are given in Chapter 10.

Carboniferous–Permian igneous processes and their evolution

Structural control of igneous activity

It is inferred that the relatively rapid onset of widespread and voluminous igneous activity in the Dinantian was a result of significant lithospheric attenuation, whereas the subsequent Silesian–Permian activity was related to smaller-scale lithospheric re-adjustments. These extensional events permitted partial melting in the underlying mantle. Although most of the transitional to strongly alkaline magmatism resulted from relatively small degree mantle melting, the Stephanian tholeiitic event marked a much larger-scale melting episode, which is discussed more fully below.

The ascent of magma was probably controlled by planes of weakness in the deep crust that gave rise to faulting at higher levels and volcanic lineaments at the surface. These lineaments, defined by elongate outcrops, chains of plugs and/or diatremes and rarely by dyke swarms, are particularly well developed in the Dinantian and generally display SW–NE to WSW–ENE trends that reflect a Caledonian fabric in the basement. The Birrenswark and Kelso lavas (Figs 9.8, 9.19) were probably erupted from a series of small volcanoes sited along south-facing fault-scarps and monoclines related to initiation of the Solway, Northumberland and Tweed basins.

In the Midland Valley, there is no evidence of volcanism directly associated with the Highland Boundary Fault and the most northwesterly activity is concentrated within a 2 to 3 km wide zone that extends ENE for some 27 km, from Dumbarton towards Stirling (Fig. 9.22). The North Campsie Linear Vent System lies at the northeastern end of this zone. Most of the lavas lie south of it, suggesting that higher ground limited their northwards extension. Two slightly younger linear vent systems form separate en echelon lines within the Campsie lava block to the southeast (Forsyth *et al.* 1996). On the south side of the Campsie Block, the South Campsie Linear Vent System forms a 15 km-long lineament close to the East Campsie Fault (Craig & Hall 1975; Forsyth *et al.* 1996). Other local lineaments are aligned WNW–ESE to NW–SE and may reflect less extensive conjugate Caledonian fractures. Notable examples occur at each end of the Kilpatrick Hills, where their extrusive products may have acted as barriers between adjacent lava fields (Hall *et al.* 1998).

Other WSW–ENE to nearly W–E trending faults throughout the Midland Valley that may have been utilized by rising magmas also probably formed active escarpments controlling local accumulations of lava. Consequently they are commonly marked by significant changes in thickness of the volcanic piles (see above). These faults include the Paisley Ruck, Dusk Water and Inchgotrick faults in Ayrshire (McLean 1966; Hall 1974; Rollin in Monro 1999), as well as the Campsie and Ochil faults (Figs 9.19, 9.24; Rippon *et al.* 1996). At the southeastern limit of the Midland Valley, the northeastern extrapolation of the main Southern Upland Fault, together with NE-trending splays to the southeast, are thought to pass beneath Carboniferous strata (Max 1976; Floyd 1994) and to have controlled the rise of magma throughout much of the Carboniferous (Upton 1982).

The Caledonian structural influence became less obvious in the Silesian when rapidly subsiding basins developed in the Midland Valley (Fig. 9.24). The margins of these basins were controlled in some instances by Caledonian features, such as the fault-bounded NE–SW tectonic high now represented by the Pentland Hills and by other Lower Old Red Sandstone volcanic piles such as that of the Ochils (Fig. 9.21). However, the substantial lava piles built up during the Dinantian were themselves now also exerting a strong control on basin development. Locally, large intrusions, assumed to be contemporaneous with the volcanism, may also have influenced the sub-basin topography. Probably the best example is represented by the Bathgate gravity and magnetic anomalies, now thought to be caused by up to 1 km of Dinantian and Namurian volcanic rocks intruded in their lower part by a large basic mass extending to a depth of about 8 km (Rollin in Cameron *et al.* 1998; and see Chapter 1, fig. 1.11).

Many Silesian basins developed along N–S or NNE–SSW axes and contemporaneous volcanism was located along hinge lines such as the Bo'ness Line on the eastern edge of the Kincardine Basin (Read 1988). Many of the well-established NE- to ENE-trending faults continued to be active and had a local influence. Thus the Troon Volcanic Member shows marked changes in thickness across the Dusk Water and Inchgotrick faults (Monro 1999) and the Ardross Fault in East Fife is a classic example of alignment of vents along a fault (Francis & Hopgood 1970). This fault is associated with right-lateral strike-slip movement and local folding (Plate 17) prior to the emplacement of the necks. The northeastern extension of the Southern Upland Fault also continued to influence the siting of intrusions, particularly analcime-dolerite sills.

During the Early Permian the most obvious structural controls were the newly developed NNW–SSE half-grabens, commonly on the site of Late Carboniferous basins, and still reflecting conjugate sets of Caledonian fractures (Anderson *et al.* 1995). However, some basins such as Mauchline, have no strong alignment with little sign of Caledonian trends. Here E–W orientated dykes suggest a continuation of the N–S tension that was responsible for the emplacement of the tholeiitic magmas in the Stephanian (Rippon *et al.* 1996).

Styles of eruption

The earliest Carboniferous eruptions in the south of Scotland and the Midland Valley, took place on low-lying semi-arid floodplains, with outwash fans and playa lakes, that graded locally into deltas, coastal plains and shallow marine environments (see above). The explosive interaction of magma with surface and ground water resulted initially in phreatomagmatic eruptions. In East Lothian, abundant small vent structures and bedded pyroclastic rocks, with base-surge and ash-fall characteristics, are interbedded with the sedimentary succession, and suggest the development of tuff-rings, probably less than 1 km in diameter (Fig. 9.38). Lacustrine sedimentary rocks in some of the vents suggest the presence of crater lakes (maars).

The plains were divided initially by NE–SW trending ridges and escarpments formed from pre-Carboniferous rocks but, with a rise in magma productivity, the eruptions built up undulating composite lava fields such as those of the Clyde Plateau and the Garleton Hills that formed long-lasting topographic highs (Fig. 9.13b). In such areas, eruptions were almost entirely subaerial and lavas were usually of aa type, though rare pahoehoe features have also been reported. Flow surfaces are rarely preserved and thick red-brown lateritic boles occur on the tops of most flows, marking tropical or subtropical weathering during significant interludes of quiescence between eruptions.

Basaltic to mugearitic lavas, typically between 5 and 30 m thick, were erupted through relatively small shield volcanoes and cinder cones that commonly coalesced along the NE-trending lineaments described above. These lineaments are marked by upstanding plugs, by volcanic necks and by thick accumulations of coarse, proximal pyroclastic rocks (Fig. 9.22). However, more laterally extensive flows can be traced for more than 6 km in the escarpment of the Gargunnock Hills, where such features are absent (Fig. 9.19; Francis *et al.* 1970), suggesting eruption from fissures. Regional dyke swarms that may have acted as feeders to the fissure eruptions are not obvious, except possibly between the Renfrewshire Hills and south Bute (Paterson *et al.* 1990). Despite their apparent rarity at current erosion levels, it is possible that dyke-like feeders are more abundant in the deeper crust. Outwith the major lava fields, individual volcanoes, such as Arthur's Seat (Fig. 9.20) and the Heads of Ayr were possibly up to 5 km in diameter and rose to heights of about 1000 m above the plains (Whyte 1964; Black 1966).

More-evolved lava compositions are locally common in the Dinantian lava fields. The abundance of trachytic extrusive rocks in the southwestern outcrop of the Clyde Plateau Volcanic Formation between Greenock and Strathaven implies that higher stratovolcanoes may have developed in this region (MacPherson *et al.* 2001). The best documented is the 8 km wide Misty Law Trachytic Centre in the Renfrewshire Hills, which comprises trachytic pyroclastic rocks, massive lavas of trachyte and rhyolite and trachytic plugs and necks (Johnstone 1965; Stephenson in Paterson *et al.* 1990). Trachyte lavas are also abundant in the upper parts of the Garleton Hills and Machrihanish successions, and rhyolites occur locally in the upper part of the succession in the western Campsie Fells and near the base of the succession in the Cleish Hills. Flow banding in many of these evolved lavas indicates viscous flows, which probably never extended more than a few kilometres from their source and may even have formed steep-sided lava domes.

Calderas may have developed over some of the principal salic centres and the thick trachyte lavas forming the Garleton Hills of East Lothian may have been ponded in a caldera. However, the best-documented evidence occurs in the Waterhead Volcanic Complex of the Campsie Fells (Craig 1980; Forsyth *et al.* 1996). Here, a large multiple neck and several smaller necks, plugged by a wide variety of rock types, occur within an oval ring-fault 2 km by 2.5 km (Fig. 9.22). The complex is underlain by a positive gravity anomaly (Cotton 1968) and the enclosed basic lavas show intense brecciation and hydrothermal alteration and are intruded by a variety of dykes (MacDonald 1973). Some of the dykes are salic, and trachytic pyroclastic rocks in the adjacent tephra cone of Meikle Bin have been attributed to the centre, although there are no salic lavas preserved. Despite the abundance of salic volcanic rocks and the inferred presence of calderas in some areas, there is little evidence for the pyroclastic flows that are typical of such activity elsewhere.

In the West Lothian Oil-shale Basin, the land surface remained close to sea-level during the Dinantian and similar conditions prevailed during most of the Silesian throughout the eastern Midland Valley (see above). Relatively small basaltic volcanoes erupted onto coastal plains with lagoons and into shallow seas, locally building volcanic islands fringed by reefs that were periodically eroded and submerged. Initial eruptions were explosive (phreatomagmatic), leading to widespread pyroclastic deposits, but later eruptions in any one area were dominantly of subaerial lavas. Pillow lavas and hyaloclastites at Kinghorn and Westfield testify to subaqueous eruptions, but most of the lavas were probably subaerial.

The morphology of the Fife volcanoes has been studied in great detail (e.g. Francis 1970, 1991*b*; Francis & Hopgood 1970; Forsyth & Chisholm 1977). The volcanic necks of east Fife (Plate 18) are exposed at a deeper structural level than the earlier vents of East Lothian and their surrounding proximal products have been eroded away. However, various stages in the evolution of the volcanoes are preserved. Initial stages involved updoming with associated radial and concentric fracturing, followed by gas-fluxioning and wall-rock stoping. Intrusive tuffisites were commonly injected along the fractures and small 'cryptovolcanic' structures, representative of this stage, are particularly common. Larger necks have the form of funnel-shaped tuff pipes, containing masses of proximal bedded pyroclastic rocks, together with blocks and comminuted debris of sedimentary wallrock, all with dominant inward dips (Fig. 9.38). Included plant fragments demonstrate that this material accumulated on the surface and attained its present position due to inward collapse of the surface cones and post-eruptive subsidence along ring-faults. The lithologies and textures of the pyroclastic rocks provide classic illustrations of the interaction of magma with wet sediments or groundwater to give phreatomagmatic eruptions that formed tuff-rings and maar-type shallow cones. Farther afield, bedded tuffs, assumed to be contemporaneous, are indicative of ash-fall into shallow water. Later conduits within the necks were filled by basaltic magma giving rise to plugs, dykes and irregular intrusions (Plate 18).

Compositional variation

In south and central Scotland the Dinantian activity mainly involved transitional to mildly alkalic basalt and hawaiite magmas, characterized by relatively small amounts of normative hypersthene or nepheline. Basanites (basalts with >5% normative nepheline) are largely confined to the Silesian and Permian. Basalts with some tholeiitic affinity are recognized among the Tournaisian Birrenswark and Kelso lavas, and low-K tholeiitic basalts occur in the Viséan at Machrihanish (Macdonald 1975). Subsequently tholeiitic magmas were intruded in copious quantities during the Stephanian.

The basic lavas are almost invariably porphyritic to varying degrees. This feature was utilized by MacGregor (1928) to devise a nomenclature based in part on phenocryst size (microporphyritic or macroporphyritic) and in part on the phenocryst assemblages (olivine + clinopyroxene, olivine + clinopyroxene + plagioclase, plagioclase ± olivine). This scheme (Francis 1991*b*, table 11.1) was widely used for many years as a convenient 'shorthand' way of representing the wide range of petrographical types that are distinctive in the field and hence formed mappable units. It also enabled lavas such as the feldspar-phyric 'Markle' and 'Jedburgh' types, which commonly range in composition from basalt to hawaiite, to be assigned a name without the need for chemical analysis. However, the scheme has now fallen into disuse in favour of less parochial descriptions.

In the Dinantian, basic magmas were commonly accompanied by lesser amounts of more differentiated associates including mugearites, benmoreites, trachytes and rhyolites. Although there is a notable compositional continuity from basic to salic components, supporting the contention that the series was related by crystal-liquid fractionation (Macdonald 1975), there is a maximum volume in the basalt to hawaiite range. Many rocks of intermediate composition have also been described as trachybasalt and trachyandesite, but do not differ significantly from the intermediate composition mugearites and benmoreites of other areas in whole-rock K/Na ratio (Macdonald 1975). Some flows of trachybasalt in East Lothian appear to have contained leucite that was subsequently pseudomorphed by analcime. Apart from one other flow in the Campsie Fells which is phonolitic (Forsyth *et al.* 1996), these are the only known silica-undersaturated evolved lavas in the Dinantian. Trachytes, quartz-trachytes and comenditic rhyolites occur as sills or laccoliths in the Dinantian Eildon Hills complex in the Scottish Borders near Melrose (see above). Phonolitic trachytes are found as plugs or laccoliths in the Dunlop–Eaglesham–Strathaven uplands (e.g. Loudoun Hill), in the Campsie Fells at Fintry and in East Lothian (e.g. North Berwick Law, Traprain Law and Bass Rock). Production of salic extrusive rocks and intrusions was confined to the Dinantian activity and was related to the growth of large central-type volcanoes, underlain by substantial magma chambers.

The Silesian and Permian alkali basaltic magma batches were volumetrically small and significant differentiates are rare, although late-stage pegmatoidal veins occur in the thicker alkali dolerite sills, as exemplified by veins of kaersutite- and/or titanaugite-rich nephelinolite ('lugarite') in the Lugar Sill (Henderson & Gibb 1987; Francis 1991*b*, fig. 11.13). Similarly the thick Stephanian quartz-dolerite sills contain *in situ* granophyric differentiates, but there are no separate and discrete salic associates.

More compositionally extreme K-rich lamprophyric magmas characterized many of the Carboniferous and Permian dykes of the Highlands and Hebrides (Fig. 9.37b). Some are spectacularly porphyritic as, for example, the biotite-rich analcime monchiquite of the Kilchatten Dyke on Colonsay (Upton, in Stephenson *et al.* in press). Some of the monchiquitic dykes of Orkney are very primitive olivine melanephelinites (Upton *et al.* 1992).

Alkaline basic sill-complexes and regional dyke swarms

Subvolcanic minor intrusions, such as plugs, dykes and sills, form an integral part of all eruptive centres and a genetic association is usually clear from close geographical links and petrological similarities. More extensive sill-complexes and regional dyke swarms, representing voluminous injections of alkaline basic magma, are also widespread in parts of Scotland (Fig. 9.39; Dunham & Strasser-King 1982; Stephenson, in press). Some may well be contemporaneous with local extrusive events, but others occur well outside known volcanic fields or are demonstrably younger than any local volcanic rocks.

Most of the alkaline sill-complexes are of Namurian or younger age and hence post-date the voluminous outpourings of lava that occurred during the Viséan (Fig. 9.8). They are, however, coeval with intermittent, more localized volcanic events that continued until the Early Permian. Francis (1968) argued that the increasing thicknesses of sediments in the rapidly developing Silesian basins of the Midland Valley were of too low density to support columns of magma. Being unable to rise to the surface, the magmas spread laterally to form sills (Francis 1991*b*). Associated dyke swarms of alkaline basic rocks are not recognized in the Midland Valley, except in the Ayrshire Basin. In contrast, in the more competent 'basement' rocks of the NW Highlands, and to a much lesser extent in those of the Southern Uplands, there are several alkaline basic dyke swarms but no basic sills (Fig. 9.37).

From a detailed study of Namurian sills in western and central Fife, Francis & Walker (1987) concluded that magma had flowed down bedding planes that were already dipping inwards at up to 5° at the time of intrusion (see Francis 1991*b*, fig. 11.8). Magma accumulated in the bottoms of the basins and in some cases flowed up dip on the opposite side, due to hydrostatic pressure. In this respect the model is similar to that proposed by Francis (1982) for the later tholeiitic sill-complex.

However, whereas the tholeiitic magmas rose along dykes that extended above the sills and hence provided the head of magma, there are no dykes associated with most of the alkali sills. Instead, there is a close geographical and petrological association with volcanic necks that mark the sites of conduits for surface eruptions. Francis & Walker (1987) suggested that it was degassed magma in the volcanic pipes that provided the feeders for the alkali sills, bursting out along radial and concentric minor fractures to flow down dip when the pipes became plugged following an eruption.

Most of the Silesian volcanism was phreatomagmatic, driven by the interaction of magma with water within the sedimentary pile (see above). The effects of this interaction are well exhibited at the advancing edges of some sills, where peperitic textures occur. The contact effects are particularly dramatic where sills have been emplaced along planes of weakness created by seams of wet lignite, now coal (Mykura 1967; Walker & Francis 1987). The dolerite is commonly altered to 'white trap' (see below) and productive coal seams may be totally replaced or coked.

The sills and dykes (Fig. 9.39) are mostly varieties of alkali basalt, dolerite or gabbro, with some basanites, foidites and alkali lamprophyres. More-fractionated rocks occur only as minor segregations in otherwise basic sills. The basic rocks exhibit a remarkable range of mineralogy and textures and nomenclature has been simplified here following Cameron & Stephenson (1985) and Le Maitre (1989). The following groups of related lithologies may be recognized:

(a) olivine-dolerite, basalt and basanite, mildly silica-undersaturated, but with no modal nepheline and little analcime. These are commonly microporphyritic (olivine ± augite), resembling local basaltic lavas of the former 'Dalmeny type';

(b) more-strongly silica-undersaturated basic rocks with modal nepheline and/or analcime. These include analcime-dolerite/gabbro (formerly 'teschenite'), nepheline-dolerite/gabbro (formerly 'theralite') and nepheline-monzogabbro (formerly 'essexite'), together with olivine-rich (picritic) variants;

(c) strongly silica-undersaturated, highly alkaline, feldspar-poor or feldspar-free rocks, mostly fine-grained basanite, foidites and alkaline lamprophyres (all formerly classified as 'monchiquitic' types). Typically they comprise phenocrysts of olivine and augite in a mesostasis of glass, analcime or nepheline and are best termed olivine analcimite and olivine nephelinite. With increasing groundmass feldspar they grade into analcime basanite, nepheline basanite and, rarely, leucite basanite. Rock types of this group tend to occur in thinner sills, seldom more than 2 m thick, and in dyke swarms.

However, some olivine-bearing dolerites defy classification, particularly where they have suffered alteration. Some have residual analcime and many have secondary quartz, whereas primary quartz and other petrographical features in a few sills suggest possible affinities with the latest Carboniferous tholeiitic intrusive suite.

More general alteration, affecting all the basic intrusions, is particularly intense close to fault planes and adjacent to sedimentary rocks that were probably saturated with water at the time of intrusion. Zones of 'white trap', in which the normal rock is transformed into a pale cream or yellowish brown alteration product, are common. The primary igneous texture is usually preserved, but the constituent minerals are pseudomorphs, comprising kaolinite, chlorite, leucoxene, amorphous silica and carbonate minerals. 'White trap', commonly containing solid

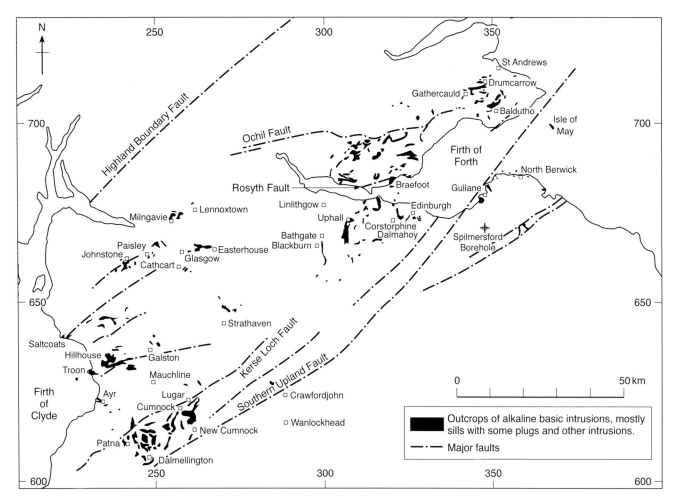

Fig. 9.39. Map showing the main outcrops of alkaline basic intrusions, mostly sills, of Carboniferous and Early Permian age in the Midland Valley. After Cameron & Stephenson (1985).

or viscous hydrocarbons on joint surfaces, is particularly widespread in dolerites that are associated with carbonaceous mudstones, coals or oil-shales. It has been suggested that the alteration was caused by volatiles released during the distillation of such rocks by heat from the intrusions (Mykura 1965).

Highlands and Islands
Rock (1983) divided the numerous dykes of alkaline lamprophyre (camptonite and monchiquite), with subordinate foidite, basanite and basalt that are in the Highlands into nine swarms (Fig. 9.37b). K–Ar radiometric dates appeared to confirm a late Carboniferous to Permian age for most of the dykes and Baxter & Mitchell (1984) suggested that they represent three tectonomagmatic events, as follows:

(a)   ?late Viséan (*c.* 326 Ma, measured on E–W trending dykes, dominant in the central part of the Northern Highlands). A comparable date for these swarms was obtained by palaeomagnetic measurements (Esang & Piper 1984);
(b)   late Stephanian to Early Permian (*c.* 290 Ma, measured on NW–SE dykes, dominant in the western and south-western Highlands and Islands). A NNW-trending dyke on Mull has yielded an Ar–Ar age of 268 ± 2 Ma (Upton *et al.* 1998);
(c)   Late Permian (*c.* 250 Ma, measured on the WSW–ENE Orkney Swarm).

Criteria for distinguishing the dykes of various ages were listed by Rock (1983), but the correlation of trend with age,

although broadly applicable, cannot be applied to individual dykes (Morrison *et al.* 1987).

Collectively, these dykes are the most silica-undersaturated, and the most primitive suite of basic igneous rocks recorded anywhere in Britain. They are an important source of information on Late Viséan to Permian magma genesis and the nature of the upper mantle over a far wider area than that sampled by the more voluminous magmatism of the Midland Valley of Scotland (Baxter 1987; Upton *et al.* 1992). They commonly contain xenoliths and xenocrysts derived from upper mantle and lower crustal sources (Praegel 1981; Upton *et al.* 1983, 1998) and, together with the coeval volcanic necks, are the most prolific source of such material (see below).

Western Midland Valley
In Ayrshire, most of the transitional to mildly silica-undersaturated olivine-dolerites have a petrographical and spatial association with the Troon Volcanic Member and cut rocks only of that member and older; thus they are probably Namurian in age. The more-strongly silica-undersaturated dolerites, basanites and foidites (former 'teschenitic', 'kylitic' and 'monchiquitic' types) cut Coal Measures, but none cut the Early Permian Mauchline Sandstone Formation. Accordingly, they may be slightly older than, or broadly coeval with, the Early Permian volcanism. An ^{40}Ar–^{39}Ar age of 288 ± 6 Ma has been obtained from the Lugar Sill (Henderson *et al.* 1987). Palaeomagnetic data on some of the sills also support a Permian age (Armstrong 1957).

A few of the sills have been studied in detail, especially those of Saltcoats and Lugar and these composite intrusions have acquired international recognition. The observed ranges in lithology have been variously attributed to differentiation *in situ* aided by gravitational settling of crystals; to multiple injections of magma; to enrichment in residual liquid and volatiles; or to some combination of these (Henderson & Gibb 1987).

Numerous dykes of alkali dolerite and basalt, with a variety of trends, are exposed in coastal sections of Ayrshire and were recorded in underground workings. They are clearly younger than the Coal Measures and some must be late Westphalian to Early Permian. However, few have sufficient analcime or nepheline to compare with the 'teschenitic' sills, and many are certainly members of the extensive Palaeogene dyke swarms that cross the area. Hence it is seldom possible to assign an age to an individual dyke with any confidence.

In the Glasgow–Paisley area, four major 'teschenitic' sill-complexes, some consisting of up to three leaves and up to 80 m thick, can be traced over wide areas (Hall *et al.* 1998). They are probably linked to the Early Permian volcanism of Ayrshire. Two plug-like intrusions, close to the Campsie Fault at Lennoxtown, of similar age are of a distinctive augite-phyric nepheline-monzogabbro.

Eastern Midland Valley

Major alkali dolerite sills are widespread throughout Fife and the Lothians (Fig. 9.39), where there are also numerous minor intrusions associated with the local volcanic centres. In the Lothians, the major sills cut strata as low as the Ballagan Formation and extend up to the Lower Limestone Formation, whereas in west and central Fife they extend up to the Upper Limestone Formation. They are not present in the overlying Passage Formation, nor in the Coal Measures and it has been suggested therefore that they are of Late Viséan to Namurian age, contemporaneous with volcanism at Burntisland, the Bathgate Hills and western Fife. Some individual sills and the marginal facies of others are of olivine-microphyric basalt or basanite, with strong petrographical and geochemical similarities to the local lavas (e.g. Walker 1986). However, many of the thicker sills are of analcime-dolerite ('teschenite') which is more silica-undersaturated and may form a separate, slightly later group which, however, pre-dates the latest Carboniferous tholeiitic dyke swarm. The Salisbury Crags Sill in Holyrood Park, Edinburgh provides a well known, and historic, example (Plate 19; Fig. 9.20).

In west and central Fife, a major sill-complex extends over 750 km^2 and has a total volume of 7.25 km^3 (Francis & Walker 1987; Walker & Francis 1987). Correlation of the many individual leaves has defined nine component sills, some of which may originally have been joined. Walker (1986) also recognized at least three separate pulses of magma injection based on distinctive geochemical signatures. The Braefoot Outer Sill, in the same area but intruded into lower, Viséan strata, is noted for its layered structure attributable to gravitational sinking of olivine, a pegmatitic facies and well-developed chilled margins. Radiometric dates from Lothian and east Fife sills generally appear to confirm a Late Viséan to Westphalian age, but some of the former are earlier (A. A. Monaghan, pers. comm.) and some of the latter may be Early Permian (see Stephenson *et al.* in press for summary).

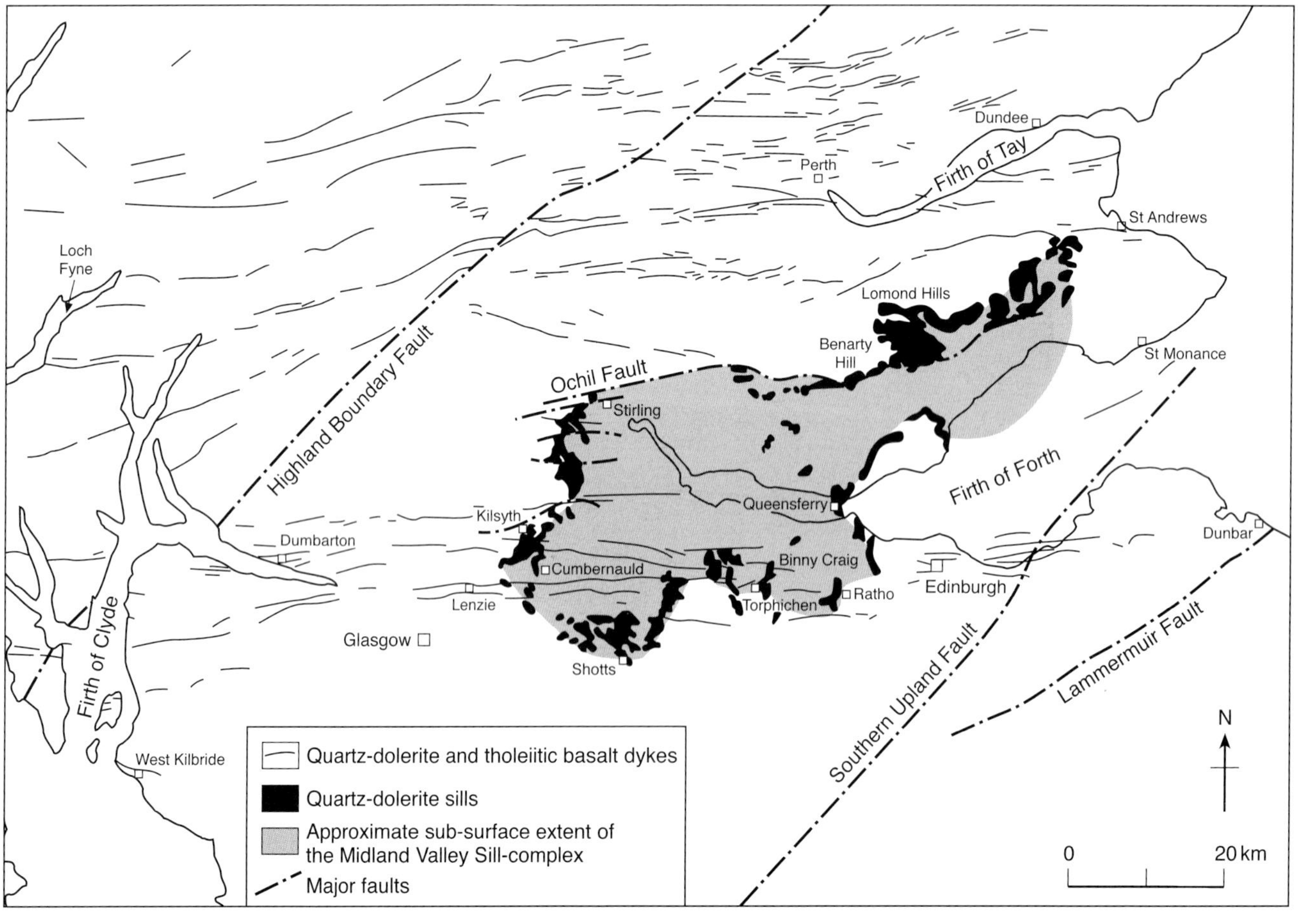

Fig. 9.40. Map of the Midland Valley, showing the distribution of latest Carboniferous tholeiitic basic intrusions. After Cameron & Stephenson (1985).

Southern Uplands

Thin sills of analcime-dolerite and a few NW-trending dykes of monchiquite and alkali dolerite cut Coal Measures in the Sanquhar Basin, and Lower Palaeozoic rocks are cut by rare dykes of monchiquite and nepheline-gabbro ('essexite'). All are assumed to be latest Carboniferous or Early Permian.

Latest Carboniferous tholeiitic sills and dykes

The transitional to alkaline magmatism that dominated northern Britain throughout most of the Carboniferous and Early Permian was interrupted in the Late Carboniferous by a short-lived period in which silica-oversaturated tholeiitic magmas were generated (Dunham & Strasser-King 1982; Loughlin & Stephenson in press). There are no extrusive rocks, but voluminous high-level intrusions include the Whin Sill-complex of northern England and the Midland Valley Sill-complex of Scotland (Figs 9.40, 9.41). The latter is associated with an extensive swarm of WNW- to ENE-trending dykes that constitutes one of the major dyke swarms of northwest Europe, extending from the Outer Hebrides eastwards at least as far as the Central Graben of the North Sea (Smythe 1994). This episode may be related to the earliest lavas of the Late Carboniferous to Early Permian rift of the Oslo region and other tholeiitic rocks of similar age in southern Sweden (Francis 1991*b*; Smythe *et al.* 1995).

In Scotland the tholeiitic dykes cut rocks ranging from Archaean to the Middle Coal Measures and the sills intrude strata between the Devonian–Carboniferous boundary and the

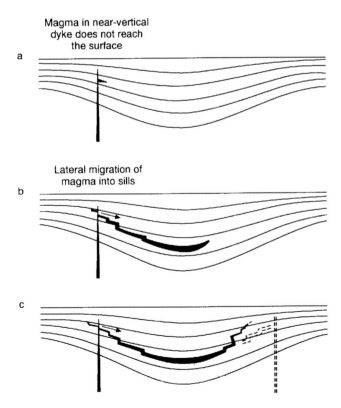

Fig. 9.41. Mechanism of intrusion of tholeiitic sills: (**a**) dykes are intruded 0.5 to 1.0 km below the surface; (**b**) Lateral accumulation of magma leads to gravitational flow down dip and accumulation of magma at the bottom of the sedimentary basin; (**c**) to achieve hydrostatic equilibrium, magma advances up dip on the other side of the basin, with en echelon fingering at the leading edge. Broken lines indicate variations inherent in multiple dyke sources. After Francis (1982).

Middle Coal Measures. Blocks of quartz-dolerite occur in sub-volcanic necks in east Fife, which are considered to be late Stephanian in age, and in the western Highlands camptonite dykes cut quartz-dolerites. No Permian strata are cut by the tholeiitic intrusions and clasts of quartz-dolerite, assumed to be from the Whin Sill-complex, occur in basal Permian breccias in northern England. The tholeiitic magmatism therefore occurred between the Duckmantian (Westphalian B) and the latest Carboniferous. Radiometric dates (De Souza 1979; M. Timmerman, pers. comm. 2002), backed by palaeomagnetic studies of the Midland Valley Sill-complex (Torsvik *et al.* 1989; Thomas *et al.* 1995), indicate rapid intrusion during the latest Carboniferous to earliest Permian.

The tholeiitic dyke swarm occurs across a 200 km-wide band that stretches for over 300 km from Barra in the Outer Hebrides and Kintyre in the west, to the east coast between Peterhead and Dunbar. Regionally the swarm is arcuate, trending 110° on the west coast, E–W in the central Midland Valley, and 070° along the northeast coast. Locally some dykes are deflected to a northeast trend along the Highland Boundary Fault. In the Midland Valley (Fig. 9.40), the dykes were emplaced partially along active or recently active E–W tensional faults (Read 1959). Cross-cutting relationships demonstrate that emplacement involved repeated pulses of magma. In the Bathgate Hills, boreholes have revealed an intimate relationship between faulting, multiphase dyke emplacement and mineralization (Stephenson 1983). Individual dykes may be traced as en echelon offsets and for up to 130 km. They average 30 m in width but may reach up to 75 m onshore. Quartz-dolerite forms pod-like fault-intrusions along the E–W west Ochil Fault.

The Midland Valley Sill-complex

This sill-complex has a volume estimated at over 200 km^3 and underlies an area of about 1900 km^2 around the inner Firth of Forth (Fig. 9.40). In places the composite thickness is about 200 m (Francis 1982). Its scarp features form many prominent landmarks, such as the Lomond Hills and Benarty Hill in Fife, Cockleroy Hill and Carribber Hill in the Bathgate Hills, and the Castle Rock and Abbey Craig at Stirling (Figs 9.21, 9.40). The complex commonly consists of several leaves, 25 to 100 m thick, which are linked by transgressive dyke-like intrusions along pre-existing fault planes ('fault risers').

The thicker sills show an increase in grain size from the chilled margins to the centre and a pegmatitic zone may be developed about one third of the way down from the top. Patches and veins of pink fine-grained quartzo-feldspathic material are also common. Late-stage veins of fine-grained basalt from later pulses of magma have been recorded in both sills and dykes. Late-stage hydrothermal mineralization developed locally, mainly in joints, during the final stages of cooling of both sills and dykes and quartz–calcite–chlorite veins are abundant locally.

Field evidence, as well as geochemical evidence (Macdonald *et al.* 1981), strongly suggests that the Midland Valley Sill-complex was fed by the associated E–W dyke swarm. The detailed relationship of the dykes to the sills was explained by Francis (1982), who suggested that the sills were emplaced into recently formed sedimentary basins at a lower structural level than the upper limit of dyke emplacement. The suggested mechanism of intrusion is illustrated in Fig. 9.41. However recent studies of magnetic grain alignment in the Whin Sill-complex and associated dykes of northern England suggest that there the pattern of magma flow was more complex (Liss *et al.* 2001).

Sharp contacts of the sills and dykes with their host sedimentary rocks provide evidence that the sediments were compacted and lithified prior to intrusion. The sills have had a marked effect on organic maturation in the adjacent lithologies and hence extensive thermal aureoles can be detected (Raymond & Murchison 1988; Murchison & Raymond 1989). This is in marked contrast to earlier alkaline basic sills of similar thickness in the same area, that were intruded into unlithified, water-saturated sediments and hence show lesser aureoles and complicated intrusive relationships (Walker & Francis 1987).

Like the alkaline basic intrusions, both sills and dykes of the tholeiitic suite have been affected by external fluids and volatiles circulating either during or shortly after intrusion. Zones of 'white trap' are common and in the Bathgate Hills, where dykes have passed through oil-shale-bearing strata, sticky black hydrocarbon deposits occur in calcite veins and as a coating to joints (Parnell 1984). In the Ochils, the Bathgate Hills and the Renfrewshire Hills, dykes have acted as both a heat source and a channel for the circulation of metalliferous brines, and some have mineral veins of former economic significance on their margins (Francis *et al.* 1970; Hall *et al.* 1982; Stephenson 1983; Stephenson & Coats 1983: see also Ch. 16).

Geochemistry and petrogenesis

Dinantian magmas

The Dinantian eruptions followed significant regional uplift, and accumulation of the lava plateaux in the Viséan was rapid. These conditions are typical of continental flood basalt sequences associated with the rise of anomalously hot deep mantle (mantle plumes). However, it seems more likely that the Dinantian, together with all of the Silesian and Permian alkali basaltic magmatism, was solely due to pressure-release melting of the subjacent mantle during extensional regimes (Smedley 1986a, b). Trace element and isotopic data from the Dinantian basaltic and hawaiitic rocks indicate that they were derived from heterogeneous mantle by partial melting (<5%) of garnet lherzolite at depths of 80 to 60 km. Trace element patterns resemble those of oceanic island basalts, suggesting that the magmas probably originated in the asthenosphere and that involvement of the subcontinental lithosphere was minimal. However, Smedley (1986b, 1988b) also showed that trace element and isotope values of the basic Dinantian lavas are similar to those of the earlier, late-Caledonian calc-alkaline magmatism and show similar spatial variations, implying that the mantle sources were immobile, non-convecting and therefore lithospheric. The lithospheric component is most obvious in the Dinantian lavas of the western Midland Valley (Wallis 1989).

Macdonald (1975) noted that particular petrographic associations could be recognized in different parts of the Dinantian lava successions and that these have distinct chemical signatures. This geochemical provinciality was subsequently confirmed by the contrasting trace element and isotopic characteristics that in some areas persisted throughout the Silesian and into the Permian (Macdonald 1980). The most likely model involves varying degrees of partial melting of slightly heterogeneous asthenosphere as the lithospheric plate migrated rapidly northwards during the Dinantian (Smedley 1988a).

Subsequent evolution of the primitive Dinantian magmas was largely by fractional crystallization. Mineralogical studies have suggested that some crystallization commenced at pressures of up to 11.5 kbar. It appears likely that primitive picritic magmas were arrested at, or close to, the crust–mantle boundary as 'underplated magmas', where they resided until fractionation of olivine, clinopyroxene and subordinate spinel had reduced the melt densities sufficiently for further crustal ascent to take place. The strongly porphyritic nature of many of the Dinantian extrusive and intrusive rocks, together with their broad compositional range, further suggests that magma resi-

dence in crustal magma chambers was general and widespread. As a result of these sub-crustal and crustal holding stages, the bulk of the Dinantian magmas erupted in a relatively fractionated condition so that in some areas, basaltic hawaiites and hawaiites predominate over basalts proper. Further crystal fractionation in small, near-surface magma chambers is suggested by hawaiitic lavas in the Renfrewshire Hills and Campsie Fells. These exhibit slight variations in composition during the course of a single eruption, producing composite flows. The trachytes, phonolitic trachytes and rhyolites are all regarded as derivatives by further crystal fractionation from the mugearitic stage of magma differentiation (Macdonald 1975).

Silesian and Permian magmas

Much of the later Dinantian, Silesian and Permian magmatism involved ascent of silica-poor, alkalic basic magmas that were markedly more primitive than their Dinantian predecessors. In general, the basic rocks are olivine- or olivine–augite-microphyric varieties with MgO contents >8%. They were erupted in small volumes reflecting their origin as small melt-fractions from relatively great depths (c. 80–90 km?) and accounting for the typical absence of low-temperature differentiates (Wallis 1989). In marked contrast to the preceding Dinantian magmatism, high overall ascent rates are suggested by their having undergone relatively little fractionation and, in many instances, by their containing fragments (xenoliths) of mantle and lower crustal wall-rocks (see below).

A study of the alkaline basic dykes of the Highlands and Islands by Baxter (1987), and a broad-scale geochemical survey of the Silesian to Early Permian basic rocks of Scotland by Wallis (1989) both indicated that the magmas originated through variable degrees of partial melting (0.5–15%) of heterogeneous phlogopite- and garnet-bearing asthenospheric mantle, with negligible crustal contamination. Wallis divided the lavas and intrusions into two broad geochemical groups on the basis of their incompatible trace element contents. The more enriched of these groups includes most of the Highland dykes and about half of the Fife and Lothian sills, together with the smaller basanitic intrusions associated with volcanic necks in the eastern Midland Valley. These represent the smallest degrees of partial melting and show no evidence of lithospheric contamination. The less-enriched group includes the remainder of the Fife and Lothian sills, the Ayrshire sills, the Troon lavas and most of the Mauchline lavas, deduced to have originated through larger degrees of partial melting of similar asthenospheric sources, with some minor interaction with lithospheric mantle material. The magmas rose rapidly, with little or no residence time in high-level magma chambers but some polybaric fractionation (<36%) of olivine ± clinopyroxene did occur during ascent.

Tholeiitic magmas

In contrast to the deeper, asthenospheric sources of the alkali magmas, the voluminous generation of Stephanian tholeiitic basalt magmas may be attributed to much larger-scale and shallower melting of depleted (probably MORB-source) mantle well to the east of Scotland. Such high Ti–Fe tholeiitic magmatism tends to occur in regions where active lithospheric spreading is taking place due to the influence of a mantle plume (Brooks & Jakobsson 1974). Ernst & Buchan (1997) have suggested that a mantle plume in the Skaggerak area, between Denmark and Norway, may have been the focus of a giant radiating dyke swarm, with the dyke- and sill-complexes of northern Britain, the Oslo Rift and the dykes of southern Sweden marking the arms of a 'triple junction'.

Macdonald *et al.* (1981) showed that, although most of the quartz-dolerite dykes fall within a restricted compositional range (which reflects the same compositional variation observed in the Midland Valley Sill-complex), there are also slight, non-systematic trace element variations between dykes. Some individual dykes were found to have a unique chemical 'fingerprint'. These authors concluded that the dykes were fed, not by a single homogeneous magma, but by a number of small, partly independent, magma chambers reflecting a heterogeneous source. Although he found no evidence for crustal contamination in the dykes, Howard (1999) concluded, from trace-element considerations, that crustal contamination was important in the evolution of the sill-complex. Systematic variations in both major and trace element geochemistry between the Whin Sill-complex and the Midland Valley Sill-complex suggest that they were not comagmatic (Howard 1999).

Xenoliths and megacrysts

For much of Scotland, post-Permian modification of the lithosphere may have been very minor and limited to thinning. Hence xenoliths and discrete crystals (megacrysts) carried up by the more silica-undersaturated Carboniferous and Permian basic magmas are important for the light they throw on the nature of unexposed rocks at depth, not only in the late Palaeozoic, but also at the present time.

The xenoliths include spinel lherzolites and, more rarely, spinel harzburgites (Fig. 9.42; Chapman 1976; Praegel 1981; Upton *et al.* 1983) and are inferred to be samples of the lithospheric upper mantle, acquired at depths between about 70 and 30 km. Rare garnet pyroxenites may originate from streaks or layers within this dominantly peridotitic mantle. Other forms of pyroxenite are more common and can be the dominant xenolith type (e.g. Elie Ness in Fife, the Gribun Dyke on Mull, and the Tingwall Dyke on Orkney). These vary widely from magnetite clinopyroxenites and spinel websterites, to amphibole- and biotite-pyroxenites, and some present evidence for several episodes of metasomatism (Upton *et al.* 1999, 2001). It has been argued that underplated pyroxenitic rocks form a substantial layer between lherzolitic upper mantle and lower feldspathic crust (Upton *et al.* 2001). Some of the pyroxenite inclusions are regarded as high-pressure cumulates cognate to the alkalic basic magmas that entrained them (Chapman 1976) and should strictly be regarded as autoliths rather than xenoliths.

Granulite-facies xenoliths (Fig. 9.42) of basic and intermediate composition (gabbro, diorite, quartz-diorite, tonalite and anorthosite) are regarded as samples of lower crustal rocks from depths of about 15–30 km (Hunter *et al.* 1984, Halliday

Fig. 9.42. Xenoliths in a monchiquite dyke at Streap, near Glenfinnan, Inverness-shire. Most are from the upper mantle and are spinel lherzolite, but the darker xenolith (top left of centre) is a pyroxenite. The pale xenolith in the centre is a granulite-facies basic gneiss from the lower crust. Coin 20 mm diameter. Photo B. G. J. Upton.

et al. 1993, Upton *et al.* 2001). Quartzo-feldspathic xenoliths are scarce, almost certainly because these more fusible crustal compositions are less likely to survive in high-temperature basaltic host magmas than the more refractory ultramafic and granulite-facies basic rocks. They include tonalitic (trondhjemitic) gneisses as well as sillimanite–garnet quartzo-feldspathic gneisses of presumed metasedimentary origin (Graham & Upton 1978).

Discrete crystals or 'megacrysts' include an assortment of anorthoclase, Fe-rich pyroxene, amphibole, biotite, zircon, apatite and Nb-rich phases, together with related xenoliths (e.g. anorthoclasites). The inference is that geochemically extreme melts, present in the deep crust and/or upper mantle at the time of the basaltic magmatism, became intimately intermixed with the basic host magmas. The ultimate origin of these enriched melts remains enigmatic. It has been proposed that they are related to asthenosphere-derived carbonatitic melts, permeating and interacting with the uppermost mantle and lowermost crust (Upton *et al.* 1999).

Much remains to be learned of the ages of the xenoliths (see also Chapter 7). On the basis of radiometric determinations by U–Pb zircon methods, ages appear to range from Palaeoproterozoic to those which were penecontemporaneous with the Late Palaeozoic magmas that entrained them (Halliday *et al.* 1984).

10 Permian and Triassic

K. W. GLENNIE

Permian and Triassic rocks are widely distributed beneath the seas surrounding Scotland but have only limited, mostly basin-margin, exposures on land (Fig. 10.1). They occur on the coast of the Moray Firth near Elgin and Golspie, in several small basins in the south and southwest of Scotland, including Dumfriesshire, Ayrshire and the Isle of Arran, and in a series of small exposures along the western seaboard of Scotland from Kintyre, through Mull and Ardnamurchan, Skye and

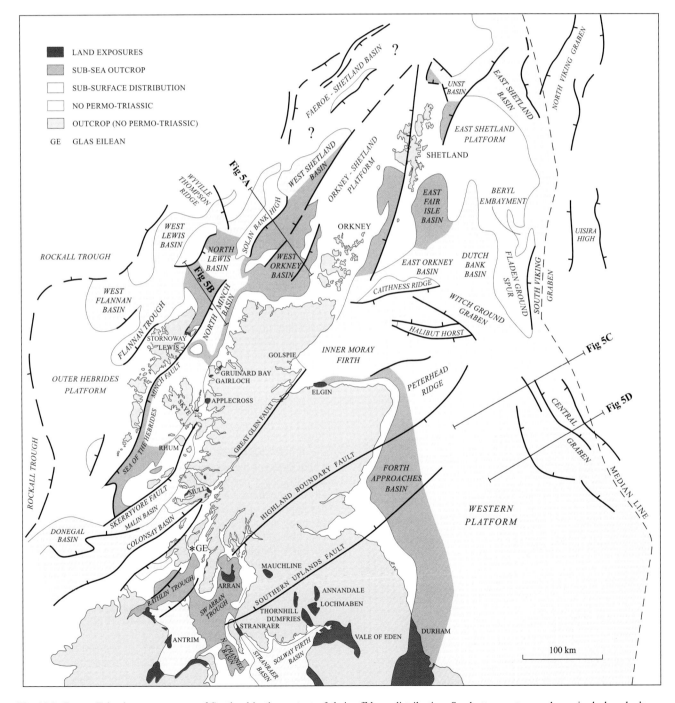

Fig. 10.1. Permo-Triassic outcrop areas of Scotland in the context of their offshore distribution. Sea-bottom outcrops shown in darker shade. Locations shown of cross-sections in Fig. 10.5.

Raasay to the vicinity of Stornoway on the Isle of Lewis. Each of these areas will be described in the context of the adjacent, mostly offshore, basinal development. The widespread distribution of rocks of Permo-Triassic age is indicative of a former very extensive cover. The historical reasons for the offshore extent but limited onshore exposure of the Permo-Triassic sequences are outlined below.

Global sea level during the Permian and Triassic was generally fairly low (Vail *et al.* 1977), and Scotland was located far from the coast within the former Laurussian part of the megacontinent Pangaea (Fig. 10.2), thus onshore exposures of Permian and Triassic rocks are almost entirely the product of terrestrial sedimentation. Over parts of continental Europe, such conditions of deposition commenced during the Late Carboniferous.

Several (4–6) Late Permian (Zechstein) marine transgressions, with intervening evaporation almost to dryness, affected the North Sea area. No route can be found for marine flooding of the time equivalent Bakevellia Sea of the Irish Sea and Antrim (Smith & Taylor 1992; Jackson & Mulholland 1993); like the Rotliegend of the Southern Permian Basin (Glennie 1998*b*) its deposition possibly occurred under a climate of varying aridity and a fluctuating water table that created lacustrine conditions in structural lows with a cyclicity similar to that of the Zechstein (see end of chapter).

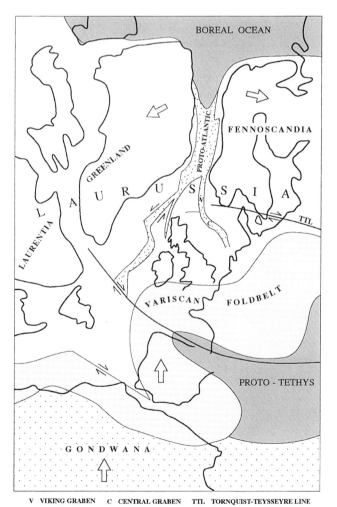

V VIKING GRABEN   C CENTRAL GRABEN   TTL TORNQUIST-TEYSSEYRE LINE

Fig. 10.2. Cartoon implying the development of the North Atlantic and North Sea rift systems in response to the northward squeezing of the Variscan orocline into the re-entrant formed by the Laurentia–Greenland and Fennoscandian components of Laurussia.

A reversion to terrestrial deposition occurred over continental Europe just before the end of the Permian (Kozur 1999), and probably applied also to Scottish waters (see Bosies Bank Formation of the Inner Moray Firth, below). The Mid-Triassic Muschelkalk Sea did not reach Scotland, but during the later Triassic, another marine transgression extended from Tethys northwestward across central Europe and, separately, northward via the Irish Sea, reaching the Scottish area only in the late Rhaetian (Fig. 10.3) (Warrington & Ivimey-Cook 1992).

Post-depositional basinal subsidence beneath the seas around Scotland was responsible for the early preservation of the Permo-Triassic sequences; this contrasts with the early Cenozoic thermal uplift of NW Scotland, where erosion resulted in a clastic influx to the North Sea Basin and brought the Permo-Triassic sequences of many basins west of Scotland to, or close to, the present sea floor (Fig. 10.1; Ziegler 1990, p.130; Stoker *et al.* 1993). It is pertinent to note that much of the current coastline of Scotland is controlled by the presence of offshore basins of sedimentation, each dating from the Permo-Triassic.

Regional development

The above brief historical outline of events can be considered as having its origin in the Late Carboniferous–Early Permian Hercynian (Variscan) Orogeny, which resulted from a collision between Gondwana and Laurussia (Fig. 10.2). The rigid margins of the Greenland–Laurentia and Baltic Shield portions of Laurussia formed a re-entrant into which the orogen was squeezed from the south. This gave rise to E–W extension across the foreland area in NW Europe: W–E right-lateral movement along the Tornquist–Teyssere line, and perhaps SW–NE left-lateral movement along the western margin of the Outer Hebrides Platform. Maximum extension probably occurred between Greenland and Norway, utilising that old line of weakness the Iapetus Suture, reducing in amount but becoming more complex to the south, where small-scale movement was taken up across a series of transtensional faults. Thus the Variscan Mountains of Brittany and Central Europe had hardly formed before they began to break up, and a series of roughly N–S trending grabens was initiated across the northern foreland (e.g. the en echelon Cheshire–Irish Sea–North Channel–Minch basins of western Britain and the Viking-Central and Horn–Bamble–Oslo graben systems of the North Sea (Fig. 10.3a) (see also Coward 1995; Chadwick & Evans 1995). Where the orogen approached the southern edge of the Baltic Shield, the crust was cut by a series of transtensional faults, which were associated with extensive volcanism that straddled the Carboniferous–Permian boundary, especially in northern Germany and Poland, but included early development of the Horn–Bamble–Oslo and Central grabens. In many parts of Scotland, these movements were associated with three phases of volcanism that possibly extended to the end of Early Permian time (e.g. Mauchline, Ayrshire) and the intrusion of sills and E–W trending dykes into older strata (Francis 1991*b*, and see Chapter 9).

Following a more equatorial location during the Carboniferous, Scotland slowly drifted northward during the Permian and Triassic periods into latitudes (15° to 30°N) that today are occupied by modern Arabia or the Sahara, and was subjected to a climate similar to that of a northern hemisphere desert or semi-desert. The Permian and Triassic continental sediments of the area are characterized by essentially unfossiliferous terrestrial red beds.

Towards the end of the Permian period, oceanic waters flooded the low-lying basins of the North Sea area several times,

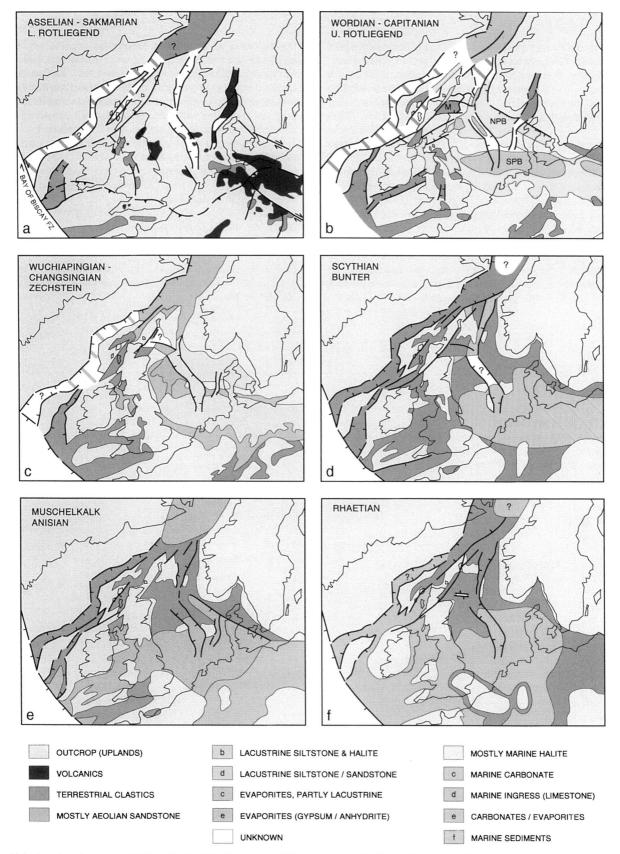

Fig. 10.3. A series of cartoons depicting Scotland in the context of the structural and sedimentological development of NW Europe (modified from Ziegler 1988*a*, 1989, 1990*a*: Smith & Taylor 1992; Warrington & Ivimey-Cook 1993; Glennie *et al.* 2002). (**a**) Early Permian (Asselian-Kungurian/Roadian) Lower Rotliegend, with associated igneous activity. The Viking and Central grabens were a late-stage development of this activity, which also caused thermal uplift and widespread erosion (e.g. Coward 1995). (**b**) Upper Rotliegend (Wordian–Capitanian) terrestrial sedimentation in the North Sea (fluvial, lacustrine and aeolian) was controlled by subsidence of the Northern and Southern Permian Basins (NPB, SPB) and the separate Inner Moray Firth Basin (M), and by the creation of a series of half-grabens between England and Ireland and west of Scotland. (**c**) Successive (Wuchiapingian–Changsingian) marine transgressions by the Late Permian Zechstein Sea resulted in cyclic deposition of basin-margin carbonates and basin-centre evaporites, including halite. Cycles are better developed in the North Sea than west of Scotland, where terrestrial clastics dominate, as also in the Inner Moray Firth. (**d**) Lacustrine mudstones (green) and terrestrial sandstones (orange) dominate basinal sedimentation during the Early Triassic (Scythian); marine ingressions are confined to eastern Europe. (**e**) Widespread (Anisian) marine flooding extends northward from the ocean Tethys. Basins marginal to Scotland remain terrestrial. (**f**) In the east, the Late Triassic (Rhaetian) marine transgression extends only into the southern Central Graben, whereas it seems to have been fairly extensive west of mainland Scotland.

leading to the cyclic deposition of carbonates and evaporites of the Zechstein Group in an essentially land-girt sea. The cyclicity was caused by the repeated formation and melting of ice caps in the vicinity of the South Pole (e.g. Crowell 1995; Glennie 1998*b*) leading to fluctuations in global sea level that must have been similar to those experienced during the Late Pleistocene (100 m or more; see e.g. Shackleton 1987; and Chapter 15). The Zechstein Sea occupied basin-centre locations, and although widely recognized in wells drilled for hydrocarbons beneath the North Sea, and represented by the Magnesian Limestone of North England and Ulster, it has no known marine representatives on-shore in Scotland.

With exposures of Scottish Permian and Triassic sediments consisting largely of unfossiliferous terrestrial red beds, it is very difficult to separate them in the absence of intervening Zechstein carbonates and evaporites. This lack of stratigraphic control led to use of the term 'New Red Sandstone', to differentiate the combined Permo-Triassic sedimentary rocks from the lithologically similar Devonian to earliest Carboni-

ferous Old Red Sandstone. Indeed, in small outcrop areas where red clastics overlie Caledonian metamorphic rocks, it can be difficult to decide whether it is a New Red or Old Red sandstone (or even similarly reddened Precambrian Torridonian Sandstone) that is exposed, the decision sometimes being taken on the rather subjective grounds of the presumed darker colour and greater induration of the older sequences.

The pre-Zechstein Permian continental strata of northwest Europe (Rotliegend Group) are divided into Upper and Lower units. In the North Sea area, the Lower Rotliegend is almost entirely absent apart, perhaps, from some volcanic rocks and associated fluvial sediments in and to the east of the Central Graben (Karl Formation, Stemmerik *et al.* 2000; Glennie *et al.* 2002). In the extensive sequences of Germany, the Upper Rotliegend can be divided into two units, Upper Rotliegend 1 and 2 (Schneider *et al.* 1998); correlations indicate that only Upper Rotliegend 2 (about Mid-Wordian to Early Wuchiapingian (see Jin *et al.* 1997; Wardlaw 2000)) is present in the North Sea area.

WEST AND SOUTH SCOTLAND

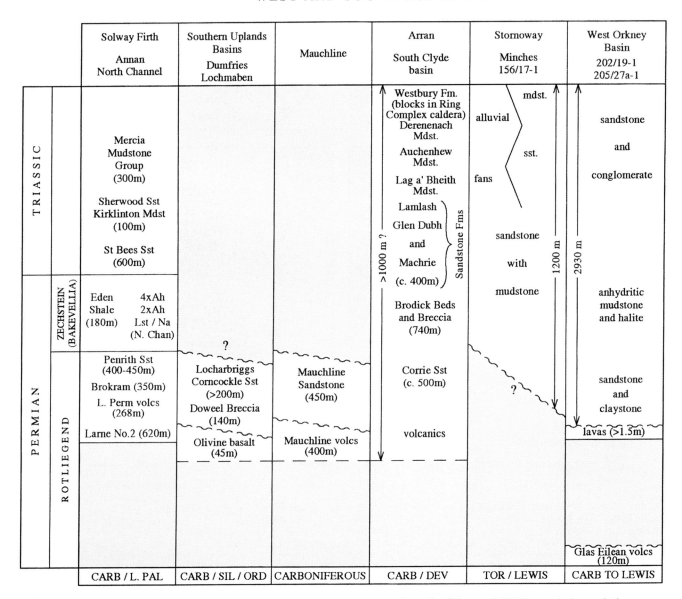

Fig. 10.4. Simplified Permo-Triassic lithostratigraphy of Scotland and adjacent seas. Timescale of Jing *et al.* (1997) tentatively matched to Permian lithostratigraphy. Ah, anhydrite; Lst, limestone; Na, halite.

Because of a paucity of dated correlatable horizons within most of the Permo-Triassic succession, and the virtual absence of radiometric ages after the Early Permian (Lower Rotliegend) volcanic activity, it has been almost impossible to obtain accurate time spans for the different depositional units within or around Scotland. Long-ranging non-marine palynomorphs known in Zechstein strata (*Leuckisporites virkkiae, Perisaccus granulatus* and *Vittatina sp.*) also occur near the top of the Rotliegend sequence in the Auk and Argyll oilfields (Pennington 1975; Heward 1991) and indicate a Wordian or younger age.

Since much of the Rotliegend stratigraphy is based on magnetostratigraphy and K–Ar dating of associated volcanics, ties to global chronostratigraphy have been open to debate, and depended on the choice of timescale used. Menning (1995) for example, has a 16 Ma duration for the Tatarian stage, which he considers covers the depositional time span of both the Upper Rotliegend 2 and the Zechstein. In contrast, Harland *et al.* (1990) and Gradstein & Ogg (1996) regard the Tatarian as of much shorter duration, respectively 6 Ma (245–251 Ma) and 4 Ma (248–251 Ma).

More recently, the names, boundary levels and stages of the Permian System, based on marine successions, have been approved by the Permian Subcommission, ICS (Jin *et al.* 1997). A few key radiometric ages help to define some of the stage time spans, and the ages of intervening stage boundaries have been recommended by Wardlaw (2000). These data indicate that the start of the Permian Period is probably about 291.6 Ma and the Permo-Triassic boundary at about 251.4 Ma, the division between Early and Late Permian being taken at the base of the Roadian stage (269 Ma) (Fig. 10.4). The Illawarra magnetic reversal has a probable age of 265 Ma. In Germany, Upper Rotliegend 2 sedimentation began just before the reversal at, say, 266 Ma, while closer to Scotland, the dating of volcanics (269–261 Ma) in the Danish Central Graben (Stemmerik *et al.* 2000) indicates a similar age for the start of the flanking and overlying Rotliegend sedimentation. At Mauchline, Ayrshire, Upper Rotliegend 2 sedimentation post-dates the youngest of the Permian volcanics (275–272 Ma) (Cameron & Stephenson 1985) and could be assigned a tentative age of 266 Ma for its start. Menning (1995), places the Rotliegend–Zechstein boundary at

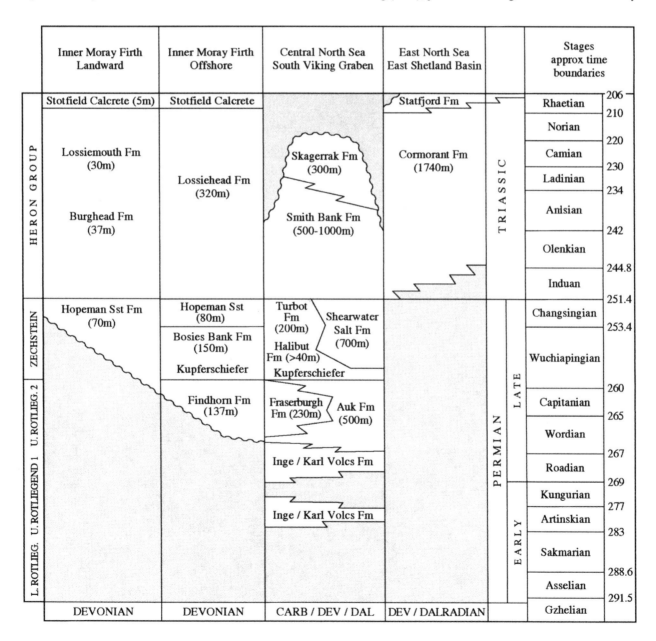

Fig. 10.4. (*continued*)

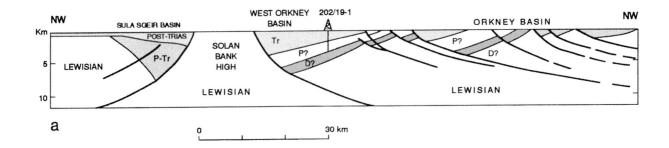

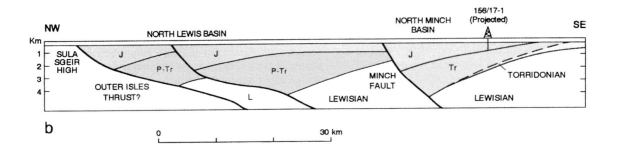

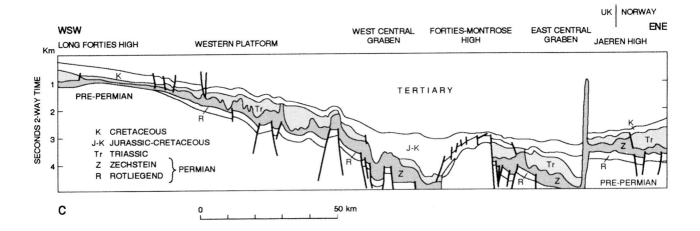

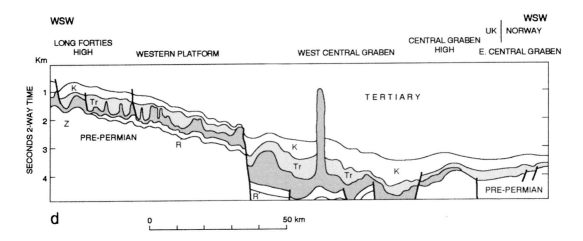

Fig. 10.5. Simple cross-sections that contrast the near-surface half graben preservation of the Permo-Triassic west of the Scottish mainland with the basinal development within the North Sea area. Based on Duindam & van Hoorn (1987), Fyfe *et al.* (1993), Stoker *et al.* 1993, Glennie & Underhill (1998).

about 258 Ma. Thus, following Jin *et al.* (1997), both the Upper Rotliegend 2 and the Zechstein were deposited during the Late Permian.

In the southern North Sea the earliest Buntsandstein (lacustrine Bröckleschiefer) is treated pragmatically as basal Triassic but was probably deposited at the same time as the last of the Permian Zechstein cycles (Ze5–7) (Aigner *et al.* 1999; Kozur 1999; Geluk & Röhling 1999); in Scottish waters, a fifth or possibly sixth Zechstein cycle, has been recognized in the Morag oil field (Quadrant 23) in the Central Graben (Taylor 1998).

In Scottish waters of the North Sea, the Upper Rotliegend 2 is characterized by basal fluvial (wadi) sands, dune sands and lacustrine or sabkha sediments that, collectively, indicate conditions of marked aridity. Fluvial sediments within much of the remaining Permo-Triassic sequence can be taken as evidence of a higher rainfall or perhaps the products of only intermittent flash-floods; locally they are the only sediments preserved on the periphery of upland areas. The oceanic flooding that created the Zechstein Sea took place in the Late Permian (Wuchiapingian). Apart from the carbonates and evaporites of the Zechstein Group, the presence of halite over 1000 m thick within the Zechstein succession of the eastern Scottish North Sea indicates not only marked aridity at that time, but also rapid subsidence to enable such a thick sequence to be accommodated (Glennie 1997).

With the passage of time, the areas of terrestrial sedimentation increased at the expense of upland areas of erosion. In the Early Triassic there were contrasting time-equivalent sedimentary facies in the North Sea and Solway Firth/west of Scotland/Moray Firth areas. The Sherwood Sandstone Group in the west and Lossiehead Formation of the Moray Firth were matched by mudstone-dominated deposition of the Smith Bank Formation in the Central Graben. Later in the Triassic, all basinal areas tended to be dominated by mudstone deposition with the Mercia Mudstone Group in the west and Cormorant Formation mudstones and sandstones in the central and northern North Sea (Fig. 10.4). Especially in the west, anhydrites, and even intervals of halite, are indicative of a near-surface water table and periods of increased aridity, whereas in the North Sea area the Triassic salts of the southern North Sea failed to extend into Scottish waters. A rise in global sea level eventually led to shallow-marine conditions encroaching the southern and western offshore areas of Scotland by the end of the Triassic (Rhaetian). The palaeogeography and lithofacies of the Scottish Permian and Triassic sequences are shown in their wider regional context by, respectively, Smith & Taylor (1992) and Warrington & Ivimey-Cook (1992).

Half-graben extension west of the Scottish mainland involved fault-block rotation in two directions. From the Solan High and West Orkney Basin southward, a series of westerly dipping half grabens (Fig. 10.5a, b) formed in response to extensional faulting in the hanging wall of easterly dipping late Caledonian thrusts (e.g. Moine and Outer Isles thrust zones). West of the West Shetland Platform, the fill of a series of half-grabens thickens to the east (Fig. 10.5a), possibly in response to Early Permian extensional subsidence into a postulated proto-Atlantic rift (Russell & Smythe 1983; Ziegler 1990*a*; Duindam & Van Hoorn 1987); this rift was later occupied by the Rockall Trough and Faeroe-Shetland Basin. Outcrop and well data show that the early fill of these half grabens west of Scotland comprised mostly terrestrial conglomerates and sandstones.

Permian and Triassic tensional events, with their associated fault-block rotations and axial subsidence, are largely responsible for rocks of those ages being represented on land in Scotland mostly in basin-margin locations. Beneath the surrounding seas, however, the situation is quite different, Permo-Triassic sedimentary sequences being preserved over more

than half of Scotland's offshore area, the bulk beneath the North Sea (Figs 10.1, 10.5c, d). The structural activity that led to this irregular sediment distribution is exemplified northwest of the Orkney Isles, where the exploration well 202/19-1 penetrated almost 3000 m of undated redbeds and evaporites of presumed Permo-Triassic age without reaching the base of the sequence (Fig. 10.5a). Seismic evidence indicates that further west, in the thickest part of the half-graben fill, these red beds may be almost 8000 m thick (Stoker *et al.* 1993). A little to the south, in the North Minch Basin (Fig. 5b), well 156/17-1 proved 1115 m of Triassic sandstone and mudstone overlying Torridonian Sandstone (Fyfe *et al.* 1993). The early Zechstein-age carbonates of the coast of Antrim may have had a lacustrine origin, but if marine, they would have had to derive their sea water via a more southerly route across northern Ireland from the postulated proto-Atlantic rift west of the Outer Hebrides Platform; this problem will be referred to again near the end of this chapter. Resting unconformably on, or faulted against, the Lewisian, just south of Stornoway on the Isle of Lewis, Steel & Wilson (1975) identified 600 m of braided-stream deposits overlain by another 600 m of conglomerates and mudstones that they ascribed to the Permo-Triassic.

Up to 3000 m of Permo-Triassic sediments may occur in the hangingwall of the Minch Fault (Fyfe *et al.* 1993) although on land, the thickness reduces to 75 to 90 m on Raasay and Scalpay (Lovell 1991). Still further southwest, up to 2000 m of Permo-Triassic sediments are suspected to be present in the Malin Basin just east of the Skerryvore Fault (Fig. 10.1).

Anderson *et al.* (1995) stress that the basement rocks of SW Scotland and Northern Ireland influenced the location and shape of the overlying Permo-Triassic basins and half grabens. For example, the Arran and Rathlin sub-basins offshore SW Scotland are separated by the Dalradian rocks of the Kintyre Peninsula, whereas the axis of the WSW–ESE trending Solway Firth Basin, lies above the Iapetus Suture. In contrast to the latter example, the NW–SE to N–S trending Permian basins of the adjacent Southern Uplands lie unconformably on, or in fault contact with, a wedge of Ordovician and Silurian sedi–ments that accreted during northwest-directed subduction between the Midland Valley of Scotland and the Iapetus Suture (McKerrow *et al.* 1977). The axes of these Permian basins, including the North Channel Basin, are possibly parallel to shear faults associated with the Late Silurian subduction direction. In some cases, partially eroded Devonian or Carboniferous sequences separate Permo-Triassic from underlying Caledonian rocks, indicating a possible late Caledonian initiation of these basin axes. The presence of Permian basins over the Southern Uplands and Ayrshire imply a formerly more extensive distribution of Permian, possibly also with Triassic strata, south of the Highland Boundary Fault.

Differential erosion associated with the early Tertiary tilting of Scotland by uplift of its NW Atlantic margin has resulted in Permo-Triassic strata being extensively exposed in some half grabens at or near seabed to the west of Scotland (Figs 10.1, 10.5a, b; Cheshire *et al.* 1972; Fyfe *et al.* 1993; Stoker *et al.* 1993), although not to the exclusion of younger Mesozoic strata in other half grabens (e.g. possibly over 2500 m of Jurassic strata in the North Lewis and North Minch basins; Stoker *et al.* 1993). In contrast, east of mainland Scotland (Fig. 10.5c, d), Permo-Triassic sequences can be buried beneath several thousand metres of younger sedimentary rocks (Ziegler 1990*a*; Glennie 1998*b*; Fisher & Mudge 1998).

Permian igneous activity

Both Permian and Triassic sedimentation took place within essentially the same basins, whose depositional areas extended with time (Figs 10.3a–e). From their distribution, the origin of the basins was clearly connected with the subsidence of E–W trending basins followed by the E–W transtensional extension of the crust that developed at the end of the Variscan Orogeny or later in the Permian. These movements seem to have been marked by fairly widespread Early Permian igneous activity (Fig. 10.3a), whereas no confirmed igneous activity of latest Permian (Zechstein) or Triassic age is known from Scotland's mainland or beneath its adjacent seas.

Permian igneous rocks are well developed within the Midland Valley, with isolated occurrences in the Thornhill and Sanquhar areas of the Southern Uplands. Overlying the Westphalian Coal Measures at Mauchline, Ayrshire, basaltic lavas reach a maximum thickness of 238 m, and within 30 km of the surrounding area occur over 60 necks, which probably acted as their feeders (Francis 1991b). The Mauchline lavas are intercalated with agglomerates, tuffs, sandstones and mudstones and overlie basal tuffs and sediments. On the western side of the Thornhill Basin in the Southern Uplands, the Coal Measures are overlain by about 20 m of olivine basalts of the Carron Volcanic Formation (McMillan in Stone 1996). Nearby are five small volcanic necks presumed to be of the same age (Greig 1971). The most westerly occurrence of Permian basaltic lavas occurs at Glas Eilean between the islands of Islay and Jura (Upton et al.1987; Stephenson & Gould 1995). Thin (2 m) beds of slaggy (sub-aerial) olivine lavas of aa type dip gently to the WSW and reach a thickness of c. 120 m. The lavas are intercalated with beds of limestone, of possible hot-spring origin, and shallow-water calcareous sandstone. Two samples give K–Ar ages of 282 ± 7 and 287 ± 6 Ma. Their mean age of 285 Ma makes them the oldest known Permian extrusives in Scotland, and compares reasonably well with the 291 ± 5 Ma date at the Carboniferous–Permian time boundary assigned to the more northerly Ardgour dyke swarm by Baxter & Mitchell (1984).

Teschenite, monchiquite and dolerite sills up to 150 m thick are intruded into Carboniferous strata over much of the Midland Valley and have widespread exposures from West Lothian to East Fife. In the Ayrshire coalfield the sills are younger than all major faults in the area, have strong petrographic and geochemical affinities with the Mauchline lavas, and are cut by necks and dykes associated with the lavas (Cameron & Stephenson 1985). Four major sill complexes occur in the Glasgow–Paisley area, some with three leaves and a maximum known individual thickness of 36 m. SE of Mauchline, the classic Lugar Sill is believed to have formed by multiple injection of progressively less evolved teschenite magma, followed by a pulse of theralitic magma that differentiated in situ and, enriched by residual liquid and volatiles, gave rise to lugarite (Francis 1991b).

WNW, W–E and WSW-trending dykes, up to 75 m wide and 300 km long, are exposed not only in the Midland Valley but, as alkaline lamprophyres, basanites and basalts, have been recognized across the Highlands as far north as the Orkney Isles and are believed to extend across the North Sea to Sweden (Ziegler 1990a; Torsvik et al. 1997); sub-vertical Caledonian lines of weakness are presumed to account for their relatively uniform orientation and mafic composition. Rock (1983) recognizes over 3000 dykes grouped into nine swarms. K–Ar dating suggests three phases of activity, Visean, Early Permian and Late Permian.

On Orkney and at Duncansby Ness in Caithness, the dykes are associated with small volcanic vents (Francis 1991b). Dyke swarms on Orkney are dated 252 ± 10 Ma, while three other dykes from the Thurso area give K–Ar ages of 268–249 Ma (Baxter & Mitchell 1984); if the younger age is correct, it dates the only igneous event in Scotland to straddle the Permo-Triassic time boundary.

The accuracy of especially older, whole rock, radiometric dating is suspect. Compare, for instance the 273–270 Ma K–Ar mineral dates for dolerite sills in the Glasgow–Paisley area quoted by Cameron & Stephenson (1985) with the 279–276 Ma given by De Souza (1979; quoted by Francis 1991b), and 268 ± 6 Ma by Henderson et al. (1987). The age distribution of Permian igneous activity displayed on Figure 10.6 was prepared with these doubts in mind and the more doubtful ages are not included. The diagram emphasizes that, whereas some of

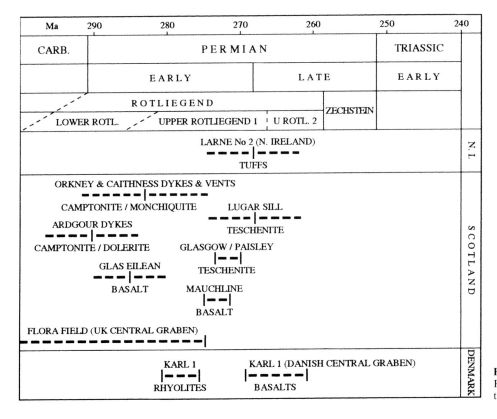

Fig. 10.6. Age ranges of some Rotliegend volcanics of Scotland and the North Sea. For discussion, see text.

the dyke swarms of the Scottish Highlands may have been intruded during the Early Carboniferous and Early Permian, the only supporting ages for Late Permian igneous activity (other than the Karl volcanics flanking and underlying the Upper Rotliegend 2 Auk Formation in the Danish Central Graben; see Stemmerik *et al.* 2000) seem to come from the Larne No. 2 well in Ulster, where all except the 268 Ma age for the basal tuffs must be rejected as indicating extrusion later than deposition of the overlying Rotliegend dune sands.

In the UK Central Graben, the Lower Rotliegend Inge Volcanics Formation (Karl Formation in Danish waters) was named by Cameron (1993) from the nearby Danish well P-1 on the Inge High. Volcanics in the same stratigraphic position in the Danish Central Graben have been named the Karl Formation, based on the succession seen and dated in the well Karl-1 (Stemmerik *et al.* 2000).

Permo-Carboniferous igneous activity in the Danish Central Graben and western Danish–Norwegian Basin seems to have taken place as two separate events: *c.* 281–276 Ma and 269–261 Ma (Stemmerik *et al.* 2000). The degree to which this general timing applies to Scotland and the rest of NW Europe is uncertain but, allowing for individual inaccuracies, there is a reasonable match. The above figures indicate the same age range for igneous activity as within the Central Graben, where crustal extension, mostly in the form of half grabens, is believed to have resulted from the effects of transtension. Even though the published ages for Permian igneous activity in Scotland must still be treated with caution, the available evidence indicates that it possibly occurred as three pulses spread between the latest Carboniferous and early Late Permian (269–261 Ma?). The mafic nature of much of the igneous material suggests that its source lay deep within the crust.

Thus most of the volcanic activity was confined to the Early Permian. With the doubtful exception of Caithness and the Orkney Isles, the Late Permian and Triassic seem to have been devoid of igneous activity in Scottish waters and on the mainland, although Late Triassic tuffs are reported from an offshore well in the Erris Trough, west of County Donegal (Tate & Dobson 1989; Hitchen *et al.* 1995).

Moray Firth and Central and Northern North Sea

The Permian and Triassic sedimentary rocks east and north of the Scottish mainland are divided into three groups (Fig. 10.4):

(1) Triassic Heron Group: terrestrial conglomerates, sandstones and shales.
(2) Late Permian (Wuchiapingian to Changhsingian) Zechstein Group: marine carbonates, anhydrites and salts and, locally, terrestrial siliciclastics.
(3) Late Permian (Wordian to Wuchiapingian) Rotliegend Group – dominated in Scottish waters by aeolian sandstones and sabkha/lacustrine? and fluvial shales and sandstones.

The Lower Rotliegend Inge Volcanics Formation has been recognized in a few wells in the UK Central Graben (Figs 10.3a, 10.6, Flora Field area), reaching a thickness of at least 350 m. Mudstones, sandstones and conglomerates are interbedded with thick basaltic lavas and tuffs (Cameron 1993). Unpublished radiometric ages indicate a time span of eruptions from 308 to 270 Ma (Scot Fraser, pers. comm. 1999); with closer sampling, these eruptions can probably be confined to two or three distinct periods. Similar rocks have been recorded on the Danish side of the Graben where the igneous rocks of the Karl Formation were extruded during two different time spans, 281–276 and 269–261 Ma (Stemmerik *et al.* 2000). The younger extru-

sions possibly indicate the start of crustal extension to form the Central Graben; they are flanked or overlain by sediments of the Upper Rotliegend 2.

Late Permian Upper Rotliegend 2

The Upper Rotliegend 2 of the central and northern North Sea areas is divided into two formations, the Auk and Fraserburgh formations. They are described here in some detail for comparison with similar units occurring beneath the Moray Firth and exposed on land, the Findhorn and Hopeman formations respectively.

Auk Formation. Named after the Auk oilfield where it reaches a thickness of *c.* 500 m, this formation is generally underlain in the south by Devonian Old Red Sandstone or Lower Carboniferous sequences or, north of the NE extension of the Highland Boundary Fault, by metamorphic rocks of the Dalradian Supergroup. It is overlain by the thin Kupferschiefer, the lowermost unit of the Upper Permian Zechstein Group. Although the formation is characterized by aeolian sandstones, these are commonly underlain by coarse sandstones and conglomerates that, near the Central Graben (e.g. Auk Field), contain pebbles of basalt.

The reddish-brown to grey aeolian sandstones were derived from the north and west and deposited on large dunes of both linear and transverse type. Bedding styles recognized include slipface sands with dips of between 25° and 30°, dune-apron sands with dips that increase from sub-horizontal to about 25° before being covered by the next migrating sequence, and sub-horizontal, bimodal sheet sands that were deposited around dune margins and in interdune areas. The sandstones are fine to medium grained with some coarse laminae. Individual grains of quartz are commonly frosted and coated with a thin film of haematitic clay whose reddish colour gave rise to the name Rotliegend. Locally, the uppermost 50 m or so of the Auk sandstones are grey coloured, and have been compared with the Weissliegend of Germany (Glennie & Buller 1983); these partly homogenized and deformed sandstones have been subjected to mass-flow mechanisms. In the Auk and Argyll fields the mass flows are associated with thin organic-rich lacustrine shales that contain a Late Permian micro-flora typical of the overlying Zechstein (Pennington 1975; Heward 1991), and associated freshwater limestones in Auk are unknown elsewhere in the North Sea (Heward 1991).

The Auk Formation has a fairly wide distribution north of the Mid-North Sea High within and flanking the Central Graben and in the South Viking Graben (Figs 10.3b, 10.4), and a similar sedimentary sequence occurs to the east in Norwegian and Danish waters. South of the Mid North Sea High the Upper Rotliegend equivalent is known as the Leman Sandstone Formation (Cameron *et al.* 1992; Glennie 1998*b*).

Fraserburgh Formation. On the Western Platform, west of the Central Graben, the Auk sandstones grade laterally into reddish-brown dolomitic and anhydritic mudstones and sandstones of the Fraserburgh Formation. Wavy adhesion-ripple sandstones indicate deposition in a probably saline sabkha environment, whereas shalier horizons may have been deposited within temporary shallow desert lakes. The formation is locally up to 230 m thick, but more generally nearer half that thickness. In a few wells (e.g. Well 20/12-1) the formation both overlies and underlies dune sands of the Auk Formation, perhaps indicating a fluctuating water table and aeolian activity controlled by aridity. The main area of deposition SE of the offshore extension of the Highland Boundary Fault may have been controlled by crustal uplift adjacent to the Central

Graben. There is local evidence for the presence of the formation along the axis of the Central and Viking graben system (mainly in Danish and Norwegian wells; Glennie *et al.* 2002), but a lack of deep wells in the area prevents its distribution from being mapped, and is shown on Fig. 10.3b only conceptually. The formation has many similarities with the Silverpit Formation of the Southern Permian Basin, but lacks any horizons of bedded halite.

Findhorn Formation. The above two formations are confined to the east of an area of non-deposition in the Outer Moray Firth, but beneath the Inner Moray Firth the Findhorn Formation has affinities to both. It comprises both fluvial and aeolian sandstones as well as anhydritic sandstone indicative of deposition on a sabkha, and the possible local development of a desert lake (Well 13/18-1). In the uppermost part of the Findhorn Formation, clean sandstones of probable aeolian origin are considered to be similar to the uppermost Weissliegend (Cameron 1993), which in the southern North Sea is locally deformed in a manner similar to that seen in the cliffs of Hopeman Sandstone east of Hopeman harbour (Glennie & Buller 1983) (see below). Well data released by oil companies indicates a Findhorn Formation up to 700 m thick in the middle of the Inner Moray Firth Basin. Re-examination of the well cuttings in several of these wells, however, indicates that the deeper parts of the former Findhorn Formation contain Devonian spores of lacustrine origin. The maximum thickness of the formation is now believed to be closer to 140 m (e.g. Well 12/28-1 in Fig. 10.7; Glennie *et al.* 2002). Although not drilled, a possible Rotliegend sequence similar to the Findhorn For-

mation, recognized seismically within the East Orkney Basin, is about 1000 m thick (Andrews *et al.* 1990).

Zechstein Group

Late Permian (Wuchiapingian to Changxinian?) sequences of the Zechstein are dominantly carbonates, evaporites (anhydrite and halite) and minor shales. The Zechstein is best developed in the southern and central North Sea, where a thickness of 700 m is exceeded locally in salt diapirs. In the Inner Moray Firth, the time equivalent Bosies Bank Formation (Figs 10.4; 10.7) was probably deposited entirely within a terrestrial environment. Marine rocks of the Zechstein Group are not known on land in Scotland.

The basal *Kupferschiefer* is a characteristically thin (mostly <1 m) organic-rich shale that caps the Rotliegend sandstones with apparent conformity. Limestones of the Halibut Carbonate Formation were deposited in the shallowest waters, fringed in slightly deeper water by the Turbot Anhydrite Formation. In the deep water of basin centres, thin anhydritic shales are overlain by halite and polyhalite of the Shearwater Formation, which in diapirs can be well over 1000 m thick. Diapiric movement of Zechstein salt, which probably continues today, was responsible for deforming all overlying sequences and creating structural traps for oil and gas. By balancing the geological sequences across the North Sea, Buchanan *et al.* (1966) calculate that the maximum depositional thickness of Zechstein salt was 1 km.

Halite is not known in the North Viking Graben or the Outer Moray Firth, where the Zechstein is generally less than

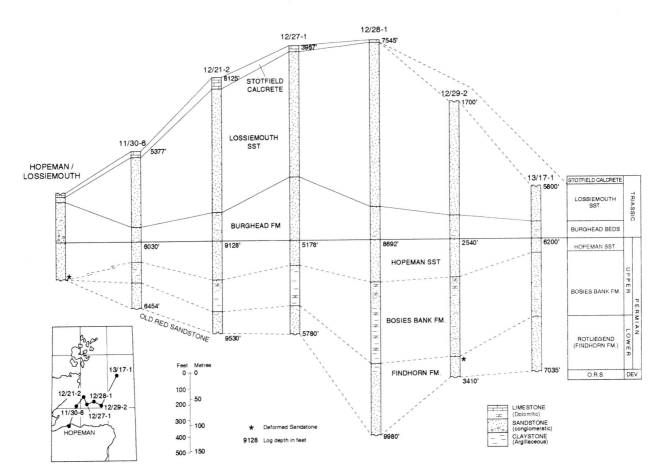

Fig. 10.7. Cross-section correlation sketch of the Inner Moray Firth; datum top Permian. (* = deformation structures correlated with those of the North Sea Weissliegend; Glennie & Buller 1983; Cameron 1993). The Triassic sequence is capped by the Stotfield Calcrete, which forms an excellent seismic marker where preserved.

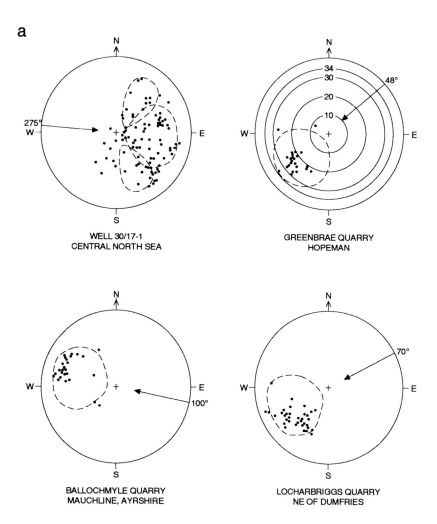

Fig. 10.8a. Evidence of sediment-transport directions. Four polar nets of bedding attitudes (dip angle and azimuth) of dune bedding near Hopeman, Morayshire, at Mauchline, Ayrshire and Lochmaben, Dumfriesshire. The maximum angle of repose of dry dune sand is 34°. No corrections have been made for slight (<10°) tectonic tilt.

200 m thick, and over much of the Central North Sea the combined Halibut and Turbot formations can be less than 100 m. The Zechstein is absent over a broad zone extending NE along the Peterhead Ridge and Halibut Horst to the Witch Ground Graben (Fig. 10.1).

Bosies Bank Formation. This formation has its widest distribution within the Inner Moray Firth, where it is a terrestrial time equivalent of the marine Zechstein Group of the Central North Sea. It is dominated by sandstones and shales with minor dolomitic limestone and anhydrite, and reaches a thickness of *c.* 140 m in the basin centre where the carbonates are developed best (Fig. 10.7). The environment of deposition is interpreted as mainly fluvial and lacustrine or sabkha, with some clean aeolian sandstones near the base (Cameron 1993). In a siliciclastic facies, the Bosies Bank Formation is thought to extend across the East Orkney and West Fair Isle basins (Andrews *et al.* 1990) and also in basin-margin locations in the Beryl Embayment and Unst Basin (Cameron 1993). A high sandstone content in well 20/9-1 near the offshore extension of the Highland Boundary Fault, probably indicates exposure of underlying Old Red Sandstone close to an active fault scarp.

Within the Inner Moray Firth, bedding attitudes deduced from dipmeter logs indicate regional fluvial transport toward the northwest (depositional slope? Fig. 10.8c). The formation is underlain by grey or black shales interpreted as the Kupferschiefer, but where this is thick (5 m or more), lacustrine deposition in local sub-basins, perhaps controlled by the regional water table, can be inferred to have been continuous from the Findhorn Formation into the Bosies Bank Formation.

In some parts of the Inner Moray Firth, the aquatic Bosies Bank Formation is overlain by up to 80 m of aeolian sandstone (Fig. 10.7) that has been interpreted as a correlative of the cliff exposures of Hopeman Sandstone north of Elgin (Fig. 10.9). Because of its position overlying the Zechstein-age Bosies Bank Formation (Fig. 10.7), deposition of the aeolian sand was believed by the well operators to have taken place during the earliest Triassic. The discovery in 1997 of a mould of the skull of *Dicynodon* (Fig. 10.10) within the upper Hopeman Sandstone (Clark 1999) has placed the entire Hopeman Sandstone and, by inference, its offshore equivalent, firmly within the later Permian. Thus a late Zechstein reversion to aeolian conditions in the Moray Firth seems to match a similar late Permian reversion from marine Zechstein to terrestrial conditions recognized in Germany (Aigner *et al.* 1999; Kozur 1999) and The Netherlands (Geluk & Röhling 1999).

Hopeman Sandstone Formation. Along the southern coast of the Moray Firth, the dominantly aeolian Hopeman Sandstone has a thickness of 200 feet (60 m) in the Clarkly Hill borehole SE of Burghead (Fig. 10.9), where it underlies the Triassic Burghead Formation and rests on the Upper Old Red Sandstone (Peacock 1966a; Peacock *et al.* 1968). In a shallow borehole near Inverugie House SE of Hopeman, the formation is overlain by Triassic sandstones and conglomerates of the Burghead Formation (Peacock *et al.* 1968), but the only visible contact east of Burghead is faulted.

The Hopeman Sandstone is well exposed in the cliff section east of Hopeman harbour, where it has a visible thickness of around 70 m (base not exposed) in the vicinity of the Clashach

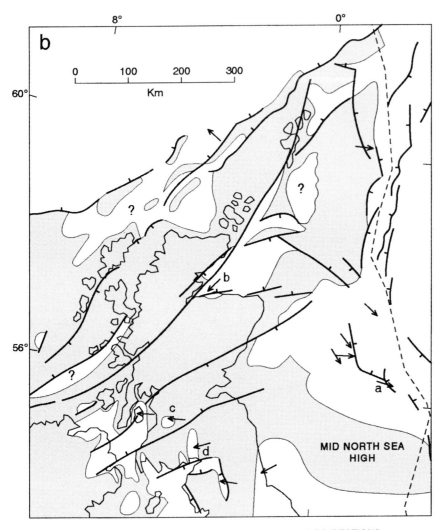

Fig. 10.8b. Aeolian sandstones, mostly Permian where known but includes a Triassic (Scythian) direction west of Shetland.

EARLY LATE PERMIAN (ROTLIEGEND) AEOLIAN TRANSPORT DIRECTIONS

Quarry. There, the formation is dominated by aeolian sandstone with foresets dipping mostly to the south and SW but in places also NE and east (for details of the bedding attitudes see Clemmensen 1987). These sandstones were probably deposited under the influence of northerly winds that were partly convected up-slope over the adjacent Old Red Sandstone and Dalradian outcrop areas. The dunes were possibly mainly of transverse type (see uniformity of dip direction in Fig. 10.8a), although Clemmensen (1987) interprets some of the variable bedding attitudes as indicating deposition on a star dune. Sheet sands are also developed especially east of Gow's Castle.

The sandstones are hosts to minor galena coatings and non-commercial barite (crystals and veinlets) and fluorspar cements. At the beach edge east of Hopeman harbour, south-dipping dune sands contain small star-like barite crystals suggestive of minute desert roses, and such cementation can be found at other localities along the coast (e.g. beneath the Covesea lighthouse and on Halliman Skerries) as well as in Old Red Sandstone in the Buckie area. Fluorspar is likewise scattered, in the Hopeman Sandstone both east and west of Hopeman, in the Triassic sandstones of Lossiemouth and Hill of Spynie, and in Old Red Sandstone just west of Lossiemouth. The presence of fluorspar and galena coatings on joint surfaces in Lower Jurassic rocks penetrated in the Geological Survey Lossiemouth borehole indicate the lower limit for the time of mineralization (Peacock et al. 1968). The early Mid-Jurassic thermal dome centred over the Central North Sea and subsequent structural adjustment (Underhill & Partington 1993; Glennie 2000) sug-

gests a possible driving mechanism and timing for this mineralization. Ferruginous staining (liesegang rings) cross-cuts the dune bedding of the Hopeman Sandstone where a sub-recent water table lay close to the surface.

Reptile footprints (Fig. 10.11a) and tail drags are preserved on many south-facing slopes where the bedding surfaces display adhesion warts formed by wind-blown sand accreting on a surface possibly dampened by early morning dew. These creatures were apparently all heading north towards the Moray Firth Basin where fresh water could be expected in the rivers and lakes of the Bosies Bank Formation (Hopkins 1999).

The Hopeman Sandstone was correlated by Watson & Hickling (1914) with an outlier of similar (Cuttie's Hillock) sandstones at Quarry Wood, west of Elgin (Fig. 10.9) that contained reptiles (*Elginia*, a pareiasaur, and the dicynodonts *Geikia* and *Gordonia*), of uppermost Permian age. A faunal revision by Walker (1973) suggested a possible Permo-Triassic age for these sandstones, but Benton & Walker (1985) and Benton & Spencer (1995) redated these fossils to 'uppermost Permian or at the extreme summit of the Permian'. Benton & Spencer (1995) state that there are no comparable localities in the British Isles or in Europe. As already described, determination of *Dicynodon* (Fig. 10.10) from Clashach Quarry has placed the whole of the Hopeman Sandstone within the Permian, making it a depositional time equivalent to the offshore Bosies Bank Formation of the Zechstein Group, its overlying (Hopeman) dune sands, and possibly also the uppermost part of the Findhorn Formation.

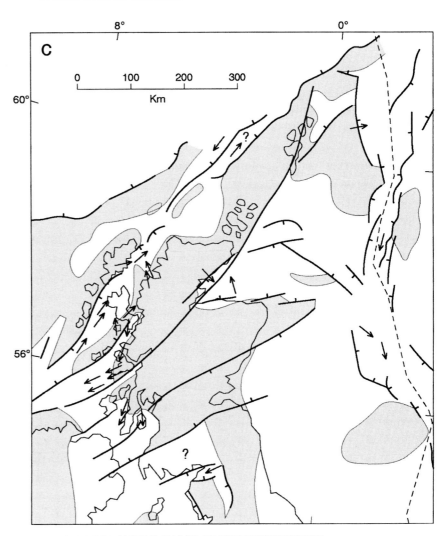

Fig. 10.8c. Fluvial, mostly Triassic but includes Upper Rotliegend 2 in the Moray Firth.

MID TRIASSIC (~ANISIAN) FLUVIAL TRANSPORT DIRECTIONS

Along the foreshore and visible in some cliffs are discontinuous zones of highly deformed and homogenised bedding, up to some 20 m thick (Fig. 10.11b), with a strong vertical component to the deformation. Locally, some exposures show signs of fluid flow and are overlain erosively by thin, finely conglomeratic (granule to small pebble) beds, possibly deflation lags of former fluvial origin.

The zones of deformation are 50–60 m below the top of the Hopeman Formation and, as already mentioned, could correlate with the top of the offshore Findhorn Formation (Cameron 1993), making correlation of the two events seem very plausible. Similar deformation structures immediately below the basal Zechstein Kupferschiefer at the top of the Auk Formation in the Central North Sea and in the Weissliegend Sandstone of the Southern Permian Basin, make the phenomenon a regional event. Glennie & Buller (1983) ascribed the deformation to the escape of air trapped and compressed hydrostatically beneath the wetted surfaces of sand dunes by flooding associated with the Zechstein marine transgression. But if the Bosies Bank Formation is entirely terrestrial, then the Zechstein Sea cannot have flooded the Inner Moray Firth (Glennie et al. 2002); the required internal increase in air pressure now seems more likely to have resulted from fluvial flooding, a surface seal having been formed by rain-wetted dune surfaces that deformed during air escape.

At many localities (e.g. along the foreshore just west of the coastguard tower), the deformed beds are underlain by structureless sandstones in which occasional rafts of laminated sand

indicate an origin by brittle fracture. Here, the 'cement' enabling brittle fracture to occur, is the reversal of what allows sand castles to stand up on a beach. The castle maintains its shape because of the the mutual capillary attraction of moist but not saturated sand grains in a sub-aerial environment. The rafts, on the other hand, comprised dune sand whose pore spaces were originally filled with air. The surrounding sands became homogenized as the water table rose through them to replace the upward-escaping air that deformed the overlying rain-wetted sands, but were unable to replace the air within the rafts, which thus retained their entity. Brittle fracture can also occur when the surface sands of a dune are wetted with rainwater, become heavier and slide down the dune's surface over underlying dry sand. East of Hopeman, overturned dune sandstones are overlain by about 4 m of slightly contorted sandstone containing some clasts of clay (Peacock 1966, pl. IX.3). The overturning may have resulted from the drag effect of a flow of water-saturated sand, including rip-up clasts, during the same catastrophic flash flood that caused other deformation in the area (cf. McKee et al. 1962).

Triassic Heron Group

Relatively thin continental clastics of the Heron Group crop out along the Moray coastline between Burghead and Lossiemouth on either side of the Hopeman Sandstone, and as faulted outliers north of Elgin. They comprise the Burghead Sandstone, Lossiemouth Sandstone and Stotfield Calcrete

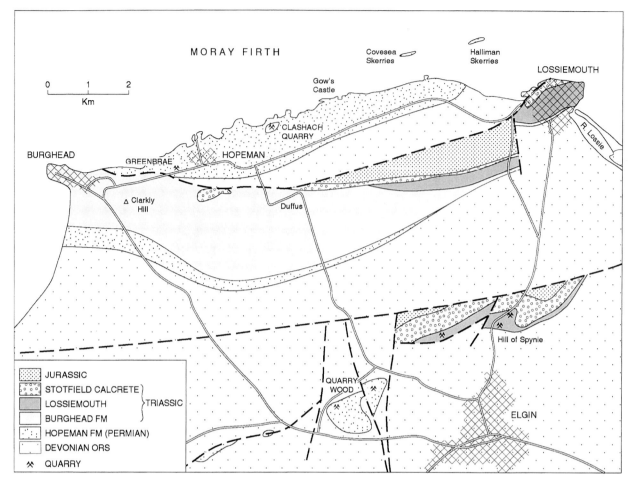

Fig. 10.9. Simplified geological map of the Hopeman–Elgin area, Morayshire showing access roads and some important quarries.

(formerly 'Cherty Rock') formations (Fig. 10.4). For the most part, the offshore formations of the Heron Group in the North Sea will be described only briefly. A fuller discussion can be found in Lervik & Spencer (1989), Cameron (1993) and in Fisher & Mudge (1998).

Burghead Sandstone Formation. Almost 40 m of fluvial reddish-brown, pebbly (up to 50 mm diameter) sandstone was drilled in a well near Duffus (Fig. 10.9) and many small abandoned quarries are now the sites of poor exposures of the

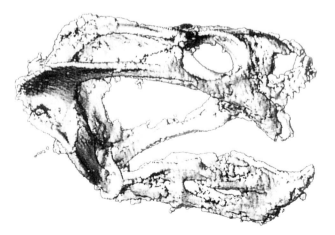

Fig. 10.10. Right lateral view of the skull of the Late Permian reptile *Dicynodon* derived from an MRI scan of its mould. Discovered high in the Hopeman Sandstone at Clashach Quarry, Hopeman. From Clark (1999), with permission.

formation (for details see Peacock *et al.* 1968). The sandstone is distributed in a long wedge, sub-parallel to the coast, extending eastward from Burghead Harbour to a point SW of Lossiemouth, where it is cut out by a N–S fault. It is underlain by the Hopeman Sandstone and is overlain either by sandstones of the Lossiemouth Sandstone Formation or by the Stotfield Calcrete Formation. The contact with the Hopeman Sandstone is faulted east of Burghead and is not exposed further south. The Burghead Formation is best exposed at Burghead Harbour, where foresetting and lensing, together with some imbrication of the pebbles, indicates fluvial transport to the NE (Gillen 1987). In the adjacent cliff and foreshore north and east of the town, the yellow and brown sandstones have low-angle to horizontal plane bedding with discontinuous pebble stringers and clay intraclasts that indicate subaerial exposure; Frostick *et al.* (1988), compared these deposits with those of ephemeral streams. These authors also compared the Triassic strata of the Inner Moray Firth with the Tertiary to Recent rift sequences of East Africa, and interpreted the Great Glen Fault as a dip-slip rift margin with the thicker and finer-grained sequence close to the fault and the coarser lithologies and thinner succession at the unfaulted margin at Burghead. This interpretation, however, is not well supported by Triassic isopach data, which fails to show the implied influence of the Great Glen Fault. Roberts *et al.* (1990) discuss this interpretation and conclude that the Triassic of the Inner Moray Firth does not conform to their rift model.

Lossiemouth Sandstone Formation. The Lossiemouth Formation includes sandstones that formerly went under the names of sandstones of Spynie, Findrassie and Lossiemouth (Fig. 10.9).

Fig. 10.11. (**a**) Reptile trackways from south-dipping dune bedding of the Hopeman Sandstone. Displayed at the entrance to Clashach Quarry, Hopeman. (**b**) North-dipping dune bedding flattening-out to the right. Cliffs just seaward of Clashach Quarry, Hopeman. (**c**) Lower part of very large (air?) escape structure in Hopeman Sandstone in cliffs just east of coastguard tower at Gow's Castle (see Fig. 10.6). Context of escape structure shown in Fig. 11 of Glennie & Buller (1983).

For the most part they are isolated exposures, reaching a known thickness of about 30 m on the Hill of Spynie, in which the style of cross-bedding indicates an aeolian origin. Fossil reptiles (e.g. *Stagonolepis, Leptopleuron*) of Upper Triassic age (Benton & Walker 1985) from this formation were among the earliest described in Scotland.

Stotfield Calcrete Formation (formerly, Cherty Rock). At Stotfield, NW Lossiemouth (Fig. 10.9), the Heron Group is capped by about 5 m of variably silicified carbonate (silcrete), which in extreme cases becomes almost pure chalcedony, and calcite-cemented sandstone. These rocks are interpreted to be a former soil horizon, which beneath the Moray Firth is more commonly calcareous rather than siliceous, hence its preferred modern name of Stotfield Calcrete Formation (Cameron 1993). Offshore it forms an excellent seismic marker horizon of presumed Rhaetian age that thickens to about 25 m in the west.

On the western margin of the Moray Firth, in the vicinity of Golspie, the Stotfield Calcrete is overlain by an alluvial conglomerate of the Dunrobin Bay Formation, which contains plant spores of earliest Jurassic (Hettangian) age and numerous reworked clasts of the calcrete and underlying sandstones, indicating reworking and possible early activity on the Helmsdale Fault (Batten *et al.* 1986; Trewin 1993*c*).

Lossiehead Formation. Beneath the Moray Firth, the Burghead and Lossiemouth formations cannot be separated with certainty, so the term Lossiehead Formation was introduced by Cameron (1993) for the reddish-brown, white and grey sandstones, siltstones and mudstones that lie between the Stotfield Calcrete and Hopeman Sandstone formations (Fig. 10.4).

Smith Bank Formation. In the Central North Sea and southern Viking Graben the Zechstein (Turbot Anhydrite Formation) is overlain by monotonous red mudstones, up to 600 m thick in Quadrant 15, of the Smith Bank Formation (Fig. 10.4), that were deposited in saline lakes and playas. In the Central Graben these mudstones, in turn, were overlain by sandstones of the Skagerrak Formation (Cameron 1993; Fisher & Mudge 1998). The lower parts of the formation can be equated with the Bunter Shale Formation of the southern North Sea, its sediments likewise being interpreted as the deposits of a broad, shallow playa lake, but shale deposition dominated some parts of the Central North Sea until the end of the Triassic. In this respect, it matches the Mercia Mudstone Group of the Solway Firth and North Channel basins west of Scotland. In more basin-margin locations, sandstone stringers probably represent nearby fluvial input.

Skagerrak Formation. This formation comprises a monotonous sequence of reddish brown, grey or white, relatively poorly sorted fluvial (flash-flood) sandstones with rare conglomerates containing clasts of sandstone and Zechstein dolomite, and common rip-up clasts of clay. The sandstones alternate with thinner units of overbank and flood-basin siltstones. Fluvial transport directions are away from highland areas but with the ultimate transport direction southward along the Central Graben (Fig. 10.8c), the streams being deviated locally around rising Zechstein diapers (Goldsmith *et al.* 1995; Pooler & Amory 1999). There is some doubt, however, as to whether a fluvial connection with the Southern North Sea Basin was maintained through the Mid-North Sea High (Fisher & Mudge 1998). Mica is generally a minor constituent, but can be abundant in the Witch Ground Graben. Locally, the sand-stones are calcite cemented and form calcretes. With the use of distinct wireline responses and the palynofloral assemblages present in three mudstone intervals, the formation in the south Central Graben can be sub-divided into eight members; the mudstones are indicative of quasi-marine influxes along the graben axis from the south (Goldsmith *et al.* 1995; Pooler & Amory 1999).

Cormorant Formation. The Cormorant Formation is present in the North Viking Graben and East Shetland Basin areas, where a thick (commonly 1000 to over 1700 m) sequence of fluvial and lacustrine, grey to reddish-brown sandstones with minor mudstones and rare limestones (calcretes) was deposited in a series of half-graben sub-basins sub-paralleled to the axis of the Viking Graben (Fig. 10.4). Steel & Ryseth (1990) suggest that contemporaneous tectonic movements permitted the exten-sion of sand sheets across the basins from marginal bajadas.

Southwest Scotland

A series of Permian basins (Stranraer, Thornhill, Dumfries, Lochmaben and Annandale) overlie the western Southern Uplands with axial trends that vary between NNW–SSE and N–S, and contain sequences of red breccias, aeolian sandstones and water-laid sandstones (Fig. 10.12). The distribution of breccia and sandstone in these basins suggests active faulting at the time of deposition, so the sequences were unlikely to have been part of a once continuous sheet (Greig 1971). The sedi-mentary sequences in the basins indicate that deposition was controlled by climatic changes in humidity. Arid conditions of aeolian sandstone deposition over the Southern Uplands (Permian wind to WSW: Fig. 10.8a) are comparable to those at Mauchline in Ayrshire (Permian wind to WNW; see also Fig. 10.8b).

Thornhill and Dumfries Basins

Unconformably overlying Carboniferous or older strata, these basins are filled mainly with red aeolian sandstone underlain by, and locally intercalated with, breccias derived from pre-Permian rocks. In the northern Thornhill Basin, the breccias are interbedded with basaltic lavas (McMillan 1996). Although undated, the lavas are presumed to have an age similar to those at Mauchline (275–272 Ma; pre-Upper Rotliegend 2) and Sanquhar. Wind-facetted pebbles ('dreikanter') have been described from the breccias of the Thornhill Basin (Brookfield 1978), indicating lengthy periods of exposure to the wind (hundreds, if not thousands, of years).

Braided-stream conglomeratic sandstones were deposited on alluvial fans and grade down-stream into sheet-flood deposits that drain towards the south (Brookfield 1980). Along the western side of the Thornhill Basin, an upward increase in grainsize of the conglomerates and the absence of reworked aeolian sand near the top of the sequence may indicate a change to a more humid climate (Brookfield 1980); specula-tively, this may have been coeval with the late Rotliegend terrestrial flooding or Zechstein marine transgression seen in the North Sea, or the Bakevellia carbonates and evaporites of the Irish Sea and Ulster.

Thin aeolian sandstones are interbedded with the water-laid deposits of the basin margins, and overlie them in the basin centres. There, the sandstones are typically dune-bedded, the bedding attitudes indicating a wind that blew fairly consis-tently to the southwest. Wind-rippled bedding planes are relatively common. Rare localized clay drapes indicate at least some intermittent rainfall.

Even though no more than about 200 m of basin fill has been proven in water wells, and much less in quarries for building stone, Brookfield (1979) computed a minimum thickness of 700 m, while a gravity survey implied that the sedimentary fill of both the Dumfries and Lochmaben basins may be at least

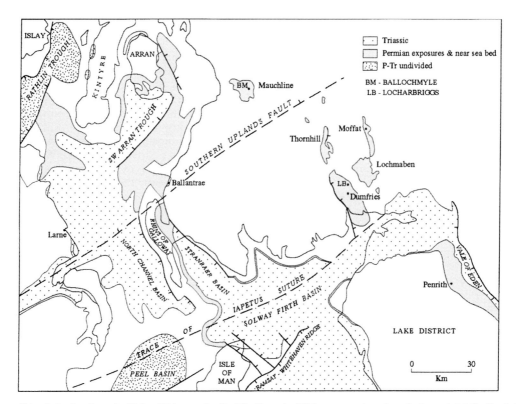

Fig. 10.12. Permo-Triassic basins from the Vale of Eden to the Rathlin Trough. Offshore areas based on Jackson & Mulholland (1993) and Fyfe *et al.* (1993).

1000 m thick (Bott & Masson-Smith 1960; Greig 1971). Akhurst & Monro (1996) consider that the Dumfries basin fill may reach a thickness of 1600 m. In the western half of the Dumfries Basin, the aeolian sandstones are closely associated with debris-flow breccias and water-laid sandstones of the Doweel Breccia Formation (Fig. 10.4), which may be the product of intermittant eastward-flowing basin-margin flash floods that eventually drained to the south; tongues of aeolian sandstone are intercalated with the breccias. Two different breccia fans have been recognized on the basis of their contained clasts (Criffel granodiorite and Carboniferous limestone in the south and greywacke and porphyry further north (Akhurst & Monro 1996)).

Lochmaben and Moffat Basins

Breccias and water-laid sandstones in the north grade southward into several hundred metres of mostly aeolian sandstones deposited by winds from the NE (Brookfield 1979). The aeolian sand is interbedded with wind-facetted clasts of basalt in the Hartfield Breccia (Brookfield 1978). The aeolian Corncockle Sandstone is noted for its reptilian footprints, and finds continued to be made at Locharbriggs Quarry following their first discovery in 1820 (Haubold 1971; Sarjeant 1974), the latest description being by McKeever (1994). As at Hopeman (Elgin area), the footprints seem to indicate that the reptiles were probably heading towards the nearest source of water, in this case south to the lower-altitude Solway Firth Basin.

Stranraer and North Channel (Portpatrick) Basins

The NNW–SSE trending North Channel and Stranraer basins are half grabens bounded by faults to their ENE. Along the western edge of the Stranraer Basin, especially in Loch Ryan, Permian breccias, with clasts dominated by greywacke, overlie Late Carboniferous and Ordovician strata; they terminate to the north before the Southern Uplands Fault is reached. The sequence becomes sandy upwards as it youngs eastward towards the Loch Ryan Fault.

The Late Permian Bakevellia sequence has a poorly developed basal limestone overlain by shales and two or three anhydritic zones that probably represent the glacially induced Zechstein cycles of the North Sea; halite, of uncertain Zechstein cycle, is present in the North Channel area. Triassic sediments (St Bees Sandstone) are interpreted to occur within Luce Bay, extending into the Solway Firth where the full Triassic sequence is present (Fig. 10.4; Jackson & Mulholland 1993).

The Late Triassic basin fill of the North Channel (or Portpatrick) Basin, lying between the Rhinns of Galloway and the NE coast of Ireland, terminates to the SE over Carboniferous strata. Further to the north, a full Late Permian to Triassic sequence similar to that drilled in the Larne No. 2 borehole (Penn et al. 1983) is expected to be present; over 1000 m of Rotliegend volcanics and sandstones are capped by 21 m of basal Bakevellia carbonates and 185 m of mudstones and evaporites, which are overlain in turn by another 1600 m of Triassic sandstones, mudstones and evaporites.

Solway Firth Basin

The Permo-Triassic basins of the Southern Uplands trend are flanked to their south by the WSW–ENE trending Solway Firth Basin, whose axis overlies the Iapetus Suture and in which the Permian and Triassic strata reach thicknesses, respectively, approaching 600 and 1000 m (Jackson & Mulholland 1993). The southern margin of the Solway Firth Basin is marked by the Ramsay–Whitehaven Ridge, and its western end by the

Rhinns of Galloway Uplift. West of this uplift is the isolated Peel Basin, to the north of which the North Channel Basin is continuous with the Clyde Basin (Fig. 10.12).

The Permo-Triassic is exposed at the eastern end of the basin in the vicinity of Annan and Carlisle, where it is in continuation with similar eastward-younging sequences in the Vale of Eden half graben. Jackson & Mulholland (1993) describe the Solway Firth sequences in terms of northern Irish Sea and Vale of Eden stratigraphy (Fig. 10.2). The Permo-Triassic succession comprises, from bottom to top, the Permian Rotliegend and 'Zechstein' (see later comments on *Zechstein/Bakevellia transgression*), and the Triassic Sherwood Sandstone and Mercia Mudstone groups.

Central Scotland

Mauchline Basin

Brick-red aeolian dune sandstone, about 450 m thick, overlies up to c. 300 m of lava flows, tuffs and agglomerates with interbedded aeolian sandstone and mudstone near the base. At one locality on the banks of the River Ayr, a tuffaceous mudstone has yielded a variety of plant impressions of probable Early Permian age (Wagner 1983). Radiometric (K–Ar) dates from the overlying lavas of 275 and 272 Ma (Fig. 10.6) support an Early Permian floral age.

The red foresetted Mauchline Sandstone (Fig. 10.13) was formerly exposed at Ballochmyle Quarry, Mauchline, but since the mid-1960s has been buried beneath household refuse. Bedding attitudes indicated that at this locality the Permian wind blew from the east. (Fig. 10.8a). Similar aeolian sandstones reported from near Ballantrae may indicate a more widespread distribution of the Mauchline Sandstone within the Midland Valley.

Arran and the Clyde Basin

The coastal regions of the Isle of Arran contain widespread exposures of Permian and Triassic redbeds. These rocks dip away from the Tertiary granite that dominates the northern half of the island. In the north of the island, the relatively small coastal exposure of Permian breccias and sandstones at the Cock of Arran extends offshore through 90° of arc as a narrow belt to the west and south (Fig. 10.12). The Cock of Arran sequence consists mostly of aeolian sandstones that are interbedded with, and overlain by, breccias and sandstones rich in clasts derived from Dalradian strata in the north or northwest. The fluvial sediments scoured channels into horizontally laminated aeolian sands. After correction for tectonic tilt, the bedding attitudes of the dune sands indicate a Permian wind that blew from about ENE (Piper 1970).

On the east coast, the c. 500 m thick Corrie Sandstone lies unconformably over Carboniferous strata. The contact is placed where a 3 m thick ridge of highly convolute-bedded white Carboniferous sandstone is overlain by undeformed Permian red aeolian sandstone (e.g. Piper 1970; McKerrow & Atkins 1985). At the contact small fissures filled with red Permian sand extend into the Carboniferous sandstone, showing that the latter was well lithified prior to the Permian, having suffered significant burial and uplift. The contact dips south at about 30°. Further south, the 740 m thick Brodick Beds were deposited as three climatically controlled sequences within a pull-apart basin SE of the Highland Boundary Fault (Frederiksen et al. 1998). The sequences comprised: (1) aeolian and sheet-sand sediments; (2) a similar sedimentary sequence reworked by fluvial floods; (3) alluvial gravels that were spread

Fig. 10.13. Large-scale aeolian cross-bedding in Mauchline Sandstone, Ballochmyle Quarry, Mauchline, Ayrshire. BGS photo. This quarry later became a landfill site.

towards the SE. The overall succession was controlled by climatic oscillations ranging between arid and sub-humid that seem to match Milankovitch cyclic theory.

The southern half of the island is dominated by south-dipping Permian sandstones and breccias and the overlying red Triassic mudstones. The sequence is cut by the Tertiary Central Ring Complex and is intruded by many related dykes and sills. To the south, a broad trough occupies the Firth of Clyde area between the Kintyre Peninsula and the Midland Valley of Scotland and could contain over 1000 m of Permian and Triassic sedimentary rocks. The regional extent of this Permo-Triassic basin is indicated by its southeastward limit on the coast at Ballantrae (Fig. 10.12), where Permian breccias and aeolian sandstones are exposed similar to those seen at Mauchline.

The general Permian sequence on Arran (Brodick, Corrie and Machrie Formations; Fig. 10.4) comprises aeolian sandstones that are interbedded with, and cut into by, fluvial breccias whose clasts were derived from pre-Permian rocks. In the southern part of the island these grade up into the Lamlash Sandstone, whose bedding structures are indicative of deposition in water, possibly a lake or series of lakes in which water-escape structures suggest possible flash floods, whereas desiccation cracks and mud-filled salt-crystal hoppers indicate at least seasonal aridity. The Lamlash Sandstone grades up into silty shales of the Mid to Late Triassic Mercia Mudstone Group. A time equivalent of the Zechstein marine flooding and succeeding Early Triassic Sherwood Sandstone has not been recognized, which raises the possibility that part of that time span could be represented by the Lamlash Sandstone (Lovell 1991). How far the Zechstein-age strata of the Larne wells extend north into the SW Arran Trough is not known; they are possibly limited to the North Channel and westward for an unknown distance under the Tertiary lavas of Ulster. The presence of Rhaetian strata (Penarth Group) within the Central Ring Complex indicates that a marine transgression reached this area in Late Triassic times.

Because of relatively strong tidal scour, Permo-Triassic sequences are exposed over the sea floor of much of the greater Firth of Clyde. British Geological Survey shallow boreholes (Cheshire *et al.* 1972) have enabled a simple subdivision into

Triassic (grey mudstones of the Mercia Mudstone Group; red sandstones with gypsum of the Sherwood Sandstone Group) and Permo-Triassic (red sandstones). Extrapolation from land exposures, coupled with interpretation of seismic data, has permitted a tentative assignment of much of the sea floor sequence to the Permian (Rotliegend) (Fig. 10.12).

Rathlin Trough and Loch Indal Basin

The Rathlin Trough extends to the NE from Northern Ireland to between the Kintyre Peninsula and Islay, while the smaller Loch Indal Basin lies SW of Islay, the margins of both being controlled by the underlying grain of the Dalradian basement (Anderson *et al.* 1995). Apart from limited BGS shallow sea-bottom boreholes, the only real stratigraphic evidence comes from the Magilligan and Port More boreholes in Northern Ireland (e.g. Fyfe *et al.* 1993). The Magilligan borehole shows that, beneath the Lias, the Penarth Group comprises 22 m of mudstone. This is underlain by 370 m of the Mercia Mudstone Group and 400 m of the Sherwood Sandstone Group, which unconformably overlies Namurian strata. In the Port More borehole, the Triassic sequence has thickened to almost 1200 m and is underlain by red sandstones containing rounded wind-blown sand grains and is tentatively ascribed to the Permian (Fyfe *et al.* 1993). All sea-floor occurrences in the Rathlin Trough are likely to be of Triassic age (Fig. 10.12). Late Permian (Bakevellia) carbonate or evaporite strata have not been recognized, although this could be an artefact of a lack of drilling in the basin.

Seismic evidence indicates that up to 2500 m of Permo-Triassic strata occur within the Loch Indal half graben. At its NE end, a Rhaetian marine bivalve fauna and microflora was recovered from a BGS shallow borehole; these identify the Westbury Formation in its most northerly known occurrence (Fyfe *et al.* 1993).

West of Scotland basins

A series of en echelon half grabens extend from offshore NW Ireland (Fyfe *et al.* 1993) to west of the Shetland Isles (Stoker *et al.* 1993). These basins evolved as part of the same structural development as those of SW Scotland and the Irish Sea. Here they are treated separately with the Great Glen Fault providing a convenient dividing line. Following an early almost complete lack of stratigraphic control, oil-related surveys are beginning to result in a few firm guidelines.

Stornoway

Prior to the seminal studies by Steel (1971) and Steel & Wilson (1975) on the Stornoway Formation of Lewis (formerly shown on Geological Survey maps as Precambrian Torridonian), several of the smaller unfossiliferous red-bed exposures in the area were assigned to the Torridonian or the Devonian Old Red Sandstone successions. Steel demonstrated that the 1200 m thick Stornoway Formation was deposited over the faulted western margin of the Minch Basin, the eastern feather edge of which on Skye, Raasay, Mull and at Applecross and Gruinard Bay, passes up into fossiliferous Rhaetian or Liassic sequences. A Permo-Triassic age has now been adopted for many other isolated sequences that are considered to have close sedimentological affinities with the dated land exposures. Samples from the Stornoway Formation give a magnetic pole that corresponds with the Late Permian pole for Europe (Storetvedt & Steel 1977), thus strongly supporting a Permo-Triassic age.

The Stornoway Formation (Steel 1971; Steel & Wilson 1975) is in fault contact with and lies unconformably over the Lewisian. It comprises mostly alluvial-fan sediments that spread their debris eastward into the Minch Basin, where it was then transported down the regional slope to the north, becoming finer (sandier) in the process. Mudflow, streamflow and braided-stream deposits were recognized but the whole sequence is devoid of any indication of age. Some 600 m of braided stream deposits are overlain by a similar thickness of conglomeratic mudflow sediments. Speculatively, the braided stream deposits are possibly of Permian age while the mudflow sediments possible correlate with the more argillaceous Mercia Mudstone Group of the Triassic that is better developed further south. It is worth noting that in well 156/17-1, 45 km NE of Stornoway, some 450 m of Triassic sandstones and mudstones are overlain by the Lower Jurassic and underlain by the Torridonian.

Other west of Scotland basins

Exploration wells have been exceedingly valuable in deciphering local sedimentary successions even when devoid of faunas, floras or datable lavas, and regional inferences can be made when associated with a seismic profile. Towards the base of the thick (up to 8000 m) West Orkney succession, an 817 m-thick interval of halite beds, anhydritic mudstone and claystone, limestone and dolomite as well as thin sandstones has been logged in well 202/19-1 (Fig. 10.5a; Stoker *et al.* 1993). This interval, which is tentatively correlated with the Zechstein of the North Sea area, is underlain by anhydritic sandy mudstones (Rotliegend-age desert lakes?) below which conformable, parallel seismic reflectors of unknown age and lithology possibly also represent the Rotliegend. The upper almost 1500 m of this well section, which reaches the sea floor in the West Orkney Basin, consists mostly of sandstones ascribed to the Triassic.

Other thick sequences have been recognized seismically and, in some cases, have been calibrated by drill and wireline logs as Permo-Triassic. For example, in 205/27a-1 in the East Solan Basin, the upper part of a *c.* 500 m succession of sandstones and calcareous and anhydritic claystones has been dated as earliest Triassic (Scythian) (Stoker *et al.* 1993). Just to the west, where it is overlain by 900 m of Triassic sandstones

that are capped unconformably by Jurassic strata; the same claystone has more recently been given a Griesbachian (basal Scythian) age. It is underlain by Kazanian and Tatarian shales and sandstones that contain non-marine palynomorphs (*Vittatina* sp. & *Leuckisporites virkkiae*) that are correlated with the Zechstein Group (Swiecicki *et al.* 1995; Herries *et al.* 1999). These palynomorphs also occur near the top of the Rotliegend in the North Sea. Lithologies and palynology indicate that these Late Permian shales were probably deposited in a lacustrine environment.

The former more extensive distribution of Permian strata has been confirmed in several wells (e.g. 206/13-1) where Permian microflora have been reworked into Late Cretaceous to Danian sediments (Hitchen & Ritchie 1987). Although not confirmed by the drill, a seismic interpretation by Mudge & Rashid (1987) infers the presence of Permo-Triassic strata in half grabens in the Faeroe Basin, but the presence of Permo-Triassic sequences beneath the adjacent Tertiary lavas has yet to be confirmed. At other localities, shallow BGS boreholes have shown that red beds of presumed Permo-Triassic age occur at or just below the sea bed in many areas. Seismic data indicate the presence of up to 2000 m of sediments in the Flannan Trough and perhaps 4000 m in the West Flannan Basin (Fyfe *et al.* 1993; Stoker *et al.* 1993; Hitchen *et al.* 1995). A trough adjacent to the southwestern extension of the Great Glen Fault in SE Mull is reported to contain very thick sediment (Johnstone & Mykura 1989); to the SW in the Colonsay and Malin basins, the Permo-Triassic may attain a thickness of 2000 m (Fyfe *et al.* 1993).

Red-bed inliers in the vicinity of Tongue, Sutherland, were long considered to belong to the Old Red Sandstone. Johnstone & Mykura (1989), however, prefer a Permo-Triassic age on the grounds of similarity with offshore cores of presumed Permo-Triassic sediments, the presence of incipient calcretes ('cornstones') and fossil soils, not known in the local ORS, and the bright red colours of the sediment, which contrast with the dull purple of similar ORS lithologies of the north coast.

Thick Permo-Triassic sequences in half grabens are recognized on seismic and inferred from occasional deep wells in the West of Scotland area but the few outcrops of probable time-equivalent sediments are confined to their basin edges. Such outcrops have been mapped on Mull and Ardnamurchan, the northern tip of Rhum, on Skye, Raasay and Scalpay, at Applecross, Gairloch and Gruinard Bay, Ardnamurchan and Morvern and the west coast of Kintyre. Rare indications of age occur as in Skye, for example, where orthoconglomerates and rythmites are overlain conformably by basal Jurassic (Hettangian) marine limestones (Nicholson 1978), and on western Mull where 12 m of marine, Late Triassic (Rhaetian Penarth Group) carbonates, sandstones and shales are locally exposed. The Rhaetian age of its bivalve fauna is supported by the occurrence of diagnostic miospores in the shale sequence (Warrington & Pollard 1985). At many of these localities, small outcrops of conglomerate (locally with a basal breccia) and brick-red sandstone variously overlie Torridonian or Moine rock, a few of which are overlain by Liassic marine mudstones. Some of these are described below in a little more detail.

Gruinard Bay and Isle of Ewe

A succession of over 100 m of interbedded purple, pebbly sandstone and conglomerate laid down in southerly derived alluvial fans is overlain by 135 m of northward-flowing fluvial sandstones deposited by meandering rivers. These latter comprise well-defined upward-fining cycles of pebbly sandstone, bright orange wind-deposited sandstone, and fine sandstone showing evidence of fossil-soil formation (Johnstone & Mykura 1987).

Raasay and Scalpay

Fining-upward sequences of conglomerates, sandstones and concretionary carbonates ('cornstones'), total 75–90 m in thickness and grade up into Lower Jurassic marine sediments on Raasay (Bruck *et al.* 1967). The coarser sequences were probably deposited on alluvial fans close to their source. The Triassic fluvial sequence is similar to that seen at Gruinard Bay and was derived from a structurally high area to the SW in Skye (Fig. 10.8c); aeolian beds are not reported. The Permo-Triassic sedimentary rocks of Raasay and Applecross were possibly deposited in the same fault-controlled half graben.

Skye

The Triassic alluvial-fan and floodplain sedimentary sequences exposed in central Skye between Broadford Bay and Loch Eishort are thought to overlie a former ridge that had been the source of the Triassic sediments on Raasay; the Skye sequence must therefore be younger. East of Loch Slapin an alluvial-fan system of streamflood and mudflow conglomerates spreads eastwards, whereas the pebbly sandstones of a possibly coeval floodplain facies were transported to the SW (Steel *et al.* 1975); Nicholson (1978) interprets associated laminated siltstones (graded rhythmites) underlying the Liassic on the eastern shore of Loch Slapin as turbidites that were deposited on the floor of a lake. This part of Skye seems to mark a watershed for Triassic fluvial transport directions, essentially to the north into the Minch Basin and to the south into the Inner Hebrides Trough (Fig. 10.8b), whose northern limit migrated northward with time.

Fluvial transport directions

In the basins and troughs to the west of Scotland, conglomerates and sandstones were deposited mostly on alluvial fans that fed braided streams. Transport was northward in or marginal to the Sea of the Hebrides and Minch basins and, east of the Skerryvore Fault, to the SW or south along the Inner Hebrides, Rathlin and SW Arran troughs, (Fig. 10.8b); in the latter there is a gradation southward into playa-lake siltstones and mudstones with developments of calcrete ('cornstone').

Zechstein/Bakevellia transgression

The Zechstein Sea transgressed the North Sea basins from the north via the Viking Graben, but to find any route for a suggested marine transgression of the Irish (Bakevellia) Sea is far from easy. The existence of the sea was first proposed by Smith (1970), who suggested a link with the open ocean via the west of Scotland. Such a transgression would have to cross a series of Caledonian structural highs (e.g. Islay–Donegal Platform, Middle Bank; Fyfe *et al.* 1993) or the Irish landmass, for which there is no evidence prior to the Jurassic. The sea did not transgress northward via the Irish Sea as both the Permian and Triassic pinch out against the Welsh highlands and Anglesey–Isle of Man Uplift (Jackson *et al.* 1987; Jackson & Mulholland 1993). A possible route across the Pennines via the mixed aeolian and sabkha environments of the Eden Shales was ruled out by Skipsey (1989), with the possible exception of a marine Belah Dolomite, and a route around the southern end of the Pennines to the Cheshire Basin seems even more implausible.

The character of the Bakevellia carbonate and evaporite sequences is very restricted both in lithology and organisms, the latter commonly being represented by little more than the rare alga (*Calcinema*) and one bivalve (*Bakevellia binneyi*). These fossils also occur in the near-shore carbonates of the Zechstein succession of NE England (Smith *et al.* 1970), their presence in both the Zechstein and Bakevellia sequences possibly resulting from a tolerance to highly saline conditions, whether marine or lacustrine. Colter & Barr (1975) refer to the sparse microfloras in the Bakevellia sequences as particularly disappointing.

Many workers (e.g. Fyfe *et al.* 1993) quote the presence of dolomite and evaporites, especially halite, as indicative of deposition in a marine environment. Lacustrine dolomite, however, is known in association with evaporites (e.g. Dean & Fouch 1983); and bedded halite is an important constituent in the wholly terrestrial Rotliegend desert lake of the North Sea's Southern Permian Basin (e.g. Glennie 1972), and occurs in many Holocene lakes in areas of marked aridity (e.g. Great Salt Lake, Utah; Umm as Samim, Oman) that are well above the level of any conceivable marine transgression. Lakes can develop in areas of low rainfall if a subsiding land surface intersects a regional water table, and in an arid climate that soon leads to an increase in salinity and eventually to halite precipitation.

Outline of oil and gas reservoirs

Permian

The Rotliegend sandstone reservoirs of the southern North Sea contain gas of Carboniferous origin. They provided the first offshore objectives for the hydrocarbon industry in UK waters in 1964/1965. In several fields in Scottish waters (e.g. Auk, Argyll), both Zechstein dolomites and Rotliegend sandstone reservoirs contain the commercially more valuable oil of Late Jurassic origin. The Kimmeridgian source rock matured deep within the Central Graben, enabling the oil to migrate up the graben flanks to the shallower reservoir sandstones (see Fig. 10.5c, d). In Auk (block 30/16), the Rotliegend reservoir comprises up to 500 m of aeolian sandstone, and other slightly less permeable sands that had been reworked into a lacustrine environment just prior to deposition of the basal Zechstein Kupferschiefer (Trewin & Bramwell 1991). The Argyll and Innes fields also contained oil in Rotliegend dune-sand reservoirs (Robson 1991), but are now abandoned.

The earliest production of oil in both Auk and Argyll was from Late Permian Zechstein dolomites, which have a vuggy porosity created by pre-Chalk (?pre-Triassic) subaerial exposure and karstification. The Zechstein reservoir has an average thickness of around 8.5 m in Auk (probably all Zechstein cycle 1), whereas in Argyll, the 10–31 m thickness probably represents the first two cycles of the Zechstein.

Oil-bearing Zechstein reservoirs have been encountered in a number of fields in the Outer Moray Firth area, Claymore, Ettrick and Morag (Taylor 1998), although none of them contain large volumes. Of Claymore's 500×10^6 barrels of recoverable oil, only about 1% is from the Zechstein Halibut Formation reservoir (Harker *et al.* 1991). The Morag accumulation underlies the Maureen oilfield.

Triassic

The only known oil in the Smith Bank Group occurs in the Josephine Member in the Josephine Field, but this has yet to be confirmed as commercial. Cementation of the Skaggerrak sandstones of the Kittiwake Field (block 21/18) on the Western Platform has reduced permeability to the extent that oil in the reservoir is virtually immovable; economic production is confined to the overlying Jurassic reservoir of the Fulmar Formation (Glennie & Armstrong 1991).

Better results were encountered in fields of the East Shetland Basin. In the giant Brent Field, the main reservoir is within the Middle Jurassic Brent Group, but the latest Triassic to Early Jurassic Statfjord reservoir has porosities in excess of 20% and permeabilities reaching several Darcies (see Chapters 11 & 19). The greater part of the giant multi-reservoired Statfjord Field lies in Norwegian waters, and only a small area of its Statfjord reservoir is in UK (Scottish) waters (Roberts *et al*. 1987). In the Cormorant Field, the Cormorant Formation is typically argillaceous and carbonate cemented, and thus a poor reservoir, but oil has been produced locally on test. The Statfjord Formation reservoirs gas condensate in the Penguin Field (block 211/13).

Hydrocarbons within the Central Graben have been discovered in Triassic reservoirs in several fields. In Judy (Block 30/7a) (Goldsmith *et al.* 1995), the Department of Energy (1998) give recoverable reserves of 5.23×10^9 m^3 (33×10^6 bbl) of liquids. There are several small fields in close proximity to each other (Marnock, Skua and Egret in block 22/24 and Heron, which straddles blocks 22/29 and 22/30). The total recoverable reserves for these four fields is given by Pooler & Amory (1999) as 180×10^6 STB of oil, and 779×10^9 SCF of gas.

The fluvial sandstones of these fields were deposited in N–S trending depocentres or 'pods' (Hodgson *et al.* 1992) located between diapiric salt ridges that confined flow across an alluvial braidplain. The Skagerrak reservoir sands were probably deposited by perennial streams whose flow rates were highly variable. The quality of good channel-type reservoir sands (Porosity, 18–21%; Permeability, 1D) was damaged by proximity to faults. The preservation of useful porosity and permeability at depths below 12 000 feet (3658 m) in Heron and Egret is possibly explained by the presence of thin chlorite rims to the sand grains, which is thought to prevent the formation of quartz overgrowths. Heron and Egret are HP/HT (high pressure >12 000 psi; high temperature >340°C) fields.

To the west of Scotland, Strathmore (blocks 204/30a, 205/26a) in the East Solan Basin, is the only field with a Triassic reservoir. It is estimated to have over 200×10^6 barrels of oil in place but, because of generally low matrix permeabilities, recovery will probably be only 36×10^6 barrels, a recovery factor of less than 18%. The Otter Bank Sandstone reservoir, with a thickness 550 to 800 feet (168–244 m) comprises a stacked sequence of alternating braided stream (highly variable flow apparently to NE, SE and SW) and sabkha deposits with extensive aeolian dune sands (wind mainly from east). Overlying the reservoir is the Foula Sandstone, which acts as a top seal because of its very poor permeability. This is thought to result from a higher content of immature ductile lithic grains, which compact on burial, and an upward increase in pore-clogging kaolinite. The grains of Otter Bank Sandstone, by contrast, have a chlorite coating that preserves the pore throats from later diagenesis (Herries *et al.* 1999).

Summary

With the exception of minor (late Triassic?) horizons on the west coast with marine fossils, the Permo-Triassic strata exposed on land over the rest of Scotland are entirely of terrestrial origin. Most of the more extensive Permian exposures are dominated by aeolian sandstones indicative of an arid climate, although there was sufficient water and vegetation for reptiles to live. The Triassic strata of the west contain more evidence of fluvial and lacustrine deposition, suggestive of a more humid climate, but even here, aeolian sandstone and the widespread occurrence of anhydrite (e.g. West Orkney Basin) is evidence of post-depositional playa or sabkha aridity.

Offshore well and seismic data have placed the mostly basin-edge exposures into their regional context. Early Permian volcanic activity, especially in Germany, resulted from an early breakdown of the Variscan orogen; thermal uplift resulted in widespread erosion at this time. Upper Rotliegend 2 fluvio-lacustrine and aeolian sedimentation followed a second phase of volcanic activity, perhaps coinciding with initial opening of the Viking–Central system of grabens. In the Late Permian, basin centres seem to have been well below global sea level at the start of the Zechstein transgression. At least four cycles of marine flooding led initially to deposition of basin-margin carbonates followed by evaporation and anhydrite deposition basinward of the carbonates, and halite in the basin centres. The Inner Moray Firth Basin was not flooded by the Zechstein Sea, fluvial and lacustrine sedimentation possibly adjusting to a water table that fluctuated with a combination of climate and a subsiding basin floor. A similar situation may have occurred west of Scotland where no transgression route can be recognized and, arguably, dolomites and evaporites of the time equivalent Bakevellia sequences lack clear confirmation of a marine environment of deposition.

A reversion to terrestrial conditions of deposition probably took place just before the end of the Permian (e.g. latest Permian dune sands in the Inner Moray Firth; erosion and karstification of the Zechstein reservoir in the Auk Field). East of Scotland, lacustrine mudstones of the Smith Bank Formation in the Central North Sea were later covered by increasing amounts of fluvially transported sands (Skagarrak Formation); these are replaced upward and northward by cleaner fluvial sands of the Cormorant Formation.

Early Triassic sandstone deposition west of Scotland was replaced upwards by the Mercia Mudstone Group, which was deposited mostly in small evaporative lacustrine basins or, perhaps, influenced by rare marine incursions from the south. Eventually, a major marine transgression extended northward via the Irish Sea, reaching the vicinity of the Minches only in the latest Triassic (Rhaetian). East of Scotland, the Rhaetic transgression seems not to have reached Scottish waters.

The marine areas west and east of Scotland have had very different structural histories. Because of Early Tertiary uplift in the west related to the opening of the Atlantic, very thick sequences of mostly Triassic continental sediments in half grabens now lie at, or just below, the sea floor. In the east, however, Late Permian continental Rotliegend and Zechstein marine sedimentation was controlled to a large extent by the opening of the Central–Viking graben system, with Zechstein halite diapirs controlling much of the ensuing Triassic continental sedimentation. Late Mesozoic subsidence centred over the graben system has carried Permo-Triassic sequences to depths of some 3–5 km.

11 Jurassic

J. D. HUDSON & N. H. TREWIN

Until the late 20th century, accounts of the Jurassic rocks of Scotland mainly comprised descriptions of the fine coastal outcrops of the Inner Hebrides region, with emphasis also on the east Sutherland coast with its spectacular boulder beds of Kimmeridgian age. That changed with the discovery and development of the North Sea oilfields, where much of Britain's oil is found in Jurassic sandstone reservoirs and has its source in Kimmeridge shale. Thus for many geologists the Jurassic is known principally from seismic reflection lines and down-hole geophysical logs. Hydrocarbon exploration also revealed a major episode of Jurassic volcanism in the Central North Sea. Nevertheless, the onshore outcrops retain their relevance. Those along the Moray Firth are directly marginal to the Inner Moray Firth Basin and provide many analogies to the other North Sea Basins. The western outcrops, with a much more

complete section exposed, were important in the history of geology and continue to stimulate research in biostratigraphy, sedimentology and palaeoecology. They also serve as onshore guides to the stratigraphy of the recently explored basins to the west of Scotland.

Palaeogeographic and structural outline

During the Jurassic, Scotland and the North Sea lay at approximately 37°N latitude, at the southern opening of a strait, separating the Precambrian shields of Greenland and Fennoscandia, that connected the Arctic Sea to a broader, island-studded epeiric sea covering most of Europe. This sea then connected southwards to the Tethys (Bjerrum *et al.* 2001,

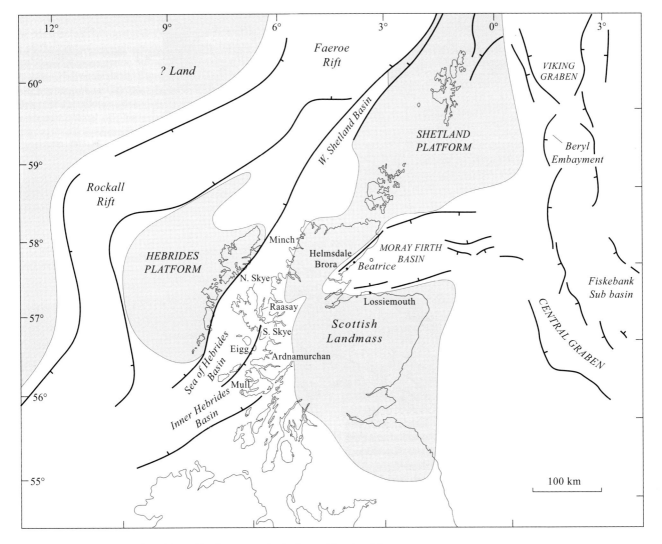

Fig. 11.1. Map to show general position of land areas, major basins and key localities.

fig. 2). Modelling results suggest that the climate was strongly seasonal, with warm, relatively dry summers (mid-20s °C) and cool wet winters (below 10°C), especially to the north of our region. This resulted in a strong latitudinal gradient in temperature and run-off, and hence salinity in the seaway, that varied through the Jurassic in response to changes in sea level and wider palaeogeographic shifts in the North Atlantic region (Sellwood *et al.* 2000; Bjerrum *et al.* 2001; Sellwood, pers. comm. 2001).

The local palaeogeographic framework comprises a Scottish landmass, which was generally emergent, and Shetland and Hebrides platforms of variable extent depending on relative sea level and tectonic events (Fig. 11.1). The structural style of the Scottish Jurassic basins is dominated by regional extension associated with North Sea rifting to the east and stretching, premonitory of the later opening of the Atlantic, to the west.

Basins are separated by tilted fault blocks that were affected by footwall uplift at times of extension. The position and orientation of these faults varied over time; they are not parallel to the present Atlantic spreading ridge. There is controversy as to whether the faults in the Hebridean area are reactivated Caledonian structures, or are entirely the result of Mesozoic extension (Roberts & Holdsworth 1999).

In the North Sea, sedimentation was mainly controlled by the structural evolution of basins centred on the Viking and Central Graben, together with the Moray Firth Basin closer inshore. Jurassic outcrop bordering the North Sea is confined to the coastal strip from Golspie to Helmsdale in Sutherland, with borehole evidence of onshore Lower Jurassic at Lossiemouth, south of the Moray Firth. The Helmsdale Fault forms the western margin of the Inner Moray Firth Basin (Fig. 11.2), and actively controlled sedimentation in the Kimmeridgian

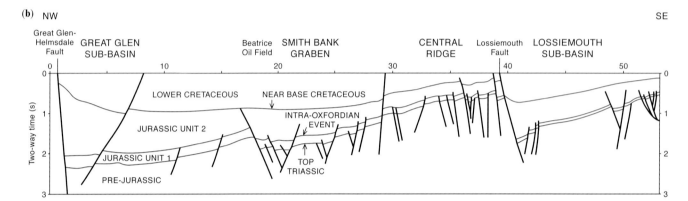

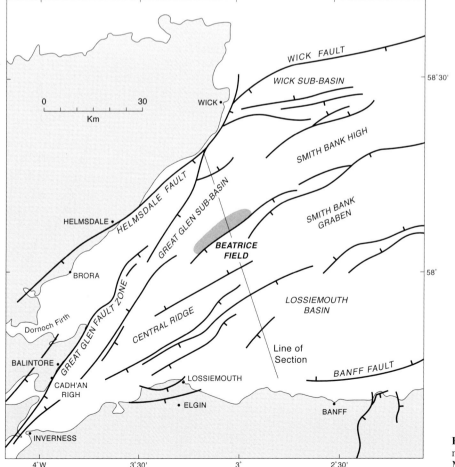

Fig. 11.2. (a) Location and structural map and **(b)** cross-section of the Inner Moray Firth.

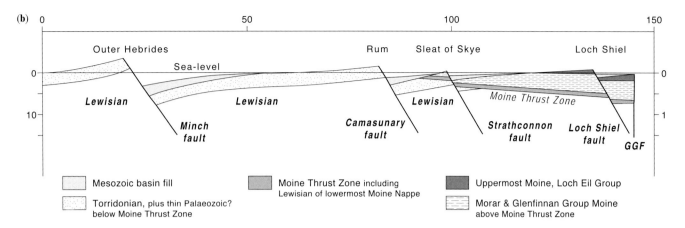

(b)

Mesozoic basin fill

Torridonian, plus thin Palaeozoic?
below Moine Thrust Zone

Moine Thrust Zone including
Lewisian of lowermost Moine Nappe

Uppermost Moine, Loch Eil Group

Morar & Glenfinnan Group Moine
above Moine Thrust Zone

(a)

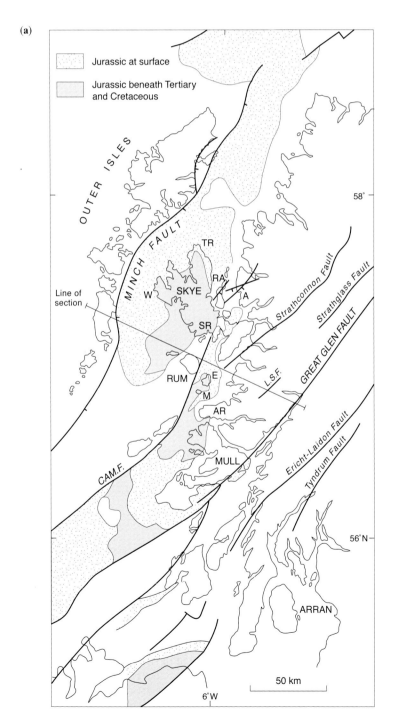

Jurassic at surface

Jurassic beneath Tertiary
and Cretaceous

50 km

Fig. 11.3. (a) Location and structural map for the Jurassic of western Scotland. A, Applecross; CAM. F, Camasunary Fault; LSF, Loch Sheil Fault; E, Eigg; M, Muck; RA, Raasay; SR, Strathaird; TR, Trotternish; W, Waterstein. Based on Fyfe *et al.* (1993). (b) Schematic cross-section of the Hebrides basins during the Jurassic, showing Mesozoic sediments and marine deposition in half-graben, and uplifted pre-Caledonian basement in the footwalls of faults. Stratigraphic thicknesses and water depths are not intended to be accurate and are conjectural on the mainland east of Skye. The present level of erosion is about 1–2 km below the sea level datum of the section. Simplified from Roberts & Holdsworth (1999).

when the fault formed a sea-bed feature against which the debris-flow deposits of the Helmsdale Boulder Beds accumulated. These outcrops provide valuable onshore analogues for offshore graben-margin oilfields such as those of the Brae area. The North Sea Jurassic has been summarized in Evans *et al.* (2003) and by Underhill (1998), thus only a brief outline is included here.

To the west of Scotland, the Hebrides Basin (Fig. 11.3) is a complex half-graben, initiated in Triassic (or possibly late Palaeozoic) times and continuing to subside throughout the Jurassic. The major bounding fault is the Minch Fault, which hugs the east coast of the Outer Isles, coming onshore only near Stornoway on Lewis where Triassic red-beds are exposed (see Chapter 10). It dips steeply east, into the basin. It probably coincided with the average position of the western shoreline of the Hebridean sea, though evidence is lacking and the exact position of the shoreline doubtless fluctuated. The eastern flank of the basin is less well-defined, but probably approximately follows the west coast of the Scottish mainland. This margin was not generally faulted, but the land to the east of it was subject to recurrent uplift, and was the source for most of the sediment delivered to the Hebridean seaway; this sediment was coarse and voluminous at times, particularly during the Mid-Jurassic. Other faults, notably the Camasunary–Skerryvore Fault that runs SSW from south Skye, between Rum and Eigg, were active at times during the Mesozoic. The Camasunary Fault divides the present Sea of the Hebrides sub-basin from the Inner Hebrides sub-basin, but its influence on Jurassic topography and sedimentation is uncertain. There is a general gentle dip of the Jurassic towards the bounding faults. Major complications occur in the vicinity of the Tertiary plutonic centres.

The Hebrides Basin is the best known of a series of basins, with intervening tilted fault-blocks, that extended westwards across the Scottish continental shelf, and originally, before the opening of the North Atlantic, to Greenland (Fig. 11.1). The other basins do not have onshore outcrops, and in most the Jurassic is concealed beneath Cretaceous sediments and Tertiary lavas. Their structure and stratigraphy is being revealed by petroleum exploration. Only a brief outline is given here; for further information refer to Parnell (1992), Fyfe *et al.* (1993) and Stoker *et al.* (1993). Overviews of the whole Atlantic margin can be found in Fleet & Boldy (1999).

Stratigraphic outline

In this account the Jurassic is divided into three parts corresponding broadly to Early, Mid- and Late Jurassic. The breaks are taken at a sea level fall within the Toarcian and a major sea level rise in the Early Callovian, so that Late Toarcian sediments are considered along with the Mid-Jurasssic and Callovian ones with the Late Jurassic (Fig. 11.4). The onshore exposures of each subdivision are described, and put into the context of regional basin development. It is outside the scope of this volume to provide details of the offshore geology; offshore stratigraphic detail has been omitted or simplified as far as possible.

In a very broad sense, the stratigraphical history of the Scottish Jurassic is similar to that of the English: a marine transgression in the Late Triassic–Early Jurassic, marine and mostly offshore Lower Jurassic, shallow-water and partly non-marine Aalenian to Bathonian, and renewed transgression in the Callovian, continuing into the Kimmeridgian.

At the end of the Triassic, continental red bed deposition continued in basins to the west and east of Scotland. The Scottish landmass, including parts of the Shetland Plat-

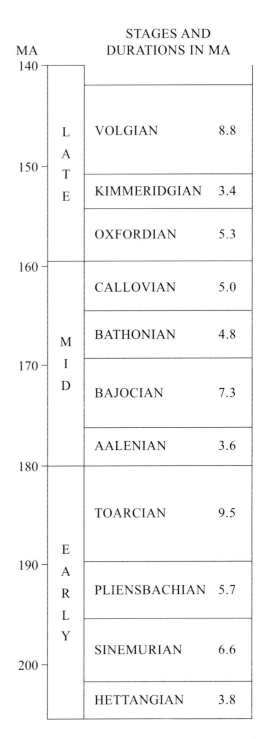

JURASSIC STAGES

STAGES AND DURATIONS IN MA

MA			
140			
	L A T E	VOLGIAN	8.8
150		KIMMERIDGIAN	3.4
		OXFORDIAN	5.3
160		CALLOVIAN	5.0
	M I D	BATHONIAN	4.8
170		BAJOCIAN	7.3
		AALENIAN	3.6
180		TOARCIAN	9.5
190	E A R L Y	PLIENSBACHIAN	5.7
		SINEMURIAN	6.6
200		HETTANGIAN	3.8

Fig. 11.4. Jurassic stages and absolute ages, based on Gradstein & Ogg (1996).

form and the Hebrides Platform, was undergoing erosion, and deposition took place in a variety of fluvial and alluvial environments where evaporation rates were high. Caliche soil profiles attest to slow deposition in a semi-arid climate. Scotland lay about 35–40°N of the equator at the boundary of arid and seasonal humid climatic belts. In Late Triassic (Rhaetic) and Early Jurassic times basin areas were progressively flooded by shallow seas invading the region from the south. The extension of shallow seas was accompanied by a change to a more humid and possibly more temperate climate. A lush vegetation and higher run-off resulted in development of rivers with deltas at the marine margin, and the red bed deposition characteristic of the Permo-Trias generally ceased. A Scottish landmass still existed and was possibly breached by the sea in the region of the Great Glen. Occurrences of

Hettangian–Sinemurian ammonites at two localities in Arran serve to link the Scottish and Northern Irish Lias successions.

The Hebridean Jurassic succession (Fig. 11.5) is more complete than that of the east coast or the North Sea. Sea level was generally rising in the Early Jurassic with highly variable shallow marine carbonate and clastic deposits at basin margins (e.g. south Skye) but thick shaly Lias in local fault-bounded

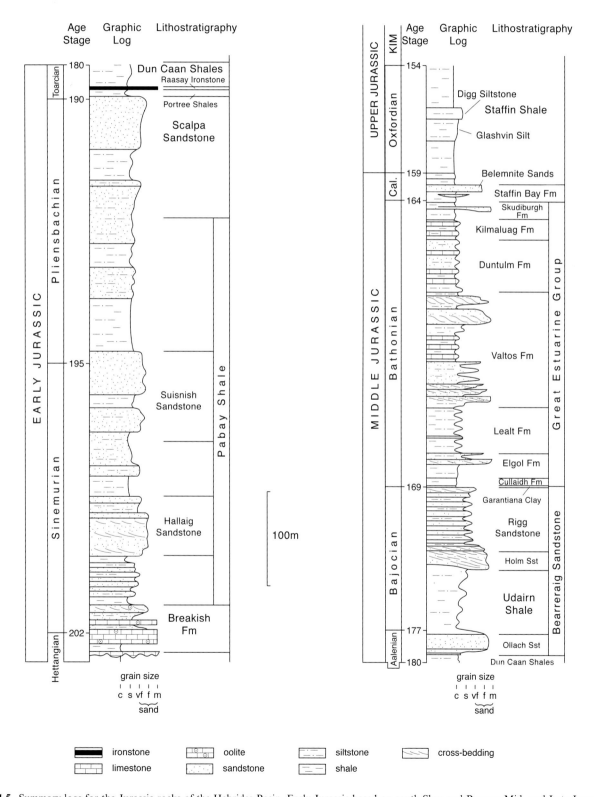

Fig. 11.5. Summary logs for the Jurassic rocks of the Hebrides Basin. Early Jurassic based on south Skye and Raasay, Mid- and Late Jurassic on Trotternish, north Skye. Modified from Hesselbo & Coe (2000).

troughs (north Skye). The succession contains a higher proportion of coarse clastic material than its English equivalents. The Middle Jurassic features marine sandstones of Aalenian–Bajocian age, of very variable thickness but including the thickest sandstones of the British Jurassic, overlain by Bathonian mixed salinity lagoonal to freshwater deposits of the Great Estuarine Group. Although deposition clearly took place in very shallow water, the Hebridean succession lacks the delta-top and fluvial facies of the Middle Jurassic that is found in parts of the North Sea and in Yorkshire.

To the east of Scotland, clastic deposition characterizes the Lower Jurassic of the Moray Firth region. In the North Sea, at the junction of the Viking, Central and Moray Firth grabens, Mid-Jurassic volcanism and doming (Stephen et al. 1993; Underhill & Partington 1993) resulted in intra-Jurassic erosion producing the Mid-Cimmerian Unconformity, and Toarcian–Bajocian strata are consequently absent from the coastal outcrops of the Moray Firth. A major rise in sea level in Callovian times is recorded in outcrops both east and west of the Scottish landmass (Sykes 1975) and rapid deepening resulted in marine shale deposition, culminating in the organic-rich deposits of the Kimmeridge Clay Formation in basinal areas.

Facies and sequences

In general, the Scottish Jurassic contains more coarse clastic material than its English or European equivalents. It lacks thick, pure limestones, and nearly all the so-called shales are micaceous, ferruginous and silty or even sandy. Hallam (1969, 1975) refers to this facies association as the 'arenaceous, argillaceous and ferruginous facies of northern Europe'. Although this is generally regarded as a proximal facies association, there are few examples of Jurassic rocks resting directly on pre-Triassic basement, so that the position of shorelines is poorly defined. Morton (1989; summary in Morton & Hudson 1995) interprets the Hebridean succession in sequence stratigraphic terms as seven sequences, each in general floored by a disconformity (sequence boundary), followed by a transgressive fine-grained unit that coarsens-up to the next hiatus. The final sequence is incomplete because of pre-mid-Cretaceous erosion, and the sequences may not all be of comparable nature. Lower Jurassic sequence stratigraphy is discussed in detail by Hesselbo & Jenkyns (1998).

In the North Sea a sequence stratigraphic approach is successfully used in offshore correlation, frequently relying on the recognition of Maximum Flooding Surfaces (MFS) that can be correlated on log characteristics. Hence a sequence-stratigraphic template has been established (e.g. Partington et al. 1993; Underhill & Partington 1993, 1994) and related to ammonite and palynological biostratigraphy. With more than 33 MFS regionally correlated in the North Sea (Underhill 1998) a detailed template is established for correlation within much of the Jurassic, but problems still exist in non-marine parts of the sequence such as the Bathonian. Some caution must be exercised in the sequence stratigraphic approach, as advocated by Underhill (1998), particularly in areas of active faulting where the effects of sea level change on deposition are overprinted or even masked by structural activity.

In general the facies sequences in the basins were controlled directly by sea level. However, hinterland uplift, climatic variations affecting the basinal areas, run-off from land areas and the terrestrial vegetation all exerted important influences. Interpretation of these factors is increasingly aided empirically by geochemical studies (e.g. Hendry et al. 2001; Holmden & Hudson 2000), and by modelling of global and regional climate (e.g. Sellwood et al. 2000; Bjerrum et al. 2001).

Regional and Historical Survey

Hebrides Basin

The most extensive Jurassic outcrops in Scotland occur in the Inner Hebrides and adjacent areas: Skye, Raasay, Eigg, Muck, and Mull have the most important sections (Fig. 11.5). Smaller outcrops are present on Rum and the Shiant Isles, and at Applecross, Ardnamurchan and Morvern on the mainland. There are also small and poorly known occurrences, of Lias only, on the coast of Wester Ross, and as blocks in a Tertiary igneous centre on Arran. Because they are easily eroded and abundantly fossiliferous, the rocks of the main outcrop are very distinctive within their region, both topographically and in the geological opportunities they afford.

The Hebridean Jurassic was important in the early development of historical geology and palaeontology, being investigated by Macculloch, Murchison, Sedgwick, Forbes and Miller, among others. The foundations for later work were laid by Judd (1873, 1878). The Geological Survey produced a series of Memoirs in the early 20th century; the delayed North Skye Memoir (Anderson & Dunham 1966) is a continuation of this tradition. Interest revived in the 1950s in response to the growth of sedimentology and palaeoecology as disciplines.

The area is of wide importance in Jurassic biostratigraphy and biogeography because many horizons yield excellent ammonite faunas, and it occupies a critical position between the North-west European Province of the Tethyan Realm, and the Sub-Boreal Province of the Boreal Realm (e.g. Page 1996). It is also important in correlating palynological with ammonite-based zonal schemes (e.g., Riding et al. 1991), a matter of great significance given its proximity to the North Sea oil province. Public interest has been generated by the discovery of dinosaur footprints and remains on Skye (Andrews & Hudson 1984; Clark et al. 1995; Clark & Barco Rodriguez 1998). Investigations of the offshore successions beneath the Minch have been conducted by the BGS using geophysical surveys and shallow boreholes (Binns et al. 1974; Fyfe et al. 1993). A deep onshore borehole has been drilled near Dunvegan, Skye by Pentex (Upper Glen No.1.) and B.P. drilled well 156/17-1 in the North Minch Basin. Deeper exploration of basins west of Shetland, the Hebrides and Ireland has been pursued by BGS (Stoker et al. 1993) and by the oil industry; well 206/5-1 in the Faeroe-Shetland Basin is particularly informative for Jurassic stratigraphy (Haszeldine et al. 1987).

Reviews of the Hebridean Jurassic have been published by Hallam (1965, 1983, 1991) in previous editions of Geology of Scotland, and by Hudson (1983). Field guides to Skye and Raasay by Morton & Hudson (1995) and to Skye by Hesselbo & Coe (2000) include reviews of the literature, as does the Memoir on Rum and adjacent islands (Emeleus 1997). Detailed field information from these sources will not be repeated here. The Jurassic rocks of Mull and Ardnamurchan have not been as well covered in recent field guides. The Lower Lias of both the Skye and the Mull-Morvern areas has been reviewed by Hesselbo et al. (1998); see also Morton (1999a, b).

Burial history, metamorphism and hydrothermal activity. It was once thought surprising that the Hebridean Jurassic in view of its situation within a Tertiary volcanic province should contain preserved fossil aragonite, dolomite-micrite with pristine isotopic composition, straw-coloured spores, vitrinite particles with low reflectance, and unstable biomolecules. Many studies have now established that this is the case for places such as north Trotternish on Skye, and Kildonnan on Eigg. Hudson & Andrews (1987) summarize earlier work; see also Thrasher (1992), and Lewis et al. (1992). Mesozoic burial history as a component of basin evolution has been assessed by Morton

(1987). Burial beneath lavas in the Palaeocene has evidently had no noticeably greater effect than burial under an equivalent mass of sediment. Only in proximity to intrusions is this situation modified. With most sills and dykes, the effects are limited to an immediate contact zone. Feeder dykes, such as the gabbro dyke on Muck, produce high temperature aureoles (Emeleus 1997), but only for a few metres from the contact. The only widespread zones of alteration are those around the major plutonic centres of Skye and Mull, where meteoric-water hydrothermal circulation systems extended several kilometres from the igneous centres. The main Jurassic hydrothermally affected outcrops are in Strathaird on Skye (Hudson & Andrews 1987), and parts of the Loch Don area on Mull. Within these areas shales are blackened, hardened and lose fissility, no aragonite is preserved, unstable clay minerals are recrystallized, oxygen isotopic composition of calcite becomes lighter due to interaction with circulating meteoric-derived waters, and vitrinite reflectance increases to anthracite grade.

North Sea and Sutherland Coast

Stratigraphic nomenclature. Jurassic nomenclature is exceedingly complex, in large measure due to the detail in which the rocks have been studied, both offshore and onshore (Figs 11.6, 11.7). Lithostratigraphic schemes have generally been applied to the onshore sequences, with minor variations between different accounts. The rapid development of offshore exploration resulted in numerous schemes, some specific to particular companies; the result being that names change across offshore block boundaries. Deegen & Scull (1977) brought some order to offshore nomenclature, but proliferation of lithostratigraphic names continued. Richards *et al.* (1993) produced a revised lithostratigraphic scheme for the North Sea (Fig. 11.6). Greater success in offshore stratigraphic analysis has been achieved by combining the principles of sequence-stratigraphy with biostratigraphic data derived mainly from ammonites, foraminifera and palynology (summary in Underhill 1998).

Burial History. The Jurassic of the coastal outcrops of the Inner Moray Firth has not been deeply buried and is immature with respect to hydrocarbon generation. However, as traced NE along the Helmsdale Fault the base of the Jurassic is buried to over 4 km in the Wick Basin, and hydrocarbons have been generated which have charged the Jurassic reservoirs of the Beatrice oilfield (Fig.11.7). The oil source rocks are likely to have been Devonian lacustrine sediments (see Chapter 8) and Early Callovian lagoonal deposits (see below).

Early Jurassic (Hettangian to Toarcian)

Although deposition was more widespread, the present distribution of Lower Jurassic strata in the North Sea has been greatly affected by Mid-Jurassic doming and erosion centred on the rift junction. Thus Lower Jurassic strata only remain in the western Moray Firth, North Viking Graben and as a small area in the Fiskebank Sub-basin to the east of the Central Graben. The only onshore exposures are at Golspie in Sutherland (Fig. 11.7), but Lower Jurassic is also present to the south of the Moray Firth near Lossiemouth (see below). Sedimentation generally commenced in a fluvial setting, giving

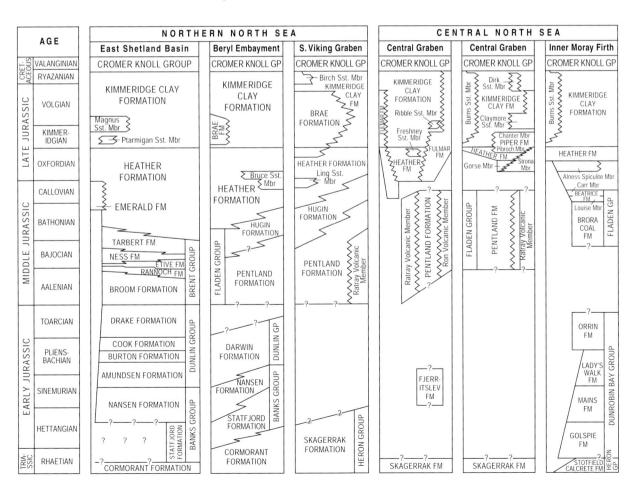

Fig. 11.6. Stratigraphic framework of the North Sea Jurassic, modified after Richards *et al.* (1993).

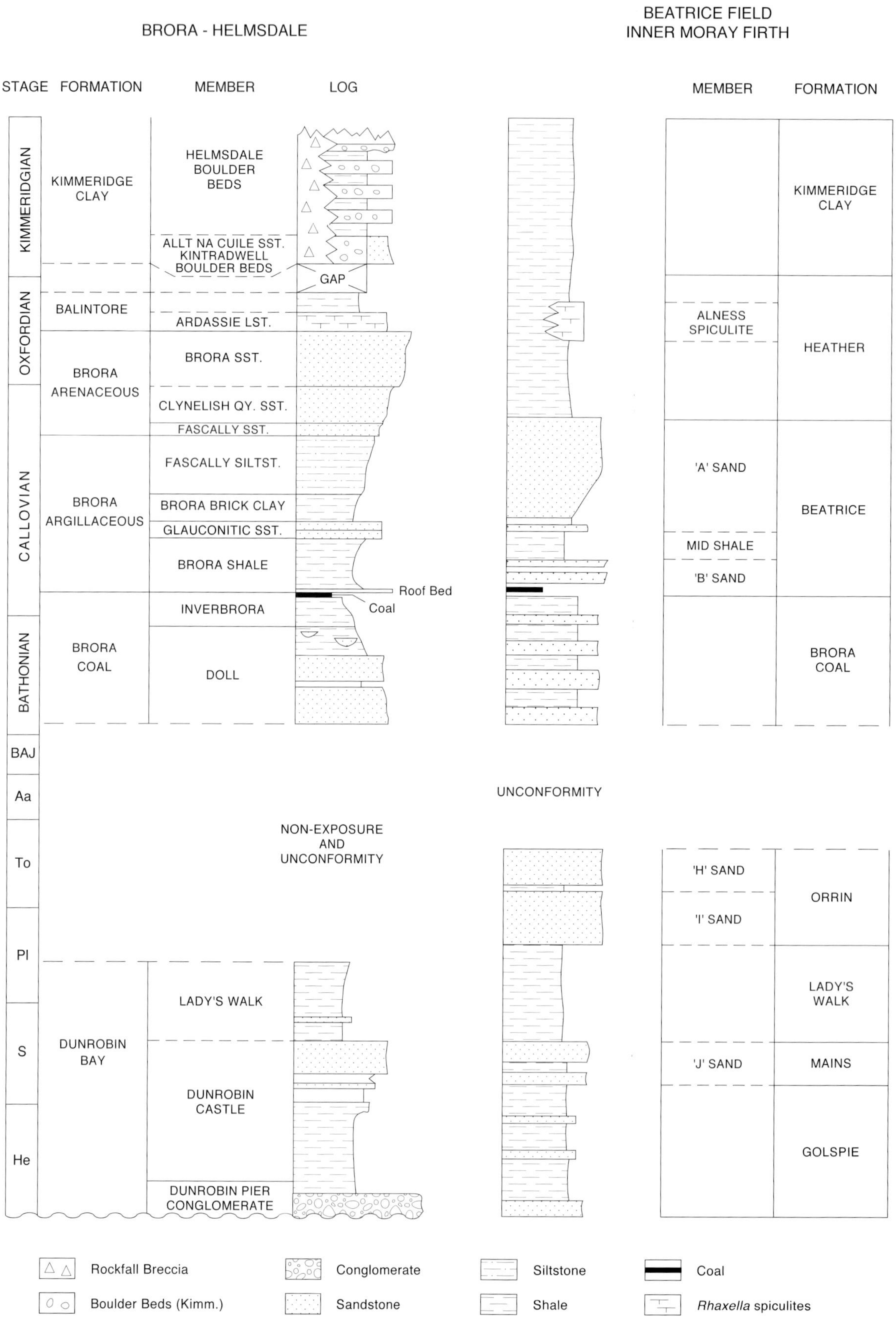

Fig. 11.7. Stratigraphic comparison of the Jurassic of the onshore section and the Beatrice Field, Inner Moray Firth.

way in the Late Sinemurian to normal marine conditions in an epeiric basin experiencing thermally driven subsidence that followed earlier Triassic rifting. To the west of Scotland, Early Jurassic ranging from shoreline to basinal facies is present in the Hebrides and Minch basins and excellent exposures, mainly of basin margin facies are seen onshore, particularly on Skye and Raasay.

Viking Graben, North Sea

Richards *et al.* (1993) divide the Lower Jurassic of the Viking Graben into the Banks Group and the Dunlin Group (Fig. 11.6). Within the Banks Group the Statfjord Formation is dominated by sandstones deposited in cyclic sequences; the sandstones tend to have erosive bases with pebble lags, rip-up mud clasts, and are frequently trough cross-bedded. Sandstones fine upwards into mudstones that are red to grey, and certainly near the base of the sequence contain caliche soil profiles. Higher in the Statfjord Formation rootlet beds and thin coals occur in grey mudstones between the sandstones. The succession is dominately fluvially with the sandstones interpreted as channel fills and the finer deposits those of the alluvial plain. The upward change from arid conditions with caliche soil profiles to grey mudstones reflects climatic change at the Triassic–Jurassic boundary.

The Nansen Formation of the Banks Group comprises pale coloured sandstones, frequently well sorted and with a carbonate cement. These sandstones progressively onlap the east Shetland Platform, and are interpreted as transgressive shallow-marine deposits. The formation is probably diachronous, being part time-equivalent to the Statfjord Formation.

The Dunlin Group is shale-dominated and ranges from Sinemurian to Toarcian in age and has been divided into four formations in the Viking Graben area (Fig. 11.6). These formations are probably equivalent to the Darwin Formation in the Beryl Embayment. The Amundsen Formation is a coarsening-up sequence of bioturbated mudstones, siltstones and fine-grained sandstones deposited in an offshore marine environment. The overlying Burton Formation is mudstone dominated with occasional sandy laminae and ripples, and sparse bioturbation. It contains horizons with authigenic phosphate, chamosite,

siderite and glauconite. This formation was deposited under low-energy shelf conditions and water circulation may have been poor. Iron and phosphate-rich horizons probably accumulated at times of very low clastic supply.

Sandstones of shallow marine origin with bioclastic debris and abundant bioturbation characterize the Cook Formation. Several units of sandstone are present, and one, Cook A, shows the typical coarsening and cleaning-upward trend of a prograding shallow-marine sandstone sheet. The overlying Drake Formation comprises marine calcareous mudstones and sandstones with thin oolitic sideritic ironstones. This formation is eroded beneath the Mid Cimmerian Unconformity in many sections. In the Beryl Embayment the Darwin Formation of bioturbated siltstones and sandstones is of Pliensbachian to Toarcian age and represents a similar shallow marine shelf environment to that of the north Viking Graben.

Inner Moray Firth

The only onshore outcrop of the Early Jurassic ('Lias') of the Moray Firth Basin is at Golspie in Sutherland. Exposures (usually poor) of Triassic to Jurassic occur on the beach between tide marks. The Dunrobin Bay Formation, as defined by Batten *et al.* (1986), corresponds with part of the Dunrobin Bay Group of Richards *et al.* (1993). The Jurassic strata overlie sandstones, mudstones and calcretes of presumed Triassic age. The junction is not seen but the overlying Dunrobin Pier Conglomerate Member at the base of the Formation (Fig. 11.8) contains abundant reworked caliche, chert and sandstone clasts from the Trias, hence the junction is considered to be locally erosive. The conglomerate records fluvial conditions with fining-up cycles of conglomerate, cross-bedded sandstone and grey muddy sandstones. The latter yield a terrestrial flora with spores of probable Hettangian age (Batten *et al.* 1986). Current directions indicate transport to the NE; parallel to the Helmsdale Fault. It is possible that this represents the earliest evidence of activity on the fault, with reworking of Triassic deposits. The conglomerate does not occur in offshore boreholes and is probably restricted to the basin margin close to the Helmsdale Fault. The climatic change marked by the transition from caliche in the Trias to grey plant-rich lithologies

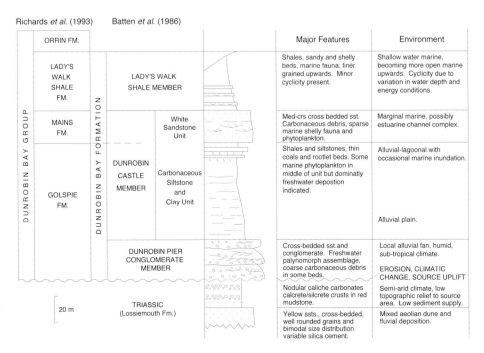

Fig. 11.8. Lower Jurassic nomenclature, succession and interpreted depositional environments, Golspie section. Modified after Batten *et al.* (1986).

in the Hettangian represents a change to a more humid climate with a rich vegetation cover on the Scottish Landmass.

The Dunrobin Castle Member (Fig. 11.7) is seldom exposed apart from the White Sandstone Unit (Mains Formation of Richards *et al.* 1993). Evidence from drilling (Neves & Selley 1975) shows that 73 m of shales and siltstones are dominantly of freshwater alluvial plain origin, but towards the top, occasional high abundances of marine dinocysts record possible lagoonal conditions. The White Sandstone is a clean, cross-bedded sandstone that shows increasing marine influence at its top; it has been interpreted as an estuarine channel, but may represent a barrier bar which separated dominantly alluvial from marine conditions (Trewin 1993c). Richards *et al.* (1993) elevated this sandstone to the status of Mains Formation, including it as the equivalent of the sandstones, siltstones and organic-rich mudstones that comprise the lowest (J sand of Linsley *et al.* 1980) reservoir of the Beatrice Field (Fig. 11.7).

The overlying Lady's Walk Shale Member (Lady's Walk Formation of Richards *et al.* 1993) was studied in detail by Lee (1925), but only a few of the beds in his numbered sequence can usually be seen. The lower part of the member comprises shales, siltstones and sandstones in which individual beds have characteristic faunas of bivalves (*Ostrea, Gryphaea, Modiolus, Pleuromya* and pectinids) and rhynchonellid brachiopods. Thin coarsening-up cycles represent shallowing with increased energy and reworking. The highest strata seen are blue-grey shales with calcareous concretions, representing more open marine conditions. Rare ammonites of Sinemurian (*raricostatum* Zone) and Pliensbachian (*jamesoni* Zone) age are present, together with belemnites. Nearness to shore may be indicated by the presence of erosional gutters filled with sandstone containing pebbles, belemnites, rhynchonellids and woody debris (Trewin 1993c). Offshore the Lady's Walk Shale Formation fines up to a horizon with calcareous concretions, once considered to represent an unconformity, but now recognized as a continuous but condensed sequence (Stephen *et al.* 1993).

The only other Early Jurassic on the east coast is recorded in the Lossiemouth borehole (Berridge & Ivimey-Cook 1967; Peacock *et al.* 1968) where a similar upward transition from non-marine to marine strata with *raricostatum* Zone ammonites is present. Detrital mineralogy indicates that the sandstones were probably derived from the Grampian area to the south of Lossiemouth (Hurst 1985).

The Orrin Formation (Richards *et al.* 1993) is not seen onshore, but offshore it consists of up to 60 m of strata. A lower coarsening-upward sandstone (The I sand of Beatrice Field) representing shoreline sands capped by a deltaic distributary mouth bar complex, is overlain by sandstones (H sand of Beatrice Field) of fluvial channels, alluvial plain mudstones, thin coals and lagoonal facies. The Orrin Formation (Toarcian) is truncated by the Mid-Cimmerian Unconformity, and overlain by Bathonian strata (Fig. 11.6).

West of Scotland

The general succession in the Lias Group is shown in Fig. 11.5. As in much of northern Europe, the Rhaetian and Hettangian stages saw a marine transgression over the terrestrial and partly arid plains that characterized basinal areas during most of the Triassic; upland areas were progressively eroded so coarse breccio-conglomerates, widespread in the Triassic alongside scarps are unknown in the Jurassic. Rhaetian is known on Arran and Mull, but on Skye and Raasay the earliest horizon that can be dated biostratigraphically is Hettangian. Marine sandstones and limestones in the Skye–Raasay–Applecross area comprise the Breakish Formation of Morton (1999a); the Broadford Formation of Hesselbo *et al.* (1998) and the Lower

Broadford Beds of earlier literature. The dated Hettangian rocks rest apparently conformably on red sandstones usually regarded as of Triassic age, but Morton (1999b) believes that in central Skye these may be of Jurassic age, and that the Jurassic transgression was diachronous. The Ob Lusa coral bed, near the base of the type section at Breakish near Broadford, Skye, contains large massive colonies of *Isastraea*, and probably formed near a shoreline. 20 m higher is the Breakish coral bed with branching colonies of *Thamnasteria* forming a small patch reef. Oolitic limestones also indicate shallow, warm, agitated seas. These occurrences are noteworthy so near the northern limit of the European Jurassic. The Breakish Formation is progressively overlapped by later strata in a southwesterly direction in central Skye, indicating the drowning of an island within the basin; see below. For further details of the Breakish Formation on Skye see Hallam (1959), Searl (1992, 1994), and summaries by Morton & Hudson (1995) and Hesselbo *et al.* (1998).

On Raasay the Breakish Formation has about the same exposed thickness as at Broadford but is more limestone-dominated. It yields mid-Hettangian ammonites (Morton 1999b). The succession in the Breakish Formation at Applecross is in nearshore facies, though Hesselbo *et al.* (1998) dispute some of the evidence of emergence claimed by Searl (1989). There is a small outcrop of Breakish Formation at Dibidil on Rum, where 35 m of metamorphosed strata, overlain by Tertiary basalt, are exposed as a sliver within the main ring fault that formed around the Rum Tertiary plutonic centre (Emeleus 1997). The facies is similar to that in Skye; it includes corals. Ammonites are rare in the Breakish Formation (but see Morton 1999b) and the benthic fauna is of restricted variety, notably including the oyster *Liostrea* and the thick-shelled shallow-burrowing bivalve *Cardinia*.

The approximately correlative strata on Mull and Morvern are mainly in a more offshore facies of alternating fine-grained limestones and marls, with more ammonites: the Blue Lias Formation (Hesselbo *et al.* 1998). The succession in Ardnamurchan is transitional to the northern, Breakish Formation facies, and small thicknesses of Blue Lias facies occur at outcrop in Skye and Raasay (Hesselbo *et al.* 1998, fig. 19); more notably, the thick succession (c. 600 m) in Upper Glen No 1 in North Skye is mainly in Blue Lias facies. Occurrences of Hettangian–Sinemurian ammonites at two localities in Arran serve to link the Scottish and Northern Irish Lias successions.

The Pabay Shale Formation combines the Upper Broadford Beds and the Pabba Shale of earlier literature, a disconformity that was thought to separate the two having been disproved by recent research (Hesselbo *et al.* 1998). The rocks are strongly micaceous and ferruginous bioturbated siltstones and fine sandstones, with many beds in the lower part (the former Upper Broadford Beds) containing abundant *Gryphaea arcuata*, the 'devil's toe nail'. These strata are well exposed at Ardnish, near Broadford, Skye. Ammonites are much more common than in the beds below, and allow accurate correlation with the standard zonal sequence. This facies is generally interpreted as deeper-water and more off-shore, but clearly clastic input to the basin increased and the clay mineralogy changed from montmorillonite to illite-kaolinite (Amiri-Garroussi 1977). Abundant nodular phosphate and the presence of berthierine (chamosite), including an oolitic iron-stone bed at Ardnish, are also consistent with the onset of a wetter climate with increased run-off of both solid and dissolved load from the source areas; the positions of the shore-lines are not well defined. An exception to this is the outcrop on Loch Slapin in Skye, where Pabay Shales with *Gryphaea* rest unconformably on Ordovician Durness Limestone. Karstic cavities in the limestone, some surfaces of which bear *Gastrochaenites* borings, are filled with laminated sediments of probable Early Jurassic age (Nicholson 1978; Amiri-Garroussi 1982; Farris *et al.* 1999).

The upper part of the Pabay Shale Formation is more uniform across the area than the preceding units; it is predominantly ammonite-bearing, micaceous, bioturbated silty shale. It is notably thicker than its English equivalents, testifying to continued subsidence combined with abundant clastic supply to the basin from a well-vegetated hinterland. Sellwood (1972) describes minor coarsening-upwards cycles with corresponding changes in bivalve faunas and trace-fossil assemblages. At Allt Fearns on Raasay, for instance, ammonites are common (sometimes enclosed in sideritic concretions) as are large bivalves; such as surface-living pectinids, *Gryphaea*, and *Hippopodium*; shallow-burrowing forms such as *Cardinia*, and deeper-burrowing *Pholadomya*. The Breakish/Blue Lias and Pabay Shale Formations are much thicker in the Upper Glen No.1 borehole in northwest Skye, which is near the depocentre of the basin. The total thickness of the Lias Group there (*c.* 2400 m) is approximately double that seen at outcrop in the central Skye–Raasay area (Hesselbo *et al.* 1998).

The upper part of the Pabay Shale Formation generally coarsens upwards, and beds of micaceous sandstone appear. Thus the base of the overlying Scalpa Sandstone Formation is gradational. In general terms, the sandstone represents an episode of shallowing and clastic influx shown by the 'Middle Lias' (Domerian or Upper Pliensbachian) over much of England, but it is much thicker. Thus renewed uplift of a nearby source of coarse detritus is implied, taking effect earlier in the north: sand appears in the Lower Pliensbachian (*ibex* Zone) in Raasay but Upper Pliensbachian (*margaritatus* Zone) in Mull. The top of the sandstone extends into the early Toarcian. The most noticeable member of the fauna is the large scallop *Pseudopecten aequivalvis*. Large calcareous concretions occur, as in most Hebridean Jurassic sandstones. The sandstone is one of the major scarp- and cliff-forming units in the succession, and landslips occur where it caps steep slopes of incompetent Pabay Shale, as at Hallaig on Raasay.

The main part of the Toarcian is represented, as in much of northern Europe, by dark shales, the Portree Shale Formation, overlain in the Hebrides by the Raasay Ironstone Formation. The shales are at maximum 14 m thick and the ironstone less than 2.5 m; the formations are sandwiched between thick sandstones so are generally poorly exposed. The shales yield characteristic Lower Toarcian ammonites such as *Dactylioceras*, which also occur along with common belemnites in the berthierine-oolite ironstone, which was mined on Raasay from 1912 to 1919 (see Draper & Draper (1990) for mine history). The ironstone is stratigraphically condensed and probably includes hiatuses, as also indicated by rolled and worn belemnites within it. It may not be of the same age everywhere in the basin. This Toarcian episode of slow and intermittent sedimentation, offshore and probably deep water by Hebridean standards, is unique within the Jurassic succession of the region. It is followed by a major hiatus, and deposition only resumes close to the end of the Toarcian, with rocks that are best described along with the Middle Jurassic.

Western Offshore Basins

Lower Jurassic strata are widely distributed in basins lying to the west of Scotland, both north and south of the Hebrides Basin with its exposed Jurassic. The present disposition of the Jurassic, and indeed of the 'basins' themselves, is the result of a combination of original deposition and subsidence and later tectonic and erosional activity. The North Minch Basin is separated from the Skye area by the Rubha Reidh basement ridge, though this may not have existed in the Jurassic

(Morton 1992). It contains up to 2500 m of Jurassic sediments east of the Minch Fault, thinning eastwards. 360 m of Lower Jurassic strata, comparable to the Skye succession, have been drilled near the centre of the basin (Well 156/17-1) (Fyfe *et al.* 1993). Small outcops near Gruinard Bay on the mainland are marginal to this basin. Poorly known Jurassic stata in the Colonsay and Malin basins were probably once connected to the Inner Hebrides sub-basin as exposed from south Skye to Mull. The sparse information on basins west of the Outer Hebrides and of the Shetland islands is summarized by Morton (1992), who also considers basins to the west of Ireland, and by Stoker *et al.* (1993).

Early Jurassic Palaeogeography

With so little preserved evidence there are many uncertainties in any palaeogeographic reconstruction for the Early Jurassic of Scotland (Fig.11.9). The extent of land areas is difficult to determine, and would have fluctuated considerably as sea level changed. Any interpretation in the region of the North Sea triple junction is based on supposition that facies extended normally across the area prior to uplift and erosion.

The exceptionally thick Lower Jurassic of Northern Skye was presumably sourced from the Scottish Landmass and possibly also from the Hebrides Platform. The thin marginal calcareous Broadford Beds of the initial transgression imply that there was no great relief to the western margin of the Scottish Landmass at the start of the Jurassic. In the Moray Firth derivation from the northern part of the Scottish Landmass and the Grampian area can be demonstrated, and it is possible that the landmass was split along continuations of the Helmsdale Fault trend (but the Great Glen Fault does not seem to have been active at this time). There is no strong evidence for the close connection between west and east on the basis of sedimentology and faunas, and since the two areas had open connection to the sea in the south they would have been equally affected by sea level changes. Large pieces of fossil wood in the Hettangian at Golspie show that the land was well vegetated early in the Jurassic, following the arid environment of the Late Trias.

'Mid' Jurassic (Aalenian to Bathonian)

Over much of the North Sea the Mid-Cimmerian Unconformity underlies deposits of Mid- or Late Jurassic age. The unconformity is most marked in the area of the North Sea triple junction where doming and erosion took place in Aalenian–Bajocian times, followed by volcanism in the Bathonian to Early Callovian, and progressive subsidence and marine incursion of the area into the Oxfordian (Figs 11.10, 11.11). The unconformity is most marked in the central area of the North Sea where sub-unconformity erosion proceeded down to sub-Triassic basement. The subsequent progressive marine onlap began in Aalenian times, but did not completely cover the central area of doming until Late Oxfordian. Thus the unconformity is defined by erosional truncation, followed by progressive marine onlap. The material eroded from the dome contributed sand to the surrounding basins, and resulted in a basinward facies shift (see Underhill 1998, fig. 8.26). Thus, fluvial, deltaic and lagoonal facies are present in the Aalenian–Bathonian Brent Group of the Northern North Sea, the Pentland Formation of the Central North Sea, the Bathonian Great Estuarine Group of the Hebrides, and Brora Coal Formation of the Inner Moray Firth. However, in regions distant from the centre of domal uplift (e.g. Skye, Brent Province) sea level fluctuations had an increasingly dominant effect.

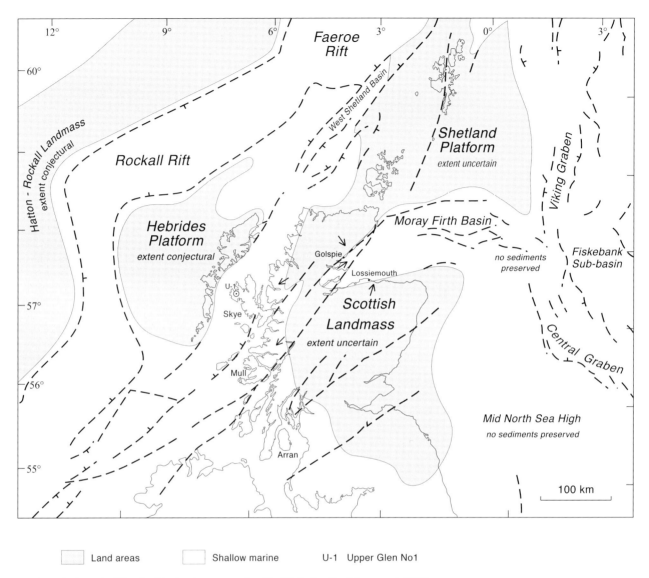

Fig. 11.9. Early Jurassic (Pliensbachian) palaeogeography. Modified after Bradshaw *et al.* (1992).

Viking Graben, North Sea

The Brent Group of the northern Viking Graben is Aalenian to Bathonian in age and up to 500 m thick. The sandstones and mudstones record the northward progradation and subsequent drowning by southerly transgression of a major wave-dominated delta that was supplied with sediment from the eroding North Sea dome to the south. The Group comprises the Broom, Rannoch, Etive, Ness and Tarbert formations (Fig. 11.6). Whilst general models of Brent Group sedimentation (Budding & Inglin 1981) give a good impression of the facies and depositional environments, delta development was subject to widespread variation due to the interaction of flooding events due to relative sea level rises, subsidence providing accommodation space for the sediments, and sediment supply. Thus units such as the Mid-Ness Shale provide time lines and record rapid and widespread changes in the delta top environment; such events are superimposed on the overall sedimentation trends.

Within the Brent Group, the Broom Formation (Aalenian) is dominated by coarse sandstones, sometimes pebbly, that rest on the Mid-Cimmerian Unconformity surface or its correlative conformable junction. The Formation is variable in derivation reflecting mainly lateral supply through fan-deltas to the Viking Graben. The sandstones vary from massive and poorly sorted to crossbedded and are generally interpreted as marine.

The Rannoch Formation is a coarsening-up sequence commencing with thin micaceous fine-grained laminated sandstones and mudstones with minor bioturbation. Sand content increases up-section and strata display low-angle lamination with frequent scours and wavy lamination. Laminae onlap the margins of scours in the manner of hummocky cross-stratification and the formation is interpreted (e.g. Scott 1992) as a prograding shoreface environment subject to wave action due to storms. The general coarsening-up character represents progressive shallowing.

The overlying Etive Formation is interpreted as a shoreline complex. It displays two major facies types. The first is a continuation of the upward coarsening of the Rannoch, culminating in parallel laminated units displaying low angle cut-offs and interpreted as upper shoreface and barrier beach deposits. The second comprises erosively based channels with cross-bedding and mudstone rip-up clasts. These have been interpreted as micro-tidal channels cutting a wave-dominated barrier island complex, but could also represent incised valley-fills.

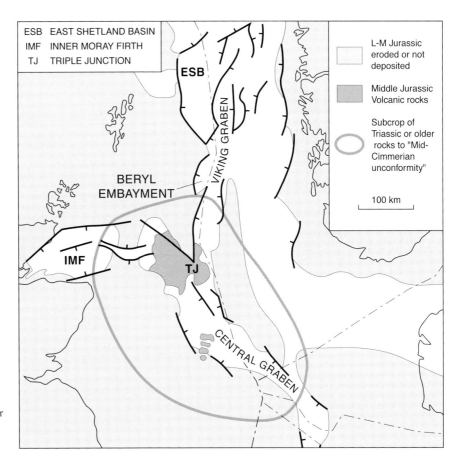

Fig. 11.10. Sketch map to show location of Middle Jurassic volcanics at the North Sea triple junction, and the area over which Lower Jurassic rocks are absent beneath the Mid-Cimmerian Unconformity. Modified after Spencer *et al.* (1996) and Underhill (1998).

A great variety of lithofacies comprise the Ness Formation; sandstones, mudstones and coals with rootlet beds. Environments represent a varied delta top with levée-bounded distributary channels, distributary mouth-bars, lagoons and vegetated delta plain. This plexus of environments was probably highly susceptible to sea-level variation, and the Mid-Ness Shale that divides the formation represents a marine incursion over the delta top. The Ness Formation records the end of the dominantly northward progradation of the Brent delta.

The Tarbert Formation consists of fine to medium-grained grey to brown sandstones. The formation is strongly diachronous due to progressive southerly stepped transgression of the delta top. Transgression is also recorded onto the Shetland Platform at this time. The Tarbert Formation is locally separated from the underlying formations by an unconformity (Underhill *et al.* 1997) and shows a distribution related to extensional faulting at the margins of fault-bounded blocks. The Heather Formation completes the Mid-Jurassic sequence in the Viking Graben and ranges from Bathonian to Oxfordian. It is a shale-dominated offshore marine sequence.

Central North Sea

In the Central North Sea, South Viking Graben and Moray Firth, the Fladen Group (Deegan & Scull 1977) now includes the Pentland, Brora Coal, Beatrice and Hugin formations (Richards *et al.* 1993) (Fig. 11.6). These formations are highly variable sandstones and shales deposited in paralic environments, and are frequently coal-bearing.

The Pentland Formation occurs in the South Viking Graben, Central North Sea, and Outer Moray Firth. The dominantly paralic sequences were deposited on the flanks of the eroding North Sea dome and have generally been difficult to correlate,

but the use of Maximum Flooding Surfaces and a sequence stratigraphic approach has proved successful (Underhill 1998).

A feature of the Pentland Formation is the volcanics that occur in the region of the North Sea triple junction. These rocks comprise the Ron Volcanics Member and the Rattray Volcanics Member (Richards *et al.* 1993) and consist of volcaniclastic sediments and undersaturated porphyritic alkali-olivine basalts (Dixon *et al.* 1981). The Rattray volcanics occur over a large area at the triple junction, and the Ron volcanics form a separate centre to the south in the Central Graben (Fig. 11.10). Geochemistry suggests derivation from an enriched lithospheric mantle source with possible contribution from the asthenosphere. The volcanicity has been ascribed to a short-lived warm mantle plume-head source (Underhill & Partington 1993, 1994); limited extent and geochemistry of the volcanics militating against a long-lived hot mantle jet. Radiometric dating indicates that volcanic activity took place in the Bathonian and Callovian (Ritchie *et al.* 1988; Latin *et al.* 1990*a, b*) following formation of the dome (Figs 11.10, 11.11).

Inner Moray Firth

At Brora the presumed Bathonian strata of the Brora Coal Formation (Fig.11.7) are exposed beneath the Brora Roof Bed which contains rare basal Callovian ammonites of the *macrocephalus* Zone (Sykes 1975). The Doll Member of the Brora Coal Formation is of fluvial origin with channel sandstones and alluvial plain mudstones (Hurst 1981). The cross-bedded channel sandstones contain concentrations of plant debris and rare silicified logs. Grey kaolinitic shales with weakly pedified horizons were deposited on an alluvial plain cut by small channels. Sideritic bands attest to low available sulphate and a record of the freshwater bivalve *Unio* from the top of the

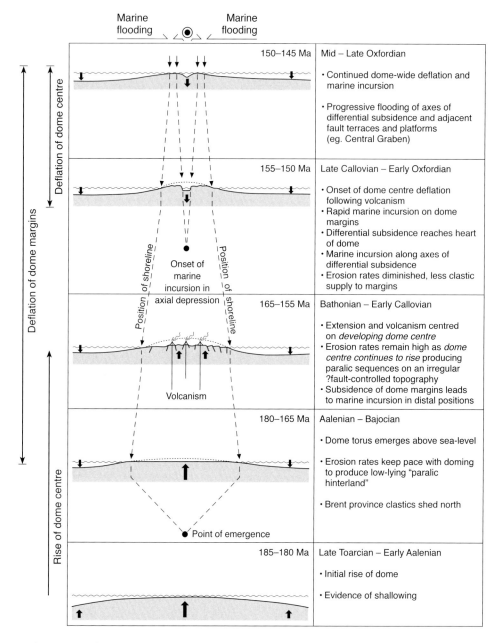

Fig. 11.11. Diagrammatic depiction of the history of the North Sea Dome from the Late Toarcian to the Late Oxfordian. After Underhill & Partington (1993,1994).

Member (Neves & Selley 1975), together with the occurrence of freshwater ostracods strengthens the non-marine interpretation. The overlying Inverbrora Member is now thought to be of Callovian age and records the start of marine transgression; it is considered in the next section.

West of Scotland

The Aalenian, Bajocian and Bathonian stages are typified in the Hebrides by the thick marine sandstones of the Bearreraig Sandstone Formation, overlain by varied non-marine strata, the Great Estuarine Group. They are the approximate correlatives of the Inferior and Great Oolite Groups, respectively, of southern England. The Callovian sees a renewed transgression and it will be described in the next section.

The Bearreraig Sandstone Formation varies from 38 m in Mull to 480 m in south Skye, the latter making it by far the thickest sandstone in the British Jurassic. The facies also varies

strongly over short distances, as do palaeocurrent orientations, so that differential subsidence of the basin floor must have been accompanied by uplift of a nearby hinterland and changing directions of sediment supply. The type section at Bearreraig in Trotternish, Skye (Fig. 11.12), has been described by Morton (in Morton & Hudson 1995). The lower part of the succession is dominantly poorly sorted silty or sandy shale, the Dun Caan Shale. Above this, at the base of the Ollach Sandstone Member, beds with ammonites beautifully preserved in small calcareous concretions are developed. The type specimen of the zonal index ammonite *Ludwigia murchisonae* was collected from near here by Lady Murchison, wife of Sir Roderick, hence its feminine termination. Fossils have been over-collected from these important outcrops in the past, and collecting should only be done from loose blocks on the shore. These beds were perhaps deposited near storm wave-base to account for the gentle concentration of complete ammonites and the preservation in life position of burrowing bivalves such

Fig. 11.12. The type section of the Bearreraig Sandstone at Bearreraig Bay, Trotternish, Skye. The ledges in the foreground contain *Ludwigia murchisonae*, and are overlain by the Ollach Sandstone. In the main cliff the Holm and Rigg sandstones are capped by a Tertiary dolerite sill.

as *Gresslya*. Within the concretions, ammonites, belemnites and bivalves are preserved in a variety of orientations due to disturbance by burrowing animals. The higher parts of the succession are mainly sandy, forming coarsening-upwards cycles, with large calcareous concretions. Within the Udairn Shale Member, a finer-grained interlude, is an international reference section for the Aalenian–Bajocian boundary (Morton 1990). *Graphoceras* species characterise the top Aalenian *concavum* Zone, and the basal Bajocian *discites* Zone is marked by the incoming of species of *Hyperlioceras*. The Udairn Shale coarsens upwards into the Holm Sandstone Member, and beneath the waterfall at Bearreraig there are large-scale crossbeds. The overlying Rigg Sandstone Member is mainly tabular bedded. As well as ammonites, large belemnites, some with phragmacones intact, are conspicuous members of the fauna; belemnite guards occur as lags at the base of some sandstone beds. The top of the Member is a shelly granule-conglomerate, as it is throughout the area. In the Bearreraig Sandstone, drifted plant material is common; it is per-mineralized and in some cases fusainized, thus testifying to the occurrence of wildfires in a forested hinterland.

Concretions of various kinds occur throughout the succession. Small early-formed calcareous or sideritic nodules are important in preserving fossils, especially in the Udairn Shale. They formed early, just beneath the sea floor. Large concretions ('doggers') are conspicuous in the Ollach and Holm Sandstones. They probably started to form around small marine-cemented nuclei, but mostly grew during burial from meteoric-derived waters (Wilkinson 1991).

A very different, cross-bedded, facies of the Bearreraig Sandstone is to be seen in Strathaird, where it comprises virtually the whole of the Formation, and in Raasay, where it diachronously appears in the upper part of it. In Strathaird strongly cross-bedded strata rest discordantly on the Raasay Ironstone, and form most of the east coast of the peninsula to Strathaird Point, where south-dipping planar cross-sets are well exposed. The rocks are calcareous with shell fragments and much bryozoan and crinoidal debris. Towards Elgol on the west coast the style and orientation of the cross-bedding changes, and near the top of the formation spectacular troughs with unimodal northwesterly directed palaeocurrents are exposed (Plate 20); U-shaped burrows (*Diplocraterion*) occur on beds within the troughs. Ammonites are virtually absent from this facies. The north–south trend of the dominant tidal currents is approximately parallel to the trend of the basin-crossing Camasunary Fault system, which runs to the west of the main area where this facies is developed, and may well have affected sea-floor topography (Morton 1983). Crinoid colonies would have lived on swept-clear rock platforms on the upthrown side of the faults.

Detailed sedimentological interpretations of parts of the Bearreraig Sandstone have been presented by Mellere & Steel (1996); their main proposal is that there is a change from predominantly regressive, pro-delta settings in the lower part of the succession, to transgressive 'estuarine' ones in the upper part. They place the change-over at a horizon of regional channeling which they correlate with the *sauzei* Zone, seen for instance at the base of the cross-bedded strata within the Holm Sandstone Member, beneath the waterfall at Bearreraig in Trotternish, and at a possibly correlative horizon in southern Strathaird corresponding to the change from predominantly southerly to northerly palaeocurrent orientations. As in Morton's interpretation (1983), currents were channeled along narrow sub-basins created by differential movements on faults that obliquely cross the main basin. In a wider context, it is notable that whereas Morton (e.g. 1983) does not recognize major breaks in the succession, Underhill & Partington (1993) suggest a break, corresponding to maximum uplift of the North Sea dome, at the base of the Ollach Sandstone (close to the *opalinus–murchisonae* Zone boundary), while Mellere & Steel (1996) place a break later, beneath the *sauzei* Zone. Thus interpretations differ, and the field evidence is equivocal.

In Trotternish and Raasay the Bearreraig Sandstone is the main cliff-former of the Jurassic succession. The coastal cliffs are lower in Strathaird, but the combination of a dyke swarm with slight hardening of the sandstone by the Tertiary hydrothermal system means that they are extremely dissected, providing excellent three-dimensional outcrops (Plate 20). There is an exposure of the cross-bedded facies in Ardnamurchan, but the Bearreraig Sandstone is generally thin, both in this area and in Mull.

The uppermost part of the main Bearreraig Sandstone in most places is a coarse shelly sandstone or even granule-conglomerate. (This is the only part of the Formation that is seen on Eigg, where it is the lowest horizon exposed.) Above, there is an abrupt facies change to grey mudstones, the Garantiana Clay Member of Upper Bajocian age. This contains diagnostic ammonites of the *garantiana* Zone, *dichotoma* subzone. It seems evident that this change corresponds to a major and widely-recognized transgressive event; it was long ago described in the Cotswolds by Buckman. However such an abrupt cutting-off of coarse terrigenous detritus remains mysterious. There may be a minor hiatus but this is not proved (Morton 1989). The Garantiana Clay, together with the basal unit of the Great Estuarine Group, is a recessively eroded shale horizon between two sandstones, so it is poorly exposed. It forms a distinct terrace in the cliffs south of Bearreraig, Skye.

The Great Estuarine Group ('Series') was so named by Judd (1878), and, ignoring quibbles about precise depositional environment (Hudson 1963), it deserves its name. In the Hebrides it is the most widespread of all the divisions, cropping out in west Skye, Eigg and Muck as well as Trotternish, Strathaird and, less well exposed, Raasay. Occurrences in Mull and Ardnamurchan are minor, and truncated by pre-Cretaceous erosion. It is also the thickest and most varied of all the non-marine ('estuarine') developments of the British Jurassic, which had been previously named and investigated by Judd. A striking feature of the formations of the Great Estuarine Group, especially the finer-grained ones, is their lateral continuity, despite the fact that they are of lagoonal facies. This continuity even applies to some individual beds such as the stromatolite of the Kildonnan Member, and contrasts with the lateral variability of the marine Bearreraig Sandstone. Even more remarkably, some of the individual formation names can be applied in the Slyne Trough off the west of Ireland (Trueblood & Morton 1991) and a facies identical to the non-marine Kilmaluag Formation occurs even farther away in the Porcupine Trough (Chen & Hudson 1991; Morton 1994). However, neither continuity of facies, nor age equivalence can be assumed.

The base of the Group is marked by a transition from marine, ammonite-bearing grey clay, the Garantiana Clay described above, to dark, fissile, organic-rich shale, the Cullaidh Shale Formation. At the type locality on Elgol shore this yields a sparse fauna including mytilid bivalves, conchostracans, freshwater to oligohaline ostracods and teleost and coelacanth fish, normally only found as isolated scales. This fauna is predominantly non-marine, and the organic content and scarcity of benthos suggests that, for much of the time, the sediment surface was inhospitable, perhaps anoxic. The shale has a TOC of around 5% and has attracted attention first as an oil shale (Lee 1913) and more recently as a potential source rock for petroleum. In north Trotternish both the Garantiana Clay and the Cullaidh Shale are either absent or represented by a sandy facies with a marine fauna (Morton & Hudson 1995).

In the upper part of the Cullaidh Shale thin beds of siltstone appear; these become gradually thicker, coarser and more bioturbated, forming a gradational transition into the Elgol Sandstone Formation in a classic coarsening-upwards sequence (Plate 21; Fig. 11.13). This is seen on the shore at Elgol itself, between the school and the overhanging cliff formed by the sandstone. The north–south cliff north of the school shows south-dipping surfaces outlining the form of a delta. The shore exposures of the same horizon show small-scale cross-beds representing small sand waves moving down the delta front. Regionally, the Elgol Sandstone Formation is interpreted as a series of deltas built into the restricted basin in which the Cullaidh Shale had been deposited. The type of delta formed depended on the salinity and tidality of the receiving basin and the quantity and grain-size of the fluvial input. In Strathaird a lobate delta form has been reconstructed from the shore outcrop and additional sections exposed along the scarp formed by the sandstone through and beyond Elgol village (Harris 1989; Fig. 11.13). This is interpreted as due to active input into a low-salinity basin. Different delta morphologies occur in Trotternish and Raasay, where the basin was more saline, and on Eigg and farther south no substantial sand body occurs at this horizon. Later history also has its effect; in Strathaird slight metamorphism due to hydrothermal circulation around the Cuillin plutonic centre has converted a soft sandstone, like that seen in Trotternish, to a hard quartzite. Probably because it is unfossiliferous and so lacked a source of calcium carbonate, the Elgol Sandstone does not contain calcareous concretions, unlike most of the other sandstones, but it is resistant enough to form a striking escarpment in the terraced cliffs of east Trotternish north of Portree, as well as in Strathaird.

The top of the Elgol Sandstone is a granule-conglomerate, representing wave-winnowing of the delta top. Above this is the sharp base of the Lealt Shale Formation. This is the lowest

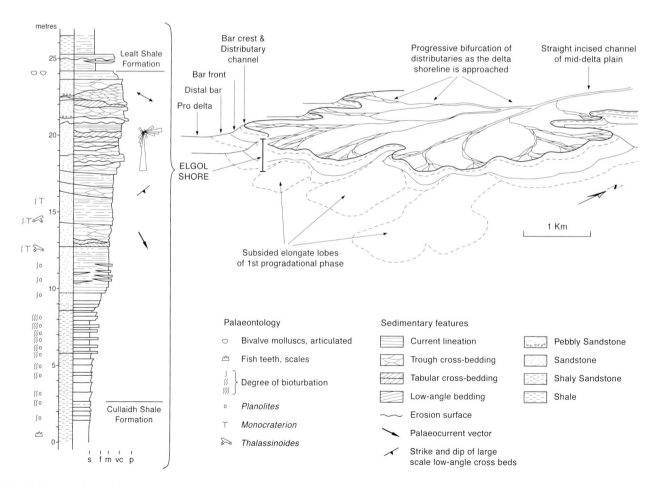

Fig. 11.13. The Elgol Sandstone Formation in Strathaird, Skye, interpreted as a lobate, fluvial-dominated, lagoonal delta (Harris 1989). (**a**) Example of log from Elgol shore (cf. Plate 21) (**b**) Reconstruction of delta based on additional logs (see text).

of the Great Estuarine Group formations that is abundantly fossiliferous. It can be divided into two Members. The lower Kildonnan Member is particularly well developed at its type locality on Eigg. It can also be traced in Skye and Raasay. It records variously brackish lagoonal environments, inhabited by mussels (*Praemytilus*), sharks and, at one horizon, plesiosaurs; the last a famous discovery made by Hugh Miller in 1844 (Miller 1858). A notable horizon is a cyanobacterial stromatolite marking the top of the Member. It is never more than 300 mm thick but can be traced from north Trotternish to Eigg and is virtually identical petrographically throughout (Hudson 1970; Harris & Hudson 1980). This demonstrates that the basin was interconnected at that time, not split into separate sub-basins. The palaeoecology of the type section on Eigg has been studied in some detail (Hudson *et al.* 1995). The rocks contain exquisitely preserved, though fragile, molluscan fossils, still with the microstructure, mineralogy and geochemistry of their original aragonite intact. In the laboratory they yield ostracods, acritarchs, dinoflagellates, the freshwater alga *Botryococcus* and fish otoliths. Thus indications for environmental conditions, such as palaeosalinity, from one group of organisms can be cross-checked with the others (Fig. 11.14). Oxygen and strontium isotopes in molluscs and otoliths also contribute to quantifying tempertures and salinities. Patterson (1999) studied oxygen isotopes in otoliths, some perhaps from migratory fish. He concluded that the temperature out to sea was 19.8 to 22.2°C, whereas the isotopic composition of estuarine species correlated with salinity variations. Most recently, strontium isotope analyses on shells, particularly *Praemytilus*, indicate a dominance of freshwater inflow, together with strong evaporation in controlling the hydrology of the lagoons, rather than seawater-freshwater mixing as previously believed (Holmden & Hudson, 2000; Fig. 11.14). Hybodont sharks lived in the lagoons; it is perhaps more likely that plesiosaurs swam in from the sea outside. The faunas are among the earliest from which such detailed environmental records can be obtained.

The stromatolite at the top of the Kildonnan Member bears pseudomorphs after gypsum and thus records a brief episode of desiccation. No species of ostracod crosses the boundary into the succeeding Lonfearn Member (Wakefield 1995). The Lonfearn Member is mainly shale with thin limestones, mainly shelly but some oolitic. The lowest part has a brackish-marine bivalve and ostracod fauna but the main part is characterized particularly by very abundant conchostracans (Chen & Hudson 1991). The conchostracans inhabited very shallow waters of fresh or freshwater-brackish salinity. Desiccation cracks demonstrate recurrent emergence of the lagoon floor. The Lonfearn Member yielded the first dinosaur footprint to be described from the Scottish Jurassic (Andrews & Hudson 1984). In Trotternish, Skye, this fissile unit proved favourable for the intrusion of thick sills of dolerite, which form spectacular cliffs and waterfalls along the northeast coast.

At the top of the Lonfearn Member silty and then sandy beds appear; also shell beds composed mainly of the small bivalve *Neomiodon* increase in frequency and thickness. Thus the base of the Valtos Sandstone Formation is gradational in a way similar to that of the Elgol Sandstone, except that the rocks are fossiliferous. The Valtos Sandstone also represents deltas built into lagoons, but instead of being one major, albeit internally complex, delta advance, there were several advances and retreats (Harris 1992). The formation is thus highly variable in facies architecture within a single section. It also varies markedly within the basin, being thick, dominantly sandy but also containing much siltstone and limestone in Trotternish, slightly less thick but even more sand-dominated on Eigg, and thin and devoid of thick sandstone bodies in Strathaird, between the two. The two sandstone-dominated successions have differing feldspar contents and heavy minerals. Whether this is due to two sources of sand from the Scottish landmass entering a single basin, or whether at the time there was separation between northern (Sea of the Hebrides) and southern (Inner Hebrides) sub-basins, is uncertain (compare Harris (1992), with Morton (1992)). The Valtos Formation also provides evidence for a source of sediment from the Outer Hebrides to the northwest. From the small outcrop below Waterstein Head at the far western tip of Skye, the Outer Isles

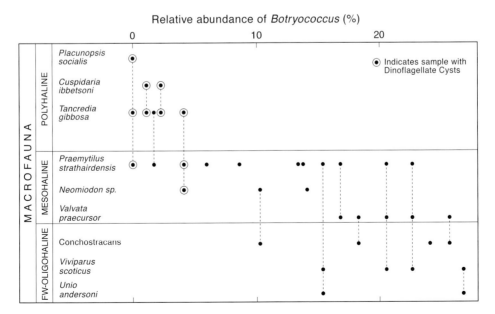

Fig. 11.14. Comparison of macrofossils and palynomorphs as palaeosalinity indicators in the Kildonnan Member, Lealt Shale Formation, Isle of Eigg. A high relative abundance (proportion of total palynomorphs) of the alga *Botryococcus* indicates freshwater influence. Dinoflagellate cysts indicate a marine connection. The molluscan and conchostracan taxa are arranged with presumed marine indicators at the top and freshwater forms at the bottom. Vertical lines indicate co-occurrence of fossils on the same bedding-plane. Note the good consistency between indicators, and the implied wide salinity tolerance of *Praemytilus*. However, recent studies on strontium isotopes in *Praemytilus* shells indicate that this bivalve calcified in waters of freshwater origin; see text. From Hudson *et al.* (1995).

Fig. 11.15. Cliff formed by the lowest sandstone unit of the Valtos Sandstone Formation that contains large calcitic concretions. Valtos, Trotternish, Skye.

lie only 25 km away, across the basin-bounding Minch Fault, and the sandstones yield a heavy mineral suite diagnostic of a Lewisian source (Harris 1992). The abundance of *Neomiodon* within the formation is remarkable; it often forms monotypic shell beds. These can be thin beds in pro-delta silts from the lagoon floor, and reworking of delta-tops produces all transitions between calcite-cemented granule conglomerates and cross-bedded *Neomiodon* biosparites. It seems that this bivalve was an opportunistic coloniser of transiently inhabitable environments. Recently, dinosaur remains have been discovered in the Valtos Formation. Clark *et al.* (1995) describe the large femur of a sauropod, probably related to *Cetiosaurus*, and Clark & Barco Rodriguez (1998) describe a trackway.

Most of the sandstones of the Hebridean Jurassic bear large calcareous concretions (nodules, doggers) that cut across the bedding and are therefore post-depositional, but those in the Valtos Sandstone Formation are perhaps the most conspicuous (Hudson & Andrews 1987; Fig. 11.15). Work by Wilkinson & Dampier (1990) on the chemical processes governing the growth of calcite concretions in sandstones, and by Wilkinson (1992, 1993) using stable isotopic and trace element analyses on the Valtos Formation examples, has gone some way towards answering questions concerning the controls on their growth and its timing. In summary, the concretions grew after some compaction of the rock, and after the depositional waters had been displaced by meteoric-derived waters flowing down confined aquifers from the hinterland, but before the deep burial of the rocks beneath Palaeocene lavas. The main source of calcite was intra-formational, from dissolution of aragonitic *Neomiodon* shells Pore waters were flowing only very slowly during concretion growth, but were recharged intermittently. Best estimates for time of growth for 1 m diameter concretions from Valtos, Skye, are that they started to grow 8 Ma after deposition (in the Oxfordian), and each took 5–10 Ma to grow. Smaller (240 mm) concretions from Eigg took about half a million years to grow.

The Valtos Sandstone forms coastal cliffs, as seen on the north Trotternish coast at the type locality (Fig. 11.15). It forms the lower part of the famous view of the Kilt Rock (Plate 24), capped by a Palaeocene dolerite sill. At Camas Sgiotaig, Eigg, modern beach sand derived from Valtos Sandstone cliffs forms the well-known 'Singing Sands'.

The top of the Valtos Formation and the base of the overlying Duntulm Formation can be seen in two excellent sections 80 km apart, at the type locality in north Trotternish, and at Camas Mor on the Isle of Muck. In both sections the top Valtos is alternating shale and limestone with low-salinity faunas of *Neomiodon, Unio* (Duntulm) and conchostracans

(Muck). The sea then crept back into the lagoons, and first small marine bivalves such as *Placunopsis* arrived, and then oysters, *Praeexogyra hebridica*, which become the dominant members of the fauna and characterize the Formation. These oyster beds were among the first features of the succession to attract attention in the 19th century; the species *hebridica*, so widespread in southern England, was first described from Skye by Edward Forbes in 1851. The distribution of this species has wider significance as recording the first entry of oysters into marginal-marine brackish waters, an environment in which they have remained outstandingly successful to the present day (Hudson & Palmer 1976). Other marginal-marine fossils accompany the oysters, such as one species of rhynchonellid brachiopod, and the mussel *Modiolus*. There are also intercalations showing a return to freshwater deposition within the Duntulm Formation in Trotternish, where coarse clastic sediment from time to time entered the basin. The formation is finer-grained and thinner in Strathaird, Eigg and Muck.

Interbedded with the oyster-bearing limestones of the Duntulm Formation are several thin beds of algal (more accurately cyanobacterial) nodular limestone, which are interpreted as having accumulated on the partially exposed margins of the lagoons (Hudson 1970; Andrews 1986; Andrews & Walton 1990). The geological history of stromatolites (in the wide sense) is well known: a maximum in the Proterozoic followed by an irregular decline to their present restriction to environments inhospitable to most metazoans, such as intertidal flats of abnormal salinity. Most attention has been paid to the earlier part of this history, but it is of interest to enquire how far back in the geological record close analogues of modern assemblages and environments can be found. The two main occurrences in the Great Estuarine Group are relevant (Hudson 1970; Andrews 1986): that at the top of the Kildonnan Member, as described above, and those in the Duntulm Formation. Both can be compared closely with modern Bahamian examples. The Duntulm Formation examples, in their 'algal nodule' facies (porostromate micrites of Andrews (1986)) contain calcified (*Cayeuxia*) and non-calcified filamentous structures similar to those of modern cyanobacteria (*Scytonema* and *Schizothrix*); unlike most stromatolites which are essentially sedimentary structures without evidence of their makers. Isotopic and facies evidence shows that the cyanobacteria were living on supralittoral flats, marginal to microtidal lagoons, and that growth and initial calcification took place when the flats were flooded by rainwater. Subsequently, complex fabrics formed in response to bacterial decay of the 'algal' tissue. Oyster fragments and foraminifera were washed onto the supra-littoral flats by storms. Desiccation then caused gypsum to precipitate, and cement fringes that had formed around the nodules to brecciate. (Fig.11.16). The gypsum was subsequently dissolved and replaced by pseudomorphic calcite. It all adds up to a convincing picture of a palaeo-environment very similar to that presciently described by Black (1933) from the Bahamas, and subsequently elaborated by Monty (1967) and Monty & Hardie (1976) (Fig. 11.16).

Above the Duntulm Formation, the Great Estuarine Group succession is regressive. On the shore north of Elgol and at Laig Gorge on Eigg continuous sections show oysters dying out; in the top bed containing them the shells are fragmentary and bored. Concurrently, ostracods and conchostracans appear, and these make up the most abundant fauna of the Kilmaluag Formation. This is mainly fine-grained shale and marl, entirely so in the south but including some sandstone in Trotternish, the type locality. Horizons with desiccation cracks are common. Shelly macrofossils are sparse and comprise mostly the freshwater gastropod *Viviparus* and the bivalve *Unio*. In Muck, extremely well-preserved lagoonal dolomites

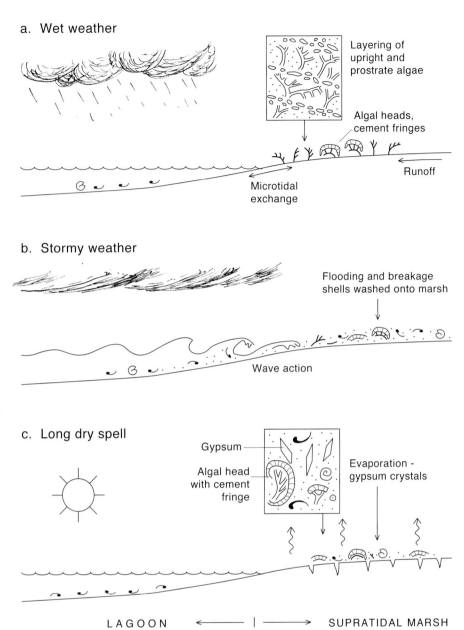

a. Wet weather

Layering of
upright and
prostrate algae

Algal heads,
cement fringes

Runoff

Microtidal
exchange

b. Stormy weather

Flooding and breakage
shells washed onto marsh

Wave action

c. Long dry spell

Gypsum

Algal head
with cement
fringe

Evaporation -
gypsum crystals

LAGOON ⟵——— | ———⟶ SUPRATIDAL MARSH

Fig. 11.16. Diagrammatic sketches to show stages in the development of cyanobacterial ('algal') limestones in the Duntulm Formation. It is not implied that weather conditions always alternated in this order. Based on Hudson (1970), Andrews (1986) and Andrews & Walton (1990).

occur, in association with strong desiccation (Andrews *et al.* 1987). In the lower part of the Group the conchostracan faunas are endemic, but in the Kilmaluag Formation of Trotternish and Muck the species *Pseudograpta murchisoniae* occurs; it is also found in northeast China thus giving a long-range correlation of these non-marine faunas (Chen & Hudson 1991). The most notable fossils of the Kilmaluag Formation, from Strathaird in Skye, are small amphibians, reptiles (including lizards, turtles and crocodiles) and mammals that variously inhabited the lagoons themselves and exposed mud surfaces around them, or were washed in from the hinterland. The assemblage rivals those from Oxfordshire and the Cotswolds in diversity and has the advantage of producing articulated or partially articulated bones (Evans & Waldman 1996). The Kilmaluag Formation is another favoured horizon for the intrusion of thick dolerite sills of Palaeocene age, including most of those forming the cliffed coast of northwest Trotternish.

The freshwater–lagoonal Kilmaluag Formation passes with gradation into the overlying, largely alluvial, Skudiburgh For-

mation. Ostracods and conchostracans disappear, and beds of red and green unfossiliferous mudstone appear. Some of these bear calcareous concretions regarded as caliche (calcareous soils) by Andrews (1985). In Trotternish there are also thin beds of cross-bedded, probably fluvial, sandstone. The Skudiburgh Formation is unusual as a Jurassic 'red-bed'; parts of it could be mistaken for Triassic Mercia Mudstone. It implies a seasonally dry climate at least in the basin, and perhaps regionally. Above is an abrupt transgression, of Early Callovian age. These strata are described in the next section.

Western Offshore Basins

Middle Jurassic rocks are apparently absent from the North Minch basin, probably because of later erosion (Fyfe *et al.* 1993). They are present in non-marine facies in the West Lewis Basin (Stoker *et al.* 1993). In the West Shetland and Faeroe–Shetland Basins the tectonic and stratigraphic history appears to be more similar to that of the North Sea, with Middle

Jurassic locally unconformable on early Mesozoic or on base-ment, thus indicating tectonic activity. Over 500 m of Middle Jurasssic strata, interpreted as submarine fan deposits, occur in sub-basins along the fault-bounded eastern side of the Faeroe–Shetland Basin, which is thus inferred to have been deep marine (Haszeldine *et al.* 1987). However, much of the basin lacks preserved Middle Jurassic.

Mid-Jurassic Palaeogeography

The snapshot chosen (Fig. 11.17) approximates to Mid-Bathonian times when the North Sea Dome with its lavas was subsiding, and the Brent Delta was being transgressed from the north as the dome collapsed. Paralic facies of the Pentland Formation surrounded the dome, but areas such as the Halibut Horst probably remained high. In the Inner Moray Firth, alluvial and fluvial facies of the Brora Coal Formation were deposited, whilst in the Inner Hebrides varied facies of the Great Estuarine Group were laid down. Marine connection may have been established between west and east Scotland at end Bathonian.

Rifting was starting in the graben systems of the North Sea and to the west of Shetland, where sands were introduced to deep-water basins by gravity-driven processes. At the end of the Bathonian, sea levels were generally rising and marine areas were being extended. The extent of the landmasses undergoing erosion is generally speculative.

'Late' Jurassic (Callovian to Kimmeridgian)

An Early Callovian marine transgression across previously paralic environments is seen in both western Scotland (Staffin Bay Formation) and in the east at Brora (Inverbrora Member and Brora Roof Bed). This flooding occurs in the *macroceph-alus* Zone of the Callovian in both areas. It represents a sudden rise in sea level, which led to the establishment, later in the Callovian, of open marine conditions, dominant dark shale or siltstone deposition, and a fauna including abundant ammo-nites and belemnites. Generally rising sea levels continued through the Oxfordian and Kimmeridgian, but superimposed on this trend were fluctuations in sea level resulting in the intro-duction of turbidite sands to basins at times of lower sea level.

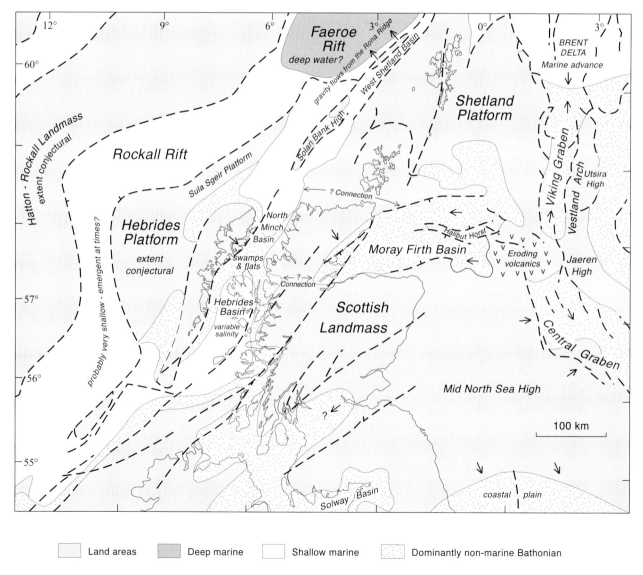

Fig. 11.17. Mid Jurassic (Bathonian) palaeogeography. Note the alternative routes for marine connection between the west and east coasts of Scotland. A northerly route is favoured by Bradshaw *et al.* (1992), and a route in the region of the Great Glen by Underhill & Partington (1993, 1994) The extent of land areas undergoing erosion, and non-marine marginal areas of deposition is conjectural. Map modified after Bradshaw *et al.* (1992).

Tectonic events, resulting in footwall uplift at basin margins and increased erosion, also contributed sand input to the basins.

A major tectonic extensional phase commenced in Mid-Oxfordian to Early Kimmeridgian times, and continued into the Early Cretaceous (Ziegler 1990a, b; Thomson & Underhill 1993). Subsidence increased as a result of extension, and the North Sea Dome finally subsided with marine deposition extending over the area of the rift triple junction.

Thus the combination of rising sea levels and extensional tectonics resulted in the establishment of deep marine conditions in the graben areas. Extensional faulting resulted in considerable footwall uplift on major faults, and footwall erosion supplied sandstones and coarser debris to the adjacent hanging wall troughs. The Brae fields area on the margin of the Viking Graben is one example, and another is the Kimmeridgian Boulder Beds associated with the Helmsdale Fault at the faulted NW margin of the Inner Moray Firth Basin (see below).

The deep rift basins received minimal clastic input, had poor water circulation and frequently became anoxic, resulting in the preservation of organic matter in black shales and mudstones. These dominantly Kimmeridgian shales are the main source rock for the oil and gas fields of the Scottish offshore areas (see Chapter 19).

North Sea

The Beatrice Formation of the Fladen Group (Fig. 11.6) overlies the Brora Coal in the Beatrice oilfield. It is entirely marine in origin with open marine conditions being rapidly established above the Brora Coal. Correlation of the Beatrice Formation with the onshore section at Brora is referred to in the following section.

The Humber Group of Deegan & Scull (1977) comprises all the strata between the Brent Group of the Northern North Sea and the Cromer Knoll Group of the Cretaceous. The Group is divided into the Heather and overlying Kimmeridge Clay formations, both of which are dominated by marine mudstones. Sandstones that occur within the group are generally either of shallow marine origin such as the Piper and Fulmar formations, or were deposited by turbidity currents and debris flows in basinal areas as in the Brae Formation and Claymore sandstone. Numerous such sandstone bodies exist adjacent to fault blocks and attract considerable exploration interest as oil reservoirs. Further details and references can be found in Underhill (1998) and Evans et al. (2003).

The Heather Formation mudstones are generally grey, silty and frequently weakly bioturbated. They generally record deposition below wavebase in an offshore marine situation. The sandstone-dominated Fulmar Formation represents shallower water, higher energy deposition in the Central Graben area and on the Fladen Ground Spur. The formation ranges from Callovian to Volgian and is thus laterally equivalent to both the Heather and Kimmeridge Clay formations. Rising sea levels caused reworking of Triassic sandstones on platform areas to supply the Fulmar sandstone. Individual, laterally continuous sandstone bodies within the Fulmar Formation reflect stepped sea level changes onlapping the platforms. Trace fossils are abundant within the Fulmar sandstones and bioturbation fabrics and ichnofacies are used to document changes in water depth and substrate (Gowland 1996; Martin & Pollard 1996). They also aid in sequence stratigraphic interpretation of the individual sandstone bodies that represent a series of progradational shorelines within a generally transgressive sequence.

The Piper Formation is another marine sandstone-dominated sequence that is time equivalent to parts of the Heather and Kimmeridge Clay formations. It forms the main reservoir in the Piper Field (Maher 1981) and several others. The sandstones were mainly deposited in shallow marine environments but also grade landwards into deltaic and fluvial deposits, and seawards to shales. The sandstones were derived by the reworking of high areas such as the Fladden Ground Spur and Halibut Horst (Harker et al. 1993). The individual sandstone bodies of the Piper Formation are laterally continuous and were deposited during brief regressions within the generally rising sea level regime of the Late Jurassic (Underhill & Partington 1993).

The Kimmeridge Clay Formation is dominated by marine shales that were deposited in an environment where bottom waters were frequently anoxic, and organic matter derived from microplankton was preserved. The most organic-rich shales correspond with periods of high sea level, low sedimentation rates and strongest anoxicity (Tyson 1995). Near basin margins, for example in the Moray Firth adjacent to the Helmsdale Fault, depositional rate was high and organic content is low. Within the Kimmeridge Clay Formation there are a number of turbiditic sandstone bodies, many of which have been productive oil exploration targets.

The Brae Formation of the South Viking Graben comprises a series of discrete conglomeratic to sandy fan deposits in the hanging wall of the faulted margin of the Fladden Ground Spur. The clastics have distinct sources and characteristics relating to their individual supply areas on the adjacent platform. Conglomerates and breccias are located close to the bounding fault, but sand transported by turbidity currents continued down the palaeoslope and is found in depocentres some 15 km from the fault margin, for example in the Miller Field. The Helmsdale Boulder Beds and Allt na Cuile sandstone (described below) accumulated adjacent to the Helmsdale Fault in the Inner Moray Firth in an analogous situation to the Brae Formation. In the Outer Moray Firth the Piper sandstone is succeeded by deep marine sandstones within the Kimmeridge Clay Formation and these form excellent reservoirs in fields such as Claymore, Galley and Tartan. The turbidite sandstones in this area are frequently fairly well sorted, and occur in packages of amalgamated beds that show little evidence of grading. The sands sometimes contain displaced shallow water fauna and represent clean shallow marine sands transported by gravity-flow mechanisms into deep water. Individual sand bodies have markedly different petrographic features depending on source. Some are clean quartz sands, but others are highly feldspathic and derived from a granitic source.

Inner Moray Firth Outcrop area and Beatrice Field

At Brora, the base of the Inverbrora Member of the Brora Coal Formation marks a change from grey, kaolinitic, freshwater to terrestrial mudstones into generally black and occasionally pyritic shales, some of which have up to 20% TOC and are virtually oil-shales. This lithological and chemical change heralds the Callovian marine transgression.

Within the Inverbrora Member two thin shell beds with *Neomiodon*, *Isognomon* and ostracods are present, and winnowed phosphatic debris is locally present. A thin coaly band is present and plant debris also occurs as drifted fragments, which include *Equisetum*, *Ginkgo*, *Goniopteris*, *Todites* and *Cladophlebis*; these genera formed the subject of Marie Stopes' first palaeobotanical paper (Stopes 1907). The environment is considered to have been lagoonal, the evidence being the presence of marine microplankton (dinoflagellates), first noted by Lam & Porter (1977). A detailed study by MacLennan & Trewin (1989) showed extensive marine influence with high abundance/low diversity assemblages present indicative of a Callovian age. The shell beds were winnowed on the lagoon floor under higher than normal energy conditions. Hendry *et al.* (2001) have shown that isotopic and trace element data from *Isognomon* shells are consistent with periodic flooding of a brackish water lagoon by cooler sea water. At other times fresh water invaded the lagoon and reduced salinity. The presence of pyrite implies sulphate availability, again consistent with marine influence. The strata are closely comparable to the Upper Ostrea Member of the Staffin Bay Formation in Skye (see below).

At the top of the Inverbrora Member is the Brora Coal, commercially worked intermittently from prior to 1598 until 1974 (Owen 1995). The coal is no longer exposed on the shore at Brora, but from mine records is known to generally lack a true seatearth. It appears to have started by the accumulation of drifted plant material, latterly becoming a subaerial swamp. The lagoonal area was cut off from the sea at this time, and swamp conditions, perhaps similar to a floating bog, spread over the lagoon. The coal is found in the Beatrice oilfield, and to the south at Cadh' an Righ. The coal contains coniferous wood and masses of *Equisetum*; palynological preparations are highly variable representing local plant communities including ferns, and marine microflora is absent (MacLennan & Trewin 1989).

Whilst the Brora Coal is found in the Beatrice area, the underlying organic-rich shales of the Inverbrora Member are very thin or absent. It appears that the lagoon was confined to the NW margin of the basin adjacent to the Helmsdale Fault. The sea may have entered the lagoon from the north as suggested by MacLennan & Trewin (1989), but Underhill & Partington (1993, 1994) give regional information to suggest marine invasion of the Moray Firth from the SW through the region of the Great Glen.

In the Brora shore section the Brora Coal is overlain by a bioturbated sandstone known as the Brora Roof Bed, since it formed the roof to the coalface in the Brora mine. The Roof Bed forms the base of the Brora Argillaceous Formation (Fig. 11.18). This 2 m thick sandstone contains a shelly marine fauna with the gastropod *Pietteia* and bivalves *Pholadomya*, *Myophorella*, *Gervillella*, *Corbula* and *Pleuromya*. Rare ammonites of *macrocephalus* Zone of the Callovian have also been found. The base of the Callovian has frequently been taken at the top of the coal but MacLennan & Trewin (1989) give palynological data that indicate that part of the underlying Inverbrora Member is also Callovian in age.

The Roof Bed represents a marine transgression due to sea level rise, the same event being present in the offshore area and on the coast at Cadh' an Righ, where the Roof Bed can be seen overlying the coal and sand-filled burrows of marine animals extend down into the coal. Eroded clasts of the coal are present in sandstones of the Roof Bed.

Rapid sea level rise combined with subsidence resulted in deposition of the black to grey Brora Shale that contains a rich marine fauna of bivalves, belemnites and ammonites. The shale is equivalent to the fossiliferous Mid-Shale between the A and B sandstones of the Beatrice oil field (Linsley *et al.* 1980; MacLennan & Trewin 1989; Fig. 11.7). The thin B sandstones of Beatrice were deposited as shallow marine bars and are equivalent to the Roof Bed, but above the Mid Shale in Beatrice lies the A sandstone – the main reservoir of the oil field. However, whilst sand was being deposited in the Beatrice area, fine-grained deposition dominated the Brora region (Fig.11.7). The Glauconitic Sandstone contains abundant belemnites in a muddy, bioturbated glauconitic sandstone with scattered phosphatic concretions. Similar phosphatic concentrations occur at the base of the A Sand in Beatrice and within shales in the Cadh' an Righ section (Sykes 1975), and this phosphatic event forms a regional marker horizon. The Brora Brick Clay was previously worked in Brora, the kilns being fired with Brora Coal. The Brick Clay and the Fascally Siltstone are only poorly fossiliferous, but are of marine origin. Prominent septarian concretions occur within the Brick Clay.

The sequence coarsens upwards into the Brora Arenaceous Formation, which was deposited in increasingly shallow water in a high-energy coastal setting adjacent to the Scottish landmass. Details are given by Hurst (1993), but the scattered nature of present outcrop makes detailed interpretation of the stratigraphy speculative. At the base of the Formation the Fascally Sandstone is bioturbated and contains moulds of bivalves in thin-bedded muddy sandstones with calcareous

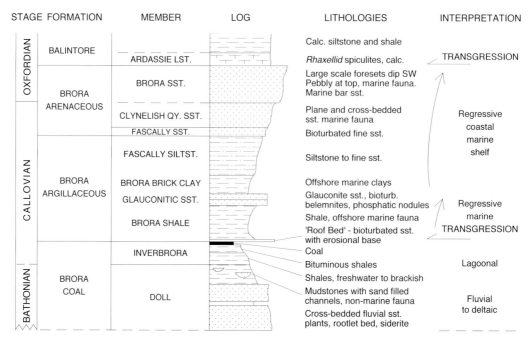

Fig. 11.18. Stratigraphic framework and depositional environments of the Bathonian to Oxfordian of the coastal outcrops of East Sutherland. Modified from Trewin (1993*d*).

concretions. The succeeding Clynelish Quarry Sandstone displays primary sedimentary structures such as low angle cross-bedding, scours and thin units of rippled sand with mud drapes. Locally (at Clynelish Quarry), the sandstone is silica cemented and abundant moulds of rhaxellid spicules are present; elsewhere it is a poorly lithified quartzose sandstone (Block Vagle *et al.* 1994). Offshore in the Moray Firth, the Allness Spiculite Member of the Heather Formation provides evidence of widespread sponge communities in the Oxfordian. The upward increase in depositional energy is continued into the overlying Brora Sandstone that displays a variety of features in the area. Most impressive is the large-scale SE-dipping bar form seen at Strathsteven Cliff south of Brora (Plate 22). Marine bivalves are locally common and include types (e.g. pectinids) characteristic of sandy substrates. Similar large-scale structures are also seen in the river gorge at Brora where a large scour is floored with pebbles, and medium to coarse-grained quartzose sandstones contain rounded quartz, and a few chert pebbles. The Brora Sandstone could represent a coast parallel bar complex cut by channels, possibly tidal in origin. At the time the Brora Arenaceous Formation was being deposited at the NW basin margin, shale was deposited in the Beatrice Field area and at Cadh' an Righ. Thus, the A Sand of Beatrice and the Brora Arenaceous Formation are not of exactly the same age, and marine sand deposition switched from Beatrice to Brora, probably reflecting fault control on basin subsidence, and changing source areas of sand.

There is a rapid deepening (in strata seldom exposed) from the Brora Sandstone to the Balintore Formation. The clean sandstones are succeeded by finer muddy sandstones in the thin-bedded sequence of the Ardassie Limestone Member. Bioturbation by *Chondrites* and *Thalassinoides* is ubiquitous, and a shelly fauna with the oyster *Gryphaea dilatata*, *Pinna lanceolata* (fan-mussel) *Cucullaea* and *Chlamys* is present. Open marine conditions are indicated by belemnites and ammonites (*Cardioceras* species) of the *vertebrale* Subzone of the Oxfordian. The lithologies present are bioturbated mudstones, and dark grey 'limestones', which are *Rhaxella* spiculites, consisting of fine sand-sized sponge spicules, and detrital grains. The originally siliceous spicules have been largely replaced by calcite, and a calcite cement is present. To the south in the Balintore area (Sykes 1975) the Brora Argillaceous and Brora Arenaceous formations are thin (31 and 12 m) and fine-grained, forming a condensed sequence deposited out of the reach of shallow marine clastics. The Balintore Formation comprises 2 m of muddy glauconitic red-weathering nodular limestone and 21 m of dark siltstone (Sykes 1975). Callovian to Mid-Oxfordian deposition was in a relatively deep, sediment-starved area.

Borehole cores have shown that the Ardassie Limestone Member at Brora is succeeded by thin bedded Oxfordian

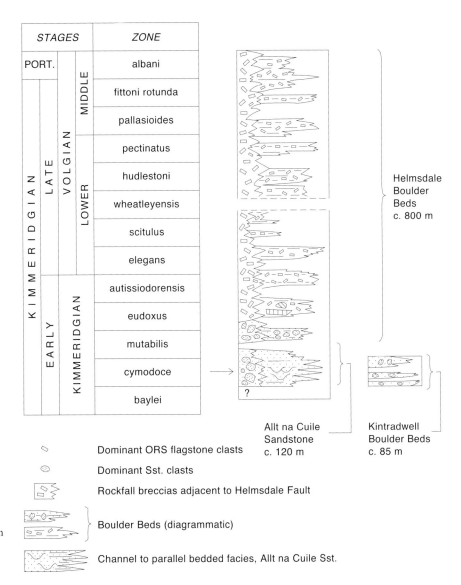

Fig. 11.19. The Kimmeridgian to Portlandian succession of the Kintradwell–Helmsdale section, East Sutherland. Modified from MacDonald & Trewin (1993).

siltstones and shales, but a break in the succession is possible since the next strata seen in the sequence are Kimmeridgian shales, sandstones and boulder beds whose deposition was clearly related to contemporaneous fault movement.

The general succession from Hettangian to Oxfordian records a variety of generally shallow marine to non-marine environments which bordered the Scottish Landmass. Whilst subsidence adjacent to the Helmsdale Fault probably formed the accommodation space for the succession, there is little direct evidence for fault activity. The reworking of Triassic calcrete and chert into the basal Lias, chert into the Brora Sandstone, and fault parallel currents in the basal Lias are only tenuous evidence of fault activity. However, the succeeding Kimmeridgian strata document movement on the Helmsdale Fault in a spectacular manner.

The Kimmeridgian succession (Fig. 11.19) is at least 800 m thick and, with minor repetition by folding, generally youngs from SW to NE along the 17 km of coastal outcrop between Kintradwell and the Helmsdale area. There appears to be a complete succession from the *cymodoce* Zone of the Kimmeridgian to the *albani* Zone of the Middle Volgian. Ammonite stratigraphy (Bailey & Weir 1932; Linsley 1972; Brookfield 1976; Wignall & Pickering 1993) and palynology (Lam & Porter 1977; Riley 1980; Barron 1989a) combine to confirm the zonal succession. The basal Kintradwell Boulder Beds appear to lie within the same ammonite zone as the Allt na Cuile Sandstone, and are overlain by a sequence containing shales, sandstones, boulder beds and breccias collectively termed the Helmsdale Boulder Beds.

The whole of the succession provides evidence for contemporaneous activity in the Helmsdale Fault zone, with clear evidence of an active submarine fault scarp with Devonian strata exposed on the footwall. Downthrow of the hanging

wall of the fault outpaced sedimentation creating a deep-water environment, with a variety of shallow marine to deltaic environments occupying a narrow shelf on the footwall adjacent to the Scottish Landmass. This shelf is nowhere preserved but its presence can be deduced from the evidence of shallow marine fauna, land-derived flora and fauna, and clasts which were swept off the shelf into deep water, to be preserved along with a pelagic marine fauna of ammonites, belemnites, fish and rare marine reptiles (Fig. 11.20).

Several reconstructions of different features of the Helmsdale Fault zone have been produced in the past (Hallam 1965; Pickering 1984; Wignall & Pickering 1993; MacDonald & Trewin 1993) and further offerings are presented in Figures 11.20 and 11.21 in an attempt to integrate the major observations on structure, sedimentology and palaeontology. The boulder beds form a narrow fringe to the Helmsdale Fault, the age-equivalent section in the Beatrice Field is entirely shale.

Considerable variation in depositional conditions and mechanisms existed along the fault line, and many geologists have contributed to facets of the depositional history of the area. Main credit goes to Bailey & Weir (1932), the first to recognize the fault-controlled nature of the sedimentation. Subsequent work by Crowell (1961), Linsley (1972), Pickering (1984), Wignall & Pickering (1993) and MacDonald & Trewin (1993) has added considerable detail to Bailey and Weir's work. Interpretations of the boulder beds prior to 1930 had included crush breccia (Murchison 1827), penecontemporaneous coastal erosion (Cunningham 1841), ice transport (Ramsay 1865), violent floods from rivers (Judd 1873), screes with an ice foot (Blake 1902) and falls from steep hillsides into the sea (Woodward 1911). Hugh Miller came close to current opinion, by finding Devonian fish in the clasts of the boulder beds which he considered came from nearby mountains (Miller 1854),

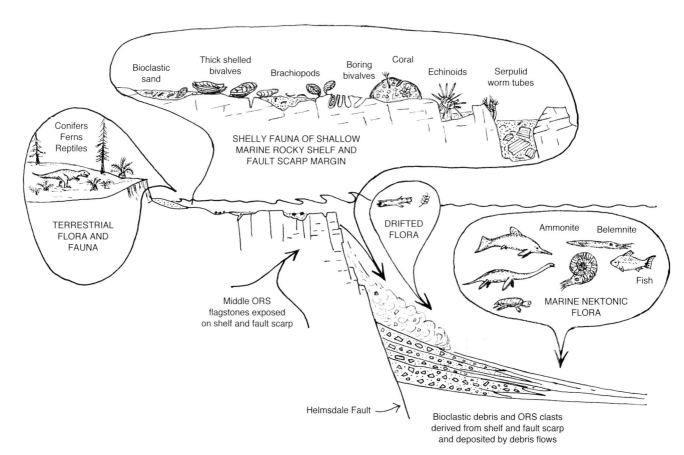

Fig. 11.20. Cartoon to show origin of flora and fauna associated with the Helmsdale Boulder Beds. Modified after MacDonald & Trewin (1993).

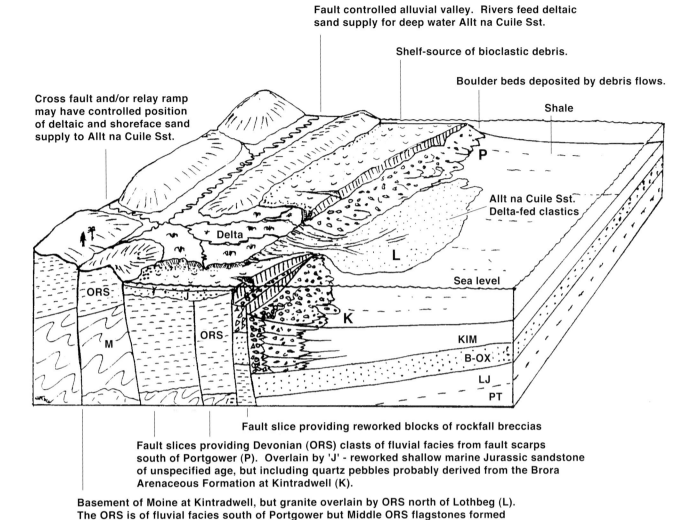

Fault controlled alluvial valley. Rivers feed deltaic sand supply for deep water Allt na Cuile Sst.

Shelf-source of bioclastic debris.

Boulder beds deposited by debris flows.

Shale

Cross fault and/or relay ramp may have controlled position of deltaic and shoreface sand supply to Allt na Cuile Sst.

P

Allt na Cuile Sst. Delta-fed clastics

Delta

L

ORS

J

Sea level

ORS

K

KIM

M

B-OX

LJ

PT

Fault slice providing reworked blocks of rockfall breccias

Fault slices providing Devonian (ORS) clasts of fluvial facies from fault scarps south of Portgower (P). Overlain by 'J' - reworked shallow marine Jurassic sandstone of unspecified age, but including quartz pebbles probably derived from the Brora Arenaceous Formation at Kintradwell (K).

Basement of Moine at Kintradwell, but granite overlain by ORS north of Lothbeg (L). The ORS is of fluvial facies south of Portgower but Middle ORS flagstones formed the fault scarps from Portgower north to Helmsdale.

Fig. 11.21. Cartoon to show features of sedimentation in the Early Kimmeridgian adjacent to the Helmsdale Fault between Kintradwell and Portgower.

and recognizing the role of earthquakes in the formation of sandstone dykes.

The Kintradwell Boulder beds are of *cymodoce* Zone and comprise shales, sandstones and boulder beds with a variety of slump folds, dislocation planes and pull-apart features which are the result of deposition on a slope directed generally to the SE away from the Helmsdale Fault (Roberts 1989). Sliding of the soft sediment was probably initiated by earthquakes caused by activity on the Helmsdale Fault; the shocks also liquified sand beds and the sand was intruded as sandstone dykes. Trace fossils such as *Rhizocorallium* and other burrows are present in some beds, as well as a sparse benthonic mollusca fauna, hence the substrate was, at least periodically, oxygenated (Wignall & Pickering 1993). Clasts in the boulder beds include well rounded quartz pebbles generally in the range of 5–20 mm, these were possibly derived from a beach environment on the adjacent shelf (MacDonald & Trewin 1993). Angular sandstone clasts up to boulder size contain internal trough cross-bedding, mud clasts and occasional pebbles. They appear to be derived from fluvial deposits, probably of Devonian age, which were exposed on the fault scarp.

In the area of Allt na Cuile and Lothbeg Point the boulder beds and shales are replaced by the Allt na Cuile Sandstone which is also within *cymodoce* Zone (Wignall & Pickering

1993). These porous, quartzose sandstones are frequently massive in appearance, and show evidence of liquification and mobilization. They are interbedded with carbonaceous sandstones and shales with both a rich terrestrial flora and also ammonites. Van der Burgh and van Konijnenburg–Van Cittert (1984) noted the dominant plants to be typical of brackish swamps (*Gleichenites*), and freshwater swamps (*Taxodiophyllum*) of a low-lying delta. Less abundant representatives of heath, moist lush vegetation, and upland forest were also recognized. On the basis of flora the sandstones were derived from a low-lying delta that spilled over the narrow shelf into deep water. The sands were deposited initially by mass-flow processes, and water-logged vegetation sank into the deep marine environment. When the Allt na Cuile sandstone is traced back towards the Helmsdale Fault, evidence of channelling and transport of large blocks of older sandstone is seen. Immediately adjacent to the Helmsdale Fault, rock-fall breccias with blocks several metres in size set in a matrix of pebbly sand are present (Fig. 11.22).

The point of entry of the Allt na Cuile Sandstone to the basin was controlled by the drainage pattern on the landmass. Possibly a relay ramp between different branches of the Helmsdale Fault controlled the delta position as suggested by Underhill (1994, 1998) or maybe a transfer fault zone influenced the delta

Fig. 11.22. Rockfall breccia adjacent to the Helmsdale Fault in Allt Choll. The large sandstone clasts are up to 5 m long. This outcrop is now very overgrown. BGS photograph.

position (Wignall & Pickering 1993). More than one fault is certainly present in the area as demonstrated by the relatively shallow intersection of granite at 695 m in the Sutherland No. 1 well near Lothbeg Point, silicified fractures cutting rock-fall breccias, and derived clasts of rock-fall breccia in the Kintradwell Boulder bed. The delta seems to have covered the shelf at this point, since no derived shallow marine fauna is present in the sandstone.

Overlying the Allt na Cuile Sandstone are shales of *mutabilis* Zone. Well-preserved drifted plants are present in calcareous cemented concretions within laminated shale, and a sparse marine benthonic fauna is present. Only a few thin turbidite sandstone beds are present and a period of quiescence on the fault is likely.

The Helmsdale Boulder Beds continue the succession from *mutabilis* Zone to the top of the section (Fig. 11.19) and occupy some 10 km of shoreline parallel to the Helmsdale Fault. A band a few hundred metres wide adjacent to the fault is normally occupied by rock-fall breccias, beyond which are boulder beds, shales and thin sandstones. Details of the sedimentology are summarised by Pickering (1984) and MacDonald & Trewin (1993). The boulder beds are up to several metres thick and contain mainly angular, but also some rounded clasts in a matrix that varies from detrital sand through mixed siliciclastic and bioclastic material to virtually pure bioclastic debris (Plate 23). Land-derived calcified logs of coniferous wood, and coral colonies (*Isastraea*) derived from the marine shelf occur as clasts up to boulder size in some beds. The matrix material of the boulder beds reflects variations in organic productivity (shell debris) and sand supply on the adjacent shelf. Rounded pebbles were derived from high-energy shelf environments, and the angular clasts from the exposed fault scarp. Transport was possibly by short-lived debris flows caused

by earthquakes triggering rock falls, and tsunamis sweeping material off the shelf. Boulder beds are interbedded with black shale, generally lacking any benthonic fauna, and thin (cm scale) sandstone beds and laminae with loaded bases and internal lamination or ripples. These thin sands may have been the result of storms washing material off the shelf. Transport directions are generally perpendicular to the line of the fault, and are revealed by the orientation of echinoid spines in some thin beds.

The most spectacular clasts in the boulder beds are seen near Portgower where one 30 m long clast is known as 'The Fallen Stack'. This was the interpretation by Blake (1902); it is now recognized as a giant clast that toppled off the fault scarp and slid downslope. The clast length gives an absolute minimum for the height of exposed rock on the submarine fault scarp.

From Portgower northwards the clasts in the boulder beds are of Middle Old Red Sandstone flagstone facies. The presence of *Coccosteus cuspidatus* in a clast indicates a stratigraphic age of topmost Eifelian for strata on the exposed footwall in Kimmeridgian times. To the south of Portgower a rapid change in clast type to a fluvial cross-bedded sandstone is seen (MacDonald & Trewin 1993). The largest clasts are red at their centres but most are bleached white. The petrography and sedimentology of these clasts point to a possible source in the Upper Old Red Sandstone. Clearly the composition of the rocks exposed on the fault scarp changed either by stratigraphic superposition or faulting to the south of Portgower. At present Moine psammites and Helmsdale granite occupy the footwall of the fault, but neither supplied clasts to the Kimmeridgian and were clearly not unroofed at that time.

West of Scotland

A transgression at or near the base of the Callovian is a major event over much of Europe, flooding the Russian platform, putting an end to the complexities of Bathonian facies distribution in England, and ushering in a period of marine sedimentation lasting until near the end of the Jurassic. A lagoonal transgression in Trotternish and a more abrupt marine one, probably above a hiatus, in Strathaird introduce the Staffin Bay Formation. In the Mid-Callovian, fully marine offshore sedimentation ensued, and persists in Trotternish, in the form of shales and silts, the Staffin Shale Formation, until the early Kimmeridgian. Correlatives in Strathaird are markedly more sandy, and a small part of the succession can also be seen on Eigg.

The exposures in Staffin Bay, Trotternish, described in Morton & Hudson (1995), are some of the most important in Europe for Late Jurassic ammonite biostratigraphy, especially for the Oxfordian, and they have many other features of interest too. One is that they dissect the toes of a major series of landslips, the biggest in Britain, where erosion of the Tertiary basalts to produce the Trotternish lava escarpment has created rotational slip-faults that also affect the shales beneath. The exposures are intertidal and complexly faulted and steeply dipping.

At the top of the Skudiburgh Formation (Great Estuarine Group, see above) there is a locally developed bed of dark clay with plant remains. Directly above occurs a thin shell bed with *Neomiodon* and the larger bivalve *Isognomon*, with a dark shale matrix and overlain by further shales and shell-beds, some of which contain oysters. This marks the base of the Upper Ostrea Member of the Staffin Bay Formation. It represents the gentlest of lagoonal transgressions. The member has a central more silty part but is generally fine grained, with a fauna of bivalves of low diversity, preserved in pristine but fragile aragonite, a feature of Staffin fossils generally. (The name of this member is inappropriate in that oysters are not the dominant fossil). Gradationally above is the lower sandy part of the Belemnite Sands Member. This contains a more varied bivalve fauna including genera usually regarded as fully marine, such as *Pleuromya*, but not belemnites. Belemnites only occur near the top of the member, where they form a 'belemnite battlefield' (Doyle & Macdonald 1993). These top beds are glauconitic and contain siderite nodules, and have yielded a plesiosaur (Clark *et al.* 1993). The Belemnite Sands Member is interpreted as representing a bar, offshore of the quiet lagoon in which the Upper Ostrea Member was deposited (Fig. 11.23). The lower part consists of wash-over sands, and the belemnite beds represent the seaward side of the barrier, with the belemnites having washed up on its shoreface. Next come offshore dark shales, possibly above a hiatus; see below. The age of the Staffin Bay Formation was uncertain for many years, but Riding (1992) and Riding & Thomas (1997) confirm from palynology that both members are Early Callovian in age; this is consistent with sparse ammonite evidence from the Belemnite Sands Member. In Strathaird, the Staffin Bay Formation is represented by the coarse, sandy Carn Mor Sandstone Member, which also contains belemnites, brachiopods and rare ammonites of the *koenigi* Zone. It rests disconformably on the Skudiburgh Member and there is no equivalent of the Upper Ostrea Member.

The Staffin Shale Formation of Staffin, Skye is argillaceous throughout, but variations in silt content and shale litho- and bio-facies enable subdivision into members and palaeoecological interpretation (Sykes 1975; Sykes & Callomon 1979; summary in Morton & Hudson 1995). The most important feature is the abundance of well-preserved ammonites. In the lowest beds Kosmoceratids of the *medea* Subzone, *jason* Zone are common. There is then a poorly-fossiliferous interval, the Dunans Shale Member, probably accumulated under mainly anoxic conditions, that is of interest as a potential source rock (Fisher & Hudson 1987). The later Callovian part of the section includes two prominent layers of septarian concretionary limestone. Thereafter, the Oxfordian succession is continuously ammonite-bearing. The faunas are dominated by the boreal Cardioceratidae (successively *Quenstedtoceras, Cardioceras, Amoeboceras*), though Tethyan Perisphinctidae also occur. The succession enables the establishment of a zonal scheme for the boreal Oxfordian, and contributes to correlation

with the Tethyan realm (Sykes & Callomon 1979). Belemnites are common, and faunas of benthic bivalves vary according to substrate consistency and oxygenation. Superimposed on generalized grain-size variations that define the members, the strata show many decimetre-scale minor sedimentary cycles; sharp-based dark shale grades up into dark grey mudstone and then into paler calcareous mudstone. Bed contacts are disturbed by *Thalassinoides, Planolites* and *Chondrites* burrows (Hesselbo & Coe 2000). A similar situation persists into the Lower Kimmeridgian beds, which are the highest exposed. They contain large septarian concretions, with successive generations of calcite and baryte in the cracks. Bentonitic clays occur at intervals in the Staffin Shale Formation, suggesting volcanic activity to the west of the British Isles from mid-Callovian to early Oxfordian times (Knox 1977; Bradshaw *et al.* 1992). In Strathaird, the succession can be correlated approximately to that of Staffin but the sandier strata are poorly exposed and much less consistently fossiliferous. On Eigg the formation is more fossiliferous, although poorly exposed. It is in part argillaceous but includes strongly glauconitic sandstones in the *cordatum* Zone.

There are no exposed Jurassic rocks on the west coast younger than Early Kimmeridgian. Upper Cretaceous sandstones and limestones overstep major faults such as the Camasunary Fault, which are thus loosely constrained in time. Analogy with the east coast sections in Sutherland, where boulder-beds accumulated against fault scarps during the Kimmeridgian, suggests a phase of rapid basin fragmentation at that time.

Western Offshore Basins

To the west of the Outer Hebrides, Upper Jurassic marine strata are proved in the West Flannan Basin and probably occur farther offshore in the Rockall Trough. In the basins west of Shetland, tectonic activity continued and Upper Jurassic rocks are more widespread than the earlier Jurassic strata, often resting unconformably on earlier Mesozoic or on basement. The sediments are predominantly argillaceous, of Kimmeridgian to Volgian age, and include organic rich (radioactive) shales comparable to the Kimmeridge Clay of the North Sea. However, facies and thickness are both variable, and submarine-fan

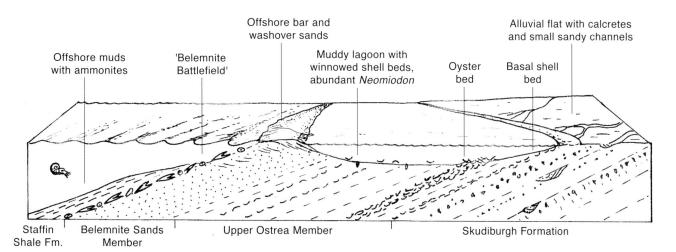

Fig. 11.23. Facies interpretation of the Staffin Bay Formation as representing a transgression over the fluvial and alluvial Skudiburgh Formation at the top of the Great Estuarine Group. The Upper Ostrea Member indicates a first lagoonal transgression, followed by the shoreward migration of an offshore sand-bar (Belemnite Sands Member), and final flooding at the base of the Staffin Shale Formation, with numerous belemnites washed up on the seaward slope of the bar (cf. Doyle & Macdonald 1993). Not to scale. The diachroneity of facies implied by this diagram is not defined, but is short compared to the length of the ammonite subzone.

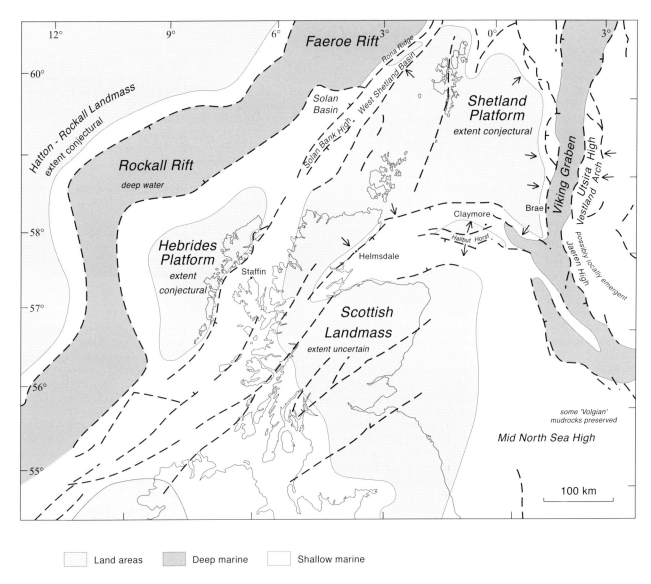

Fig. 11.24. Late Jurassic (Kimmeridgian) palaeogeography. Active rift margin faulting resulted in deep water organic-rich shale deposition in graben areas, and deposition of coarse clastics adjacent to active faults (e.g. Helmsdale, and Brae Field). Modified after Bradshaw *et al.* (1992).

deposition continued along the boundary between the Rona Ridge and the Faeroe-Shetland Basin (Stoker *et al.* 1993).

Late Jurassic Palaeogeography

A rising sea level in the Late Jurassic resulted in drowning of areas that were previously exposed (Fig 11.24). However, footwall uplift at basin margins provided local source areas for sands that were recycled through delta and shelf environments and eventually deposited as deep water clastics in adjacent basins. River systems existed on the Shetland Platform and Scottish Landmass and supplied sand and mud to coastal systems. The land areas were well vegetated with distinct lowland and upland vegetation types.

12 Cretaceous

S. D. HARKER

The Cretaceous of Scotland consists of a succession of sedimentary rocks that record episodic marine transgression, from both east (North Sea) and west (Atlantic), over the eroded rift terrains of Late Cimmerian tectonism. In common with much of NW Europe and the Atlantic borders of Canada and Ireland, the Early Cretaceous was dominated by clastic deposition in a moderately active tectonic regime (Sinclair *et al.* 1994). Passive subsidence was the dominant process in the Late Cretaceous, accompanied by carbonate and hemipelagic deposition (Hancock & Rawson 1992). The Chalk Group sediments are considered to have once covered much of what is now the Scottish mainland, only to have been removed during the Tertiary–Quaternary uplift, accompanying the opening of the North Atlantic Ocean.

The dominant NE–SW structural trend for the half graben systems to the west of Scotland, shows reactivation of old Caledonian lineaments, parallel to the Moine Thrust (Fig.12.1). This area represents the SE rifted margin of the Proto North Atlantic, across from the eastern seaboard of North America and Greenland (Ziegler 1988*a*). Atlantic rifting was rejuvenated through the Tertiary, as evidenced by extensive igneous activity (Stoker *et al.* 1993; Fyfe *et al.* 1993). The Faeroe escarpment marks the southern limit of the widespread Tertiary plateau basalts that mask the underlying Cretaceous stratigraphy to the NW of Scotland. Cretaceous North Sea rifting was inherited from the Late Cimmerian (Jurassic) tectonism that produced the triple junction of the NNE–SSW Viking, the WNW–ESE Moray Firth and the NW–SE Central graben systems. However, following the Austrian tectonic pulse during the Aptian, rifting was effectively terminated and, for the remainder of the Cretaceous, progressive sea-level rise led to transgression over most of the Scottish landmass. Onlap of the flanks of the North Sea graben system is evident from the Cenomanian onwards.

The Scottish Cretaceous succession is poorly exposed in some sparsely distributed onshore outcrops (Fig. 12.1, see Hallam (1991) for references), though much can be inferred regarding the geological history by the incorporation of offshore data. Onshore there are Lower Cretaceous shallow marine sandstones, possibly *in situ* at Moreseat, near Peterhead in NE Scotland, but Upper Cretaceous outcrops are only known on the west coast. The normal west coast section is generally shallow marine in origin and consists of basal sandstones followed by chalks and limestones which are succeeded by clastics, and this can be observed on the islands of Eigg, Mull, Raasay, Scalpay and Skye, as well as on the Argyll mainland near Morvern. Offshore, the data come largely from some shallow boreholes, many deep oil industry wells and abundant geophysical data, particularly extensive seismic records. In the deeper parts of the offshore grabens, the Early Cretaceous succession consists at the base of the youngest organic rich shales of the Kimmeridge Clay Formation, Humber Group. This is followed by calcareous shales and shallow marine to deep marine sandstone units of the Cromer Knoll Group, that were deposited in an actively developing bathymetric topography. The offshore Late Cretaceous is generally represented by chalks (Chalk Group) in the southern regions, that grade northwards into calcareous shales of the Boreal realm (Shetland Group), marking a return to more stable tectonic subsidence and widespread deep marine conditions.

Early Cretaceous

During the Early Cretaceous, the low-lying Scottish mainland remained largely subaerially exposed. Apart from some isolated fringing coastal deposits, evidence for the depositional and structural history of the Early Cretaceous comes from offshore. Deposition of organic-rich muds continued in the Atlantic and North Sea areas from the latest Jurassic into the Early Cretaceous, in restricted marine basins under anoxic bottom conditions. Thus the youngest units of the Humber Group, the uppermost Kimmeridge Clay Formation, are Ryazanian in age (Figs 12.2, 12.3; Johnson & Lott 1993; Ritchie *et al.* 1996). The Late Cimmerian tectonic episode culminated in block fault uplift and erosion, prior to deposition of calcareous muds and sands of the Vallhall Formation, Cromer Knoll Group. The resultant unconformity, commonly termed the Base Cretaceous Unconformity (or BCU) frequently does not represent a single event of simple transgression over the rifted terrain. There is commonly a composite condensed section containing intra-Valhall unconformites, as well as the underlying contact with the Kimmeridge Clay or older rocks (Rawson & Riley 1982). The change to calcareous hemipelagic sedimentation from Humber to Cromer Knoll groups represents the oxygenation of bottom waters and the connection to more open marine conditions in a pulsed transgressive episode. Intra-basinal highs, such as the Halibut Horst and Forties–Montrose High (Fig. 12.1) were prominent areas of non-deposition through into the Late Cretaceous and may have acted as sand sources for Early Cretaceous marine gravity flows.

The Valhall Formation is dominantly a pale grey to greenish-grey or reddish-grey section of marine calcareous mudstones or marls, with occasional limestones, ranging in age from latest Ryazanian to Early Aptian (Fig. 12.2). It is succeeded by non-calcareous grey marine mudstones of the Carrack or Cruiser formations. In the northern North Sea and parts of the Atlantic seaboard basins, the Cromer Knoll Group remains undivided, where the section consists of more homogeneous calcareous mudstone lithologies.

There are several sandstone units represented in the Cromer Knoll Group. Onshore the Moreseat sandstone (Barremian to Hauterivian age) is of shallow marine origin, located 30 km north of Aberdeen (Hall & Jarvis 1993*b*). This is a fine to medium grained sandstone, occasionally glauconitic with a shallow water fauna of brachiopods, bivalves and rare ammonites. Although long known from glacial erratics, this locality is now considered to be the only *in situ* onshore example of the Early Cretaceous Cromer Knoll Group. It forms a remnant of a shoreline system formed around the Moray Firth that fed the marine gravity flow systems, represented offshore by the Wick Formation (Figs 12.4 & 12.5). It is also worth noting that at Leavad, 12 miles WSW of Wick in Caithness, Tait (1910)

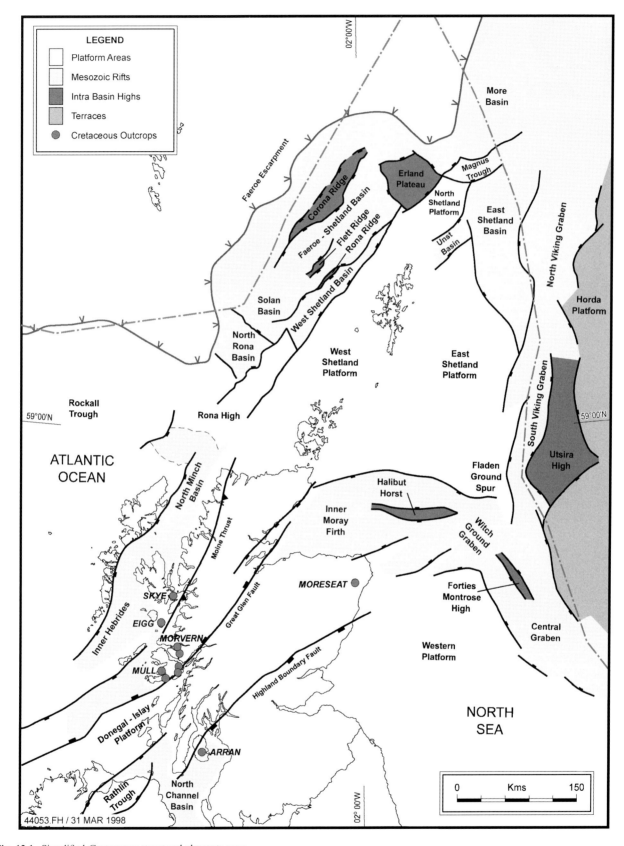

Fig. 12.1. Simplified Cretaceous structural elements map.

records an erratic of Lower Cretaceous sandstone extending to 195 by 150 yards (178×137 m), and shown to overlie shelly boulder clay. It is not known how far this large sheet of Cretaceous rocks was transported by ice, but it probably represents locally derived Early Cretaceous shoreline clastics.

The Punt, Coracle and Captain sandstone members are mappable units within the Wick Formation as defined by Johnson & Lott (1993). The Scapa Sandstone Member of the Valhall formation infills the Late Cimmerian rifted topography on the northern flanks of the Halibut Horst. Thick conglomerates

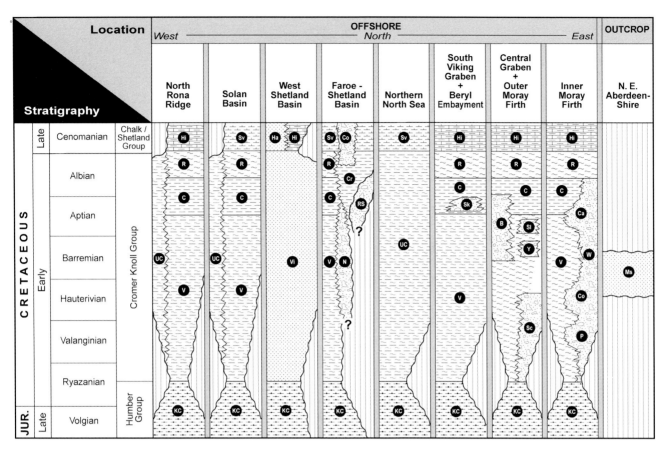

Fig. 12.2. Early Cretaceous comparative stratigraphic chart. For legend see Fig. 12.3.

Age	Group	Formation	(Member / Unit)	Lithology
Early Tertiary	Shetland	**S** Sullom		Marl
	Chalk	**E** Ekofisk		
Late Cretaceous	Shetland	**US** Undivided Shetland **J** Jorsalfare		Limestone
		F Flounder **K** Kyrre		
		Sv Svarte **M** Macbeth		
	Chalk	**T** Tor **ML** Mackerel		Dolomite
		Hi Hidra (**Ha** *Haddock Sandstone*)		
	Inner Hebrides	**Bl** Beinn Iadain Mudstone (**FS** *Feorlin Sandstone*)		Calcareous Shale
		SL Strathaird Limestone (**LG** *Lairg Gorge Sandstone*)		
		(**CA** *Clach Asdair Conglomerate*)		Shale
		GC Gribun Chalk		
		MG Morvern Greensand (**La** *Lochaline White Sandstone*)		Organic Rich Shale
Early Cretaceous	Cromer Knoll	**UC** Undivided Cromer Knoll		
		R Rodby **Co** Commodore		Marine Gravity Flow Sandstone
		Vi Victory **Cr** Cruiser		
		RS Royal Sovereign		Shallow Marine Sandstone
		C Carrack (**Sk** *Skiff Sandstone*)		
		B Britannia		
		W Wick (**Ca** *Captain Sandstone*)		Igneous
		(**Co** *Coracle Sandstone*)		
		(**P** *Punt Sandstone*)		
		V Valhall (**SL** *Sloop Sandstone*)		Hiatus
		(**Y** *Yawl Sandstone*)		
		(**Sc** *Scapa Sandstone*)		
		(**Ms** *Moreseat Sandstone*)		
Late Jurassic	Humber	**KC** Kimmeridge Clay		

Fig. 12.3. Cretaceous legend.

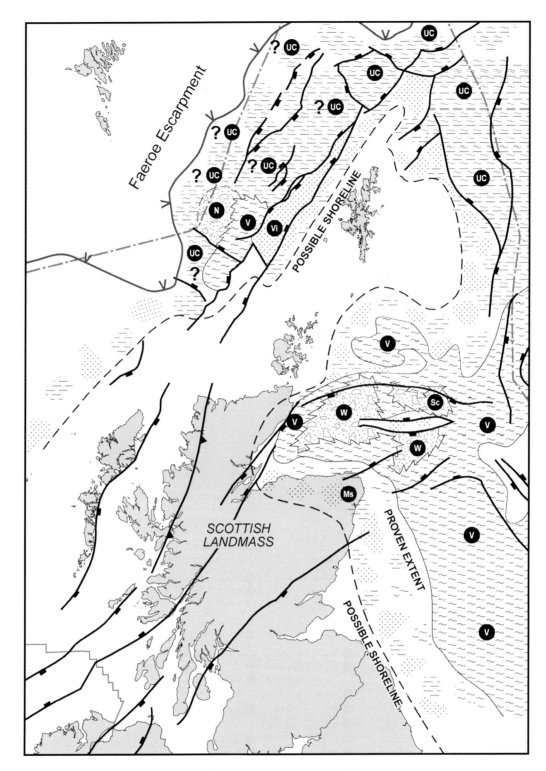

Fig. 12.4. Late Ryazanian to Hauterivian palaeogeographic map. For legend see Fig. 12.3.

(non-reservoir due to high argillaceous content and carbonate cementation) are present adjacent to the footwall block, in the southern part of the half graben topography. The reservoir quality sandstones (low argillaceous content and less cementation) interfinger with the conglomerates, thicken into the half-graben, and thin up the dip slope of the adjacent tilt block. The sandstones pass by facies change over a short distance into sealing marls of the Valhall Formation (Harker *et al.* 1987; Harker & Chermak 1991). The Brittania Formation and the Skiff, Sloop and Yawl members are marine gravity flow sand-

stones derived from the southern extension of the East Shetland Platform and Fladen Ground Spur. These sandstones are Late Barremian to Aptian in age and were sourced during the Austrian tectonic episode.

The western offshore basins contain both shallow marine and gravity flow sandstones. The Victory Formation of the West Shetland Basin ranges in age from Late Ryazanian to Albian and consists of a complex shallow marine to paralic succession of glauconitic sandstones and conglomerates with coals locally present. The basal contact is unconformable onto

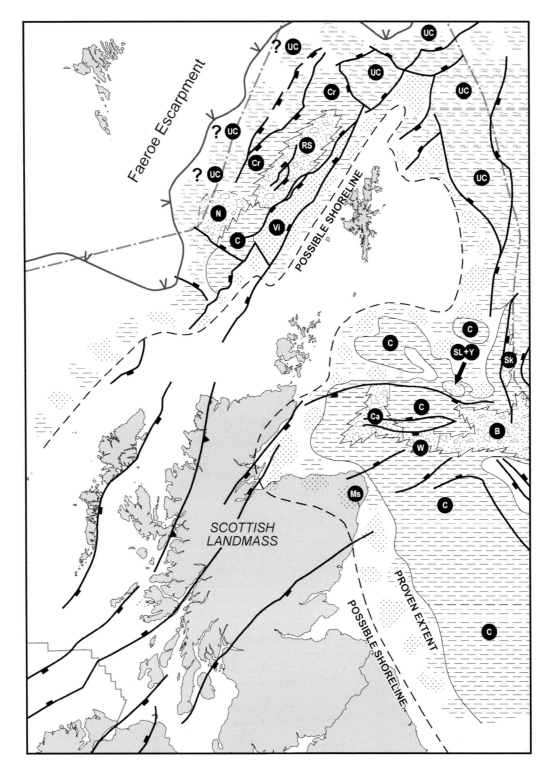

Fig. 12.5. Barremian to Aptian palaeogeographic map.

the Devonian over the Rona Ridge. To the west into the Faeroe- Shetland Basin, the marine gravity flow sandstones of the Royal Sovereign Formation represent deposition in deeper marine conditions in the Barremian to Albian. The Royal Sovereign sandstones shale out to the west and north into non-calcareous mudstones of the Cruiser Formation. Similar to the Scapa sandstones of the Moray Firth, the distribution of gravity flow sandstones was controlled by the bathymetric topography, and localized conglomerates fringe footwall blocks. The Neptune Formation is also of gravity flow origin,

but is restricted to the southern Faeroe–Shetland Basin adjacent to (and sourced from) the Rona High.

After the Austrian tectonic episode, the Cretaceous marine transgression progressed during the Albian, with hemipelagic deposition infilling a passively subsiding remnant topography. Variably calcareous mudstones and marls dominate the succession. The Rodby Formation consists of red-brown to medium grey marls, mudstones and thin limestones, distinguishing it from the underlying grey, non-calcareous mudstones of the Carrack Formation. The calcareous content decreases towards

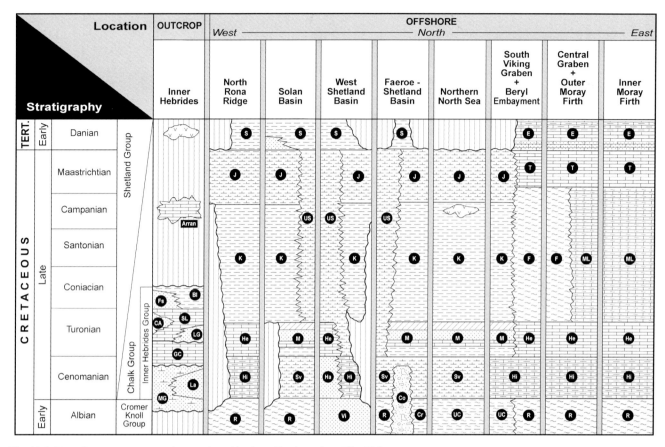

Fig. 12.6. Late Cretaceous comparative stratigraphic chart. For legend see Fig. 12.3.

the north, where the Albian succession comprises the undifferentiated Cromer Knoll Group. However, a final Early Cretaceous pulse of marine gravity flows, the Commodore Formation, is present towards the top of the Albian in the Faeroe–Shetland Basin (Fig. 12.3; Ritchie *et al.* 1996). These sandstones are more restricted to a basinward location than the older Royal Sovereign sandstones, but likewise shale-out basinward into the Cruiser Formation mudstones. The genesis of the Commodore sandstones was similar to the Royal Sovereign Formation, though they persist in age into the Cenomanian, where they are interbedded with the Svarte Formation calcareous mudstones (Figs 12.6 & 12.7).

Late Cretaceous

There are several outcrops of Late Cretaceous rocks on the Inner Hebridean islands of Eigg, Mull, Raasay, Scalpay and Skye, as well as on the Argyll mainland near Morvern (Figs 12.1 and 12.6–12.9). All the sections whether carbonate or clastic are thin and of shallow marine origin. There are also metamorphosed chalk fragments in Tertiary volcanic vents on the Isle of Arran (Hallam 1991). Many of the chalk outcrops show a high degree of silicification, which may indicate episodes of Late Cretaceous exposure to semi-arid continental conditions (Hancock 2000). Marine transgression continued through the Late Cretaceous, gradually drowning out all but small areas of the Scottish Highlands and the Southern Uplands (Figs 12.7 to 12.9; Hancock & Rawson 1992). Throughout the Late Cretaceous, carbonate deposition in warm tropical seas, with abundant coccolith distribution, resulted in the widespread occurrence of Chalk Group sediments. The colder

more Boreal waters to the north were less favourable for coccolith productivity and the sediments there are less calcareous and more mud dominated and belong to the Shetland Group.

In outcrops in southern Mull, Eigg and on the adjacent mainland in Morvern, the basal Cretaceous section is represented by calcareous shallow marine sandstones of the Morvern Greensand. These glauconitic clastics mark the late Albian–Cenomanian transgression of this region and rest unconformably on Jurassic and older rocks. Work by Braley (1990), and Lowden *et al.* (1992) has revised the stratigraphy of the Inner Hebrides Group. The Morvern Greensand, together with the Lochaline White Sandstone are equivalent to the Hibernian Greensnd Formation of the Rathlin Trough in Northern Ireland (Fyfe *et al.* 1993). The area to the south of Skye would appear to have been a shallow marine clastic shelf during Cenomanian times (Fig. 12.7). A similar development of coastal conditions is likely to have fringed the Scottish landmass, though evidence is lacking, apart from the Haddock Sandstone Member of the Hidra Formation in the eastern part of the southern West Shetland Basin.

The basal formation of the Chalk Group throughout much of the Scottish offshore areas is the Hidra, consisting of white to pale grey, argillaceous limestones. To the north and west the limestones are replaced by calcareous mudstones of the Svarte Formation of the Shetland Group. Only the intra-basin highs, such as the Halibut Horst and the Forties–Montrose High show no Cenomanian cover. The Commodore marine gravity flows and the Haddock shallow marine sands are the only clastic deposits documented from the Cenomanian. Thus the remaining Scottish land area appears to have been fairly well peneplained by this time. The Gribun Chalk succeeds the Morvern Greensand on Mull and is of similar facies to the Hidra,

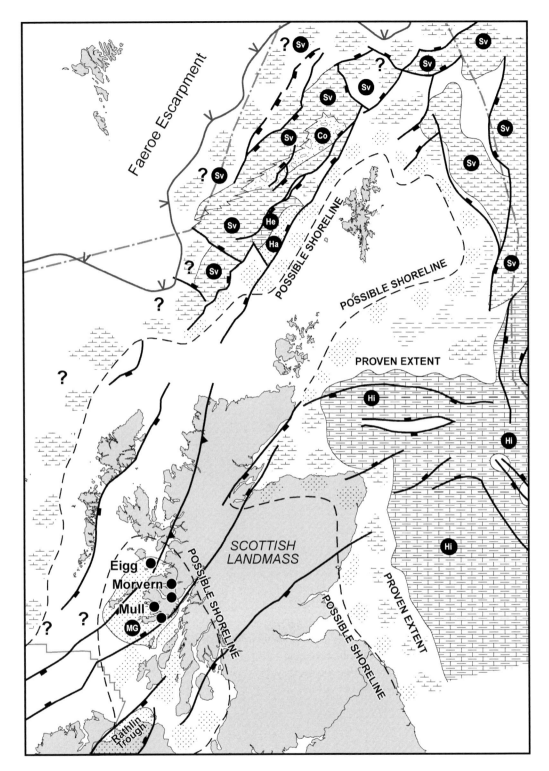

Fig. 12.7. Cenomanian palaeogeographic map. For legend see Fig. 12.3.

and ranges in age from Cenomanian to Turonian on the basis of palynology and micropalaeontological evidence (Braley 1990), but it is considered Santonian in age by Hancock (2000) on the basis of rare macrofossils.

The Turonian Herring Formation is a cryptocrystalline limestone and has its equivalent facies, the Strathaird Limestone, in outcrops of the Inner Hebrides Group. A carbonate platform area was present in the Inner Hebrides, whereas shallow marine sands continued to dominate in the Rathlin Trough to the south (Fig. 12.8). Interestingly, there are some

clastics interbedded in the Straithaird Formation, the Clach Asdair Conglomerate and the Laig Gorge Sandstone members according to Braley (1990). In contrast, Hancock (2000) proposes the name of Gribun Formation for the conglomerates that succeed the Gribun Chalk in southwest Mull and considers them to be possibly of Maastrichtian age, based on their position between the Palaeocene basalts and the underlying Chalk. Local block fault movement of the Inner Hebrides area may have resulted in the Late Cretaceous coarse clastic input, though outcrop evidence is too sparsely distributed to propose

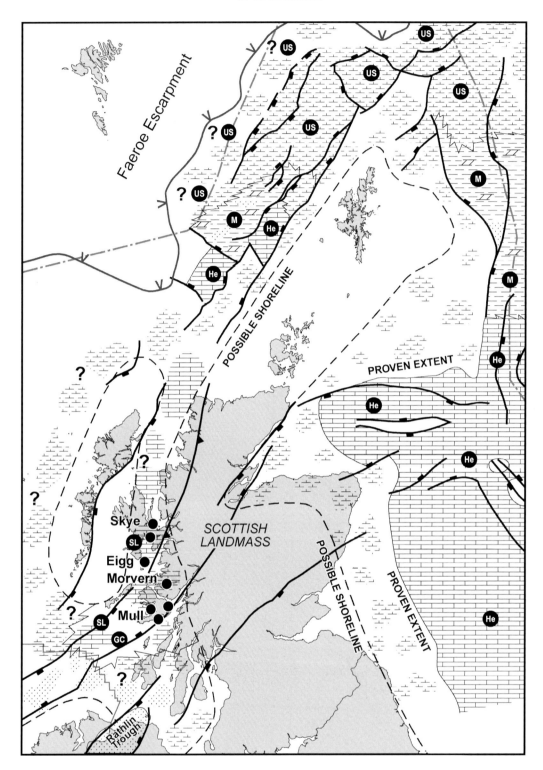

Fig. 12.8. Turonian palaeogeographic map. For legend see Fig. 12.3.

firm conclusions. Offshore and to the north of the carbonate belt of the Herring Formation are interbedded mudstones, thin dolomites and sandstones of the Macbeth Formation. Further to the north and west the Turonian is represented by calcareous mudstones of the Shetland Group.

In the Senonian (Coniacian to Campanian), the Shetland Group facies extended further to the south, as represented by mudstone of the Kyrre Formation in the North Sea, and on the western seaboard by the Beinn Iadain Formation in the Inner Hebrides area (Fig. 12.9). The Feorlain Member is the only Senonian sandstone identified by Braley (1990) and may be a shallow marine deposit. To the south these clastics are replaced by carbonates of the Ulster White Limestone in Northern Ireland and the possible Senonian age Chalk Group fragments in volcanic vents in Arran. The Senonian Chalk Group is represented by marls and chalks of the Mackerel Formation in the Moray Firth and Central North Sea. Marls and calcareous shales of the Flounder Formation separate the Kyrre shales from the Mackerel chalks in the Outer Moray Firth to South Viking Graben areas. During the Senonian,

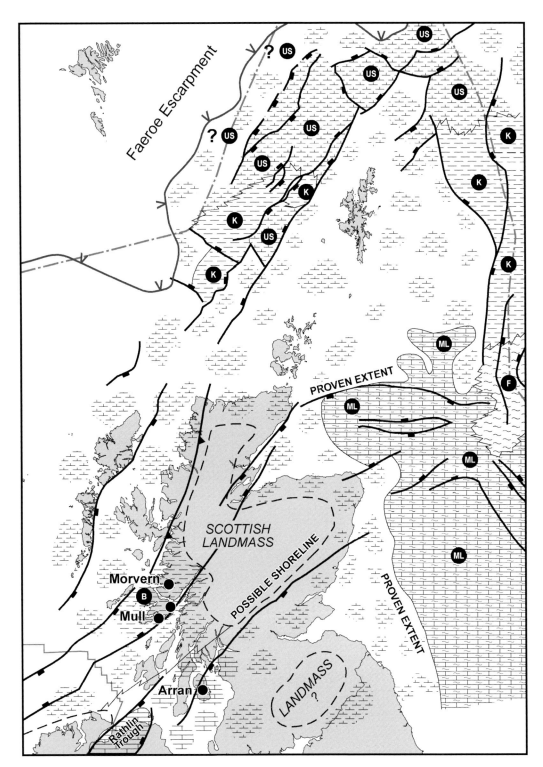

Fig. 12.9. Senonian palaeogeographic map. For legend see Fig. 12.3.

only remnants of the Scottish Highlands and the Southern Uplands are believed to have remained subaerially exposed.

In the far north of the North Sea, undifferentiated Shetland Group calcareous mudstones dominate the Late Cretaceous succession. The Maastrichtian marked a return to more wide-spread carbonate deposition with chalks of the Tor Formation (Chalk Group) in the south and Jorsalfare (Shetland Group) in the north. The Chalk Group deposition continued into the Tertiary, as represented by the sandy chalks of the Ekofisk For-

mation. Shetland Group deposition also continued into the Tertiary as represented by the sandy mudstones of the Sullom Formation (Fig. 12.6).

The onset of Hebridean igneous activity had been thought to have been within the Maastrichtian (Srivastava 1975). How-ever, recent work by Bell & Jolley (1997) revised the age assign-ment and showed that the Hebrides igneous activity did not commence until the Palaeogene (see Chapter 14). Nonethe-less, Late Cretaceous intrusives have been recorded from the northern North Sea in offshore wells (Stoker *et al.* 1993). The uplift caused by the Tertiary igneous activity that was associated with the opening of the North Atlantic, led to erosion and stripping off of the Cretaceous cover of the Scottish mainland and possibly the silicification of the Hebridean chalk outcrops. This uplift eventually led to considerable erosion of the Scottish landmass, the detritus being transported into the North Sea basinal area and deposited to form the Lower Tertiary sandstones that form major reservoirs in offshore oilfields (see Chapters 13 & 19).

13 Tertiary sedimentation

R. W. O'B. KNOX

As a result of substantial uplift and erosion during the Cenozoic, much of the Scottish landmass is devoid of Tertiary strata. In eastern Scotland, Tertiary deposits are limited to the Pliocene Buchan Gravels (Flett & Read 1921; Hall, A. M. 1985; McMillan & Merritt 1980) and an ice-rafted block of Miocene clay (Crampton & Carruthers 1914). The only substantial onshore deposits are the lavas and largely pyroclastic sediments of the Hebridean Igneous Province (see Chapter 14). These volcanic rocks constitute part of the North Atlantic Tertiary Igneous Province, which developed in response to the rise of the North Atlantic mantle plume beneath the continental crust of East Greenland during the Palaeocene. Regional plume-related uplift and associated rift tectonics in the North Atlantic region (Fig. 13.1) led to the creation of a landmass that encompassed much of present-day Scotland and what is now the largely submerged Orkney–Shetland Platform. Uplift and erosion of this landmass, especially the Orkney–Shetland Platform, resulted in substantial sediment supply to the adjacent North Sea and Faeroe–Shetland basins, where the Tertiary successions attain maximum thicknesses of around 3 and 4 km, respectively (Fig. 13.2).

The aim of this chapter is to give the reader a general account of the evolution of these sedimentary basins. Because of the long history of hydrocarbon exploration and production in these basins, a very substantial literature has developed, much of it of a highly technical nature. The following selection of references is intended to provide the reader with an introduction to this extensive literature. Comprehensive general accounts of the offshore Tertiary strata are to be found in Andrews et al. (1990), Fyfe et al. (1993), Johnson et al. (1993), Stoker et al. (1993) and Gatliff et al. (1994). Bowman (1998) and Johnson & Fisher (1998) provide general accounts that place more emphasis on the commercial significance of the offshore Tertiary sediments. Doré et al. (1999) provide a summary of the principal tectonic events that influenced the Tertiary evolution of Scotland, while White & Lovell (1997) demonstrate the correlation between offshore sand sedimentation and igneous activity in the Paleocene and Eocene. Illustrations of Tertiary sediment cores acquired during commercial drilling are to be found in Oakman et al. (1993). Palaeontological studies have been largely confined to microfaunas and microfloras (e.g. Gradstein et al. 1993). Additional references to Tertiary sedimentation in the offshore Scottish area may be found in Parker (1993), Knox et al. (1996); Fleet & Boldy (1999) and Evans et al. (2003).

Tectonic evolution

The tectonic evolution of the North Atlantic region is reflected in the depositional history of the offshore Scottish basins. Successive stages in the development of the North Atlantic Ocean are marked by major changes in the amount and pattern of uplift in the Scottish source areas and by progressive changes in the style of subsidence and fill within the offshore basins. These changes are complex in detail, but they are here viewed in terms of eight major depositional cycles, which are most clearly expressed in seismic profiles from the North Sea Basin (Fig. 13.3). The cycles are placed in their temporal context in Figure 13.4.

The earliest Tertiary sediments (Cycle 1) represent a continuation of the tectonic and depositional environments of the Late Cretaceous. In the North Sea Basin they comprise a relatively thin and uniform veneer on the underlying Cretaceous succession.

In Mid-Palaeocene times an abrupt change in tectonic and depositional regimes was brought about by rapid plume-induced uplift of the North Atlantic region, accompanied by major volcanism in the North Atlantic Igneous Province. Uplift of the Scottish landmass resulted in a substantial increase in sediment supply to the adjacent North Sea and Faeroe–Shetland basins (Cycle 2). Reduced water depths on the western margin of the North Sea Basin initially caused shallow water sands to be displaced into deeper water, where they formed substantial basin-floor sand fan complexes (Cycle 2A). The thickest accumulations took place in topographic lows that followed the Mesozoic graben system and developed through a combination of fault reactivation and relative compaction of Mesozoic basinal mudstone successions. As the rate of uplift diminished, rising sea level led to the development of major prograding shallow marine sediment wedges in shelf areas, although slope failure led to continued deposition of deep-water sands (Cycle 2B).

Following a period of high sea-level stand at the end of Cycle 2, a second major phase of regional uplift occurred in latest Palaeocene times. This was related to uplift of the North Atlantic rift margins prior to the onset of sea-floor spreading between Scotland and Greenland. A regional fall in sea

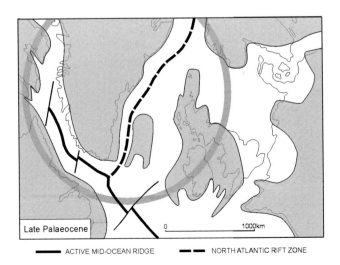

Fig. 13.1. Regional tectonic setting prior to the opening of the NE Atlantic between Greenland and Scotland. Inferred land areas shaded in grey. The circle represents the approximate extent of the proto-Icelandic mantle plume.

Late Palaeocene   0   1000km

—— ACTIVE MID-OCEAN RIDGE   – – – NORTH ATLANTIC RIFT ZONE

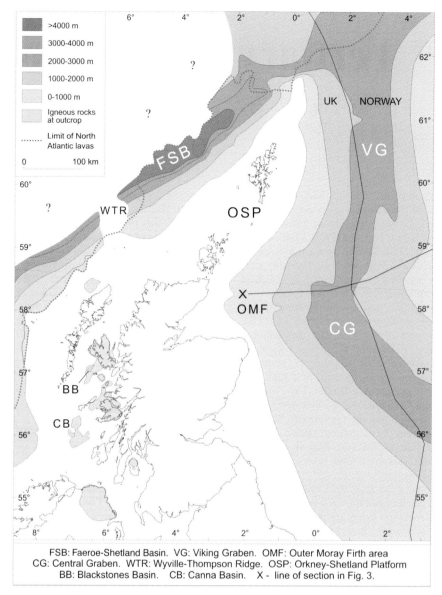

Fig. 13.2. Thickness of Tertiary sediments around Scotland.

FSB: Faeroe-Shetland Basin. VG: Viking Graben. OMF: Outer Moray Firth area
CG: Central Graben. WTR: Wyville-Thompson Ridge. OSP: Orkney-Shetland Platform
BB: Blackstones Basin. CB: Canna Basin. X - line of section in Fig. 3.

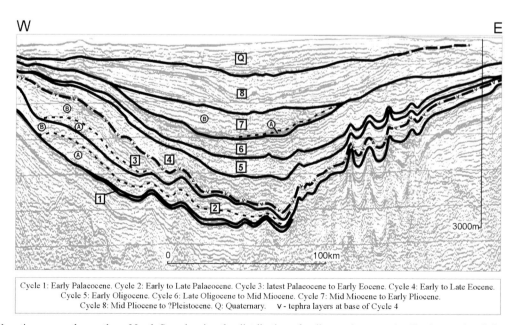

Cycle 1: Early Palaeocene. Cycle 2: Early to Late Palaeocene. Cycle 3: latest Palaeocene to Early Eocene. Cycle 4: Early to Late Eocene.
Cycle 5: Early Oligocene. Cycle 6: Late Oligocene to Mid Miocene. Cycle 7: Mid Miocene to Early Pliocene.
Cycle 8: Mid Pliocene to ?Pleistocene. Q: Quaternary. v - tephra layers at base of Cycle 4

Fig. 13.3. E–W section across the northern North Sea, showing the distribution of sediments in successive Tertiary cycles. Subcycles A, B are shown where a distinct package of early, basin-restricted sediments can be recognized. Sharp anticlinal structures are the result of salt diapirism. See Fig. 13.2 for the line of section. Modified from Hartog Jager *et al.* (1993, fig. 3).

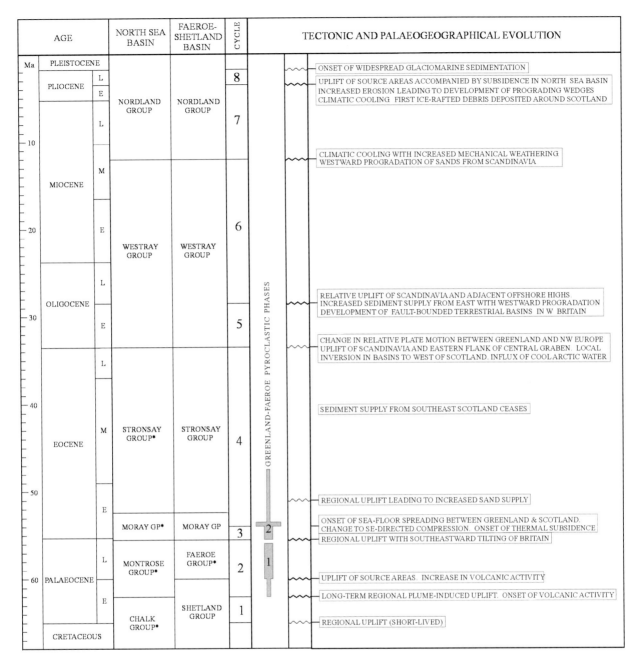

Fig. 13.4. Timing of the most significant developments in the tectonic and palaeogeographical evolution of the Scottish landmass and the adjacent offshore basins. Timescale from Cande & Kent (1995). Lithostratigraphic nomenclature from Knox & Holloway (1992) and Knox *et al.* (1997). Tephra phases from Knox & Morton (1988). Asterisks indicate lithostratigraphic units that include hydrocarbon reservoirs.

level, accompanied by renewed uplift of the Scottish source areas, led to renewed progradation into the basins. The initial sea-level fall led to substantial deep-water sand sedimentation in the North Sea Basin (Cycle 3A), with the thickest accumulations again being confined to the Mesozoic graben zones. A subsequent rise in sea level, accompanied by continued uplift and eastward tilting of the Scottish landmass, led to the development of a major shallow marine to terrestrial shelf wedge, while relatively thin, condensed, deep water sediments continued to be deposited in central parts of the basin (Cycle 3B).

With the onset of Atlantic sea-floor spreading at the beginning of Cycle 4 sedimentation (Early Eocene), the pre-existing NW–SE extensional regime gave way to a SE-directed compressional regime that persists to the present day. Thermal

subsidence of the North Atlantic region was associated with a reduction in structural differentiation within the depositional areas and by a rise in sea level that caused widespread flooding of the shelf areas. An initial period of subaerial explosive volcanism along the developing mid-ocean ridge led to the widespread deposition of basaltic air-fall tephras. Throughout Cycle 4 deposition the Scottish landmass continued to supply the bulk of sediments to the North Sea Basin, with the development of a broad, prograding sandy shelf along the western basin margin. Deep water environments persisted in central and eastern parts of the basin, with accumulation of relatively condensed, mud-dominated sediments.

The base of Cycle 5 marks a profound change in the tectonic and sedimentary regime in earliest Oligocene times, resulting from changes in the configuration of plate movement in the

North Atlantic region. Sea-floor spreading in the Labrador Sea ceased, while in the NE Atlantic the movement of NW Europe from Greenland changed from a southeasterly to more east-southeasterly direction. This led to a switch in the focus of ridge-push related uplift from Scotland to Scandinavia. The consequent influx of sediment from the rejuvenated Scandinavian landmass combined with that from the Scottish landmass to produce a more uniform pattern of sediment distribution within the basin. At the same time, rapid global cooling resulted in glacioeustatic lowering of sea level. Mild inversion within the North Sea Basin may have served to decrease water depths in central parts of the basin, leading to higher rates of largely muddy sedimentation.

The onset of Cycle 6 sedimentation (Late Oligocene to Miocene) was marked by renewed relative uplift of Scandinavia, probably resulting from further changes in the pattern or rate of spreading along the North Atlantic ridge system. This led to a significant fall in relative sea level on the eastern margin of the North Sea Basin, resulting in the development of a major westward-prograding sediment wedge.

A major fall in sea level in the late Mid Miocene (Cycle 7) may be largely of glacioeustatic origin, resulting from a marked increase in the volume of polar ice. Uplift of southern Scandinavia may also have taken place at this time, but the sediment was largely directed southwestwards into the central North Sea. In the Viking Graben sands were brought in from the east, but much of the muddy sediment appears to have been derived from Scotland.

Cycle 8 sedimentation was characterized by the development of large-scale progradational wedges on both flanks of the North Sea Basin during the late Pliocene, indicating rejuvenation of both the Scottish and Scandinavian landmasses coupled with rapid subsidence of the intervening basin. The renewed uplift of the Scottish landmass is a conspicuous feature of this depositional cycle, since it contrasts with the pattern of reduced uplift established in early Oligocene times. No significant change in the pattern of North Atlantic sea-floor spreading can be identified that would explain this anomaly, and it seems most likely that it is an effect of the onset of northern hemisphere glaciation at around 2.6 Ma. Modelling of the effects of ice-cover on the northern European landmasses suggests that the observed tectonic events can be accounted for by greatly accelerated erosion rates leading to sediment loading within the basin and isostatic uplift of the adjacent landmasses.

Cycle 8 sedimentation was brought to a close by an intensification of glacial activity in latest Pliocene to earliest Pleistocene times, reflected in the onset of widespread glacio-marine sedimentation.

During the Palaeocene and earliest Eocene, the Faeroe–Shetland Basin displays a history of basin fill broadly similar to that of the North Sea Basin. However, with the onset of sea-floor spreading in the Early Eocene, the basin lost its structural identity and became incorporated into the developing North Atlantic Ocean. The post-Eocene succession is thin and incomplete compared with that of the North Sea Basin, with the most complete sections preserved along the southeastern basin

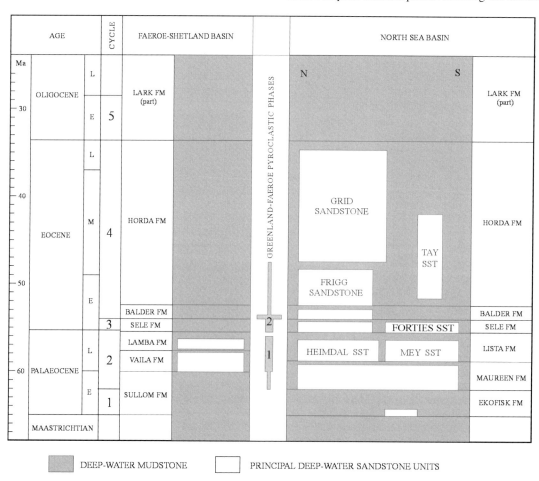

Fig. 13.5. Stratigraphic distribution of deep-water sandstones in the Faeroe–Shetland and North Sea basins, showing the principal named sandstone members. Time scale and tephra phases as in Fig. 13.3. Lithostratigraphic names (basinal facies only) from Knox & Holloway (1992) and Knox et al. (1997). The Mey Sandstone Member (Lista Fm., Cycle 2) includes the Andrew and Balmoral sandstone units. Other named North Sea sandstone units (not shown) are the Cromarty, Flugga and Teal sandstone members (Sele Fm., Cycle 3), and the Skroo Sandstone Member (Horda Fm., Cycle 4).

margin. Two factors account for this apparently anomalous situation: basin inversion resulting from SE-directed compression from the Late Eocene onwards and erosion by increasingly powerful deep-water geostrophic currents, reflecting the increased influence of the Antarctic ice cap on the Atlantic deep-water circulation system.

Stratigraphic framework

The contrasting styles of sedimentary fill within the North Sea and Faeroe–Shetland basins have led to the establishment of significantly different lithological successions, reflected in the differing lithostratigraphic schemes for the two basins (see Figs 13.4, 13.5). Because of these differences, the common history of crustal evolution and sea-level change in the two basins is best appreciated by reference to the long-term tectono-sedimentary cycles identified in the preceding section. Significant tectonic and depositional events of lower magnitude took place during deposition of each of these cycles, but while an understanding of this greater stratigraphic complexity has proved essential in the offshore search for hydrocarbons, a simplified approach is deliberately adopted here.

Also shown on Figure 13.4 is a summary of the tectonic and volcanic history of the region. Of particular significance in establishing the relative timing of sedimentary and volcanic phases is the presence of abundant tephra layers in the Palaeocene and Eocene successions of the North Sea Basin and Faeroe–Shetland Basin. A distinctive feature of this tephra succession is that it includes a high proportion of layers of basaltic composition, whose geochemistry points to sources in the Greenland–Faeroe province. Two main periods of pyroclastic activity (Phases 1 and 2) have been recognized from the stratigraphic occurrence of tephras and are believed to reflect periods of increased volcanic activity within the North Atlantic province as a whole. Phase 1 pyroclastic activity was associated with the rise of the North Atlantic plume beneath the continental crust of East Greenland and was at a maximum during the uplift phase of Cycle 2. Phase 2 activity was associated with the development of the North Atlantic rift zone. It was initiated during the uplift phase of Cycle 3, but maximum pyroclastic activity took place during the transgression that accompanied the initial, subaerial phase of sea-floor spreading.

Our understanding of the location and timing of uplift of the Scottish landmass in Palaeocene and Eocene times is greatly enhanced by the presence of deep water sandstones in otherwise mudstone-dominated basinal successions. The distribution of these sandstones is summarized in Figure 13.5.

Palaeogeographical evolution

Cycle 1: Early Palaeocene

The tectonic and depositional environments that had prevailed throughout the late Cretaceous persisted with little change into the Early Palaeocene. The offshore basins continued to develop as structurally simple basins, with widespread deposition of chalky lime muds in the central and southern North Sea Basin and variably calcareous terrigenous muds in the northern North Sea Basin and Faeroe–Shetland Basin. The sediments are characterized by diverse marine microfaunas and microfloras dominated by benthic and planktonic foraminifera, radiolaria, calcareous nannoplankton and dinoflagellate cysts. These assemblages indicate free connection with oceanic Atlantic waters to the south and west.

Terrigenous input to the basins was for the most part restricted to mud-grade material, with any sands accumulating on the shelf, in near-shore environments. In earliest Palaeocene times, however, a fall in sea level led to a seaward shift of the beach zone, with the result that sand was locally displaced into deeper water via canyons cut into muddy slope sediments. Well-sorted sandstones thus occur in channel fills and small basin-floor fans (Fig. 13.6a). The distribution of these deep water sandstones indicates that they were supplied mainly from the Orkney–Shetland Platform, but with minor supply from southeast Scotland. Subsequent transgression led to a drowning of the shelf areas, culminating in the deposition of clean chalky limestones throughout central and southern parts of the North Sea Basin and over much of mainland Britain (Fig. 13.6b).

Cycle 2: Mid to Late Palaeocene

Regional uplift in Mid-Palaeocene times was accompanied by accelerated uplift of the Orkney–Shetland Platform. Associated rapid subsidence of the offshore basins led to a marked differentiation into shallow water shelf and deep water basin environments. Widespread volcanic activity took place in the North Atlantic region, reflecting the impingement of the North Atlantic mantle plume beneath the continental crust of East Greenland. In the offshore basins, this activity is largely represented by thin, distal tephra layers derived from the Greenland–Faeroe region (Phase 1; see Fig. 13.3). However, relatively thick beds of reworked basaltic tephra in the Outer Moray Firth area of the North Sea Basin (Fig. 13.6c) are believed to have been derived from one of the Hebridean volcanic centres to the southwest. Reworked tephras in the Faeroe–Shetland Basin area are believed to have been derived from the Greenland–Faeroe province to the northwest.

The sedimentary expression of the plume-induced uplift is most pronounced in the North Sea Basin, where, as illustrated in Fig. 13.6c, the regional fall in sea level led to the accumulation of deep water sand deposits in extensive submarine fans. The sands were almost exclusively derived from the Orkney–Shetland Platform, with minor output from southeast Scotland, possibly reflecting drainage from the Midland Valley. Deep water sand sedimentation was initially restricted to deeper parts of the North Sea Basin (Cycle 2A; Fig. 13.3), where the lowest sandstones are associated with reworked chalky limestones. The limestones represent erosion of Cretaceous and Early Palaeocene (Cycle 1) sediments exposed on the flanks of the Central Graben area during the period of lowest sea-level stand. They mostly consist of re-sedimented lime muds, together with rounded, glauconite-coated chalk pebbles of coastal origin and angular fragments and occasional large blocks derived from slope failure along the graben margins. The sandstones and limestones are interbedded with grey, silty, variably calcareous mudstones. Sandstone beds are mostly internally structureless, and were deposited by mass-flow processes.

A subsequent rise in sea level led to renewed sedimentation on the shelf, with the result that the reworking of limestones largely ceased. Continued relative uplift of the Scottish source areas led to further accumulation of Cycle 2A deep water sands in the North Sea Basin and to the initiation of substantial deep-water sand sedimentation in the Faeroe–Shetland Basin.

The rise in sea level eventually led to increasing accumulation of sediments on the shelf areas, with the development of well-defined prograding sediment wedges (Cycle 2B; Fig. 13.2) along the margins of both basins. Sediment supply was initially sufficient to maintain supply to the deep water sand fans

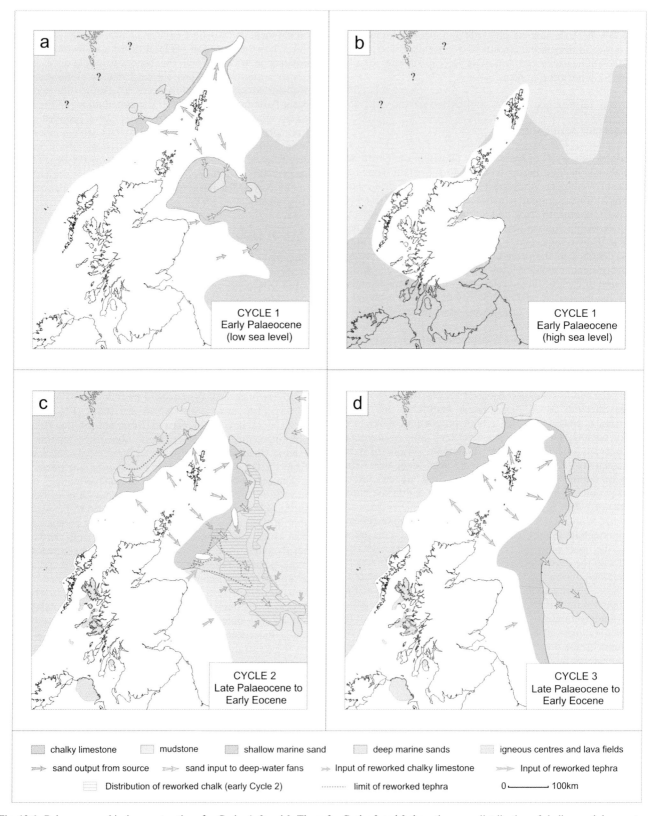

Fig. 13.6. Palaeogeographical reconstructions for Cycles 1, 2 and 3. Those for Cycles 2 and 3 show the gross distribution of shallow and deep water sandstones, spanning both low and high sea-level periods of each cycle.

through slope failure on the prograding sediment wedges. Sand deposition reached its maximum extent at this time (Fig. 13.6c). An influx of reworked Hebridean tephras to the North Sea Basin took place early in this phase of sedimentation. At about the same time, reworked tephras entered the Faeroe–Shetland Basin from the west.

The deep water sand fans of Cycle 2 resulted from slumping of sediments that had accumulated on the shelf edge during rapid coastal plain progradation. As a result, the slumped sediments consisted of both sand and mud, leading to the formation of lithologically heterogeneous fan deposits. These typically consist of interbedded sandstones and mudstones interspersed with relatively thick sandstone units that represent submarine channel fills. The channel sandstones are typically up to 30 m thick, but locally reach over 100 m as a result of vertical amalgamation. Coalescence of individual submarine fans led to the development of an extensive and more or less continuous basin-floor submarine fan complex.

Away from the main focus of sand sedimentation, the sediments are dominated by mudstones. In the Faeroe–Shetland Basin, the mudstones are characteristically dark grey and silty, indicating that they were derived from the shelf through slope failure. In the more distal parts of the North Sea Basin, however, the mudstones are characteristically fine grained, often with a distinctive greenish colour. These mudstones are interpreted as hemipelagic muds and probably include a substantial amount of altered pyroclastic material of both detrital and primary air-fall origin. Though mostly confined to central and eastern parts of the basin, they also occur interbedded with sandstones in outer parts of the submarine fan systems.

Eventually, continued sea-level rise and decreased relative uplift of the source areas led to sand sedimentation becoming increasingly confined to inner shelf areas. Deep water environments persisted over much of the North Sea Basin, with accumulation of fine-grained muds, while relatively rapid deposition of silty muds continued in the Faeroe–Shetland Basin.

Diverse microfaunas and microfloras prevailed throughout deposition of Cycle 2, indicating that the basins were fully marine throughout. However, the disappearance of calcareous foraminifera from the basinal microfossil assemblages early in Cycle 2 indicates that free communication with oceanic waters was reduced. The subsequent dominance of agglutinated foraminifera reflects increased stratification of the water column, with consequent acidification of the bottom waters. No macrofossils have been recorded from the deep water sediments. Since burrows are present within the hemipelagic mudstone facies, it seems likely that this absence is the result of dissolution of skeletal material by acidic pore-waters.

The sandstones of Cycle 2 include important hydrocarbon reservoirs, including the Foinaven and Schiehallion fields of the Faeroe–Shetland Basin and the Andrew and Maureen fields of the North Sea Basin.

Cycle 3: Late Palaeocene to Early Eocene

The uplift that immediately preceded opening of the North Atlantic led to a gross eastward tilting of the British Isles and caused much of the sediment to be directed into the Outer Moray Firth area (Fig. 13.6d). This led to major sand fan development in the Central Graben, augmented by sand supply from the southeast. Reduced uplift of the Orkney–Shetland Platform resulted in relatively minor submarine fan development in the Viking Graben. The North Sea Basin became more or less landlocked as a result of the uplift of western Britain, leading to a sharp change in facies from open marine to restricted marine environments throughout the NW European region.

In the deep water successions of the North Sea Basin, bioturbated hemipelagic claystones of Cycle 3 give way rapidly to dark grey, organic-rich claystones. This lithofacies change is accompanied by an equally sharp change in the marine microfossil assemblages, with a marked reduction in the abundance and diversity of benthic foraminifera and an increasing abundance of diatoms. The mudstones display a rapid upward increase in lamination, indicating progressive elimination of sea-floor oxygenation in response to the development of a highly stratified water column. The development of low-diversity, specialized dinoflagellate cyst assemblages probably reflects lowered salinity in the surface waters. Comparable biofacies changes take place in the more rapidly deposited

proximal successions of the Moray Firth area and the Faeroe–Shetland Basin, although little or no change in lithofacies is evident. A distinctive feature of the biota is the presence of teleost fish (illustrated in Thomas et al. 1975).

Along the western margin of the North Sea Basin, and most especially in the Moray Firth area, uplift and eastward tilting of mainland Scotland led to a rapid increase in sediment supply to the shelf. As in Cycle 2, rapid progradation of coastal plain sediments led to slumping of mixed sand/mud deposits to form lithologically heterogeneous basin-floor fans. Sand sedimentation was much less extensive than in Cycle 2, reflecting both diminished uplift of the East Shetland Platform and the shorter duration of uplift.

In the Faeroe–Shetland Basin, where rapid sediment aggradation during Cycle 2 had led to reduced water depths, regional uplift led to a rapid northwestward progradation of shallow marine sands. Most of the sands were deposited in littoral and sublittoral environments, but local slumping led to the accumulation of mounded sand deposits in a slope environment.

In the later stages of Cycle 3, a rapid rise in sea level led to the development of a large progradational wedge that extended over much of the northwestern margin of the North Sea Basin (Fig. 13.3; Cycle 3B). Basinwards of this progradational wedge, deep water conditions persisted. Slumping along the front of this wedge led to the development of minor submarine fans above the earlier, more extensive fans. The Faeroe–Shetland Basin was the site of relatively minor sand progradation at this time.

The submarine fan sandstones of Cycle 3 host important hydrocarbon reservoirs. They are restricted to the North Sea Basin and include the Arbroath, Everest, Forties, Montrose and Nelson fields.

Cycle 4: Early to Late Eocene

Cycle 3 sedimentation was brought to an abrupt close by changes in stress pattern that immediately preceded opening of the North Atlantic. Progradation in the Outer Moray Firth area ceased, and flooding of the broad coastal plain led to the formation of extensive lakes and lagoons in which thick accumulations of peat took place. The occurrence of abundant basaltic tephra layers in the basinal mudstone facies marks the acme of pyroclastic activity in the North Atlantic Igneous Province (Fig. 13.4; early Phase 2). These tephras are believed to represent a short-lived period of subaerial volcanism along the newly formed mid-ocean ridge. Over 200 tephra layers have been identified in the basal part of the Cycle 4 succession, where they are associated with siliceous laminated mudstones. This tephra-rich unit forms a prominent seismic reflector, often referred to as the Ash Marker.

With the onset of sea-floor spreading, the region experienced a long-term rise in relative sea level. In the Faeroe–Shetland Basin this led to passive basin fill, with the deposition of dominantly muddy shallow marine sediments. In the North Sea Basin, however, relative uplift of the East Shetland Platform led to renewed sand supply and to the development of deep water submarine fans (Fig. 13.7a). An entirely separate submarine fan system developed further south in response to sand supply from the southeast, possibly representing drainage along the Midland Valley. Later in Cycle 4, sand supply became confined to the northern North Sea, where sediment aggradation, possibly combined with the onset of inversion (see below), reduced water depths to the point where deep water sand fan development virtually ceased (Fig. 13.7b).

The deep water sandstones of Cycle 4 are very different from those of the preceding cycles, reflecting a fundamental change in the nature of sand supply to the shelf edge. In the preceding

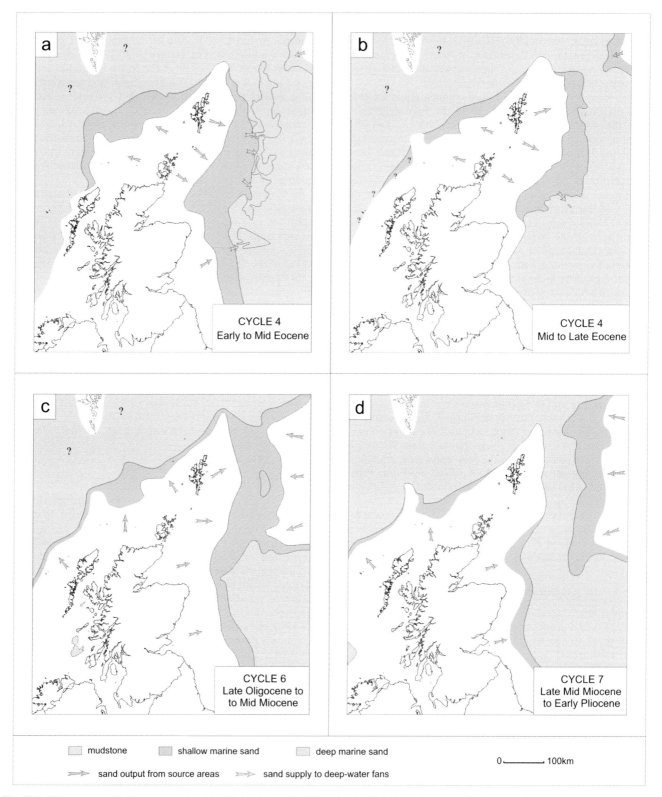

Fig. 13.7. Palaeogeographical reconstructions for Cycles 4, 6 and 7. Those for Cycle 4 shows the gross distribution of shallow and deep water sandstones, spanning both low and high sea-level periods of the cycle.

cycles, submarine fans were fed directly by prograding coastal plain sediments that extended to the shelf edge. By contrast, the lower rate of sediment supply in Cycle 4 allowed a much greater degree wave reworking on the shelf, leading to the concentration of sand on the shelf in the form of beaches and offshore bars and the dispersal of the mud into the offshore zone. Substantial offshore mud sedimentation led to the devel-

opment of prograding muddy slope wedges. Unstable accumulations of sand at the shelf edge were transported down these muddy slopes in relatively narrow erosional channels. In this way, well-sorted, mud-free sands were carried down into deeper water, where they accumulated as relatively small, channel-dominated fans. Vertical amalgamation of channel fills led to the accumulation of over 100 m of sand in some places.

In the early stages of Cycle 4, mudstone facies continued to reflect a stratified water column, with dark grey, laminated sediments accumulating in the deeper basinal areas. The restricted biota established in Cycle 3 persisted, with a particularly distinctive feature being the common occurrence of the large diatom *Coscinodiscus* (illustrated in Jacqué & Thouvenin 1975). A progressive rise in sea level led to a gradual increase in bottom-water circulation, however, culminating in a return to rich and diverse microfaunas and microfloras.

The sandstones of Cycle 4 include the youngest commercial hydrocarbon reservoirs in the UK offshore. Reservoirs are restricted to the North Sea Basin and include the Alba, Frigg, Gannet and Harding–Griffin fields.

Cycle 5: Latest Eocene to Early Oligocene

The onset of Cycle 5 was marked by initial uplift and shallowing throughout the North Sea Basin, followed by widespread transgression. In the Faeroe–Shetland Basin, Cycle 4 sedimenta-

tion was brought to a close by powerful bottom-water currents that created a widespread erosion surface and cut major channels up to 250 m deep. The same scouring event may be responsible for the absence of Late Eocene sediments in some of the more basinal areas of the North Sea. It is believed to have resulted from the establishment of free connection between Atlantic and Arctic oceanic waters, which also caused a lowering of water temperatures throughout the region. Significant faunal changes also take place across the Cycle 4/Cycle 5 boundary, with shallower and more oxygenated bottom water environments being reflected in a sharp increase in calcareous benthic foraminifera at the expense of agglutinated foraminifera.

In the North Sea Basin, sediment was supplied from both Scotland and a rejuvenated Scandinavian landmass. Muddy facies dominated in both the North Sea and Faeroe–Shetland basins, with sands being restricted to near-shore settings. In deeper parts of the North Sea Basin, a change in mudstone character is evident, with the dominantly green-grey mudstones of Cycle 4 giving way to brown-grey, more organic-rich

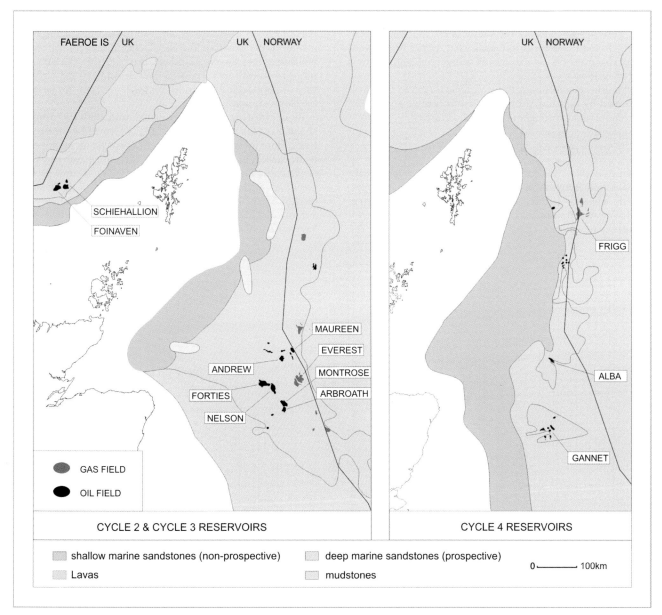

Fig. 13.8. Distribution of oil and gas fields within the sandstone facies of the Palaeocene and Eocene. Cycle 1 fields (limestone facies) in the Norwegian sector are not shown.

mudstones of Cycle 5. The marginal sands are commonly glauconitic and commonly contain bivalves, echinoid spines and ostracods.

Cycle 6: Late Oligocene to Mid Miocene

In the late Oligocene, accelerated uplift of Scandinavia resulted in major progradation from the east (Fig. 13.3; Cycle 6), resulting in sand sedimentation extending across the Norwegian shelf and into the Viking Graben (Fig. 13.7c). Uplift of the Scottish source areas appears to have been minimal at this time, but shelly, locally coarse, glauconitic sands continued to accumulate in the near-shore zone. In western Scotland and elsewhere in western Britain, the development of small fault-bounded basins led to the local preservation of sediments of Oligocene or presumed Oligocene age. Three such basins occur in the Malin–Hebrides area: the Canna Basin, the Blackstones Basin and a small basin in the Little Minch. Little is known of the sediments within these basins, but analogy with the Lough Neagh Basin of Northern Ireland (Wilkinson *et al.* 1980) suggests that they consist of freshwater mudstones and lignites of Late Oligocene age.

In the Faeroe–Shetland Basin, shallow marine sands and muds were deposited along the southeastern margin, passing westwards and northwards into somewhat deeper water mudstones. However, the basinal record is highly incomplete as a result of erosion.

Full marine connection with the oceanic waters to the north is indicated by rich and diverse calcareous benthic and planktonic microfaunas throughout the offshore area.

Cycle 7: Mid Miocene to Pliocene

The base of this cycle marks a major fall in sea level, with sedimentation initially being confined to more basinal areas. Climatic changes led to increased mechanical weathering, reflected increased siltiness of the mudstones and in an increased proportion of chlorite in the clay mineral assemblages. The initial sea-level fall led to a major influx of sand from the east (Fig. 13.3, Cycle 7A; Fig. 13.7d), which may in part have resulted from reworking of the shelf sands of Cycle 6. The sandstones are commonly glauconitic and micaceous, and locally contain abundant bivalve, echinoid and gastropod debris. Overlying silty mudstones were derived from both east and west.

Cycle 8: Late Pliocene to Early Pleistocene

In the Late Pliocene and Early Pleistocene, uplift of both Scotland and Scandinavia led to major progradation along the basin margins, with both Scotland and Scandinavia acting as sediment sources (Fig. 13.3). Despite the very high rates of erosion and sedimentation, the sediments are largely of silty mudstone facies. Sandstones are restricted to marginal areas, where they are commonly coarse grained with abundant shell debris.

Hydrocarbon reservoirs

The lower part of the offshore Tertiary succession includes important hydrocarbon reservoirs, which fall into two groups (Fig. 13.8). Those associated with the widespread, sheet-like fans of Cycles 2 and 3 are mostly formed by structural traps in the deeper parts of the basin, where fine-grained basinal mudstones act as the reservoir seal. Outside the structural traps, hydrocarbons have been able to escape to the surface by way of permeable sandstones that extend from the basin, via the slope, up onto the shelf.

By contrast, reservoirs associated with the more restricted channelized fans of Cycle 4 are largely formed by stratigraphic traps. Here the muddy slope deposits provide an up-dip seal to hydrocarbon migration from the lower slope and basin floor sandstones. For this reason, the reservoirs occupy proximal positions within the fans. Further details of hydrocarbon distribution in Tertiary strata are contained in Chapter 19, and a more detailed account of the petroleum geology of the Tertiary is given by Bowman (1998).

14 Tertiary igneous activity

B. R. BELL & I. T. WILLIAMSON

During the Palaeogene, the NW European continental margin was the site of intense volcanic activity in response to lithospheric thinning and, ultimately, at $c.\,55\,Ma$, the formation of a new ocean crust (e.g. White 1988, 1992; Saunders *et al.* 1997) (Fig. 14.1). Along the west coast of Scotland, vestiges of this period of magmatism take the form of continental (flood) lava sequences, together with shallow intrusive centres and associated lava shields, dyke swarms and sill complexes (Emeleus & Bell 2003). The igneous activity spanned the interval $c.\,60.5\,Ma$ to $55\,Ma$ and appears to have been intermittent, with significant hiatuses between periods of rapid growth of the lava fields and intrusive activity (Bell & Jolley 1997).

The magmatism is attributed to the impact of the proto-Iceland plume at the base of the lithosphere, which produced approximately contemporaneous volcanic and intrusive activity between NW Europe and Arctic Canada. The siting of the lava fields was largely controlled by crustal thinning events in the Mesozoic (Thompson & Gibson 1991), whereas the location of the central complexes was strongly influenced by considerably older lineaments. Subsequently, ocean floor spreading took place between NW Europe and East Greenland and between central West Greenland and Baffin Island. The magmas that were erupted or emplaced at the time of continental break-up were not typical of plumes sourced from deep levels in the mantle, and involved much MORB-like material, derived from the upper (depleted) mantle (Saunders *et al.* 1997). The rate of melt production waned after $55\,Ma$. The plume, now considerably smaller and located below Iceland, is still responsible for significant volcanic and subvolcanic activity.

In NW Scotland, the Hebridean Province comprises remnants of three lava fields: Eigg (including Muck, $c.\,60.5\,Ma$), Skye (including Canna, $c.\,58\,Ma$) and Mull (including Morvern, $c.\,58.5/55\,Ma$, see below). These take the form of stratiform sequences of predominantly subaerial facies lavas of the alkali olivine basalt to trachyte lineage, along with considerably less abundant tholeiitic basalt and its derivatives (Thompson 1982). Eruption was from fissure systems (now represented by the dyke swarms) and from central vents fed by the central complexes (Walker 1993*a, b*). Interlayered with the lavas are a variety of pyroclastic, epiclastic and volcaniclastic deposits. These include tuffs and lahars, together with fluviatile and lacustrine facies sedimentary sequences which were deposited during periods when the contemporaneous land surface developed a significant drainage system (e.g. Williamson & Bell 1994). Palaeosols formed in areas with good drainage and low rates of erosion.

The climate within the region during the Palaeogene was controlled by latitude, altitude and probably marine influence. Palynological analysis of sedimentary sequences interbedded with the lavas indicates the development of a wide range of surface environments, from upland forests through to swamps and estuarine/lacustrine systems, mainly influenced by the elevation of the lava field (Jolley 1997). Weathering of the lavas during hiatuses in the volcanic activity, as evidenced by reddened flow tops, was strongly influenced by altitude and biological activity. In general, the climate was warm temperate to subtropical and no major periods of deterioration (glaciation) are recognized.

Intrusive activity comprised the growth of central complexes, consisting of ring intrusions and stocks with a common (or nearly so) focal point, and interpreted as the shallow (less than $2\,km$) hearths of volcanoes which developed throughout the Palaeogene (e.g. Walker 1993*a, b*; Emeleus & Bell 2003). These include: Rum, Skye, Mull, Ardnamurchan, Arran and St Kilda. At the present level of erosion, each central complex comprises a myriad of coarse-grained intrusions, together with suites of cone-sheets and dykes. Sill complexes developed separately, typically being emplaced within the pre-volcanic (Triassic to Cretaceous) sedimentary sequences.

The absolute time interval spanned by the growth of each of the lava fields and emplacement of each of the central complexes may be deduced from isotopic age dates and from palynological data. These age data also enable magma production rates to be estimated (Bell & Jolley 1997; Hamilton *et al.* 1998). Many new age data have become available in recent years and provide a much clearer picture of the chronological development of the Province and the inter-relationships of the extrusive and intrusive units.

Information concerning the geometries of the lava fields (lateral extent and thickness) and central complexes (vertical extent and diameter at depth) has been provided by field observations and various geophysical surveys. Geophysical investigations have proved to be of particular value for the offshore areas, especially where younger sedimentary sequences (Eocene to Recent) obscure the Palaeogene igneous rocks (Ritchie & Hitchen 1996). To the NW and west of Scotland, within the Faeroe–Shetland Basin and the Rockall Trough respectively, thick sequences of lavas and a number of central complexes have been recognized from their seismic, gravity and magnetic characteristics (Fig. 14.2). These offshore igneous rocks provide us with valuable data not available from the more deeply eroded (up to $2\,km$) onshore exposures, especially with respect to the nature of the volcanic-subvolcanic interface and the geometry of the lava shields which developed above the central complexes (Walker 1993*a*). The offshore volcanic rocks also provide unique data concerning certain magma compositions not recognized in the onshore exposures and extend our knowledge of the chronological and spatial development of the Province (e.g. Kanaris-Sotiriou *et al.* 1993).

Pre-Tertiary tectonic events appear to have played an important role in the siting of the lava fields and the central complexes. Rifting and basin development in the North Atlantic may be traced back to at least the Mesozoic, with thick sequences of Triassic, Jurassic and Cretaceous strata overlying Proterozoic (Moine) or Archaean (Lewisian) basement. These rifting and basinal development events involved stretching and thinning of the lithosphere which, during the Palaeogene, focused the upward migration of the mantle-derived magmas and influenced the geometry of the lava fields (Thompson & Gibson 1991). Central complexes developed where there were

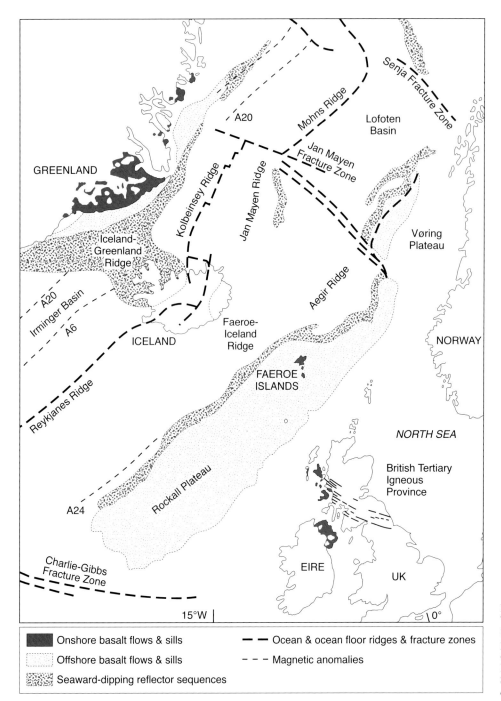

GREENLAND

A20

Mohns Ridge

Lofoten
Basin

Senja Fracture Zone

Jan Mayen
Fracture Zone

Kolbeinsey Ridge

Jan Mayen Ridge

Iceland-
Greenland
Ridge

Vøring
Plateau

A20

Irminger Basin

A6

Aegir Ridge

ICELAND

Faeroe-
Iceland
Ridge

Reykjanes Ridge

NORWAY

FAEROE
ISLANDS

NORTH SEA

British Tertiary
Igneous
Province

Rockall Plateau

A24

EIRE

UK

Charlie-Gibbs
Fracture Zone

15°W

0°

Fig. 14.1. The North Atlantic
Tertiary Igneous Province (NATIP).
Sketch map showing the extent and
principal features of onshore and
offshore igneous activity in the
Province (after Stoker *et al.* 1993;
Saunders *et al.* 1997; Sinton
et al. 1998).

■ Onshore basalt flows & sills	– – Ocean & ocean floor ridges & fracture zones
▢ Offshore basalt flows & sills	- - Magnetic anomalies
▨ Seaward-dipping reflector sequences	

pre-existing fault systems within the thinned lithosphere. The
emplacement of ascending batches of magma into the upper
crust, either into the central complexes or the associated dyke
swarms and cone-sheet complexes, was strongly influenced by
the contemporaneous regional and local stress fields (Walker
1993*b*). Thus, volcanic activity associated with the edifices of
the central complexes was most likely of the fissure type,
although possibly also from isolated vents located along the
dyke swarms.

Chapters on Tertiary igneous activity in the three previous
editions of *Geology of Scotland* (Stewart 1965; Emeleus 1983,
1991) provide a wealth of information concerning the various
lithologies and their distribution within the Hebridean Province. Rather than repeat all of these data, attention is drawn
here to many of the new insights which have occurred through

the extensive research which has been undertaken in the past
decade (Emeleus & Bell 2003). Important themes addressed
since the third edition include: the geochemistry of the lava
sequences (Kerr 1995*a*, *b*; Scarrow & Cox 1995); the stratigraphy of the lava fields (Williamson & Bell 1994; England
1994; Emeleus 1997), the geochemical evolution of the central complexes (Bell *et al.* 1994; Kerr *et al.* 1999); mechanisms
of emplacement of intrusions (Walker 1993*b*); regional tectonics (White 1992; Saunders *et al.* 1997); and, the chronology
of the Hebridean Province (Bell & Jolley 1997; Hamilton *et al.*
1998, 1999; Chambers & Pringle 2001). Furthermore, our
knowledge of the offshore area, within the Faeroe–Shetland
Basin and the Rockall Trough, has greatly increased due to
intense exploration for hydrocarbons within this part of the
Atlantic Margin.

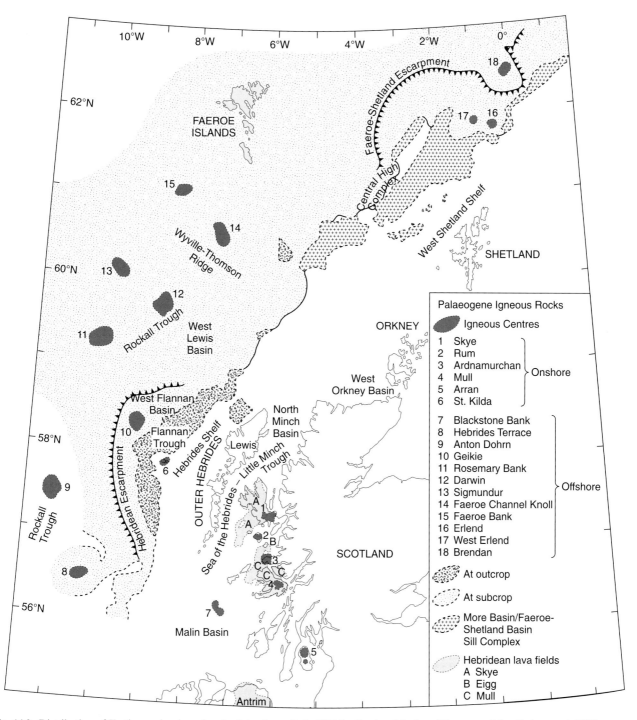

Fig. 14.2. Distribution of Tertiary volcanic and major intrusive units in NW Scotland and in the offshore area (after Stoker *et al.* 1993).

Timing of igneous activity

The timing of the various volcanic and intrusive events may be determined by a variety of isotope measurements on whole-rock and mineral samples. Palynological analysis of sedimentary rocks interbedded with the lavas also provides valuable data on the age and duration of the volcanism. Previous reviews include Mussett *et al.* (1988), Hitchen & Ritchie (1993) and Ritchie & Hitchen (1996), which deal with onshore and offshore material, respectively. Although there are discrepancies between the two dating techniques, it is evident that the growth of the lava fields and the emplacement of the central complexes were very rapid events, each often involving less than a million years.

Volcanism within the (onshore) Hebridean Province commenced in the Danian, indicated by an ^{40}Ar–^{39}Ar age of $c.\,60.5 \pm 0.08$ Ma for sanidines from a tuffaceous sandstone close to the base of the Eigg Lava Formation (Chambers & Pringle 2001). No other ages are available for this formation, which is unconformably overlain by a fluvial conglomerate and the valley-filling Sgurr of Eigg Pitchstone. The latter is dated at 58.72 ± 0.07 Ma by Chambers & Pringle (2001). Thus, the erosional surface below the conglomerate developed over as long as $c.\,2$ Ma.

The only high-precision isotope age for the Skye Lava Field is an ^{40}Ar–^{39}Ar age of 58.91 ± 0.18 Ma for anorthoclase crystals from a trachytic tuff close to the top of the preserved sequence. In addition, Hamilton *et al.* (1998) derived an age 'window' on the basis of $^{206}Pb/^{238}U$ zircon ages for ultrabasic and basic rocks of the Rum and Skye central complexes of 60.53 ± 0.08 Ma and 58.91 ± 0.07 Ma, which pre-date and post-date the Skye lavas, respectively. An $^{40}Ar-^{39}Ar$ age of 57.6 ± 1.2 Ma has been determined for biotites from a trachyte dyke (Hamilton et al. 1998), assumed to represent a feeder to a lava high up in the Skye Lava Field stratigraphy. This date extends the youngest possible age by c. 1 million years and consequently overlaps the isotopic age of the lava field with the palynological age range of 58–58.25 Ma deduced by Jolley (1997).

The $^{206}Pb/^{238}U$ zircon age of Hamilton et al. (1998) for an alkaline pegmatite from ultrabasic layered rocks of Rum is at variance with data from the older Western Granite (based upon the observation of an intrusive relationship), which has a Rb–Sr age of 59.8 ± 0.4 Ma (Mussett 1984), highlighting possible problems with certain of the older whole-rock age data. The $^{206}Pb/^{238}U$ zircon age for a quartzo-feldspathic pegmatite from the Cuillin Centre on Skye is in general agreement (based upon intrusive relationships) with the $^{206}Pb/^{238}U$ zircon ages for the younger Western Red Hills and Eastern Red Hills granites, 57–58.5 Ma and 55.7–55.9 Ma, respectively (Hamilton et al. 1999).

Whole-rock samples from the Mull Lava Field yield an isotopic ($^{40}Ar-^{39}Ar$) age range of 58.66–60.56 Ma (Chambers & Fitton 2000). Palynological analysis of sedimentary rocks interbedded with the lavas of SW Mull suggests a considerably younger age, c. 55 Ma, for the lower (older) part of the lava succession (Jolley 1997). The youngest major granitic intrusion of the Mull Central Complex, the Loch Ba Ring-dyke, yields a sanidine $^{40}Ar-^{39}Ar$ age of 58.5 ± 0.5 Ma (Chambers & Pringle 2001) and a $^{206}Pb-^{238}U$ zircon age of 58.5 ± 0.1 Ma (Hamilton et al. 1999).

The North Granite Centre on Arran has been dated at c. 58.5 Ma ($^{40}Ar-^{39}Ar$; Chambers & Pringle 2001) and related quartz porphyry intrusions in SW Arran yield an age of 58.5 ± 0.8 Ma ($^{40}Ar-^{39}Ar$; Mussett et al. 1987). A somewhat older age of 61.5 ± 0.5 Ma has been reported for the peralkaline Ailsa Craig Granite, south of Arran (Rb–Sr; Harrison et al. 1987).

The age of the St Kilda Central Complex is poorly constrained, with various gabbroic rocks dated at c. 60 Ma (K–Ar; Miller & Mhor 1965) and the Conachair Granite at 55 ± 1 Ma (Rb–Sr; Brook, in Harding et al. 1984). To the west, the Rockall Granite has a most likely (and similar) age of c. 55 Ma (as reviewed by Ritchie & Hitchen 1996: Rb–Sr; Hawkes et al. 1975).

Offshore data are considerably more sparse, and certain of the whole-rock isotopic ages are of relatively poor quality. The North Rockall Trough–Hebrides Lava Group was erupted in the interval 63–50 Ma (K–Ar; reviewed by Ritchie & Hitchen 1996). However, these data were obtained from altered material and represent a very limited sample set. As such, it is possible that the volcanism was intermittent and that there were significant hiatuses in the extrusive activity.

Tholeiitic basalt lavas in Well 163/6-1A on the NW side of the Darwin Central Complex (Fig. 14.2) have an average age of c. 55 Ma (K–Ar, Morton et al. 1988). Similar lavas overlying the Erlend Central Complex yield a roughly equivalent age ($^{40}Ar-^{39}Ar$ whole-rock data; unpublished, discussed in Ritchie & Hitchen 1996). Sinton et al. (1998) reported an $^{40}Ar-^{39}Ar$ whole-rock age for dacites underlying the basaltic lavas in Well 163/6-1A of c. 55 Ma.

Hamilton et al. (1998) calculated a magma production rate of $2.2 \times 10^3 km^{-3} yr^{-1}$ for the Skye Lava field, which they estimate was originally 1.6 km thick with a volume of 1400 km^3, and was (based upon their $^{206}Pb/^{238}U$ zircon ages) erupted over 1.6 ± 0.2 million years This is considerably less than the 1 m/200 years estimated by Bell & Jolley (1997), based upon an estimated thickness of the lava pile of 1200 m and a duration of c. 250 000 years.

Volcaniclastic deposits preserved within the offshore sedimentary sequences of the Faeroe–Shetland Basin and the North Sea, together with the equivalent onshore sequences in SE England, are the products of widespread tephra eruptions and may be dated biostratigraphically (Knox & Morton 1983, 1988). The first phase occurred in the interval 60–57.5 Ma (nannofossil zones NP5-9) and the second more voluminous phase occurred during the interval 56–50 Ma, synchronous and post-dating the time of lithospheric rifting and the commencement of ocean floor spreading at c. 55 Ma.

Location and architecture of the igneous units

In general terms, the lava fields were erupted into the same rifted blocks of crust which contain thick sequences of Mesozoic strata, synchronous with renewed tectonism from c. 60.5 Ma, through to the time of lithospheric break-up at c. 55 Ma (England 1992a). Following a major phase of post-Palaeocene subsidence, a substantial proportion of the (present-day) offshore lavas were buried by thick sequences of Eocene–Recent sediments. The southern extension of the Skye Lava Field, within the Canna Basin, is partially covered with Oligocene sediments (Fig. 14.3).

The architecture of the oldest part of each lava field was controlled by the Danian palaeogeography, commonly assumed to have been relatively subdued, subsequent to the erosion of a (?substantial) thickness of Upper Cretaceous and older strata. However, there is abundant evidence for considerable relief prior to and during the development of the lava fields, for example, the eastern margin of the Mull Lava Field appears to onlap Moine basement psammites and pelites, and the southern extent of the Skye Lava Field filled a valley system on the northern flank of the then exhumed Rum Central Complex (Emeleus 1985, 1997; Williamson & Bell 1994). Throughout the development of the lava fields, poorly understood tectonic uplift and subsidence events associated with the magmatism influenced the palaeogeography, and hence the distribution of individual flows, or packages of flows (Walker 1995).

The bases of the lava fields are typically not well exposed, in particular due to landslipped material and scree around many of the present-day lava escarpments. Each of the lava fields overlies a major unconformity surface, especially in the vicinities of the central complexes, where Palaeogene uplift brought basement (Lewisian) gneisses, Neoproterozoic (Moine) schists, and Neoproterozoic and Lower Palaeozoic sedimentary rocks to the contemporaneous land surface. These uplift events may be attributed to the initial stages of growth of the central complexes.

Pre-Palaeogene deformation events may be recognized within the Mesozoic strata which typically underlie the lava sequences. In north Skye, NE-trending broad anticlines and synclines occur within the Jurassic strata, but do not affect the thin sequences of Cretaceous strata which survived the major post-Cretaceous uplift and erosion events which affected NW Scotland (England 1994) (Fig. 14.4). Thus, a major pre-Cretaceous period of erosion may be recognized. The axes of these folds trend parallel to the major bounding faults to the Mesozoic basins (e.g. the Camasunary–Skerryvore Fault) and preserve a record of pre-Cretaceous compressive tectonic events within the basins.

At the end of the Cretaceous, uplift lead to the development of various early Palaeocene clastic sediment accumulations,

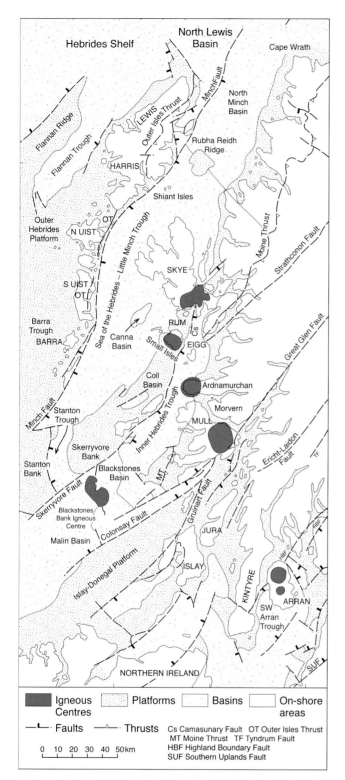

Fig. 14.3. Sketch map of the Inner Hebrides area, showing the main structural elements (after Fyfe *et al.* 1993).

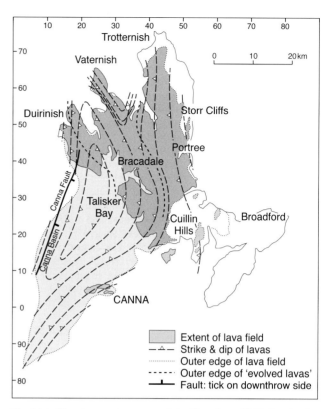

Fig. 14.4. Structure contour map of the Skye Lava Field showing its broad synclinal form (after England 1994).

breccias are common, suggesting eruption of magma into shallow water and the formation of hydroclastic deposits. The common presence of pollen and spore assemblages within these deposits attests to their aqueous mode of deposition. Also present during this initial phase of volcanism are hyaloclastite accumulations (e.g. Fiurnean, north of Portree, north Skye) and pillowed lavas (e.g. the Macculloch's Tree Flow, Ardmeanach, west Mull), both formed when basaltic magmas were emplaced into shallow bodies of water. Certain of the classic columnar-jointed lava flows near to the base of the Mull Lava Field were emplaced into water, based upon their upward gradation into pillowed and fragmental (tuffaceous) material (e.g. at Carsaig Arches, SW Mull).

The volumetrically dominant basaltic and hawaiitic flows of the lava fields are typically thin (<5 m and <10 m, respectively), sheet-like, and were generally erupted onto relatively low relief land surfaces. The younger parts of the lava sequences on Skye and Mull contain higher proportions of evolved flows, typically mugearites, benmoreites and trachytes (Bailey *et al.* 1924; Anderson & Dunham 1966). Such flows tend to have more dome-like or ribbon-shaped geometries, giving rise to, and infilling, shallow valley systems (Williamson & Bell 1994; England 1994). The locations of these evolved flows were also controlled by the distribution of their fissure feeders, now represented by dykes and stocks of similar composition, for example, within the Bracadale region of central west Skye (Anderson & Dunham 1966). There are also rare but spectacular examples of larger-scale valley-fill lavas within the Skye and Eigg lava fields.

The central complexes occur within basement highs, typically where they are intersected by NE-trending ('Caledonian') fault systems. Richey (1961) argued convincingly that where such ancient lineaments intersected the thinned (<30 km) and tectonically high N–S corridor of crust which ran along the west coast of Scotland (Meissner *et al.* 1986), then central intrusive

including valley-fill flint- and chert-bearing conglomerates and sandstones (e.g. the SW portion of the Mull Lava Field, on the Ross of Mull).

Uplift and subsidence events during the growth of the lava fields may be recognized by recourse to sedimentological and palynological analysis of interbedded sedimentary rocks, and by interpretation of the environment of eruption (or 'facies') of the volcanic products. During the initial stages of growth of the Skye and Mull lava fields, various basaltic tuffs and activity occurred. Thus, the Skye and Rum central complexes are located on or close to the Camasunary–Skerryvore Fault (Butler & Hutton 1994), whereas the central complexes of Mull and Arran were emplaced into the Great Glen Fault and the Highland Boundary Fault, respectively. Faults associated with St Kilda and many of the offshore central complexes are not so obvious and further geophysical studies are required in order to understand their locations. However, deep-seated structures within the basement (Lewisian) gneisses along the continental shelf in the vicinity of the St Kilda and the (submerged) Geikie central complexes suggest that pre-Palaeogene rifting events were at least partially responsible for their locations (e.g. Harding *et al.* 1984). Imaging the deep basement structures within the Faeroe–Shetland Basin is hampered by the seismic opacity of the often thick lava sequences and much work is required here before a clear picture can emerge.

The level within the crust at which the central complexes were emplaced was influenced by the crustal density profile, typically close to the base of the older lava sequences. The sill complexes were typically emplaced into the thick sequences of Mesozoic sedimentary rocks as a consequence of the over-lying (older) lavas acting as a density filter (e.g. the Little Minch Sill Complex (Gibb & Gibson 1989) and the Faeroe–Shetland Sill Complex (Gibb & Kanaris-Sotiriou 1988)). The Loch Scridain Sill Complex, SW Mull, does, however, breach to a shallower level, within the lava sequence, but differs in that many of the sills are highly xenolithic (Preston *et al.* 1999).

During the emplacement of the central complexes, the adjacent country rocks accommodated the new material by extensional faulting, uplift and the development of arcuate fold systems. Uplift may be measured by the structural elevation of pre-Palaeogene lithologies, whereas the marginal fold systems, involving substantial crustal shortening adjacent to the central complexes, may be quantified by detailed field observations (Walker 1975; England 1988). Examples of such arcuate fold systems include Skye, Mull, Rum and Arran, and most likely involved gravitational collapse of the country-rocks around the margins of the central complexes as they were emplaced (e.g. Holroyd 1994).

The subsurface geometries of the central complexes may be modelled from their gravity and magnetic signatures (see Chapter 1). All are characterised by significant positive Bouguer

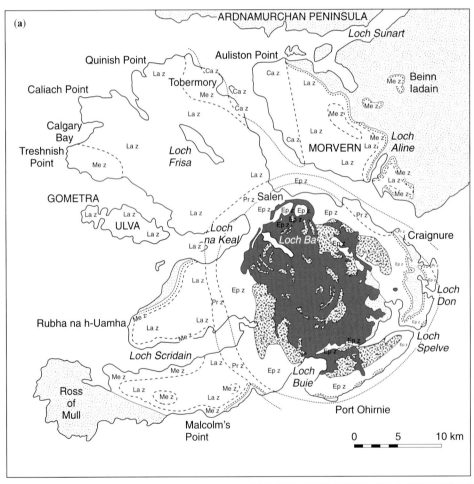
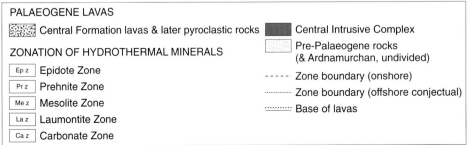

Fig. 14.5. (a) Sketch map indicating the distribution of hydrothermal secondary mineral zones superimposed upon the Mull Lava Field. (b) Schematic cross-section illustrating paragenesis depth profiles for the mineral zones (after Walker 1971).

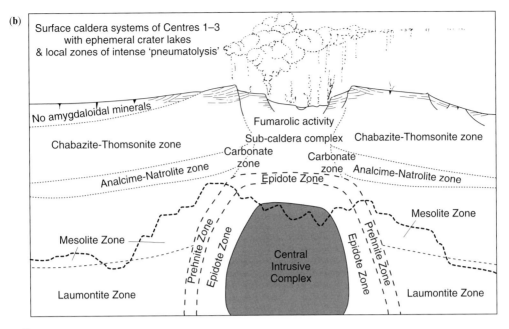

Fig. 14.5. (*continued*)

gravity anomalies, with localised and steep gradients suggesting steep-sided margins of dense material (olivine-rich gabbro and/or peridotite). The anomalies have been modelled and indicate that these basic and ultrabasic rocks extend to depths of at least 15 km and that the granites, although voluminous at the present level of erosion, are most likely very thin and extend to a depth of only 1–2 km (McQuillin & Tuson 1963; Bott & Tuson 1973; Bott & Tantrigoda 1987; England 1992b). The magnetic anomalies of the central complexes reflect the modal percentages of magnetic minerals, likely to be relatively high and low in the gabbros and peridotites, respectively. Thus, where central complexes are dominated by ultrabasic rock types there is less of a magnetic anomaly than where gabbroic rocks are abundant.

Thermal and hydrothermal alteration of the country-rocks is also pronounced in the vicinity of each of the central complexes (e.g. Almond 1964). The development of steep geothermal gradients around the margins of the central complexes during their development may be recognized from the mineral assemblages and textures which are preserved within the various country-rock lithologies. Heat was also removed from the central complexes by convective flow of meteoric waters, as deduced from the significantly lowered values of $\delta^{18}O$ and δD within the minerals that have interacted with the fluids. The convective cells were of substantial size, involving at least 2000 km³ of meteoric water and extending up to 10 km from the margins of the central complexes (i.e. very approximately half of the diameter of the central complex) (Taylor & Forester 1971; Forester & Taylor 1977). In the immediate vicinity of the margins of the central complexes at the time of emplacement the temperature of metamorphism may have been in excess of 1000°C; however, the anhydrous mineral assemblages preserved in these rocks indicate that there was no mineral-fluid reaction below c. 900°C (Ferry et al. 1987). With time, the fluid flow became channelised, as evidenced by the myriad of vein networks which dissect the country rocks and the various lithologies of the central complexes. Mineral assemblages within these veins are dominated by amphiboles, prehnite, epidote, chlorite, various carbonates and zeolites, together with quartz. Mineral geothermometry indicates temperatures of precipitation, which are <500°C (Ferry 1985a, b). Ion probe studies of individual crystals of quartz suggest that even at the micro-

scopic scale, fluid flow was channelized, with adjacent portions of crystals recording small and large degrees of isotopic exchange (Elsenheimer & Valley 1993). Rock–fluid reaction was not entirely isochemical, with minor changes recognized for both gabbroic and granitic rocks (Ferry 1985a, b).

Another form of hydrothermal alteration recorded by the lava piles may be attributed to their burial. Regionally near horizontal, stratified zones of amygdale mineral assemblages indicate increasing temperature with depth (Walker 1970) (Fig. 14.5). By comparison with the distribution of amygdale mineral assemblages in lavas from the Antrim Lava Field of Northern Ireland and the lava fields of Eastern Iceland, it may be deduced that as much as 1500 m of lava has been eroded from the Mull lava pile since the Palaeogene (Walker 1970). Thus, the original thickness of the lava pile in the vicinity of Ben More (970 m at the present day) was likely to have been over 2000 m. Similar zonation patterns in the lavas of Skye indicate comparable amounts of erosion (King 1977).

The lava fields

Remnants of three lava fields are preserved in western Scotland: Eigg (including Muck and SE Rum) (Emeleus 1997); Skye (including Canna and NW Rum) (Anderson & Dunham 1966; Emeleus 1985, 1997; Williamson & Bell 1994) and Mull (including Morvern) (Bailey et al. 1924; Kerr 1995) (Fig. 14.6). Offshore, west of Scotland, the submerged Faeroe–Shetland, Erlend and North Rockall Trough–Hebrides lava fields/groups comprise considerably thicker sequences, covering significantly larger areas (Ritchie & Hitchen 1996) (Fig. 14.2).

The vast majority of the lavas appear to be sheet-like, and were erupted into a subaerial environment. Weathered tops, boles and palaeosols are common features within the preserved sequences. Pyroclastic rocks are relatively rare (Emeleus et al. 1996a). Intercalated with the volcanic rocks are various sedimentary units, ranging from coarse debris flow facies through fluvial sandstones, siltstones and coals, to lacustrine mudstones. Stratigraphical subdivision of the lava fields is most effectively achieved by using these sedimentary sequences, deposited during hiatuses in the volcanism, to define (both volcanic and sedimentary) allostratigraphical formations and

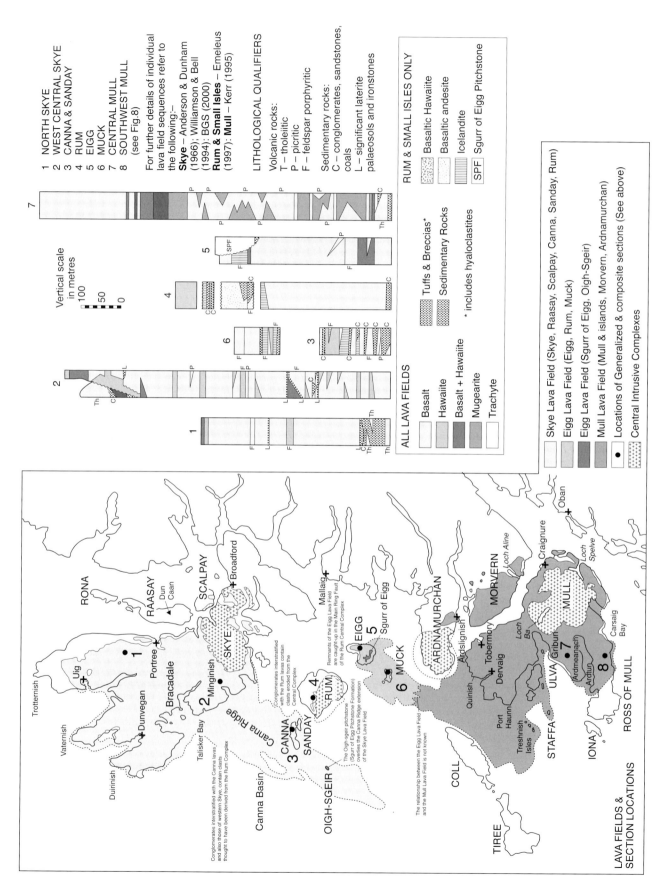

Fig. 14.6. Sketch map depicting the distribution of, and inferred relationships between, the Palaeogene lava fields in the Hebridean Province, and representative generalized vertical stratigraphical sections through the Hebridean lava fields.

members. Further evidence of subaerial environments is palae-ontological and includes the presence of fossil trees entombed within flows, for example, Macculloch's Tree, the Carsaig Tree (Plate 26) and the Quinish trees, all on Mull. Leaf macrofloras are preserved within sedimentary intercalations, for example in the Allt Mor and Glen Osdale members of the Skye Lava Field (Williamson & Bell 1994; Anderson & Dunham 1966), the Upper Fionchra Member on Rum (Emeleus 1997), and the famous Ardtun Conglomerate Member of the Mull Lava Field (Bailey *et al.* 1924; Boulter & Kvacek 1989). The latter also includes a terrestrial insect fauna.

A'a flows appear to be less common than pahoehoe types, with an example of the latter described in detail from the Mull Lava Field by Kent *et al.* (1998). Typically, the less evolved flows are thin (up to 5 m), comprising stacked flow units commonly with scoriaceous tops. Lava tubes are recognized in a number of flows, for example, the Macculloch's Tree Flow on the Ardmeanach Peninsula, west Mull and a flow towards the base of the sequence exposed on Staffa. Gas cavities are commonly filled with secondary hydrothermal (amygdale) minerals, for example, calcite, quartz, and various zeolites. Pipe amygdales are common in the basal parts of flows where they have been erupted over a wet substrate.

More evolved flows are thicker (up to 20 m) and generally have greater volumes. The large areal distribution of the evolved flows, with some flow lengths greater than 10 km, suggests high effusion rates. These more viscous units commonly exhibit flow structures (including folds) due to the alignment of groundmass plagioclase, grain-size banding and modal variations in mineral content. Such fabrics are particularly obvious in the more evolved compositions, mugearite and trachyte.

Columnar jointing is a common feature within basaltic flows which have ponded within valleys (allowing slow, uninterrupted cooling) where the substrate comprised either shallow standing water or wet sediment. Some of the most famous flows within the Hebrides exhibit near-perfect columnar jointing, for example, the Fingal's Cave Flow on Staffa, the Macculloch's Tree Flow, and the Preshal More flows at Talisker in west central Skye. Within more evolved flows, less perfect prismatic jointing is common. However, columnar jointing is known from more evolved flows, for example, the rhyodacite flow on the Sgurr of Eigg.

The initial phases of volcanism within the Skye and Mull lava fields were dominated by pyroclastic eruptions and the formation of hyaloclastite units where basaltic flows brecciated and pillowed upon entering generally shallow water. Thereafter, although there is evidence for eruptions onto surfaces covered by standing water, the lava sequences developed, predominantly, in a subaerial environment.

The Eigg Lava Field and the Sgurr of Eigg Pitchstone Formation

The Eigg Lava Field (or Formation, see Fig. 14.6) crops out on Eigg, Muck and SE Rum and pre-dates the intrusion of a NW-trending dyke swarm and the emplacement of the Rum Central Complex. This early position in the igneous stratigraphy is confirmed by an ^{40}Ar–^{39}Ar age date of *c.* 60.5 Ma for the sanidine-bearing Port Mor trachytic 'tuff' (a volcaniclastic sandstone), close to the base of the sequence (see above) (Emeleus *et al.* 1996*a*; Chambers & Pringle 2001). Alkali olivine basalts are dominant, although hawaiites and mugearites are also present. Intercalated with the lavas are thin orange-red mudstones, some of volcanic origin (Emeleus *et al.* 1996*a*).

Overlying the Eigg Lava Formation in the south of the island is a valley-fill conglomerate sequence, bedded in part, with clasts of local lava field lithologies, together with red

(Torridonian) sandstone and rare Palaeogene silicified woody material (*Pinites eiggensis*; Harker 1908). The sequence is of variable thickness, up to a few tens of metres. The overlying rhyodacite pitchstone was erupted into the same valley system, extending west to the skerries of Oigh-sgeir and also draining towards the west. It is a black, glassy, columnar-jointed rock with microphenocrysts of anorthoclase, plagioclase and pyroxene and is at least 120 m thick. The basal part of this flow is brecciated in part and, locally, has well-developed flow banding. Fragments of basaltic rock are dispersed throughout its mass. Emeleus (1997) interpreted the eruption history to have commenced with an ash flow, giving way, with time, to one or more lavas.

The Skye Lava Field

The Skye Lava Field crops out in north and west-central Skye, extending south through the islands of Canna and Sanday, to NW Rum (Fig. 14.6). Of the four districts, northern Skye covers the largest area, but is the least well understood.

West–central Skye. In west–central Skye several formations are recognized (BGS 2000 (Minginish); groups of Williamson & Bell (1994)). Interbedded sedimentary units and prominent palaeosurfaces are used to create the subdivision. The stratigraphically lowest sequence, the An Leac Formation, crops out on Soay Sound and unconformably overlies various Mesozoic and Torridonian sedimentary rocks. Flat-lying, laterally impersistent volcaniclastic deposits and interbedded sedimentary rocks are dominant and eruption of magma into shallow water is inferred. The succeeding Meacnaish and Creag Mhor members complete the Rubh' an Dunain Lava Formation and comprise various basaltic and rarer more evolved flows, with several hiatuses indicated by the presence of lacustrine siltstones and mudstones and many palaeosols. Proceeding up through the formation, the relative proportion of interbedded siltstones and mudstones diminishes. The overlying Bualintur Lava Formation, dominated by porphyritic basalts and hawaiites, crops out west of Glen Brittle and may interdigitate with the upper part of the Rubh' an Dunain Lava Formation.

The first major sedimentary interlude is marked by the Minginish Conglomerate Formation, subdivided into geographically dispersed members: Culnamean, Allt Geodh' a' Ghamhna and Allt Mor. These conglomerate–sandstone–siltstone–coal sequences were deposited within alluvial braided stream systems. Clasts within the conglomerates are predominantly of Torridonian sandstone and siltstone, together with felsite and granite interpreted as the erosion products of the unroofed (between 60.5 Ma and 59 Ma) Rum Central Complex (Meighan *et al.* 1982; Williamson & Bell 1994), together with only a surprisingly small population of local lava field lithologies. Siltstones within the Allt Mor Member contain superb leaf impressions, similar to the famous Ardtun (Leaf Bed) Conglomerate Member of the Mull Lava Field (see below).

The overlying Cruachan and Glen Caladale lava formations are dominated by interbedded basalt and hawaiite flows, rare picritic basalts, and a few evolved flows, typically flow-banded mugearites, the most prominent of which defines the Stac a' Mheadais Member. The Cruachan Lava Formation appears to interdigitate with the basalt, hawaiite and mugearite flows of the Coire na Circe Lava Formation to the NE, the latter overlain by the rhyolite-dominated Fionn Choire Lava Formation immediately adjacent to the Cuillin Centre.

A significant hiatus in volcanic activity is marked by the development of a weathering profile and the subsequent deposition of the Eynort Mudstone Formation. The latter comprises mudstones and fine-grained volcaniclastic deposits which accumulated in shallow bodies of water. Of the four sequences identified, the most complete is the Ben Scaalan Member.

The Fiskavaig Lava Formation appears to interdigitate with the upper part of the Glen Caladale Lava Formation. It is dominated by basalt and hawaiite flows, many of which are plagioclase porphyritic. Within the McFarlane's Rock Member there is a distinctive, thick mugearite flow with well developed flow folding.

The overlying Gleann Oraid Lava Formation records a significant increase in the relative proportion of evolved flows, with two members, Sleadale and Cnoc Scarall, being defined on the basis of thick, valley-ponded trachyte domes. The Sleadale trachyte is underlain by an anorthoclase-bearing trachytic tuff which provides the only precise isotopic age date (58.91 Ma, see above) for the Skye Lava Field. Close to the base of the formation is a composite hawaiite flow, with aphyric base and plagioclase macroporphyritic interior. Similar flows are recognized from the Beinn Totaig Formation of north Skye (see below), suggesting a possible correlation.

The lower flows of the Gleann Oraid Lava Formation appear to be intercalated with the laterally-restricted Loch Dubh Lava Formation, the latter dominated by plagioclase and olivine microporphyritic hawaiites and basalts.

At the base of the twin summits of Preshal More and Preshal Beg, near Talisker, the laterally-restricted Preshal Beg Conglomerate Formation crops out (Fig. 14.7). These heterogeneous sedimentary rocks include debris flow (?lahars), alluvial fan and fluviolacustrine facies volcaniclastic deposits accumulated within a substantial and long-lived valley drainage system which developed upon the Glen Oraid Lava Formation surface. Subsequently this topography was inundated by two thick (at least 120 m) intracanyon flows of compositionally distinctive tholeiitic basalt belonging to the Talisker

Lava Formation. These flows mark a significant change in the chemical signature of the lava sequence and have a strong compositional affinity with the various intrusive units of the Cuillin Centre (Bell *et al.* 1994). Williamson & Bell (1994) concluded that the Preshal More flows may represent the only remnants of an originally significant lava shield that developed above the Cuillin Centre.

North Skye. Volcanic activity in north Skye commenced with the eruption of the subaqueous facies Portree Hyaloclastite Formation (up to 40 m thick), comprising palagonite hyaloclastite breccias, pillowed lavas and various volcaniclastic sandstones and siltstones. The Formation crops out in the vicinity of Portree, and especially north of Portree below Craig Ulatota and on Fiurnean, together with many other minor outcrops around the present-day lava escarpment.

The overlying, predominantly subaerial facies flows of north Skye have an aggregate thickness of at least 1200 m and have been subdivided into five formations (groups of Anderson & Dunham 1966): Beinn Edra (lowest), Ramasaig, Beinn Totaig, Bracadale, and Osdale (highest), separated by various thin sedimentary sequences of alluvial braided stream and lacustrine association. Stratigraphically up-sequence, the relative proportion of evolved flows (hawaiites to trachytes) to basaltic flows increases. This is a common motif throughout the Hebridean lava fields.

The Beinn Edra Formation crops out on the Trotternish Peninsula in the classic east-facing escarpment from The Storr, north through Beinn Edra, to The Quirang (Plate 27). Rotational landslips and rock failures partially obscure this more or less 300 m thick basalt-dominated section. Crystal-rich tuffaceous mudstones occur within the sequence around The Quirang and preserve evidence of pyroclastic basaltic volcanism during

Fig. 14.7. Preshal Beg in west–central Skye, as seen from the NW face of Beinn Bhreac, looking NW. This isolated hill forms one of two outliers of an olivine tholeiite flow of the Talisker Formation, erupted late in the development of the Skye Lava Field. This massive intracanyon (valley-fill) flow lies upon a surface of Preshal Beg Conglomerate Formation, underlain by stratiform sheet flows ('trap topography') of hawaiite and basalt flows belonging to the Arnaval Member of the Gleann Oraid Lava Formation. In the distance are the twin summits of Healabhal Mhor and Healabhal Bheag (also known as Macleod's Tables) comprising near flat-lying lavas, NW of Loch Bracadale.

the early stages of growth of the Skye Lava Field (Bell *et al.* 1996). The top of the formation is marked by the Trotternish Shale Member.

The Ramasaig Formation crops out on the Duirinish and Waternish peninsulas, for example, at Waterstein Head, Dunvegan Head, at Idrigill Point and on the twin summits of Healabhal Mhor and Healabhal Bheag (Macleod's Tables). Most of the *c.* 800 m thick sequence comprises flows of basaltic or hawaiitic composition, some of which are plagioclase porphyritic. The Beinn Edra and Ramasaig formations both rest upon the pre-volcanic land surface and therefore were most likely contemporaneous.

North of Loch Harport, including the area around Mugeary, the Beinn Totaig Formation crops out. Within this *c.* 600 m thick formation are basalts, hawaiites, mugearites and composite hawaiite flows, the latter suggesting a correlation with the Gleann Oraid Lava Formation in west central Skye (see above). The Roineval and Sligachan lava formations of BGS (2000) may be southern extensions of the Beinn Totaig Formation.

The overlying Bracadale Formation (*c.* 130 m) crops out in a relatively narrow corridor of ground, possibly defining a broad palaeovalley, NE of Bracadale. Many of the flows are evolved: hawaiites, mugearites and trachytes, with restricted flow lengths, and are relatively thick.

The youngest preserved unit is the Osdale Formation (*c.* 500 m) which contains both basaltic and more evolved flows and crops out west of Bracadale. Separating the Osdale Formation from the locally subjacent Ramasaig Formation is a trachytic, tuffaceous sandstone and leaf-bearing shaly siltstone sequence which crops out in the Hamara River in Duirinish. Within the same stratigraphic interval are the conglomerates and leaf-bearing shaly siltstones of Glen Osdale, Healaval Mhor (Fig. 14.6) (Anderson & Dunham 1966), the former dominated by clasts of Torridonian sandstone, together with Palaeogene felsite and granite, similar to the Minginish Conglomerate Formation, further south (Williamson & Bell 1994).

Other lava occurrences on Skye. Metamorphosed basaltic and hawaiitic lavas also crop out in and around the margins of the Skye Central Complex, for example a roof pendant on Glamaig and a screen at Creagan Dubh in the Eastern Red Hills. Their equivalence to particular formations in north Skye and west central Skye has not been ascertained. On the Strathaird Peninsula, *c.* 300 m of predominantly basaltic flows have been altered by the hydrothermal systems which developed during the emplacement of the central complex, with pyroxene hornfels facies assemblages within basaltic lavas south of Sgurr na Stri at the head of Loch Scavaig (Almond 1964). On Raasay, an outlier of the lava field forms the summit of Dun Caan (Fig. 14.6).

Canna, Sanday and NW Rum: The Canna Lava Formation. The Canna Lava Formation comprises both alkali olivine basalts and tholeiitic basalts, and their evolved differentiates, interbedded with fluviatile conglomerate–sandstone–siltstone sequences (Emeleus 1973, 1985, 1997). The clasts within the conglomerates are of local lava field lithologies, together with fragments of basement, and granite and felsite shed from the unroofed Rum Central Complex, further south. At times there was a considerable (several tens of metres) topography on the lava field, for example, in NW Rum.

On Canna and Sanday, at least 200 m of lavas are preserved, with more evolved compositions more common up-sequence. One particularly distinctive flow, a columnar-jointed tholeiitic basaltic andesite overlying a bed of conglomerate, crops out on Eilean a' Bhaird in Canna Harbour. At Compass Hill, east Canna, *c.* 50 m of sedimentary breccia of debris-flow associa-tion, with blocks of basalt and red feldspathic sandstone, crops out. The submerged Canna Ridge connects the Canna and southwest Skye parts of the lava field.

In NW Rum, four members are recognized: Lower Fionchra (lowest), Upper Fionchra, Guirdal, and Orval (highest). Steep-sided palaeovalleys are identified both within the lava sequence and at the base of the pile, where one side of a valley eroded in the Western Granite crops out on the north side of Orval. At the base of the Upper Fionchra Member is *c.* 60 m of hyaloclastite breccia and pillowed lava, indicating that the earliest eruptions associated with the member were into a (shallow) lake-filled valley. Associated lacustrine sediments include siltstones with leaf impressions. Within the conglomerate units, in addition to clasts of local lava field lithologies and basement rock-types, there are blocks of various igneous lithologies derived by the unroofing and erosion of the adjacent Rum Central Complex. In particular, clasts of bytownite troctolite and gabbro are found, of Layered Suite association (see below), which are missing from the assemblages found further north on Canna, Sanday and Skye (Fig. 14.6), presumably because of their physical instability.

The Mull Lava Field

The internal architecture of the Mull Lava Field (Fig. 14.6) is considerably less well understood than that of the Skye Lava Field. Three informal Formations are recognized at present. In stratigraphical order (oldest first) they are the Staffa Lava Formation, the Mull Plateau Lava Formation and the Mull Central Lava Formation. The main outcrops are throughout northern Mull, the coastal peninsulas of south Mull (including various small offshore islands, Ulva, Gometra, the Treshnish Isles, Staffa), and on the Morvern Peninsula. Small outliers of the lava field are preserved along the south coast of the Ardnamurchan Peninsula, in particular around Ben Hiant. This account relies mainly upon the original Geological Survey mapping of Mull (Bailey *et al.* 1924), together with the geochemical stratigraphy established by Kerr (1995a) and more recent observations by the authors.

The present-day thickness of the lavas on Mull is *c.* 1800 m, which includes a crudely estimated 900 m thickness of tholeiitic basalt flows preserved as screens within the Central Complex. The sequence on Morvern is *c.* 400–500 m thick. On the basis of hydrothermal mineral distribution with depth, it would appear that a thickness of at least 1200 m has been eroded from the lava pile in the Ben More area (Walker 1970) (Fig. 14.5). The lavas typically overlie Moine basement rocks, with or without intervening sections of Triassic, Jurassic and Cretaceous strata. In SW Mull, the lavas terminate at the Assapol Fault. In contrast to the Skye lava field, sedimentary interludes within the Mull Lava Field appear, in general to be much less common, and, therefore, subdivision into lithostratigraphic formations is less easily achieved. Only in SW Mull, on the Ross of Mull (Plate 25), are significant interlava sedimentary units recorded (Fig. 14.8).

The base of the volcanic sequence is locally marked by either a *c.* 1–3 m thick, laterally persistent reddish-orange mudstone, the Gribun Mudstone Member, interpreted as a ferrallitized basaltic ash, or by a thin impersistent clastic sequence, the Croggan Member.

The Staffa Lava Formation immediately overlies this sequence except in the Morvern and Croggan areas where it appears to be absent. It is on average a few tens of metres thick and dominated by subaerial lavas most likely erupted from NW-trending fissures now represented by the Mull Dyke Swarm. The first major hiatus in the volcanic activity is marked by the *c.* 6 m thick Ardtun Conglomerate Member, an alluvial

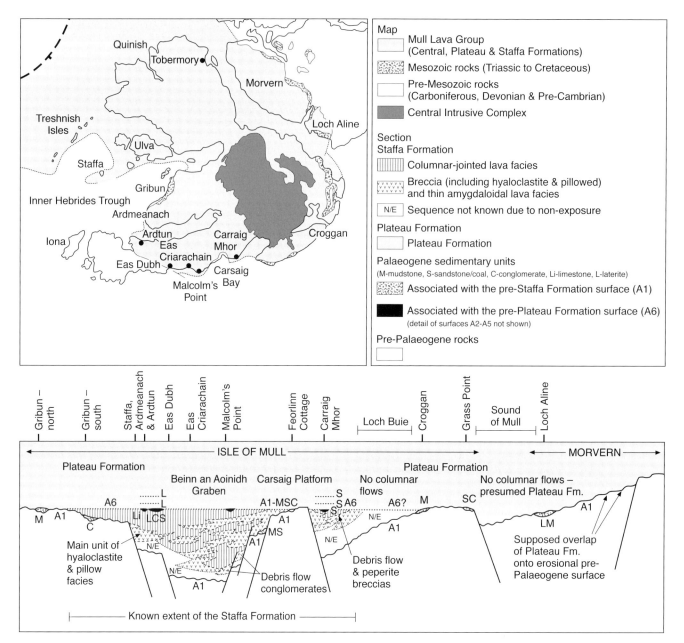

Fig. 14.8. Schematic cross-section of the lava succession in SW Mull illustrating the possible relationships between the various volcanic facies and intercalated sedimentary rocks of the Staffa Formation, to 'basement' structures and the succeeding Mull Plateau Lava Formation.

debris fan, fluvial and lacustrine conglomerate–sandstone–siltstone sequence which, within the argillaceous units, contains remarkably well preserved leaves from ginkgo, hickory, plane, ash, redwood and swamp cypress trees (Boulter & Kvacek 1989; Jolley 1997).

The lava sequence between the Gribun Mudstone and Ardtun Conglomerate members contains, in places, a substantial thickness of basaltic flows, many, but not all, of which exhibit well-developed columnar jointing and invasive lava tubes, both features indicative of lava ponding. Examples of such flows include: the Macculloch's Tree Flow on the Ardmeanach Peninsula, which contains the cast of *Taxodixylon*; the Fingal's Cave Flow on Staffa; together with several flows which crop out along the south coast of the Ross of Mull from Eas Dubh through Malcolm's Point to East Carsaig (Fig. 14.8). The presence of columnar jointing within these flows, together with their overall geometries, the presence of pillowed facies and the nature of interbedded sedimentary rocks, indicates that they

were erupted into broad valleys containing impounded lakes. Within these valleys substantial swamps developed, resulting in coal beds up to 3 m thick (e.g. at Loch Codh' an Dunain, above Malcolm's Point), over which lavas flowed, entraining trees and other surface materials, for example, the recently discovered Carsaig Tree (Plate 26).

Detailed mapping indicates that the Fingal's Cave and Macculloch's Tree 'lavas' are, in fact, parts of the same flow. This flow overlies a thick heterogeneous sequence of bedded volcaniclastic sandstones and siltstones with abundant woody debris, hyaloclastite breccias and primary spatter deposits (Fig. 14.9). East of Malcolm's Point on the Ross of Mull, at the 'Pulpit Rock', the Staffa Lava Formation overlies a heterogeneous sequence of conglomerates containing flint clasts derived from Cretaceous (Turonian) chalk deposits and clasts of local lava field lithologies. Fossil trees are also preserved within the lavas of north Mull. By far the best examples are found on the Quinish Peninsula, where several trees are preserved both as

Fig. 14.9. Cross- and surge-bedded hyaloclastite breccias within the sedimentary and volcaniclastic deposits underlying the columnar jointed Macculloch's Tree lava flow of the Staffa Formation, Ardmeanach, west Mull. Note the well-developed colonnade-entablature pairing in this flow.

casts on the reddened top of an a'a flow and as aligned moulds in the overlying lava.

The Mull Plateau Lava Formation may be divided into the Main Member, overlain by the Pale Member. Kerr (1995a) referred to a Coire Gorm magma-type, essentially represented by the Pale Member, but showing a degree of transitional interleaving with the underlying Main Member. Correlation of groups of flows across the lava field, based mainly upon their geochemical signature was presented by Kerr (1995a). The most common lava types are basalt and picritic basalt. The relative proportion of evolved flows increases up-sequence within the Formation, with a significant number of evolved flows, hawaiites and mugearites, in the Main Member and a preponderance of benmoreites and trachytes in the Pale Member. Within the Pale Member, close to the summit of Ben More, are dark shaly siltstones with poorly preserved plant remains, together with lenses of conglomerate containing clasts of Moine psammite.

Towards the base of the overlying Mull Plateau Lava Formation, at Laggan Bay, is a thick sequence of basaltic ashes, epiclastic breccias and debris flow deposits. These deposits are most likely proximal to a small vent and, north of the mugearitic flow of Na Torranan, lava flows bank up against a thick (tens of metres) mound of volcaniclastic material. Kent *et al.* (1998) described an inflated pahoehoe flow from north Mull, within an interval considered to be close to the base of the lava pile.

The Mull Central Lava Formation is largely obscured by younger intrusive units of the Mull Central Complex. Many of the isolated exposures are of intensely hydrothermally altered pillowed basalt lava. Bailey *et al.* (1924) concluded that the body of water involved was a caldera-filling lake. The estimated thickness of *c.* 900 m implies that the caldera floor progressively subsided, creating accommodation space, during the eruption of these intra-caldera lavas.

Submerged lava fields and volcaniclastic deposits

West of Shetland, within the Faeroe–Shetland Basin, and further south in the Rockall Trough, are thick, extensive lava fields of Palaeogene age, buried by Eocene and younger strata (Fig.

14.2). The volcanic rocks within the western side of the Faeroe–Shetland Basin are referred to as the Faeroes Lava Group and crop out on the Faeroe Islands. The Erlend Lava Group is located towards the northern end of the basin, overlying the Erlend Central Complex and is not exposed above sea level. The North Rockall Trough–Hebrides Lava Group occupies the northern end of the Rockall Trough and is also not exposed above sea level (Ritchie & Hitchen 1996; Ritchie *et al.* 1999).

Offshore volcaniclastic deposits. Interbedded with the Palaeogene strata of the North Sea and Faeroe–Shetland basins (Ch. 13) are various wind-transported tuffs and volcaniclastic deposits (e.g. Knox & Morton 1988; Morton & Knox 1990). Within the North Sea Basin, two phases are recognized: an earlier (Late Palaeocene) Phase 1, comprising volcaniclastic sandstones, together with graded ashfall deposits ranging from basaltic through to silicic compositions, and with alkaline types also present (Knox & Morton 1988); and, a later (latest Palaeocene through to Early Eocene) Phase 2, comprising thick graded airfall ashes within the Sele and Balder formations. The Balmoral Tuff(ite) of the Lista Formation in the North Sea (see Chapter 13) belongs to the Phase 1 activity.

Phase 2 activity has been subdivided into four 'subphases', a–d, the most significant of which is represented by the 'subphase b' thick basaltic tuffs within the Balder Formation (a laminated mudstone), and referred to as the Balder Tuff(s) (Jacque & Thouvenin 1975). These tuffs, although reworked in places, are an important regional (6×10^6 km²; Knox & Morton 1988) seismic marker in North Sea and Faeroe–Shetland basinal stratigraphies and comprise thin (typically <20 cm) graded layers of basaltic ash with MORB affinity, and with an aggregate thickness of several metres, representing an eruption volume of several 10^3 km³. The thickness distribution of the Balder Tuff(s), their MORB compositions and the estimated volume of magma involved, together with their Early Eocene age, suggest a link with the initial cataclysmic period of continental break-up and the commencement of ocean floor spreading between the Faeroe Islands and East Greenland. The subsequent subphases c and d are similar to subphase b and appear to represent small-volume eruptions which post-dated the commencement of ocean-floor spreading.

The central complexes

The central complexes have diameters of up to c.15 km and represent foci of intense intrusive activity. They comprise a wide variety of rock-types and display a range of intrusion geometries and mechanisms of emplacement. The complexes may be regarded as the root zones of central volcanoes, the extrusive products of which have now largely been removed by post-Palaeogene weathering and erosion. Evidence of (typically early) surface volcanism associated with the central complexes is locally preserved, particularly on Rum, Skye and Mull.

The geometry and mode of emplacement of the component intrusions are strongly dependent upon the lithologies involved. Coarse-grained ultrabasic and basic units (e.g. peridotite, troctolite, gabbro) commonly form sequences which are either relatively flat-lying or dip at shallow angles towards a focal point (i.e. centrofocal dips) at a few kilometres depth. In many cases (e.g. parts of the Cuillin Centre, Skye) they have the appearance of extremely complicated confluent cone-sheet complexes resulting from the emplacement and slow cooling of countless pulses of magma (cf. Walker 1975). Fine-grained basic units (e.g. dolerite) occur in suites of cone-sheets (e.g. Skye, Ardnamurchan and Mull), typically emplaced into older coarse-grained ultrabasic and basic units, and adjacent country-rocks, and may be related to periods of dyke emplacement and the growth of the central complexes (Walker 1993b) (Fig. 14.10a). Granitic rocks typically occur as nested sets of plutons, comprising steep-sided stocks, with the youngest located within the 'core' of the complex. Intermediate (commonly hybrid, mixed-magma) rock-types typically take the form of narrow ring-dykes, for example, the Marsco Hybrids of the Western Red Hills Centre on Skye and the Loch Ba Ring-dyke on Mull (Fig. 14.10b).

Cone-sheet emplacement was related to the intrusion of linear dyke swarms (Walker 1993b). The cone-sheets comprise conical basalt and dolerite intrusions, typically less than 5 m thick, with a common focal point at depth (and approximately coincident with the focal point of the layering present within the various coarse-grained ultrabasic and basic units). Central uplift in excess of 1 km may be attributed to individual suites of cone-sheets. Cone-sheets are typically more common within the NW and SE quadrants of central complexes, related to the dominant (NW–SE) dyke swarm trend. The period of cone-sheet emplacement overlaps that of dyke emplacement. Walker (1993b) has developed a model which suggests that during periods of slow crustal dilation, cone-sheets were emplaced, whereas during more rapid periods of dilation, dyke intrusion was dominant (Fig. 14.10a).

Ring-dykes of hybrid and granitic rock were emplaced into steep, outwardly dipping fractures which developed as a consequence of the foundering or subsidence of central cylinder-like blocks (cf. Butler & Hutton 1994). Where these fractures breached the land surface, a caldera formed and there was associated surface volcanism. A cauldron subsidence developed where the ring fracture 'topped out' at some subsurface horizon (Fig. 14.10b). Emplacement of magmas into these ring fractures led to magma-mixing (tapping magmas from underlying compositionally stratified chambers), stoping and gas brecciation.

Surface volcanic activity took the form of primary pyroclastic materials (agglomerate, tuff, breccia, ignimbrite) and associated volcaniclastic deposits (breccias, lahars, reworked tuffs) and covers a wide range of compositions. Much of this material is only seen today as proximal facies deposits preserved as screens between later (subsequent) intrusions. Offshore, within the North Sea, Faeroe–Shetland and Rockall Trough basins, distal facies deposits are preserved within the thick Palaeogene sedimentary sequences (Knox & Morton 1988).

(a)

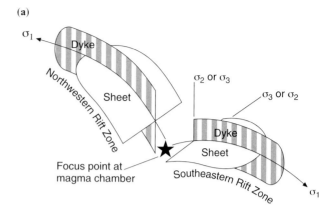

(b)

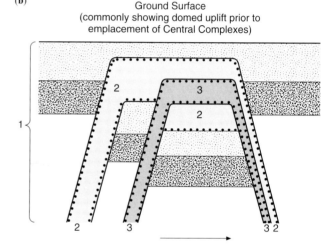

STRATIGRAPHICAL SEQUENCE AND EMPLACEMENT EVENTS

TYPICAL COUNTRY ROCK SEQUENCE IN THE HEBRIDES

Palaeogene volcanic sequences
Mesozoic and Palaeozoic sedimentary sequences
Archaean and Proterozoic metamorphic 'basement' sequences

PALAEOGENE CENTRAL COMPLEXES

| 3 | Later Ring-dyke |
| 2 | Early Ring-dyke |

Chilled intrusive contact

Fig. 14.10. (a) Schematic diagram illustrating the relationship between (bladed) dykes and inclined sheets (cone-sheets) due to magma migration into the (NW–SE-trending) rift zones of the Cuillin volcano, Skye. Dykes are injected when the principal deviatoric stress axis σ_3 is horizontal, and cone-sheets are injected when σ_3 is vertical (after Walker 1993b). (b) Schematic cross-section through two ring-dykes. The country rock between the ring-dykes forms what is referred to as a 'screen'.

St Kilda

The St Kilda Central Complex crops out on the St Kilda Archipelago, comprising the islands of Hirta, Dun, Soay, Boreray, Levenish and minor sea stacks. No in situ Palaeogene volcanic rocks or pre-Palaeogene country-rocks are preserved above sea level. The most recent account of the Complex is by Harding *et al.* (1984).

The oldest intrusion is the Western Gabbro, exposed on the west side of Hirta and most of Dun. It occurs in a number of textural varieties and is commonly layered, with dips of *c.* 45° towards the east or NE. The presence of modal and grain-size layering, slump structures and intrusive breccias indicates that the formation of this intrusion has much in common with gabbroic and peridotitic intrusions elsewhere in the Province. In the cliffs at Cambir, west Hirta, the Cambir Dolerite comprises sheets of fine-grained olivine dolerite invading the Western Gabbro.

The outlying islands of Boreray, Soay and Levenish are composed of an igneous breccia, consisting of pegmatitic gabbro, commonly sheared in places, and veined and brecciated by dolerite. Similar material occurs at Glacan Mor on Hirta. Some of the gabbro blocks are identical to material from the Western Gabbro. The olivine-bearing Glen Bay Gabbro on Hirta crops out in two discrete masses, separated by the younger Glen Bay Granite. The gabbro has an obvious splintery chilled margin against the older brecciated gabbros of Glacan Mor. The western outcrop is very sheared and granulated, with, in places, a steeply dipping mineral lamination.

The Glen Bay Granite crops out at the head of Glen Bay and has a chilled margin against the Glen Bay Gabbro. It is a medium-grained plagioclase microporphyritic rock, sheared throughout its mass. On Hirta, various brecciated intrusions of microgranite, microdiorite and dolerite, together with fragments of dolerite and gabbro derived from the early igneous breccias and gabbros of Mullach Mor, the Western Gabbro and the Glen Bay Gabbro comprise the Mullach Sgar Complex. At least four generations of dolerite and microgranite intrusion are recognized, with abundant evidence for the interaction and mixing of basaltic and silicic magmas, for example, pillowed masses of dolerite with glassy selvedges in a microgranitic matrix. Elsewhere, dolerite and basalt are fractured and invaded by stringers and veins of felsite and microgranite.

The Conachair Granite crops out in the eastern part of Hirta, between Conachair and Oiseval, and is the youngest major intrusion in the St Kilda Central Complex. It is a pale-weathering, drusy, medium-grained rock, with a very blocky appearance due to the development of various joint sets. A variety of sheets of basic and silicic compositions, some composite, invade all of the major intrusions, most obviously, the Conachair Granite. The attitudes of the sheets suggest a focal point at depth, east of Hirta.

Fig. 14.11. (a) Generalized geological map of the Skye Central Complex. (b) Geological map of the Cuillin and Strath na Creitheach centres. (c) Geological map of the Western Red Hills and Eastern Red Hills centres (after Emeleus & Bell 2003).

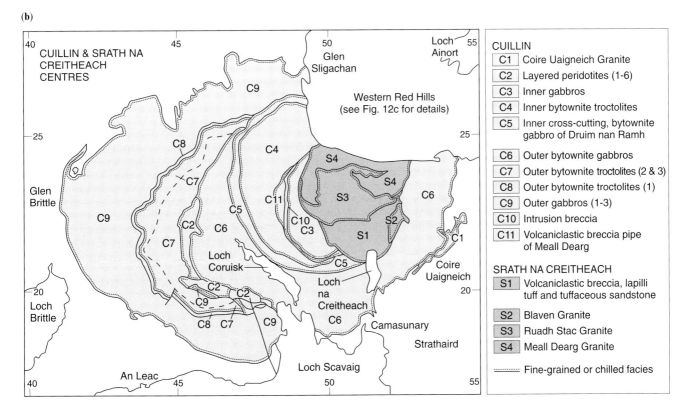

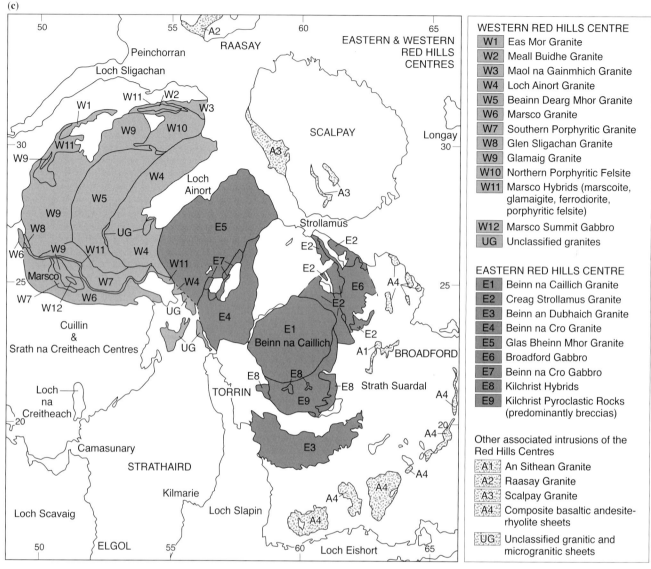

(c)

WESTERN RED HILLS CENTRE
- W1 Eas Mor Granite
- W2 Meall Buidhe Granite
- W3 Maol na Gainmhich Granite
- W4 Loch Ainort Granite
- W5 Beainn Dearg Mhor Granite
- W6 Marsco Granite
- W7 Southern Porphyritic Granite
- W8 Glen Sligachan Granite
- W9 Glamaig Granite
- W10 Northern Porphyritic Felsite
- W11 Marsco Hybrids (marscoite, glamaigite, ferrodiorite, porphyritic felsite)
- W12 Marsco Summit Gabbro
- UG Unclassified granites

EASTERN RED HILLS CENTRE
- E1 Beinn na Caillich Granite
- E2 Creag Strollamus Granite
- E3 Beinn an Dubhaich Granite
- E4 Beinn na Cro Granite
- E5 Glas Bheinn Mhor Granite
- E6 Broadford Gabbro
- E7 Beinn na Cro Gabbro
- E8 Kilchrist Hybrids
- E9 Kilchrist Pyroclastic Rocks (predominantly breccias)

Other associated intrusions of the Red Hills Centres
- A1 An Sithean Granite
- A2 Raasay Granite
- A3 Scalpay Granite
- A4 Composite basaltic andesite-rhyolite sheets
- UG Unclassified granitic and microgranitic sheets

Fig. 11. (*continued*)

Skye

The Skye Central Complex comprises the Cuillin (oldest), Srath na Creitheach, Western Red Hills and Eastern Red Hills (youngest) centres (Bell & Harris 1986) (Fig. 14.11).

Cuillin Centre. The Cuillin Centre is dominated by various coarse-grained layered and unlayered basic and ultrabasic ring intrusions which have a focal point below the Red Hill, Meall Dearg, at the southern end of Glen Sligachan (Fig. 14.11b). These units are cut by a suite of cone-sheets, members of the NW-trending dyke swarm, and numerous small breccia pipes. The country rocks are predominantly basaltic lavas which have been subjected to localized high grade pyroxene hornfels thermal metamorphism facies (Almond 1964; Ferry *et al.* 1987) south of Sgurr na Stri and on the east side of Glen Brittle. Along the SE margin of the centre, in Camasunary Bay, the underlying Torridonian sandstones and shales crop out and there is abundant evidence for intense thermal alteration and, locally, partial melt formation and injection of these melts into marginal gabbros.

The centre may be subdivided as follows: (i) the Outer Gabbros (oldest); (ii) the Outer Layered Suite; and, (iii) the Inner Layered Suite.

The Outer Gabbros form a heterogeneous group of layered and unlayered gabbro and bytownite gabbro intrusions that (predominantly) crop out west of the main summits of the Cuillin Ridge, from Sgurr nan Gillian in the north to Garsbheinn in the south (Plate 21).

The Outer Layered Suite comprises a narrow, fluxioned, xenolithic, tholeiitic dolerite (or Border Group) grading inwards (towards the east) into a massive, coarse-grained, plagioclase-rich, bytownite troctolite of strikingly white coloration (the White Allivalite of Hutchison 1968). Inwards, this bytownite troctolite is layered, consisting of plagioclase-pyroxene and plagioclase-olivine cumulates. The younger Layered Peridotites have been subdivided into six units (Claydon & Bell 1992) and range from dunite through to feldspathic peridotite (Fig. 14.12). The structurally lowest unit is dominated by dunite and contains discontinuous layers of chrome-spinel (Bell & Claydon 1992). Units 2 and 3 are of feldspathic peridotite and Unit 4 is a mass of intrusive heterogeneous breccias comprising plagioclase-dominated blocks in a matrix dominated by olivine, and vice versa. Within Units 5 and 6 are a variety of peculiar textural varieties of peridotite, for example, spherical and hemispherical masses of 'poikilo-macrospherulitic' structures, and peridotite 'fingers' penetrating upwards and partially replacing

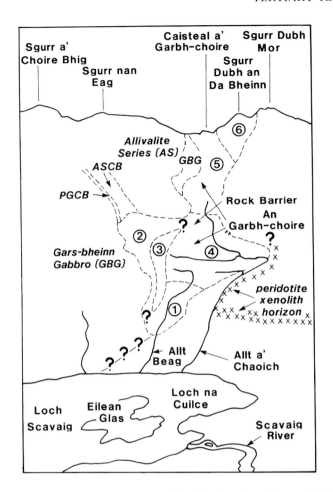

Fig. 14.12. An Garbh-choire, Cuillin Hills, Skye, from the summit of Sgurr na Stri, looking west. Forming much of the floor of the corrie are the ultrabasic rocks of the Layered Peridotites; the peridotites extend from just above the shore of Loch na Cuilce, westwards in the low ground north of the southern portion of the Main Ridge, and south of Sgurr Dubh Beag, Sgurr Dubh Mor and Sgurr Dubh an Da Bheinn. The Layered Peridotites cut across into Coir' a' Ghrunnda at the low ground on the horizon, at Caisteal a' Garbh-choire. The extents of the six units are indicated (after Claydon & Bell 1992).

troctolite (Claydon & Bell 1992). Interior to the Layered Peridotites are the Outer (Layered) Bytownite Gabbros, which contain abundant xenoliths derived from the Layered Peridotites, especially along their mutual contact.

The Inner Layered Suite consists of a number of discrete layered and unlayered masses of gabbro, bytownite gabbro and bytownite troctolite. The outermost of these is the steep-sided unlayered Bytownite Gabbro of Druim nan Ramh. Interior to this are the Inner Bytownite Troctolites and the Inner Gabbros, which are separated by a 50 m wide vertical zone of shattered tuffaceous rocks invaded by xenolithic basalt and dolerite sheets. The Inner Gabbros are exposed on the ridge of Druim Hain, and contain some of the best examples of modal layering within the Cuillin Centre, with layers dominated by magnetite, and layers of anorthosite. The layering dips inwards at a steep angle, commonly up to 70°, towards the focal point below Meall Dearg. Xenoliths of basalt and dolerite are common, with flattened shapes, suggestive of plastic deformation soon after incorporation.

Late-stage components of the Cuillin Centre include a suite of cone-sheets, together with larger multiple intrusions of tholeiitic basalt and dolerite, commonly xenolithic, and locally with highly brecciated facies. The breccia pipes that pierce the Centre are composed of angular to rounded masses of locally derived igneous rock in a matrix of similar, comminuted material. Brecciation was by volatile escape during emplacement.

The only silicic intrusion associated with the Cuillin Centre is the Coire Uaigneich Granite, which crops out along the margin of the SE sector. The intrusion appears to have been emplaced along the unconformity between Torridonian strata and Palaeogene lavas. It is heterogeneous, containing abundant xenoliths of partially digested (Torridonian?) sandstone and siltstone. Needle-like crystals of hypersthene are set in a pale granitic groundmass that also contains paramorphs after tridymite (Wager et al. 1953). The Coire Uaigneich Granite is cut by cone-sheets, in contrast to the younger granites of the Srath na Creitheach, Western Red Hills and Eastern Red Hills centres, further north and east.

Erosion of up to 2 km of rock from above the Cuillin Centre has removed virtually all of the evidence concerning the nature of the volcanic edifice. However, the geochemical similarity and late stratigraphical position of the Talisker Lava Fomation flows in west central Skye suggest that these intracanyon lavas were erupted from the Cuillin Volcano and/or an associated part of the Skye Dyke Swarm, and are unrelated to the main volcanic succession of the Skye Lava Field (Williamson & Bell 1994; Bell et al. 1994). These flows are discussed above in the section on the lava fields.

Srath na Creitheach Centre. The Srath na Creitheach Centre was emplaced into the NE quadrant of the Cuillin Centre and comprises three granites: Meall Dearg, Ruadh Stac and Blaven

(Fig. 14.11b). Metre-wide spherulitic rhyolite (dyke) apophyses of the Meall Dearg Granite invade the Inner Gabbros on Druim Hain. The Meall Dearg Granite comprises sheets of two types, a fine-grained, hornblende-bearing variety, and a younger, coarse-grained, hedenbergite-bearing variety. They crop out on the upper slopes of Meall Dearg and Ruadh Stac and are underlain by the younger dome-shaped Ruadh Stac Granite. The Blaven Granite crops out on the lower western slopes of Bla Bheinn and its age relationships to the other two granites cannot be deduced.

Western Red Hills Centre. The Western Red Hills Centre occupies an area of *c.*35 km^2 and comprises ten granites, a composite ring-dyke (the Marsco Hybrids), a number of pipes/masses of explosion breccia, and a gabbro (Wager *et al.* 1965; Thompson 1969) (Fig. 14.11c). The Centre was emplaced into Palaeogene lavas to the west, Torridonian and Mesozoic sedimentary rocks to the north, and the granites of the Srath na Creitheach Centre to the south. To the east, it is cut out by the younger Eastern Red Hills Centre.

Early explosion breccias are preserved on Belig and Meall a' Mhaoil, with subangular blocks of a wide variety of lithologies (pre-Palaeogene and Palaeogene). Juvenile material is not recognized.

The main granite intrusions of the Centre fall into two natural groupings (Thompson 1969): (i) a N–S-trending suite (Glamaig, Beinn Dearg Mhor and Loch Ainort), emplaced sequentially inwards; and, (ii) two E–W-trending suites, one in the north (the Northern Porphyritic Felsite, and Maol na Gainmhich, Meall Buidhe and Eas Mor), and one in the south (Southern Porphyritic (± felsite), and Glen Sligachan and Marsco), both suites emplaced sequentially outwards. The focal point for all of the intrusions is approximately east of Loch Ainort.

A cauldron subsidence model for the development of the centre best explains the field observations (Thompson 1969). Following the formation of the early explosion breccias and the emplacement of the Marsco Summit Gabbro, the hybrid (mixed-magma) Glamaig Granite was intruded. This was followed by the Beinn Dearg Mhor and Loch Ainort granites, forming a set of nested plutons. Subsequently, the two E–W-trending suites of granites were emplaced as the block of crust composed of the early granites subsided, most likely in a complex, piecemeal fashion.

The classic Marsco Hybrids form a complex ring-dyke intrusion within the Western Red Hills Centre (Wager *et al.* 1965). First described by Alfred Harker (Harker 1904), this composite intrusion is particularly well exposed on the west side of Marsco in what is now referred to as Harker's Gully. The intrusion comprises the hybrid rock-type marscoite (with xenocrysts of plagioclase, quartz and alkali feldspar), flanked by (the Southern) Porphyritic Felsite (a variant of the Southern Porphyritic Granite, with phenocrysts of quartz and alkali feldspar) and ferrodiorite (an Fe-rich tholeiitic differentiate, with phenocrysts of plagioclase). Simple mixing calculations suggest that marscoite is the product of thorough mixing of one part felsite magma with two parts ferrodiorite magma. This simple explanation requires some modification, for example, the ferrodiorite contains xenocrysts of quartz and therefore is, in fact, also partly hybrid. Also of note, the ferrodiorite contains rare xenoliths of partially melted Lewisian gneiss (Thompson 1981). Further north, on the SW side of Glamaig, a more heterogeneous hybrid, glamaigite, crops out within the ring-dyke (Wager *et al.* 1965).

Eastern Red Hills Centre. The Eastern Red Hills Centre is the youngest focus of intrusive activity on Skye and occupies much

of the district of Strath, SW of Broadford (Fig. 14.11c). Many of the granites were emplaced into pre-Palaeogene country-rocks, giving rise to significant thermal aureoles. The dominant intrusions are of granite, comprising (in order of emplacement): (i) Glas Bheinn Mhor; (ii) Beinn na Cro–Beinn an Dubhaich–Creag Strollamus–Allt Ferana, collectively referred to as the Outer Granite; and, (iii) Beinn na Caillich (or Inner Granite).

The Glas Bheinn Mhor Granite cuts out the eastern margin of the Western Red Hills Centre, whereas the Beinn na Cro portion of the Outer Granite chills against the Glas Bheinn Mhor intrusion. The southernmost portion of the Outer Granite, Beinn an Dubhaich, was emplaced into Cambro-Ordovician dolostones, resulting in the development of skarn mineralisation and a substantial zoned thermal aureole (Tilley 1951; Holness *et al.* 1989). These dolostones have been subjected to Caledonian thrusting events, together with pre-granite annular folding, possibly gravity driven, during the early stages of Palaeogene central uplift and intrusive activity (Holroyd 1994). Further evidence of this early uplift event comprises a narrow screen of Lewisian gneiss, overlain by hornfelsed lavas preserved between the Inner and Outer Granites, NW of the Beinn na Caillich Granite, at Creagan Dubh. The margin of the Beinn na Caillich Granite is steeply inclined, has a near-perfect circular outcrop pattern, and a well-developed marginal porphyritic felsite facies containing ferrohedenbergite and fayalite, exposed, for example, in the Allt Slapin.

The Broadford Gabbro crops out in the northern part of the Centre and has both faulted and intrusive contacts. Part of its outcrop is a *c.* 200 m wide dyke-like extension. On Creag Strollamus the gabbro is in contact with bedded pyroclastic rocks which overlie a weathered surface of the Allt Fearna granite intrusion (Johnston 1996).

Peripheral to the granites of the Eastern Red Hills Centre is a suite of composite sills and dykes (Harker 1904; Walker & Skelhorn 1966; Bell & Pankhurst 1993) (Fig. 14.11c). The sills are co-focal with the centre of the Beinn na Caillich Granite, with an inward dip of *c.*15°, and comprise marginal basalt facies (0.5–2.5 m thick) and central rhyolite or felsite facies (up to 50 m thick). These sills and dykes can be traced from Rubha Suisnish in the south, to Rubha na Sgianadin in the north and are typically emplaced into Mesozoic strata. The contact relationships between the contrasting lithologies are highly variable: (i) veins of rhyolite penetrating the basalts; or (ii) fragments of basalt within the rhyolites; or (iii) compositionally gradational (e.g. Rubh' an Eireannaich, north of Broadford). In common with the Marsco Hybrids and other intrusions of the Skye Central Complex, the nature of these contacts indicate that the basaltic and rhyolitic magmas were intruded over such a short period of time that they were both liquid at the same time, with the basaltic liquid intruded prior to the rhyolitic liquid, the latter emplaced subsequently along the central axis of the basalt intrusion.

Volcaniclastic breccias. Two large and compositionally distinctive masses of volcaniclastic rocks are preserved within the Skye Central Complex, but which have no obvious link with the main intrusive events. These are in Srath na Creitheach (Jassim & Gass 1970) at the southern end of Glen Sligachan (Fig. 14.11b), and near Kilchrist, in the district of Strath (Bell 1985) (Fig. 14.11c).

The Srath na Creitheach breccias crop out over an area of *c.* 2 km^2 and post-date the Cuillin Centre (deduced by the presence of large slabs (or megablocks) of gabbro within the breccias), but pre-date the granites of the Srath na Creitheach Centre (deduced by the chilled margin of the Ruadh Stac

Granite). The dominant clast types are basalt and dolerite, commonly altered and supported in a matrix of similar, comminuted material. Juvenile material has not been recognized from these breccias. Formation of the breccias may have involved gas escape from magma at a deeper level, together with fluidization processes. Certain exposures of the coarse breccias have textures similar to those seen in debris flows and lahars, indicating that the conduit was opened to the surface. Surface reworking is also suggested by the presence of rare, laterally discontinuous, stratiform deposits of fine-grained tuffaceous sandstones and siltstones.

The Kilchrist breccias are extremely heterogeneous and comprise a wide range of lithologies. The main mass crops out over an area of $c.\,2\,\mathrm{km}^2$ and is invaded by five hybrid (mixed-magma) intrusions referred to as the Kilchrist Hybrids. Three of these occur around the margin of the breccia outcrop and form part of a discontinuous ring-dyke, suggesting that the structural level of the breccia mass is due to cauldron subsidence, and that it originated at a higher level in the crust. These hybrids comprise small rounded fragments of basaltic material with diffuse margins set in a granitic host.

The breccias are poorly sorted, unstratified and are dominated by sub-angular to rounded fragments of pre-Palaeogene country-rocks, together with basalt, dolerite, gabbro, rhyolite, tuff (including ignimbrite), granite, pitchstone, and blocks of earlier breccia, set in a matrix of similar, comminuted material in both clast- and matrix-supported relationships. Intercalated with the breccias are volcaniclastic sandstones and rhyolitic tuffs. Within the Allt nan Suidheachan–Cnoc nam Fitheach area there are two large masses of rhyolitic ignimbrite (Bell & Harris 1986). Intruded into the breccias are small stocks of brecciated porphyritic rhyolite: (i) west of Cnoc nam Fitheach; (ii) in the Allt Coire Forsaidh; and (iii) in the Allt Slapin.

The extremely heterogeneous nature of the Kilchrist breccias and associated deposits may be interpreted as the products of surface and near-surface explosive volcanism and associated epiclastic processes within or marginal to a vent system. The ignimbrites and other silicic tuffs appear to be *in situ* extrusive deposits and may be generally related to the stocks of brecciated rhyolite. Elsewhere, there is evidence of surface weathering, in the form of lateritized breccia horizons, for example, north of Loch Cill Chriosd. As such, the Kilchrist breccias may offer the best evidence as to the nature of the volcanic and subvolcanic activity associated with the Red Hills (granite) centres, with the formation of epiclastic breccias and the eruption of various silicic pyroclastic materials.

Rum

The Rum Central Complex was emplaced into a horst of Palaeogene volcanic rocks (Eigg Lava Field), Mesozoic and Torridonian sedimentary rocks and basement Lewisian gneiss (Fig. 14.13). Three phases of growth and decay are recognized (Emeleus 1997; Emeleus & Bell 2003): Stage 1, dominated by silicic magmatism (granites and felsites) and the development of a system of ring faults; Stage 2, the emplacement of minor intrusions, together with gabbros and layered peridotites and troctolites (the Rum Layered Suite); and, Stage 3, substantial subaerial erosion and the unroofing of the central complex, prior to intermittent burial by subaerial lavas and coarse clastic detritus eroded from the volcanic edifice and roof zone of the central complex to form part of the Skye Lava Field (described in the lava fields section).

Stage 1. This comprises the Northern Marginal Zone, the Southern Mountains Zone and the Western Granite. The first recognized events consist of uplift by as much as 2 km, tilting,

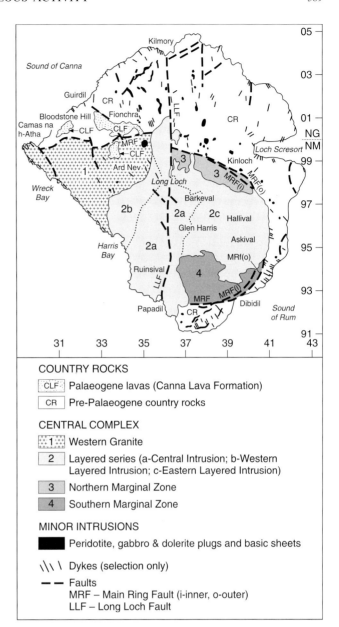

Fig. 14.13. Geological map of the Rum Central Complex (after Emeleus & Bell 2003).

deformation and doming within the Main Ring Fault of Torridon Group strata and Lewisian gneiss. As doming proceeded, large masses of Torridonian sandstone (Mullach Ard and Welshman's Rock) detached along low angle faults and slid, gravitationally, off the dome. Subsequent subsidence of the block interior to the Main Ring Fault produced a caldera, into which were erupted rhyodacitic ignimbrites and crystal-vitric tuffs (e.g. Dibidil, Cnapan Breaca and Meall Breac; Troll *et al.* 2000). Interbedded with these juvenile deposits are tuffaceous sandstones and unbedded megabreccias and breccias dominated by fragments of Torridonian sandstone, together with rare gneiss, basalt and dolerite. These caldera-fill breccias formed by collapse of caldera wall material onto the caldera. The finer-grained units were deposited by an intra-caldera fluvial (or fluviolacustrine) system. The breccias are intruded by dykes of porphyritic rhyodacite, breccia and tuff. Intrusive masses of porphyritic rhyodacite (e.g. Coire Dubh and Dibidil) contain rounded fragments of basaltic material and indicate interaction between the silicic and basic magmas.

The Am Mam Breccias of the Northern Marginal Zone consist principally of blocks and megablocks of gabbro, together with blocks of gneiss, sandstone and feldspathic peridotite, all set in a dioritic matrix. The obvious significance of these breccias is that plutonic basic and ultrabasic rocks had formed by this stage, well before the Rum Layered Suite of Stage 2. In the SE sector of the Main Ring Fault (along the Allt nam Ba and southeast of Beinn nan Stac), fault-bounded slivers of Lower Jurassic strata (Broadford Beds) and Eigg Lava Formation basalts are preserved due to a relatively early subsidence event. Subsequent uplift along the Main Ring Fault resulted in Torridon Group sandstones overlying them (Smith 1985). The microporphyritic Western Granite and related small granite masses in the Papadil (south Rum) and Long Loch (central Rum) areas post-date the porphyritic rhyodacites, but are of similar composition.

Stage 2. Stage 2 was dominated by the emplacement of basic and ultrabasic magmas. NW-trending dykes of the Muck Regional Dyke Swarm, together with dykes trending N and NNE and cone-sheets, were intruded into the Northern Marginal Zone and the Southern Mountains Zone, with a focus beneath upper Glen Harris. The volumetrically dominant intrusive activity involved the development of the Rum Layered Suite, which crops out in the southern and central parts of the island. In east Rum a number of gabbro sheets intrude these layered rocks (e.g. Askival and Atlantic Corrie). Also invading the layered rocks and the surrounding country-rocks are over forty stocks of gabbro and massive and layered feldspathic peridotite (Wadsworth 1994). The peridotites, troctolites, and bytownite gabbros of Rum exhibit a wide variety of layering and associated features. Typically the layering is modal, involving differing proportions of olivine, clinopyroxene, plagioclase and chrome-spinel, although layering due to textural features is also present. The peridotites tend to form dark easily weathered layers, in contrast to the more resistant troctolites (allivalites of Harker (1908)).

Various models have been presented in order to explain the development of these layered rocks in terms of magmatic sedimentation, involving crystal settling and sorting, together with post-depositional deformation, reaction and pore space infill and crystallization (Emeleus *et al.* 1996b; Emeleus 1997; Emeleus & Bell 2003). Sedimentary features include: graded bedding, cross-bedding, slump and flame structures, drop stones and associated deformation of the surrounding layered rocks, and breccia development. Indeed, it was through investigations of the Rum Layered Suite that the term igneous cumulate was coined and models for crystal accumulation were developed (Wager *et al.* 1960; Wager & Brown 1968). Within the cumulate pile, considerable post-cumulus reactions have taken place, involving crystal–melt and crystal–crystal reactions, and which have modified mineral compositions and textures during slow cooling (cf. Emeleus *et al.* 1996b). Features such as finger structures involve reaction with, and dissolution of, troctolites by hot picritic magmas which produce replacement rocks (e.g. NW Hallival). Other thermal effects of the hot parental magmas to the Layered Suite include the partial melting of country-rock sandstones, gneisses, felsites and granites. Such melts were capable of back veining and shattering the marginal facies of already crystallized intrusions, yielding various types of intrusion breccia (e.g. at Harris Bay).

Detailed mapping over the past four decades has shown that the Rum Layered Suite may be subdivided into three intrusions: the Eastern, Western and Central layered intrusions. The Eastern Layered Intrusion is at least 700 m thick and comprises sixteen peridotite–troctolite macro-rhythmic units (or doublets) (Brown 1956; Volker & Upton 1990). The Western

Layered Intrusion comprises a sequence of layered bytownite gabbros (at Harris), overlain by peridotites (on Ard Mheall), with a minimum thickness of *c.* 600 m (Wadsworth 1961). Within this sequence are the classic 'harrisites': elongate crystals of olivine, often perpendicular to the layering, which have been interpreted as the product of upward crystal growth from the contemporaneous floor of the chamber. The Central Intrusion, several hundreds of metres across, is the youngest of the three layered sequences, occupying the central portion of the Layered Suite (McClurg 1982; Volker & Upton 1990). It comprises a complicated assemblage of megablocks (up to 1500 m by 400 m by 30 m thick) of layered troctolite surrounded either by massive peridotite or heterolithic peridotite breccia. The dip of the layering within individual blocks is relatively constant; whereas the different blocks have different layering orientations, suggesting disruption, rotation and slumping. Zones of intrusive breccia, up to 400 m wide and typically trending north, occur within the Central Intrusion (Wadsworth 1992). More than one generation of breccia development is recognized and some of these breccia zones have a focal point north of the summit of Ruinsival. A schematic reconstruction of possible events involved in the development of the Central Series is shown in Figure 14.14.

No direct local evidence is preserved concerning the nature of the volcanic edifice which developed above the Rum Central Complex. However, it is evident from the age and clast contents of sedimentary deposits interlayered with lavas of the Skye Lava Field (on Rum, Canna and west central Skye; Emeleus 1973, 1985; Williamson & Bell 1994) that rapid and substantial erosion took place soon after the cessation of any agradational volcanic activity associated with the Rum volcano. Clasts of Rum intrusive lithologies occur within conglomerates which were deposited by northward flowing rivers soon after the Skye Lava Field started to develop and are more appropriately discussed within the context of the growth of the lava fields.

Ardnamurchan

The Ardnamurchan Central Complex is located on the Ardnamurchan Peninsula on the Scottish mainland, north of Mull (Fig. 14.15). Three discrete centres of intrusive activity are recognized (Richey & Thomas 1930): (i) Centre 1 (oldest); (ii) Centre 2; and, (iii) Centre 3 (youngest). The country-rocks comprise a basement of low-grade Moine psammites and pelites, overlain by a thin sequence of Triassic breccias, conglomerates and sandstones, Jurassic sandstones, limestones and shales, and Palaeogene lavas (an outlier of the Mull Lava Field). Emplacement of the Centre 2 and 3 intrusions involved substantial doming and uplift, although no peripheral annular folds similar to those developed on Mull and Skye are present within the country-rocks.

Volcaniclastic breccias and Centre 1. Overlying the thin outlier of the Mull Lava Field is a *c.* 200 m thick sequence of volcaniclastic breccias, forming the prominent crags above Maclean's Nose on the south side of Ben Hiant. The link between these breccias and the various ring intrusions which define Centre 1 is unclear and it may be that the vent system with which the breccias were associated is considerably older. However, based upon the spatial association of the breccias with the cone-sheets of Centre 1 they will be dealt with here.

The breccias are typically poorly stratified and extremely heterogeneous, dominated by matrix-supported clasts mainly derived from the older lava field. Fragments of basement (Moine) rocks and the Mesozoic cover sequence are relatively uncommon. One clast type which cannot be matched with *in situ* material is blocks of rhyodacite ignimbrite. This material

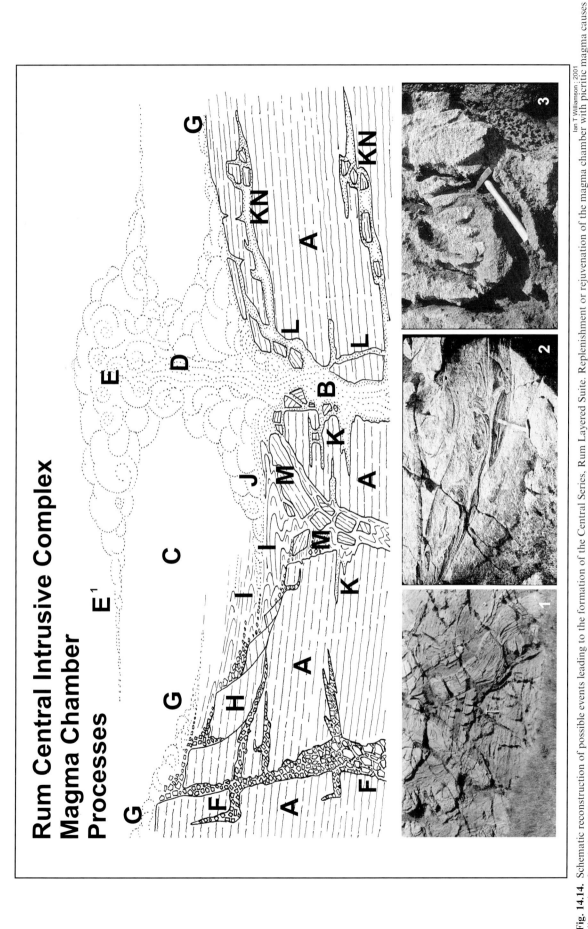

Fig. 14.14. Schematic reconstruction of possible events leading to the formation of the Central Series, Rum Layered Suite. Replenishment or rejuvenation of the magma chamber with picritic magma causes disruption, foundering, sliding and slumping of earlier formed layered sequences (after Emeleus *et al.* 1996*b*). Abbreviations are as follows: **A**, pre-existing cumulates of the Eastern and Western Layered Series; **B**, conduit system delivering ultrabasic (picritic) magmas (±olivine crystals) into the chamber; **C**, magma column overlying floor of chamber; **D**, plume of magma rising into chamber, driven by momentum and thermal buoyancy; **E**, turbulent mixing within the plume head and lateral stratification of (newly intruded) magma; **E**[1], stratification of new magma along thermal boundary layers and rain of crystals; **F**, igneous breccias due to injection and/or faulting; **G**, gravity-driven turbidity or density currents developing along chamber walls and flowing towards centre of chamber; **H**, slippage of large coherent masses of already-crystallized cumulates along listric faults; **I**, slumping, folding and shearing of unstable partially lithified cumulates; **J**, gravity density currents and base surge-type activity at foot of column; **K**, intrusion of sills of ultrabasic (picritic) magma, with associated melting of pre-existing troctolite cumulates, formation of 'finger' structures etc.; **L**, plug-like masses of ultrabasic material; **M**, foundering of coherent megablocks into incompletely lithified cumulates; **N**, intrusive sheets of ultrabasic (picritic) magma, causing instability and block foundering within the upper part of the cumulate pile; **1**, breccia of large blocks and slump structures within the Central Series, Long Loch; **2**, typical minor slump feature in the Eastern Layered Series, Askival; **3**, finger structures, Minishal.

Ian T Williamson : 2001

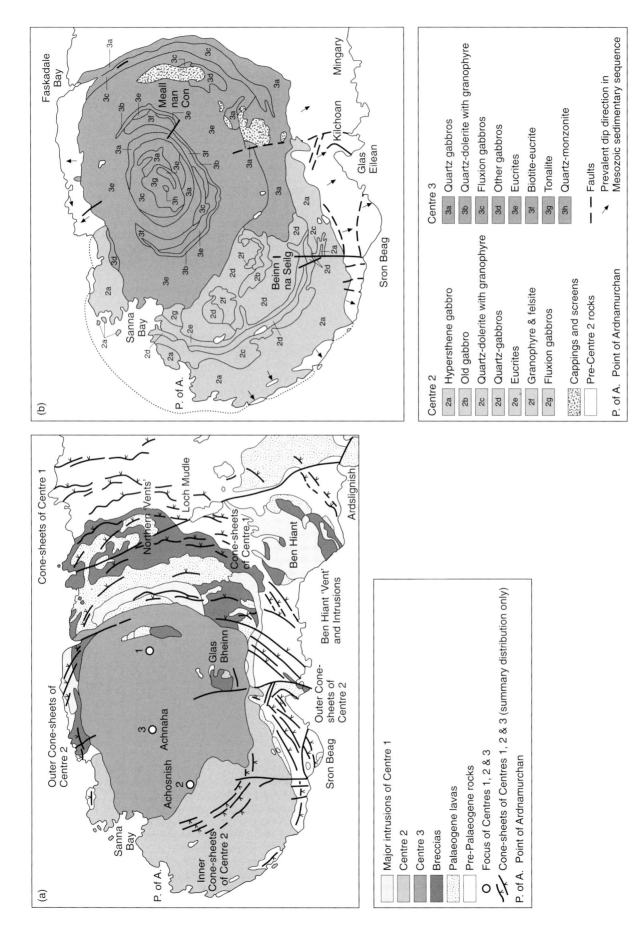

Fig. 14.15. (a) Geological map of the Ardnamurchan Central Complex. (b) Geological map of Centres 2 and 3, Ardnamurchan Central Complex (after Emeleus & Bell 2003).

is clearly the product of earlier explosive volcanic activity, although the vent(s) from which the magma was erupted has not been recognized.

Fragments within the breccia range in size from blocks several metres across, down to sand and silt grade material. Bedding, where present, is defined by thin layers of tuffaceous sandstone and siltstone interstratified with the breccias. Fragments within these finer-grained deposits are dominated by lava field lithologies, together with trachyte, not recognized from the local outcrops of the Mull Lava Field on the Ardnamurchan Peninsula and on North Mull. The environment of formation of the Centre 1 breccias is poorly understood. By comparison with active volcanic areas, similar heterogeneous epiclastic deposits occur in areas marginal to vents and accumulate by a variety of mass flow processes.

Emplaced into the breccias are sheets of andesitic pitchstone. These have previously been interpreted as lavas, although in at least one example (in Richey's Gully on the SE side of Ben Hiant) the invasive nature of the sheet is particularly obvious, with columnar jointing fanning away from the leading edge of this shallow intrusion where it cooled in contact with the (water-saturated?) breccias. The breccias are also intruded by various sheets and stocks of plagioclase porphyritic and aphyric dolerite. The main intrusive sheets are of tholeiitic quartz dolerite and form part of the Centre 1 suite of cone-sheets with a focal point, at depth, c. 1 km west of Meall nan Con. The outermost cone-sheets are inclined inwards at shallow angles (15–20°), whereas those towards the interior have inclinations of up to c. 40°.

Associated with the Centre 1 cone-sheets are breccias referred to by Richey & Thomas (1930) as forming the Northern Vents. This material is similar to the Ben Hiant Breccias although the degree of exposure is not good and no detailed investigation has been undertaken since the original survey of Richey & Thomas (1930). Other intrusions associated with Centre 1 are either sheet- or dyke-like and appear to pre-date the cone-sheets.

Centre 2. Centre 2 comprises four phases of intrusive activity, all with a focal point, at depth, below Aodann (Fig. 14.15). The first phase involved the intrusion of an outer ('older') suite of basic cone-sheets, emplaced into the Mesozoic cover sequence and underlying Moine basement. These cone-sheets are of similar tholeiitic composition to the Centre 1 suite. In the vicinity of Kilchoan, the density of cone-sheets is very high, resulting in either the elimination of country-rock, with cone-sheets emplaced into cone-sheets, or, where the country rock is still present, its extreme thermal metamorphism. Multiple and composite (with felsite) members of the suite occur, but are not particularly common. Intrusion of the outer cone-sheets produced a (relative) central uplift of c. 1300 m, although central subsidence may also have taken place.

The first major ring intrusion of Centre 2 is the Hypersthene Gabbro, which cuts across the older suite of cone-sheets strongly transgressively at several places along its southern outer margin. The Hypersthene Gabbro has excellent modal layering, dipping inwards towards a focal point below Achosnich. Augen structures and upward penetrating finger structures occur in the section north of Sanna Bay and suggest that significant post-cumulus modifications have taken place. The Hypersthene Gabbro has a major thermal aureole associated with it. Within this are various rocks of rheomorphic origin, generated by melting of basement and Mesozoic lithologies. Also, at Glebe Hill, NW of Kilchoan, there are outcrops of high grade hornfelses, with sapphire, spinel and plagioclase, produced from a highly aluminous parent, possibly a Palaeogene lateritic claystone, or a Jurassic shale, or pelitic material from the Moine basement.

Interior to the Hypersthene Gabbro is a steep-sided hybrid (mixed-magma) intrusion, consisting of dolerite veined by microgranite and felsite (Blake *et al.* 1965; Skelhorn & Elwell 1966). The classic exposures at Eilean Carrach, NE of the Point of Ardnamurchan, illustrate the nature of these rocks very clearly (Fig. 14.16). Silicic material either veins (millimetres to centimetres wide) large masses of dolerite, resulting in relatively angular outlines to the dolerite 'clasts', or acts as a 'matrix' to more rounded masses of dolerite with irregular (crenulated), chilled margins indicating that the basic material was liquid when it came into contact with the silicic magma. Thus, mixing of hot (c. 1200°C) basic magma with cooler (c. 900°C) silicic magma will, as the former loses heat and the latter gains heat, during mixing, produce these two phenomena (i.e. veins of microgranite in fractured dolerite and 'pillows' of dolerite with chilled margins within microgranite).

The third phase of Centre 2 intrusive activity was the emplacement of the inner suite of basic cone-sheets, which are steeply inclined (up to 70°) inwards, towards the focal point below Aodann. They are typically plagioclase porphyritic dolerites. The final phase of Centre 2 intrusive activity was

Fig. 14.16. Net-veining and intrusion breccia, Eilean Carrach, Centre 2, Ardnamurchan Central Complex.

the emplacement of more (incomplete) ring intrusions, mainly of quartz gabbro.

The Glas Eilean Vent crops out on the east side of the promontory (tidal island) on the east side of Kilchoan Bay. It developed after the intrusion of the outer suite of cone-sheets, but contemporaneous with the development of younger intrusions of Centre 2. The fragmental material within the vent consists of blocks of Moine psammite and pelite, Jurassic sandstone and limestone, together with various basic igneous rock-types (some derived from the outer suite of cone-sheets?). Brecciation appears to have been almost *in situ,* possibly by gas action, and fragments were not subsequently transported any significant distance. The 'matrix' forms vein-like features, up to 0.5 m across, with fine-grained margins against the blocks. It is composed of comminuted block material together with juvenile pumiceous and shard-like fragments of devitrified (silicic?) glass, forming a network of veins emplaced as pyroclastic material during rapid volatile loss, also most likely responsible for the initial (and subsequent) brecciation of the block lithologies (Paithankar 1967).

Centre 3. The youngest centre consists of a suite of annular basic intrusions (gabbros) with near-complete ring geometries (Fig. 14.15). The dips of the margins (and inter-intrusion contacts) are most likely inwardly-inclined, giving rise to a nested suite of funnel-shaped intrusions. Intermediate and silicic intrusions associated with the Centre preserve evidence of magma-mixing during their formation.

The focal point of Centre 3 is located below a point 1 km ENE of Achnaha, directly below compositionally evolved intrusions. The Centre measures *c.* 7 km WSW–ENE and *c.* 6 km NNW–SSE. The largest of the Centre 3 intrusions and the one which helps to define the Centre's overall geometry and give it topographic expression, is an olivine bytownite gabbro (the Great Eucrite), which crops out on the summits of Meall Clach an Daraich, Meall an Fhir-eoin, Meall Meadhoin, Creag an Airgid and Beinn na h-Imeilte. Within the interior of Centre 3 is a narrow, steep-sided, hybrid ring-dyke which was formed by the partial mixing of basic and silicic magma. It crops out over *c.* 270°, implying some form of rotational or 'trap door' subsidence model. Some of the gabbroic ring intrusions within the inner part of Centre 3 crop out over the same sector as this ring-dyke. The innermost part of Centre 3, above the focal point, is composed of a small mass of amphibole-rich tonalite and a central quartz monzonite with large biotite crystals. Given their location and their hybrid mineralogical and compositional characteristics, it is likely that these evolved rocks are the product of reaction between evolving basic magmas and partially melted roof rocks. Very few minor intrusions are associated with Centre 3: these are restricted to some dolerite cone-sheets cutting the older intrusions in the south and rare NNW–SSE-trending dykes.

Mull

Our understanding of the Mull Central Complex (Fig. 14.17) is still, largely, due to Bailey *et al.* (1924). The only available summary of more recent observations is presented by Skelhorn (1969), together with a small number of mainly petrological studies of certain of the main intrusions (see Kerr *et al.* 1999).

Three centres are recognized: 1, 2 and 3, with the first and last considered to have been related to the development of calderas (1, the Early Caldera (or Glen More Centre); and, 3, the Late Caldera (or Loch Ba Centre)) (Skelhorn 1969). Centre 2, the Beinn Chaisgidle Centre, is dominated by cone-sheets and ring-dykes. During the formation of the Central Complex, from Centre 1 through to Centre 3, there was a gradual

migration of the focus of intrusion along a SE to NW axis, by a few kilometres, parallel to, and coincident with, the Mull Regional Dyke Swarm trend.

Marginal annular folds of the country rocks appear to have developed in response to early intrusive events. These structures include the Loch Don and the Loch Spelve anticlines and the Duart Bay and Coire Mor synclines. The age of the annular folds is not well understood, although a maximum (relative) age may be provided by the cross-cutting volcaniclastic breccias on the east side of the complex.

Centre 1 (Glen More Centre; 'Early Caldera'). Some of the screens of country rock between the numerous intrusions of the Mull Central Complex are composed of hornfelsed and hydrothermally altered pillowed basaltic lavas and have been interpreted by Bailey *et al.* (1924) as having originated from a localized part of the stratigraphically youngest part of the lava field. These flows are attributed to the Central Lava Formation (also see the section on magmas and magmatic processes, below).

The earliest of the main intrusions of the Glen More Centre (Fig. 14.17a) are the steep-sided granites of Glas Bheinn and Derrynaculean, possibly forming portions of ring-dykes or steep-sided stocks. Emplacement of these granites was, in part, controlled by ring faults, with central collapse. Brecciation, due either to gas escape or ring faulting, is common throughout these granites. In addition, the Glas Bheinn intrusion was emplaced into the core of the (somewhat imperfectly developed) Loch Spelve Anticline, part of the annular fold system peripheral to the central complex.

Along the trace of the ring fault, which defines the extent of the Early Caldera, are numerous masses of explosion breccia (e.g. on the eastern side of Sgurr Dearg) consisting of chaotic assemblages of sub-angular to rounded fragments of lava lithologies, Mesozoic sedimentary rock, Moine gneiss and a wide variety of coarse-grained igneous rocks. The breccias appear to have formed by gas streaming from silicic magmas, as suggested by the presence of brecciated rhyolitic rocks as blocks in the breccia (Bailey *et al.* 1924). The deeper structural level of the basement Moine gneisses interior to the main caldera-bounding fault is indicated by the general absence of this material as a clast lithology interior to the fault. These observations also suggest that the breccia-forming events occurred at a relatively shallow level in the crust.

In Coire Mor there are deposits of unstratified volcaniclastic breccia (agglomerate of Bailey *et al.* 1924) containing sub-angular to rounded blocks of various igneous rocks and pre-Tertiary sedimentary rocks, together with large masses of flow-banded rhyolite. The Coire Mor rocks were interpreted by Bailey *et al.* (1924) as surface accumulations and contemporaneous rhyolite lava flows. Richey (1961) subsequently expressed doubt as to the surface origin of the Coire Mor material, preferring a model of subsurface gas brecciation, similar to the explosion breccias of Sgurr Dearg.

Approximately contemporaneous with the breccia-forming event(s), was a period of intrusion of silicic magma, represented by the Beinn Meadhon, Torness and Creag na h' Iolaire flow-banded felsites (rhyolites). Disruption and intrusion by younger basic intrusions (mainly cone-sheets) greatly restricts any understanding of the original geometries of these intrusions.

A suite of (early) basic (and rare intermediate and silicic) cone-sheets was then emplaced into the Glas Bheinn and Derrynaculean granites, the explosion breccias and the early felsites/rhyolites. These minor intrusions dip inwards at *c.* 45° towards a focal point below Beinn Chaisgidle. Bailey *et al.* (1924) estimated their aggregate thickness as approaching 1000 m, and considered that they were responsible for substantial central

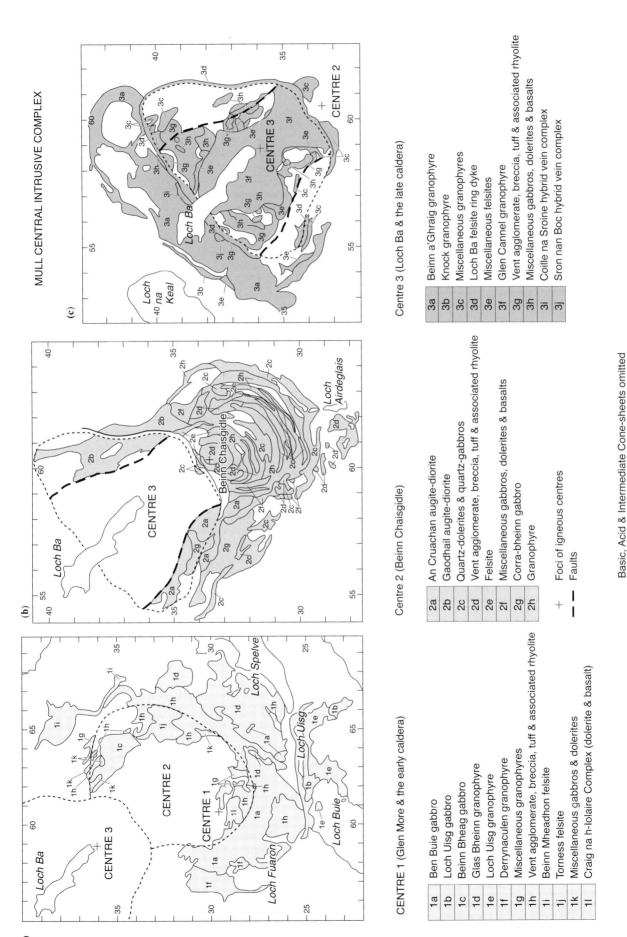

MULL CENTRAL INTRUSIVE COMPLEX

CENTRE 1 (Glen More & the early caldera)

1a	Ben Buie gabbro
1b	Loch Uisg gabbro
1c	Beinn Bheag gabbro
1d	Glas Bheinn granophyre
1e	Loch Uisg granophyre
1f	Derrynaculen granophyre
1g	Miscellaneous granophyres
1h	Vent agglomerate, breccia, tuff & associated rhyolite
1i	Beinn Mheadhon felsite
1j	Torness felsite
1k	Miscellaneous gabbros & dolerites
1l	Craig na h-Iolaire Complex (dolerite & basalt)

Centre 2 (Beinn Chaisgidle)

2a	An Cruachan augite-diorite
2b	Gaodhail augite-diorite
2c	Quartz-dolerites & quartz-gabbros
2d	Vent agglomerate, breccia, tuff & associated rhyolite
2e	Felsite
2f	Miscellaneous gabbros, dolerites & basalts
2g	Corra-bheinn gabbro
2h	Granophyre

Centre 3 (Loch Ba & the late caldera)

3a	Beinn a'Ghraig granophyre
3b	Knock granophyre
3c	Miscellaneous granophyres
3d	Loch Ba felsite ring dyke
3e	Miscellaneous felsites
3f	Glen Cannel granophyre
3g	Vent agglomerate, breccia, tuff & associated rhyolite
3h	Miscellaneous gabbros, dolerites & basalts
3i	Coille na Sroine hybrid vein complex
3j	Sron nan Boc hybrid vein complex

+ Foci of igneous centres

– – – Faults

Basic, Acid & Intermediate Cone-sheets omitted

Fig. 14.17. (**a**) Geological map of Centre 1 (Glen More), Mull Central Complex. (**b**) Geological map of Centre 2 (Beinn Chaisgidle), Mull Central Complex. (**c**) Geological map of Centre 3 (Loch Ba), Mull Central Complex (after BGS 1992).

uplift. Emplacement of the intermediate and silicic cone-sheets overlapped with the intrusion of the basic cone-sheets. Movement of the fault defining the Early Caldera had, essentially, ceased by the time of emplacement of the early cone-sheets.

Three large gabbroic intrusions were then intruded into the complex: Ben Buie in the SW, exterior to the main bounding fault; Corra-bheinn in the west, mainly, but not wholly exterior to the main bounding fault; and, Beinn Bheag interior to the bounding fault in the NE quadrant of the centre. Skelhorn & Longland (in Skelhorn 1969) suggested that, originally, the Ben Buie intrusion (and possibly the Corra-bheinn intrusion) was circular in plan, and that central subsidence, interior to the main bounding fault, removed to a deeper structural level much of the intrusion. Modal layering close to the outer margin of the Ben Buie intrusion dips inwards at 15–20°, whereas adjacent to the bounding fault the layering dips at an angle in excess of 35°. The outer margin of the Ben Buie intrusion dips outwards at a shallow angle (Lobjoit 1959). On the basis of the inward dipping nature of the layering, it appears to have a confluent cone-sheet geometry and its base may be at no great depth. Consequently, emplacement may have resulted in significant central uplift. The three gabbro intrusions were subsequently invaded by various cone-sheets, basic through to silicic, which belong to the Ben Chaisgidle Centre (Centre 2; see below).

The Loch Uisg intrusion may also belong to the Glen More Centre. Two different lithologies are identifiable, granite and gabbro. The junction between the two comprises a zone of hybrid material formed by the mixing of the two contrasting magmas. This asymmetric composite intrusion appears to have the geometry of a flat-lying sheet emplaced into flows of the Mull Plateau Lava Formation. At the west end of Loch Uisg, the upper contact of the granite dips at a steep angle to the north. Emplacement of the Loch Uisg intrusion post-dates the annular folding event(s) and the development of the explosion breccias of the Glen More Centre.

Centre 2 (Ben Chaisgidle Centre). Subsequently, the focus of igneous activity shifted several kilometres towards the NW, to the area around Beinn Chaisgidle (Fig. 14.17b). This centre is dominated by thin, steeply inclined, outward-dipping ring (-dyke) intrusions varying in composition from basalt through to rhyolite (felsite), and inwardly inclined basalt and dolerite (Late Suite) cone-sheets. Associated with the Centre is the Glen More Ring-dyke, a steeply inclined, hybrid intrusion (Bor 1951). The ring-dykes are predominantly of silicic composition, with steeply inclined margins. They vary from relatively coarse-grained types such as granite, through to felsite and rhyolite, with thicknesses varying between 50 and 500 m. Basic ring-dykes are much less common, and vary from gabbro through to dolerite. Certain of the ring-dykes are composite, with gradational internal variation from silicic to basic.

The Glen More Ring-dyke crops out from the floor of Glen More to the summit of Cruach Choireadail, over a vertical distance of almost 500 m. It grades upwards from a gabbro, through dioritic rocks, into a mafic granite. Bailey *et al.* (1924) and Koomans & Kuenen (1938) interpreted the vertical variation in composition as the product of *in situ* differentiation by crystal-liquid fractionation, whereas others (Holmes 1936; Fenner 1937) concluded that the dioritic rocks resulted from the mixing of silicic and basic magmas. Bor (1951) advocated a combined process involving fractionation of a basaltic magma to produce an intermediate liquid, the latter subsequently mixing with unrelated silicic magma.

The Late Basic cone-sheets, a suite of tholeiitic quartz dolerites, mark the last obvious event in the development of the Beinn Chaisgidle Centre. As these cone-sheets were emplaced,

the focus of intrusion migrated further NW towards Loch Ba and Centre 3 became established.

Centre 3 (Loch Ba Centre; 'Late Caldera'). The suite of Late Basic cone-sheets continued to be emplaced during the development of the Loch Ba Centre and are symmetrically disposed about an axis trending NW, parallel to the length of Loch Ba (Fig. 14.17c). These cone-sheets cut the Beinn a' Ghraig and Glen Cannel granites, the latter of which is relatively thin and exposed as an upper domed surface. The emplacement of the hybrid, mixed-magma, Loch Ba Ring-dyke was the last major event in the development of the Loch Ba Centre. Space for this intrusion was achieved by the combined action of gas brecciation and central subsidence.

The first major intrusion to be emplaced within the Loch Ba Centre was the Glen Cannel Granite, an oval, dome-shaped mass with a NW-trending long axis. This intrusion contains abundant gas cavities and is preserved, predominantly, within the subsided block interior to the late-stage Loch Ba Ring-dyke. The Glen Cannel Granite cuts numerous Late Basic cone-sheets within the central subsided block, but, exterior to the block, to the SE, the granite is cut by similar cone-sheets.

The Beinn a' Ghraig Granite is located external to the Loch Ba Ring-dyke along its NW margin and is considered to be younger than the Glen Cannel Granite. The Knock Granite is of similar age, taking the form of a steep-sided elongate mass, separated from the Beinn a' Ghraig Granite by a screen of hornfelsed basaltic lavas. Similarly steep-sided granitic, dioritic and hybrid ring intrusions occur to the NE of Loch Ba, in the vicinity of Toll Doire, Maol Bhuidhe and Killbeg.

The final major silicic intrusion of the Centre is the Loch Ba Ring-dyke. It has an external diameter of *c.* 8 km and a width varying from 400 m down to parts which, at the present level of erosion, are devoid of igneous rock and where the trace of the ring fault is marked by brecciation of the country rocks. In general, the ring-dyke is close to vertical, although steep outward dips along the NW portion may be recognized. The intrusion was first described by Bailey *et al.* (1924), and its petrology and origin have subsequently been discussed by Walker & Skelhorn (1966) and Sparks (1988). The latter two studies recognized the hybrid nature of the intrusion, involving dominant silicic rock (rhyolite or felsite) with inclusions (typically <10 mm across) of more basic material ranging in composition between ferrobasalt and dacite. The presence of (<10 vol%) dark, rounded to lenticular, globular, glassy inclusions may be attributed to liquid immiscibility with the silicic host. The rhyolite component is partially devitrified with an obvious flow banding and the preservation of fiamme (eutaxitic texture), are indicative of a 'pyroclastic' mode of formation (Sparks 1988). Given the glassy hybrid nature of the intrusion and the development of textures typical of welded tuff, it is evident that its emplacement involved the mixing of magmas during the intrusion of pyroclastic material. Sparks (1988) concluded that the basic glass fragments dispersed throughout the Loch Ba Ring-dyke were generated in a compositionally stratified magma chamber (ferrobasalt through dacite to rhyolite) which was overlain by a cap of rhyolitic magma. Emplacement involved the thorough mixing of the rhyolitic magma with the subjacent magma(s), which were most likely close to their liquidus temperature(s). During mixing, the excess heat from the hotter basic magma(s) was absorbed by the rhyolitic magma, causing rapid and violent vesiculation of the latter and ultimately the formation of pyroclastic material during ascent within the ring fracture and emplacement of the ring-dyke. Flaring of the ring-fracture by the gas-charged pyroclastic material may have occurred as it was explosively emplaced. Limited central subsidence, most likely not exceeding a few hundred metres, also occurred. Although there is no direct evidence preserved, venting of hybrid (mixed-magma) material may have occurred during the emplacement of the ring-dyke, giving rise to a Plinian eruption column.

Arran

The island of Arran in the Firth of Clyde contains the most southerly major intrusive complexes of the Scottish sector of the Province. They were emplaced into Dalradian Supergroup phyllites overlain by various Palaeozoic and Mesozoic sedimentry rocks. There are two main discrete centres of igneous activity: (i) the Northern Granite Centre; and, (ii) the Central Ring Complex. A third centre, the Tighvein Complex, is less well documented (Fig. 14.18).

Northern Granite Centre. This centre has an outcrop diameter of 10–12 km and comprises a coarse-grained Outer

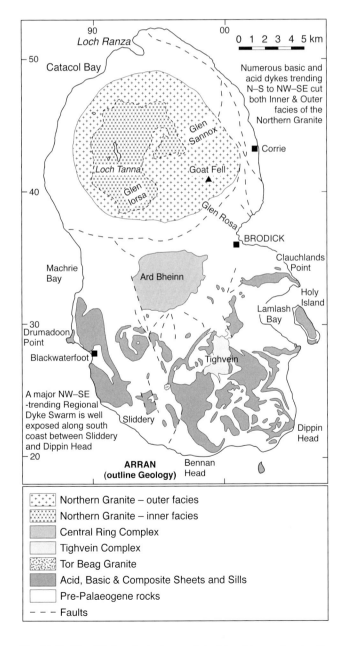

Fig. 14.18. Simplified geological map of the Isle of Arran showing the distribution of Palaeogene igneous formations.

Granite and a fine-grained Inner Granite. Both intrusions are non-porphyritic and biotite-bearing and contain miaolitic cavities (druses). A suite of rare earth element bearing accessory minerals, ferusonite and gadolinite, has been found in some (Hyslop *et al.* 1999). The Outer Granite was emplaced into phyllites of the Dalradian Supergroup, except along the NE and eastern margins, where it is in contact with Ordovician and Lower Old Red Sandstone strata. The thermal aureole created by the granite has a width of several hundreds of metres. Xenolithic marginal facies occur locally, as does veining of the country-rocks by apophyses of the granite. A substantial system of joints, which may be attributed to unloading, characterizes the Outer Granite and gives rise to typical castellated rock exposures, especially in the Goatfell area. Emplacement of the Outer Granite involved the diapiric intrusion of magma into the downward dipping limb of a major synform in the Dalradian country rocks, refolding and upwardly displacing it to produce a marginal (rim) synform (England 1992*b*). The younger, fine-grained Inner Granite crops out in the western part of the Northern Granite Centre, approximately centred on the Loch Tanna area, and has sharp, well defined and generally steeply dipping contacts with the Outer Granite. Suites of basaltic dykes trending either NW–SE or N–S, and numerous thin aplite sheets and veins cut both granites. A late-stage 'crush zone' affects both intrusions, trending approximately north, along the west side of Loch Tanna.

Central Ring Complex. This poorly-exposed, heterogeneous assemblage of rocks located in the centre of the island (Fig. 14.18) includes various shallow-level intrusions of basic, intermediate (hybrid, mixed-magma) and silicic compositions, together with extrusive rocks, interpreted mainly as hydrothermally altered lavas with some tuffs and breccias. At least four separate associations of volcanic rocks are recognized: (1) Ard Bheinn Centre; (2) Binnein na h-Uaimh Centre; (3) Creag Dubh Centre; and, (4) Creag an Fheidh Centre. The overall circular outcrop and structure of the Central Ring Complex suggests these were associated with the development of a now deeply eroded major caldera. The country rocks are of Devonian to Permian age. The NE sector of the Complex cuts across Devonian, Carboniferous and Permian rocks, which were previously domed by the emplacement of the Northern Granite Centre, implying a younger age for the Central Ring Complex.

In the area around Ard Bheinn, andesitic and basaltic lavas crop out and are attributed to several centres of eruption (King 1955). Associated arcuate masses of tuffaceous sandstones and volcaniclastic breccias contain a variety of igneous and sedimentary clasts. Of particular note are several megablocks of Devonian and Permian–Triassic sandstone, Cretaceous chalk and sandstone, Lower Jurassic shale, and Rhaetic (Penarth Group) shale overlying a large mass of Triassic sandstone. Preservation of this material may be attributed to caldera collapse processes and provides clear evidence for the former existence of a Mesozoic cover to the area. The coarse-grained igneous masses are interpreted as parts of ring intrusions, emplaced to shallow levels in the crust.

Tighvein Complex. A further small centre may exist at Tighvein (Fig. 14.18). This poorly exposed complex comprises felsite, microgranite, dolerite and hybrid rocks. Little is known in detail about their form and modes of emplacement.

Ailsa Craig

The Ailsa Craig peralkaline microgranite boss crops out in the Clyde Estuary *c.* 20 km south of Arran. At the present level of erosion it intrudes Triassic sedimentary rocks. It is a distinctive blue-grey rock which is characterized by alkali pyroxenes and amphiboles (Harrison *et al.* 1987). Most recent research has involved its detailed mineralogy (Howie & Walsh 1981; Harding 1983).

Rockall

The peralkaline granite which forms the conical-shaped islet of Rockall is located *c*. 250 km west of the St Kilda Archipelago (Hawkes *et al.* 1975). It stands *c*. 20 m above sea level and has a width of only 30 m. The nearby microgabbro which forms Helen's Reef may be part of the same complex. The granite is intruded by veins and thin sheets of a rock rich in alkali pyroxene and amphibole, referred to as rockallite.

Submerged central complexes

Very little is known about the (offshore) submerged central complexes, which have been identified by their magnetic and gravity profiles and seismic expression (Hitchen & Ritchie 1987; Fyfe *et al.* 1993; Stoker *et al.* 1993; Ritchie & Hitchen 1996). To date, samples of intrusive rocks have not been recovered from any of these submerged complexes, other than the Blackstones Bank Central Complex, SSW of Tiree (Durant *et al.* 1982).

Blackstones Bank. The Blackstones Bank Central Complex crops out on the sea bed and is located *c*. 30 km SSW of Tiree, within the Blackstones Basin (Fig. 14.2). This basin is flanked by the Camasunary–Skerryvore Fault and extensions of the Great Glen Fault (Fig. 14.3). Simple geological maps have been constructed based upon a relatively large number of *in situ* samples (Durant *et al.* 1982; Fyfe *et al.* 1993). These include: gabbro, granite, microgranite and tuffisite, all cut by basaltic sheets and dykes, giving rise to a rugged (sea bed) topography. Retrieved samples suggest that the country rocks to the Complex comprise calc-silicate hornfels thought to be Jurassic in age, and calcareous metasediments and quartzite.

Faeroe–Shetland Basin and Rockall Trough. Several offshore submerged central complexes have been recognized (Ritchie & Hitchen 1996; Mould *et al.* 1996; Ritchie *et al.* 1999). Those in the Faeroe–Shetland Basin are (from north to south): Brendan; Erlend, West Erlend; Suduroy; North Westray/Judd; South Westray; Faeroe Bank; Faeroe Channel Knoll. In the Rockall Trough (approximately from north to south) are: Bill Bailey Bank; Sigmundur; Darwin; Lousy Bank; Rosemary Bank; West George Bligh Bank; East George Bligh Bank; Geikie; Mammal; Swithin; (Rockall); Rockall Bank; Lyonesse; Sandarro; Sandastre; Reschora; Owlsgard; Aramassa; Mentone; Anton Dohrn; Hebrides Terrace.

No wells or boreholes have penetrated these central complexes, although the (overlying) volcanic sequences above Erlend and Darwin have been seismically imaged (Gatliff *et al.* 1984; Abraham & Ritchie 1991) and sampled (Morton *et al.* 1988), together with the Erlend Sill Complex (Ridd 1983; Kanaris-Sotiriou *et al.* 1993). The offshore central complexes are all assumed to be Palaeogene in age. The lithologies involved are presumed to be similar to those observed in the dissected onshore central complexes.

Dyke swarms and plugs

The regional dyke swarms represent batches of magma that have crystallized within the near-vertical fissure conduits, which fed the lava fields and central complex-associated lava shields (Fig. 14.19). They trend NW to NNW and achieve high

intrusion densities in the vicinities of the central complexes, in particular Skye, Mull and along the south coast of Arran. Plugs are considerably less common and have a more random distribution. Individual dykes are composed predominantly of dolerite/basalt, are typically less than 2 m across, and may be simple or multiple, the latter types being more common in the vicinity of the central complexes. Wider dykes are known, for example, one up to 100 m wide on Muck (Emeleus 1997) and, offshore, the Minch Magnetic anomaly is interpreted as the response of a *c*. 1100 m wide dyke (Ofoegbu & Bott 1985). Composite dykes also occur, typically with a central silicic unit (felsite/microgranite/quartz porphyry) flanked by dolerite. Good examples of such composite dykes crop out in west Arran along the Tormore shore section (Kanaris-Sotiriou & Gibb 1985).

The main swarms are: Skye; Rum–Muck; Mull; Jura–Islay; Arran (Speight *et al.* 1982). Where close to central complexes, local crustal dilation/extension, oriented SW–NE, of up to 25% was achieved. In addition to the main swarms, in the vicinities of the Skye, Mull and Rum central complexes, there are NE-trending dykes which may be attributed to subswarms associated with the central complexes. Alternatively, they represent a separate period of crustal dilation oriented NW–SE, parallel to the NE Atlantic margin. Emplacement of the dyke swarms overlapped with the growth of the spatially-associated

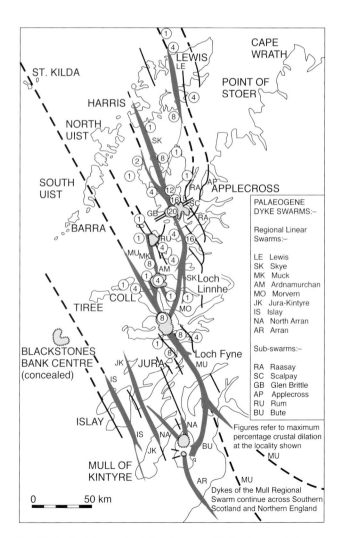

Fig. 14.19. Sketch map depicting the main dilational axes of the regional dyke swarms. Figures refer to maximum percentage dilation at the localities shown (after Speight *et al.* 1982; Ofoegbu & Bott 1985).

central complexes. Furthermore, Walker (1993b) has developed a model which suggests a close link between dyke injection and cone-sheet emplacement within the central complexes.

A structural study of the Mull Regional Swarm by Jolly & Sanderson (1995) has revealed systematic changes in the form, orientation and widening direction of dykes with increasing distance from the Mull Central Complex: the number of dykes declines although individual intrusions are, on average, wider and more widely-spaced. The importance of the dominance of the regional stress field lessens 'down axis' and there is less crustal extension. Close to the central complex, the dykes are irregular and commonly display en echelon features. However, in the farthest parts of the swarm, they are represented by thicker planar sheets, aligned normal to the minimum principal stress field. For example, the Cleveland Dyke is c. 25 m thick in the Durham–North Yorkshire area, approximately 350–400 km from Mull. Such distal dykes appear to have been emplaced with a degree of lateral migration of magma. The complexity and emplacement dynamics of individual dyke intrusions may also be modelled. Platten & Watterson (1987) and Platten (2000) for example, demonstrated that some multiple and zoned dykes of the Skye Regional Swarm were emplaced in a series of sequential fracturing and incremental dilation events over a period of time.

Ultrabasic/picritic dykes (Fig. 14.20) are less common and are typically closely spatially and compositionally associated with the ultrabasic units in the central complexes, for example, the Layered Peridotite Series on Skye and the Layered Suite on Rum. Within the areas of the lava fields where evolved lavas are common, remnant feeder dykes are also evident, for example, trachyte dykes at the head of Loch Harport on Skye, close to the central axis of the Skye Dyke Swarm.

The distribution of the dolerite/basalt dykes within the swarms is also compositionally controlled (Mattey et al. 1977). Close to the axis of a swarm and close to the associated central complex, the dykes are of (tholeiitic) depleted, MORB-like basalt (see below in magmas and magmatic processes), whereas dykes in more peripheral locations are of the alkali olivine basalt type. It is likely that the tholeiitic dykes were emplaced during the same interval as the growth of the central complexes, which have similar magmatic affinities.

Plugs of a variety of compositions occur throughout the Province. Many are of common lava field lithologies and are interpreted as localised feeder systems. Other plugs, for example, the peridotite plugs of Rum, are spatially and genetically associated with the central complexes (Wadsworth 1994; Emeleus 1997). Thermal aureoles around many plugs are insignificant, whereas some have substantial zones of thermal and hydrothermal alteration, for example, 'S Airde Bheinn in north Mull (Bailey et al. 1924), and the remotely located Sithean Sluaigh Plug south of Strachur on Loch Fyne (Smith 1969). Certain plugs are elongate, possibly representing the distended head of a dyke. One excellent example of this is the Cnoc Rhaonastil Plug in south Islay which contains late-stage segregations of nepheline syenite, produced by the extreme in situ fractionation of alkali olivine basalt magma (Hole & Morrison 1992; Preston et al. 1998, 2000a, b).

Sill complexes

Sill complexes are spatially associated with the Skye and Mull lava fields. In north Skye, a substantial complex, the Little Minch Sill Complex (Gibb & Gibson 1989), of picrite-alkali olivine dolerite type, invades Jurassic strata and can be traced offshore to the west and NW. The other major onshore sill complex occurs in SW Mull, the Loch Scridain Sill Complex (Bailey et al. 1924; Preston et al. 1998), of tholeiitic basalt-rhyolite type, invades basement rocks, together with the overlying Mesozoic sedimentary rocks and Palaeogene lava sequence. On Arran, alkaline sills crop out in the Holy Island–Dippin area, whereas in SW Arran there are sills of quartz-feldspar porphyry. The Raasay Sill is related to the Red Hills granites of Skye (e.g. Butler & Hutton 1994) and the Garsbheinn Sill, south of the Cuillin Hills, is related to the Cuillin Centre of the Skye Central Complex (Harker 1904).

West of Shetland, the Faeroe–Shetland Sill Complex comprises a large suite of tholeiitic basalt and dolerite sills with MORB-like compositions that invade Cretaceous and Palaeogene strata in the Faeroe–Shetland Basin (Gibb et al. 1986; Ritchie & Hitchen 1996). Underlying the Erlend basaltic lavas of the Faeroe–Shetland Basin are Cretaceous and Palaeogene sedimentary rocks intruded by rhyolitic and dacitic sills (Kanaris-Sotiriou et al. 1993; Kanaris-Sotiriou 1997). Further south, the Rockall Trough Sill Complex invades strata of similar age, although no detailed geochemical data are available (e.g. Ritchie et al. 1999).

The Little Minch Sill Complex. The Little Minch Sill Complex crops out on the Trotternish (and, to a lesser extent, the Waternish and Duirnish) peninsulas of north Skye, on Raasay, and on the Shiant Isles (Gibson & Jones 1991; Gibb & Henderson 1996). The complex has an aggregate thickness of c. 250 m, with individual leaves 10–100 m thick, dipping at a shallow angle towards the west. Many of the coastal cliffs of the Trotternish Peninsula are formed from these columnar-jointed

Fig. 14.20. Picritic dyke cutting bytownite troctolite ('White Allivalite'), Coir' a' Ghrunnda, SW Cuillin Hills, Isle of Skye.

rocks, for example, the Kilt Rock at Loch Mealt and north of Bornesketaig in west Trotternish (Plate 24). The sills are commonly transgressive, for example, on Ru Meanish at Duntulm, and composite, with interleaved picritic, doleritic and more evolved (crinanitic, i.e. analcime olivine-basalt/dolerite) units with chilled contacts. Buchites (melted inclusions of country rock) are found, for example, on Ru Meanish at Duntulm. Also within the Duntulm and Ascrib Islands sills, are excellent examples of mineral layering, involving textural and modal variations in the constituent olivine, clinopyroxene and plagioclase. Crystal settling does not appear to be the dominant cause of the layering, which is more effectively explained in terms of *in situ* crystallization involving a migrating crystallization front due to heat loss from the roofs and floors of the sills (Gibson & Jones 1991). On the basis that a few sills invade the overlying lavas, it may be inferred that intrusion of the sill complex post-dates the development of at least the oldest part of the Skye Lava Field (Anderson & Dunham 1966).

The Loch Scridain Sill Complex. The Loch Scridain Sill Complex invades Moine basement, Mesozoic sedimentary rocks and the Palaeogene lava sequence of SW Mull, but does not cut the Palaeozoic granitic Ross of Mull Pluton. Individual sheets vary from 0.5 to 10 m thick, commonly with well developed chilled margins. Evidence of localized melting of the country rocks at sill margins is reported by Kille *et al.* (1987). Basic types are dominant and many of the more evolved types (andesite through to rhyolite) are glassy (pitchstones of Bailey *et al.* 1924). Many of the sills are highly xenolithic, with cognate types (peridotite through to gabbro) representing crystal cumulates (Preston & Bell 1997), together with accidental (upper crustal) types (Preston *et al.* 1999; Fig. 14.21). Within the accidental category, in addition to easily recognized types such as quartzite and sandstone, are xenoliths of aluminous buchitic, crustal melt material. These comprise either a lilac-tinted glassy core with needles of mullite (mullite buchite) or a black glassy core with small crystals of cordierite (cordierite buchite), both commonly rimmed with an anorthositic shell. At the junction between the buchite core and the anorthosite rim are crystals of sapphire and/or aluminous spinel. Trapped within the plagioclase crystals of the anorthosite shell are quenched pockets of basalt melt.

The origin of the buchites requires some form of melting of an aluminous protolith. Preston *et al.* (1999) concluded that their origin involved the two-stage melting of pelitic layers within the Moine basement. The first melt was of rhyolitic composition, represented by the evolved sills of the complex, whereas a second stage of melting produced the more aluminous liquids represented by the buchites. The mullite and cordierite crystals are the residual phases after complicated incongruent melting reactions involving muscovite and biotite, respectively. The anorthositic rim was produced by reaction between the aluminous (buchitic) liquid and the basaltic sill magma(s), resulting in excess plagioclase precipitation (Dempster *et al.* 1999).

Holy Island and Dippin sills, Arran. On Holy Island, off the coast of SE Arran (Fig. 14.18), a *c.* 250 m thick sill of peralkaline sanidine-microporphyritic trachyte is emplaced into Permian sandstones. Similar sills crop out around Lamlash Bay. Also in SE Arran is the Dippin Sill, a *c.* 40 m thick composite intrusion with a central thick, analcime-bearing olivine dolerite unit flanked by analcime dolerite units. It intrudes Triassic strata and displays pronounced hydrothermal alteration (Dickin *et al.* 1984). A flow differentiation model has been applied to explain its genesis (Gibb & Henderson 1978), involving the initial intrusion of evolved liquids from the upper part of

Fig. 14.21. Loch Scridain Sill, with large plagioclase-mantled mullite buchite (xenolith), at Killunaig on the north shore of Loch Scridain, Ross of Mull, SW Mull.

the feeder chamber to provide the marginal intrusions, followed by the injection of less-evolved porphyritic magma to give the central unit. Flow differentiation occurred during intrusion, with late-stage filter pressing to yield pegmatitic segregations.

Quartz-feldspar porphyry sills of Arran, and the Raasay Sill. The Arran and Raasay sills are most usefully considered within the context of the nearby, associated intrusive complexes of the Northern Granite Centre on Arran and the Red Hills centres of the Skye Central Complex, respectively. Dykes of similar composition occur in close spatial association. The SW Arran sills are several tens of metres thick and form conspicuous crags such as at Brown Head and Bennan Head. In SE Arran there are similarly thick composite sills with dominant central quartz-feldspar porphyry units flanked by thin basaltic units. The contacts between the silicic and basic lithologies are either gradational or comprise pillows of the basic material within the silicic material and indicate an origin by sequential intrusion of the two contrasting magmas and their intimate interaction. The silicic portions of many of these sills are glassy (pitchstone), for example at Drumadoon. Similar intrusions occur within the Mull Central Complex and around the periphery of the Eastern Red Hills Centre of the Skye Central Complex, including the classic intrusion of Rubh' an Eireannaich (Bell & Pankhurst 1993).

The granitic Raasay Sill, *c.* 30 m thick, was emplaced transgressively into Triassic and Lower Jurassic sedimentary rocks. (Butler & Hutton 1994). Its riebeckite-bearing alkaline composition suggests a possible link with the Maol na Gainmhich Granite of the Western Red Hills Centre on Skye. A similar granite crops out on Scalpay, south of Raasay.

The Gars-bheinn Ultrabasic Sill, Skye. On the south side of the summit of Gars-bheinn, intruded into hornfelsed lavas adjacent to the Cuillin Centre, the Gars-bheinn Ultrabasic Sill is composed of feldspathic peridotite, the uppermost *c.* 15 m of which displays conspicuous horizontal olivine- and plagioclase-rich layers. At the base of the intrusion is an apparently connected feeder dyke of similar composition. The origin of the layering has variously been attributed to crystal settling (Weedon 1960) and the injections of 'feldspathic fluid sills' into already-crystallised peridotite (Bevan & Hutchison 1984).

Faeroe–Shetland Sill Complex. The Faeroe–Shetland Sill Complex comprises a large number of leaves which invade Cretaceous and Palaeogene sedimentary rocks over an area of *c.* 750 km by *c.* 100 km within the Faeroe–Shetland Basin, and extending north into the More Basin and south to the Wyville-Thomson Ridge (Stoker *et al.* 1993) (Fig. 14.2). The extent of the complex to the NW is poorly constrained due to the seismically opaque Faeroes Lava Group, although at least three significant sills crop out on the Faeroe Islands, suggesting an Early Eocene age. Isotopic age data suggest older ages but are of variable quality (e.g. Ritchie *et al.* 1999). The sills are of tholeiitic basalt and dolerite of MORB affinity (Gibb *et al.* 1986; Gibb & Kanaris-Sotiriou 1988).

Erlend Sill Complex. The Erlend Sill Complex, sometimes referred to as the Acidic Suite, comprises silicic (glassy and crystalline rhyolite and dacite) sheets interlayered with claystones and siltstones (Ridd 1983; Kanaris-Sotiriou *et al.* 1993; Kanaris-Sotiriou 1997). Ridd (1983) described peperitic textures from these strata and suggested an extrusive volcanic origin. However, thermal alteration of pollen and spores from the interbedded Cretaceous and Palaeocene strata and diachronous relationships between the sills and their host strata, as seen in wells 209/3-1, 209/4-1A and 209/9-1, suggest that the sheets are more likely to be intrusions.

Rockall Trough Sill Complex. This suite of sills occurs within Palaeogene and Cretaceous strata within the northern part of the Rockall Trough, from the Wyville-Thompson Ridge,

south, into the Southern Rockall Trough (e.g. Ritchie *et al.* 1999). Its age is most likely Late Palaeocene to earliest Eocene.

Magmas and magmatic processes

The volcanic and subvolcanic rocks of the Hebridean Province have, over the last century, acted as a testing ground for virtually all models and theories of magmatic processes. In early landmark studies Harker (1904) identified fractionation trends within the Skye Lava Field and magma mixing/interaction and crystal fractionation processes within the intrusive rocks of the Skye Central Complex, and Bailey *et al.* (1924) recognized and developed the concepts of magma-types and magma series. Many more recent investigations have attempted to quantify a wide range of magmatic processes. Here, it is only possible to summarize some of the important historial developments and current state of knowledge; see reviews by Thompson (1982), Saunders *et al.* (1997) and Emeleus & Bell (2003) for more detail.

The important concepts of magma-types and magma series were developed by Bailey *et al.* (1924) from their study of the Mull Lava Field and the Mull Central Complex. Within the Normal Mull Magma Series are the Plateau Magma-Type, the Non-Porphyritic Magma-Type, the Intermediate to Sub-Acid Magma-Type and the Acid Magma-Type. The Plateau Magma-Type, of alkali olivine basalt affinity, was attributed a parental status relative to the derivative status (by fractional crystallization) of the others. Bailey *et al.* (1924) identified the problem of such a silica-undersaturated magma producing the rhyolitic rocks of the Acid Magma-Type and invoked that the assimilation of sialic crust must have been involved. Bowen (1928) essentially agreed with this model but proposed that efficient removal of early-precipitated olivine was the dominant process. Kennedy (1930) suggested a totally opposing model, whereby the Non-Porphyritic Magma-Type, of tholeiitic basalt affinity, was parental to the (therefore derivative) Plateau Magma-Type. Kennedy (1933) revised his ideas and suggested that both

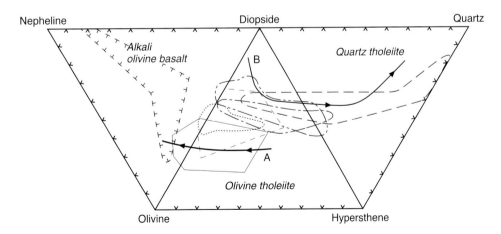

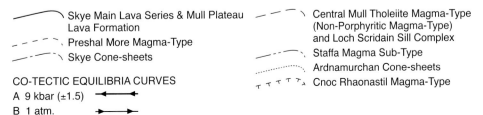

Fig. 14.22. Normative CIPW plot showing the compositional fields of Hebridean Palaeogene magma-types and 1 atmosphere and 9 kbar (anhydrous) cotectic curves for the equilibria: olivine + plagioclase + clinpyroxene + natural basic/basaltic liquids (after Thompson 1982). See main text for discussion and references.

magma-types, renamed olivine basalt (later alkali olivine basalt of Tilley (1950) and nepheline-normative) and tholeiitic basalt (hypersthene-normative) were of parental status. From the experimental studies of Yoder & Tilley (1962) it was evident that under low-pressure conditions, one type could not yield the other type by fractionation.

The current phase of geochemical studies of magmatic processes within the Province commenced with the classic investigation of the major-element compositions of Skye lavas by Thompson *et al.* (1972). This study demonstrated that although the Skye lavas, which they assigned to a Skye Main Lava Series (SMLS), were petrographically of alkali olivine basalt type, in detail they varied from nepheline- to hypersthene-normative in composition. Nepheline-normative flows have a typical alkali olivine basalt major-element composition, but with many of the minor- and trace-element concentrations more typical of tholeiitic basalt. The fractionation trend of the SMLS can be successfully depicted on a modified 'Basalt Tetrahedron' (from Yoder & Tilley 1962), which clearly illustrates how the least evolved members straddle the thermal barrier defined by the 'Critical Plane of Silica Undersaturation'. This operates at pressures less than 8 kbar (0.8 GPa, *c.* 30 km depth) (Fig. 14.22). These observations indicate that the major-element compositions of the SMLS were imparted at depth, where the thermal barrier does not operate. Experimental studies (Thompson 1974) indicate that the most primitive compositions developed at pressures of up to 17 kbar. Relatively fast eruption rates are implied, with no re-equilibration during ascent having occurred.

Two evolutionary trends then developed: (i) alkali olivine basalt–hawaiite–mugearite–benmoreite; and, (ii) alkali olivine basalt–Si-rich and Fe-poor intermediates–trachyte (Fig. 14.23). The Benmoreite Trend developed deep within the crust under high pressures, whereas the Trachyte Trend is the result of low pressure fractionation. The major-element signatures of flows of the Skye Lava Field also occur within the Mull lavas: the Mull Plateau Lava Formation (MPLF) (former Mull Plateau Group, MPG; Beckinsale *et al.* 1978; Morrison *et al.* 1980; Kerr 1995a; Kerr *et al.* 1999) and a similar model is implied.

The tholeiitic basalt flows of the Staffa Lava Formation of the Mull Lava Field have a complex origin, involving fractional crystallization and significant crustal contamination of transitional magmas of the MPLG (Thompson *et al.* 1986; Kerr 1998). The distinctive Preshal More lava flows at the top of the preserved sequence on Skye, together with dykes from the axial portion of the Skye Swarm (Esson *et al.* 1975; Mattey *et al.* 1977) and cone-sheets of the Cuillin Centre (Bell *et al.* 1994), differ from the Mull tholeiitic basalts, and have distinctive high Ca, and low K, Ti and P compositions, akin to Mid Ocean Ridge-type basalts (MORB).

The primary nature of the basic magmas was imparted by variable degrees of partial melting of an heterogeneous mantle.

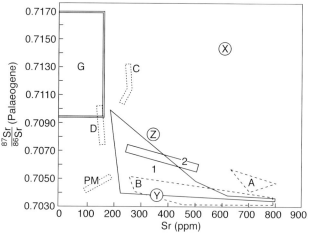

Fig. 14.24. $(^{87}Sr/^{87}Sr)_{Palaeogene}$ against total Sr for basaltic rocks, granites and crustal materials. Depicted fields are: G, Skye, Mull and Arran granites; 1, Mull Plateau Lava formation; 2, Central Mull Tholeiite Magma-type (or Non-Porphyritic Magma-type); A, SMLS Trachyte Trend; B, SMLS Benmoreite Trend; C, Ferrodiorite unit of the Marsco Hybrids, Western Red Hills Centre, Skye; D, Basic units of the Rubh' an Eireannaich Composite Sill, Eastern Red Hills Centre, Skye; PM Preshal More Magma-type; X, 'Average' amphibolite-facies Lewisian gneiss; Y, 'Average' granulite-facies Lewisian gneiss; Z, 'Granitic' granulite-facies Lewisian gneiss. See main text for discussion and references.

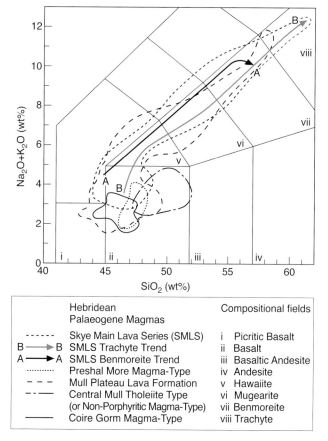

Fig. 14.23. Plot of total alkalis ($Na_2O + K_2O$) against silica (SiO_2) illustrating Hebridean Palaeogene magma-types and trends superimposed upon the compositional fields of alkali & tholeiitic basalts and their related differentiates. See main text for discussion and references.

The SMLS and MPLF, together with the Little Minch Sill Complex (Gibson 1990) and non-axial dykes of the main swarms (Mattey *et al.* 1977), were derived from a Ca-poor basalt. The tholeiitic basalt magmas (i.e. Non-Porphyritic Magma-Type) are richer in Si and Ca, but poorer in Fe, Ti and P. However, given that there is significant compositional overlap between the two magma-types, it is important to note that the distinction between them can only be made for the least evolved compositions.

Contamination mechanisms and their geochemical signatures

Interaction between mantle-derived magmas and continental crust causes detectable modifications of the trace-element and isotope geochemistry (Sr, Nd and Pb) of the magmas. Contamination is possible due to the exothermic nature of (fractional) crystallization, leading to the partial melting of wall-rocks. The timing of contamination can be assessed: before, during or after fractional crystallization. Of particular interest, assimilation during fractional crystallization (AFC) can be recognized by certain geochemical correlations. Within the Hebridean area, the likely crustal contaminants are lower crustal (granulite-facies) Lewisian gneiss, upper crustal (amphibolite-facies) Lewisian gneiss, Moine pelites and psammites, Dalradian pelites, and Torridonian arkoses and shales.

The Sr-isotope signatures of the SMLS indicate different histories for the Benmoreite and Trachyte trends (Moorbath & Thompson 1980; Figs 14.23 & 14.24). Within the former, fractional crystallization in granulite-facies lower crust has left the mantle signature unmodified, whereas in the latter contamination by (radiogenic) amphibolite-facies upper crust occurred. Taking Nd-isotope data and trace-element concentrations into account, it is evident that the SMLS magmas underwent fractional crystallization near to the base of the crust (Thirlwall & Jones 1983; Dickin *et al.* 1987). By combining Sr- and Nd-isotope data it is possible to show contamination trends and the fields occupied by particular contaminants (Fig. 14.25). Similarly, Pb-isotope data can be used to identifiy lower and upper crustal contaminants and the available data suggest that in most instances almost complete equilibration between magma and crust took place, possibly by some sort of vapour transfer mechanism and involving the dominant intermediate composition crustal rocks (Dickin 1981; Fig. 14.26).

Magmas of the SMLS and the MPLF which show significant amounts of contamination, based upon their relatively high values of $(^{87}Sr/^{86}Sr)_{Palaeocene}$, have relatively higher concentrations of Ba, Rb, Sr, Th and the light rare-earth-elements (LREE), introduced during the incorporation of crustal melts produced by wall-rock melting (Thompson *et al.* 1982). The most contaminated lavas have the most primitive compositions because they had the highest temperatures (Kerr *et al.* 1999). Contamination of the Preshal More basalts (or magma-type) differs for that of the SMLS and the MPLF and was of the AFC type, involving upper crustal amphibolite-facies Lewisian gneiss or Moine psammites and pelites. A similar contamination story has been deduced for the various intrusive units of

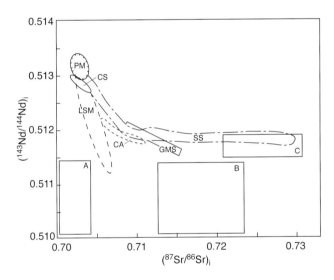

Fig. 14.25. $(^{87}Sr/^{87}Sr)_{Palaeogene}$ against $(^{143}Nd/^{144}Nd)_{Palaeogene}$ for Hebridean basaltic rocks and crustal materials. Depicted compositional fields are: LSM, SMLS and Mull Plateau Lava formation; PM; Preshal More Magma-type; CS, Skye cone-sheets; CA, Ardnamurchan cone-sheets; GMS, Mull and Skye granites; SS, Loch Scridain Sill Complex magmas; A, 'Average' granulate-facies Lewisian gneiss; B, 'Average' amphibolite-facies Lewisian gneiss; C, 'Average' Moine schist. Sr and Nd isotopes corrected for 55 Ma. See main text for discussion and references.

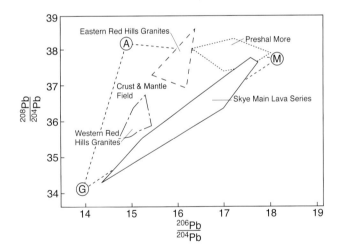

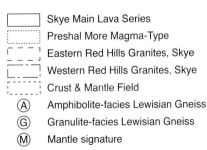

Fig. 14.26. Plot of Pb isotopes for Skye lavas and granites compared to compositions of crustal and mantle mixing components involved in their formation (after Dickin *et al.* 1987). M, Estimated 'average' composition of mantle-derived magmas for Skye at 60 Ma; G, 'Average' granulite-facies Lewisian gneiss; A, 'Average' amphibolite-facies Lewisian gneiss.

the Cuillin Centre (Dickin *et al.* 1984; Bell *et al.* 1994). The tholeiitic basalt Staffa Magma-Type flows close to the base of the lava sequence in SW Mull have different trace-element characteristics from the Preshal More flows. Contrasting opinions exist as to the origins of these isotopically contaminated flows. One model involves picritic melts which underwent fractional crystallization at the Moho, followed by contamination involving partial melting of fusible quartzo-feldspathic lithologies in granulite-facies gneisses, then AFC type contamination involving Moine psammites and pelites in the upper crust (Thompson *et al.* 1986). Kerr (1999) offered a different model, involving SMLS/MPLF type magma, which underwent crustal contamination.

Primary compositions of mantle-derived magmas and depths of generation

Experimental and trace-element studies of the SMLS magmas indicate an origin by partial melting of a garnet lherzolite at a depth of *c.* 60 km (Thompson 1974; Thompson *et al.* 1980). The Preshal More basalt (magma-type) was subsequently generated by a greater degree of melting of the residuum. The remaining (unmelted) mantle was of harzburgitic composition. A similar model may be applied to the Mull lavas (Thompson 1982; Emeleus & Bell 2003). For the Mull lavas, Kerr *et al.* (1999) suggested a model involving three groups (or magma series), each achieving their composition by differing depths of melting, with time. First, deep melting of garnet lherzolite produced the MPLF magmas, giving way to shallower melting of garnet-poor lherzolite to yield the Coire Gorm and Central Mull Tholeiite magma-types (the latter a re-named Non-Porphyritic Central Magma-Type). Involved in this model are variable amounts of fractional crystallization and contamination by a range of crustal materials.

Scarrow & Cox (1995) re-examined the geochemistry of the Skye lavas and advocated a model involving decompressive melting of abnormally hot mantle to yield picritic magmas, which then evolved by fractionation of olivine and chrome-spinel. Final melt segregation (i.e. equilibration) from the mantle took place within the depth range *c.* 60–110 km (at temperatures in the range 1390–1510 °C). The melts which separated at the greatest depth were nepheline-normative, whereas the shallower melts were hypersthene-normative. This model is in broad agreement with that advocated by Thompson *et al.* (1972) and Thompson (1974).

In order to explain the overall relatively low concentrations of incompatible trace-elements within the Palaeogene lavas of NW Scotland, Morrison *et al.* (1980) and Thompson (1982) suggested that prior extraction of highly alkaline (lamprophyric) melts during the Permian resulted in a depleted mantle which then yielded up the various magmas in the Palaeogene. Lateral mantle heterogeneity may also have been (at least partially) responsible for the depleted geochemical characteristics, although this is very difficult to model, given that crustal contamination processes were also involved in producing the final geochemical signatures of the lavas (Morrison *et al.* 1980).

Ultrabasic and basic magmas of the central complexes

Evidence for parental magma compositions to ultrabasic and basic units of the central complexes may be deduced from uncontaminated chilled margins where no fractionation events have occurred. Alternatively, spatially and genetically associated suites of minor intrusions may provide insights to magma compositions. Among the latter, the suites of cone-sheets associated with the Cuillin Centre of the Skye Central Complex (Bell *et al.* 1994), the Ardnamurchan Central Complex (Geld-

macher *et al.* 1998) and the Mull Central Complex (Kerr *et al.* 1999), are of the MORB-like Preshal More Magma-Type (akin to the Central Mull Tholeiite Magma-Type; cf. Kerr *et al.* 1999). Fractionation of these centrally emplaced magmas appears to have taken place at relatively shallow depths (*c.* 10 km, 3 kbar). Chilled margins to gabbroic intrusions are of similar composition, for example, the Ben Buie Gabbro, Mull (Skelhorn *et al.* 1979).

The parental magmas to the various bodies of ultrabasic rock were of a somewhat more primitive composition. The layered peridotites of the Eastern Layered Intrusion on Rum had a parental picritic magma with 15–20 wt% MgO (Greenwood *et al.* 1990; Volker & Upton 1990), whereas the troctolitic and gabbroic units formed from a basaltic melt with *c.* 10 wt% MgO. Alkaline affinities are suggested for the Rum magmas on the basis of late-stage segregation veins of teschenitic composition (Kitchen 1985).

Minor intrusions

Dykes, sills and plugs all provide geochemical data concerning magma-types and magmatic processes involved in their formation. In particular, they provide unique evidence of high-level, *in situ* processes which are inferred to have been involved in the geochemical evolution of the lavas, but for which no obvious 'visual' evidence is retained. For example, they reveal the presence of crustal xenoliths and the significance of contamination processes; and, the accumulation of crystal rich-zones in dykes and sills and flow differentiation.

Dyke swarms. Within the Skye Dyke Swarm, *c.* 70% of the intrusions are of the Preshal More Magma-Type and are most abundant within the axis of the swarm and close to the Cuillin Centre (Mattey *et al.* 1977). Such dykes appear to be genetically related to the suite of cone-sheets which are dominant within the NW and SE quadrants of the Cuillin Centre. Walker (1993*b*) suggested that the dykes were emplaced, downrift, during periods of relatively rapid crustal extension, whereas the cone-sheets were emplaced during intervals of slower extension. The xenolithic, plagioclase-megacrystic gabbro-anorthosite dykes of north Skye also appear to have been formed from the Preshal More Magma-Type and show abundant evidence of flow differentiation and the incorporation of cognate xenoliths (Donaldson 1977). The remaining dykes are dominated by compositions belonging to the SMLS Magma-Type, although dykes with a 'hybrid' composition are also noted, the Fairy Bridge Magma-Type, with a major-element signature akin to the SMLS Magma-Type but trace-element characteristics of the Preshal More Magma-Type (Mattey *et al.* 1977). Dykes with SMLS affinities and with evolved compositions, for example, trachytes, tend to occur only in the vicinity of remnants of the lava fields which contain abundant evolved flows and are, in general, close to the central complexes.

Within the Mull Dyke Swarm, members of the MPLF and the Central Mull Tholeiite magma-types are represented (Kerr *et al.* 1999). The distal members of the Mull Swarm in NE England, for example, the Cleveland Dyke, belong to the Central Mull Tholeiite Magma-Type (Macdonald *et al.* 1988) and have Sr-isotope signatures indicating significant crustal contamination, predominantly by Moine metasedimentary material (Moorbath & Thompson 1980).

The sapphire-bearing xenolithic monchiquite dyke of Loch Roag, Harris, has high concentrations of Ba and the light rare-earth-elements (Menzies *et al.* 1989), unlike all other dykes within the Hebridean Province. However, an isotopic age of *c.* 47 Ma implies a Palaeogene affinity, even though the chemistry of the dyke is more akin to Permo-Carboniferous lamprophyres, common throughout NW Scotland (Upton *et al.* 1998).

The Cnoc Rhaonastil Boss, South Islay. This relatively small doleritic boss or stock contains dominant alkali olivine dolerite and analcime dolerite facies of SMLS/MPLF association/ magma-type. However, rare segregations or pods of coarse-grained nepheline syenite attest to extemely efficient closed-system fractionation, most likely involving some form of filter pressing (Hole & Morrison 1992). Such evolved compositions are very uncommon, only approached elsewhere by facies within the Shiant Isles Sill of the Little Minch Sill Complex (see below). Minerals with high concentrations of trace-elements within the syenites are documented by Preston *et al.* (1998, 2000*a, b*).

Sill complexes. The two significant onshore sill complexes outlined above are of contrasting compositional affinities: (i) the Little Minch Sill Complex, of SMLS/MPLF Magma-Type (alkali olivine basalt); (ii) the Loch Scridain Sill Complex, of Preshal More Magma-Type (tholeiitic basalt).

The Little Minch Sill Complex comprises leaves which range in composition between picrite, through alkali olivine dolerite, to crinanite and rare syenite (Gibson 1990; Gibb & Henderson 1996). The alkaline affinities of the sills are similar to the SMLS/MPLF magmas. However, Sr- and Nd-isotope data indicate that AFC processes have taken place, involving up to 20% of amphibolite-facies Lewisian gneiss (Gibson 1990).

The xenolithic Loch Scridain Sill Complex comprises three distinct groups: Group 1, tholeiitic basalts and andesites, mainly aphyric and with Preshal More Magma-Type affinities; Group 2, plagioclase- and pyroxene-phyric andesites and dacites; and, Group 3, rhyolites (Preston *et al.* 1997, 1999). The geochemical trend from Group 1 through 2 to 3, is one of increasing concentrations of incompatible trace-elements and elevated values of radiogenic Sr and Pb, interpreted as an AFC process involving a high Nd partial melt of Moine metasedimentary material, but not wholesale assimilation of pelite. The Group 3 rhyolites represent partial melts of Moine pelite, whereas the Group 2 andesites and dacites formed by bulk mixing of Group 1 basalt magma and Group 3 rhyolite magma.

The xenoliths within the Loch Scridain sills are of two types: cognate, mainly of gabbroic and peridotitic material representing cumulate assemblages (Preston & Bell 1997) and accidental crustal types (Preston *et al.* 1999). Within the latter category, certain of the xenoliths have behaved in a relatively refractory manner, for example, Moine quartzites. The unusual mullite- and cordierite-bearing aluminous buchites, however, are the result of melting of crustal materials. A two-stage process is recognized by Preston *et al.* (1999), involving a first stage which yields a rhyolitic melt, now represented by the Group 3 rhyolite sills, and a second stage bulk melting of the residual, more aluminous pelites. Reaction between these aluminous melts and the hot basaltic sill magmas resulted in abundant crystallization of plagioclase around the buchite rims, producing anorthosite mantles (Preston *et al.* 1999; Dempster *et al.* 1999). Essentially within these xenolithic sills we are seeing evidence of a contamination process 'frozen in', which more typically is deduced from elevated radiogenic isotope signatures in, for example, xenolith-free lavas.

Silicic rocks

Rocks of silicic composition occur predominantly within the central complexes, as ring intrusions, bosses and stocks, and

range in composition between monzogranite and peralkaline granite. More rarely, dykes, sills, lavas and pyroclastic deposits cover a similar compositional range. The most controversial aspect of these silicic rocks is their origin: are they the products of extreme fractional crystallization of basic magma, and, if so, which type of magma?; or, are they the consequence of partial melting of crust by the voluminous basic and ultrabasic magmas as they migrated through the crust? Most likely, both mechanisms will have occurred in tandem and in examining the geochemistry of the silicic rocks attempts should be made to distinguish examples where one or other process has been dominant. Useful reviews are provided by Bell (1976), Gass & Thorpe (1976), Thompson (1982) and Emeleus & Bell (2003).

Early ideas on the genesis of the granites were dominated by fractional crystallization (e.g. Harker 1904, 1908; Bailey *et al.* 1924; Richey *et al.* 1946). Following this, the pendulum swung towards favouring partial melting processes (e.g. Wager 1956; Wager *et al.* 1953, 1965; Brown 1963; Dunham 1968; Thompson 1969). With the development of rapid geochemical analysis, including isotope spectrometry, significant progress was made in trying to recognize how the two contrasting processes could be distinguished through the compositions of the magmas/ rocks produced. Early isotope studies include Moorbath & Bell (1965) and Moorbath & Welke (1969), who considered the whole-rock Sr- and Pb-isotopes of various volcanic and intrusive rocks from Skye. The Sr data suggested a partial melting model, whereas the Pb data inferred a mixed model, involving mantle and crustal lead. Subsequent studies have confirmed that mantle and crustal isotopic components are present in all of the igneous units of the Province: although mantle- and crust-dominated examples are recognized (Walsh *et al.* 1979; Moorbath & Thompson 1980; Dickin 1981; Dickin *et al.* 1984; Figs. 14.24, 14.25 & 14.26). The crustal component comes from the same sources recognized for the lavas: lower and upper crustal Lewisian gneiss (granulite- and amphibolite-facies, respectively), Moine metasedimentary rocks (pelites and psammites), Dalradian pelites, and Torridonian arkoses and shales. Interpretation is hampered by the hydrothermal alteration processes associated with the development of meteoric water circulation systems during and after emplacement, and which had the potential to cause modifications to rock chemistry (Taylor & Forester 1971; Forester & Taylor 1977; Ferry 1985*a, b*). Careful sampling appears to have minimized this potentially serious problem.

Three compositional groups are recognized by Thompson (1982) for Palaeogene granitic rocks throughout the British Tertiary Volcanic Province, on the basis of mineralogy (hence major-elements), trace-elements and isotope geochemistry. Thompson (1981) concluded that granites within the primitive and peralkaline categories are the product of simple crystal-liquid fractionation, involving quartz, plagioclase, alkali feldspar, Fe–Ti oxides and apatite. From a study of the whole-rock rare-earth-element signatures of Skye granites, Thorpe *et al.* (1977) and Thorpe (1978) identified the similarity between the REE profiles of lavas of the SMLS/MPLF Magma-Type and the granites and suggested a link through fractional crystallization (Fig. 14.27). Thompson (1982) demonstrated, however, that a similar match could be made by mixing *c.* 80% of un-contaminated Preshal More basalt magma with *c.* 10% each of granulite- and amphibolite-facies gneiss to yield a contaminated liquid which, after fractional crystallization, would give granitic liquids. It is therefore possible that both basaltic magma-types were capable of producing granitic liquids.

The peraluminous granites can be produced by melting granodioritic to tonalitic Lewisian gneiss or Torridonian arkose and shale at low pressures (1 kbar H_2O pressure) at temperatures above 715°C (Thompson 1981). Such lithologies bulk melt

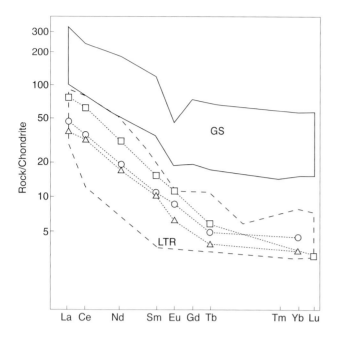

Fig. 14.27. Chondrite-normalised Rare-earth-element (REE) abundance data for Skye granites compared to Lewisian and Torridonian crustal formations from Skye and Rhum (after Thorpe *et al.* 1977). Depicted compositional field and symbols are: GS, Skye granites; LTR, Rum Lewisian and Torridonian rocks; □, Lewisian gneiss (Eastern Red Hills, Skye); ○, △, Typical Torridonian arkoses from close to the Skye Central Complex.

at temperatures above 930°C, similar to the liquidus temperatures of Hebridean granites (Thompson 1983). If a bulk melting model were appropriate, then there would be the expectation that a typical granodioritic or tonalitic gneiss would have the same trace-element signature as a peraluminous granite. This is not the case and, therefore, such a model cannot be correct.

Dickin (1981) concluded from his analysis of radiogenic isotope data for Skye granites that the dominant (but not the only) crustal component is amphibolite-facies gneiss (Figs 14.25 & 14.26), i.e. the same contaminant identified for the Preshal More magmas (see above). Contamination appears to have been selective, with the initial breakdown of certain accessory minerals within granulite-facies gneiss but without significant partial melting of the gneiss. Subsequently, these contaminated Preshal More magmas underwent AFC within amphibolite-facies gneiss in the upper crust. Here, partial melting did occur and these melts mixed with the silicic liquids generated by the fractionation of the contaminated Preshal More basaltic magma. Thus, a hybrid origin for Skye granites is advocated.

An example of a granitic intrusion containing at least a proportion of partial melt of Torridonian sedimentary rock is the Coire Uaigneich Granite of the Cuillin Centre on Skye (Wager *et al.* 1953; Brown 1963). Dickin & Exley (1981) demonstrated a hybrid origin for this granite, involving the combination of a partial melt of arkose and shale and liquids produced by fractional crystallization of Cuillin-type (i.e. Preshal More) basic magma. The presence of zircons of Torridonian type (detrital) within the granite emphasizes the link with partial melting processes (Exley 1980).

The origin of the granites within the Mull Central Complex is discussed by Kerr *et al.* (1999). Two groups of granites are recognized by Walsh *et al.* (1979): 'early granites' belonging to Centre 1, and 'late granites' belonging to centres 2 and 3. Kerr *et al.* (1999) concluded that the two types can be distinguished on a variety of geochemical plots. All the granites have hybrid origins, involving fractional crystallization combined with crustal input. The amount of crust appears to be greatest in the oldest granites and the youngest granites have the most evolved compositions.

The granites of the Northern Granite Centre on Arran are the product of fractional crystallization of basaltic liquids, but also contain a crustal contribution from the basement (late Proterozoic) Dalradian metasedimentary rocks (Dickin *et al.* 1981; Meighan *et al.* 1992). To the south, the peralkaline Ailsa Craig Granite contains virtually no crustal component (Harrison *et al.* 1987).

Magma mixing processes

Magma mixing was an important magmatic process throughout the Hebridean Province, particularly within the intrusive environment. Classic examples of intrusions involving contrasting basic and silicic magmas include the composite dykes and sills associated with the Skye, Mull, Ardnamurchan and Arran central complexes, and hybrid ring-dykes such as Marsco, Loch Ba and Glen More. Mixing appears to have taken place prior to and during emplacement: within the basic units xenocrystic quartz and alkali feldspar are preserved, whereas in the silicic units clots of basic material are common. The basic magmas involved tend to be somewhat evolved, within the compositional range ferrobasalt through to ferroandesite, with low Ti/P values (Bell 1983; Marshall & Sparks 1984; Sparks 1988; Bell & Pankhurst 1993).

Within the classic composite sill at Rubh' an Eireannaich in the Eastern Red Hills district on Skye, there are completely gradational contacts between the marginal basic units and the central silicic unit (Harker 1904). Trace-element and Sr-isotope data indicate that the basic magma has a composition consistent with *c.* 50% fractional crystallization of a tholeiitic basalt magma contaminated with crust (Bell & Pankhurst 1993). Mixing at the interface between the contrasting magmas has lead to a compositionally gradational zone over a distance of *c.* 30 cm.

Within the ring-dykes of the central complexes, more thorough mixing has occurred, although each intrusion displays certain unique characteristics. Analysis of the compositions of the rocks, however, points to similar liquids being involved. The Loch Ba Ring-dyke of Centre 3, Mull, comprises a dominant felsite-rhyolite-welded tuff, with up to 10 vol% of dark glassy inclusions ranging in composition from ferrobasalt throught to rhyolite, with tholeiitic ferroandesite particularly common (Sparks 1988). Within the dominant silicic material are phenocrysts of quartz, sanidine and other minerals, all of which are present as xenocrysts within the inclusions. Similarly, within the Marsco Hybrids of the Western Red Hills Centre, Skye, the basic unit, ferrodiorite, carries xenocrysts of quartz and is therefore of hybrid character. Within the silicic unit, a porphyritic felsite, the quartz occurs as phenocrysts. Simple bulk mixing calculations suggest that the hybrid rock found in close association with the basic and silicic units, referred to as marscoite by Harker (1904), was produced by the mixing of two parts ferrodiorite (i.e. ferroandesite) magma with one part porphyritic felsite magma (Wager *et al.* 1965; Bell 1983). Further north, on Glamaig, another part of the ring-dyke contains the less homogeneous hybrid, glamaigite, comprising small basic inclusions within a pale (more silicic) matrix. Such heterogeneous materials would be, even at moderate temperatures, homogenized by diffusion in less than two years, or less than one year at magmatic temperatures (Thompson 1980). Thus, the preservation of such textures implies very rapid quenching after mixing. Also within the Western Red Hills Centre, the Glamaig Granite carries abundant small xenoliths of basaltic material and clots of mafic minerals. Thompson (1980) interpreted these as evidence for the mixing of basaltic magma into a dominant granitic magma body. The basaltic material has the characteristic evolved Ti/P signature typical of tholeiitic andesite.

In order to explain the genesis of these hybrid intrusions, and others throughout the Province such as the Glen More Ring-dyke on Mull and the classic net-veined complexes in Centre 2, Ardnamurchan and in the St Kilda Central Complex, it is necessary to infer compositionally zoned magma bodies or chambers at depth (Thompson 1980; Bell 1983; Marshall & Sparks 1984; Sparks 1988; Preston 2001). The roof zone of such chambers will be dominated by a cap of low density rhyolitic magma. Below this, will be a strongly zoned more basic body of magma, zoned downwards from rhyolite through dacite to ferrobasalt. The compositional range of the glassy inclusions within the Loch Ba Ring-dyke is particularly compelling evidence for the zoned nature of such an underlying basic magma body (Sparks 1988). Mixing along the interface between the rhyolite magma cap and the underlying zoned body of magma will cause the initial stage of hybridization recognized by the presence of xenocrysts in the essentially unmixed basic and silicic units preserved within the intrusions.

Emplacement of these ring-dykes and the final disposition of the remnant parental basic and silicic magmas and the newly formed hybrid materials caused by their mixing, will depend upon the dynamic processes which occur within the ring fractures as the central blocks subside and the magmas mix and are forced upwards. Sustained high temperatures will lead to thorough mixing and homogenization. Superheating of the rhyolitic magma by the hotter basic magma may lead to vesiculation in the former and the formation of a gas-charged pyroclastic fluid, as suggested for the Loch Ba Ring-dyke (Sparks 1988). Surface eruptions of mixed-magma material may occur, but are not preserved within the now deeply dissected lava fields of the province.

The nature of the plume(s) associated with North Atlantic volcanism in the Palaeogene

The magmatism which commenced in the early Palaeocene with the impact of the proto-Iceland Plume in the North Atlantic region continues today on Iceland, which is located on the axis of a now substantially smaller plume (Saunders et al. 1997).

The source of the plume is assumed to have been a thermal boundary layer deep (but at unknown depth) within the mantle (White & McKenzie 1989, 1995). There are some obvious problems with the simple plume model proposed by White & McKenzie (1989): high-temperature picritic magmas were involved with the magmatism around the margins of the North Atlantic Igneous Province (NAIP), for example, on Mull and Rum (Kerr 1995; Emeleus 1997), and MORB-type basalts are recognized within the marginal areas, for example, Skye (Thompson 1982) and appear to have been derived from a depleted mantle. To produce picritic melts would require a mantle temperature in excess of 1450°C, at least 150°C above the normal, or ambient, temperature.

To explain the very rapid commencement of the magmatism associated with the plume (White & McKenzie 1989, 1995; Saunders et al. 1997), together with the spatial, temporal and volumetric relationships of the various magmas throughout the NAIP, it may be concluded that the plume had the following characteristics: (i) high initial temperatures; (ii) melting which may be attributed to the decompression of upwelling mantle during lithospheric rupture and plate separation; and, (iii) magma ascent which appears to have been controlled by pre-existing lithosphere 'topography' or 'thin-spots' (Thompson & Gibson 1991), or magma ascent along a planar surface rather than a point source (Saunders et al. 1997).

The widespread magmatism which occurred during the initial impact phase of the plume collapsed into a linear rift system during and subsequent to plate separation and the commencement of sea floor spreading at c. 55 Ma. However, continued sporadic activity away from the rift zone at this time suggests a degree of lateral migration away from the site or sites of upwelling.

In order to identify hot, plume-related magmas which were generated at depth from melts derived from the relatively cooler mantle through which the plume ascended, geochemical discriminants have been sought. Fitton et al. (1997) concluded that normal mid-ocean ridge basalts (N-MORB) can be distinguished from 'plume' magmas derived from a deeper and less-depleted mantle source by their Nb–Y–Zr signatures and that, on a log (Nb/Y)–log (Zr/Y) plot, it is possible to distinguish between magmas derived from these contrasting sources. The degree of melting, crustal contamination processes and any subsequent hydrothermal alteration do not appear to upset the Nb–Y–Zr signature, and therefore offer a simple discriminant as to whether a particular batch of magma (now represented by extrusive or intrusive units) may be attributed to a deep-sourced plume, or was simply the product of partial melting in the upper, depleted mantle.

Within the Iceland Neovolcanic Zone, Iceland plume magmas with depleted and enriched signatures have been erupted. N-MORB basalts (i.e. derived from the depleted upper mantle and not related to mantle plume magmatism) occupy a field below the 'plume array'. Thus, in order to identify plume-related magmas within the Hebridean Province, their location on this plot should reveal their affinities.

The wealth of geochemical (major, trace, REE and isotope) data now available for the basalts of the Hebridean Province (lavas, dykes and cone sheets) provides considerable insight as to the nature and dynamics of the proto-Iceland Plume and its source region. Scarrow et al. (2000) concluded that early Palaeogene magmatism was dominated by the polybaric melting of an anhydrous Fe-rich plume source mantle. Kent & Fitton (2000) have suggested that the geochemical data are consistent with the derivation of the basaltic magmas not from a single mantle source but two sources: (1) Icelandic (plume) mantle; and, (2) hot N-MORB-like mantle forming an outer envelope to the plume. With time, the proportion of 'Icelandic' material being involved in the melting regime below the Hebrides, more than 1000 km from the axis of the plume, increased, and then decreased, relative to N-MORB type.

Chambers & Fitton (2000) have demonstrated a change in the geochemical signature of the lavas on Mull, essentially coincident with the incoming of the Coire Gorm Magma-type (Kerr 1995), at the base of the Pale Member. The underlying Main Member has an N-MORB signature, derived from the relatively cool outer part of the plume, whereas the younger volcanic rocks have been sampled from the hotter, 'core' of proto-Iceland Plume material. Helium isotope data for certain Skye lavas are consistent with an origin from the proto-Iceland Plume (Stuart et al. 2000).

From the foregoing account, we may conclude that as new techniques are developed to decipher the formation, evolution and crystallization of magmas, we can be sure that the Palaeogene volcanic and intrusive rocks of NW Scotland will play a significant role in testing hypotheses and modelling new data.

15 Quaternary

G. S. BOULTON, J. D. PEACOCK & D. G. SUTHERLAND

From time to time in its history, the Earth has suffered an 'Ice Age', when large parts of its land surface have been covered by glaciers and its ocean surface by sea ice. This has happened at least during the late Precambrian, the Ordovician and the Carboniferous. The earth is again in an Ice Age. It began to develop during a phase of global cooling at the Eocene–Oligocene boundary (35–40 Ma) and has intensified during the late Tertiary and Quaternary.

Antarctica is the continent most susceptible to glaciation, and evidence of the first growth of the Antarctic ice sheet from the Middle Miocene (c. 14 Ma) is the first sign of severe cooling. Some stages in progressive cooling are:

2.4 Ma: the first icebergs dropped detritus in the North Atlantic;
2 Ma: the first Arctic marine microfaunas in the North Sea;
0.75–0.8 Ma: detritus dropped from icebergs and glacial tills in the Forth approaches, showing that Scottish-centred ice sheets extended into shallow waters;
0.55 Ma: the first time that a Scottish-centred ice sheet extended to the edge of the western continental shelf.

The cooling of global climate has not however been smooth and gradual. It has shown complex patterns of variation on all timescales. The best continuous evidence of global climate change through the Late Tertiary and the whole of the Quaternary comes from low sedimentation rate cores from the deep ocean that preserve a record of changing oceanic water temperature in changing microfaunal assemblages (Fig. 15.1a). They show strong oscillations between cold and warm periods, and also that these oscillations change through time in both amplitude and frequency. Although the warm periods have shown similar temperatures through time, cold periods seem to have become progressively colder. There appear to have been sudden increases in coldness during periods at about 2.5–2.3 Ma (coinciding with the onset of glaciation in the North Atlantic region) and at 0.8 Ma (coinciding with first expansion of a Scottish ice sheet into the North Sea). At 0.8 Ma there was also a change in the dominant wavelength of climatic cycles, from one of 40 ka (thousand years) prior to 0.8 Ma to one of 100 ka afterwards.

This last 0.8 Ma has been characterized by the rhythmic growth and decay of large ice sheets in the middle latitudes of North America and Europe during so-called *glacial periods*, separated by relatively short *interglacials*. These glacial/ interglacial oscillations have involved exchanges of up to 50×10^6 km^3 of water mass between the oceans and centres of ice sheet growth in Europe and North America, where ice sheets up to 3–4 km thick were formed. No part of the surface or near surface environment has been immune to these cyclical changes. There has been cyclical loading of the lithosphere with excess pressures of up to 0.344 kilobars; lowering of global sea levels by up to 150 m; major shifts in the global distributions of animals and plants; and fundamental changes in atmospheric and oceanic circulation patterns.

The ice sheets of Antarctica and Greenland represent a continuous stratigraphic sequence of frozen atmospheres. Because of temperature-controlled fractionation between the light isotope of oxygen (^{16}O) and the heavier isotope (^{18}O) during precipitation over the ice sheet, variation of the ^{16}O/^{18}O ratio of ice can be used as a direct measure of palaeotemperature. Figure 15.1b shows the palaeotemperature record from the central part of the Antarctic ice sheet for the last four glacial/interglacial cycles. This remarkable record is obtained because the accumulation (sedimentation) rate of snow in central Antarctica is very slow. It gives a long record, but the details of change are smoothed out. By contrast, the southern Greenland ice sheet has a very rapid accumulation rate, and therefore produces a shorter, but much higher resolution record (Fig. 15.1c). It shows very large and rapid temperature changes at frequencies higher than previously expected, and it shows that the last interglacial period (125 ka) was considerably warmer than that of the present, but with greater climatic variability.

The large-scale climate changes reflected in Fig. 15.1a–c appear to be driven by predictable changes in the intensity of solar radiation reaching the Earth as a consequence of geometrical variations in the Earth's orbit around the sun. However, air bubbles trapped at the time of ice formation in the Earth's great ice sheets and sampled in cores from boreholes reveal that 'greenhouse gas' (e.g. carbon dioxide, methane) concentrations were low during glacial periods and high during interglacials, and thus that a natural 'greenhouse effect' may have played a key role in governing the magnitude of change between glacials and interglacials. Extrapolation of the climatic cycles of the recent past into the future suggests that the present interglacial would naturally come to an end within the next 5000 years, unless a man-made greenhouse effect prevents or delays it.

The base of the Quaternary is now taken at 1.8 Ma, at the boundary between the Olduvai and Gilsa geomagnetic events (Fig. 15.1a). As little evolution of species has occurred during this period, climatic change, which has had a dominant influence on sedimentation, is used to define a series of climatostratigraphic stages, in contrast to the bio-stratigraphically defined stages of earlier geological periods, which are based on evolutionary changes. An alternating sequence of glacial and interglacial stages has now been defined which, in lowland Scotland, include both glacial and tundra environments during the glacial stages, and boreal (equivalent to the modern pine/ spruce forest areas of central Scandinavia) and temperate environments during the interglacial stages.

The global stratigraphic record is overwhelmingly derived from marine sediments. Apart from a unique contribution from ice sheet stratigraphy, the Quaternary is no exception. The difficulty is that whereas earlier marine sediments have been tectonically built into the structure of continents and are easily accessible to study, Quaternary marine sediments are still largely submarine. Figure 15.2 shows a schematic cross-section across Scotland from the North Sea to the foot of the western continental shelf. The thick sediment masses that occur in the marine areas are of course largely derived from erosion of the Scottish land mass. It is this erosional activity that has shaped much of the form of the land.

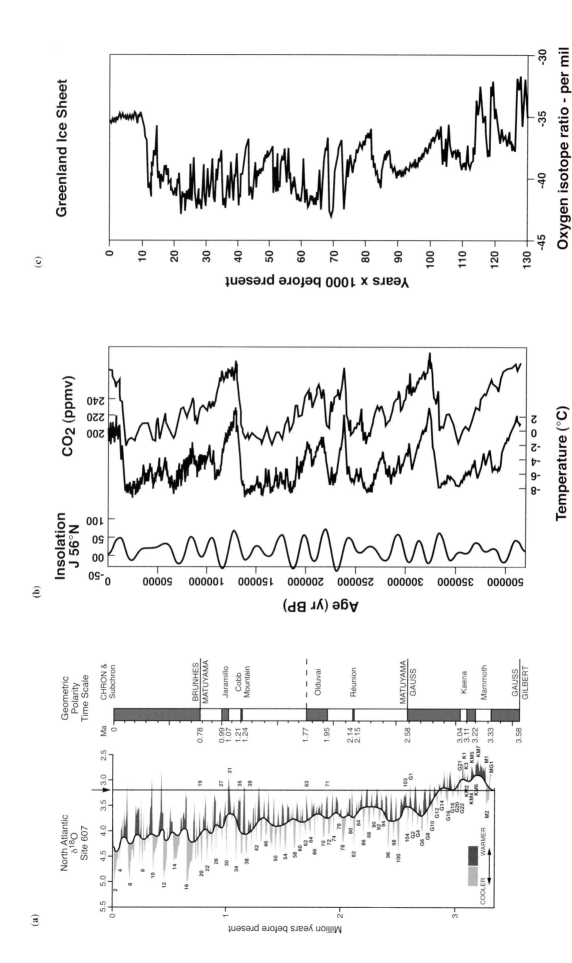

Fig. 15.1. The spectrum of Quaternary climatic change. (**a**) Oxygen isotope record from the North Atlantic indicating global ice volume change. Low global volumes to the right, high volumes to the left (data from Barendregt & Irving 1998). It shows the increasing intensity of cold periods after 3 million years ago, and the even greater intensity and increasing length (>100 000 years) of cold periods after 750 000 years ago. The geomagnetic polarity timescale is also shown. (**b**) The record of atmospheric temperature and carbon dioxide concentrations from Vostok Station (Antarctica) during the last 500 000 years. Cold. 'glacial' periods are about 100 000 years in duration, and temperate, interglacial periods are about 10 000 years in duration (data from Petit *et al.* 1999). There are slow, but fluctuating build-ups to the glacial maxima, and then rapid amelioration to interglacial conditions. Note that temperature and carbon dioxide concentrations are strongly associated. There is no significant change in one without a correlative change in the other. (**c**) The last 130 000 years in the stratigraphic record taken from the Greenland ice sheet (data from Dansgaard *et al.* 1993). More negative oxygen isotope values show colder conditions. It shows the strong and dramatic changes in climate during the glacial period from 115 000 to 10 000 years ago, compared with the relatively unvarying climate since 10 000 years ago. Note however the much more strongly varying climate of the warmer last interglacial period 115 000 to 130 000 BP. A possible warning about conditions in a warmer, 'greenhouse' world.

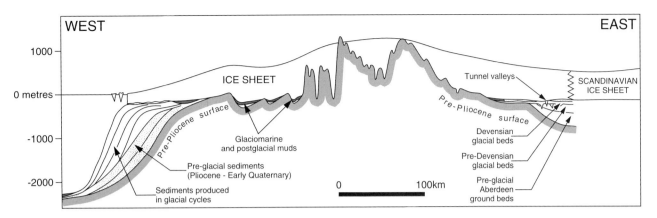

Fig. 15.2. Schematic diagram across Scotland from the eastern North Sea (east of Aberdeenshire) to the Atlantic west of the Hebrides. It shows the modelled ice sheet surface of the last glacial maximum, the massive building out of the western continental shelf, particularly during the strongly erosive period of Quaternary glaciation, and the sediment infill in the North Sea basin. Notice the 'tunnel valleys' in the central North Sea which represent major drainage features formed beneath the ice sheet during successive glacial periods.

Evolution of the landscape

The form of the land reflects events on a spectrum of timescales. Large topographic features take a long time to form and are likely to reflect events over long time periods. Small features can be produced relatively quickly. The largest topographic elements, the Southern Upland and Highland blocks, the Midland Valley, the Minch and North Sea Basins and the continental shelf edge, have been part of the relatively stable landscape skeleton for a very long time period, and arose as a consequence of major tectonic events:

405 Ma: Uplift associated with closure of the Iapetus Ocean so that Scotland became a tectonically elevated area. The location of the main Grampian watershed was inherited from this event.
350–355 Ma: Rifting to create the subsiding basin of the Midland Valley.
250–265 Ma: Basin subsidence initiated in the North Sea and in the Minch.
55 Ma: Opening of the Atlantic, flood basalt extrusion in the Hebridean area, thermal uplift in the west and subsidence in the North Sea area.

Through the Cenozoic, there has been a relatively stable tectonic pattern of perennial uplift of structural blocks in the west and relative down-warping in the east, which has been superimposed on the main landscape elements listed above. High-level erosion surfaces, which some have regarded as a product of marine erosion (e.g. George 1955) and others as a product of subaerial weathering (e.g. Hall 1991), are widespread and are warped upwards towards the main Scottish watershed which runs north–south through the western Highlands and western Grampians. Such high level surfaces are common around the North Atlantic, in western Norway, Spitsbergen, Greenland and Iceland and reflect uplift around the opening rifted margins of the ocean. This relatively stable pattern of uplift in the west and subsidence in the North Sea, and the stable block structure of Scotland, has ensured that a relatively stable pattern of drainage has been maintained from at least Early Tertiary times (Hall 1991), and that the continually subsiding North Sea has been a locus of continuous sedimentation through the Cenozoic.

The long post-Palaeozoic history of landscape evolution has been associated with a surprisingly low average long-term rate of erosion of about 1.5 km in the last 300 Ma. This is a rate of 0.05 mm/a, compared with an average modern global rate of 0.03 mm/a, and a typical rate of glacial erosion of about 1 mm/a. An extreme example of this relatively low erosion rate comes from Buchan, in northeastern Scotland. Here, granites and metamorphic rocks that were intensely weathered during warmer Tertiary climates still show 50 m thick weathering profiles, having survived being overridden by successive ice sheets during the last 0.75 Ma.

The Quaternary events that have left the strongest mark on the landscape and in the terrestrial sedimentary record have been the frequent growth of ice sheets. These flowed radially outwards from centres in the Highlands and Southern Uplands and were powerful agents of erosion and deposition, moulding the uplands, removing earlier sediments from the lowlands, locally depositing great thicknesses of till directly from the ice, and depositing sand and gravel from meltwater rivers. Rates of glacial erosion have clearly varied dramatically from place to place.

The most dramatic large scale erosional features are the deep U-shaped glens and sea lochs of the Highlands (Figs 15.2, 15.3). These have been produced, or at least deepened by glacial erosion at rates that were much faster than the long-term rates suggested above. Dating of carbonates precipitated in the caves of Assynt suggests rates of valley erosion per 100 ka glacial/interglacial cycle of between 47 and 68 m (Hebdon *et al.* 1997). Assuming that Assynt was ice covered for between 15% and 25% of the time during the last glacial cycle, implies a valley erosion rate of between 2 and 4.5 mm/a, typical of normal glacial erosion rates. The deepest sea loch, Loch Morar, attains a depth of 300 m below sea level. In order for rates of glacier erosion of between 2 and 4.5 mm/a to excavate such a trough would require it to be continuously sustained for some 150 000–67 000 years. The excavation of such troughs must clearly reflect repeated glacial occupancy if the length of glacial phases is no greater than those shown in Figure 15.1a, b, and probably requires the order of a million years of Quaternary time. Although we have no direct evidence of when the Scottish Highlands first began to suffer repeated widespread glaciation, it seems most likely that it must have begun by 0.75–0.8 million years ago (Fig. 15.1) at the very least, suggesting that the great troughs of Scotland (Fig. 15.3a) could have been almost entirely excavated by glaciation.

There is a strong contrast in the intensity of glacial erosion between the western Highlands with its highly indented fjord-coastline, deep troughs and sharp ridges, and the smoother mountain outlines of the eastern Highlands and the coastline of eastern Scotland (Fig. 15.4). Contrasts such as these are

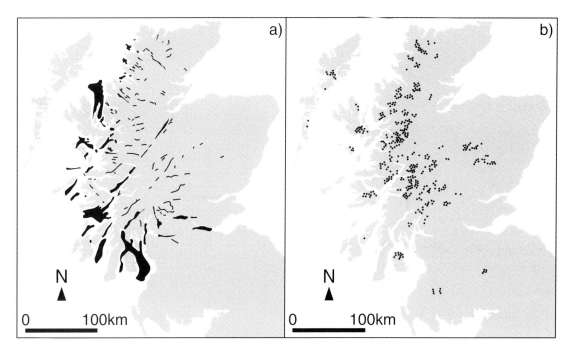

Fig. 15.3. (**a**) Distribution of major glacially eroded troughs in Scotland. (**b**) Distribution of corries in Scotland.

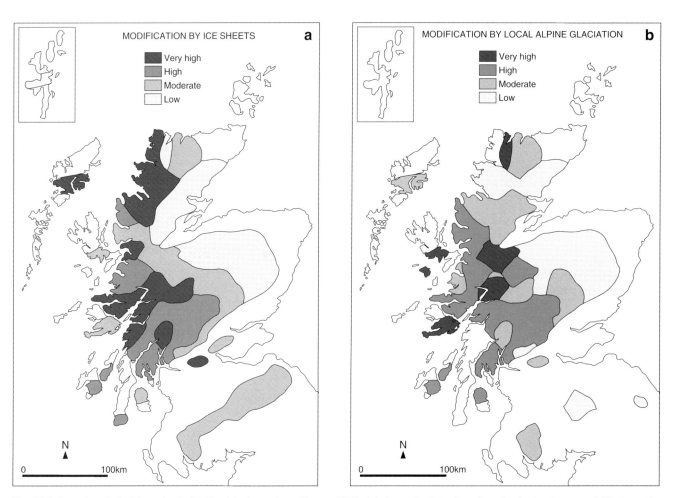

Fig. 15.4. Intensity of glacial erosion in Scotland (redrawn from Haynes 1995). (**a**) shows the intensity of erosion by ice sheets, and (**b**) shows the intensity of erosion produced by local valley and cirque glaciers. Note that the highest intensity of erosion from both sources is found along the northwestern seaboard, and lowest erosion intenstities are found in the east.

Fig. 15.5. The glacially eroded trough of the Lairig Ghru valley in the Cairngorms. BGS photograph.

frequently seen in areas covered by the same ice sheet, between mountainous areas of recent uplift, which tend to be penetrated by fjords, and more stable areas where uplift has been less and where fjords have not been produced. It is a contrast seen between the western coast of Norway on the western side of the Scandinavian ice sheet, and the eastern coast of Sweden on its eastern side; or between the fjord-indented western coast and the smoother eastern coast of Canada. There is strong evidence that where there is continuous strong uplift, erosion occurs at a high rate to keep up with uplift and is able to produce deep erosional trenches, thus preventing the development of a stable graded erosional profile.

To a large degree, the orientations of the major over-deepened glacial troughs in the Highlands reflect structural or lithological contrasts in bedrock which define relatively easily eroded zones, such as the Great Glen Fault. However, there are other areas where glacier flow appears to have super-imposed a large-scale erosional pattern on the landscape. One such area is in the Grampian Highlands (Fig. 15.3a) where a series of major troughs. Loch Leven, Glen Coe, Loch Etive, Loch Awe, Loch Fyne, Loch Long, Loch Lomond, Loch Katrine, Loch Voil, Loch Earn, Glen Dochert, Loch Tay, Glen Lyon, Loch Rannoch, Loch Ericht and Loch Treig, radiate from Rannoch Moor, suggesting that this area has been a persistent ice sheet centre from which ice flow has radiated during the successive Quaternary glaciations, thereby imposing a dominant radial grain on the landscape.

Glacier thermal regime also has a strong influence on erosion rates. Where the ice/bed interface is at the melting point, the glaciers slide their beds and have a strong erosional potential.

Fig. 15.6. A moraine formed at the terminus of a small glacier of the Loch Lomond Stadial in the north eastern Corrie of Beinn Dearg Mor, Wester Ross. (Crown copyright).

Fig. 15.7. Terrace and fossil sea-cliff cut by marine erosion during high relative sea levels. Lismore, Loch Linnhe. BGS photograph.

Where the interface is below the melting point, the ice is frozen to its bed, no sliding occurs and there is limited capacity to erode. This can explain strong local erosional contrasts. For example, Figure 15.5 shows the deep glacially eroded trough of the Lairig Ghru in the Cairngorms. On the plateau tops through which this trough has been eroded (Plate 30), there are remnants of tors and of Tertiary weathering, which are indices of only very slight erosion. The greater thickness of ice in the Lairig Ghru would have provided greater insulation of the bed against the penetration of surface cold than the thinner ice above the

Cairgorm plateau, which would have suffered much lower subglacial temperatures. As a consequence, the ice/bed interface in the valley may have been at the melting point for extended periods, producing strong erosion, whereas on the plateau, the bed may have been frozen, inhibiting erosion.

A similar logic can be applied to the evidence of slight Quaternary erosion in the Buchan area. The eastern flank of the British ice sheet is likely to have suffered a much more continental climate than the western, with the low summer temperatures and cold, dry winters which are conducive to cold ice conditions. The ice sheet bed in this zone may therefore have been cold for much of its subglacial history, as also suggested by the evidence of Cairngorm plateau tors and the survival of (presumably Tertiary) deep weathering

Other features of glacial erosion which are too large to have been produced during the last glacial period alone, and must reflect repeated glaciation, are the corries of the high mountains (Figs. 15.3b, 15.5, 15.6, Plate 30). Corries were excavated by small glaciers at times when climate was not severe enough to develop an ice sheet or before the mountains were enveloped by growing ice sheets. They are more numerous and occur at lower altitudes in the west Highlands than further east (Linton 1959), reflecting the importance of moisture-bearing westerly winds which nourished the corrie glaciers. The majority of corries face between north and east, an aspect which favours snow accumulation and glacier growth because of the protection of snow beds on northeasterly slopes from direct radiation, and blowing of snow from summit areas onto northeasterly facing lee-side slopes.

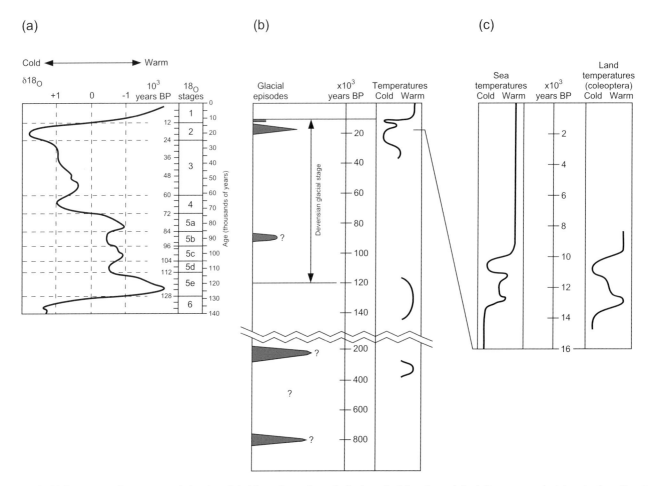

Fig. 15.8. (a) Deep ocean isotope record showing global ice volume through the last glacial cycle, and (b, c) Quaternary glacial and other climatic events in Scotland for which evidence exists.

Other large-scale, multi-phase landscape features are the remains of rock terraces cut by the sea and backed by fossil cliff lines on parts of the west coast (Fig. 15.7). These, the 'pre-glacial beaches' of the Geological Survey memoirs, are to be found at heights ranging from a few metres OD in Kintyre to 34 m on Islay and Jura and over 40 m on Colonsay. They are overlain by till in places and may have been glaciated more than once. It is believed that they were formed during periods of rapid combined marine and periglacial erosion. A more widespread member of this 'family' of landforms, the Main Late-glacial Shoreline, is discussed below. The high cliffs of parts of the Moray Firth and North Sea coasts may also have been shaped in part prior to the last glaciation.

Pre-Late Devensian history

The last glacial stage, termed the Devensian in Britain, began about 120 000 years ago (Fig. 15.8). Its coldest period occurred in the Late Devensian at about 20 000 years ago, when an ice sheet centred in the Highlands and Southern Uplands had expanded from the Highlands to cover most of Britain. At its maximum it was over a kilometre thick in the Midland Valley. Because of the erosive power of the ice sheet, very little sedimentary evidence of events prior to this last major ice sheet expansion has survived. Such evidence is concentrated in the Buchan area, which had suffered little glacial erosion, possibly

for the reasons given above, the off-shore zone, and isolated fragments of the earlier Quaternary stratigraphic record which have survived because of local circumstance. It is therefore difficult to re-integrate this scattered evidence to give a coherent picture of the varied sequence of environments that characterised pre-Late Devensian Scotland in the Quaternary. The evidence is summarised below, firstly from the land area and then from the sea areas.

Pre-Late Devensian sediments on land

Tertiary and Quaternary sediments that pre-date the Late Devensian glacial episode are widespread in Buchan. Tertiary sediments include the Buchan Gravels which are up to 25 m thick and deeply weathered. They contain clasts of flint and quartzite within a kaolinitic clayey silt, and appear to have derived some of their components from an intensely weathered rock which developed under a subtropical climate in Miocene times (Hall 1984). East of a line from Elgin to Strathmore, rock has been patchily but extensively decomposed to a gruss (granular sand), locally to depths of several tens of metres. Hall (1984) has suggested that this weathering took place under temperate conditions post-dating the Miocene, and as such it is distinct from the clayey gruss associated with the Buchan Gravels Group. Similar deeply weathered rock occurs further west within the outcrop of the Foyers Granite and in the Gaick and Helmsdale areas.

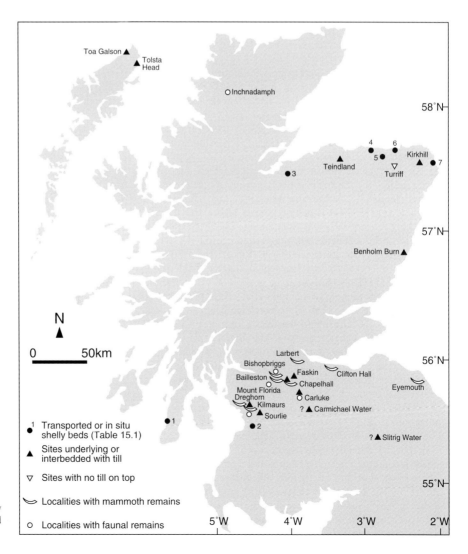

Fig. 15.9. Dated fossil-bearing sites underlying, interbedded with, or immediately overlying the Main Devensian till in Scotland (see also Tables 15.1, 15.2).

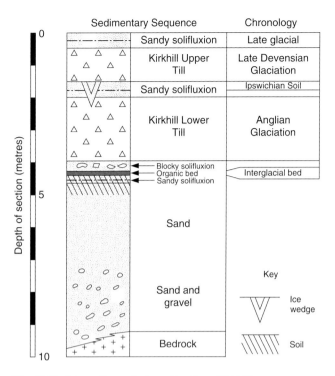

Depth of section (metres)

Sedimentary Sequence | Chronology

Sandy solifluxion	Late glacial
Kirkhill Upper Till	Late Devensian Glaciation
Sandy solifluxion	Ipswichian Soil
Kirkhill Lower Till	Anglian Glaciation
Blocky solifluxion / Organic bed / Sandy solifluxion	Interglacial bed
Sand	
Sand and gravel	
Bedrock	

Key

Ice wedge

Soil

Fig. 15.10. Schematic, synthetic section from Kirkhill, near Fraserburgh (Fig. 15.9) (based on Hall & Jarvis 1993*a*). The sands and gravels near the base of the section contain granitic erratics that are probably re-worked from glacial sediments. The site shows more pre-Late Devensian events than any other land section in Scotland.

The best record of pre-Devensian Quaternary events comes from a sedimentary sequence at Kirkhill near Fraserburgh (Figs 15.9, 15.10) that lies in basins and channels between tor-like prominences of partly decomposed felsite (Hall & Jarvis 1993*a*). A Kirkhill Upper Till, of Devensian age, overlies a soil of last interglacial age (about 120000 BP). This is underlain by the Kirkhill Lower Till which is underlain by an organic bed with an interglacial pollen flora of pine, alder and lime. Gravels underlying these tills contain erratics of biotite-granite and red sandstone, suggesting that they may have been fluvially reworked from a glacial source before the time of the Kirkhill Lower Till. It is very likely that these tills and glacially derived sediments were deposited during the glacial events between 300 000 and 130 000 BP (Fig. 15.1b).

The last interglacial, the Ipswichian, lasted from about 130 000 to 117 000 BP. Although in general it was a period during which the climate was similar that of the present day, there is evidence that part of it was significantly warmer. Evidence from the Greenland ice sheet (Johnsen *et al.* 1992) suggests that the warmer part of the interglacial was also stormier, at least in the North Atlantic region. This evidence has been used to support the view that, if global warming creates a much warmer world in the near future, it would be characterized by much stormier conditions.

Very little evidence remains of the last interglacial in Scotland, largely because of erosion by the glaciers of the succeeding Devensian glaciation. However, at Fugla Ness on Shetland, till and periglacial slope deposits overlie a peat of last interglacial age which contains Scots pine stumps and a pollen flora similar to those of the maritime heathlands of southwest Ireland (Hall *et al.* 1993). The cool windy climate of the modern Shetland is not one in which such a flora would flourish, and it probably reflects warmer, less windy conditions during the last interglacial compared with those of the present. The end of the last

interglacial is recorded by a fossil soil at Teindland (Fig. 15.9), which has a pollen spectrum showing progressive replacement of hazel and alder woodland by pine and then by cold heathland reflecting the deteriorating climate and the onset of colder glacial conditions.

The early part of the glacial period between 117 000 and 75 000 BP was characterized by rapid oscillations of climate (Fig. 15.1c) between *stadial* (periods when there was significant glacial growth) and *interstadial* (periods when glaciers decayed but climate did not warm in our latitudes to interglacial conditions) periods. There is evidence that the Scandinavian ice sheets grew rapidly after the end of the last interglacial, retreated during the Brorup interstadial at about 100 000 BP, and subsequently expanded and contracted again during the Odderade interstadial at about 80 000 BP. Scottish equivalents of these interstadials were identified from the pollen flora of a peat bed near Peterhead (Whittington *et al.* 1993), which showed the existence of birch-pine woodland. There is, however, no clear evidence of the growth of glaciers in Scotland during this early Devensian period. The Scandinavian ice sheet expanded rapidly after 72 000 BP, and after retreat during a long interstadial, eventually expanded to its last glaciation maximum in northern Germany and Poland at about 20 000 BP.

Scotland was probably glaciated during early Devensian cold phases, but the extent of glaciation is unknown. Sutherland (1981), Sissons (1982), Connell & Hall (1987) and Davies *et al.* (1984) have all presented data that can be interpreted in favour of an extensive early Devensian ice sheet, but unequivocal evidence is still lacking.

Shelly muds laid down in a marine environment not far from glacier fronts are widespread in parts of the northeast (Buchan, Caithness and Orkney), the southwest (Ayrshire), and locally on low ground elsewhere. These muds probably date from the end of the long mid-Devensian interstadial period and prior to the last glacial maximum. Many of the derived faunas are high-boreal to low-arctic with a few boreal–lusitanian species. Earlier workers (e.g. Jamieson 1865, 1866) argued that they were *in situ*, but more recent work has suggested that they have been reworked or transported as rafts by glaciers (e.g. Merritt *et al.* 1995). Shells of high arctic species (see below) have been recorded in Islay and adjacent to a mass of marine clay at Clava (Peacock 1975) where they are considered to be ice-transported rafts of marine or glaciomarine sediment (Table 15.1).

A large part of Scotland was ice-free towards the end of the Middle Devensian and was not glaciated in the Late Devensian until after 25 000–30 000 BP, after which the ice sheet spread from centres in the Highlands and Southern Uplands to cover most of Britain. The absence of dates younger than 25 000 BP on the mainland and 23 000 BP in the Outer Hebrides may indicate expansion of the ice sheet by these dates. Table 15.2 summarizes sites where radiometrically dated organic materials underlie till. At Crossbrae, near Turriff (Fig. 15.9), a thin peat below soliflucted till has yielded radiocarbon ages of 29 000 and 26 000 BP. At Airdrie, two undated peats antedating Late Devensian till have yielded coleopteran evidence for severe, but possibly interstadial conditions (Coope 1962).

Mammalian fossils have been recovered, chiefly from below a till assumed to represent the Late Devensian glacial maximum, at 13 sites (Table 15.3; Fig. 15.9). The best documented is at Sourlie, near Irvine where organic-rich silts within a 7 to 8 m thick stratified sequence, with lodgement till above and below, have yielded remains of reindeer (*Rangifer tarandus*) dated to about 30 000 BP, possibly together with woolly rhinoceros (*Coelodonta antiquitatis*) (Jardine *et al.* 1988). Other important sites that give evidence of Devensian maximum ice-free conditions include Bishopbriggs (Rolfe 1966) and the Inchnadamph caves (Lawson 1984). Sourlie appears to be the only site, apart

Table 15.1. *Notable sites for transported or in situ shelly beds*

Site	Fauna	[14]C Age	Amino-acid Age	Remarks
1. Cleongart	Chiefly derived			Glaciomarine
2. Afton Lodge	High boreal/low-arctic		Ipswichian?	Marine, possibly transported
3. Clava	High boreal/low-arctic			Marine, probably transported
4. Boyne Limestone Quarry	Probably arctic			Glaciomarine?, transported
5. King Edward	Boreal or arctic	>40 k	<80 k*	Marine or glaciomarine, 45.7 m OD. Said to be *in situ*, but base not seen.
6. Castle Hill, Gamrie	High boreal/low-arctic	>40 k	Devensian/Ipswichian	Marine, possibly *in situ*, but with some derived shells (e.g. *Arctica*)
7. Annachie	Possibly arctic			Marine/glaciomarine; widespread, thick deposits

1. Jessen (1905) with earlier references.
2. Eyles *et al*, (1949), D. Q. Bowen (pers. comm.1984).
3. Horne *et al*, (1893), Peacock (1975), J. Merrit (pers. comm.1988).
4. Peacock (1966*b*, 1971 and unpublished).
5. Jamieson (1865, 1866), Miller *et al*, (1983), Sutherland (1984).
6. Jamieson (1865), Peacock (1971), Sutherland (1984).
7. Jamieson (1865), McMillan & Aitken (1981).

Table 15.2. *Mammalian remains within or beneath glacial deposits (Modified from Sutherland 1984)*

Location	Site description	Remains
Bishopbriggs	In sands and gravels overlain by till	Left metacarpel, upper molar, left tibia and left humerus of woolly rhinoceros (*Coelodonta antiquitatis*)
Bishopbriggs	Uncertain. In till or sands and gravels under till	Molar tooth of mammoth (*Elephas primigenius*)
Baillieston	In bed of laminated sandy clay that laterally passes under till	Tooth of mammoth (*Elephas primigenius*)
Mount Florida	In sand and gravel overlain by till	Antler and bones of reindeer (*Rangifer tarandus*)
Chapelhall	In till	'Remains' of mammoth (*Elephas primigenius*)
Carluke	In till	Right antler of reindeer (*Rangifer tarandus*)
Larbert	In esker gravels	Tooth of mammoth (*Elephas primigenius*)
Clifton Hall	In till	Tusk of mammoth (*Elephas primigenius*)
Kilmauars	In probable till at base of marine glacigenic deposits	Molar and nine tusks of mammoth (*Elephas primgenius*) and antlers of reindeer (*Rangifer tarandus*)
Dreghorn	In sands and gravels under till	Tusk of mammoth (*Elephas primigenius*)
Eyemouth	Uncertain. In till or sands and gravels under till	Molar tooth of mammoth (*Elephas primigenius*)
Inchnadamph	Resting on silty sand in inner chamber of cave	Antler and leg bone of reindeer (*Rangifer tarandus*)
Sourlie	Organic silts in stratified sediments between tills	Antler fragments of reindeer; fragments of woolly rhinoceros

Table 15.3. Radiometrically dated sediments closely predating the Late Devensian ice sheet

Site	Material	Lab No.	Radiocarbon age (a BP)
Sourlie	bone	SRR-3023	29 900 ± 420
	plant debris	SRR-3146	29 290 ± 350
	clay/silt	SRR-2147	30 230 ± 280
	clay/silt	SRR-3148	33 270 ± 370
Bishopbriggs	bone	GX-0597	27 550 ± 520
Tolsta Head	peat	SRR-87	27 333 ± 240
Garrabost	marine shell	SRR-2367	26 300 ± 320 (o) 23 000 ± 230 (i)
Inchnadamph	bone	SRR-2103	25 360 ± 750
	bone	SRR-24,590	24 590 ± 750
Assynt	speleothem	SUI-80A	26 000 ± 3000
Assynt	speleothem	AUZ-80	30 000 ± 4000
Assynt	speleothem	SUIZ-80B	26 000 ± 2000
Crossbrae Farm	peat	SRR-2401	26 400 ± 170 22 380 ± 250

from the Inchnadamph caves, where the deposits are *in situ*, though at others, such as Kilmaurs (Bishop & Coope 1977) the faunal remains may not have been transported far. The Inchnadamph caves (Fig. 15.9) have also yielded a Loch Lomond stadial fauna of reindeer, collared lemming (*Dicrostonyx rorquatus*) and tundra vole (*Microtus gregalis*) (Lawson & Bonsall 1986).

Pre–Late Devensian sediments in the offshore zone

The most detailed record of Quaternary events in Scotland is contained in thick sedimentary sequences lying in the offshore zone. However, this record has only become accessible during the last 25 years through marine seismic surveys and borehole investigations.

There is a strong, tectonically determined contrast between the sedimentary sequences lying to the west and northwest of Scotland and those in the North Sea area (Fig. 15.2). To the west, Quaternary sediments have continued the process of building out of the shelf edge that was initiated after the formation of the eastern rifted margin of the opening North

Atlantic. To the east, in the North Sea, Quaternary sediments continued the process of filling of the subsiding North Sea basin at a rate that has largely been controlled by the rate of subsidence. Neither the style nor the character of sedimentation in western and eastern areas changed at the Tertiary–Quaternary boundary. It was dominantly of non-glacial origin, with occasional events that reflected the progressive Quaternary cooling of the Earth.

In the central North Sea and Moray Firth areas, the early Quaternary is represented by the Aberdeen Ground Formation, consisting of muds and sands deposited on and beyond the margins of the deltas of southern North Sea rivers such as the Rhine and Thames (Stoker & Bent 1987). Micropalaeontological data shows that deposition of the formation began in the late Tertiary, and palaeomagnetic signatures show it to extend at least to the Jaramillo event (*c.* 1.07–0.99 Ma BP; see Fig. 15.1a). Within the Aberdeen Ground Formation there occurs the so-called 'crenulated reflector' (Holmes 1977), shown by three-dimensional seismic reflection data to be a surface criss-crossed with furrows analogous to those created by iceberg keels dragging through sea bottom sediment. The crenulate reflector lies within the Matuyama palaeomagnetic epoch (Fig. 15.1a), probably near to 2 Ma BP, with its icebergs derived from calving of the Scandinavian ice sheet rather than a Scottish ice sheet. The first till in the Aberdeen Ground Formation, reflecting the flow of a grounded ice sheet from the Scottish mainland into the North Sea, occurs just above the Jaramillo event (Fig. 15.1a) and therefore dated at just after 0.99 Ma BP.

After this period there is extensive evidence of Scottish based ice sheet extending into the North Sea on a number of occasions, including during the Cromerian (stage 13), Elsterian (stage 8), Saalian (stage 6) and Devensian glacial stages (Fig. 15.1a). Each of these latter glacial events is associated with the development of so called 'tunnel valleys', anastomosing channels (e.g. Praeg 1996) trending roughly parallel to the palaeoflow of the ice sheet, 50–200 m deep, and of the order of 1 km wide, and representing the locations of erosive subglacial drainage channels. Although the extent of Cromerian ice sheets is poorly known, both the Saalian and Elsterian ice sheets were very much larger than the ice sheet of the last glacial cycle, and were confluent with Scandinavian ice sheets over Europe. The extent of Late Devensian ice sheets will be discussed later.

A similar distinction to that established in the North Sea has been identified in the sediments on the western and northwestern continental margin (Fig. 15.2), which shows an earlier, largely non-glacial sequence accumulating before about 0.75 Ma and a later, dominantly glacial sequence. The lower sequence is primarily sandy, derived from current reworked sediments on the shelf. When these sediments were transported over the shelf edge they were deposited on the upper part of the continental slope. As the slope built out and steepened it became unstable and local failure and collapse produced debris flows and turbidity flows that carried sediments down the continental slope into deep water. Strong, ocean-margin contour currents produced by geostrophic forces, re-suspended and reworked sediment to create the large sediment drifts that are a feature of the lower continental slope all around the margin of the North Atlantic Ocean.

Glacial tills are found in the upper part of the sequence on the western continental margin. When ice sheets, with their powerful sediment transporting capacity, reached the continental margin, they produced a strong transport of sediment to the continental shelf edge, which then flowed down the continental slope and built it out at a rate much greater than during non-glacial periods. As yet, the earliest dated tills probably belong to the Saalian glaciation (Fyfe *et al.* 1993), although it is likely that ice sheets centred over the Scottish

mainland have extended to the shelf edge from time to time since 0.75 Ma. In Figure 15.2, a disproportionately large thickness of post-Pliocene sediments is shown belonging to this post-0.75 Ma period, reflecting higher erosion and sedimentation rates.

The Late Devensian stage: the last glacial maximum

After about 30 000 BP, there was strong global cooling that culminated about 20 000 years ago. On the European continent, an ice sheet expanded from the mountains of Scandinavia, eastwards across the Baltic Sea as far as the vicinity of modern Copenhagen, Berlin, Warsaw and Moscow on the European Plain; and westwards as far as the edge of the continental shelf of Norway. Permafrost (permanently frozen ground) developed to depths in excess of 100 m and extended as far south as central France. At the coldest part of the glacial stage, Scotland, when not covered by an ice sheet, was a cold tundra environment, and all of Britain lay north of the tree line, which was located in northern France.

In Britain an ice sheet nucleated and then grew out from the Scottish Highlands, merging with ice from other centres in Britain; eventually reaching the northern coast of East Anglia in the southeast, the Severn estuary in the southwest and the western edge of the continental shelf beyond the Hebrides. In Ireland, an ice sheet developed from centres in the mountains of Antrim and of western Ireland and, after coalescing, expanded as far south as the vicinity of Dublin in the east and the Shannon estuary in the west. As it grew, the British ice sheet became confluent with the European ice sheet in the central North Sea and with the Irish ice sheet in the Irish Sea.

There is widespread evidence of glacial erosion of bedrock, producing striated and streamlined surfaces (Plate 28). The products of such erosion were then largely deposited as till (Fig. 15.11) which covers much of the lowlands. The smearing out of till beneath the moving ice sheet created streamlined drumlins (Fig. 15.12), which are particularly common in the Midland Valley and the large valleys of the Borders and on the Solway plain. The drainage of meltwaters from beneath the ice sheet created large esker systems (Plate 29), which are widespread in valley and lowland areas.

The dispersal by ice sheet flow of rock clasts from glacially eroded bedrock gives evidence of the patterns of ice sheet flow (Fig. 15.13). Their distribution can be largely attributed to the last glaciation in the central and western part of Scotland, although the varied transport directions of those derived from major igneous bodies in NE Scotland is evidence of a complex glacial history in that area. Boulders of Norwegian larvikite and rhomb porphyry have been found at several localities, notably on the coast south of Aberdeen where some occur in gravels below the main Late Devensian till. These may have been carried across the North Sea by the Scandinavian ice which reached the east coast before the main ice sheet developed over Scotland, although they may also have been deposited by the Scandinavian ice that reached the Durham coast during the Saalian glaciation, immediately prior to the Last (Ipswichian) Interglacial. Erratics of Jurassic and Cretaceous rocks have probably been derived largely from the sea-floor of the Moray Firth during the last as well as earlier glaciations. Some Cretaceous rocks near Peterhead are now thought to be outcrop (see Chapter 12)

The evidence of dated organic beds summarized in Figure 15.9 and Table 15.2 suggests that the ice sheet advancing from the Highlands crossed the Midland Valley shortly after 26 000 BP. Along the northern margin of the Southern Uplands there are a number of sites where a lower till containing

Fig. 15.11. Bishopbriggs. Till from the last glaciation (3–4 m thick) resting on outwash gravels which elsewhere have yielded reworked bones of woolly rhinoceros dated at 27 500 BP. BGS photograph.

Fig. 15.12. Drumlins at Myrehead, Linlithgow. The drumlin crests are clearly seen across the picture. They were formed beneath ice flowing from west to east (from left to right). Viewed from the air they are streamlined landforms which reflect the shape of the base of the ice as it flowed over the surface. BGS photograph.

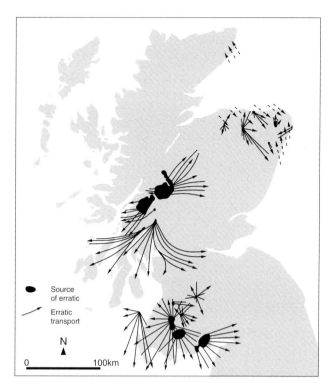

Fig. 15.13. Glacial dispersion of erratics from distinctive bedrock sites in Scotland. Dispersal of Mesozoic sediments from the Moray Firth is also shown, as is the transport on-shore in northern Aberdeenshire of marine sediments derived from the western North Sea.

Highland erratics is overlain by an upper till with Southern Upland erratics (Kirby 1969; Sutherland 1984). They suggest that the growing ice sheet expanded initially most rapidly from Highland centres and that only later was there sufficient growth of independent ice centres in the Southern Uplands to fend off Highland ice. The northern limit of Southern Upland erratics (Fig. 15.13) probably indicates the location of a zone of confluence with Highland ice at the maximum of glaciation. At the maximum of glaciation, presumed to have coincided with the coldest phase of the last glacial period at about 18 000–20 000 BP, there was not a single, simple ice dome over the British Isles, but a complex ice sheet with separate centres of outflow over the Highlands, the Southern Uplands, the Outer Hebrides, the Lake District, Wales and the Wicklow Mountains of southeast Ireland. In the Outer Hebrides, striations and landforms parallel to former ice flow directions suggest a pattern of glacial radiation from southern Lewis (Fig. 15.14), with another dome over South Uist and Barra. Selby (1989) has suggested that the Outer Hebridean dome of the ice sheet extended near to the shelf edge south of St Kilda (see above). As a consequence of the growth of an Outer Hebridean ice dome, ice derived from the mainland may not have reached the Outer Hebrides during the Late Devensian.

In the northern North Sea, there is evidence that the Scottish and Scandinavian ice sheets were confluent at a surprisingly early date between 22 800 and 29 400 BP (Sejrup *et al.* 2000). This could only happen if a large and extensive ice sheet had existed over Scotland. The post-26 000 BP date for ice advance over the lowlands suggests that the confluence must have occurred between 26 000 and 22 800 BP. Dates on marine sediments from the northern North Sea (Sejrup *et al.* 2000) demonstrate that this confluence must have broken shortly after 22 800 BP, with the Scandinavian ice sheet retreating to the vicinity of the Norwegian coast by about 20 000 BP (Valen *et al.* 1996). The Wee Bankie Formation, 60 km east of the

mouths of the Forth and Tay estuaries, which is part of a moraine produced at the margin of the Scottish ice sheet (Thomson 1978; Sutherland 1984; Stoker *et al.* 1985), probably represents the margin of the Scottish ice sheet shortly after this confluence broke.

It was formerly believed that the late Devensian ice sheet had a limited extent in northeast Scotland. Sutherland (1984) and Hall (1984) argued that the shelly grey tills of eastern Caithness, with Mesozoic erratics derived from the Moray Firth, were of pre-Devensian age, and that the line dividing these from tills with inland erratics to the west marked the easterly limit of the ice sheet. However, Hall & Whittington (1989) have shown that the Moray Firth-derived tills in Caithness overlie the inland tills, and therefore that both are probably of Late Devensian age. This is consistent with the existence of a major ice dome over the northern North Sea from which ice flowed over the Moray Firth area, with North Sea-derived ice pushing back Scottish ice that had previously been more extensive.

Further to the north, the last direction of ice movement over the Orkney Islands was towards the northwest (Mykura 1976), and although its age is unknown it may have been coeval with the northwesterly ice flow over eastern Caithness, both being consistent with the existence of a northern North Sea ice ridge between the Scandinavian and Scottish ice sheets. In Shetland, the most recent glacier cover took the form of an ice dome on the main island (Mykura 1976). The presence of till overlying a presumed Ipswichian peat (Birks & Peglar 1979) suggests that the glacial phase was of Devensian, possibly Late Devensian age. Moraine-like features near the continental shelf edge some 100 km west of Shetland are assumed to mark the maximum extent of Late Devensian ice flowing from Shetland (Peacock & Long 1994). Its position suggests that it must at least have been part of an ice ridge extending from the northern Scottish mainland, over Orkney and as far as Shetland, but may possibly represent the most westerly extent of ice flow from the ice saddle between the Scandinavian and British ice sheets.

The existing evidence suggests that different parts of the British ice sheet did not reach their maximum extents at the same time. This is likely to have arisen because of flow from the many centres of ice outflow and the interactions between ice masses from different centres. Although attempts to characterize the form of the maximum of glaciation over Britain as if all maximum extents were coeval are almost certainly misconceived, it is possible to create an approximation of the form of the ice sheet at the coldest part of the last glacial period by geophysical models that match the geological evidence.

Modern glaciers and ice sheets have a repetitive surface profile. This arises because most lie on rigid rock beds and their movement is determined by the effective yield strength in shear of ice; about 100 kPa (about 1 kg/cm^2). However, where ice sheets overlie soft, water saturated sediments, there is evidence that the sediments offer much less frictional resistance to ice flow than rock surfaces, so that flow occurs at shear stresses much lower than 100 kPa, resulting in a much flatter ice sheet than one resting on a rigid bed.

There is geological evidence of the maximum elevation of the Late Devensian ice sheet surface over northwest Scotland. Ballantyne (1987, 1999) has demonstrated in that area the existence of a prominent contrast between the uppermost parts of some of the highest peaks, which are mantled by thick frost-weathered *in situ* detritus, and lower slopes which show glacially scoured bedrock. The transition between the two is abrupt, occurring over a few tens of metres. It was suggests that this 'trim-line' marked the highest extent of the ice sheet surface. A reconstruction of this surface over Easter and Wester Ross, Skye, Mull and Jura shows that it descends from about 900 m in the Sound of Mull and the Sound of Sleat to 600 m between Coll and Tiree and 500 m over western Skye. This is consistent with a model produced by Boulton *et al.* (1991) (see Fig. 15.15) in which the shear stress over the sea area is about 30 kPa and about 70 kPa over the land area. These approximate values probably reflect the reducing proportion of the subglacial bed that consisted of exposed rock surfaces and the greater proportion of soft sediment in going from the mainland to the shelf area. The glaciological model in Figure 15.15, which represents the ice sheet after the North Sea confluence with the Scandinavian ice sheet had been broken, shows a prominent N–S ridge over the Highlands, a dome over the Western Isles, and a dome over the Southern Uplands which is connected by saddles to the Highland and Irish domes.

The model shows a very restricted extent of ice over northeast Scotland. If the Moray Firth were an unglaciated embayment as some have claimed, the northeastern side of the ice sheet would need to have been very cold and dry to ensure that a location near the centres of accumulation remained unglaciated whilst the ice sheet extended far to the south. As very little erosion is believed to occur when the temperature at the bed of an ice sheet is significantly lower than the melting point of ice, this is consistent with the evidence of little erosion of the Cairngorm plateau (Plate 30) and the limited erosion that appears to characterize northeast Scotland. There is now evidence from the northeastern North Sea (Sejrup *et al.* 2000) that an ice dome extended out from southwest Norway over the northern and central North Sea by 28 000 BP. Given the evidence that many parts of Scotland were ice-free at this time (Table 15.2), it implies that eastern Scotland was approached by ice from Scandinavia before there had been major outgrowth of ice from Scottish centres. This would be compatible with evidence of an ice dome over the Moray Firth and the Northern

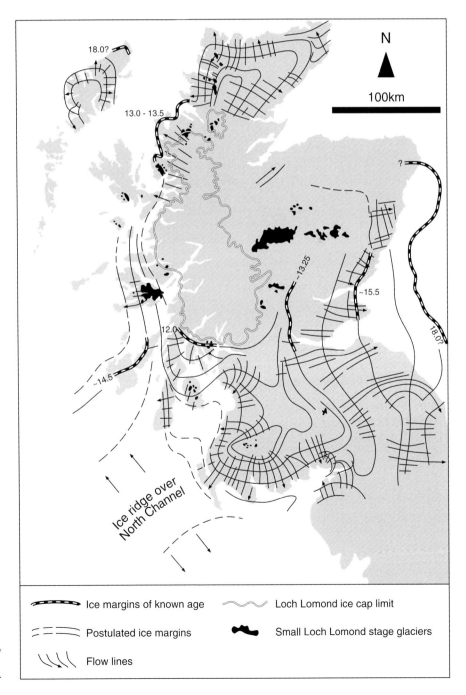

Fig. 15.14. Inferred pattern of decay of the Late Devensian ice sheet in Scotland. Heavy lines show ice margin position for which there is evidence of age in thousands of years.

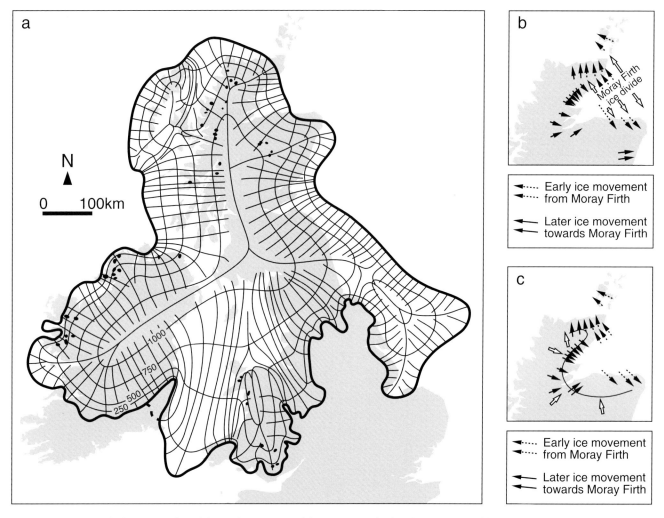

Fig. 15.15. (**a**) Theoretical reconstruction of the maximum extent of the Late Devensian ice sheet over the British Isles at a time when confluence with the Scandinavian ice sheet had been broken. (cf. Fig. 15.2). Principal nunatak areas are shown as dots. (**b, c**) Explanation of the evidence of the last ice flow directions in the Moray Firth area. Evidence of a landward flow in the outer Firth suggests an ice divide in the Firth (**b**), whilst seaward flow in the inner Firth (**c**) must have occurred after collapse of the ice dome. The change could reflect a Wolstonian/Late Devensian contrast (e.g. Sutherland 1984) or stages in decay in the last Devensian ice sheet (e.g. Boulton *et al.* 1985).

North Sea, and north-westward Late Devensian ice flow over Caithness and Orkney prior to the glacial maximum over Britain. It is suggested that this ice ridge connecting Scandinavia to Scotland had decayed, possibly because of isostatic depression of the North Sea and rising relative sea level, before the glacial maximum over Britain had been reached.

Deglaciation and sea level change

After the coldest part of the last glacial period, there is evidence that the ice sheet in Europe had begun to retreat all round its margin by about 16 000 BP (Boulton *et al.* 2001), with strong global warming after about 14 600 BP producing fast rates of retreat. Substantial retreat of the Late Devensian ice sheet in Scotland appears to have begun on the west by about 15 200 BP, whilst its eastern margin in the North Sea was retreating by 14 100 BP (Sejrup *et al.* 1994) at the latest. Moraines produced by halts in retreat or readvances of the ice sheet margin are rare, suggesting that retreat was relatively uninterrupted, although an extensive moraine system in Wester Ross (Robinson & Ballantyne 1979), which reflects deglaciation as

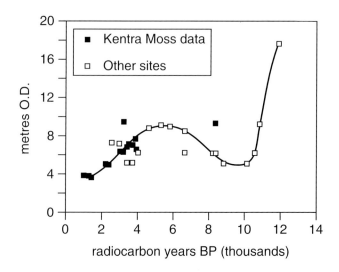

Fig. 15.16. Relative sea level curve through the last 12 000 years as drawn from data in the Kentra Moss area of western Invernesshire. (Redrawn from Shennan *et al.* 1995.)

far as the western mainland, may be tentatively dated at about 13 500–13 000 BP. It is possible to use features such as drumlins and eskers and striae on bare rock surfaces, most of which formed parallel to glacier flow immediately prior to retreat of the glacier, as indicators of the trend of the ice margin during retreat (Boulton *et al.* 2001). This suggests (Fig. 15.14) that as the ice sheet retreated from both east and west it formed a ridge running N–S from Wester Ross to the western side of the Southern Uplands, and that this then separated into a Southern Uplands dome and a ridge lying along the western seaboard from the upper Clyde to Wester Ross.

Much of the evidence for the period of retreat comes from the pattern of sea level change during deglaciation. Although global, *eustatic* sea levels were low during deglaciation, *isostatic* depression of the lithosphere due to the ice-sheet load was of greater magnitude, with the consequence that local relative sea levels around the Scottish ice-sheet were high. Careful analysis and dating of sediments that formed very close to sea level during and after the period of deglaciation (e.g. Shennan

et al. 1994) clearly shows the pattern of deglacial relative sea level change (Fig. 15.16). They show that deglaciation was accompanied by a fall rather than rise in relative sea level. Data such as that shown in Figure 15.16 can be used to construct *isobases* (Fig. 15.17), which show the current form of the surface that lay at sea level at a given time in the past. They show the pattern of isostatic uplift of the lithosphere, which reflects the pattern of earlier lithosphere depression caused by the load of the ice sheet.

In eastern Scotland, the Errol Beds occur within this area of strong glacio-isostatic depression and later uplift (Peacock 1981) (Fig. 15.17). They are dominantly reddish-brown clays, silts and sands, sometimes laminated, with scattered ice-rafted pebbles and boulders (Paterson *et al.* 1981), and contain an arctic marine fauna. On land they are rarely more than a few metres thick, although several tens of metres have been recorded in deep channels and estuaries. The Errol beds are nearshore equivalents of the St Abbs Formation in the western North Sea and the Barra and Hebrides Formations in the

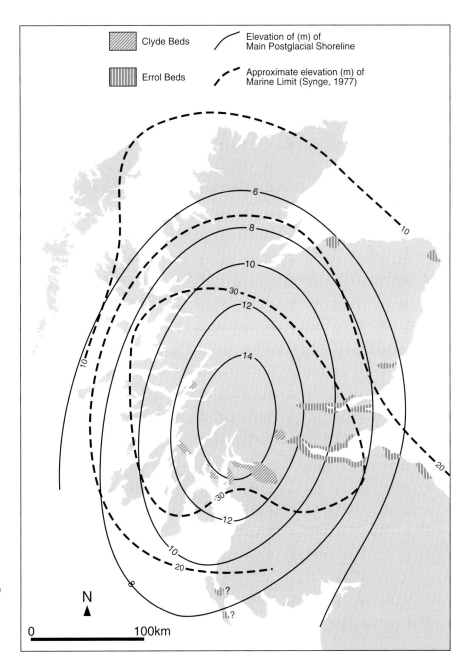

Fig. 15.17. Elevation of presumed isobases on the Main Postglacial Shoreline, (7500 BP) and the elevation of the marine limit. Glaciomarine Clyde and Errol Beds, which probably formed more than 10–20 m below sea level, are now found above sea level where isostatic uplift has been greatest.

western sea lochs and the Sea of the Hebrides. They probably formed between about 17 000 and 13 000 BP (Peacock & Browne 1998). Glaciomarine silts at St Fergus, near Peterhead dated at 15 320 ± 200 BP (Hall & Jarvis 1989), which contain an arctic molluscan fauna, are probably their lateral equivalents. They represent glaciomarine sediments formed in a sea area occupying a glacio-isostatic depression into which icebergs calved from the retreating ice mass (Fig. 15.18).

The most detailed sequence of shorelines that reflect relative sea level fall due to isostatic uplift occurs in SE Scotland (Sissons 1983), where an approximate chronology for the ice retreat can be established on the basis of a simple model relating shoreline gradient to age (Andrews & Dugdale 1970; Sissons 1976a, p. 120). Such a calculation suggests that five shorelines identified by Cullingford & Smith (1980) along the east coast of Central Scotland formed progressively between around 16 000 BP and about 14 000 BP (Fig. 15.18). The ice margin appears to have retreated very slowly in eastern Fife and the Strathmore coast, from evidence that there was considerable change in shoreline gradients during this period. The ice sheet margin may be placed in this area at around 15 500 BP with some confidence (Fig. 15.14). These shorelines (gradients, 0.94 m/km to 0.54 m/km) and those formed up to the time of the Main Perth Shoreline (Fig. 15.18; gradient, 0.43 m/km) (Sissons & Smith 1965; Cullingford 1977) were contemporaneous with the Errol Beds, and their offshore equivalent, the St Abbs Formation.

The formation of the Main Perth Shoreline and the end of the deposition of the Errol Beds occurred at around 13 000 BP. In places their inland limit can be related to outwash terraces or dead-ice terrain. In east central Scotland this inland limit approximately indicates the position of the ice at or slightly prior to 13 000 BP (Figs. 15.14, 15.18). In those areas where extensive searches have failed to find the Errol Beds (for example, much of the Clyde sea area, and the Cromarty Firth) it may be argued that there was ice-cover at the time of Errol Beds deposition. The shoreline sequences on the west coast are less clear than on the east but a tentative calculation of shoreline gradient against age can be made for the area of the SW Highlands and neighbouring islands. This suggests that the shoreline Ll of Dawson (1982) was formed at approximately 14 500 BP, implying that parts of western Jura and NW Islay were deglaciated by this time.

The Clyde sea area may have been covered by an ice dome centred over Arran at a late stage of glaciation, with ice flowing to the east across Ayrshire and to the west across the Kintyre peninsula. A minor local readvance of this ice is indicated by a distinct till unit in central Ayrshire. Deglaciation of the Clyde sea area was followed by deposition of the Clyde Beds (Fig. 15.17), which are chiefly greyish brown clayey silts and sands with pebbles rafted by sea ice. Like the Errol Beds these are thin onshore, but may be many metres thick in estuaries. Their deposition commenced by about 13 000–12 800 BP (Peacock & Harkness 1990; Sutherland 1986) as glaciers retreated to within the mouths of the sea lochs in response to the sharp climatic amelioration at this time. Rapid deglaciation of the Clyde sea region appears to have taken place as a consequence of calving of icebergs as the ice front receded into the deeper waters of the inner sea area (Sutherland 1984). Elsewhere along the coast still-stands during ice sheet retreat have been inferred from breaks in the marine limit near the mouths of sea lochs (Sutherland 1981). In the SW Highlands, such a still-stand or minor readvance has been dated to approximately 13 000 BP (Sutherland 1981). It is possible that these breaks in the marine limit relate to topographic control on ice flow near the mouths of sea lochs (Sutherland 1984).

The pattern of relative sea level change during the late glacial and Flandrian periods can be used to infer the pattern and magnitude of loading by ice sheets of the lithosphere. Lambeck (1993) has used such evidence from around Britain to reconstrust the approximate form and thickness of the ice sheet, and is consistent with the model shown in Figure 15.15.

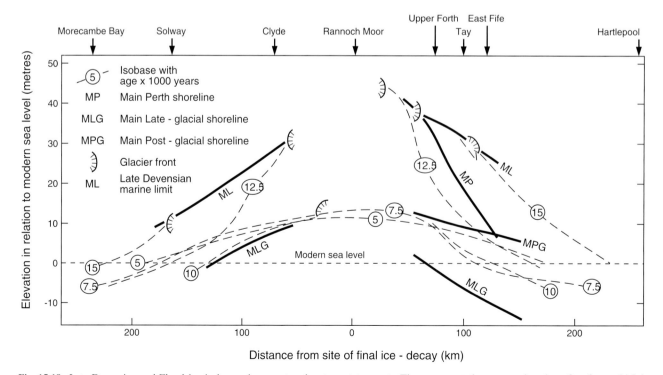

Fig. 15.18. Late Devensian and Flandrian isobases along west and east coast transects. They represent the present elevation of surfaces which lay at sea level at the times shown, and reflect the magnitude and pattern of crustal uplift since that time. The marine limit shows the highest point to which these features extend.

The Late Glacial Period

One of the most interesting and informative periods of strong climatic change that we know from the geological record occurred at the end of the last glacial period. It is particularly well reflected in the marine stratigraphic record of sediments on the western continental shelf west of the Hebrides. Figure 15.19b (Kroon *et al.* 1997) shows the inferred pattern of sea surface temperature change in winter (T_{min}) and summer (T_{max}) during the period from about 15 000 to 9000 years BP, inferred from changes in the isotopic composition of the shells of foraminifers that lived in near-surface waters and were buried in sediments after their death. They show rapid warming in the northeastern North Atlantic after about 15 500 BP. This warming ended at about 14 300 BP and was followed by a long phase of cooling that culminated between 12 500 and 11 500 BP, followed initially by very rapid and then slower warming. The pattern almost precisely follows that in the Greenland ice sheet cores (Fig. 15.19a), and is also clearly recorded by the evidence of fossil beetles (Coope 1977; Atkinson *et al.* 1987) from the land area of Britain.

In the warming after 15 500 BP, the ice sheet retreated rapidly and may have disappeared completely in Scotland during the period (Sissons 1976a). During the subsequent cooling after about 14 300 BP, the climate had deteriorated sufficiently to produce significant re-growth of ice in the Highlands. By about 12 000 BP, a large ice cap had re-developed in northwestern Scotland that stretched from what are now the northern suburbs of Glasgow to Wester Ross. These periods of warming followed by cooling are together known as the Late Glacial period, the early warm phase being the Windermere Interstadial, and the later, cold phase as the Loch Lomond Stadial. Rapid warming after 11 500 BP ushered in the present interglacial period, the so-called Flandrian.

The Windermere Interstadial

During the Windermere interstadial, conditions of arctic severity were rapidly replaced by a milder climate as the oceanic polar front in the North Atlantic migrated to the north of Scotland (Ruddiman & MacIntyre 1973) and North Atlantic Drift waters

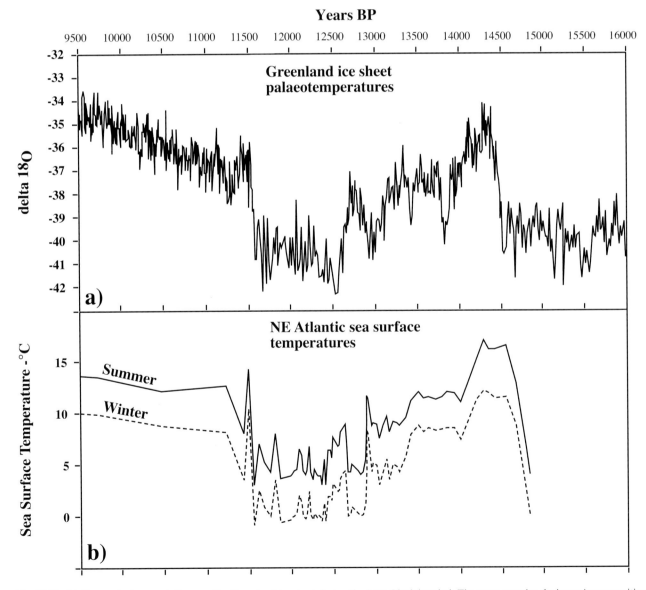

Fig. 15.19. (a) Oxygen isotope variations on the Greenland ice sheet during the Late Glacial period. The more negative the isotopic composition the lower the temperature (data from Dansgaard *et al.* 1993). (b) Seasurface palaeotemperatures inferred from the isotopic composition of planktonic foraminifers in winter (lower curve) and summer (upper curve). Material taken from cores from the continental shelf west of the Hebrides (data from Kroon *et al.* 1997).

reached the Scottish shores (Peacock & Harkness 1990). Atmospheric temperatures, as inferred from fossil coleopteran assemblages, rose dramatically, to come close to present-day values (Bishop & Coope 1977; Atkinson *et al.* 1987). Vegetation responded slowly to the climatic change and the plant communities of this period were characterized by open-habitat species typical of pioneer vegetation on recently deglaciated terrain (Walker 1984; Pennington *et al.* 1972). As the interstadial progressed, plant succession led to the development of a closed vegetation cover throughout the lowlands and in the Highland valleys.

There was considerable diversity in the interstadial vegetation communities which reached their greatest complexity following a brief phase of climatic deterioration which may be correlated with the Older Dryas chronozone of the North West European sequence (Pennington 1975; Mangerud *et al.* 1974). The vegetation zones that developed during the main part of the interstadial occupied similar geographical areas to the principal vegetation zones that developed under the different climatic conditions of the Middle Flandrian (Birks 1977) and which have been found in modern relict vegetation. Most of the country was covered by grasslands or dwarf-shrub heaths and tree development was limited to birch and pine in favoured localities (Gray & Lowe 1977). Tree birch had a northerly limit on the west coast in southern Skye (Birks 1973) but also occurred on the east coast in Aberdeenshire and possibly even Caithness (Peglar 1979) whilst pine has been recorded only locally in the eastern Central Lowlands and Aberdeenshire.

Complete deglaciation of the western sea lochs is indicated by the distribution of fossiliferous Clyde Beds within the lochs as well as the environment of deposition of these sediments. The marine fauna of the interstadial interval recorded in the Clyde Beds is of high-boreal to low-arctic affinities and appears analogous to similar but less well documented assemblages which occur throughout the Quaternary. It is characterized on the one hand by several pan-arctic species such as *Yoldiella lenticula* and *Macoma calcarea* (molluscs), *Elofsonella concinna* and *Eucytheridea bradii* (ostracods) and *Elphidium clavatum* (foraminifer), and on the other by boreal, Atlantic molluscs (e.g. *Arctica islandica*, *Modiolus modiolus* and *Corbula gibba*) which extend as far north as northern Norway today. The presence of such assemblages around the Scottish coast suggests waters approximately 3°C cooler than present, a relatively weak North Atlantic Drift off Scotland (Peacock 1983) and normal marine rather than glaciomarine conditions (Peacock 1989).

During the early interstadial, sea level around the coasts most affected by glacio-isostasy was falling rapidly (e.g. Peacock *et al.* 1978) to levels below those subsequently attained by the sea during the Main Postglacial Transgression in the middle Flandrian (Fig. 15.16). There is thus little direct evidence for the position of the shoreline during the middle to late interstadial but indirect fossil micro- and macro-faunal studies indicate that in the Highland fringes, sea level was relatively stable at altitudes within a few metres of its present level. In the outer islands and other areas peripheral to the centre of isostatic uplift, sea level throughout the interstadial was below its present level.

Loch Lomond Stadial

The Loch Lomond Stadial represents a return to conditions of arctic severity for approximately 1000 years, during which mean summer temperatures are believed to have been about 10–12°C below those of the present (Atkinson *et al.* 1987), and

marine sediments with a restricted high arctic marine fauna were yet again deposited around the coasts (Peacock *et al.* 1978). The re-growth of glaciers in Scotland is refected by moraine sequences (Sissons 1979, 1983) and by stratigraphic evidence from the SW Highlands and Mull where sediments overlain by, or incorporated into, glacial deposits associated with the advance have been radiocarbon dated, as have proglacial deposits characterized by marine faunas or terrestrial floras typical of severe climates (Peacock *et al.* 1989; Tipping 1986, 1989). These studies indicate that in the SW Highlands the readvance culminated after 10 500 BP, which agrees with the age of the High Buried Shoreline of the Forth Valley, inferred from a shoreline gradient against age model, at approximately 10 200 BP. The High Buried Shoreline is contemporaneous with the Menteith Moraine formed at the maximum of the readvance (Sissons 1966, 1976*b*).

The extent of the Loch Lomond ice cap is marked by the extent of major series of moraines. The slope of these moraines along valley sides can be used to reconstruct the gradients of the terminal zones of the ice cap. Within the area occupied by the ice cap there are broad areas of 'hummocky moraine', often regarded as evidence of stagnation and rapid decay of inactive ice. However, Horsfield (1983) and Bennett & Boulton (1993*a, b*) have demonstrated that the hummocky moraine frequently consists of linear elements analogous to modern moraines formed at actively retreating ice margins. The moraines reflect retreat of an active ice margin at a rate not dissimilar to modern glacier retreat rates in southern Iceland. Many mountain areas which lay outside the Loch Lomond ice cap, had their corries occupied by small glaciers during the stadial (Sissons 1979) (Fig. 15.6).

In many places, the Loch Lomond ice cap blocked pre-existing patterns of drainage to create ice-dammed lakes, which left behind features such as deltas and shorelines on valley sides, such as the so-called 'parallel roads of Glen Roy'.

The retreat and final disappearance of the glaciers of the Loch Lomond stadial have been studied by examination of pollen sequences in sediments deposited immediately after deglaciation. In principle, areas that were the last to have been deglaciated should show evidence of the beginning of organic growth at later sites deglaciated earlier. There is evidence of this in some areas (Walker & Lowe 1981) but not in others (Tipping 1988), whilst radiocarbon dating of basal organic sediments shows no age pattern reflecting glacier retreat. This probably reflects the fact that the global atmospheric CO_2 concentration decreased during the latter part of the Loch Lomond stadial so that a range of true ages prior to 10 000 BP tend to show the same radiocarbon age of about 10 000 BP. For these reasons the deglaciation chronology is poorly known but it seems probable that complete deglaciation was achieved prior to the Early Flandrian *Juniperus* maximum, which occurred at about 9600 BP.

The vegetation that developed during the stadial was characterised by species typical of broken ground and open tundra although there appear to be no direct modern analogues for many of the plant communities (Walker 1984). Particularly notable have been variations in the abundance of pollen of species of *Artemisia* in stadial sediments. Geographically, very high values have been found in the eastern and central Grampians with declining values to the west and south (Birks & Mathewes 1978; Macpherson 1980; Tipping 1985). These variations have been interpreted as a direct reflection of the precipitation pattern during the stadial as certain species of *Artemisia* are chionophobes and likely to flourish in areas of lower snowfall. The reduced levels of precipitation inferred from such data for the eastern and central Grampians correspond closely with the precipitation pattern deduced from glacier distribution during the stadial (Sissons 1980). Temporally, certain pollen profiles also show changes in *Artemisia* pollen values as the stadial progressed, with an early phase of low frequencies followed by higher frequencies during a later drier period during the stadial (Macpherson 1980; Caseldine 1980; Tipping 1985).

During the stadial, slope processes were particularly active resulting in the general destruction of interstadial soil profiles as well as local burial by slumping or solifluction of interstadial peats and organic sediments (Donner 1957; Dickson *et al.* 1976; Clapperton & Sugden 1977). In lakes and enclosed basins the stadial is marked by a distinct horizon of minerogenic sediments frequently containing low concentrations of organic detritus derived from the interstadial soils (Pennington 1977). In the lowlands, river activity was enhanced and large alluvial fans deposited, as in the Lochwinnoch Gap, at the foot of the Ochil Hills and at Corstorphine in Edinburgh (Kemp 1971; Newey 1970; Sissons 1976*b*, 1979).

Nearshore erosion during the stadial was severe. This is most clearly demonstrated in the Forth Valley where a distinct erosion surface has been identified over an area in excess of 28 km², cutting across Lateglacial marine sediments, till and bedrock, and directly overlain by Early Flandrian sediments (Sissons 1969, 1976*b*). The inner margin of this surface defines the Main Lateglacial Shoreline (Fig. 15.17) which is isostatically tilted eastwards with a gradient of 0.17 m/km. Around the coast of the Southwest Highlands and neighbouring islands is another erosional shoreline isostatically tilted westwards, the Main Rock Platform, which has a similar gradient to the Main Lateglacial Shoreline (Gray 1974, 1978; Dawson 1980, 1988; Sutherland 1984). The similarities between the two features led Sissons (1976*b*) to conclude that they were both produced during the stadial, an hypothesis that received support from the evidence for rapid littoral erosion of bedrock around the Glen Roy ice-dammed lakes (Sissons 1978). Uranium-series dating of speleothem material overlying the Main Rock Platform (Gray & Ivanovich 1988) has suggested, however, that the platform may have been inherited in part from a pre-existing feature or features (Sutherland 1981; Browne & McMillan 1984).

Flandrian Interglacial

The climatic amelioration at the end of the Loch Lomond Stadial was abrupt and the rate of temperature rise may have been as great as 1°C per decade (Coope 1977; Atkinson *et al.* 1987). Offshore water temperatures may have risen from near zero to a little below modern values within a few decades (Peacock & Harkness 1990; Fig. 15.19b). The change in climate coincided with the return of North Atlantic Drift waters to the Scottish coasts. The climatic ameliorations at the beginnings of both the Flandrian and the Windermere Interstadial were both of a similar magnitude and rapidity and resulted from the retreat of the oceanic polar front in the North Atlantic to the north of Scotland. At both times the vegetation inherited from the previous cold periods was dominated by open-habitat taxa, these being succeeded by shrub and scrub vegetation. In contrast to the interstadial, however, when the initial mild phase only lasted a few hundred years, to be followed by a period in which temperatures were somewhat lower than at present, the mild climate of the Early Flandrian was maintained, giving rise to a sequence of vegetational changes quite different from those of the interstadial.

The best continuous proxy for Flandrian climatic change in the North Atlantic region, the most important determinant of climatic change in Scotland, is the climatic record derived from the ice cores from the Greenland ice sheet (Dansgaard *et al.* 1993; Fig. 15.20). It shows the dramatic rise in temperature immediately at the beginning of the interglacial period and a slow climatic decline since about 5000 BP. However, this underlying trend is almost masked by high-frequency variability, much of which may be local adjustment to larger scale patterns of change. Recent analyses of proxy climatic data and the instrumental record from the Northern Hemisphere have permitted a reconstruction of hemispheric mean temperatures through the last millennium (Mann *et al.* 1999; Fig. 15.21). This also shows low-amplitude, high BP-frequency changes that may be local effects, but it also shows, prior to the last 100 years, evidence of a gradual reduction in mean hemispheric temperature, that may be a continuation of the apparent decline shown in Figure 15.20 since 5000 BP. When compared

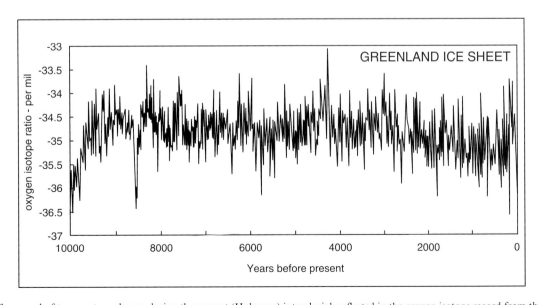

Fig. 15.20. The record of temperature change during the present (Holocene) interglacial, reflected in the oxygen isotope record from the Greenland ice sheet (from Dansgaard *et al.* 1993). It shows the end of the phase of strong warming at the end of the last glacial period, about 10 000 years ago. Although the climate varies rapidly during the Holocene, the amplitude is small (see Fig. 15.1c). The core shows evidence of the 'Little Ice Age' during the 17th to 19th centuries and the subsequent warming at the end of the 19th and the beginning of the 20th century.

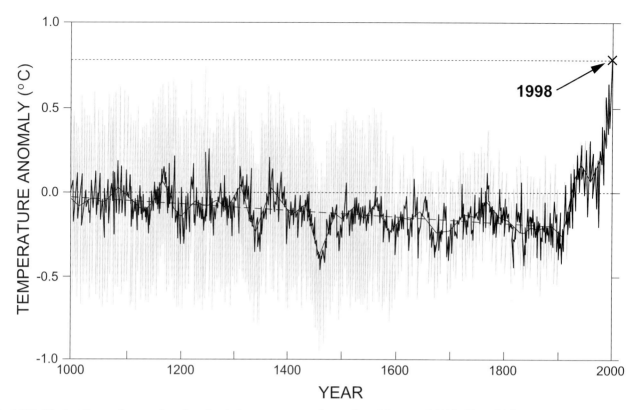

Fig. 15.21. The last thousand years of northern hemisphere temperature change (from Mann *et al.* 1999). The solid lines show the reconstructed temperature and the 40-year smoothed mean. The grey shading shows two standard error limits, and the dashed line the linear trends of the mean temperature prior to 1900. It shows that although there have been regionally important events, such as the mediaeval warm period and the 'Little Ice Age' in the North Atlantic sector, global mean temperatures have been very stable. However, the very strong warming during the 20th century seems anomalous. Is it connected to the unprecedented increase of atmospheric carbon dioxide during the last hundred years?

to the longer record of glacial/interglacial change shown in Figure 15.1c, it is entirely plausible that the change since 5000 BP could be part of the natural trend towards a further glacial period.

Changes in flora

There are now numerous peat bog and lake sites in Scotland from which pollen sequences record the sequence of interglacial floras (e.g. Walker & Lowe 1997). This is illustrated in Figure 15.22 by a site from Black Loch in Fife (Whittington *et al.* 1991). At the transition from Loch Lomond stadial to Flandrian interglacial, the vegetation was predominantly grassland, followed in rapid sequence by plant invasions in which lowland vegetation was dominated firstly at about 10 000 BP by shrub species such as juniper, willow and crowberry, with tree birch expanding into southern and central Scotland just after 10 000 BP and reaching northern Scotland by 9000 BP. By this time, most of the lowland areas were covered by birch and hazel woodland, with rowan, aspen and willow and juniper scrub at higher elevations, and even the offshore islands had a substantial tree flora (Bennett 1995). By about 8500 BP, the lowlands south and west of the Grampians were being invaded by oak, elm and Scots pine, whereas further north, birch and Scots pine forests were becoming established. Between 7500 and 5000 BP, the heyday of the great Caledonian pine forest had been reached (Bridge *et al.* 1990), with the tree line reaching some 800 m in some areas, although further north still, in Caithness and Sutherland, woodland was more sparse, dominated by birch and hazel and with relatively few stands of pine.

Throughout much of the country alder expanded into the forests during the middle Flandrian, appearing in the south at

around 7000 BP and achieving its maximum extent by around 6500 BP. After about 6000 BP there is evidence of change to a cooler, moister climate, which resulted in some forest decline and its replacement by blanket peat, heaths and grasslands.

Geomorphological and hydrological changes

The milder and less stormy climate of the Flandrian compared to the preceding Loch Lomond Stadial, together with the corresponding development of vegetation and soil cover, resulted in a marked diminution of geomorphological activity compared to the earlier period. However, the glacial legacy of large volumes of unconsolidated debris, over-steepened slopes and disrupted drainage systems meant that the Early Flandrian was a period of adjustment to the new conditions. There were a considerable number of rock slope failures (Holmes 1984) as well as extensive reworking by streams and flows of the available material producing debris cones in many Highland valleys (Brazier *et al.* 1988). In contrast, the Middle to Late Flandrian was relatively quiescent. However, the last 500 years have witnessed a major change in the rates of geomorphological processes with increased fluvial as well as renewed mountain-top periglacial activity (Innes 1983; Brazier *et al.* 1988; Ballantyne 1986; Ballantyne & Whittington 1987). This recent resurgence may partly be due to the climatic deterioration noted in Figure 15.21, although increased grazing pressure on the upland areas is an equally probable cause.

The newly deglaciated land at the beginning of the Flandrian was sparsely vegetated and relatively unstable, so that rainfall ran off rapidly into flood-prone and unstable, sediment-laden, braided river systems. The invasion of woodlands at the beginning of the interglacial dramatically changed

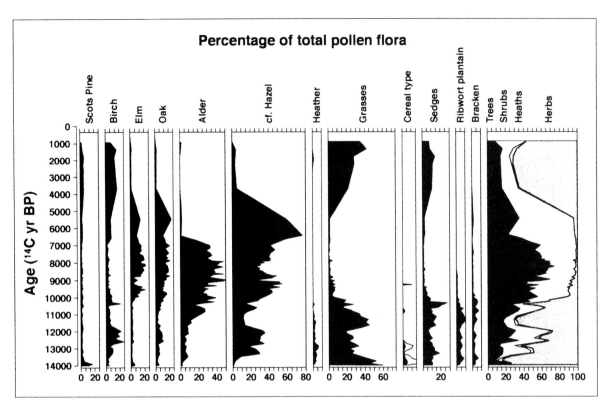

Fig. 15.22. Floral evolution in Fife (Black Loch) during the Holocene interglacial (from Edwards & Whittington 1997). At the end of the last glacial period, between 13 000 and 9000 radiocarbon years ago, open tundra and grassland were progressively replaced by forest; firstly birch, then pine, elm and oak. Hazel, then alder, reflected the onset of wetter conditions. Human impacts are seen by 4000 to 5000 years ago in forest clearance. They were the first steps in the creation of the human-engineered modern landscapes, as tree-less as the later part of the glacial period, but warmer.

the hydrological regime. Trees intercepted, reduced and slowed down runoff, permitting the river systems to adopt more stable courses, a trend enhanced in the lowlands by the spread of more varied mixed-oak forests after about 8500 BP. After about 6000 BP, the climate in Scotland became significantly wetter, which is likely to have produced faster runoff and more flood prone rivers, although the evidence of actual river regimes from this period is slender.

Sea levels and the coastal environment

Around the coasts there have been major changes in the position of the shoreline during the Flandrian due to the complex interplay of glacio-isostatic and eustatic sea-level movements. The differences in sea level change experienced from place to place are primarily a function of distance from the centre of glacio-isostatic uplift in the western Highlands (Fig. 15.17). Thus in the Outer Isles where isostatic effects have been least, there has been a net sea-level rise during the Flandrian whilst around much of the mainland coasts there has been a net fall, although the pattern of change has, generally, been complex with periods of sea-level fall during the Early and Late Flandrian being separated by a major transgression that reached its climax in the Middle Flandrian (Fig. 15.16).

The major transgression, termed the Main Postglacial Transgression, was the result of the global eustatic sea-level rise consequent upon the final melting of the North American ice sheet. It occurred because the rapidly reducing rate of isostatic uplift became temporally less than the rate of eustatic sea level rise. The maximum of the transgression was reached at different times in different parts of the country, being earliest in the western Forth Valley at around 6800 BP (Sissons & Brooks

1971; Sissons 1983) and generally later in areas further from the centre of isostatic uplift (Smith, D. E. et al. 1983). A particularly prominent depositional shoreline, the Main Postglacial Shoreline, was formed at the maximum of the readvance. Isostatic tilting of that shoreline has given it a gradient of between 0.05 m/km and 0.08 m/km. After about 5000 BP, relative sea level fall continued in Scotland as the eustatic component of sea level due to the melting of global ice sheets ceased but isostatic uplift continued.

It is possible to reconstruct the pattern of crustal warping in Scotland during the Flandrian by reconstructing the modern form of a surface that lay at sea level at some time in the past, a so-called isobase, which indicates the pattern of crustal warping since that time. Data illustrated in Figure 15.16 have been used to reconstruct the isobase for the top of the marine transgression that occurred at about 6800 BP and formed the Main Postglacial Shoreline (Fig. 15.17). It shows the net rebound of the lithosphere since 6800 BP, and is a memory of the time-varying pattern of ice loading during the latter part of the glacial period.

The sedimentary sequences deposited as a consequence of these movements of the shoreline are best developed in the estuaries of the east and southwest coasts. Here, silts and fine sands deposited during periods of marine influence are interbedded with terrestrial peats and fluvial sands and gravels (Sissons et al. 1966; Jardine 1980). Along the east coast a prominent fine-sand horizon that is present in both estuarine and near-shore terrestrial sediments was deposited at around 7000 BP. This may have been produced by a major storm surge in the North Sea basin (Smith, D. E. et al. 1985) or giant wave (tsunami). There is evidence that a large sector of the Norwegian continental margin collapsed in the mid-Flandrian to form mass flow that slid down the continental slope of western

Norway and extended as far as the mid-ocean ridge in the Norwegian Sea. It is suggested that the water displacement produced by this slide created a tsunami that broke against the northeastern shores of Scotland to create relatively high level storm deposits (Dawson *et al.* 1988; Long *et al.* 1989).

The impact of human society

In the Late Flandrian, humanity had become a major agent of geological change. In Scotland, the first signs of this are seen in pollen records (e.g. Fig. 15.22). By about 5000 BP, shortly after the change to a cooler, wetter climate, tree felling and burning by humans significantly enhanced the rate of forest decline and bog and heath development that had already started as a consequence of change to a cooler, wetter climate. This process of deforestation reached its maximum extent by the 18th and 19th centuries, with as little as 4% of the country under woodland by 1750 (Edwards & Smout 2000). This process, which mimicked the barer landscape of newly deglaciated Scotland, coupled with the climatic deterioration during the last 1000 years, and including the so-called Little Ice Age of the 16th–19th centuries, generated increased flood frequencies and may

have been the cause of the greater instability and tendency to river braiding in the 18th and 19th centuries (Macklin & Lewin 1993). As a consequence, there was widespread engineering of lowland river courses in an attempt to control both flooding and course instability.

By the end of the 20th century humanity has developed powerful processes that transport masses of Earth materials equal to about half that transported by natural transport processes and three times that created by mountain building; consume and intercept about 72% of continental runoff; has removed between 26% and 46% of global forests; and may have intervened in the biosphere in a way that has created an extinction rate of mammalian species about 40 times the 'natural' background rate. Moreover, by burning fossil fuel, humanity has released enough carbon from natural storage in 60 years or so to increase atmospheric carbon dioxide concentrations to levels not experienced through the whole of the Quaternary, and which are maybe responsible for the dramatic rise in northern hemisphere temperatures shown during the last 60 years in Fig. 15.21. It is possible, as a consequence of such human impacts, that the future geological environment of Scotland will be very different from those of the Quaternary.

16 Metalliferous minerals

C. M. RICE

The first records of metalliferous mining in Scotland appear in the 13th century and relate to lead from the Leadhills–Wanlockhead area which, over the next six hundred years, easily became Scotland's biggest nonferrous metal producer. There is no known evidence for earlier mining activities and the absence of Bronze Age mines in particular is surprising given the concentration of Bronze Age monuments in many metalliferous areas (O'Brien 1996). Leadhills–Wanlockhead is also notable as the source of the gold in the 16th century for the Scottish regalia (Gillanders 1981). During the 19th and 20th centuries substantial amounts of chromite were extracted in Unst, and of baryte and iron ore from the Midland Valley. Overall, Scotland has produced over 5×10^6 tonnes of iron ore, around 850 000 tonnes of baryte, 300 000 tonnes of lead, about 16 000 tonnes of chromium, 7000 tonnes of zinc, 200 tonnes of antimony, and a few tonnes of gold and silver. Some copper, nickel and manganese have also been recovered. Most of these deposits are now exhausted or uneconomic under prevailing conditions.

In the last 50 years Scotland has been widely explored by the British Geological Survey (BGS) and various mining companies. Exploration has been assisted by a comprehensive nationwide drainage geochemical survey conducted by BGS. This has led to many significant discoveries but the highlight has been the discovery of world class baryte deposits at Aberfeldy, strategically placed to supply the North Sea oil industry with drilling mud. In addition, significant but currently subeconomic deposits of Cu, Ni and Au have been identified.

In the foreseeable future metalliferous minerals are unlikely to make a significant contribution to Scotland's economy. The country has been thoroughly mapped and prospected and it is doubtful that world class deposits remain to be discovered. Nevertheless, there is the possibility of small, high-grade deposits, especially of gold, being found.

The most important deposits in the near future will be of industrial minerals (see Chapter 18) and more especially, from the point of view of this chapter, baryte. Currently, the Foss baryte mine and the silica sand deposit at Lochaline are the only two active mines in Scotland exploiting industrial minerals. No metalliferous deposits are being exploited at the moment (2002).

The structure of this section is based on the observation that, whereas mineralization has occurred over a protracted period of geological time, it is concentrated within the early and late Proterozoic, Ordovician, Siluro-Devonian and Carboniferous to Early Tertiary and is linked with a number of episodes of continental rifting and plate collision. The mineralization comprises examples of hydrothermal, magmatic and sedimentary deposits of which the first is especially well represented around high-level stocks, in veins and associated with hot springs. The best known examples of each deposit type are discussed in the text, others are summarized in Tables 16.1–3 and all are located in Fig. 16.1.

Mineralization in Scotland is well covered in the recent literature and the reader is referred to Dunham *et al.* (1979), Hall (1993), Rice (1993), British Geological Survey Mineral Reconnaissance Reports, and numerous papers in the Transactions of the Institution of Mining and Metallurgy for more information.

Archaean

There are extensive tracts of Archaean felsic and mafic gneisses on the mainland of NW Scotland and offshore, predominantly in the Hebrides, but there are no known mineral deposits of proven Archaean age and, indeed, these gneissic rocks are depleted in many elements of economic interest, including gold, uranium and thorium, in common with lower crustal rocks in other shield areas (Tarney *et al.* 1972; Cameron 1994). However, they do contain significant concentrations of Ba in feldspar, an important point that will be discussed later. It is probable that any early mineral deposits would have been eroded or physically disrupted by the intense deformation or dispersed to higher crustal levels by partial melting and volatile flushing (Halliday *et al.* 1985).

Proterozoic

In the early Proterozoic (*c.* 2.4–2.0 Ga) there was a prolonged episode of continental extension, emplacement of basic (Scourie) dykes and, towards the end of this period, deposition of basic volcanics and greywackes (Loch Maree Group, see Chapter 3). This group also contains numerous small lenses of banded iron formation, manganiferous horizons and pyritic beds, including one at Kerry Road, Gairloch (below), with significant gold and copper concentrations, that were precipitated from submarine hot springs. Overall these rocks constitute a typical greenstone belt assemblage which, in other parts of the world, is a rich repository of metalliferous minerals. Whereas greenstone belts may cover vast areas in some countries (e.g. South Africa and Canada), Scotland has just $100 \, \mathrm{km}^2$ remaining. Nevertheless, it has profound metallogenic implications in that it demonstrates an event that could have transported significant quantities of metals from the mantle to the upper crust. These metals would then have been available, either in place or possibly as derived sediments, for remobilization and concentration in subsequent metallogenic events (Russell 1985).

From 2.0 to 1.2 Ga the Proterozoic is represented by granites and pegmatites belonging to the Laxfordian orogeny (see Chapter 3). Compared to the Archaean gneisses they contain enrichments of K, Ba (further enriched) and U and minor Mo mineralization (von Knorring & Dearnley 1960*a, b*; Russell 1985). The remainder of the Proterozoic is characterized by an extensional regime in which various basins accumulated continental clastic sequences (Torridonian) and marine clastics with or without volcanics (Dalradian and Moine respectively). These basins may have formed during a prolonged period of lithospheric extension which began in the Torridonian (*c.* 1.2 Ga) and, propagating in a southeasterly direction, ended with Iapetus rifting and eruption of the Tayvallich volcanics in the Dalradian basin (Soper *et al.* 1998).

Table 16.1. *Mineralization associated with plutonic/volcanic rocks (modified from Rice 1993)*

Location	Host rock	Style of mineralization	References
Ardsheal	Silurian appinite breccia pipes.	Disseminated pyrite and chalcopyrite with carbonate and chlorite alteration.	Rice & Davies (1979)
Arndilly	Locally brecciated Dalradian quartzite.	Mn and Fe oxide-bearing veins. Possibly related to late chlorite alteration.	MacGregor et al. (1920)
Ballachulish	Siluro-Devonian leucocratic micro-adamellite within composite granitoid.	Weak stockwork of quartz, pyrite, chalcopyrite, molybdenite, scheelite veinlets associated with sericite.	Evans et al. (1980) Haslam & Kimbell (1981) Harmon et al. (1985)
Balmaha	Ordovician serpentinite of the Highland Border Series.	Narrow streaks and lenses of chromite with silica and carbonate alteration. Up to 0.3% Cr.	Henderson et al. (1983)
Beinn nan Chaorach	Altered porphyritic dacite and intrusion breccia.	Central quartz, pyrite, chalcopyrite, molybdenite veins and peripheral sphalerite, galena veins. Sericite, kaolinite alteration. Up to (%) Cu 0.27, Mo 0.015.	Ellis et al. (1977) Zhou (1987a, b)
Ben Loyal	Silurian syenite.	Disseminated thorite, thorianite and REE minerals in syenite and mineralized pegmatite.	Heddle (1924) Gallager et al. (1971)
Black Stockarton Moor	Late Caledonian granite veins in Moine psammite.	Zoned copper sulphides, molybdenite and pyrite with sericite, chlorite alteration. Up to (%) Cu 0.44, Mo 0.034, Au 0.66 ppm.	Leake & Brown (1979) Leake & Cooper (1983)
Blackmount	Late Caledonian granite veins in psammite.	Pyrite and molybdenite in granite veins.	Smith & Marsden (1977)
Cairngarroch Bay	Devonian granodiorite – diorite complexes, partly porphyritic.	Weakly disseminated pyrite, pyrrhotite, chalcopyrite, arsenopyrite and pyrite veins. Locally intense sericite, calcite, chlorite alteration.	Allen et al. (1981)
Carn Chuinneag	Garnetiferous albite gneiss within Cambrian granitic complex.	Cassiterite in thin magnetite-rich bands within albite gneiss. Cu–Mo mineralization in quartz-breccia vein within aureole.	Gallagher et al. (1971)
Calliachar – Urlar Burn	Dalradian quartzite, quartz mica schist, amphibolite.	Quartz veins with electrum, tellurides, pyrite, galena, sphalerite, chalcopyrite, arsenopyrite, carbonates.	Ixer et al. (1997)
Comrie	Siluro-Devonian diorite and feldspathic rocks in contact with amphibolite sill at margin of diorite.	Auriferous pyrite and chalcopyrite veinlets in shear zone in diorite. Disseminated arsenopyrite and gold in feldspathic rocks.	R. E. Hazleton (pers. comm.) Plant et al. (1989)
Corrie Buie	Dalradian metalimestones and calcareous schists.	Stockwork of quartz veins with argentiferous galena and trace gold. Possibly related to felsic intrusive.	Wilson & Flett (1921) Pattrick (1984)
Corrycharmaig	Serpentinite sill hosted by Dalradian garnet mica and quartz schists.	Chromite pods in sill. Between 1855–1856 yielded 60 tonnes ore.	Anderson et al. (1949) Harrison (1985) Hawson & Hall (1987)
Dalbeattie	Hornfelsed Silurian greywackes in aureole of Criffel granodiorite.	Quartz, carbonate veins with pitchblende, chalcopyrite, bismuth and hematite. Possible Jurassic age.	Miller & Taylor (1966) Gallager et al. (1971)
Dorback	Brecciated contact zone between Caledonian diorite and marble.	Pyrrhotite and chalcopyrite in breccia. Chlorite, sericite and epidote alteration.	P. Henney (pers. comm.)
Etive	Siluro-Devonian late adamellite in composite granitoid.	Quartz, molybdenite, chalcopyrite, scheelite veins in weakly altered (sericite, chlorite) adamellite. Up to 0.9% Mo.	Haslam & Cameron (1985) Batchelor (1987)
Garbh Achadh	Late Caledonian biotite-feldspar porphyry stock, marginal igneous breccias and epidiorite country rock.	Disseminated pyrite, pyrrhotite, chalcopyrite and molybdenite and weak sericite and kaolinite alteration. Up to 0.24% Cu.	Ellis et al. (1978) Fortey (1980)
Glen Gairn	Siluro-Devonian lithium granite cutting diorite–granite complex.	Veins of wolframite, cassiterite, scheelite and molybdenite and disseminations of sphalerite, chalcopyrite and topaz in Li granite, greisen alteration.	Tindle & Webb (1989) Webb et al. (1992)
Glendinning	Silurian greywacke.	Stratabound and disseminated Fe–As sulphides cut by quartz, dolomite veinlets containing Fe–base metal–Sb-bearing sulphides. Produced 200 tonnes Sb.	Dewey et al. (1920) Gallagher el al. (1983) Duller et al. (1997)
Glenhead Burn	Ordovician greywacke near margin of Siluro-Devonian Loch Doon granodiorite and monzonitic intrusions.	Disseminations of Fe sulphides and arsenopyrite in monzonite and quartz–pyrite–arsenopyrite–gold veins near margin of granodiorite. Up to 8.8 ppm Au.	Leake et al. (1981) Naden & Caulfield (1989)

Table 16.1. (*continued*)

Location	Host rock	Style of mineralization	References
Lairg	Siluro-Devonian adamellite and Moine–Lewisian country rocks.	Molybdenite and pyrite with Cu and Bi sulphides in quartz veins and coatings. Also younger quartz, base metal sulphide veins.	Gallagher *et al.* (1974)
Hare Hill	Siluro-Devonian granodiorite.	Early quartz, pyrite, arsenopyrite, chalcopyrite veins and later quartz, stibnite, galena, sphalerite veins. Sericite, chlorite, carbonate alteration.	Dewey *et al.* (1920) Fowler (1976) Boast *et al.* (1990)
Helmsdale	Silurian biotite adamellite and Devonian sediments.	Disseminated thorite in adamellite. Uranium minerals in shear zones and sediments. Some molybdenite, chalcopyrite veins near Helmsdale Fault.	Gallager *et al.* (1971) Tweedie (1979) Plant *et al.* (1980)
Moorbrock Hill	Contact between Siluro-Devonian granodiorite and greywacke.	Early quartz, pyrite, arsenoprite and gold as veins and disseminations and later Cu–Zn sulphides.	Naden & Caulfield (1989)
Ratagain	Silurian quartz monzonite.	Quartz, fluorite veins with Fe–Mo–Cu–Pb–Zn–Bi-bearing sulphides and gold and silver minerals.	Alderton (1988)
Souter Head	Silurian intrusion breccia pipe including granite and quartz porphyry phases.	Pyrite and molybdenite in breccia matrix cavities and in quartz, sericite veins cutting breccia pipe.	Porteous (1973)
Stobshiel	Siluro-Devonian granitoid.	Early pyrite, arsenopyrite, gold veins and later base metal sulphide mineralization.	Naden & Caulfield (1989)
Talnotry	Late Caledonian diorite sill hosted by Palaeozoic shales and greywackes.	Sulphide lens at base of sill containing Fe–Co–Ni–Cu sulphides and gold.	Wilson & Flett (1921) Gregory (1928) Stanley *et al.* (1987)
Tomnadashan	Late Caledonian granitic lenses in diorite.	Fe–Cu–As–Sb sulphides as disseminations and in quartz, calcite veinlets associated with altered granitic lenses.	Wilson & Flett (1921) Zabala (1970) Pattrick (1984)

See main text for Arthrath, Cononish, Fore Burn, Knock, Lagalochan, Rhynie, Unst. Further details and references in Hall (1993) and Rice (1993).

Table 16.2. *Stratiform mineralization of Sedex and Volcanogenic Type in the Middle Dalradian Argyll Group (slightly modified after Hall 1993). Listed in approximate geographic sequence from SW to NE (Asterisk following area refers to locality on Fig. 16.1)*

Locality	Style of Mineralization	References
Meall Mor*	Chalcopyrite in veins and disseminations in metabasites and metasediments hosted by Upper Erins Quartzite. 1 km² zone locally enriched.	Wilson & Flett (1921), Smith *et al.* (1978), Willan (1980, 1983), Willan & Coleman (1983).
Knapdale Pyrite Horizon	Thin layers of pyrite, sphalerite and scarce galena in metasediments hosted by Upper Erins Quartzite. Sporadic showings 100 m thick, 7 km strike.	Smith *et al.* (1978), Willan (1980, 1983), Willan & Coleman (1983).
Craignure	Thin (10 cm) layers of massive iron sulphides with chalcopyrite and pentlandite in metasediments hosted by Ardrishaig Phyllite. 60 m strike.	Wilson & Flett (1921), Willan (1980, 1983), Willan & Coleman (1983).
Inverary*	Thin layers of massive and disseminated iron sulphides with chalcopyrite and pentlandite in metasediments hosted by Ardrishaig Phyllite. 0.1 km².	Wilson & Flett (1921), Berridge (1969), Willan (1983).
Tom na Gobhair	Thin lenses of massive iron sulphides with chalcopyrite in metasediments hosted by Loch Tay Limestone.	Willan (1983).
Garbh Achadh	Thin layers of massive and disseminated iron sulphides with chalcopyrite and minor arsenopyrite in metasediments hosted by Crinan Grit.	Ellis *et al.* (1978), Willan (1980, 1983).
Creggans	Thin layers of massive and disseminated iron sulphides with minor chalcopyrite in metasediments hosted by Ardrishaig Phyllite.	Willan (1983), Smith *et al.* (1977).
McPhun's Cairn	Thin layers and small pods of massive iron sulphides with galena and sphalerite in metasediments hosted by Ardrishaig Phyllite.	Wilson & Flett (1921), Smith *et al.* (1977). Willan & Hall (1980), Willan (1980, 1983), Willan & Coleman (1983).
Allt Donachain	Small showing of sulphides and Ba-silicate in metasediments hosted by transition group near base of Ben Eagach Schist.	Gallagher (pers. comm.).
Tyndrum Area*		
Auchtertyre Horizon (Auchtertyre)	Disseminated iron sulphides with sphalerite and chalcopyrite in metasediments near middle of Ben Challum Quartzite. Up to 80 m thick, 9 km along strike.	Fortey & Smith (1986), Smith *et al.* (1988), Willan & Coleman (1983).

Table 16.2. (*continued*)

Locality	Style of mineralization	References
Eag Uillt Horizon (Auchtertyre)	Up to 8 wt% ZnS in quartzites in Ben Lawers Schist.	
Ben Challum Horizon (Auchtertyre)	Disseminated pyrite with sphalerite, galena and chalcopyrite in metasediments near top of Ben Challum Quartzite. Up to 20 m thick, 4 km along strike.	Fortey & Smith (1986), Smith *et al.* (1988), Willan & Coleman (1983).
Ben Challum Horizon (Creag Bhocan)	Thin massive and disseminated iron sulphides with chalcopyrite and sphalerite in metasediments with metabasites near top of Ben Challum Quartzite. 3 bands 1–3 m thick, 3 km along strike.	Scott *et al.* (1988).
Pubil (Glen Lyon)	Disseminated iron sulphides in metasediments hosted by Sron Bheag Schist. 500 m² zone with iron sulphides (IP anomaly only).	Smith *et al.* (1977).
Lower Glen Lyon (Deri Cambus to Creag Dubh)	Thin layers of sphalerite, pyrrhotite with minor galena, pyrite in metasediments hosted by transition group near base of Ben Eagach Schist.	Willan (1981, 1983).
Loch Lyon* (Ben Heasgarnich)	Disseminated baryte, barian silicates, sphalerite in metasediments hosted by Ben Eagach Schist. 1–3 m thick, 4 km along strike.	Coats *et al.* (1984a, b), Scott (1987), Scott *et al.* (1991).
Aberfeldy Area*, see main text.		
Western Sector (Foss)	Massive baryte with disseminated pyrite, magnetite, sphalerite; quartz-celsian; pods of massive iron sulphides with galena, sphalerite in metasediments; hosted by Ben Eagach Schist (subdivided into Foss West and East). Layers up to 5 m, 2 km strike, Reserves 2 × 10⁶ tonnes.	Coats *et al.* (1980, 1981), Willan (1980, 1983), Willan & Coleman (1983), Fortey & Beddoe-Stephens (1982), Russell *et al.* (1984), Swainbank & Fortey (1981), Russell (1985, 1988a, b), Parker (1980), Hall *et al.* (1991), Moles (1983, 1985, 1986).
Central Sector (Ben Eagach)	Massive baryte with disseminated pyrite; quartz-celsian; massive carbonate with galena, sphalerite, pyrite; in metasediments hosted by Ben Eagach Schist. Layer up to 2 m, 600 m strike.	
Eastern Sector (Duntanlich)	Massive baryte with disseminated pyrite; quartz-celsian; in metasediments hosted by Ben Eagach Schist. Layers up to 5 m, 1.5 km strike. Mineable reserve >6 × 10⁶ tonnes.	
Moulin (Pitlochry)	Minor showing of disseminated iron sulphides in metasediments plus Zn geochemical anomaly at Ben Eagach/Ben Lawers schist boundary.	Smith *et al.* (1977), Phillips *et al.* (1986).
Glenshee Area*		
Glenlochsie Burn	Disseminated chalcopyrite and iron sulphides with iron oxides in metasediments; Zn drainage anomaly; hosted by Ben Eagach Schist/Ben Lawers Schist in complex structural relationship.	Smith *et al.* (1977), Coats *et al.* (1984a, b, 1987), Pease *et al.* (1986).
Allt an Daimh.	Iron sulphides, galena and sphalerite in lower laminated quartzite member of Ben Eagach Schist.	
Braemar Area*		
Allt an Loch	Stratiform baryte bed (5 m thick, 0.8 km length) with disseminated pyrite at top of Ben Eagach Schist.	Gallagher *et al.* (1989a), Fortey *et al.* (1991).
Loch Kander	Stratiform iron sulphides, galena, sphalerite with armenite, hyalophane and baryte in calc-silicate schist (15 m thick, 300 m strike) near top of Ben Eagach Schist.	
Lecht*	Stratiform pyrite and strata-bound galena, sphalerite and quartz veins hosted by metasediments of Appin (or Argyll?) Group. (0.5 km NNE of Lecht Mine).	Smith (1985), Nicholson & Anderton (1989).
Huntly Area*	Sulphides in intraformational breccias, cherts, schists of Middle Dalradian Portsoy Group.	Coats *et al.* (1987).
Vidlin, see main text		

The Torridonian consists of up to 10 km of clastic fluviatile and lacustrine sediments and rare volcanics deposited in rift basins between *c.* 1.2 and 1.0 Ga (see Chapter 3). No significant mineralization is known in Scotland, but in similar sequences elsewhere, such as on the Colorado Plateau, there are important deposits of uranium, copper and vanadium. The lack of mineralization may be due to the paucity of organic matter in the Torridonian, which is an important control on precipitation in younger sequences, the nature of the source regions and possibly the absence of sufficient thermal energy (early in the rifting process) to power hydrothermal convection in the upper crust. The source regions for the Torridonian consisted of upper crustal rocks of normal composition, and therefore possible metal sources, but also locally derived Lewisian gneiss depleted in metals (Van de Kamp & Leake 1997). The Moine sequence deposited as shallow marine sands and muds also contains little known mineralization, and similar reasons as for the Torridonian may be invoked.

The opening of Iapetus (*c.* 600 Ma) marks the second major metallogenic event in Scotland. It generated widespread igneous

Table 16.3. *Principal vein deposits of lead, zinc, baryte and silver (modified from Gallagher 1991)*

Location	Productive minerals	Production 10³ t	Associated minerals	Trend	Geological age	Isotopic age	Host rocks	Reference
Blackcraig	Galena sphalerite	5 / 1.2	Calcite, dolomite, baryte, chalcopyrite	WNW–ESE	Post Permo-Carboniferous	—	Silurian greywackes, Permo-Carboniferous dolerite dyke	Wilson & Flett (1921), Gallagher (1964)
Strontian	Galena, sphalerite baryte	3.2 (Pb) / 0.03	Calcite, quartz, pyrite, minor strontianite and the barium zeolites, harmotome and brewsterite	WNW	Pre Eocene dolerite dykes, post Permo-Carboniferous dolerite and camptonite dykes	Late Permian	Carboniferous-Permian dykes, late Caledonian Strontian granite, Moine gneisses	Wilson & Flett (1921), Gallagher (1964), Ineson & Mitchell (1974), Mason & Mason (1984)
Tyndrum	Galena, sphalerite	10	Quartz, baryte, calcite, pyrite, chalcopyrite and later uraninite	NE–SW	Pre Late Carboniferous dolerite dyke; post late Caledonian quartz porphyry dyke	Pb–Zn mid Carboniferous; (uraninite, Late Permian)	Grampian Group Psammites, Early Dalradian schists	Ineson & Mitchell (1974), Pattrick (1985), Wilson & Flett (1921)
Woodhead	Galena	6.7 (Pb)	Calcite, dolomite, quartz, sphalerite, chalcopyrite	WNW–ESE	Post Ordovician	—	Ordovician greywackes	Wilson & Flett (1921)
Cumberhead	Baryte, galena	—	Hematite	NW–SE	Post Early Carboniferous	Jurassic (palaeo-magnetic)	Early Devonian felsite, Silurian sediments	Gallagher et al. (1982), Evans & El-Nikheli (1982)
Gasswater	Baryte	500	Calcite	NNW–SSE and WNW–ESE	Post Early Carboniferous	Late Carboniferous to Permian	Early Carboniferous and Devonian sediments	Scott (1967), Moore (1979)
Glen Sannox	Baryte	52	—	NNW–SSE	Post Early Devonian	Triassic	Early Devonian Sandstones, mudstone and conglomerate	MacGregor et al. (1944), Moore (1979)
Muirshiel	Baryte	300	Minor hematite, quartz, mica, calcite, strontianite	NNE–SSW; E–W	Pre Eocene dolerite dykes, post Late Carboniferous dykes	Triassic	Early Carboniferous volcanics	MacGregor et al. (1944), Moore (1979), Stephenson & Coats (1983)
Myres Burn	Baryte	—	—	NW–SE; NS to NNW–SSW	Post Early Carboniferous volcanics	—	Early Carboniferous trachytic tuffs and lavas	MacGregor et al. (1944)

See main text for Leadhills–Wanlockhead and the silver deposits at Alva and Hilderston

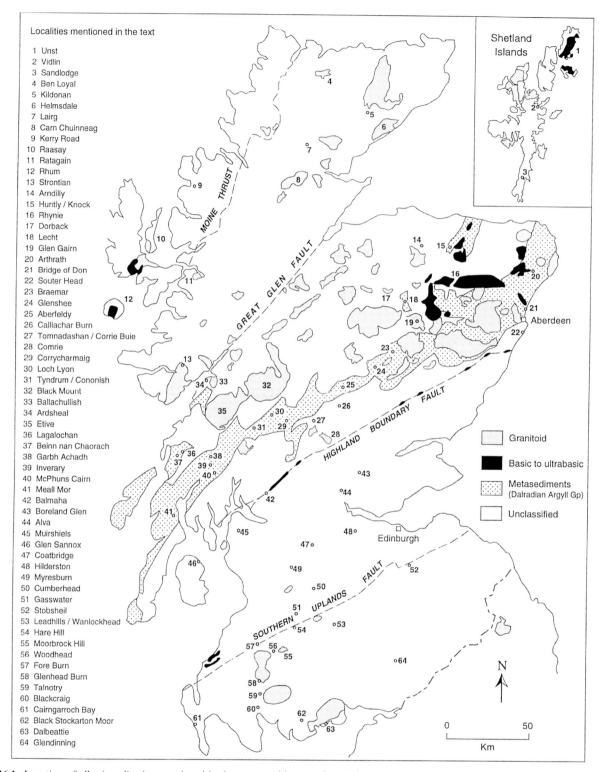

Fig. 16.1. Location of all mineralization mentioned in the text or tables superimposed on a simplified geological map.

Localities mentioned in the text

1 Unst
2 Vidlin
3 Sandlodge
4 Ben Loyal
5 Kildonan
6 Helmsdale
7 Lairg
8 Carn Chuinneag
9 Kerry Road
10 Raasay
11 Ratagain
12 Rhum
13 Strontian
14 Arndilly
15 Huntly / Knock
16 Rhynie
17 Dorback
18 Lecht
19 Glen Gairn
20 Arthrath
21 Bridge of Don
22 Souter Head
23 Braemar
24 Glenshee
25 Aberfeldy
26 Calliachar Burn
27 Tomnadashan / Corrie Buie
28 Comrie
29 Corrycharmaig
30 Loch Lyon
31 Tyndrum / Cononish
32 Black Mount
33 Ballachullish
34 Ardsheal
35 Etive
36 Lagalochan
37 Beinn nan Chaorach
38 Garbh Achadh
39 Inverary
40 McPhuns Cairn
41 Meall Mor
42 Balmaha
43 Boreland Glen
44 Alva
45 Muirshiels
46 Glen Sannox
47 Coatbridge
48 Hilderston
49 Myresburn
50 Cumberhead
51 Gasswater
52 Stobsheil
53 Leadhills / Wanlockhead
54 Hare Hill
55 Moorbrock Hill
56 Woodhead
57 Fore Burn
58 Glenhead Burn
59 Talnotry
60 Blackcraig
61 Cairngarroch Bay
62 Black Stockarton Moor
63 Dalbeattie
64 Glendinning

Granitoid

Basic to ultrabasic

Metasediments
(Dalradian Argyll Gp)

Unclassified

activity and a belt of submarine hot springs within a basin (Dalradian) that extended from the SW Highlands to the Grampians, and possibly to the Shetlands. The submarine hot springs deposited important concentrations of baryte and minor Cu, Pb, Zn and Ni. The igneous activity also includes an alkali-rich granite intrusion, Carn Chuinneag, which carries minor cassiterite mineralization (Table 16.1). Such mineralized granites are typical of continental rift settings and ones of similar age are found in the Appalachians (Hudson & Dall-

meyer 1982) and characterise the opening of Iapetus. It seems likely that the fundamental reason for the restriction of significant mineralization to the Dalradian basin is the presence of igneous activity and a high regional geothermal gradient. These factors provided thermal energy to drive hydrothermal convection cells which accessed a variety of metal sources and produced the mineralization.

The hot spring deposits are restricted to the middle Dalradian Argyll Group and may be divided into older barium-rich

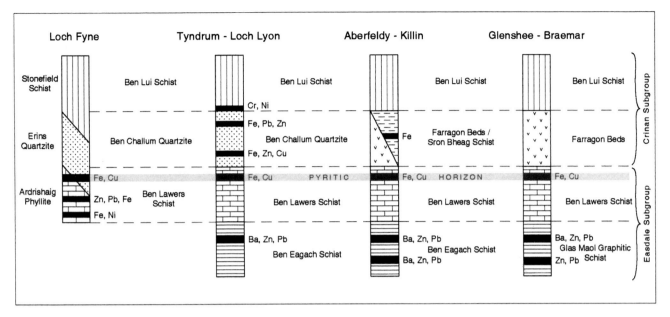

Fig. 16.2. Metallogenic stratigraphy of the Argyll Group (Middle Dalradian) (after Smith 1992; Smith & Gallagher 1994).

and younger base metal-rich varieties. The former are restricted to the Ben Eagach Schist whereas the latter are hosted by the Ben Lawers Schist and younger formations (Fig. 16.2). The most important barium deposit, now the Foss Mine near Aberfeldy, was discovered by the BGS using drainage geochemistry during the DTI funded Mineral Reconnaissance Programme (Coats *et al*. 1980). As the largest barite mine in the UK it supplies around 25% of the annual requirement. From 1984 to 1999 around 685 000 tonnes of direct shipping grade baryte has been supplied to North Sea hydrocarbon operations.

Kerry Road copper-gold deposit

The Kerry Road deposit, originally noted by Peach *et al*. (1907), consists of a 4 m thick, finely banded, quartz-carbonate schist containing about 20% of sulphides, of which the most common are pyrite and pyrrhotite with minor chalcopyrite, a little sphalerite and a trace of native gold (Fig. 16.3a, b; Jones *et al*. 1987). The footwall is chloritic hornblende schist and the hangingwall hornblende schist with minor iron formation. Deformation of the ore horizon is intense and, although the outcrop is terminated at both ends by low angle faults of uncertain age, it continues at depth to the southeast (Fig. 16.3c). The Loch Maree Group contains roughly equal amounts of hornblende schist and quartz mica schist, interpreted as basic igneous rocks (flows and sills) and greywackes respectively. All are strongly deformed and affected by lower amphibolite-facies metamorphism (Williams *et al*. 1985; see Chapter 3). The basic rocks have a MORB composition (Johnson *et al*. 1987) and may have been the extrusive equivalents of the latest Scourie dykes (see Chapter 3). The assemblage of main ore metals Cu, Zn, Au, in conjunction with mafic rocks of MORB type and continentally derived clastic sediments, are consistent with submarine exhalative activity in a back-arc setting involving continental rifting.

Aberfeldy baryte deposits

In the Aberfeldy area baryte occurs as highly folded and usually steeply dipping beds up to several metres thick. They are commonly enveloped in cherty pyritic celsian (Ba-feldspar) rock and are associated with graphitic muscovite schist, along about 7 km of strike of the Ben Eagach schist (Fig. 16.4). The

baryte beds have been divided into three sections along strike (Foss, Ben Eagach, Duntanlich) (Table 16.2). The Duntanlich orebody has a mineable reserve of over 6×10^6 tonnes but was refused planning permission in 1997 (see Chapter 20). The baryte beds usually contain more than 90% by volume of coarse granoblastic baryte together with impurities such as sulphides, carbonates, magnetite and quartz that tend to be concentrated in thin layers. Significant quantities of barium also occur in barium muscovite within the enclosing graphitic schists and the overall barium content of the Aberfeldy mineralization, as contained in baryte and barium-bearing silicates, is probably the highest in the world. At the same lithostratigraphical level there are deposits that are similar in style but smaller in size in the Loch Lyon (Coats *et al*. 1984a, b), Glen Shee (Pease *et al*. 1986) and Braemar areas (Gallagher *et al*. 1989a) (Figs 16.1, 2; Table 16.2).

The Foss Mine is exploiting the western sector of the outcrop at Aberfeldy where mineralization can be traced for 1.8 km in a highly folded, sub-vertical zone 60–110 m thick which has been tested by drilling to a depth of 350 m. The main baryte bed averages 4 m thick in the worked section of the deposit where proven reserves are 0.3×10^6 tonnes at or above API grade. The American Petroleum Institute (API) specification for baryte is independent of mineralogical composition and requires principally that the density of the delivered product is $4.2\,\mathrm{g\,cm^{-3}}$. Extraction has been successfully adapted to the pronounced folding of the baryte horizon underground (Fig. 16.5) but in the open pit, where overall grade is variable and wallrock contamination is less easy to control, sub-API specification barite is worked as blending material to reduce costs. The baryte bed on the Cluniemore property is 5–13 m thick, locally reaching 33 m, and has been proved along 750 m of strike to at least 550 m depth (Butcher 1999, pers. comm.).

Sulphur isotope studies show that baryte sulphur was mainly derived from local Dalradian sea water, whereas the sulphide sulphur is essentially of hydrothermal origin (Willan & Coleman 1983; Moles 1986; Hall *et al*. 1988, 1991). Oxygen isotope analysis of the cherty celsian rock suggests that the chert was deposited at about 200°C from sea water (Fisk 1986). Pb and Sr isotopes indicate that the Lower Appin and Grampian groups and the Lewisian were possible metal sources (Hall *et al*. 1991; Swainbank & Fortey 1981).

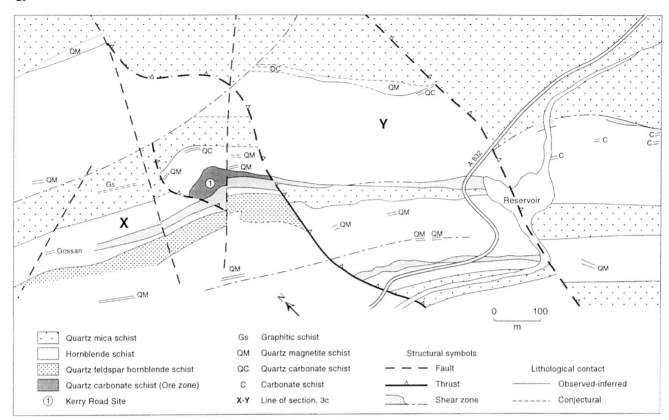

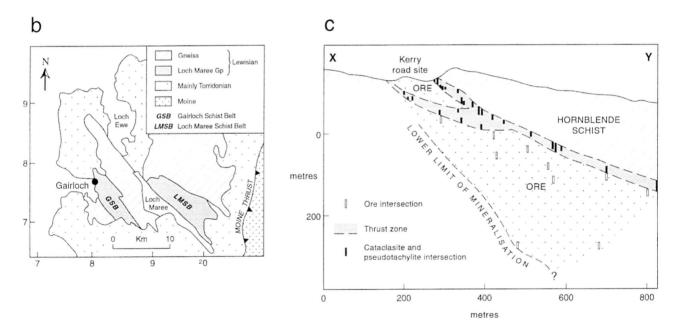

Fig. 16.3. (a) Geology of the Kerry Road Cu–Au deposit, Gairloch. (b) Regional geological setting. (c) Cross-section of the ore zone (after Jones *et al.* 1987).

There is general agreement that the baryte was deposited from hot springs debouching into fault-controlled sedimentary basins that were located on a continental margin as the Proterozoic continent started to break up (Coats *et al.* 1984*a*,*b*; Plant *et al.* 1984; Russell *et al.* 1984) (Fig 16.6). This hydrothermal activity predates the onset of significant igneous activity in the developing Dalradian basin. As such, they are classic examples of sedex-type submarine exhalative deposits.

The barium could have been sourced from feldspars in Lewisian gneisses, Laxfordian granites and pegmatites or sedimentary derivatives such as the Moine and Grampian Groups which are enriched in Ba (Plant *et al.* 1984). The formation of baryte may result from the mixing of sea water and barium-rich hydrothermal solutions emanating from hot springs (Fig. 16.7) or from the mixing of dense sulphate-rich brines from evaporitic tidal environments with barium-rich hydrothermal

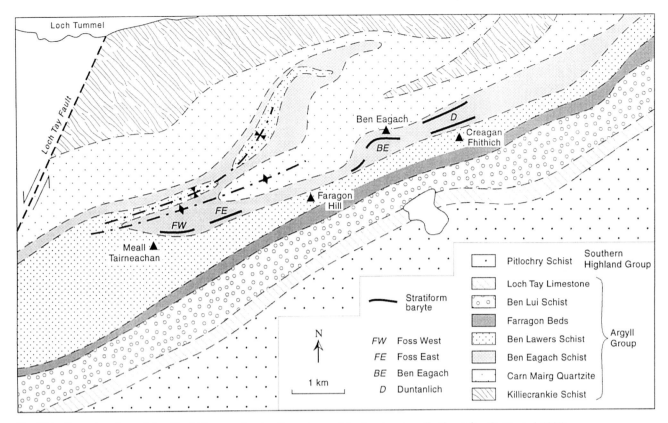

Fig. 16.4. General geology of the Aberfeldy area showing the outcrop of the baryte mineralization (after Coats *et al.* 1981).

Fig. 16.5. Stope in folded barite bed looking east. Subsidiary F2 folds lying subhorizontal with respect to a north–south section but plunging 25° west are modified by upright F3 folds (photograph by P. R. Deakin FRPS).

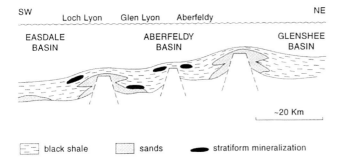

Fig. 16.6. Schematic section at time of Ben Eagach Schist deposition, showing the position of inferred second-order basins (from Hall 1993, simplified after Coats *et al.* 1984).

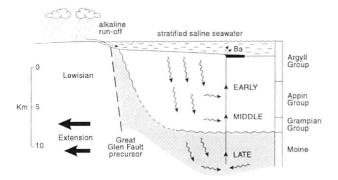

Fig. 16.7. Generalized model for the genesis of the Aberfeldy stratiform mineralization with particular reference to the origin of celsian (from Hall 1993, simplified after Russell *et al.* 1984).

solutions (Willan & Coleman 1983; Russell *et al.* 1984). It has been suggested (Russell *et al.* 1984) that the timing of the mineralization represented the first opportunity for sea water to access and leach Ba from newly fractured continental basement, possibly via downward excavating convection cells.

Minor base metal and nickel deposits

There are a number of relatively minor stratiform and disseminated Fe–Cu–Pb–Zn–Ni sulphide deposits hosted by the Easdale and Crinan Subgroups (Smith *et al.* 1977, 1988; Scott *et al.* 1988; Fortey & Smith 1986; Willan 1983).They are found within at least five horizons of which one, the pyritic horizon, can be traced from Loch Fyne in the southwest to Glen Shee in the northeast, a distance of 160 km (Fig. 16.2) (Smith *et al.* 1977). These horizons correspond in time to the first appearance of amphibolites which mark the onset of mafic igneous activity in the Dalradian basin (Scott *et al.* 1991). Examples of the sulphide deposits include Creag Bhocan, McPhun's Cairn, Auchtertyre, Ben Challum, Meall Mor and Inverary (Fig. 16.1, Table 16.2). At Creag Bochan, sulphide layers 1–3 m thick may be traced along strike for *c.* 3 km. The layers consist of laminae of pyrite, chalcopyrite and minor sphalerite in amphibolite, quartzite and chlorite–mica schist. A Cu–Zn sulphide horizon associated with hornblende schist at Vidlin in the Shetlands shows similarities to this group of deposits but its stratigraphic position within the Dalradian is uncertain (Garson & May 1976). The sulphides were probably deposited from hot springs associated with mafic volcanic activity and may be classed as volcanogenic massive sulphide deposits. Sulphur isotope studies of the sulphides are consistent with the sulphide sulphur being produced mainly by high-temperature reduction of sea water sulphate (Scott *et al.* 1986,

1991; Willan & Coleman 1983). The copper mineralization at Meall Mor in epidotised metabasites and metasediments may be related to high level emplacement of mafic sills into sediments (Mohammed 1987). The unusual nickel-rich mineralization at Inverary could also be exhalative and may involve ultramafic rocks at depth.

Ordovician

Spreading of Iapetus continued until Early or Mid-Cambrian when a compressional phase (the Grampian Orogeny) began, which lasted until the Early Ordovician. The orogeny may have been caused by collision between Laurentia and island arcs or a microcontinent, the Midland Valley terrane (see Chapter 7). Ordovician mafic intrusive rocks (the Younger Basics) assumed to represent the roots of an island arc, are found in the NE of Scotland (Yardley *et al.* 1982). These contain significant Cu–Ni mineralization in the Knock and Arthrath intrusions (Table 16.1). In addition, obduction of oceanic crust in the period Mid-Ordovician to Mid-Silurian has resulted in the exposure of historically important chromite deposits and significant Platinum Group Element (PGE) mineralization at the base of this crust in Unst.

Copper–nickel mineralization in mafic magmas

Copper–nickel mineralization was discovered in the Knock and Arthrath mafic intrusions, Aberdeenshire, during a regional exploration programme by a consortium of companies (Exploration Ventures Ltd.) (Rice 1975). The intrusions are poorly exposed and structurally complex and consist of layered peridotitic to gabbroic cumulates, granular gabbros and norites and xenolithic rocks. The most significant mineralization (2×10^6 tonnes @ 0.52% Ni and 0.27% Cu) occurs at the southern edge of the Knock mass, where disseminated to massive sulphides are hosted by gabbro and norite cumulates in a structurally complex contact zone (Fig. 16.8). Anomalous levels of precious metals also occur in these contact zone sulphides and sulphide-rich rocks (up to 380 ppb Pd and 180 ppb Au) and pyroxene pegmatites (up to 585 ppb Pt and 95 ppb Pd) (Fletcher & Rice 1989). Sulphur and oxygen isotope evidence suggests that assimilation of siliceous country rocks in the contact zone was responsible for the separation of a Ni- and Cu-rich sulphide liquid that produced the mineralization (Fletcher *et al.* 1989, 1997).

Chromite deposits in Unst

Chromite has been worked commercially in Unst, Shetlands (Hitchen 1929) and, to a much lesser extent, at Corrycharmaig in Perthshire (Table 16.1). Small chromite pods on Unst in Shetland have yielded 52 000 tonnes of ore, largely for the chemical industry, until production ceased in 1944. The chromite occurs as cumulate lenses and layers within hartzburgite and dunite units in the lower part of an ophiolite sequence emplaced onto Dalradian basement (Garson & Plant 1973; Prichard 1984). The sequence also contains thin (<1 m) PGE-enriched horizons (up to 3 ppm Pt + Pd) hosted by sulphide-rich and chromite-rich basal cumulate dunites (Prichard & Lord 1993; Lord & Prichard 1997) (Fig. 16.9). The most abundant PGE minerals include sperrylite ($PtAs_2$), stibiopalladinite (Pd_3Sb), Pt–Pd–Cu–Au alloys and potarite (PdHg) (Fig. 16.10). Some PGE enrichments are probably of magmatic origin as indicated by the sulphur isotope ratios of associated sulphides, whereas others, which occur in serpentinized zones, may be related to later hydrothermal processes (Maynard *et al.* 1997*a*; Gunn *et al.* 1985).

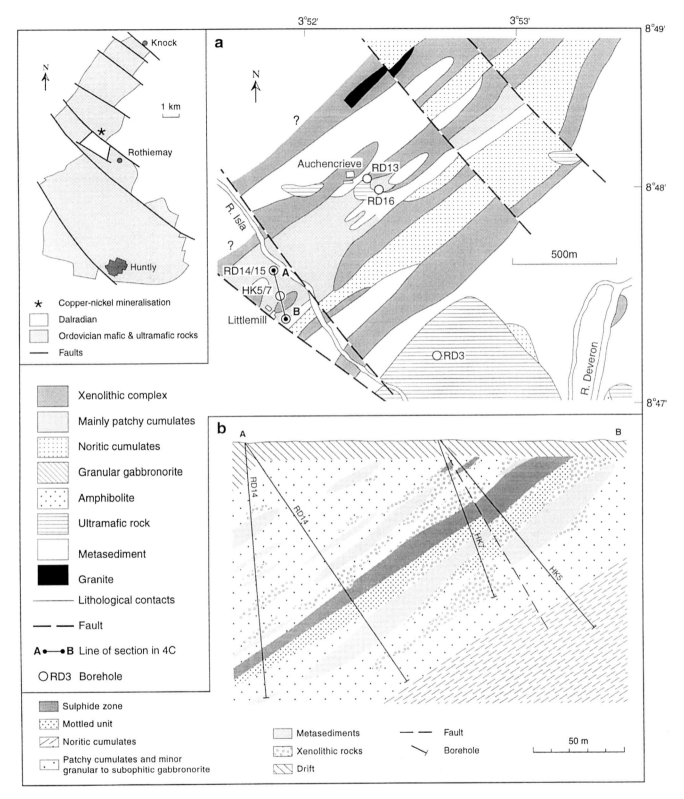

Fig. 16.8. (**a**) Geological map of the Littlemill–Auchencrieve area (after Fletcher & Rice 1989); (**b**) cross-section through the Littlemill ore zone (after Wilks 1974). Inset, location of the mineralization within the Huntly–Knock basic mass.

Silurian–Devonian

The period from the Late Ordovician to the Early Devonian is particularly interesting from the mineralization point of view. During this time the Iapetus ocean closed and was replaced in northern Britain by an essentially transtensional regime (Pattrick & Polya 1993; Treagus *et al.* 1999) with sinistral

shearing, and accompanied by major igneous activity. Batholiths and a large number of minor granitoid intrusions and andesitic lavas were produced showing predominantly calc-alkaline characteristics (see Chapter 8).

The combination of regional structures, a transtensional regime and abundant igneous activity was especially favourable for hydrothermal mineralization and a variety of styles is seen.

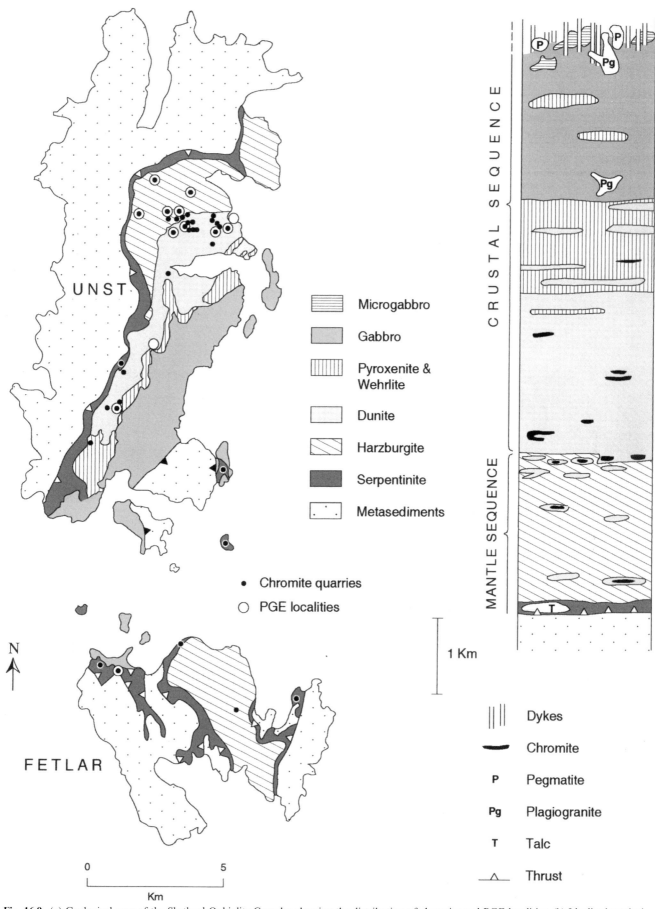

Fig. 16.9. (a) Geological map of the Shetland Ophiolite Complex showing the distribution of chromite and PGE localities. (b) Idealized vertical section through the Shetland Ophiolite Complex (both modified after Prichard & Neary 1985).

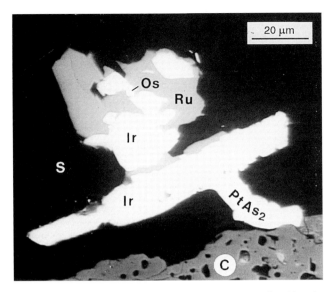

Fig. 16.10. SEM backscattered image of a composite grain of irarsite (Ir), ruthenian pentlandite (Ru), sperrylite (PtAs) and a euhedral hexagonal crystal of native osmium (Os). The grain is surrounded by silicate (S) but attached to the edge of a chromite grain (C). From Cliff, Unst (Prichard *et al.* 1986).

The most common is porphyry Cu mineralization of which Ballachulish, Beinn nan Chaorach and Garbh Achadh are good examples (Table 16.1). An unique example of granite-hosted Mo–W–Sn mineralization is associated with one of the youngest and most evolved Caledonian granitoids at Glen Gairn (Webb *et al.* 1992). However, whereas in other parts of the world porphyry deposits are a major source of copper, none of the Scottish mineralization is economically significant, a fact which has been attributed to the lack of epizonal water (Plant *et al.* 1983). Of much more economic interest is the gold and silver mineralization related to the igneous activity. Good examples of the variety seen here are Lagalochan, Foreburn and Rhynie. Cononish may also be included in this group.

Gold and silver mineralization at Lagalochan and Foreburn

The Lagalochan gold–silver prospect is hosted by a subvolcanic diatreme about 2 km in diameter on the southern edge of the Lorne Plateau (Harris *et al.* 1988*a, b*). The diatreme contains several breccia types, including molybdenite-bearing vein quartz, which are cut by felsic stocks, sills and dykes. Mineralization comprises a gold–copper–molybdenum inner zone and an outer base and precious metal zone and is accompanied by strong hydrothermal alteration. Electrum, native silver and tetrahedrite are the most important precious metal-bearing minerals. The Cu–Mo mineralization was deposited at a depth of about 1000 m from hypersaline magmatic fluids at temperatures in excess of 400°C indicating, together with the geology, clear affinities with porphyry-style systems (Kay 1985).

A rather different style of mineralization, possibly representing a higher structural level than Lagalochan, is seen at Fore Burn near Straiton. Here there is a linear zone of intense hydrothermal alteration (including sericite and tourmaline) running for about 2.5 km parallel to the nearby Southern Uplands Fault and hosted by Early Devonian diorites and volcaniclastic sediments. The zone contains veins and disseminations of iron and base metal sulphides and gold (Allen *et al.* 1982; Charley *et al.* 1989).

Rhynie hot-spring gold system

The Rhynie cherts, world renowned for their early plants and arthropods (see Chapter 8) are the exhalative manifestation of an adularia-sericite hot spring system, which is unique in the UK (Rice & Trewin 1988; Rice *et al.* 1995, 2002). It is located within a small outlier containing Early Devonian fluviatile and lacustrine sediments and volcanics. Siliceous sinters, andesitic lavas and tuffs, intensely altered to quartz and adularia in places, are centred on a major low-angle extensional fault zone defining the basin margin on the western side. They contain enrichments of Au, As, W and Mo over at least 2 km of the fault outcrop. Below the oxidation zone gold has been proved in arsenian pyrite. Multiple quartz, chert and carbonate veining and brecciation are widely developed, especially along the basin margin fault zone.

The fluids responsible for most of the hydrothermal alteration and sinter deposition were dominated by meteoric water but incursions of high-temperature magmatic fluids also occurred (Rice *et al.* 1995). The nature of the parental magma(s) is uncertain at the moment. The temporal and spatial association between the andesitic lavas and tuffs and the hot spring deposits suggest a genetic link with andesitic magma but the presence of anomalous levels of Mo and W indicate an involvement with late Caledonian granitic magmas (Fig. 16.11).

The presence of additional epithermal mineralization of possible Devonian age in Aberdeenshire, Sutherland and near Inverness, together with numerous outcrops of Devonian sediments in eastern and northeastern Scotland, indicate that much of this area is close to the Devonian palaeosurface and is prospective for further epithermal deposits (Nicholson 1989, 1990; Crummy 1993; Crummy *et al.* 1997).

The Cononish gold deposit

Mesothermal gold-bearing quartz veins are found throughout the upland areas of Scotland. Notable examples include Glenhead Burn and Glendinning in the Southern Uplands, Cononish and Calliachar Burn in the Grampians. These may represent the distal manifestations of magmatic hydrothermal systems (Leake *et al.* 1981; Patrick *et al.* 1988; Duller *et al.* 1997; Ixer *et al.* 1997). The Cononish Au–Ag deposit, near Tyndrum, is the most important precious metal deposit so far discovered in Scotland this century. Alluvial gold attracted prospectors to the area and the discovery of auriferous quartz sulphide float in 1984 led directly to outcropping mineralization on the slopes of Beinn Chuirn. The mineralization (450 000 tonnes at a cut and diluted grade of 11.3 g/t Au and 60.1 g/t Ag) is hosted by a silicified breccia zone, the Eas Anie vein, which has been proved for 700 m along strike and 500 m down dip (Fig. 16.12). It fills a structure considered to have formed during left-lateral movement of the nearby Tyndrum Fault (Treagus *et al.* 1999). The wall rocks are of psammite, pelite, amphibolite and impure limestone of the Grampian and Appin groups, which have been silicified and haematized by the hydrothermal solutions responsible for the deposit. The mineralization predates a Permo-Carboniferous dyke, and an Early Devonian age of about 410 Ma, is indicated by K–Ar dating of K-feldspar in the wall-rock (Curtis 1990; Treagus *et al.* 1999).

Ore grade mineralization is restricted to two ore shoots plunging 45° SW and correlates with the overall sulphide content, especially of galena. It is best developed where the vein cuts competent psammites and ductile pelites. The sulphides consist mainly of fine grained pyrite, chalcopyrite, galena and sphalerite and the precious metal phases are various tellurides, electrum and native gold and silver (Pattrick *et al.* 1988; Earls *et al.* 1992). The mineralization is similar to that occurring in other auriferous quartz veins in the Tyndrum area (Pattrick *et al.* 1988).

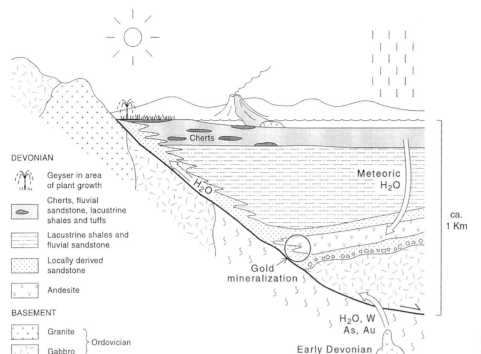

DEVONIAN

⚶ Geyser in area of plant growth

▬ Cherts, fluvial sandstone, lacustrine shales and tuffs

☰ Lacustrine shales and fluvial sandstone

⋯ Locally derived sandstone

v v Andesite

BASEMENT

⋰ Granite ⎫
          ⎬ Ordovician
∨ Gabbro ⎭

ʃ ʃ Dalradian

Fig. 16.11. Subsurface reconstruction of the Rhynie hydrothermal system at the time of deposition of the Rhynie cherts (modified after Rice *et al.* 2002).

Fluid inclusion and stable isotope studies have provided important genetic information indicating a magmatic control according to Curtis *et al.* (1993). However, their interpretation is disputed by Craw & Chamberlain (1996) who advocate a radically different model whereby gold is precipitated from oxidizing meteoric fluids during uplift (see below). A difficulty with this model is that mineralization at Cononish appears to post-date uplift by at least 30 Ma. Curtis *et al.* (1993) have shown that the ore fluids were fairly dilute (6 wt% NaCl equivalent) and CO_2-bearing and the mineralization was deposited at temperatures in the range 290 to 350°C at a depth of about 4 km. According to these workers the fluids were a mixture of magmatic and probably contemporary meteoric waters and the sulphur was obtained from both a magmatic source and the country rocks. There is geophysical evidence that the magmatic source may be a buried extension of the Late Caledonian Etive granite (Pattrick *et al.* 1988). Similarities between Rhynie and Cononish in terms of age and tectonic setting suggest that Rhynie might represent a high level manifestation of a Cononish-type system.

Sources of gold

The source(s) of gold in these late Caledonian deposits has been the subject of a vigorous debate in recent years between those advocating an upper crustal metasedimentary source and those arguing for a magmatic source. Regional geochemical surveys indicate that the Dalradian metasediments are enriched in arsenic and antimony, elements commonly associated with gold, and Plant *et al.* (1989) and Simpson *et al.* (1989) have proposed that these metals and also gold and sulphur are leached from the metasediments by hydrothermal fluids and concentrated around small intrusives or in veins along major lineaments. The derivation of sulphur, arsenic and fluids from metasediments associated with intrusive-related mineralization in the Southern Uplands is supported by stable isotope and fluid inclusion data (Lowry *et al.* 1997).

An alternative leaching model for mineralized veins in the Grampians proposes that the gold was initially mobilized into veins by metamorphic or evolved meteoric fluids and then re-mobilized by later head-driven oxidizing meteoric fluids during uplift. (Craw 1990; Craw & Chamberlain 1996). On the other hand, the observation that most of the Caledonian precious metal deposits are spatially associated with alkali-rich igneous rocks, an association that occurs worldwide, and the fact that much of the mineralization had a magmatic fluid involvement, supports a magmatic origin for the gold (Rock *et al.* 1987; Alderton 1988). The concentration of precious metal deposits between the Mid-Grampian Line and the Highland Boundary Fault is notable and this gold may have become incorporated into magmas as they traversed Dalradian basic rocks in the lower and middle crust (Russell 1985; Halliday *et al.* 1985). Although more work is clearly required, it seems likely that multiple sources are involved depending on particular geological circumstances.

Carboniferous to Early Tertiary

In northern Britain the period from the Carboniferous to the Early Tertiary was characterized by extensional tectonics and important episodes of igneous activity. A combination of geological and isotopic evidence suggests that widespread lead–zinc veins, baryte veins and a few silver- and uranium-bearing veins were formed at intervals during this period (Ineson & Mitchell 1974; Russell 1985). In addition, some important beds of sedimentary ironstones were deposited. The formation of the lead–zinc, baryte and silver veins has been linked to the early opening of the North Atlantic (Russell 1976; Mitchell & Halliday 1976). Such an event would be associated with a high heat flow and fracture formation, conditions favourable for the initiation of hydrothermal convection cells in the upper crust.

Continuing opening of the Atlantic in the Early Tertiary was associated with major igneous activity and large felsic and

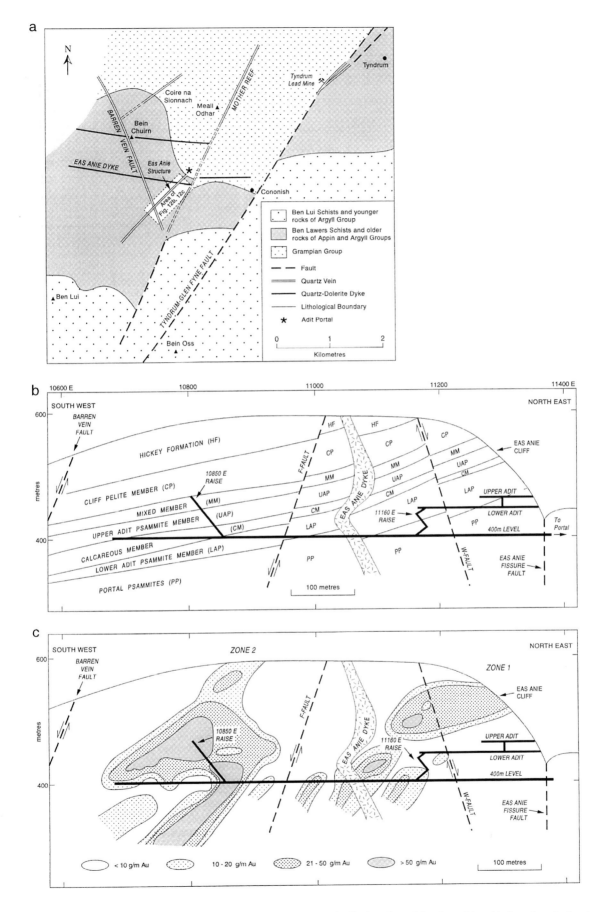

Fig. 16.12. (**a**) Generalized geology of the Cononish–Tyndrum area, (**b**) Longitudinal section of the Cononish gold-silver deposit showing stratigraphy. (**c**) Longitudinal section showing Au assay data (after Earls *et al.* 1992; see also geological map in Treagus *et al.* 1999). Gramme metres (g/m) indicates grade of sample in g/t arranged over 1 m.

mafic igneous centres and regional dykes swarms were emplaced (see Chapter 14). To date the mineralization discovered consists of some minor magnetite- and copper sulphide-bearing skarn deposits on Skye (Tilley 1951, Duff 1965) and subeconomic concentrations of platinum group minerals occurring within layered mafic intrusions in Rum, Mull and Skye (Butcher *et al.* 1999; Pirrie *et al.* 2000). The style of the mineralization is comparable to that found within the Tertiary mafic intrusions of East Greenland and indicates that the North Atlantic Tertiary Igneous province is one of the most extensive platinum-group mineral provinces in Europe (Pirrie *et al.* 2000). There is also some recent evidence that Tertiary basaltic dykes on the mainland may be linked to gold mineralization (see below).

Leadhills–Wanlockhead lead–zinc veins

The largest by far of the lead–zinc deposits is Leadhills–Wanlockhead (LW) followed by Tyndrum and Strontian (Table 16.3). The first authenticated record of mining at LW is 1239 (in Temple 1956) with peak production in the late 19th century and effective cessation of mining in 1934. Total production has been at least 270 000 tonnes of lead ore, 13 800 tonnes of sphalerite and 23 tonnes of silver (Mackay 1959). There are about 70 veins hosted by intensely deformed Ordovician greywackes. The veins are typically about a metre wide and subvertical and trend north–south and NW–SE, though the richest vein, the Susanna, has an east–west trend (Vaughan 1974). The structure in the area is dominated by reverse faulting and a major pre-mineralization reverse fault forms a NW boundary to the district (Fig. 16.13). The over-riding block includes Arenig black shales and cherts which appear to have formed a permeability barrier to the ore fluids (Temple 1956).

The major sulphides comprise galena, sphalerite, pyrite and chalcopyrite and the main gangue minerals are ankerite, calcite, quartz and barite. The upper parts of the vein are extensively oxidized and, amongst a large number of oxidation minerals, include four, leadhillite, susannite, lanarkite and caledonite, for which LW is the type locality (Plate 31) (Gillanders 1981).

The ore fluids were very saline and deposited the minerals at about $180°C$. Stable isotope data indicate that the fluids were modified meteoric waters, the reduced sulphur was derived from the Lower Palaeozoic country rocks and the sulphate sulphur was from oxidized hydrothermal H_2S or from ground-water (Samson & Banks 1988; Pattrick & Russell 1989). Radiometric age determinations on clay gouge from the veins suggests a mid-Carboniferous emplacement age for the mineralization (Ineson & Mitchell 1974).

Pattrick & Russell (1989) have argued that LW belongs to a group of lead–zinc vein deposits, including Tyndrum, that are of Early Carboniferous age and coeval with the large base metal deposits of Ireland. However, only LW compares with these in size. The ore fluids in these Scottish deposits have the characteristics of basinal fluids which may have migrated along major structures such as the Tyndrum and Leadhill faults from sedimentary basins in the Midland Valley (Pattrick & Russell 1989). The driving force may have been crustal thinning during this period of extension which generated an increased geothermal gradient and fracture permeability and thereby stimulated convection of upper crustal fluids through major structures such as the Tyndrum fault (Treagus *et al.* 1999). The BGS have suggested that metalliferous veins in the Dalradian may have been sourced from older stratiform mineralization (Smith *et al.* 1984). However, there is no evidence of similar 'older' mineralization in the Lower Palaeozoic rocks of the Southern Uplands, though metamorphosed Ordovician black shales are possible alternative source rocks.

Silver-bearing veins

The Midland Valley contains some interesting native silver-bearing carbonate–baryte veins, which are hosted by Devonian volcanics and Carboniferous sediments and show a spatial relationship to Permo-Carboniferous quartz dolerite dykes. Two deposits of this kind are known at Alva and Hilderstone and have yielded about 5 tonnes each of silver (Table 16.3) (Moreton *et al.* 1998; Meikle 1994; Stephenson *et al.* 1983; Jassim *et al.* 1983; Hall *et al.* 1982). The association of silver drainage anomalies with Permo-Carboniferous dykes in Aberdeenshire indicates that further deposits may remain to be discovered (Chung 1991). Hydrothermal clays in the wall rocks at the Alva mine have yielded K–Ar ages in the range 264 to 299 Ma (Ineson & Mitchell 1974) which, together with the strong spatial association mentioned above, suggests a genetic connection with the dykes (Russell 1985) or with the rifting event that generated the dykes (Moreton *et al.* 1998). These deposits show strong similarities to a world class of silver deposit described as five element (Ag–Co–Ni–As–Bi) type (Moreton *et al.* 1998), which includes the famous Kongsberg deposit in Norway and the Canadian Cobalt–Gowganda deposits (Kissin 1988). The Permo-Carboniferous dyke swarm mentioned above extends eastwards to the Oslo area (Smythe *et al.* 1995), where the Kongsberg deposit is located, suggesting that this and the Scottish silver deposits may be part of the same magmatic-tectonic event (Moreton *et al.* 1998).

Uranium mineralization

Following a reconnaissance programme (1968–1972), on behalf of the UKAEA, minor uranium mineralization was discovered in various parts of Scotland. This includes veins in and around Caledonian granites (e.g. Helmsdale and Dalbeattie), and veins hosted by metasediments (e.g. Tyndrum). The uraniferous veins at Dalbeattie and at Tyndrum have given Mesozoic radiometric ages (Tables 16.1, 3). Other uranium mineralization occurring as enrichments in Old Red Sandstone sediments of the Orcadian Basin may be of Devonian age (Gallagher *et al.* 1971).

Baryte veins

Baryte veins are widely distributed in Scotland but the most important at Gasswater, Muirshiel and Glen Sannox are located in the Midland Valley (Fig. 16.1; Table 16.3). Two of these, Gasswater and Muirshiel, have dominated production. In the former, the veins occur in WNW- or NNW-trending faults in rocks of Devonian to Early Carboniferous age. High grade ore shoots up to 6 m thick have been exploited for about 800 m along strike and to a depth of about 200 m. Gasswater was worked continuously from 1923–1963 and was one of the main baryte sources in Britain (Scott 1967).

The age of the baryte veins is uncertain. Direct field evidence indicates that some are contemporaneous with Late Carboniferous quartz dolerite dykes, whereas others postdate these dykes and predate Early Tertiary dykes. K–Ar ages on clay gouge associated with the veins range from Carboniferous to Triassic (Ineson & Mitchell 1974; Moore 1979) and a palaeomagnetic study of a baryte–hematite vein in the River Nethan district indicates a Jurassic age (Evans & El-Nikhely 1982). The principal veins lie within the belt occupied by the Tertiary dyke swarm leading MacGregor (1944) and others to

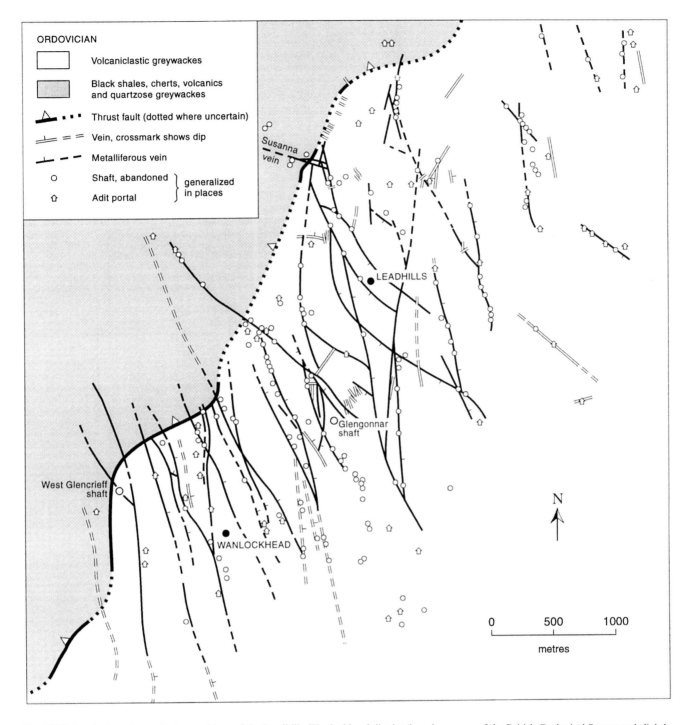

Fig. 16.13. Lead–zinc veins and mine workings of the Leadhills–Wanlockhead district (based on maps of the British Geological Survey and slightly modified after Dunham *et al.* 1979).

propose a generic connection. However, the association could be explained by reactivation of old fracture systems (Stephenson & Coats 1983). Other workers have opted for baryte vein formation over an extended period of time from late Carboniferous to the Mesozoic and possibly Early Tertiary (Stephenson & Coats 1983). Russell (1985), on the other hand, has linked the formation of the baryte (and the silver, see above) veins with the intrusion of mafic magmas consequent upon the postulated opening of the Faeroes–Shetland trough in the Late Carboniferous. Irrespective of age, limited sulphur isotope and fluid inclusion data are consistent with a model whereby rising brines carrying barium mixed with cool

sulphate-bearing waters at a high level to precipitate the baryte veins (Jassim *et al.* 1983; Moore 1979).

Sedimentary ironstones

During the Carboniferous and Jurassic ironstone deposits were laid down in deltaic and shallow marine environments respectively. In the 19th century the Carboniferous ironstones of the Coatbridge district were the main source of iron for the Scottish iron industry. The worked horizons occur mainly in the Limestone Coal Group and the Coal Measures and the ore had an average iron content of 25–30%. The ironstones are shale-hosted and overlie coal seams and consist of nodules of siderite in layers with variable amounts of clay (clay band type) or bands of dark ironstone which contain carbonaceous matter in addition to siderite and clay (blackband type). The carbonate is derived from decaying organic matter and the iron mainly from detrital iron oxides. The siderite is precipitated from pore fluids during diagenesis under reducing conditions (Curtis & Spears 1968; Pearson 1979).

A Jurassic ironstone was worked on Raasay during the First World War. This ironstone is up to 2.5 m thick and contains 23 to 25% of iron and reserves are estimated at 10 to 16×10^6 tonnes (Gribble 1983). It overlies shales of Liassic age, usually consists of chamosite ooliths in a siderite matrix and shows cross bedding. The fossil assemblage indicates that the ironstone is of Toarcian age and spans at least one ammonite zone (*bifrons* Biozone). It is succeeded by a hiatus with local evidence of a minor angular unconformity (Morton 1989). The sequence may be interpreted in terms of a transgression followed by a period of slow or non-deposition and a regression. At this time soil formation on adjacent land masses was occurring in a warm, humid climate and may have been lateritic (Hallam 1975). The precise origin of these ironstones is uncertain but they may have formed by intensive reworking of lateritic soils under shallow marine conditions (Young 1989; Hallam & Bradshaw 1979).

Quaternary

Placer gold occurs in most streams draining the upland areas of Scotland but significant amounts have been obtained only from the Leadhills–Wanlockhead area, and Helmsdale in Sutherland. At least 25 000 oz of alluvial gold was taken from the former in the 16th century and some of this was used for the crowns of James V and his queen (Gillanders 1981). The gold is derived from glacial till, earlier gravels and bedrock sources. Gold-bearing quartz clasts in lead–zinc vein breccias suggest that some of the gold is early, possibly Caledonian (Temple 1956). A comprehensive study of alluvial gold grains from Leadhills has indicated that the sources may include (a) Lower Palaeozoic sedimentary rocks, (b) Tertiary basaltic

dykes, (c) ophiolitic material and (d) Permian red beds and basalts (Leake *et al.* 1998).

During a minor gold rush in 1868–1869 at least 3500 oz were obtained from some streams draining the north side of the Strath of Kildonan, Helmsdale. The immediate source of the gold is morainic terraces bordering the streams (Joass 1869) and the ultimate source may be granitic rocks of the Strath Halladale migmatite complex (Dawson & Gallagher 1965) or an Early Devonian epithermal system akin to that described at Rhynie (above) (Crummy *et al.* 1997). Whatever the exact source, it seems likely that deep preglacial Tertiary weathering released the gold which was then upgraded by more recent fluvial action (Plant & Coleman 1972).

A rather similar story applies to a gold placer deposit recently discovered in Borland Glen in the Ochils, where the original source may have been within Devonian lavas and sediments. Here Tertiary weathering has been critical in producing a gold-enriched regolith from very low grade country rock for subsequent upgrading by recent fluvial action (Crummy 1993; Coats *et al.* 1991). It can be seen that the combination of deep Tertiary weathering followed by fluvial upgrading is a favourable combination for placer formation and further discoveries can be expected in the eastern and northeastern parts of Scotland where glacial scouring was generally limited and portions of the Tertiary weathering profiles have been preserved (Crummy 1993).

Concentrations of iron and manganese formed by supergene processes are common in Scotland. The most important of these are manganiferous iron oxides found at the Lecht, near Tomintoul (Nicholson & Anderton 1989), the Bridge of Don, Aberdeen (Chew 1978) and iron oxides at the Sandlodge Mine, Shetland (Wilson & Flett 1921).

Marine placers of chromite and olivine are found in deltas fed by streams draining the Tertiary ultrabasic and basic rocks of Southern Rum. The surficial 1m of sand in the delta contains some 70 000 tonnes of chrome spinel averaging 32% Cr_2O_3 at a grade of nearly 1% and 1.5 to 2 million tonnes of olivine averaging 47% MgO at 25% grade. Accompanying minerals are ilmenite and vanadiferous magnetite and trace amounts of platinum group elements (Gallagher *et al.* 1989b) for which there is now a possible source (Butcher *et al.* 1999).

17 Coal

J. H. RIPPON

Coal has been important to the Scottish economy for many centuries, the result of coal-rich successions through a significant stratigraphical interval, a range of coal types, and many outcrops. Scottish mining engineers were in the forefront of the Industrial Revolution, and drilling for coal reserves generally predated comparable applications in the English fields. Peak production, in the early 20th century, was over 40×10^6 tonnes/year, with a decline to a mid/late 1990s output of less than 10×10^6 tonnes, including opencasted (surface-mined) coal (Fig. 17.1), the decline reflecting competition from other fuels and the depletion of the more accessible reserves. A broad review of the pre-1990s industry is given by Beveridge *et al.* (1991); potential and possible mining resources are described below. Recently, the potential for gas production from the coals has been investigated by deep drilling: the coalbed methane interest in Scotland is also discussed below. Underground gasification is a further possible energy option. With the exception of the small coalfield in the onshore Jurassic succession at Brora, all the coals are of Carboniferous age.

Carboniferous coals

Coalfield extents and stratigraphical ranges

Coals of mining thickness occur through most of the Scottish Carboniferous, in strata from Dinantian to Westphalian C age, but with a concentration in the Namurian (E_1) Limestone Coal Formation and in the Westphalian A to mid B succession (Fig. 17.2); coals later than early Westphalian C were usually altered (or destroyed) by weathering during the time represented by the sub-Permo-Triassic unconformity. Because of the stratigraphical range, it is not unreasonable to include all the Carboniferous outcrop of the Midland Valley (Fig. 17.3) as 'coalfield', although in practice discrete areas are recognized; these were formalized by the coalfield memoirs of the Geological Survey (Scotland).

Apart from the Midland Valley fields, smaller outlier coalfields are found to the north of the Highland Boundary Fault, and at Sanquhar south of the Southern Upland Fault (in the nearby Westphalian succession at Thornhill, the coals were eliminated by post-Carboniferous/pre-Triassic weathering). To the south of the Southern Uplands, the Canonbie Coalfield is part of an extensive concealed Carboniferous basin that extends southwest into the West Cumberland Coalfield of northwest England (Chadwick *et al.* 1995).

In all fields, coal development was strongly influenced by the tectonic setting, especially during Namurian times. For example, Francis (1991a) described pronounced coal thickness variations across certain prominent strike slip fault systems, notably the Kerse Loch structure in Ayrshire. Rippon *et al.* (1996) noted the systematic thickening of coals into syndepositionally active tectonic depocentres such as the Kincardine Basin, and thinning across the adjacent high to the east.

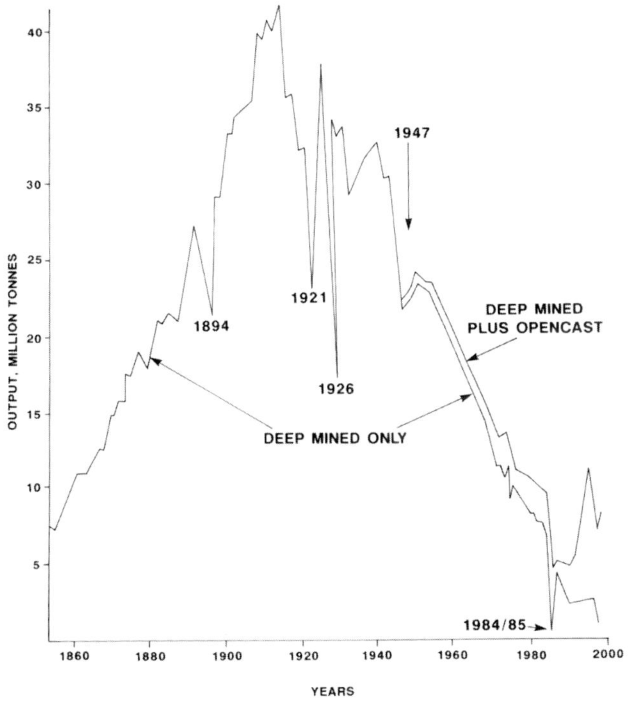

Fig. 17.1. Trends in output of deep-mined and opencasted coal in Scotland, 1853 to 1999. Modified from Beveridge *et al.* (1991) using data kindly supplied by the Scottish Coal Company Ltd and the Coal Authority.

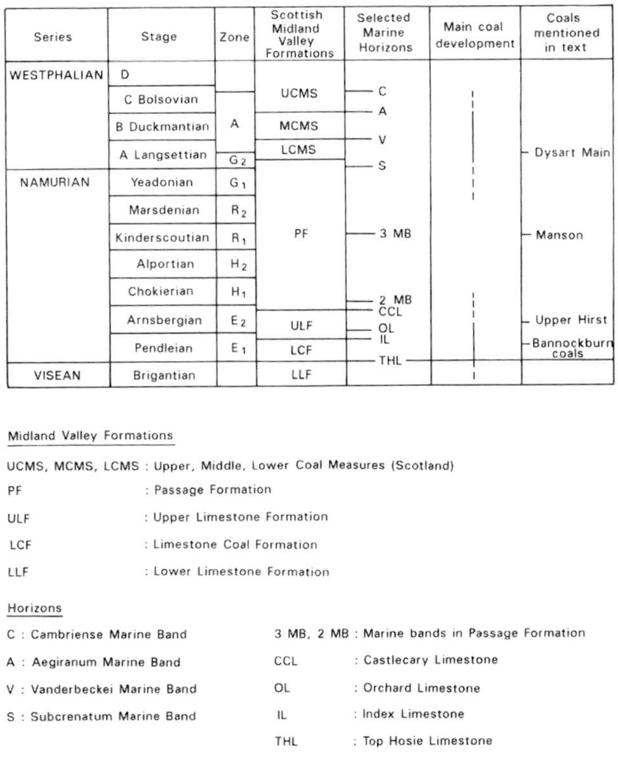

Fig. 17.2. Chronostratigraphy of the main Scottish coalfields.

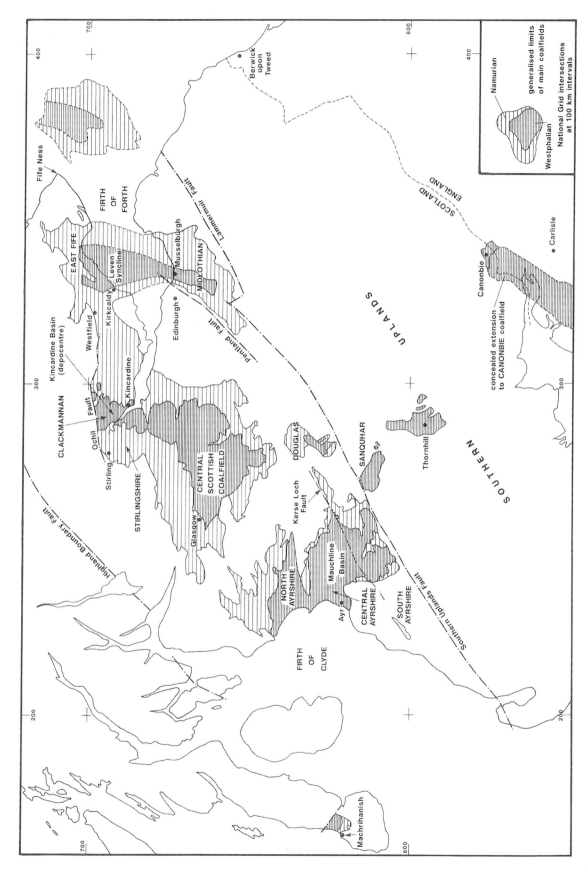

Fig. 17.3. Locations of the main Scottish coalfields.

Figure 17.4 summarizes the general stratigraphical and geographical distribution of the main coal successions, and the degree to which they remain for exploitation. Further stratigraphic, structural and palaeogeographic information is given in Chapter 9.

Coal ranks, qualities and thicknesses

The Carboniferous coals have ranks varying from high volatile bituminous to anthracite. Rank variations largely reflect proximity to igneous intrusions. As a generalization, the end-Carboniferous quartz-dolerite intrusions have produced most up-ranking, rather than intra-Carboniferous suites (Francis 1991a, b): regional thermal metamorphism characterizes the coals across wide areas underlain by the Midland Valley Sill, with progressive devolatilization of the coals with depth, those most closely underlain by the sill achieving coking ranks over much of the Stirling–Clackmannan area. However, small areas of low volatile coal are associated with the intra-Carboniferous intrusions. Because of the rapid rank variations in many areas, it is not generally suitable to produce regional rank maps, and coal prospects require careful attention to rank data for marketing evaluations.

Two key quality attributes benefit the utilization of most Scottish coals, namely the generally low chlorine, and very low sulphur contents. The geological controls on chlorine and sulphur in British coals are discussed by Rippon (1997), who related sulphur contents mainly to the inflow directions of Carboniferous palaeochannel systems. In Scotland, low sulphur contents characterize most fields, with exceptions in western areas, where generally higher values probably reflect westerly source areas comparable to central and western England. The strong marine influence in the Namurian coal-bearing successions only rarely resulted in higher-sulphur coals.

As noted above, coal thicknesses commonly reflect the disposition of tectonic depocentres (with thicker successions and thicker coals) and palaeo-highs (with condensed successions, any thicker coals being composites of individually thinner seams). Again generalizing, coalbeds of around 1 m thickness are common across wide areas, with some seams thickening to around 3 m in depocentres. However, there are various noteworthy exceptions. For example, the Dysart Main (Westphalian A) of eastern Fife is around 8 m thick over much of the local depocentre. Francis (1991a) notes the 15 m thick composite Quarrelton Thick Coal west of Glasgow, in a Dinantian succession which is condensed where it overlies the Clyde Plateau volcanic formations; he also notes the spectacularly thick coals in the Westfield Basin (Figs 9.5, 17.3), resulting from specific syn-depositional subsidence.

Mining characteristics and coal marketing

The Midland Valley may be regarded as a mosaic of structurally distinct areas, the result of compartmentalization by syn-depositionally-active structures (Rippon 1997). These areas usually present quite different geological environments for mine planning, in terms of variations in depositional patterns, bed thicknesses, the incidence of syn-depositional igneous features, bedding dips, and the density and displacement of faults. In some areas fault densities, orientations and sizes are substantially different in Westphalian, compared with Namurian, formations, and this probably results from changes in the regional stress that, in marginal coalfields (such as Douglas, Fig. 17.3) are evidenced by intra-Carboniferous unconformities. All these variations are especially significant to the identification of areas suitable for deep mining. As a generalization, the more basinal areas present the more consistent mining

environments: individual seams achieve their greatest thicknesses, there are fewer igneous disturbances, bedding dips are lower, and fault density is also lower. However, the depths in these more basinal areas will also often be greater.

As with all British coalfields, mining methods have evolved with time and economic circumstances. Since the 1950s, most deep mined output has been from longwall workings, which have been most efficient in the more basinal areas, see above. Opencast mining has also been common since the 1940s, and has proportionally been more important than deep mining since the mid-1980s (Plate 32).

The wide variation in coal ranks available in Scotland has always been beneficial to marketing, encouraging specific utilizations such as metallurgical coal, and product blending. At present, the bulk of Scottish coal is produced for electricity generation, either in local power stations, or for export. The lower sulphur and chlorine contents are particularly advantageous.

The effects of mining on the environment

The decline of deep mining in Scotland over the last few decades (Fig. 17.1) has inevitably left a legacy of landscape and hydrogeological difficulties, many resulting from earlier extractions, prior to recent more stringent environmental legislation. However, many areas have now been rehabilitated and incorporated into a variety of landscape types. The main continuing environmental issues concern new opencast mining (which in many areas has been part of the land rehabilitation process), and the rise in groundwaters following the cessation of pumping from closed deep mines. The assessment of water pathways and timings to emergence are matters for specialist geological work. Generalizations here are inappropriate, except for the observation that the composition of mine water discharges in Scotland should often have significantly lower iron carbonate contents compared with those in English coalfields. This follows from the low to very low pyritic sulphur content of most Scottish coals, and the consequently smaller amount of iron resulting from oxidation of the coals in mine workings.

A brief review of major unmined deep reserves

Despite the long history of Scottish mining, there are many remaining resources, some of which are large by European standards. Deep mining from the Longannet complex continued to 2002 in the Clackmannan Syncline (Fig. 17.3), and there are various other resources, either abandoned by a declining industry, or indeed never exploited. Given the size of some of these resources, and the variations in the energy market that can occur over the period of a decade, it is important that they should continue to be recognized.

Clackmannan Syncline. The mine at Longannet worked the Upper Hirst Coal (Fig. 17.2) from the late 1960s. In the Kincardine area, seams in the Coal Measures, some hundreds of metres above the Upper Hirst, have long been mined out, but the Upper Hirst remains largely intact. These reserves have been extensively explored by core boreholes and high-resolution seismic surveys. It is interesting to note that further extensive coal resources, including coking ranks, remain entirely unmined in the Limestone Coal Formation, below the Upper Hirst, within the depth range considered technically recoverable by the former National Coal Board (NCB, latterly British Coal Corporation, BCC).

East Fife. Large resources remain unmined in the Leven Syncline, in many Coal Measures seams (Fig. 17.3), including

	Stirling & Clackmannan	Fife (W & central)	Fife (N & NE from Kirkcaldy)	Firth of Forth offshore	Midlothian	Central Coalfield	Ayrshire (Mauchline Basin)	New Cumnock	Douglas	Sanquhar	Canonbie
Coal Measures	outcropped or shallow, generally mined out		thick coals, extensive unmined resources	outcropped or shallow, generally mined out		some thicker coal resources remain	outcropped or shallow, generally mined out			thick coals, largely unmined
Passage Formation	few / no significant coals		thick coals in places near top of succession, largely unmined offshore	local thick and inferior coals near top of succession		few / no significant coals		local thick coal, unmined	no significant coals	
Upper Limestone Formation	extensive resources in Upper Hirst seam, unmined			few / no significant coals				local thick coals, unmined at depth	few / no significant coals	few / no significant coals
Limestone Coal Formation	extensive resources in Clackmannan Syncline (unmined)	thick coals mainly mined out	local thick coals unmined at depth	probably extensive thick coals unmined but very deep		thicker coals generally mined out	few / no significant coals	some thick coals, largely unmined	thick coals unmined at depth	succession absent	few / no significant coals
Lower Limestone Formation			local thicker coals				few / no significant coals ; succession locally absent				
earlier Dinantian successions			local thicker coals				few / no significant coals ; succession locally absent				

Significant remaining deep coal resources

Main Scottish Coalfields

Generalised summary of remaining deep coal resources

Fig. 17.4. Main Scottish coalfields: generalized summary of coal development in the various Carboniferous formations, and of the remaining deep coal reserves.

the Dysart Main. Extraction extending offshore from coastal mines has a long history, with the final mine closure in 1996/1997. The Leven Syncline is characterized by wide areas with few faults, the main problem for mining being increasing depth offshore. Exploration would, however, require major capital expenditure and a long-term commitment. The seams of the Limestone Coal Formation, at depth below the Coal Measures, thicken significantly into the Leven Syncline, but are too deep for conventional mining. Northeast of the Leven Syncline, a further coalfield is known offshore from Fifeness (Fig. 17.3) but is insufficiently proved for any mining appraisal.

Midlothian. Deep mining access to the remaining resources in the onshore Midlothian Syncline is now lost and, given the complex pattern of abandoned workings, it is very unlikely to be reconsidered. Exploration of the southwestern extent of the basin by the NCB in the 1970s proved generally thin coals, reflecting proximity to the depositional basin margin. However, extensive multi-seam resources remain unmined in the Coal Measures offshore (Musselburgh prospect), and have been explored by cored boreholes and some marine seismic surveys. These resources are ultimately continuous with those of the Leven Syncline, although bedding dips are generally steeper and the area is compartmentalized by a few end-Carboniferous quartz-dolerite dykes, and some significant faults. Again as in the Leven Syncline, the seams of the Limestone Coal Formation are too deep for conventional mining.

Ayrshire and Douglas. These areas (Fig. 17.3) include more common igneous features, and often prominent faults, some of which were active during deposition of the coal-bearing successions. There are no large-scale resources comparable to the Clackmannan or Leven synclines, but 1970s and 1980s drilling by the NCB established areas of locally thickened and unmined coal. Notable amongst these is the small field at Douglas, in which the seams of the Limestone Coal Formation are largely unmined; a very thick coal in the Passage Formation (the Manson Seam) probably results from syndepositional movement on a nearby fault. The Douglas field is relatively coal-rich, although geologically more complex than most other Scottish areas. The remaining resources in Ayrshire are geologically very site specific, but are generally relatively shallow (<300 m) with the exception of the unmined Coal Measures in the deeper parts of the Mauchline Basin, which were abandoned prior to the development of more modern seismic techniques.

Canonbie. The minor exposed coalfield at Canonbie (Fig. 17.3) has long been known, and exploited on a small scale; indeed, drilling for coal in the neighbourhood is know from the late 18th century. It is only since 1970s and 1980s exploration by deep cored boreholes and some seismic reflection surveys by the the NCB that the extent of the coalfield at depth, concealed beneath Permo-Triassic sediments, has been known (Picken 1988). A number of Westphalian age coals of mining thicknesses are present over at least 70 km² (Beveridge *et al.* 1991) in the immediately-proved area, which is considered sufficient for two large collieries given favourable economic circumstances. Seismic surveys for hydrocarbon exploration since the NCB work are thought to indicate a much larger resource trending along a depocentre southwest past Carlisle, and connecting with the West Cumberland Coalfield (Chadwick *et al.* 1995). Regarding the immediate area proved by the NCB exploration, the coals lie at readily mineable depths, the resource being compartmentalized by a few large faults.

Scottish coalfield data sets

For all those areas which can reasonably be envisaged as future mining prospects, much of the exploration, sufficient to establish their mining character, has already been undertaken. The long history of mining and exploration has resulted in excellent geological data sets, comprising borehole data (core log description, coal analyses, geophysical/wireline logs), seismic surveys, coal analyses taken in mines, numerous underground observations and many other geotechnical data, together with interpretational reports, plans and sections.

As elsewhere in UK coalfields, exploration by boreholes peaked twice, in the 1950s and 1970s, reflecting the economic situations of the times. Coals in many Scottish fields seem generally less friable than their English equivalents (other than where heat-altered), aiding better core recoveries in earlier holes. Geophysical logs have been run in deep holes since the 1950s (early Schlumberger surveys) and from the 1970s onwards in most exploration boreholes for deep mines. Seismic reflection surveys generally date from the late 1970s; better 2D acquisition and processing since the late 1980s has given resolutions of fault throws to <5 m at several hundred metres depth, given good acquisition conditions. There are newly acquired 3D seismic data in the Clackmannan Syncline. Inseam seismic surveys have been undertaken in various mines.

The Scottish coal industry geological and geophysical data set continues to be of value in specialist geological and geotechnical work throughout the coalfields, and of course is available for any longer-term interest in the larger deep mineable resources that remain. However, the data also have considerable analogue value for geological appraisals in other contexts, particularly regarding offshore hydrocarbon reservoirs in Upper Carboniferous formations, and in the interpretation of fault growth and sealing mechanisms in fluvial–deltaic systems. The data set also has obvious value to coalbed methane evaluations within the coalfields themselves, and this recent development is now considered.

Coalbed methane developments in Scotland

Coalbed methane (CBM) is gas produced from unmined coal seams by drilling, the gas being released over a period of years, usually aided by hydraulic fracturing of the coal. It is to be distinguished from gas contained in mining voids, and from underground gasification. In CBM production, the evolved gas will broadly approximate to gas that would be liberated by longwall mining, and the energy resource of the coal substance that remains after CBM production is probably not dissimilar to that which would be in a mined product. CBM wells typically intersect coals at a mininum depth of around 500 m, reflecting the burial history conditions necessary for gas generation and retention over geological time. The deeper parts of the original depocentres are therefore particularly attractive. Although overall coalfield CBM resources may be large, successful prospects are likely to be site specific (especially with respect to detailed fault attributes) and much smaller operations than major offshore gas fields (see Chapter 19).

In the UK, CBM development dates only from the early 1990s. By the mid-1990s, however, most significant coalfield areas in Scotland were included in exploration licences, and the first wells were drilled in the Clackmannan Syncline to the deeper, higher rank seams in the Limestone Coal Formation, particularly to the thick Bannockburn coals. This area was deemed suitable as it combined a thickened coal succession, and a coal burial history that was different to that of the mined Upper Hirst in the overlying Upper Limestone Formation (Fig. 17.2): the Upper Hirst was known to have a generally very low gas content, compared to the underlying target coals. The overall structure of the area was also reasonably known at depth from the exploration for the Upper Hirst mining prospect. The Clackmannan Syncline (or, strictly speaking, the precursor Kincardine Basin) is likely to be of continuing interest for CBM development in the 21st century, presenting opportunities for data sharing between the mining and gas interests. Other areas of particular interest include the Canonbie field, where gas contents are known, from NCB core boreholes, to be favourable. The smaller field at Douglas is also of potential interest, but gas contents are presently unknown. The Midlothian Syncline is of little interest here, most relevant coals being mined out. The Leven Syncline, with its extensive unmined coals, is of interest, but most resources either lie offshore or beneath urban areas, making practical exploitation difficult.

Jurassic coal

The Brora Coalfield

The Jurassic successions of Scotland and adjacent offshore areas are described in Chapter 11, and this account relates only to the Brora Coalfield, which lies on the east coast of Sutherland at the town of Brora. Coal-bearing strata are present in a Lower to Upper Jurassic succession that may be compared with the offshore areas (Macgregor 1954; Hurst 1981). The Lower Jurassic Dunrobin Group unconformably overlies Permo-Triassic sediments, and includes the thin (<0.50 m) Dunrobin 'coals' (approximating to carbonaceous claystones in places). The Brora Main coal seam is of Callovian age and is overlain by the Brora Roof Bed, a marine transgressive sandstone also of Callovian age (see Chapter 11).

The Brora Main is the only seam of a consistently mineable thickness, achieving 1 m to 1.5 m in the Brora area. It is a bituminous coal with volatile matter around 35% to 40% (air dried). Its marketable attributes are generally poor, with high ash and sulphur contents. Disseminated pyrite occurs throughout the coal, with discrete horizons of nodular pyrite. The seam is underlain by a 'parrot' (that is, a cannel) coal and a bituminous shale (the Inverbrora Member, of part Callovian age) which is very pyritic. The Brora Main has been worked for local use since the 16th century by shallow mining adjacent to the coastal exposures, and, from the early 19th century, from further inland. Around 1810, shaft sinking commenced just east of Brora village to access coal downthrown by the Brora Fault. Mining from these shafts continued until the later 1960s, using the 'room' and pillar method, with working height achieved by extracting down to the bituminous shale. During the later 1960s and 1970s, several cored boreholes were drilled to ascertain the extent of the reserves, especially to the west, but unfavourable economics led to mine closure in the mid-1970s. The main market for the coal was the adjacent brickworks; quality, and distance from markets, have limited its wider use. An excellent illustrated history of coal mining at Brora has been published by Owen (1995).

Conclusions

Significant energy resources remain at depth in Scottish Carboniferous coals, especially in the Clackmannan Syncline and Canonbie areas. Any future major mining enterprises in these and other fields are likely to be capital intensive. These coals are a considerable national resource, requiring careful land use planning. It will often be appropriate for mining and CBM interests to share exploration programmes.

18 Bulk minerals

C. D. GRIBBLE

Aggregates

The distribution of rock types in Scotland has ensured that Scotland is able to produce good quality rock aggregate almost anywhere in the country. In general all aggregate is derived from two main sources: deposits of sand and gravel, which are almost exclusively of glacial origin, and crushed rock aggregate from quarries mining solid rock.

Scotland is self-sufficient in aggregate production (and, in fact, exports aggregates). The annual amount of crushed rock aggregate is more than twice that of sand and gravel, with a total annual production of about 33×10^6 tonnes. Figure 18.1 shows the annual production of aggregate from 1972 to 1998 (BGS 1972 *et seq.*) and indicates that production continued to increase (or at worst plateaued out) during the recession from 1990 to 1995, in spite of UK total production showing an overall reduction of over 20% during this period. The graph shows that the annual production of sand and gravel has fallen slightly from 12×10^6 to about 10×10^6 tonnes per annum, and that hard rock production is now more than 23×10^6 tonnes per annum. It should be emphasized that a crushed rock granite quarry at Glensanda on Loch Linnhe which started in 1987 accounts for more than 5×10^6 tonnes of the crushed rock annual production. This quarry, the first custom-designed superquarry in Scotland, sends material to south-eastern England, and also to northern Europe and the United States (see below).

Sand and gravel

For many years glacial sands and gravels have been a major source of Scottish aggregates. In the 1950s and 1960s natural sands and gravels provided by far the largest proportion of commercially produced aggregate in Scotland; it is only since 1969 that hard rock aggregate production has overtaken sand and gravel production in Scotland (Fig. 18.1)

A series of positive points concerning sand and gravel deposits is listed below:

(a) Glacial sands and gravels are of widespread occurrence in Scotland and generally are of good quality.

(b) The cost of setting up plant to work sand and gravel deposits (mainly washing and sieving) is not nearly as expensive as setting up plant to crush hard rock (crushing, sieving and sorting), so that the price per tonne (*ex*-quarry) is much less.

(c) Sand and gravel deposits merely have to have the top soil and any overlying materials removed (peat, alluvium) before extraction can begin, although a small crushing plant is usually necessary to deal with any large clasts present in the deposit (boulders, cobbles). Hard rock deposits require blasting to produce blocks of rock of suitable size for crushing to begin.

(d) Almost every sand and gravel deposit in Scotland (unlike those for example in SE England) works material lying *above* the water table; thus pumping of water is not required and extraction is relatively easy and inexpensive.

(e) Up to the present time most deposits have been more than 5×10^6 tonnes in size which, with a yearly production rate of (say) 250 000 tonnes, implies a 20-year life expectancy.

(f) Although not suitable for wearing course or other coated layers in road construction, most glacial gravels are quite suitable for most end uses (concrete aggregate, infill, lower courses in roads).

A series of negative points concerning sand and gravel deposits can also be proposed and these are listed below:

(a) The deposits are generally small in size and would not be suitable for development of a large quarry with a large annual rate of production (of say $>0.5 \times 10^6$ tonnes) because the life expectancy of the quarry would be too short.

(b) Most of the best sand and gravel deposits have been, or are being, worked at the present time. Those that remain may possess one or several of the following criteria: sited in remote places with no obvious local markets; contain material which is sited below the water table; contain material of poor quality; have a limited size of deposit available for exploitation; be subject to protection on environmental grounds.

(c) Royalty payments per tonne (or per cubic metre) to a landowner are several times higher for sand and gravel deposits than for crushed rock deposits. In Scotland royalty payments in 1996 were about 20 pence/tonne for crushed rock compared to 45–60 pence/tonne for good quality sand and gravel.

(d) Sand and gravel frequently underlie well-drained arable land (especially in the Midland Valley) whereas hard rock

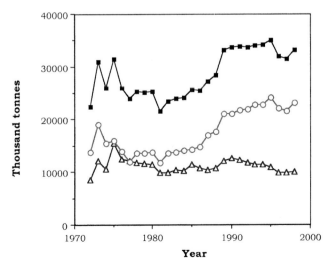

Fig. 18.1. Aggregate production in Scotland, 1972 onwards (circles are for crushed rock; triangles are for sand and gravel; and squares represent total aggregate production in Scotland).

aggregate quarries are sited on poor agricultural land. Restoration of the site after the sand and gravel has been extracted is possible but the drainage is seldom as good as before.

(e) Since sand and gravel deposits are relatively thin (usually less than 10 m thick in Scotland), a large area of land has to be stripped to allow the gravel layer to be excavated (approx. 5.5 hectares will yield 1×10^6 tonnes). This is quite different from hard rock deposits, where even quarries in dolerite sheets (about 60 m thick) yield 1×10^6 tonnes of aggregate from just over 0.5 hectare of land.

The position at the present time, bearing in mind the positive and negative points outlined above, is that the quarrying of sand and gravel is decreasing in Scotland at the expense of hard rock quarrying, and this situation is expected to continue into the future. Such a situation is also occurring in England where many regional and local authorities are refusing planning permission for working sand and gravel deposits. Along the Thames Valley the presence of leisure activity 'water parks', indicate the positions of old, exhausted sand and gravel deposits, which were worked below the water table.

However, if the use of aggregates continues to expand in the future as government predictions suggest, then there is no doubt that such an expansion will be borne by a development of new hard rock quarries together with increased production from existing hard rock quarries. Increased recycling of materials, predicted to rise to about 15% of demand (Arup Economics 1991; see also Chapter 20) will also contribute to demand.

Aggregate quality

Aggregate quality for every type of aggregate is decided by a series of engineering tests (to British Standard specifications) carried out on aggregate samples. Although different grain-sized samples can be used in some tests the vast majority of tests demand a sample in the 10 to 14 mm range. The tests can conveniently be divided into *physical tests* and *mechanical tests.*

In the physical tests a range of *relative densities* are determined (RD (oven dried), RD (saturated and surface dried), and apparent RD), as well as water absorption and porosity for all aggregates. In addition to these tests, natural gravels also require particle size distribution (PSD) which is the size grading curve for the complete sample, and sample shape (particularly flakiness index I_F, elongation index I_E and angularity number AN, which determines by how much the percentage of voids in any sample (X%) exceeds that of a sample of perfectly rounded clasts (= 33%), and with AN = X − 33).

In the mechanical tests, strength is tested by means of impact (aggregate impact value or AIV), or crushing (aggregate crushing value or ACV). Durability of an aggregate is determined by its resistance to abrasion (aggregate abrasion value or AAV; Los Angeles abrasion value or LAAV); and its frictional resistance to polishing by rubber gives the polished stone value (PSV) where the test deals only with aggregate to be used for the wearing course in roads (that is the uppermost coated layer on which the traffic runs).

Other tests include the magnesium sulphate soundness test which tests the durability of aggregate in wetting and drying cycles using saturated solution of $MgSO_4$; and represents the effects of frost action on the aggregate sample; the frost heave test which measures the expansion of an aggregate sample in water in freezing conditions; and the concrete shrinkage test which measures the drying shrinkage of concrete made with a sample of aggregate using standard cement powder, water and sand.

Table 18.1. *Engineering test results on some Scottish gravels*

BS Tests	Midland Valley Gravels*				Skye†	
	1	2	3	4	Gravel	Sand
RD (oven dried)	2.42	2.52	2.64	2.59	–	
RD (sat & surf dried)	2.53	2.57	2.66	2.64	–	
Apparent RD	2.70	2.67	2.71	2.74	–	
Water Absorption‡	4.23	2.29	1.05	2.11	–	
AIV (<30)	29	28	22	21	17	
ACV (<30)	30	–		17	–	
AAV (<15)	–	–			9	

RD = relative density; for other abbreviations see text.
* Midland Valley gravels from the Strathkelvin Valley (data from Gribble 1990).
† Allt Anavig deposit, Kyleakin (data from Gribble 1983).
‡ The ICE recommends a value of <3% for WA values.

Table 18.1 shows test values for some typical glacial gravels in Scotland, taken from the Strathkelvin Valley near Kirkintilloch (Gribble 1990); and also two samples of glacial gravels from a deposit at Allt Anavig near Kyleakin on Skye (Gribble 1983). The figures show that most Scottish gravels are acceptable for most engineering applications with the exception of wearing courses (PSV results are too low) and in very low shrinkage concrete. Generally glacial gravels are of lower quality than aggregate from crushed rock but their low cost and widespread availability make them an obvious choice by the construction industry where aggregates are required in a particular project. However, the decreasing availability in Scotland of new, large, gravel deposits of good quality that are above the water table, together with the difficulties in obtaining planning permission for exploitation from regional authorities, suggests strongly that gravel sources are declining and that crushed rock aggregate will take an increasingly larger share of the market in the future.

Sands represent a specialized part of this market. Sand is used in a number of applications but mainly for mortars, as the fine aggregate in concrete (about 20% of the total weight), and in asphalt manufacture. The main tests concerning sands are PSD graphs, as the size variation is important, and the constituents comprising the sand – this latter information also being important for gravels. Table 18.2 gives some indication of the variation in constituent particles comprising both sands and gravels in Scotland. Annual tonnages for sand production alone are not competely available but in 1998, 2×10^6 tonnes of building sand, 3×10^6 tonnes of concreting sand and perhaps 1×10^6 tonnes of sand for fill were produced, representing about 60% of the 10×10^6 tonnes sand and gravel total for that year.

Crushed rock aggregates

Approximately 70% of all Scottish aggregate is produced from crushed hard rock. Although a wide range of rock types are

Table 18.2. *Lithological content of some gravel samples, and a sand sample*

Rock type	Midland Valley Gravel				Skye	
	1	2	3	4	Gravel	Sand
Basic igneous	36	26	17	54	6	3
Acid igneous	11	4	13	0	7	10
Quartzite	7	32	32	21	39	47
Gneiss	0	13	34	11	4	8
Schist	14	15	7	10	5	7
Sandstone	32	10	8	5	6	5
Arkose	–	–	–	–	33	23

Table 18.3. *Engineering test results on some Scottish crushed rock aggregates (values in brackets indicate preferred BS test values)*

BS Tests	1	2	3	4	5	6
RD (oven dried)			2.70			2.68
RD (sat & surf dried)			2.71			2.72
Apparent RD	2.70	2.63	2.72	2.96	2.86	2.77
Water Absorption	0.70	0.37	0.30	0.43	0.40	1.21
AIV (<30)	21	27	19	9	7	8
ACV (<30)	21	27	18	19	10	17
AAV (<15)	3.2	3.4	12.5	6	3.6	4
PSV	51	49		56	57	61

1 Moine psammite from Banavie Quarry, Fort William.
2 Red granite from Peterhead Quarry.
3 Black Dalradian Islay limestone from Ballygrant Quarry, Islay.
4 Saussuritized anorthosite, Isle of Harris.
5 Gabbro & diorite, Virdins Quarry, Shetland Islands.
6 Quartz dolerite, Midland Valley.

available for exploitation as aggregate, and this is shown in Table 18.3 where the engineering properties of aggregates are given for six different rock types, only a few rock types are frequently used.

In the Midland Valley the most ubiquitous crushed rock aggregate is quartz dolerite where its high PSV (>60 in most cases) means that it can be coated and used in the upper courses of roads including motorways, thus commanding the highest prices. Olivine dolerite is rarely used, although it is a common rock type in the Midland Valley with about 50% of dolerites of Early Carboniferous age being olivine-bearing. The reasons are that the test results are much poorer probably being because olivine is usually altered to serpentine in these rocks, and this alteration weakens the rock and reduces the engineering properties. Basalts are occasionally used, but basalts suffer from a large percentage of poor rock being present (very weak and vesicular rock occurs at the tops and bottoms of lava flows) and the rock is not of as high quality as quartz dolerite. Aberdeenshire occasionally uses quartz gabbros which have the same properties as quartz dolerites.

Elsewhere in Scotland the rocks used for aggregate production depend upon the geology of the region. Thus in the Grampian Region and in the Highland Region granites are commonly used, and produce a very good quality material although the PSV is too low (poor) to use it as wearing course coated aggregate in road construction. However it is an excellent material for high grade concrete and it is interesting to note that the largest quarry ever opened in Scotland, at Glensanda on Loch Linnhe, is located on the southeastern edge of a large granite intrusion (the Loch Sunart granite intrusion). The reasons for the location of an exporting superquarry were proposed by Gribble (1989) as:

(a) at least 150×10^6 tonnes of rock reserves suitable for 30 years life at an annual extraction rate of 5×10^6 tonnes;
(b) rock must be capable of producing good quality aggregate;
(c) site must be near the sea (<2km away) so that all haulage of material can be carried out using conveyor systems;
(d) access must be on to the sea with deep water available (preferably for ships of 37 500 dwt where 9 m of water must be available);
(e) the site must be protected from the main wind directions (which in Scotland are from SW to NW).

More information on this topic can be found in a report by Arup Economics & Planning (1992) prepared for the Department of the Environment, and in Gribble (1980, 1989, 1991, 1995).

In the Southern Uplands of Scotland, including the Scottish Borders, the main rock types used for aggregate supply are greywackes of Early Palaeozoic age. These are strong, dark grey rocks which perform excellently in most aggregate applications. In some old maps of the Peebles region, quarries in the Ordovician greywackes are denoted 'whinstone' (an old name for dolerite or basalt) and the engineering properties of greywackes are very similar to those of dolerites. Several small quarries exist in this region from Hawick across to Moffat in the west but the coastline of southern Scotland prohibits the development of superquarry sites. Furthermore, apart from the lack of decent coastal sites and deep water in the region, the greywackes there are invariably found intercalated intimately with shales. Shales are not suitable for any engineering use and the amount of discard (useless materials that would still have to be quarried) would be too great to make such an operation economic. Greywackes would still be suitable materials for small quarry units to exploit because of their excellent aggregate properties, especially the PSV which is always over 60 and would allow the aggregate to be used in the wearing course on roads.

In the more remote parts of Scotland some unusual rocks have been used as aggregate, despite the fact that there are better rocks available within some of the areas. Thus, for example, Shetland quarries a phyllite (amongst others) at Scalloway; Lewis in the Outer Hebrides quarries Lewisian Gneiss near Stornoway; Skye quarries Torridonian Sandstone at Sconser; Islay quarries black Dalradian Limestone at Ballygrant, and Orkney uses crushed Middle ORS flagstones.

Thus a wide and varied assemblage of rock types is used for producing aggregate in Scotland, and considering the remote nature of parts of Scotland it is unlikely that the quarrying of many of the more unusual types will cease. But in the large population centres, such as the Midland Valley, quartz-dolerites will continue to be quarried for many decades to come. We may well see the increasing development of large superquarries in remote coastal areas (probably quarrying granites or other large igneous bodies) to supply both the Midland Valley requirements as well as to provide material for export.

About 1.6×10^6 tonnes of limestone aggregate is mined annually in Scotland. More than half of this tonnage comes from Dunbar where a very pure calcium carbonate Lower Carboniferous limestone is mined, together with a shale horizon, to eventually produce cement after mixing and sintering. The remainder of the limestone aggregate comes from several quarries in the Midland Valley (e.g. near Bathgate and south of Glasgow) where the material is used for agricultural lime and general purpose aggregate, a quarry in the Highlands at Blair Atholl where it is used for engineering purposes, and one at Ballygrant on Islay where the aggregate is used for agricultural lime as well as for general purposes.

Dimension stone

Dimension stone is rock that can be used for building purposes by being cut or sawn into shape to provide stone for building and cladding; and to provide slabs, roofing tiles, floor tiles, ashlar and paving stones. Modern machinery has improved the quarrying of large stone blocks and some quarries have reopened to provide material for this purpose. Furthermore, present-day architects are demanding more natural stone usage on new buildings to blend them in with the Victorian and earlier buildings that abound in Scotland.

Government statistics reveal that the use of granite has increased significantly in the last decade, and that the UK is self-sufficient in sandstone and limestone for building purposes. Home production is augmented by imported stone, particularly granite from Scandinavia, roofing tiles from Spain, and specialized worked marble from Italy and elsewhere.

Scotland originally produced large amounts of good quality sandstone for building purposes, particularly in the Midland Valley, using many quarries including the Lower Carboniferous Giffnock Sandstone from which most of Victorian Glasgow is built; or the Craigleith Sandstone of similar age from which most of classical Georgian Edinburgh is built. The difference in the performance of these building stones can be attributed to the particular city in which the stones reside, and sandstone composition.

The Glasgow sandstone is porous with a mainly carbonate cement and resides in an industrial city which suffered air pollution in the past. CO_2 in the air combines with rain water to give carbonic acid (H_2CO_3) which then reacts with the carbonates in the rock to give calcium bicarbonate $Ca(HCO_3)_2$ which is soluble and can be washed out. On the other hand the Edinburgh sandstone is much less porous and contains a silica cement which is non-reactive and does not get leached out, so that the sandstone has not seriously degraded with age.

The city of Aberdeen, from the 17th century onwards, was built of local granite, initially obtained by use of boulders from drift and surface outcrop, and later from deep quarries such as Rubislaw. The fresh granite is completely resistant to all air-borne pollutants. Other towns and villages in Scotland were built of local stone so that, for example, in the Midland Valley most towns and villages were built of Carboniferous sandstone although some of the towns and villages in Ayrshire used Permian red sandstones from quarries in the Mauchline area. Glasgow and some towns and villages to the immediate north (Stirling, Crieff) also used Old Red Sandstone as building stones. Elsewhere, the towns in northeast Scotland used local granite so that Peterhead and Fraserburgh are built of red granites from the Peterhead quarries; but the Turriff area used red Devonian sandstones and the town of Macduff on the Moray Firth used local Dalradian metamorphic rocks. Some villages in more remote areas often used quite exotic stone. The village of Kentallen used kentallenite (a potash-bearing gabbro) because it was built on it and it had to be excavated during the building of the Oban railway line, and North Ballachulish used diorite because it was the local rock. Similar examples are to be found throughout Scotland, thus knowledge of the local geology can often be obtained from an examination of the older houses in local villages.

Aberdeen is an interesting case in that the earliest buildings in Old Aberdeen, including the older University buildings, were built of sandstones that had to be imported by sea from the south. The reason for this was that when the older part of the city was built in the 15th and 16th centuries, techniques for working granite into architectural detail were not known, and builders used sandstone that could be carved using available skills. At the present time a few quarries (Peterhead, Ross of Mull, Dalbeattie near Dumfries, Kemnay in Aberdeenshire) can provide granite blocks for dimension stone and it is possible that such sources will increase in the future. A sandstone quarry in the grounds of Hopetoun House was re-opened to obtain material to repair Georgian buildings in Edinburgh where a perfect colour match is of crucial importance; but new stone buildings in Scotland such as Queen Street Station and the Law Courts in Glasgow were both built of northern English sandstone which matched the local building stone colours well, and it may well be some time (if at all) before Scotland develops dimension stone quarries to provide sandstones for modern natural stone buildings. However, Permian Hopeman Sandstone is currently being used in Edinburgh, and covers the recent extension to the National Museum of Scotland in Chambers Street.

The brucite marble at Ledmore in the NW Highlands of Scotland has recently been worked for dimension stone. This is a particularly handsome greyish white marble with wisps of

yellowish brucite present (brucite formation is discussed in the section dealing with talc). The marble at Ledmore is of Cambrian age and has been hydrothermally altered by an alkali igneous intrusion (called the Borolan complex), which was emplaced along the Moine Thrust.

In northern Scotland several quarries (e.g. Spital and Cairnfield) currently work Caithness flagstones of the Middle ORS. The main uses are for paving slabs in pedestrian precincts, tiling and a variety of natural stone products such as fireplaces. Roofing tiles are produced for the repair of St Magnus Cathedral in Orkney. The general demand is high and several new flagstone quarries are planned in Caithness.

Silica sand

Scotland contributes about 0.6×10^6 tonnes of silica sand to the UK total of 4.5×10^6 tonnes. Most comes from the Midland Valley where siliceous ganisters provide the high quality material, but about 75 000 tonnes comes from the Cretaceous sandstones of Loch Aline. An analysis gives SiO_2 99.69%; Al_2O_3 0.11%; total iron 0.02%; MgO 0.01% and CaO 0.02%. This is well inside the minimum quality demands for industry which require an Al_2O_3 content less than 0.4% and total iron content less than 0.07%. This material is mainly used as a scouring agent.

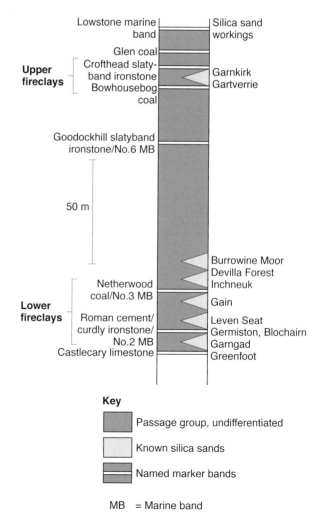

Fig. 18.2. Generalized stratigraphy of the Passage Group of the Central Basin, indicating the approximate positions of known silica sand horizons (adapted from MacPherson 1986).

The remaining annual tonnage of silica sands is produced by various quarries in the Midland Valley, and these sands, which are used for purposes other than construction, have been termed industrial sands. In the past Carboniferous sands in the Glasgow–Coatbridge area were quarried, but as industry demanded higher purity in the sands being used for glass making and moulding, production moved from the Glasgow area to western Fife where the best sands are produced from the Passage Group rocks of western Fife.

The generalized section of the Passage Formation (Fig. 18.2) shows the approximate positions of all the known silica sand horizons. The silica content varies from 94% at Garnkirk with less than 0.5% iron as Fe_2O_3, 98.6% at Levenseat (with 0.55% iron), and 99% at Devilla Forest (with 0.02% iron). The sand at Levenseat is acid treated to provide material for colourless flint glass containers, or, if left untreated, is used for wash-moulding and coloured glass production. The Devilla Forest sands are used after washing only to produce colourless flint glass. MacPherson (1986) suggested that the Devilla Forest site should be protected from complete depletion because of its uniqueness. Although other locations in Scotland have been investigated, the demand for increased sand purity, with high silica (>95%) and low iron content ($\ll$0.5%) has tended to restrict the choice of possible silica sand sites.

Fireclay and brick-making

The UK produces about 1×10^6 tonnes of fireclay annually, mainly for the production of refractories such as bricks for lining high-temperature furnaces. Scotland produced about 80 000 tonnes annually (from deposits in the Lothians) but in 1997 production dropped to 26 000 tonnes, and then ceased completely from 1998 onwards as the main company involved closed its Scottish refractory production unit. In the UK about 4600×10^6 bricks were produced annually at the end of the eighties but this has since dropped back to around 3000×10^6 in 1998. Scotland produced 172×10^6 bricks in 1998 (down from 330×10^6 in the late 1980s) and production is continuing to drop slightly each year. None of the bricks manufactured are facing bricks; but Scottish production from centres at Errol in Fife and near Denny in Stirlingshire seems set to continue into the foreseeable future.

Talc

Considerable quantities of talc are present in Unst and Fetlar of the Shetland Islands. The main deposits on Unst occur within the serpentine outcrop and near to the thrust line which separates the serpentine on the south and east from the pelites and igneous sills to the north and west (Mykura 1976).

Serpentine is formed from the hydrothermal alteration of olivine in the presence of water and silica. Under continuing hydrothermal conditions, serpentine further breaks down to give talc and brucite. If CO_2 is present then serpentine combines with the CO_2 to produce talc, and magnesite is also produced instead of brucite.

Queyhouse Quarry on Unst has been operating since 1945 with an annual production of between 4000 and 6000 tonnes. The talc is mostly used in the manufacture of roofing felt. Talc was worked on the nearby island of Fetlar but production ceased in 1914, and old Viking quarries which mined talc have been recognized on Shetland south Mainland near the Burn of Catpund, where talc occurs with magnesite.

Diatomite

Diatomite, a white siliceous material formed from the skeletons of diatoms accumulating in freshwater lakes, is widely used as an insulating material or as a filter in sugar refining. It is also used as a natural lightweight filler where its low density (0.5 tonnes m^{-3} in the natural state reducing to 0.25 tonnes m^{-3} after calcining and drying) makes it ideal for this use.

The United Kingdom imports between 10 and 20 thousand tonnes of diatomite per year and at a price well in excess of £100/tonne. Although this is not a large amount of money in total, the Island of Skye contains several natural deposits of diatomite which are capable of supplying the UK demand. Most deposits there are too small or difficult to work, and one or two deposits (such as those at Sartil) have been worked out, but a few deposits, particularly those at Eilean Chaluim Chille, north of Uig, and at Loch Cuithir, about 7 km south of Staffin merit further investigation.

These two sites may contain more than 1×10^6 cubic metres of natural diatomite, and may be commercially viable. The Loch Cuithir deposit was worked around 1914 and again around 1940. It is estimated that half of the original deposits remain, but the amount and quality of the reserves need to be ascertained.

19 Hydrocarbons

M. PYE & S. BROWN

Scotland and the adjacent continental shelf have proved to be exceptionally rich in oil and gas thanks to the presence of two source rocks. Onshore, the Carboniferous oil shales around Edinburgh were the basis of a thriving shale oil industry in the latter part of the 19th century. Offshore, the Upper Jurassic Kimmeridge Clay Formation is the source of most of the oil in the North Sea fields, discovered and produced in the latter part of the 20th century. The development of these natural resources has proved to be hugely challenging scientifically, technologically and commercially.

The economic return to Scotland and the rest of the United Kingdom has been immense; since 1965 the oil industry has generated an operating surplus of £250 billion (DTI 2000). Hydrocarbons from the UK Continental Shelf as a whole contributed £4 billion to the UK's gross domestic product in 1999, equivalent to 1.8% of the total. However, in addition to this most obvious and important impact, the production of oil and gas from the 'geology of Scotland' has left its mark in other ways. There have been changes in the science of geology as practised in Scotland, and on the history and landscape. In West Lothian the working of oil shale during the late 19th and early 20th century produced the distinctive waste heaps known as bings (see Chapter 20, Fig. 20.1). More recently oil development has brought economic benefits to the northeast of Scotland and the Shetland Islands.

This account of the economic geology of oil and natural gas builds on the geological framework presented in earlier chapters. It addresses the following subject areas, offering a historical perspective, a snapshot of current issues, and a window on the future:

- offshore oil and gas: the North Sea sedimentary basins;
- offshore oil and gas: the basins of the northeast Atlantic margin;
- onshore oil and gas: oil from sapropelic coal and oil shale;
- onshore oil and gas: coal bed methane.

Readers interested in greater detail of the offshore geology and details of individual fields are referred to Glennie (1998a) and Abbots (1991).

Offshore oil and gas

Geographical extent

The principal areas of oil and natural gas exploration and production offshore Scotland (Figs 19.1, 19.2) are as follows:

1. The Northern North Sea which includes the N–S-trending Viking Graben and its Tertiary cover, the East Shetland Basin situated in the NW, and the eastern margins of East Shetland Platform, which bound the later two basins to the west.
2. The Central North Sea, principally within and on the western flank of the NW–SE-trending Central Graben together with its overlying Tertiary cover.
3. The Moray Firth, including the Inner Moray Firth Basin, which extends onto the coastal fringe of the Moray Firth

in the west and includes the NW–SE-trending Witch Ground Graben in the east.

4. The NE Atlantic Margin, which includes all the areas under exploration west of Shetland together with the UK designated area extending westwards into the Atlantic to Rockall.

Geological overview

This distribution of oil and gas fields described above, is principally controlled by a system of Late Jurassic grabens within which the Kimmeridge Clay source rock is mature for the generation of oil and gas (Fig. 19.3). Oil and gas migrating from Kimmeridge Clay source rocks has been trapped in reservoirs. In the North Sea the reservoir rocks are principally sandstones of Jurassic and Palaeocene age, although many other formations are involved (Fig. 19.4). Reservoir rocks have the porosities and permeabilities needed to sustain the flow

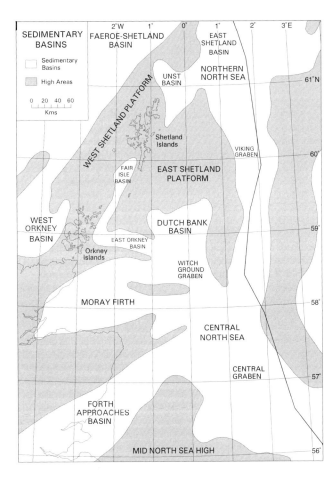

Fig. 19.1. Sedimentary basins, offshore Scotland. The Kimmeridge Clay Formation is mature for the generation of oil and gas in the Viking, Central and Witch Ground Grabens and in the Faeroe–Shetland Basin.

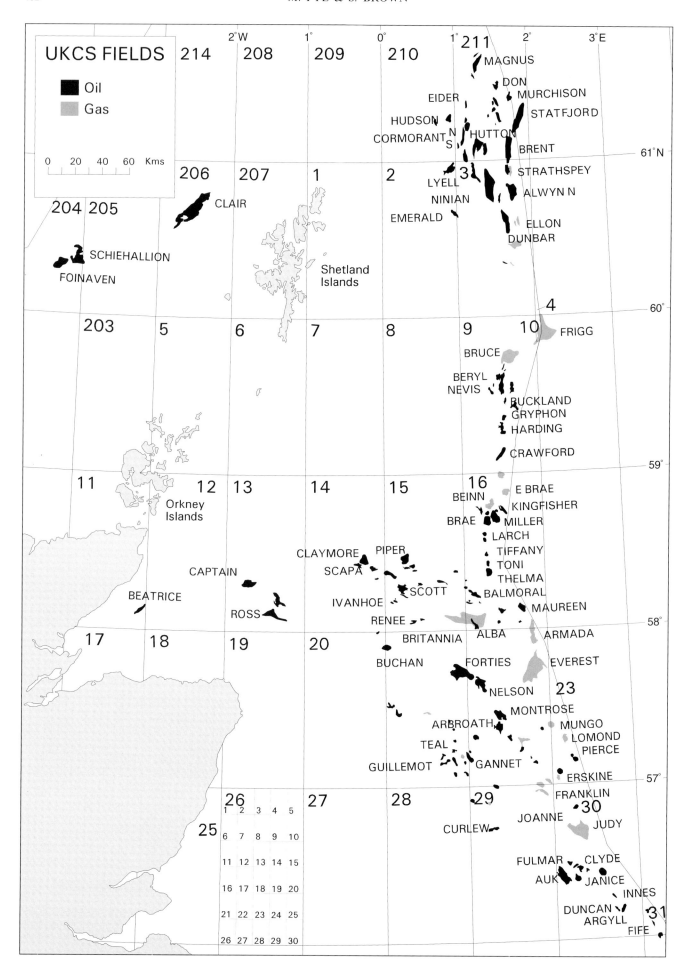

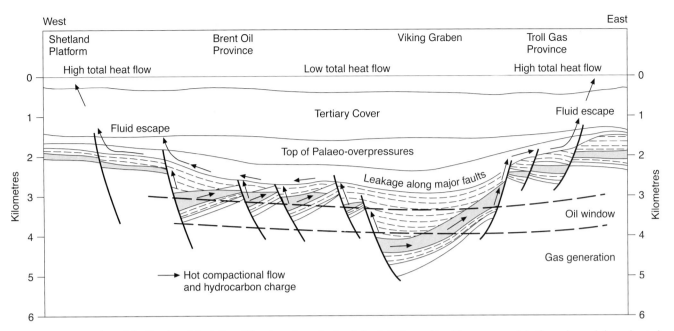

Fig. 19.3. Cross-section of the Northern North Sea. Oil and gas from the deeply buried Kimmeridge Clay source rock in the graben axis has migrated into reservoirs in the tilted fault blocks along the graben margins (after Burley 1993).

rates required for a commercial offshore development. Offshore individual wells need to flow at rates of thousands of barrels per day to be economic and this requires reservoirs with porosities generally in excess of 20% and permeabilities greater than 100 mD. In order to retain oil and gas these reservoirs need to be contained in some form of trap (Spencer *et al.* 1996). For the Jurassic reservoirs of the Northern North Sea the trap is usually a tilted fault block. In the Central North Sea the movement of underlying Zechstein salt has helped to form traps both by controlling where Jurassic sands were deposited and then by the subsequent formation of salt diapirs. At the Palaeocene level traps are mainly four-way dip closures draped over deeper structures (Bain 1993).

Production and remaining reserves

The first oil discovery offshore Scotland was in 1969 in what was to become the Arbroath Field (Central North Sea, Block 22/17, Crawford *et al.* 1991). This early phase of exploration was phenomenally successful with a lot of the large structures seen on seismic containing major oil fields. Forties was discovered in 1970, Brent, Beryl, Piper and Ninian followed in the next four years. Development of these fields was also rapid with Forties onstream by 1975, Brent, Beryl and Piper in 1976 and Ninian in 1978. By 1980 production was over half a million barrels/day and contributed 4% of the UK's Gross Domestic Product. Production continued to rise through the early 1980s but then dropped due to the oil price crash in 1986. Production rose through the 1990s to reach 2.8×10^6 barrels/day by the end of the decade. In 1999 UKCS production was 137.1×10^6 tonnes of oil and 105 bcm of gas (1 tonne crude oil = 7.5 barrels). Oil production is expected to continue at this level until 2002 before declining; gas production will increase but will probably peak before 2004. Cumulative production for the UKCS to the end 1999 was 2444×10^6 tonnes of oil and 1410 bcm of gas (DTI 2000). The total remaining reserves are estimated as $1000–4630 \times 10^6$ tonnes of oil and 1190–3465 bcm of gas. Of these figures, 665×10^6 tonnes of oil and 760 bcm of

gas are proven reserves in existing fields. There were 134 oil and gas fields in production offshore of Scotland in 2002.

The economic geology of each of the offshore areas is now considered in more detail. The accounts provide, in turn:

- a brief history of exploration and production activity in the area;
- a synoptic account of the principal reservoirs, source rocks and traps;
- field examples chosen to illustrate aspects of the economic geology.

The Northern North Sea

Exploration activity began in the Northern North Sea in 1970. Initial seismic reflection profiles revealed a major regional unconformity at depth, forming an irregular surface of high relief. Shell drilled a structural closure on this unconformity in 1971 and discovered the oil bearing Jurassic sandstones of the Brent Field beneath it (Fig. 19.5). In the subsequent seven years, 32 discoveries were made in Brent sandstones beneath Base Cretaceous closures and some 8 billion barrels of oil discovered (Bowen 1992).

Since then, the Northern North Sea has become the major oil producing area of the UK Continental Shelf (Johnson *et al.* 1993), although there have been very few subsequent discoveries of greater than 100×10^6 barrels. The productive life of the northern oilfields has been much greater than originally expected and no major field has yet been abandoned. The Brent Field is currently being depressurised to recover the associated gas and Magnus is to have gas from the fields to the west of Shetland injected into the reservoir to improve oil recovery.

Principal reservoirs, Northern North Sea

The main reservoirs of the Northern North Sea area, in order of economic importance, are as follows:

Fig. 19.2. Location map for Scotland's offshore oil and gas fields. For licencing purposes the UKCS has been divided into numbered quadrants and each quadrant is subdivided into 30 blocks as shown in quadrant 26.

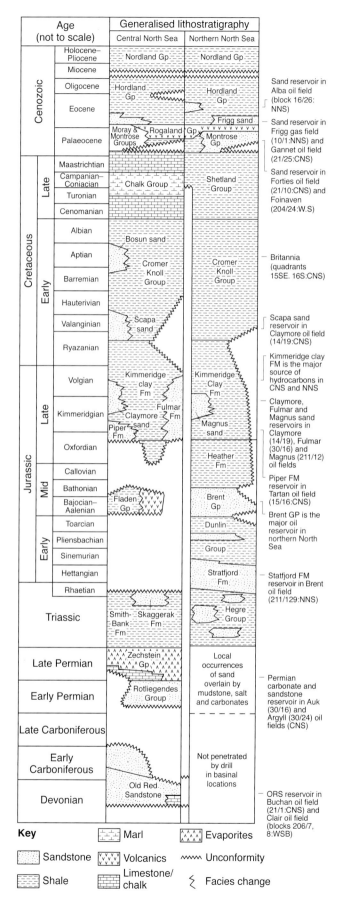

Fig. 19.4. Stratigraphy of offshore Scotland showing the wide range of ages of the different reservoirs present on the UKCS.

Middle Jurassic (Brent Group and its lateral equivalents). Distributed throughout the basins of the Northern North Sea, these strata are most productive in the East Shetland Basin and in the Beryl area (Quadrant 9) of the Viking Graben. They were deposited in deltaic and related shallow marine environments (Richards 1992). They commonly produce a layered reservoir, with laterally continuous sandstone units (the Etive and Tarbert Formations) juxtaposed stratigraphically with heterolithic sandstone–mudrock sequences (the Ness Formation), the latter containing channel-fill sands (Livera 1989). Porosity and permeability are variable but locally as high as 30% and 4 D respectively. These high permeability streaks in the Etive Formation led to early water breakthrough in producing wells and platforms had to be modified to cope with large volumes of produced water. Communication between the upper shoreface sands of the Etive and the underlying lower shoreface sands of the Rannoch Formation has reduced recovery from the Rannoch as injected water coned down from the Etive. More recently, horizontal wells have been drilled in the Rannoch to improve recovery (Black *et al.* 1999).

Fields with Middle Jurassic sandstone reservoirs include Brent (Block 211/29, James *et al.* 1999), Ninian (Block 3/3, Van Vessem & Gan 1991) and Beryl (Block 9/13, Robertson 1993). The Brent, Statfjord and North Alwyn Fields have a subsidiary reservoir, the Statfjord Formation, of Late Triassic to Early Jurassic age. It was deposited in a fluvial to shallow marine environment.

Upper Jurassic. Sandstone and conglomerate reservoirs are found locally distributed in the South Viking Graben and are also productive in the Magnus Field (Block 211/12) in the East Shetland Basin. Deposited in submarine fan environments, in the south Viking Graben they consist of thick piles of conglomerate and sandstone interbedded with mudrock (e.g. the Brae Field reservoir; Block 16/7a, Stephenson 1991), with the coarsest succession developed close to the major faults at the western margin of the Viking Graben. Porosity averages *c.* 14% and permeability *c.* 360 mD but varying between 1 mD and 4 D in places. In the Magnus Field (Shepherd 1991), the reservoir consists mostly of medium-grained sandstone with 18–24% porosity and permeability in the range 0–950 mD. Other fields with Upper Jurassic reservoirs in the Northern North Sea include Miller (Block 16/7b, Rooksby 1991) and the Tiffany and Toni Fields (Block 16/17, Kerlogue *et al.* 1994).

Palaeocene and Eocene. A major gas field, the Frigg Field (Block 10/1, Brewster 1991) was discovered in 1972 and has been in production since 1977. The reservoir sandstone was deposited in a submarine fan environment in the Early Eocene. The Frigg reservoir comprises sandstone of 29% average porosity and permeability as high as 4 D in places. More recently the Gryphon and Harding Fields have been developed (Newman *et al.* 1993). These have similar good quality, submarine fan reservoirs but contain a viscous heavy oil which required long horizontal wells to develop successfully.

Trias. Triassic sandstone, although extensive in its distribution, has had limited economic significance in the Northern North Sea. It has provided production in some fields (e.g. Beryl), and it is now being exploited from beneath some of the Brent Province fields such as North Alwyn and Tern (Black *et al.* 1999).

Source rocks, Northern North Sea

The source rock for oil and gas in the Northern North Sea is the Late Jurassic to Early Cretaceous Kimmeridge Clay

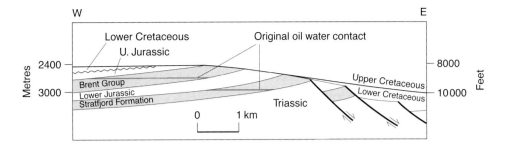

Fig. 19.5. Structural cross-section of the Brent field. The Jurassic reservoirs are truncated below the Base Cretaceous Unconformity and sealed by the overlying shales. (after Bowen 1975)

Formation. It is widely distributed throughout the Mesozoic basins and reaches maturity for oil generation at burial depths of c. 3000 m. These depths were achieved in the basins around the Mid-Tertiary. It is a dark grey, organic-rich shale deposited in an offshore marine environment. The richest part of the formation has up to 10% total organic carbon (TOC) and its characteristically high value response to downhole gamma-ray logging tools shows that it contains radioactive minerals (hence the informal name of 'hot shales').

Traps, Northern North Sea

Rotational block faulting associated with Mesozoic extension of the Northern North Sea basins played a critical role in creating structural traps for hydrocarbons with reservoirs in pre-Cretaceous strata. The typical trapping style of Northern North Sea, Jurassic fields such as Brent and Statfjord, involves the combination of tilted fault blocks and the development of an unconformity surface truncating the dipping reservoir horizon over the structural high which was then capped by younger shales. The Magnus Field with its Upper Jurassic reservoir also has a similar structural style.

In most cases there is good communication across the fields so that down-flank injectors can support crestal production wells. However, some fields were found to be severely compartmentalized by faulting; producers and injectors had to be assigned to each of the smaller fault blocks in the Northwest Hutton (Block 211/27, Johnes & Gauer 1991) and North Cormorant Fields (Block 211/21a, Demyttenaere et al. 1993). Structural instability along the crests of the major fault blocks has produced a footwall degradation complex in the Brent and Ninian Fields (McLeod & Underhill 1999). The numerous slump faults have restricted communication in the reservoir but these areas have been developed with long horizontal wells.

Upper Jurassic reservoirs in the south Viking Graben are found on the hangingwall of extensional faults, in the case of fields such as Brae the fault is the major basin margin fault separating the Viking Graben from the East Shetland Platform. The reservoir facies is lost laterally as the sandstone and conglomerate is replaced by mudrock (Kerlogue et al. 1994).

In the Eocene, stratigraphic trapping occurs with sand bodies forming as channel fills or lobes on submarine fan surfaces (Timbrell 1993). The sands pass laterally into mudrocks. Later differential compaction enhances relief.

Field example, Northern North Sea

The T-Block fields, Tiffany and Toni, are oil-fields discovered in 1977 and 1979 respectively and are located at the western margin of the Viking Graben in Block 16/17 (Kerlogue et al. 1994). The estimates of recoverable reserves initially in place are 13.2 and 5.3 million tonnes of oil. Tiffany has 36° API gravity oil and Toni 34.7° API.

The reservoir in both fields comprises sandstone and conglomerate. A range of detailed depositional interpretations have been proposed for various lithofacies types present: for the conglomerates, interpretation is dependent upon the nature of their matrix (muddy or sandy) and whether the larger clasts are matrix or framework supported. Coarse deposits from debris flows and from high density turbidity currents are interbedded with thinner bedded sandstones deposited from low density turbidity currents and with hemipelagic mudrocks. The sequences are considered to have been deposited in a submarine fan environment. Average porosity in the reservoir zones of each field is c. 10.5% and permeability on average is only 75 mD in Tiffany and 150 mD in Toni.

The trap for the Toni and Tiffany Fields is due to a combination of stratigraphic and structural features (Fig. 19.6). A structural culmination has been formed by inversion of the basin boundary fault which lies close to the west of the fields. In Tiffany, the reservoir facies is lost to north and south as a result of facies changes whereas in Toni the interpretation favours termination against sealing cross-faults. In both, up-dip sealing to the west is postulated to occur at a fault that juxtaposes the reservoir with impermeable pre-Jurassic rocks. Top seal in both cases is the Kimmeridge Clay Formation. Tiffany also has a subsidiary reservoir in the Lower Cretaceous, and Toni a subsidiary zone in the Middle Jurassic, containing gas condensate.

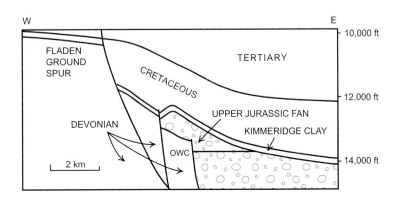

Fig. 19.6. Structural cross-section of the Tiffany field. The Upper Jurassic fan was deposited at the graben margin.

The main source of hydrocarbons is the Kimmeridge Clay Formation which overlies and is interbedded with the T-Block reservoir facies. The principal phase of oil generation is thought to have begun in the Eocene. It has been postulated that the gas condensate in Toni has a mixed source, including Middle Jurassic shales and coals as well as the Kimmeridge Clay Formation.

Central North Sea

Following the 1969 discovery of the Arbroath Field (Block 22/17, Crawford *et al.* 1991), drilling over the next five years resulted in a string of further exploration successes at stratigraphic levels ranging from the Devonian to the Lower Tertiary. Today, the Central North Sea has become a major area of oil, gas and gas condensate production (Gatliff *et al.* 1994). The latest development in the Central North Sea has been the development of a number of Jurassic, High Pressure, High Temperature (HPHT) gas condensate fields including Shearwater (Block 22/30b, Blehaut *et al.* 1999), Elgin and Franklin (Blocks 22/30 & 29/5, Lasocki *et al.* 1999). In these fields reservoir pressures exceed 10 000 psi and reservoir temperatures are above 190°C. The source of the overpressure is thought to be hydrocarbon generation (Holm 1996).

Principal reservoirs, Central North Sea

The principal reservoirs in the Central North Sea, in order of economic importance, are as follows:

Palaeocene. Sandstones of Palaeocene age form the reservoir in the giant Forties Field (Block 21/10, Wills 1991) and a number of other, smaller fields, including a clutch of fields in the north where the central North Sea area merges with the Viking Graben in Quadrant 16 (Balmoral, Andrew and Maureen). The sandstone was deposited in submarine fans, with coarser grained turbidite deposits accumulating in elongate topographic lows on the depositional surface. In Forties average porosity is around 28% and permeability averages 700 mD. It was the recognition of the channelized nature of these turbidite flows in the Montrose and Arbroath Fields that led Enterprise Oil to realise that the original well on the Nelson structure had penetrated an interchannel area and only recorded oil shows (Whyatt *et al.* 1992). Realizing that the turbidite channels were discernible on seismic, Enterprise drilled again and discovered the Nelson Field in 1988.

Jurassic. Upper Jurassic sandstones form the reservoir in major fields such as Fulmar (Block 30/16, Spaak *et al.* 1999) and Clyde (Block 30/17b, Turner 1993). The sandstone is of good reservoir quality with porosities of *c.*23% and permeability up to 800 mD. Shallow marine deposits succeeded by deeper water submarine fan sandstone are characteristic of the reservoir sequence. Broadly age-equivalent sandstone of shallow marine origin is also found on the western flank of the Central Graben forming the reservoir in the Kittiwake Field (Block 21/18, Glennie & Armstrong 1991).

Trias. Upper Triassic sandstone of fluvial origin is the reservoir in the Marnock and Skua Fields (Block 22/24, Pooler & Amory 1999) along the western edge of the Central Graben. Older Triassic sandstone has been found to contain oil in the Josephine Field (Block 30/7). The distribution of Triassic sandstone is discontinuous due to the deposition being controlled by uneven, penecontemporaneous dissolution of salt at the top of the underlying Permian evaporite sequence.

Permian. Zechstein carbonate and Rotliegend sandstone contributed to the pay zone in the Argyll Field (no longer in production, Block 30/24, Robson 1991) and the Auk Field (Block 30/16, Trewin & Bramwell 1991). Argyll also had production from Devonian Old Red Sandstone.

Cretaceous. Chalk reservoirs have proved to be of major importance in the adjacent Danish and Norwegian sectors of the Central North Sea but not so in the UK sector. The Machar Field (Block 23/26a, Foster & Rattey 1993) and the Banff Field (Block 29/2a, Evans *et al.* 1999) both produce from fractured Chalk reservoirs adjacent to salt diapirs.

Source rocks, Central North Sea. The principal source rock throughout the Central North Sea area is the Upper Jurassic Kimmeridge Clay Formation. In places the depth of burial of the source rocks is sufficient to have generated gas condensate which is now found in the reservoirs of fields such as Everest (Block 22/9 & 22/10, O'Connor & Walker 1993).

Traps, Central North Sea

In the Central North Sea traps commonly show evidence of the influence of mobile Permian salt. Anticlinal closures over the crests of salt swells and lateral closures against the flanks of salt diapirs occur (Davison *et al.* 2000). In addition, rotational block faulting coupled with movement of salt, especially the location and timing of salt withdrawal, have played a major role in forming the structure of fields such as Fulmar (Penge *et al.* 1999). In the Palaeocene, low amplitude anticlinal closures occur over fault-bounded structural highs. In the Eocene in particular, subtle traps in submarine fan lobes formed by stratigraphic pinch-out and differential compaction are found (e.g. Gannet A, Block 22/21, Armstrong *et al.* 1987).

Field example, Central North Sea

The Clyde Field (Block 30/17b, Turner 1993) is located on the SW margin of the Central Graben. It was discovered in 1978 and production commenced in 1987. It is estimated to have recoverable reserves of 17.55×10^6 tonnes of oil.

Clyde produces from the Upper Jurassic Fulmar Sand Formation, a bioturbated, arkosic, fine grained sandstone, deposited in a shallow marine environment. Average porosity is 20% and permeability varies from 1 to over 1000 mD. The oil from Clyde has a gravity of 38° API and is sourced from the Upper Jurassic Kimmeridge Clay Formation present in adjacent structural lows. It has been estimated that the oil in Clyde was generated from a source buried to depths of 2900–3100 m during the Early to Mid-Eocene.

Clyde Field has a combination structural/stratigraphic trap (Fig. 19.7). It occurs in a rotated fault block that is underlain by a wedge of Zechstein salt. The up-dip edge of the rotated block has been truncated beneath a major unconformity at the base of the Cretaceous. Locally Upper Cretaceous strata rest directly on Triassic beneath the unconformity. Top seal to the Jurassic reservoir sandstone is provided by the Kimmeridge Clay Formation and by the Upper Cretaceous where truncated up-dip by the base-Cretaceous unconformity.

Moray Firth

This area stretches from the Moray Firth coast to the eastern limit of UK North Sea Quadrant 15 (Andrews *et al.* 1990). It consists primarily of two important sub-basins from an oil and gas perspective. The Inner Moray Firth Basin is in the

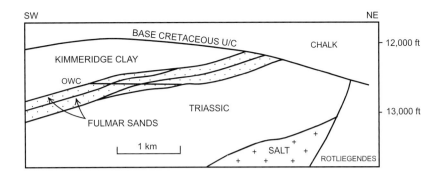

Fig. 19.7. Structural cross-section of the Clyde field. The Jurassic reservoir is truncated beneath the Base Cretaceous Unconformity and sealed by shales and chalk. Deeper salt movements helped to form the structure.

west, where Mesozoic depositional thickness is strongly influenced by faults with an inherited NE–SW Caledonian trend and in the east, the Mesozoic Witch Ground Graben has NW–SE-trending boundary faults.

The first field to be discovered in the Moray Firth area was the Piper Field (Block 15/17, Harker 1998) in 1973, located on the northern flank of the Witch Ground Graben. The first well in the Inner Moray Firth was drilled in Block 12/26 in 1967 (David 1996) but the first significant discovery in this area had to wait until 1976, with the discovery of the Beatrice Field in Block 11/30 (Stevens 1991). Beatrice and Piper both have Jurassic reservoirs; however, recent exploration has established a narrow fairway of Lower Cretaceous sand linking the two basins (Law *et al.* 2000) from Captain to just north of Buchan.

Principal reservoirs, Moray Firth

There are a number of different reservoir horizons in the Moray Firth Basin, in the Palaeozoic, the Jurassic and the Cretaceous, but by far the most important occur in the Upper Jurassic.

Jurassic. Upper Jurassic shallow marine sandstones, the Piper and Scott formations, are widely distributed in the eastern (or Outer) Moray Firth area. Typical porosities are around 25% and permeabilities can be up to 10 D. They form the reservoir in a number of important fields in addition to Piper, such as Tartan (Block 15/16, Coward *et al.* 1991), Rob Roy and Ivanhoe (both in Block 15/21, Currie 1996). Upper Jurassic deep marine turbidite deposits, the Claymore and Galley formations are also widely distributed in the Outer Moray Firth area. Porosity is *c*. 28% on average and permeability can be as high as 1.3 D. Middle Jurassic shallow marine to deltaic sandstones form the reservoir in the Beatrice Field (Stevens 1991). The uppermost sandstone unit of the pay zone, a shallow marine sandstone of Callovian age, forms the main reservoir with porosity of 10–20% and permeability of up to 800 mD (see also Chapter 11).

Cretaceous. Lower Cretaceous sandstone contributes to Moray Firth production in the giant Britannia gas field (Blocks 15/30 & 16/26, Jones *et al.* 1999), the Scapa Field (Block 14/19, Harker & Chermak 1992) and the Captain Field (Block 13/22, Rose 1999). All of these reservoirs are composed of turbidite sands but Britannia is unique in that the reservoir sequence is dominated by slurry flows of muddy sandstone.

Palaeocene and Eocene. Overlying Britannia, the Alba Field was a serendipitous discovery in Eocene turbidite sands (Newton & Flanagan 1993). Ocean bottom seismic has proved to be the key in imaging these sands. Palaeocene turbidite sands form the reservoirs in MacCulloch and the now abandoned Donan Field.

Permian and Carboniferous. Two minor Palaeozoic reservoir horizons, in the Carboniferous and in the Permian, occur in the Claymore Field (Block 14/19, Harker *et al.* 1991). The former consists of deltaic sandstone. The latter is in evaporite facies with its porosity in cavities formed as a result of freshwater leaching. Neither accumulation would have been economic in its own right; oil production has only been achieved as a consequence of production of the main Upper Jurassic reservoir.

Devonian. The Buchan Field (Block 21/1, Edwards 1991) has a reservoir of predominantly fluvial, Old Red Sandstone of Devonian–Carboniferous age. The sandstones are of poor reservoir quality and the production is from an extensive open fracture network (see also Chapter 8).

Source rocks, Moray Firth

The principal source of oil in the Moray Firth Basin is the Upper Jurassic Kimmeridge Clay Formation. Organic carbon content ranges from 2% up to 15%. Over much of the Outer Moray Firth the Kimmeridge Clay is buried to depths in excess of 3000 m and is therefore mature for oil generation. In the Inner Moray Firth however the picture is rather different: Kimmeridge Clay Formation strata are buried to depths of between 1000 to 3000 m only, depths shallower than those required to bring the organic material into the oil generating 'kitchen'. However it seems that the Inner Moray Firth may have suffered up to 1000 m of basin uplift during the Tertiary. Therefore the Kimmeridge Clay Formation is likely to be mature for oil generation at least locally.

The oil in the Beatrice Field has been considered to be anomalous due to its notably waxy nature. This indicates that its source organic material was richer in algal material than is the Kimmeridge Clay Formation. Suitable sources have been postulated in the lacustrine Devonian strata (Duncan & Hamilton 1988) or in the paralic facies of the Middle Jurassic associated with the Beatrice reservoir itself. Co-sourcing from Devonian and Middle Jurassic strata is also possible (Peters *et al.* 1989, Bailey *et al.* 1990)

Oil in the Moray Firth fields shows some variation in API gravity: Beatrice oil is of 38° API with high wax content; Captain (see below) has 19–21° API, Scapa 32.5°, and Piper 37°. Apart from Beatrice, which is due to a different source, the remaining variation reflects the maturity of the source delivering the charge to the reservoir and, in the case of Captain, the later effects of within-reservoir alteration. The Kimmeridge Clay also sources the gas found in association with the oil in many of the Outer Moray Firth fields.

Traps, Moray Firth

The predominant trapping style in Moray Firth fields is of tilted fault blocks capped by Upper Jurassic or Lower Cretaceous

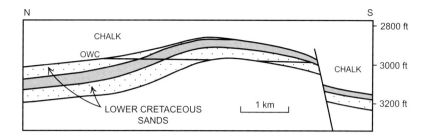

Fig. 19.8. Structural cross-section of the Captain field. The Upper Captain Sand depositionally thins onto the crest; the Lower Captain Sand forms a sand 'fairway' thought to represent a back-filled submarine canyon.

mudrocks. There are, however, a significant number of downthrown, hangingwall traps such as the Saltire Field (Moseley 1999). Jurassic traps were formed by the Mid-Cretaceous ready to receive their hydrocarbon charge in the Late Cretaceous or Early Tertiary.

Field example, Moray Firth

The Captain Field (Block 13/22, Rose 1999) is located in the western part of the Moray Firth Basin. It was discovered in 1977, production commenced in 1997 and it is estimated to have recoverable reserves of 52×10^6 tonnes. Captain produces from two horizons of Lower Cretaceous turbidite sandstone rather than the Jurassic sandstones that are the more common reservoirs in this basin. The sandstones are mainly poorly consolidated with porosities ranging from 28–34% and permeabilities of 1–12 D. Captain produces oil of 19–21° API of an especially viscous nature, which presents special production challenges, challenges that condemned the accumulation to an uneconomic status for twenty years.

The Captain trap is formed by three-way dip closure forming a broad structure of low relief, combined with reservoir pinch-out through stratigraphic onlap (Fig. 19.8). The source of the viscous crude is considered to be the organic-rich shale of the Upper Jurassic, Kimmeridge Clay Formation which is mature for oil generation in structural lows adjacent to the Captain structure. Geochemical analysis indicates that the crude was originally typical of others in the North Sea but suffered biodegradation due to flushing of the reservoir by 'fresh' water during the Tertiary. Captain has a small associated gas cap thought to have formed through a late phase of gas migration that post-dated oil emplacement and its *in situ* alteration. The economic evaluation of the Captain discovery was significantly changed as a result of the emergence of horizontal well technology in the 1980s. Captain was one of the first North Sea fields to be developed with horizontal wells.

Northeast Atlantic margin

Exploration activity began on the northeast Atlantic margin, offshore Shetland (Fyfe & Osborne, 1996; Stoker *et al.* 1993), in 1972 with the drilling of well 206/12-1 on the flanks of the NE–SW-trending basement high known as the Rona Ridge. The first significant discovery was made in 1977, in Devonian to Carboniferous strata overlying fractured Lewisian gneiss in Block 206/8, later to be known as the Clair Field (Coney *et al.* 1993; see also Chapter 8). Recently the economic potential of Clair has been re-evaluated and it will soon be developed. A second phase of exploration drilling in the northeast Atlantic margin in the late 1980s failed to reveal commercially attractive accumulations.

The next indication that the Atlantic margin might be an important new petroleum province did not come until 1990–1992 with the Solan and Strathmore discoveries in Block 205/26 (Herries *et al.* 1999), and the discovery of the Foinaven Field (Block 204/24a, Cooper *et al.* 1999). This was followed

by the discovery in 1993, of the Schiehallion Field (Block 204/20, Leach *et al.* 1999). The development of the Foinaven and Schiehallion Fields provided the first oil production from this new frontier area in 1997 and 1998 respectively.

The northeast Atlantic margin province stretches from Irish waters in the southwest to offshore northern Norway (Dore *et al.* 1999). Exploration activity is now also underway around the Faeroe Islands. Along this extensive ocean margin province, the exploration and production industry is facing different challenges from those encountered in the North Sea. Notable among these is the deeper water, reaching *c.* 1600 m midway between Shetland and Faeroe (North Sea depths are less than 200 m) but also from harsh weather and especially difficult metocean conditions.

Principal reservoirs, northeast Atlantic margin

Proven and potentially important rocks of reservoir quality have been found in horizons ranging from Precambrian to Palaeocene. However, deep burial commonly destroys reservoir potential of Mesozoic and older strata except over significantly elevated, fault-bounded structures (e.g. the Devonian–Carboniferous Old Red Sandstone facies of the Clair Field). Hydrocarbons have also been found in fractured Precambrian basement and in Triassic, Upper Jurassic and Cretaceous sandstones within the area. The principal reservoirs found to date to contain economic accumulations of hydrocarbons, in the Foinaven and Schiehallion Fields, are of Palaeocene age, developed in deep marine sandstone facies including turbidites.

The charge of the various reservoirs also varies from oil with associated gas to gas or gas condensate. One of the major operational challenges facing the industry in its assessment of the economic viability of the wide range of discoveries is how to exploit the gas reserves in this remote and environmentally sensitive area which has no existing pipeline infrastructure.

Initial exploration concepts were based on those that had proved so successful in the Northern North Sea. However in the North Sea the integrity of the top-seal in traps had not been a high risk factor. This risk factor seems, with hindsight, to have been underestimated in early exploration campaigns in the Atlantic margin. Also the widespread distribution of Tertiary lavas, formed during the opening of the Atlantic Ocean basin (see Chapters 13, 14), has been a problem for the industry as the lavas adversely affect the ability of geophysicists to image the underlying strata from seismic reflection data.

Source rocks, northeast Atlantic margin

Local hydrocarbon source kitchens have released oil from late Jurassic Kimmeridgian shales to fields such as Foinaven and Schiehallion. However, over much of the extensive area to the northeast, these source rocks tend to be more deeply buried and may have been generating gas since the Early Tertiary. Thin organic rich shales also occur in the Lower Cretaceous but this interval may be of more economic importance further south in Irish waters.

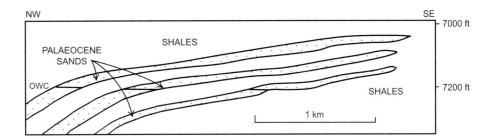

Fig. 19.9. Structural cross-section of the Foinaven field. The Palaeocene sands pinch-out updip forming a stratigraphic trap.

Traps, northeast Atlantic margin

Diverse trapping styles are encountered in the area. Rotated faults blocks similar geometrically to the northern North Sea Jurassic play do occur especially along trend from the Clair Field on the Rona Ridge. Other traps include drape anticlines, 'pop-up' anticlines resulting from deformation along transform fault zones, and stratigraphic pinch-outs associated with growth faulting.

Field example, northeast Atlantic margin

The Foinaven Field, discovered in Block 204/24 in 1992 (Cooper *et al.* 1999) following the recognition of oil and gas shows in a well two years earlier, occurs in water depths of 480 m, 200 km west of Shetland. Its subsequent development has been a major milestone in industry activity in the new Atlantic frontier province. First production was achieved in 1997, with first year of peak production in 1998. Given that development plans were sanctioned only in late 1994, Foinaven has been notable for its 'fast-track' development programme.

Located on a NE–SW trending fault-bounded ridge to the south of the main Faeroe Basin, the geology of the Foinaven Field contrasts markedly with that of the Clair Field. The Foinaven pay zone consists of Palaeocene sandstone developed as a number of thin but laterally quite extensive channelized sand bodies thought to have been derived from the east during a phase of Tertiary uplift (Fig. 19.9). Reservoir quality is excellent, with average porosity *c.* 28% and permeability up to 2 D. Faulting of the Palaeocene section segments the reservoir, with little pressure continuity between segments. Associated gas caps occur in some of the segments at different structural levels. The oil and associated gas are thought to come from Upper Jurassic shales equivalent to the Kimmeridge Clay Formation source rocks of the North Sea. The oil in Foinaven has 26° API gravity and relatively low viscosity.

Onshore oil and gas

Oil from sapropelic coal and oil-shale

James 'Paraffin' Young, a trained chemist from Glasgow, established a plant in Bathgate, West Lothian in 1851 for the destructive distillation of oil from sapropelic coal. This predated by eight years the discovery of oil in Titusville, Pennsylvania by 'Colonel' Drake, an event commonly taken as the birth of the modern oil industry. The coal used by Young, occurred within the Carboniferous Lower Coal Measures and was known as Boghead Parrot Coal or Torbanite, after its location at Boghead on the Torbanehill Estate. The deposit extended over only about 1000 hectares and was less than 50 cm thick. It was exhausted after 12 years, both as a result of local demand for the distillation product but also through export of the coal to Germany and North America (MacGregor & Anderson 1923).

A new source of oil was discovered in 1858, in the much more extensive oil-shales of the Calciferous Sandstone Measures. The shale yielded less oil than the Torbanite per unit volume but, being much more widespread, in thicker units, and less expensive to extract, its discovery permitted a large expansion of the industry. Oil-shale produced 70–200 litres of oil per tonne of shale whereas the Boghead coal yielded 535–580 litres per tonne (Cameron & McAdam 1978). Distillation of the shale also yielded 13–26 kg of ammonium sulphate per tonne of shale which was used as a fertilizer.

By 1865, when Young opened a plant to distil oil-shale at nearby West Calder, 120 plants were producing oil in east central Scotland and an important industry had grown up. By 1878, about 500 000 barrels (7.5 barrels = 1 tonne of crude oil) of oil per year were being produced and, at the peak of the industry's output during the First World War, production of some 2.1×10^6 barrels of oil per year was achieved (Hallett *et al.* 1985). In 1933 it was reported that the operations of mining the shale and the manufacturing of the downstream products supported some 40 000 people in local employment (Anon 1933).

Sapropelic coals are usually less areally extensive than the better known humic variety. Humic coals form largely from the *in situ* accumulation of woody tissue as a forest peat, whereas sapropelic coals, rich in spores, fragments of leaf cuticle and/or algal remains, accumulate initially as an organic rich ooze in ponds, lakes or lagoons deficient in oxygen (Adams 1960; Tissot & Welte 1978). The sapropelic coals are characterized chemically by a high proportion of volatile organic compounds. The variety of sapropelic coal known as 'cannel' coal (from the Scots pronunciation of 'candle' and so named because it was once burnt to supply domestic lighting) has a large concentration of plant spore material. The Boghead coal initially used by Young resembles cannel coal in appearance and mode of formation but merits differentiation because of its richness in algal remains (predominantly from *Botryococcus*-related algae).

The principal raw material for the synthetic oil produced by this industry proved therefore to be oil-shale. Tissot & Welte (1978) suggest there is no precise lithological or chemical definition of an oil-shale, only an economic one: any rock yielding commercial amounts of oil upon pyrolisis (heating to 500°C) can be termed an oil-shale. In contrast, Hutton (1982) defines an oil-shale as a rock containing more than 5% by volume of the liptinite which is derived from spores and algae.

The main oil-shale development in the Lower Carboniferous of central Scotland stretches from just cast of Linlithgow and Bathgate to the Pentland Hills (Fig. 19.10), with small workings exploiting developments in the Burntisland area of Fife (Carruthers *et al.* 1927). Extraction of the oil-shale was principally by the 'stoop and room' method (Carruthers *et al.* 1927). A series of tunnels are driven within the shale seam roughly at right angles to each other, beginning from the base of the main vertical shaft and extending out to the limits of the area to be exploited. The volumes of shale formation left between

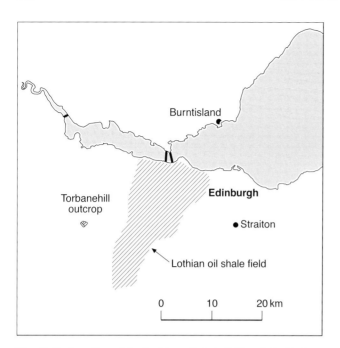

Fig. 19.10. Location of the Lothian oil shale field and the Torbane Hill outcrop.

the network of tunnels are then worked, beginning at the farthest point, by driving still further tunnels until each area is left without sufficient support. These are allowed to collapse as the working retreats progressively back toward the main shaft. Open cast production also contributed from the 1940s onwards. In 1958, experiments were conducted to produce oil by *in situ* heating but these were unsuccessful and the work discontinued. The spent shale after distillation, which represented not less than 80% of the extracted rock, has resulted in a number of 'mountains' of waste or 'bings' which remain as prominent landmarks in West Lothian (see Chapter 20).

In 1962, HM Government gave notice of its intention to withdraw in 1964 the 6.25p per gallon preferential tax concession to UK-produced oil. The Scottish oil-shale industry, which had been struggling for some time to compete with imports of naturally occurring oil, collapsed. Cumulative production of oil from oil-shale and coal in Scotland to 1962 is estimated to have been *c.* 75 million barrels (10^6 tonnes) (Hallet *et al.* 1985). Cameron & McAdam (1978) estimated the remaining reserves of oil-shale in the Lothians at 37.5 million barrels (5×10^6 tonnes) of oil upon distillation. However, there is little prospect of commercial exploitation of the oil-shale so long as secure, plentiful supplies of naturally occurring oil are available. Thin, uneconomic oil-shale also occurs in the Middle Jurassic of Skye and Raasay. Yields of between 54 and 77 litres per tonne of shale have been reported (Lee 1920; Gibson 1922).

Naturally occurring oil and gas in onshore basins

Exploration for naturally occurring oil and natural gas onshore Scotland has never succeeded in developing into a significant industrial activity. Until the 1980s onshore exploration concentrated in the central and eastern parts of the Midland Valley. The main target was the Carboniferous Calciferous Sandstone Measures, with sandstone the postulated reservoirs, oil-shale as potential source, and the traps formed by anticlinal structures sealed by Carboniferous shale. This play is viable on a limited basis and provides the circumstances responsible for the production achieved in the area of the D'Arcy-Cousland anticline, Midlothian.

Onshore exploration began in the UK in 1919 with a national programme of exploratory drilling commissioned by Government, which included two wells in Scotland. One of these, D'Arcy No. 1, found gas in Calciferous Measures sandstone at 221 m depth, which on test flowed at about 8500 m^3 per day. Oil was also found at 552 m and about 50 barrels of waxy crude were recovered over a two-month period (Carruthers *et al.* 1927).

After a long gap in exploration activity, due in part to problems over ownership of oil and rights of access to land, the D'Arcy Exploration Company (later to become British Petroleum) and the Anglo-American Oil Company obtained licences to drill the NNE–SSW trending D'Arcy-Cousland anticline. A period of exploration and appraisal drilling between 1937 and 1954 eventually led to commercial gas production from Cousland in 1957, feeding gas by pipeline 8 km to the gas works at Musselburgh where it was mixed with town gas. Some 6.4 million m^3 of gas were produced before production ceased in 1965 (Holloway 1986).

Oil production was also achieved on the D'Arcy structure (Fig. 19.11), to the SSW along trend from the Cousland gas accumulation, following a programme of exploration and appraisal drilling from 1937 to 1940. Cumulative production of *c.* 30 000 barrels of oil was achieved until it was shut down in 1965.

A number of other exploration ventures were mounted in east central Scotland during the late 1930s, 1940s and 1960s. These included wells drilled near Linlithgow, Pumpherston, Rosyth, and near Dunfermline. The activity was always at a low level and without significant commercial success. New peaks of activity were seen during the 1980s with 24 wells drilled between 1980 and 1987. The Department of Trade and Industry (2000) record the following as 'significant discoveries' during this period: Milton of Balgonie No. 1 (drilled in Fife in 1985, oil discovery) and Bargeddie No. 1 (mid-central Scotland, 1989, gas discovery). Drilling has targeted for the most part the Carboniferous of the Midland Valley. An exception was Premier Oil Company's Sutherland No. 1, drilled near Helmsdale on the Moray Firth coast. Here the target was Jurassic sandstone, similar to that which forms the reservoir for oil in the Beatrice Field (Block 11/30) lying *c.* 30 km offshore to the east. No commercial development resulted.

Considering other onshore areas together with Scottish inshore waters, areas on and around northeast Skye, in the Minch northeast of Stornoway, in the Sea of the Hebrides southeast of Barra, around the north of Mull, and in the Firth of Clyde south of Arran have all been licensed for exploration at times over the past ten years. Targeting Permo-Triassic and Jurassic prospects, no commercial discoveries have been announced. Similarly, exploration interest in the recent past has focused on areas around Thurso in the extreme north (Trewin 1989) and around Stranraer. In all these cases there has been no commercial success. The DTI (2000) records a number of areas under license onshore Scotland, around Gretna in the south, an area in mid-central Scotland and around Methil in Fife.

Coal bed methane

Coal bed methane is natural gas produced in a coal seam during the formation and burial of the coal. The coal seam forms both the reservoir and the trap for the gas. The Airth gas field, located near Kincardine, west Fife was discovered in 1994. From 1996 it has provided commercial production of gas from a Carboniferous coal seam. The estimated recoverable reserves originally in place are 541×10^6 m^3, making it a very significant accumulation when compared to the history of

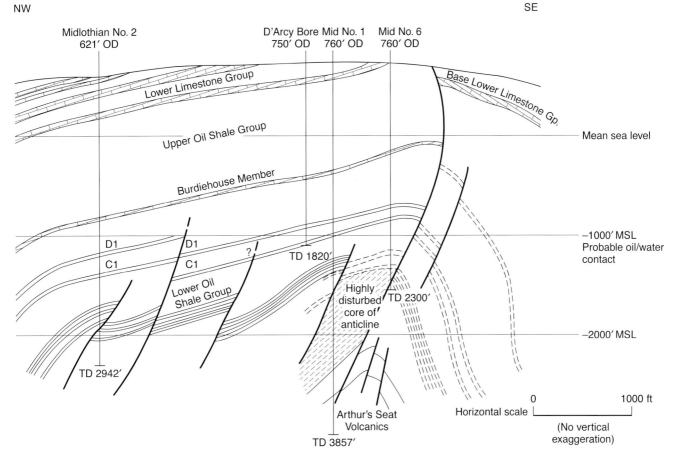

Fig. 19.11. Cross-section through the D'Arcy anticline, Midlothian (after Hallett *et al.* 1985).

onshore developments in Scotland. Airth was the first commercial development of coal bed methane in the UK.

Future oil and gas production

The number of fields in production will continue to grow as small satellite fields are tied back to existing infrastructure. PILOT, the joint industry and government taskforce has set a target of sustaining UKCS production above 3×10^6 barrels of oil equivalent until 2010. Whilst much of the offshore oil and gas production is in the mature stage, the exploration and production industry in the UK is far from being a 'sunset industry'. New field developments in mature basins, exploration and development in frontier areas to the west, plus additional recovery from existing fields will all be active and challenging issues for the future.

20 Environmental geology

A. P. McKIRDY

The most satisfactory definition of the term 'environmental geology' is the study of how humans interact with the geological environment (Woodcock 1994; Bennett & Doyle 1997; Thompson *et al.* 1998). The subject combines many traditional branches of geoscience including engineering geology, economic geology, hydrogeology and geomorphology with development control, resource management and Earth heritage conservation. The growth of this integrative subject reflects an urgent need to ensure that planned development is accomplished with minimum damage to the environment and that non-renewable resources, in particular construction materials and energy minerals, are used wisely. Practitioners of environmental geology generally acknowledge the need for a whole systems approach in dealing with dynamic physical processes. Examples of holistic approaches to environmental management include river catchment and coastal zone management.

Geoscientists have an increasingly prominent role in the development control process and in environmental management generally. As a consequence, the profession has become more aware of the need to contribute expert knowledge on geoscience to the decision-making process in an effective way (McKirdy 2000). Environmental Assessment (EA) and other environmental auditing techniques are now a mandatory part of the development control process. As a consequence, many planning decisions are largely determined on technical grounds, with the physical characteristics of the site constraining the development options.

In essence, environmental geology is the interface between the study of geology as an academic science and the real world. In the following chapter, human interactions with the physical environment are described with particular emphasis given to the issues that are relevant in Scotland.

Winning and working of aggregate reserves

The rate at which sand and gravel and hard rock reserves are being exploited in Great Britain as a whole continues to rise. Production of these commodities (Table 20.1) has almost doubled since 1965, reaching a high of 300×10^6 tonnes in 1989 (BGS 1998*b*). During the next decade, production fell back, progressively reaching a figure of 220×10^6 tonnes in 1997. In Scotland, production of crushed rock has risen from 14.8×10^6 tonnes in 1986 to 21.7×10^6 tonnes in 1997. Some 9.9×10^6 tonnes of sand and gravel was produced in Scotland during 1997. That figure has remained broadly static over the last twenty years.

Table 20.1. *Production of natural aggregate 1965–1995 in Great Britain [all quantities are in million tonnes]*

Year	1965	1970	1975	1980	1985	1990	1995
Sand and gravel	102	110	117	96	102	116	90
Crushed rock	59	98	110	103	115	162	151
Total	161	208	227	199	217	278	240

Aggregate extraction has some adverse consequences for the environment, but many benefits for society generally who 'consume' these products either in primary or secondary form. However, it is self-evident that these resources are non-renewable on a human timescale and much of the easily exploitable reserve of sand and gravel, has already been removed in areas close to the primary markets. What remains is often in areas of highly valued countryside where the extraction process and transportation from site is considered to be a threat to the landscape or other environmental attributes (Gordon & Campbell 1992; McKirdy 1994; Lindley *et al.* 2001; SNH 2000).

Aggregate working – the wider context

Aggregate is now an internationally traded commodity. Particularly with larger construction projects, crushed rock and other bulk material may not be entirely sourced from indigenous reserves. Scotland is potentially a rich source of crushed rock. Much of the country is underlain by crystalline rocks, either of igneous or metamorphic origin, and limestones that are ideally suited for use in the construction industry. Despite these resources having being exploited over many centuries for building, industrial and road-making purposes, much remains intact. Traditionally, aggregate has been quarried within 50 miles or so of its eventual end-use. As the *modus operandi* of the industry has changed, so the area of search for bulk minerals has been extended to cover the entire coastline of Scotland (Gribble & Wilson 1980).

The motive for winning and working of aggregate is to supply demand for these products, but at a profit. So the industry has, to date, been opportunistic rather than strategic in its exploitation of the mineral resource. Planning procedures exist, in part, to ensure that minimum environmental standards are maintained. Sustainability has not previously been a prime consideration in the determination of planning applications. However, this issue is now firmly on the political agenda as Government policy requires that all economic activity take due account of the principles of sustainable development. In the context of mineral development, these principles are articulated in the National Planning Policy Guidelines on 'Land for Mineral Working' (Scottish Office 1992). The guidelines acknowledge the difficulty of assessing whether the exploitation of a non-renewable resource constitutes a sustainable activity and also poses the key question whether the man-made asset created through the use of the minerals will be of greater value to society than the natural asset that is lost. The guidelines make specific reference to the development of coastal superquarries, which are considered to offer a number of positive benefits. However, the economic benefits of mineral working must also recognize and be reconciled with the following environmental and social constraints:

- environmental designations of national importance (such as Sites of Special Scientific Interest (SSSIs) and National Scenic Areas (NSAs);

- the unique scenic quality of much of the west coast of Scotland and the islands;
- the importance of tourism to the national and local economy;
- the legitimate interests of the local community.

However, the general presumption in favour of mineral working is preserved.

Coastal superquarries

Superquarries, where high-quality aggregate reserves are worked over a large area, guarantee high levels of production over substantial periods of time. It has also been argued that extraction on this scale has environmental benefits, as physical disturbance is concentrated in a clearly defined area. Glensanda, on the north shore of Loch Linnhe, has worked the southern part of the Strontian granite since 1985 with levels of production unmatched by any other single quarry in the UK.

The concept of developing very large coastal quarries, with an average output many times that of conventional extraction sites, was first put forward by the report of the Verney Committee commissioned by the Department of the Environment (Verney Committee 1976). It described superquarries as one of a number of potential solutions to the problem of aggregate supply. A Scottish Office report (Gribble & Wilson 1980) demonstrated that the superquarry concept was technically feasible and went on to identify five specific localities: South Harris, Loch Ewe, Loch Linnhe (the location of Glensanda quarry, Scotland's only working superquarry), Kentallan and Walls (Shetland). These were ranked in order of their desirability from an environmental viewpoint and also on the suitability of the rock to be exploited.

Case study: proposed superquarry at Lingerabay, South Harris

As an illustration of the potential impact of a superquarry development on the terrestrial and maritime environment, the application by Redland Aggregate Limited to develop the anorthosite resource of South Harris is briefly examined. A Public Inquiry was held in 1994 to examine this application and the decision to reject the application was announced in October 2000.

The application area lies east of Roineabhal in South Harris and covers a total of 459 hectares. The initial output was to have been around 1×10^6 tonnes per annum, achieving a final figure of 10×10^6 tonnes if there was sufficient demand for the product.

Impact of the Lingeradbay superquarry on the natural environment would have been considerable and these were the grounds on which the application was rejected. Roineabhal lies at the centre of the South Lewis, Harris and North Uist National Scenic Area. Impacts would have included a significant detrimental effect on the landscape value of an area adjudged to be of national importance in that respect, loss of montane habitat, silt runoff from the quarry and the possibility of water contamination or foreign species being introduced through ballast water dumped by rock-carrying tankers. The increased marine traffic with attendant pollution and general disturbance would also take its toll on the marine environment.

The anorthosite body which was earmarked for exploitation extends over many square kilometres so, environmental considerations notwithstanding, removal of part of the resource to satisfy a considerable proportion of the nation's aggregate requirement could arguably be a wise use of a finite resource. However, if the output of crushed rock from this

quarry is simply to be added to the world supply, then the argument for quarrying sites of such high environmental value becomes more difficult to justify.

Aggregates levy

A tax levied on every tonne of aggregate won from indigenous reserves was announced by the Chancellor of the Exchequer in March 2000, taking effect from April 2002. The purpose of this tax is to supress overall demand for aggregate and also to reduce further primary production by encouraging substitution with secondary or recycled material. A Sustainability Fund may be established at some time in the future to deliver environmental benefits to local communities affected by quarrying activities. The Quarry Products Association, trade representatives of the minerals industry, put forward counter-proposals that they claimed would do more to protect the environment, but these were rejected by Government in favour of an Aggregates Levy. The charge is levied at £1.60 per tonne and applies to sand, gravel and crushed rock sourced within the UK, and aggregate dredged from the seabed from UK territorial waters. There is a comprehensive range of exemptions for other quarried or mined products, such as coal, metal ores, industrial minerals and dimension stone. Limestone and silica sands used in prescribed industrial or agricultural processes will be exempt, as will exports of aggregate. Imports will be taxed upon first sale or use within the UK.

Use of secondary material

Use of secondary material, such as colliery spoil and construction wastes, as a substitute for virgin aggregate, is also an important factor in the supply equation (Howard Humphries 1994). In England and Wales, some 10% of all bulk construction products are derived from the existing pool of secondary material, whereas in Scotland, the figure is only 2% (Arup Economics and Planning 1991).

In Scotland, there are large quantities of secondary materials available which are capable of making a substantial contribution to the demand for aggregates (Pieda plc. 1995). Such material falls into two main categories; byproducts of industrial processes, and mineral wastes (Table 20.2).

Waste tips (Fig. 20.1) of the oil-shale industry (see also Chapter 19) comprise the largest secondary resource in Scotland, followed by colliery spoil and pulverized fuel ash (PFA). These three major sources of secondary aggregate are located in central Scotland, coincident with the area where the demand for primary aggregate is highest.

There are many potential uses for secondary materials in road construction and building projects. The British Standard (BS 6543) on 'Use of Industrial By-Products and Waste Materials in Building and Civil Engineering' gives a useful categorization of the potential uses of these materials, including bulk fill, aggregate for concrete, concrete block manufacture,

Table 20.2 *Types of secondary material*

Industrial by-products	Mineral wastes
Power station ashes • Pulverised fuel ash (PFA) • Furnace bottom ash (FBA)	Spent oil-shale and colliery waste
Demolition and construction waste	Slate waste
Road and airfield reclamation wastes	Quarry waste
Metallurgic slag	Other mineral wastes (from mining of lead, zinc, gold, barytes)

Fig. 20.1. Shale waste tip or 'bing', West Lothian. Part of the 220×10^6 tonnes reserve of secondary material that could be used in place of primary aggregate. Broxburn, West Lothian. Photo SNH copyright.

earthworks construction and capping layers in road construction. A greater use of secondary materials as substitutes for primary aggregates, would slow down the rate at which finite reserves of virgin hard rock and sand and gravel are consumed. Such substitution has the additional environmental benefit of reducing industrial dereliction by removal of spoil tips and reducing land take arising from the disposal of mineral wastes. It is estimated that there is around 220×10^6 tonnes of secondary material located in the central belt of Scotland. Assuming 100% substitution of secondary material for primary aggregate used for fill, demand for construction fill could be met from this source for the next 22 years.

The use of secondary aggregates is, therefore, likely to result in net environmental benefits, although further work needs to be done to quantify these savings and promote greater use of this material. However, there is evidence of continuing consumer resistance to the use of secondary material, which is rooted in a limited knowledge of the availability of this material, concerns about increased risk of liability and preference for use of established sources of primary aggregate. However, in some instances, increased transportation requirements will be incurred where recycled or secondary material is used in preference to primary aggregate, so it does not automatically follow that this form of recycling is always environmentally benign and economically beneficial.

Restoration of disused quarries

The quality of reinstatement and reuse of quarry and land-fill sites often represents the most visible action by the minerals industry in pursuit of sustainable development. Until recently, extraction sites were restored for agricultural or forestry after use, but a wider range of reinstatement options is now considered. Nature conservation, amenity, recreation and commercial after-uses for disused quarries and pits are now commonplace. Restoration schemes must now be agreed in advance of new permissions for mineral working being granted, so considerable effort is made by the industry to achieve high standards of site aftercare (RSPB 1990; DoE 1992a, 1996a; QPA & English Nature 1999). Sites of geological importance have also benefited from these more benign environmental practices through schemes designed to incorporate the conservation of key geological exposures into final restoration plans (McKirdy & Wright 1988; SNH 1996). A summary of the environmental issues and effects associated with mineral working is presented in Table 20.3.

Opencast coal

Since the deregulation of the coal industry in 1994, there has been a considerable acceleration in the number of applications made for opencast coal working, although overall production of coal has continued to fall since 1950s. The reduction has been particularly marked since 1970, with UK production falling from around 150×10^6 tonnes to 50×10^6 tonnes in 1997 (see also Chapter 17). Output of coal from sites in Scotland during 1997/1998 were 1.9×10^6 tonnes from deep mining and 6.3×10^6 tonnes from opencast operations. A reduced level of output has been coupled with a change in working from deep mined to opencast. All production comes from around 25 opencast operations. Opencast sites are restricted exclusively to the central belt in Scotland, with extraction sites concentrated in Fife, Lothians, Ayrshire and Lanarkshire. In terms of direct effects on the environment, opencast operations have much in common with large-scale aggregate working. The same imperative applies to return the land to a beneficial after-use on completion of the extraction process (Bradshaw & Chadwick 1980; RSPB & SNH 2000). Proposed opencast coal developments are subject to the same planning controls and constraints as hard rock quarries (Scottish Executive 1999a, b, 2000).

Table 20.3. *Summary of environmental issues and effects associated with mineral working*

Environmental issues	Environmental effect
Industry is reluctant to use secondary material as primary resources of sand and gravel and rock are plentiful. Sustainable development has not yet fully taken root, although there are now signs that the concept is being taken more seriously	Exploitation of reserves takes place more rapidly than necessary
Lack of a strategic view taken by the minerals industry – most applications are made on an opportunistic rather than strategic basis	There is little evidence that the mineral resource is being developed in a strategic fashion
Environmental assessment is now almost universally required for new mineral operations	Environmental issues receive a profile commensurate with their importance in determining individual applications
Restoration schemes are now more imaginative than hitherto	Restoration to afteruses such as recreation, amenity and conservation are now more frequent
Applications for mineral working are for larger areas and greater outputs than hitherto. Superquarries are now a reality	Environmental damage is arguably greater at the extraction site than for smaller operations, but fewer quarries are required to generate a similar output
Mineral extraction is now an international business, with large quantities of bulk materials exported from and imported to this country	Detrimental environmental effects can now be 'exported' and 'imported' – a process largely determined by external economic drivers

Environmental assessment

Environmental Assessment (EA) was introduced in 1988 following Directive 85/337/EEC on the 'Assessment of the Effects of Certain Public and Private Projects on the Environment.' The principal aims of the Directive are:

- to ensure that the environmental consequences of new developments are known and taken into account before planning consents are issued;
- to encourage developers to consider environmental concerns from the earliest stage of project planning and design, where potential adverse effects can be most effectively and economically addressed.

Developers are thus required to prepare an environmental statement which describes the potential environmental effects of certain specified types of development (Scottish Office 1988, Scottish Executive 1999a). There is now a general acceptance that environmental assessment greatly enhances the planning decision-making process and allows for a full exposition of all the relevant geological factors. The EA process also allows for the effects of the development on the environment to be monitored over time and the predicted impacts measured against the actual effects that arise. This procedure is particularly relevant in relation to major developments such as the construction of a nuclear facility or trunk road system. Other developments, such as quarrying and opencast mining (over 25 ha) and peat extraction (over 150 ha), groundwater abstraction exceeding $10 \times 10^6 \, m^3$ per year and installations for the production of non-ferrous crude metals all require environmental impact studies to be carried out as part of the planning process.

The environmental statement must address the following issues:

- a description of the proposed development;
- data necessary to identify and assess the main effects of the proposed development;
- description of likely significant effects (direct and indirect) on human beings; flora and fauna; soil, water, air and climate; the landscape; the interaction between any of the foregoing; material assets and the cultural heritage;
- proposed mitigation measures, where significant adverse effects are identified;
- a non-technical summary of the above.

Although geology is not referred to specifically within the regulations, it would not be possible to describe environmental impacts fully without reference to geological issues.

Case study: proposal to extract barytes at Duntanlich, Perthshire

The proposal to extract barytes at Duntanlich, Perthshire (see also Chapter 16) was refused by the Secretary of State after it was debated at a public inquiry in 1992. Barytes is used as a weighting agent in drilling mud. The case in favour of development was supported by an environmental statement, prepared by consultants to the developer. This unpublished statement provided information on the stratigraphy and structural position of the orebody, details of the mineralized bed and the genesis of the deposit. The national economic need to work this orebody at this particular time was also discussed in some detail, as was supply and demand for this commodity internationally. Other factors, such as a positive effect on the balance of payments, proximity of the resource to market and boost to the local economy were all cited as factors in favour of

development. The environmental statement also considered ways in which the effect of the development on the landscape and on potable water supplies currently taken from the area, could be minimized. The statement also contained a non-technical summary of the application. The case for development was supported by the Department of Trade and Industry.

Objections to the development were presented to the public inquiry by Perth and Kinross District Council, Tayside Regional Council, Scottish Natural Heritage and local residents. The environmental consequences of transporting the ore for milling in Aberdeen, the predicted effect of the development on the landscape and disruption to the local community were the main grounds for objection. Evidence was also heard on the potential threat to potable water supplies as a result of 'groundwater rebound'. This phenomenon occurs when groundwater levels are depressed to facilitate mining operations, but after working ceases and pumping stops, groundwater recovers to its original levels and comes into direct contact with sulphides, now oxidized, exposed on the rock walls of the shafts and adits. Groundwater becomes acidified and enriched in heavy metals, causing a potential pollution threat. No mine closure plan had been proposed to deal with this eventuality by the developer and this was considered to be an important omission from the environmental statement.

Around twenty witnesses were called to consider the wide range of issues, scientific, technical, economic, political and social, raised by both developers and objectors. The reporter, who heard the evidence on behalf of the Secretary of State, recommended refusal of the application on the grounds that the environmental objections could not be satisfactorily mitigated.

The Environmental Assessment process allows the geoscientist to make a vital input to planning and development control decision making. In the case described above, geoscientists were involved in promoting both sides of the argument. The non-technical summary is an important part of the process that allows a wider audience than hitherto to understand the scientific arguments involved.

Water management

Water is one of society's most basic requirements. The geoscientist is involved in many aspects of the management of this resource, from the siting and construction of reservoirs to the treatment and disposal of wastewater. As the world's population increases and water consumption for industrial purposes rises at a commensurate rate, so the challenge to the water engineer to keep the taps running becomes all the greater. Scotland has an extensive water resource of rivers and lochs, so there is comparatively little need for underground reserves to be utilized. This is in sharp contrast to the south of England, where approximately 60% of all potable water comes from groundwater.

Management of natural systems is now seen in the context of the catchment as a whole and not as individual river reaches or bodies of standing water. This approach will be further reinforced when the EU Water Framework Directive is introduced. Catchment management has implications for both land managers and the Scottish Environmental Protection Agency (SEPA), the main regulatory authority on water pollution. In addition, SEPA has prepared a groundwater protection policy for Scotland which will direct both public and private sector strategy in this area (SEPA 1999).

Pollution of surface and groundwater

Pollution caused by contaminated water flowing from derelict mineworkings is a major environmental concern. Coal has been exploited since the Industrial Revolution, but with the rationalization of the industry since privatization, many workings have been taken out of production. During the working life of many of these mines, pumping was routinely carried out to lower the water table. When the pumps are switched off, the water table then rises to its former level. Underground water may be significantly contaminated by iron depending on the mineralogy of the strata being drained (Babtie Geotechnical 1997). Iron pyrites and marcasite, both sulphides of iron, are present in all coals and coal measures to a varying extent. These minerals are readily oxidized as soon as they are exposed to oxygen, forming ferrous and ferric sulphates, sulphuric acid and ferric oxide. These primary reaction products can react to form other metal sulphates.

It is often the case that ferruginous minewaters do not emerge until several years after the cessation of pumping. The South Ayrshire Coalfield was closed in 1976 and pumping ceased a year later, but the major outbreak of polluted minewater at Dalquharran did not occur until October 1979. The Central Fife Coalfield was closed and pumping ceased in 1966, but the Foordell outbreak did not occur until ten years later. The larger the area drained, the longer the time taken for rebound of the water table to occur.

Both the iron content and discharge rate of ferruginous minewaters tend to decrease with time. There is often a fairly rapid decrease from very high initial values. This approximates to a 'half-life' rule, in that iron content reduces by half over the period required for the water table to re-establish at its original level. This still results in long term discharges with high iron and low pH values. It will take decades, possibly hundreds of years, before water quality is likely to return to its original purity before mining began.

Concentrations of less than 1.0 mg/l of iron have little effect on the biota of rivers or streams. Ochre staining is visible on the river bed at concentrations of around 10 mg/l, with a commersurately more significant detrimental effect on biological productivity of the waterbody.

Pollution may arise from many other sources, such as opencast mines, surface water runoff from stockpiles, roadways and contaminated land, and oil from vehicles and machinery. Clearly, prevention is better than cure, but where water treatment is required, most systems rely on the use of lagoons or settlement ponds. More recently, reed beds have been used on a pilot scale to treat part of a seepage from a former coal mine tip in East Lothian. The system appears to be effective in removing iron solids from the system. However, there are some practical problems in setting up these biological filtering systems and their application is likely to be in treating long-term problem sites and also for 'polishing' effluents from which solids have already been removed.

Since 1995, licensing and regulation of discharges has been the responsibility of SEPA. The practice of setting consent levels is the primary method of controlling pollution likely to be generated by new developments. It is then the responsibility of the operator to ensure that the permitted pollution levels are not exceeded. A financial agreement, in the form of a guarantee or bond, may be required to ensure against pollution following decommissioning of the development.

Natural heritage value of rivers and flood alleviation

Flowing water, in the form of rivers, is also an important feature of the natural heritage. Ten river reaches are notified in Scotland as SSSIs to demonstrate the wide variation in river forms, associated processes, habitats and species.

In recent years, flooding has regularly occurred at the confluence of the Rivers Spey and Feshie, prompting land-

Fig. 20.2. The River Tay floods Perth in 1992 – an aerial view of the event. Photo D. C. Thomson Ltd, copyright.

owners to undertake remedial measures, such as channel straightening, that has done little to alleviate the problem of flooding, but much to detract from the 'naturalness' of the system. This conflict stimulated research which lead to the development of lower impact river bank protection strategies (Hoey et al. 1998).

Recent flooding of the River Tay in Perthshire (Fig. 20.2) has increased pressure for flood alleviation schemes. The Muirton housing estate is built on the flood plain of the River Tay and is separated from the flowing water by a few metres of flat ground and a low flood bank. The River Tay drains much of central Scotland and carries more water than any other river in Britain. This river has a long history of flooding and it therefore, may seem surprising that this location was selected as the site for a major public housing development. It is clear that these natural processes can only be managed and not controlled, so landowners, developers and planners need to take a more realistic view of what land uses are possible within the floodplain of active rivers systems (McKirdy et al. 1998). Planners are now being actively encouraged to take such geoscience considerations into account when planning applications are being determined (Hine et al. 1998).

Integrated Catchment Management (ICM) is clearly the way forward. ICM requires that rivers and their surrounding catchments are managed in a holistic and integrated way. The co-operation of all land and water managers is required to achieve this objective.

Climate change and river management

Climate change, brought about by global warming, is likely to make the UK more flood prone. Flood defences on the Tweed, Tay and Ness for example are unlikely to be able to cope with the greater volumes of water and towns along the banks of all Scotland's major rivers are likely to be at increased risk from flooding. Increased levels of greenhouses gases, such as carbon dioxide, released to the atmosphere as a by-product of energy production, are considered to be the most important driver for this global phenomenon. The Kyoto meeting of the world's environment ministers in 1997 identified target levels of carbon dioxide emissions for each of the participating nations. For example, the UK target was to achieve a reduction from 150×10^6 to 140×10^6 tonnes per year. The UK Climate Change Programme recognizes the need to adapt to climate change, primarily by reducing the emissions of greenhouses gases (DETR 2000a, b, c).

Evaluation of natural and man-induced hazards

Slope instability

Slope instability may directly result in damage to property or other infrastructure, and has in some instances indirectly affected natural heritage interests. Rockfalls and landslides are the commonest manifestations of such instability and in certain circumstances, remediation measures are required to stabilise the slope. Relatively minor forms of instability can be responsible for considerable repair bills to roads, buildings and other structures and may also cause delays to traffic flow or other commercial interests. Rockfalls or scree slopes are generally confined to mountainous and/or remote areas where such instability is not usually in conflict with other landusers. Mountaineers and hill walkers may occasionally be put at risk from rockfalls, but the remediation measures in such remote settings are unlikely to be justified. Landslides are another widespread natural hazard which may need to be managed, depending on their proximity to commercial or other interests (DoE 1994a, 1996b). However, some landslides, such as those involving the Tertiary lavas of The Storr and Quirang on Trotternish, Skye (Plate 27), are of significant cultural, scenic and scientific importance. Where natural or man-made rock faces occur close to developments, stabilization measures, such as netting or rock bolting may be required. Such measures will normally be implemented in response to safety or restoration requirements imposed on the site by the relevant regulatory authorities.

Natural settlement and man-induced subsidence

Settlement and subsidence involve vertical displacement of the ground, ranging from a few millimetres in scale to catastrophic collapse. Settlement involves compaction of poorly consolidated material and the amount of compaction can normally be predicted if the ground conditions and the loading to be applied are known. Subsidence may be natural, resulting from the collapse of natural underground cavities (DoE 1996c). In other cases, subsidence is caused by the collapse of shallow mineworkings (DoE 1992b). Shafts, adits or mine entrances to abandoned workings are often close to the surface. Roof collapse can be a gradual process, leading eventually to a sudden failure with the formation of a 'crown hole' (Fig. 20.3). Many underground workings are unrecorded, so there is an increased reliance on site investigations to pick up the occurrence of such problems. The location and extent of more recent workings, particularly those related to the winning of coal, are available from the British Geological Survey (BGS).

Environmental geology mapping

Attempts have been made at various times to provide geological information in an accessible format with the purpose of informing decisions taken by land use planners. The scale, nature and distribution of natural resources, such as sand and gravel or coal, are important factors that may constrain development. Natural hazards, such as landslides or areas prone to flooding, and identification of poor foundation conditions are also important considerations that guide the location of housing or other infrastructure developments. Thematic maps have been used as a means of translating complex technical data into a form that lay readers, such as planners and elected councillors, are able to understand. Although maps of this kind are no substitute for site investigations or ground surveys, they are of considerable assistance in the development of strategic plans.

In Britain, the practical need for environmental geology maps was first recognized in the 1980s (Monro & Hull 1986; Browne

Fig. 20.3. As a result of an insufficient site investigation, the existence of the crown hole only comes to light in catastrophic circumstances. Achamore Road, Drumchapel, Glasgow. Photo NERC copyright.

et al. 1986; Brooks & Marker 1987; Browne & McMillan 1991). Glenrothes and a surrounding area which comprised 100 km² in total, was chosen for a pilot study, as that part of Fife had a range of land uses and natural resource potential, and no planning disputes were in progress (Nickless 1982). In presenting the data, BGS, who carried out this work on contract to the Department of the Environment, were required to ensure that it was made available in a format which could be used 'in the decision-making process.' Specifically, DoE's objectives were 'to ensure that geological information is taken into account at the earliest possible stage in development and renewal, and also to provide an up-to-date interpretation of the existing geological database and present this in the format of environmental geology maps relating geological ground conditions to development, redevelopment and the maintenance of existing buildings.'

Many potential land use conflicts were identified within the study area, including:

- the rapidly expanding new town of Glenrothes with associated industrial and housing developments impacting upon conservation areas such as the Lomond Hills Country Park and the historic village of Falkland;
- the interaction of agriculture and forestry with exploitation of opencast coal and sand and gravel workings;

- abandoned deep coal mines and limestone workings as a constraint on development;
- the effects of other land uses on the development of water resources – surface water and from aquifers.

Monro & Hull (1985) report that 'the study was mostly concerned with the collation and interpretation of extant geological information (geological mapping at 1:10 560 scale, borehole and mining data, sand and gravel assessments, numerous site investigations and a hydrogeological study). This process revealed deficiencies in the database, some of which were remedied by limited fieldwork. The accumulated geological data were then interrogated on a thematic basis.' The resulting syntheses were presented as a series of thematic maps, displaying basic geological data and then reworked to create a series of derived maps (sand and gravel potential, foundation conditions and groundwater resources), which in turn gave rise to a series of Environmental Potential Maps. Separate maps were then produced identifying:

- areas showing development potential for housing or light factory development;
- priority areas for site investigation;
- mineral resources, including water.

This pilot has provided the basis for a number of similar studies in other parts of Britain and environmental geology maps are now available for many different parts of the country, including Glasgow, Coatbridge and Bridgend (Smith & Ellison 1999).

Waste disposal and management

Earth scientists play a key role in the disposal of society's solid and liquid wastes. A understanding of the behaviour of host rocks and local hydrology is an essential prerequisite to the design and construction of disposal facilities for domestic, industrial and nuclear wastes.

Disposal of domestic and inert wastes

Problems associated with waste disposal are most acute in the urban environment. Large conurbations generate increasing volumes of waste, which have to be disposed of responsibly and with minimal environmental impact. Most domestic waste is disposed of in landfill sites or exceptionally, in landraise sites, where new topographic features are created from waste materials (Gray 1998). The former are usually mineral excavations or natural depressions in the ground surface. Landfill sites can be either *containment* or *dispersal* sites. Containment sites are designed such that any leachate generated from the breakdown of putrescible waste is prevented from leaving the site and polluting the groundwater by an impermeable barrier. The barrier can be created from naturally occurring puddled clays, butyl rubber sheeting or other types of synthetic membrane. The host rocks for landfill sites normally have a very low permeability, such as clays, marls and other mudrocks, so any leakage through the barrier that does occur is contained locally. Management of landfill gas, also generated from putrescible wastes, is an important task for those operating containment sites. With dispersal sites, no effort is made to contain any leachate generated, so this type of landfill site is designed to accept only inert material, such as demolition waste. The design criteria for such sites are less stringent, as the potential for environmental impact is considerably smaller.

Most sites are concentrated in the central belt, reflecting the distribution of population in Scotland. Good technical guidance exists for the selection and operation of landfill sites (Department of the Environment 1990). Most sites are efficiently operated and the leachate generated from putrescible waste is well-managed, although combustion of landfill gas has given rise to injury (Williams & Aitkenhead 1991).

Landfill tax

The Landfill Tax was introduced in October 1996 with the objective of reducing the total volume of waste material going to landfill. The tax is levied on waste deposited at licensed landfill sites, with higher rates payable for active or putrescible wastes and a lower rate for inert construction wastes. This has led to a substantial reduction in the amount of material going to licensed sites, although there is clear evidence of wastes being disposed of through unregulated or 'exempt' routes. However, benefits accrue from this tax, as funds from the Landfill Tax Environmental Trust Fund are invested locally to enhance the quality of restoration work on mineral sites and other environmental projects.

Disposal of high-level nuclear waste

Since the beginning of the 'nuclear age' some sixty years ago, significant quantities of highly toxic and radioactive waste have been generated by many countries around the world. Dealing with the nuclear waste has become a very high profile issue and the public have a keen interest in, and a partial understanding of the issues involved. The role of the geoscientist is to identify the most promising locations for waste disposal and to assist the competent authorities in the implementation of appropriate disposal solutions. However, despite a concerted research effort, no purpose built, deep geological repository for high-level waste has been constructed and nearly all wastes are currently in storage awaiting a decision on how best to achieve their permanent disposal (Couples *et al.* 1998). However, deep underground burial is currently considered to offer the best and most effective environmental option for the disposal of high-level waste (Chapman & McKinley 1987). Although exploration drilling was undertaken by UK NIREX Ltd. during the 1980s to assess the suitability of both crystalline and sedimentary rocks, there are no current proposals to dispose of high-level nuclear waste in Scotland (NIREX 1989, 1992, 1994).

If safe disposal of high-level nuclear waste is to be achieved, then the site selected for repository construction must display the following characteristics. The lithology must be impermeable and impervious to minimize fluid migration; there must be evidence of limited tectonic activity in the immediate vicinity of the repository site; current seismic activity must be low and the hydrogeology should be demonstrably incapable of disrupting the engineered containment barriers.

Disposal of intermediate nuclear waste

A vertical shaft at Dounreay, constructed in Old Red Sandstone strata, was licensed by The Scottish Office as a nuclear waste disposal facility in 1959, the only extant licence of its kind in Scotland. It was routinely used for the disposal of unconditioned Intermediate Level Waste (ILW) between 1959 and 1970, and occasionally thereafter until May 1997 (W. Jones, pers. comm.). An estimated 700 m³ of ILW was disposed of down the shaft during that period. Because the original role of the shaft was as a temporary access route, the sides were unlined and continuous pumping was necessary to remove groundwater. On completion, pumping was discontinued and subsequently, the shaft filled naturally with water to the level of the surrounding watertable.

However, to reduce the potential for escape of contaminated material to the surrounding rocks, water was pumped from the shaft during the waste disposal operation. This encouraged a net inflow of water into the shaft. In 1977, following gas accumulation in the space above the waste column, an explosion occurred in the air space above the water. Disposal subsequently ceased and the facility is now on a care and maintenance regime.

Since 1975, the United Kingdom Atomic Energy Authority (UKAEA) have commissioned a series of studies to establish options for the long-term management of the shaft facility. The most recent of these, begun in 1996, established that it was now possible to retrieve the waste safely. During current care and maintenance, approximately $16 \, m^3/day$ of water is removed from the shaft. This is discharged to sea via the authorised route as it contains almost no radioactivity.

Fault zones are potentially very influential because they can form highly permeable pathways and control the route of contaminant transport from any below ground repository. During driving of the site discharge tunnel, no major groundwater transmitting discontinuities were recorded until the tunnel encountered a fault approximately 280 m from the ILW Shaft, at which point water inflows increased to greater than $270 \, m^3 \, hr^{-1}$. Despite the potential high transmissivity of faults at the site (and the high inflows experienced during driving of the tunnel) recent groundwater modelling studies suggest that the presence of these faults does not significantly impact upon groundwater flow pathways or travel times (Pitty et al. 1989).

A number of studies have been carried out at the site to evaluate the rate at which the coastline in the Dounreay area is migrating landward as a result of coastal erosion. The most recent of these studies has identified that the rate of coastline recession is likely to lie between 59.2 and 93.5 mm/year, with an anticipated 'average' rate of 70 mm/year for the 'Dounreay' rocks (Hutchinson et al. 2001). Lithological variation within the ORS sequence, combined with fault zones and joint patterns, has already led to the development of an indented coastline in response to coastal erosion and this will be further accentuated over time, particularly if predictions of sea level rise due to global warming are correct. Thus, in the longer term, the Dounreay facility is potentially vulnerable to coastal erosion.

Contaminated land

Much of the soil resource, particularly in the Midland Valley, has been adversely affected by years of industrial activity. Conservative estimates put the number of potentially contaminated sites throughout the UK in the hundreds of thousands and recent estimates suggest that $10–22 \times 10^4$ hectares of land is potentially affected by contamination. This represents approaching 1% of the total UK land area (Pollard & Herbert 1998). In recognition of the requirement for proactive management of the soil resource, The Royal Commission on Environmental Pollution has recommended that a UK Soil Protection Strategy be implemented to redress the balance (Royal Commission on Environmental Pollution 1996). This recommendation was subsequently accepted by Government.

Much of the contaminated land in Scotland is concentrated in the Midland Valley where there is a legacy of pollution through coal and metalliferous mining, industrial processes and waste disposal (Puri & Gordon 1998). New approaches will be required from all the competent authorities, including industry, SEPA and local authorities to address the problem. Innovative techniques of soil remediation are under development, including bio-remediation, which will obviate the need for more drastic measures, such as soil removal or burial. However, further

research is required before the economic viability and environmental acceptability of this technique can be demonstrated.

The ban on disposal of sewage sludge at sea, which ceased in 1998, and tighter restrictions on discharges to watercourses has resulted in higher rates of application of this material to agricultural land. Sludge can contain appreciable amounts of substances such as heavy metals, pathogenic organisms and organic contaminants which are potentially detrimental to soil fertility and animal health if application to agricultural land is badly managed (Aitken 1996). Currently, only 2400 ha of land in Scotland has received sewage sludge, but as 75% of this material has been disposed of at sea to date, this figure is set to rise dramatically. However, regulations and codes of practice are currently in place to ensure that application is properly regulated and adverse environmental impacts do not arise. However, enforcement of these regulations is critically important in this regard.

Coastal zone management

Achieving effective management of the coastline is one of the most important environmental challenges for this century. Scotland has a diverse and dynamic coastline which is around 13 000 km in length. Evidence of coastal erosion is widespread, particularly on the 'softer' east coast and the Atlantic coasts of the Western and Northern Isles, where beach-dune and machair systems are retreating at variable rates (Lees et al. 1998). Extensive residential and industrial development is rare on soft coasts where the land is more likely to be used for golf courses, caravan parks or Ministry of Defence facilities. But unregulated development and a lack of appreciation of the importance of active processes in shaping the coastline has led to a piecemeal approach to coastal planning. Where properties are threatened by coastal retreat, ad hoc protection works have been undertaken, with no strategic approach to guide the process.

Coastal management

Shoreline Management Plans (SMP) have been promoted in England and Wales as a mechanism for managing erosion and defence construction along the coastline (MAFF 1995). These plans are founded upon an understanding of physical parameters, such as longshore drift, wind and waves. This approach to erosion management has been endorsed by The Scottish Office (1997) in their National Policy Planning Guidelines on Coastal Planning. Recent research suggests that implementation of such an approach would be useful along most of the developed Scottish coastlines (Hansom 1999). In England, Shoreline Management Plans have been constructed for distinct and self-contained coastal process units, known as coastal cells. On mainland Scotland, seven major cells have been identified, divided into 24 sub-cells (HR Wallingford 1997). Further research has added detail to these cells, including identification and descriptions of patterns of longshore drift, areas of erosion and accretion, existing coastal protection and management measures and assessment of the potential effect of climate change on the coastline (HR Wallingford 2000a). If this approach is taken to a logical conclusion, plans will be written for cells or sub-cells wherever potentially conflicting pressures exist, thus guiding the location of all future residential, industrial and recreational developments. To date, two Shoreline Management Plans have been completed in Scotland. The first covers an area of the Inner Moray Firth, from Burghead to the Sutors of Cromarty, and the second encompasses the entire coastline of Fife. A further SMP extends from Northumberland to St Abbs Head in Berwickshire.

Alternative methods of coastal protection

Alternative approaches to coastal protection have been developed which require a minimum of hard engineering (Lees *et al.* 1998; HR Wallingford 1991, 2000*b*). Such schemes are based on a fuller understanding of the natural processes at work, trusting more to nature than man's sometimes clumsy interventions. Retention of beach material in the inter-tidal zone is the most effective way of absorbing the energy generated by the sea. Beach re-charge, off-shore groynes and cliff drainage are some of the ways in which coastal stability can be enhanced at lower cost and with less environmental intervention.

Sea level rise and managed retreat

Throughout the Holocene the Scottish landmass has been recovering from the crushing weight of ice which it had previously supported (see Chapter 15). Average rates of uplift have been greatest where the ice was thickest, around the Western Highlands, and least in areas closer to the margins of the last ice sheet, such as the Western and Northern Isles. For most of this period global sea levels too have been rising but, except in these island groups, this has been outpaced by crustal uplift. Thus, raised shoreline features are prevalent on much of the mainland whereas the islands are being progressively submerged, albeit at rates of 1–2 mm per year.

Though this pattern of change has persisted for the last 5000 to 6000 years it now looks likely to change dramatically in the present century partly as a result of human influence upon the climate. Global warming is expected to cause a significant increase in rates of sea level rise worldwide, from 1–2 mm/year at present to at least 4 or 5 mm/year by 2050, though predictions vary widely (Hulme & Jenkins 1998). This is due, essentially, to thermal expansion of ocean water and increased melting of mountain glaciers. Should such levels be attained, then all Scottish coastlines will experience relative sea level rise and submergence (Pethick 1999).

The impact of such a rise will, naturally, be most keenly felt on Scotland's lowest lying coastlines, especially where saltmarshes dominate as in the Forth and Solway Firths (Pethick 1999). In such areas saltmarshes will gradually transgress landwards, where not constrained by topography or land use. Where flood embankments exist, however, the position of the high water line will be fixed resulting in a progressive loss of intertidal flats and saltmarsh as the low water level continues to rise. This has been termed 'coastal squeeze'.

One possible means of managing rising sea levels and mitigating habitat losses in such settings is to build a second line of defence inland of the first and allow the seaward line to breach naturally (French 1997). This may even be encouraged by creating a breach if none exists or lowering the existing flood embankments. In so doing saltmarsh becomes re-established upon the formerly protected land. This, in itself, can have a valuable coastal defence role, with 10 m width of saltmarsh having, roughly, the same protective effect as 1 m height of sea wall. This practice, known as managed retreat or managed re-alignment, is clearly not appropriate where built development or services are at risk of flooding, but may prove viable where farmland has been claimed from former inter-tidal areas, as for example in the Forth Estuary.

Of potentially greater significance still to the Scottish coastline may be any increases in storminess associated with climate change. More frequent, long-lasting or severe storms or even a slight shift in prevailing wind directions may all cause increased coastal erosion. This is likely to be of particular concern on sandy beaches, especially where the associated dune and links environments have been developed, for example as golf courses. Indeed, in such situations it may ultimately prove cheaper, as well as more environmentally sensitive, to re-align threatened tees and greens than to perpetually extend and enhance coastal protection in the face of these pressures.

Environmental consequences of off-shore hydrocarbon exploration and transportation

The hydrocarbon reserves under the North Sea have been exploited since the 1960s, but this body of water has also been one of the world's most productive fishing grounds for many generations (Davies & Kingston 1992). The North Sea is also of considerable nature conservation interest and recreational importance (Frances *et al.* 1992).

Oil and gas production pose a potential threat to the marine environment of the North Sea principally through pollution from pipeline and platform discharges and the decommissioning of obsolete exploration and production installations.

Sea bed pollution

Davies *et al.* (1988) estimate a total area of 106 km^2 of the seabed is seriously affected by these discharges in the UK North Sea sector alone with some 1600 km^2 showing some signs of oil-based contamination. Around seven million cubic metres of toxic waste have been dumped on the floor of the North Sea as a result of exploration and production operations over the last thirty years. The most harmful components of this waste from drilling operations are biocides, corrosion inhibitors and demulsifiers. In a recent study, it was demonstrated that heavy metals and lubricants have leaked from the piles of cuttings generated by the 1500 drilling and production installations that have been active in the North Sea. It was formerly thought that heavy metal and other pollutants would remain trapped within the piles. High concentrations of nickel and arsenic have been found in the water column around cutting piles, at limits that exceed British environmental quality standards. Concentrations of metal were even higher in pore water sampled within the cutting piles. It has been claimed that the effects of these oily and metal rich wastes can spread up to 5 km from the drilling rigs leading to a demonstrable and serious impact on marine life. These findings, however, are disputed by the industry. Clearly, further work is required to resolve this issue and identify any measures that are required to safeguard the marine environment.

Oil spills

Oil spills from platforms and pipelines are another source of marine pollution. Despite the remoteness of many oilfields in the North Sea and the rough seas which do much to disperse any spills that do take place, oil has come ashore on many occasions in the past, affecting sensitive habitats, such as salt-marshes and estuaries supporting bird colonies and other marine life (Dicks & White 1992). Major offshore spills are rare, and by their nature, unpredictable events which makes effective planning to deal with their environmental consequences difficult to achieve in practice. Between 1979 and 1988, some 1101 incidents were reported by offshore operators on the UK continental shelf, involving an estimated 9000 tonnes of crude oil (Department of Energy 1989). In most cases, oil spills are left to disperse naturally, as long as they are carefully monitored. Although mechanical recovery is perhaps more environmentally desirable, this is rarely effective in the difficult operating conditions that prevail in the North Sea, especially when large volumes of oil are involved. Aerial spraying also has limited application in the North Sea. Consequently, all countries bordering the North Sea have been affected by shoreline oiling at some time over the last thirty years and this situation is unlikely to change during the remaining period that these fields remain in production.

Oil spills also result from shipping accidents and tanker discharges. The sinking of the oil tanker Braer off Shetland in 1992 was one the most serious shipping incidents in recent years which led to some 8.47×10^4 tonnes of crude oil being discharged into the sea (Ritchie & O'Sullivan 1994; Davies & Topping 1997).

Decommissioning of oil installations

Concern has been raised that little provision has been made for the removal and disposal of offshore platforms once their production lifetimes have come to an end (Side 1992). With some 1500 facilities involved in exploration and production, the potential problem is considerable. The UN Convention on the Law of the Sea 1982, as amended, currently requires any installation which is abandoned to be removed. However, non-removal may be considered to be an acceptable option where there are demonstrable concerns over the technical feasibility or hazards involved in dismantling or removal operations. Abandonment strategies require purging of production facilities, which inevitably leads to short-term increase in water contamination. The cutting up and dismantling of topside facilities will also generate additional pollutants. However, it is anticipated that the most acute environmental effect will arise from the use of explosive charges in dismantling the steel jacket, as all marine organisms can potentially suffer injury through exposure to explosive blasts. Suggested alternative uses for installations left intact include research facilities, communication bases or power generation from wind or waves.

Earth heritage conservation

Conservation of the best and most representative features of Scotland's Earth heritage has been a legal requirement since the *National Parks and Access to the Countryside Act* was passed in 1949. Geological and geomorphological Sites of Special Scientific Interest (SSSIs) have been in place since that time and now number some 500 across Scotland. The site coverage, which is constructed on a GB basis, was recently updated during the conduct of the *Geological Conservation Review* (GCR). Individual site descriptions are published in a series of 40 subject volumes (e.g. Emeleus & Gyopari 1992; Gordon & Sutherland 1994; Stephenson *et al.* 1999). The purpose of Earth heritage conservation is to protect nationally and internationally important geological and geomorphological features from development that would lead to significant damage or destruction of the notified scientific interest. SSSIs are of significant interest for teaching and research purposes and as such represent an irreplaceable scientific resource (Wilson *et al.* 1994).

Selection of conservation sites

The site selection process is described in *An Introduction to the Geological Conservation Review* (Ellis *et al.* 1996). In summary, the review sought to identify the key Earth science sites in Britain, which reflect the range and diversity of the geological and landform resource. Each site selected has to satisfy the legal 'test' outlined in the 1949 Act prior to its endorsement as

an SSSI. To ensure an objective site assessment process, criteria and supporting guidelines were developed to aid the selection process. The criteria are as follows:

1. Sites that are of importance to the *international* community of Earth scientists (Dob's Lin SSSI, e.g. the internationally accepted boundary stratotype between the Ordovician and Silurian, and Siccar Point SSSI, Berwickshire (Plate 16), where James Hutton first described the 'abyss of time' and developed his modernizing views on the science of geology).
2. Sites that are scientifically important because they contain *exceptional* features (e.g. Rhynie SSSI, for example, because of the exceptional preservation of the cellular structure of the plant fossils contained in the Rhynie chert).
3. Sites that are nationally important because they are *representative* of a feature, event or process which is fundamental to Britain's Earth history (e.g. Pabbay SSSI, Western Isles, representing machair and dune surfaces important for interpreting the development of features associated with coastal landform evolution).

In addition, there should be minimum duplication of interest between sites; each site should be practically capable of being conserved, demonstrate an assemblage of geological features or scientific interest; show an extended, or relatively complete record of the feature of interest, have been studied in detail, have the potential for future study and have played a significant part in the development of the Earth sciences in Britain.

Threats to Earth science sites

Active steps must be taken to maintain these sites, as many are under threat through changes in landuse. Blanket afforestation, quarry infill, removal of fluvio-glacial features and commercial fossil collecting are some of the current issues of concern (Gordon 1996; Gordon & MacFadyen 2001). Scottish Natural Heritage (SNH) are statutory consultees for all matters relating to the conservation of SSSIs and their views are sought by the competent planning authority on any development affecting notified sites. Where development is considered to pose a significant threat to the notified interest, SNH have the statutory right to object. However, the planning authority only have a duty to take SNH's views into consideration in determining each application and factors, other than environmental considerations, may weigh more heavily in the balance. Where SNH feel that an unacceptable threat to the natural heritage is posed by development, they may petition the Environment Minister at The Scottish Parliament and ask for developments to be 'called in' for determination at a public inquiry. Such steps were taken by SNH in 1993 when the application to develop a superquarry at Lingerabay, South Harris, was made.

Scotland's fossil heritage is a major scientific, economic, educational and leisure resource, that has a wider range of users, including research scientists, geology students, amateur and commercial collectors, school pupils and the general public (Wimbledon 1988; MacFadyen 1999). Some 84 sites are identified as being of national or international palaeontological importance in Scotland. Most require no regulation or management, as the resource of fossil material is relatively abundant. Also, there is a general recognition that visits by informed groups are largely beneficial, as new specimens, of interest to the palaeontologist, are turned up during the course of these professional or recreational visits (Forster 1998). However, some sites yield fossil material of such rarity or value to science that collecting must be regulated. Four sites are covered by management agreements, limiting access and the quantity of material permitted for collection. In one case, a security fence has been constructed to ensure that commercial collectors are excluded from the site. Unlike many countries, Britain has no legislation specifically designed to regulate fossil collecting or the sale of fossil material. Fossils are regarded as any other mineral and no specific recognition is given to the scientific or monetary value of individual specimens. However, there have been instances in Scotland where prosecutions have been pursued and convictions secured after sites covered by management agreement were raided by commercial fossil collectors.

The need for greater public awareness

The need for greater public awareness of the subject is now considered by many in the profession to be of the greatest importance. Professor R. H. Dott Jr. (University of Wisconsin), in his closing remarks to the Royal Society of Edinburgh conference held in August 1997 to commemorate the bicentennial of James Hutton's death, thought that there were few activities more important to the survival of our many geological institutions than explaining to the general public the need for and value of geological information (Dott 1999). He contends that, without broad-based support, public funding for national museums, geological surveys and university departments in many countries throughout the world, is unlikely to be sustained at present levels. A number of publications and television programmes have been produced to achieve that objective in Scotland (Baird 1991; Grayson 1992; SNH & BGS 1993–1999; McKirdy & McKirdy 1995; McIntyre & McKirdy 2001), but a great deal remains to be done to engage and inform a wider cross-section of the public.

Planning professionals and land managers also require to have a greater awareness of Earth science issues. Many planning and land use decisions have been taken in the past without an adequate understanding of natural processes or resource constraints. Where such mistakes have been made, expensive remediation measures are usually required or opportunities missed for resource exploitation. The Department of the Environment, Transport and the Regions has targeted local authority planners and land managers with publications entitled *Environmental Geology in Land Use Planning* and a *Guide to Sources of Earth Science Information for Planning and Development* (Thompson *et al.* 1998; BGS 1998*b*). The purpose of these publications is to explain the relevance of the Earth sciences to an audience that is largely unaware of the importance and significance of the subject in taking development control and land management decisions. Plans are also in hand to

ensure that Earth science issues are addressed as part of the formal training of town and country planners and that refresher courses are available as required.

Towards a sustainable future

Sustainable development is a key objective to which every developed country in the world aspires. Most were represented at the United Nations Conference on Environment and Development held in 1992 and signed the resultant treaty, which has become known as the Rio Treaty. The World Commission on Environment and Development defined sustainable development as 'development that meets the needs of the present without compromising the ability of future generations to meet their own needs. At a minimum, sustainable development must not endanger the natural systems that support life on earth: the atmosphere, the waters, the soils and the living beings' (World Commission on Environment and Development 1983).

The UK government's response to the Rio Earth Summit was comprehensively set out in the paper 'Sustainable Development – The UK Strategy' (DoE 1994*b*). The strategy advocates waste minimisation, encourages recycling and endorses the effective protection of high quality landscapes and wildlife from development in all but exceptional circumstances.

However, economic imperatives to build our infrastructure required that resources, non-renewable on a human timescale, such as sand and gravel and coal, have been consumed in considerable quantities. So is sustainable development achievable in reality, and if so, what changes in current practice are necessary to realize this goal?

Magnus Magnusson, past Chairman of Scottish Natural Heritage, in an address to the Natural Environmental Research Council (Magnusson 1992), argued that market forces will tend towards over-consumption and the exploitation of the reserves that are cheap to work will be targeted, with less consideration given to the impact on the environment. This situation will continue until strategy replaces opportunism in, for example, the winning and working of minerals. The need for these raw materials is unlikely to diminish significantly in future years, so the demand that society makes on the environment to provide these resources, will increase. People need houses, roads and fuel for their cars, but society also demands that the built and natural heritage enjoys effective protection. This is one of the many challenges that we face in the third millennium, but it surely not beyond us to make adequate provision for both.

References

ABBOTTS, I. L. (ed.) 1991. *United Kingdom Oil and Gas Fields 25 Years Commemorative Volume.* Geological Society, London, Memoir, **14**.

ABRAHAM, D. A. & RITCHIE, J. D. 1991. The Darwin Complex, a Tertiary centre in the Northern Rockall Trough. *Scottish Journal of Geology,* **27**, 113–125.

ADAMS, P. J. 1960. *The Origin and Evolution of Coal.* HMSO, London.

AFTALION, M. & VAN BREEMEN, O. 1980. U–Pb zircon, monazite and Rb–Sr whole-rock systematics of granitic gneiss and psammitic to semipelitic host gneiss from Glenfinnan, northwestern Scotland. *Contributions to Mineralogy and Petrology,* **72**, 87–98.

AGASSIZ, L. 1838. Upon glaciers, moraines, and erratic blocks. *Edinburgh New Philosophical Journal,* **24**, 364–383.

AGASSIZ, L. 1844. *Monographie des Poissons Fossiles du Vieux Grès Rouge ou Système Dévonien (Old Red Sandstone) des Iles Britanniques et de Russie.* Neuchâtel.

AHLBERG, P. E. 1991. Tetrapod or near-tetrapod fossils from the Upper Devonian of Scotland. *Nature, London,* **354**, 298–301.

AHLBERG, P. E. 1992. A new Holoptychiid porolepiform fish from the Upper Frasnian of Elgin, Scotland. *Palaeontology,* **35**, 813–828.

AHMED-SAID, Y. & TANNER, P. W. G. 2000. P-T conditions during emplacement and D2 regional metamorphism of the Ben Vurich Granite, Perthshire, Scotland. *Mineralogical Magazine,* **64**, 737–753.

AIGNER, T., HORNING, J., JUNGHANS, W.-D. & PÖPPELREITER, M. 1999. Baselevel cycles in the Triassic of the South German Basin: a short progress report. *Epicontinental Triassic. Zentralblatt für Geologie und Paläontologie,* **1**, 537–544.

AITCHISON, J. C. 1998. A Lower Ordovician (Arenig) radiolarian fauna from the Ballantrae Complex, Scotland. *Scottish Journal of Geology,* **34**, 73–81.

AITKEN, M. N. 1996. Sustainable use of sewerage sludge on agricultural land. *In:* TAYLOR, A. G., GORDON, J. E. & USHER, M. B. (eds) *Soils, Sustainability and the Natural Heritage.* HMSO, Edinburgh, 152–169.

AKHURST, M. C. & MONRO, S. K. 1966. Dumfries: a Permian desert. Excursion 9. *In:* STONE, P. (ed.) *Geology in South-west Scotland: an Excursion Guide.* British Geological Survey, Keyworth, 80–87.

ALDERTON, D. H. M. 1988. Ag–Au–Te, mineralisation in the Ratagain complex Northwest Scotland. *Transactions of the Institution of Mining and Metallurgy,* **97**, B171–B180.

ALDRIDGE, R. J. & PURNELL, M. A. 1996. The conodont controversies. *Trends in Ecology and Evolution,* **11**, 463–468.

ALDRIDGE, R. J., BRIGGS, D. E. G., SMITH, M. P., CLARKSON, E. N. K. & CLARKE, N. D. L. 1993. The anatomy of conodonts. *Philosophical Transactions of the Royal Society, London,* **B340**, 405–421.

ALLAN, D. 1928. The geology of the Highland Border from Tayside to Noranside. *Transactions of the Royal Society of Edinburgh,* **56**, 57–88.

ALLAN, D. 1940. The geology of the Highland border from Glen Almond to Glen Artney. *Transactions of the Royal Society of Edinburgh,* **60**, 171–193.

ALLEN, P. 1991. Provenance research: Torridonian and Wealden. *In:* MORTON, A. C., TODD, S. P. & HAUGHTON, P. D. W. (eds) *Developments in Sedimentary Provenance Studies,* Geological Society, London, Special Publications, **57**, 13–21.

ALLEN, P. A. & MANGE-RAJETZKY, M. A. 1992. Devonian–Carboniferous sedimentary evolution of the Clair area, offshore north-west UK; impact of changing provenance. *Marine and Petroleum Geology,* **9**, 29–52.

ALLEN, P. A. & MARSHALL, J. E. A. 1981. Depositional environments and palynology of the Devonian East Shetland Basin. *Scottish Journal of Geology,* **17**, 257–273.

ALLEN, P. M., BIDE, P. J., COOPER, D. C., PARKER, M. E. & HASLAM, H. W. 1981. Copper-bearing intrusive rocks at Cairngarroch Bay, south-west Scotland. *Institute of Geological Sciences, Mineral Reconnaissance Programme,* Report **39**.

ALLEN, P. M., COOPER, D. C., PARKER, M. E., EASTERBROOK, G. D. & HASLAM, H. W. 1982. Mineral exploration in the area of the Fore Burn igneous complex, southwestern Scotland. *Institute of Geological Sciences, Mineral Reconnaissance Programme,* Report **55**.

ALLWRIGHT, A. E. 1980. *The Structure and Petrology of the Volcanic Rocks of Eigg, Muck and Canna, NW Scotland.* MSc thesis, University of Durham.

ALMOND, D. C. 1964. Metamorphism of Tertiary lavas in Strathaird. *Transactions of the Royal Society of Edinburgh,* **65**, 313–434.

ALSOP, G. I. 1992. Late Caledonian sinistral strike-slip displacement across the Leannan Fault system, northwest Ireland. *Geological Journal,* **27**, 119–125.

ALSOP, G. I. & HOLDSWORTH, R. E. 1993. The distribution, geometry and kinematic significance of Caledonian buckle folds in the western Moine Nappe, northwestern Scotland. *Geological Magazine,* **130**, 353–362.

ALSOP, G. I. & HOLDSWORTH, R. E. 1999. Vergence and facing patterns in large-scale sheath folds. *Journal of Structural Geology,* **21**, 1335–1349.

ALSOP, G. I., HOLDSWORTH, R. E. & STRACHAN, R. A. 1996. Transport-parallel cross folds within a mid-crustal Caledonian thrust stack, northern Scotland. *Journal of Structural Geology,* **18**, 783–790.

ALSOP, G. I., PRAVE, A. R., CONDON, D. J. & PHILLIPS, C. A. 2000. Cleaved clasts in Dalradian conglomerates: possible evidence for Neoproterozoic compressional tectonism in Scotland and Ireland? *Geological Journal,* **35**, 87–98.

AMIRI-GARROUSSI, K. 1977. Origin of montmorillonite in early Jurassic shales of NW Scotland. *Geological Magazine,* **114**, 281–290.

AMIRI-GARROUSSI, K. 1982. Age of the Camas Malag Formation, Skye. *Scottish Journal of Geology,* **18**, 247–249.

ANDERSON, F. W. 1951. The Geological Survey bore at Rashiehill, Stirlingshire (1951). *Bulletin of the Geological Survey of Great Britain,* **20**, 43–106.

ANDERSON, F. W. & DUNHAM, K. C. 1966. *The Geology of Northern Skye.* Memoirs of the Geological Survey, Scotland, HMSO, Edinburgh.

ANDERSON, J. 1841. On the geology of Fifeshire. *Transactions of the Highland and Agricultural Society,* **7** (new series), 376–431.

ANDERSON, J. 1859. *Dura Den, A Monograph of the Yellow Sandstone and its Remarkable Fossil Remains.* T. Constable, Edinburgh.

ANDERSON, J. G. C. 1946. The geology of the Highland border: Stonehaven to Arran. *Transactions of the Royal Society of Edinburgh,* **61**, 479–515.

ANDERSON, J. G. C., DUNHAM, K. C. & HARVEY, C. O. 1949. The Corrycharmaig serpentinite intrusion, Glen Lochay, Perthshire. *Wartime Pamphlet, Geological Survey England and Wales,* **9**, supplement No. 1.

ANDERSON, L. I. & TREWIN, N. H. (In Press) An Early Devonian arthropod fauna from the Windyfield chert, Aberdeenshire, Scotland. *Palaeontology.*

ANDERSON, L. I., DUNLOP, J. A. & TREWIN, N. H. 2000. A Middle Devonian chasmataspid from Achanarras Quarry, Caithness, Scotland. *Scottish Journal of Geology*, **36**, 151–158.

ANDERSON, T. B. 1968. The geometry of a natural orthorhombic system of kink bands. In: BAER, A. J. & NORRIS, D. K. (eds) *Proceedings of the Conference on Research in Tectonics*. Geological Survey of Canada, Paper **68–52**, 200–228.

ANDERSON, T. B. 1987. The onset and timing of Caledonian sinistral shear in County Down. *Journal of the Geological Society, London*, **144**, 817–825.

ANDERSON, T. B. & CAMERON, D. 1979. A structural profile across Co. Down. In: HARRIS, A. L., HOLLAND, C. H. & LEAKE, B. E. (eds) *The Caledonides of the British Isles – Reviewed*. Geological Society, London, Special Publications, **8**, 263–267.

ANDERSON, T. B. & OLIVER, G. J. H. 1986. The Orlock Bridge Fault: a major late Caledonian sinistral fault in the Southern Uplands terrane, British Isles. *Transactions of the Royal Society of Edinburgh: Earth Sciences*, **77**, 203–222.

ANDERSON, T. B. & OLIVER, G. J. H. 1996. Xenoliths of Iapetus Suture mylonites in County Down lamprophyres, Northern Ireland. *Journal of the Geological Society, London*, **153**, 403–407.

ANDERSON, T. B., PARNELL, J. & RUFFELL, A. H. 1995. Influence of basement on the geometry of Permo-Triassic basins in the northwest British Isles. In: BOLDY, S. A. R. (ed.) *Permian and Triassic Rifting in Northwest Europe*. Geological Society, London, Special Publications, **91**, 103–122.

ANDERTON, R. 1980. Distinctive pebbles as indicators of Dalradian provenance. *Scottish Journal of Geology*, **16**, 143–152.

ANDERTON, R. 1985. Sedimentation and tectonics in the Scottish Dalradian. *Scottish Journal of Geology*, **21**, 407–436.

ANDREWS, I. J., LONG, D., RICHARDS, P. C., THOMSON, A. R., BROWN, S., CHESHER, J. A. & McCORMAC, M. 1990. *The Geology of the Moray Firth*. British Geological Survey Offshore Regional Report, HMSO, London.

ANDREWS, J. E. 1985. The sedimentary facies of a late Bathonian regressive episode: the Kilmaluag and Skudiburgh Formations of the Great Estuarine Group, Inner Hebrides, Scotland. *Journal of the Geological Society, London*, **142**, 1119–1137.

ANDREWS, J. E. 1986. Microfacies and geochemistry of Middle Jurassic algal limestones from Scotland. *Sedimentology*, **33**, 499–520.

ANDREWS, J. E. & HUDSON, J. D. 1984. First Jurassic dinosaur footprint from Scotland. *Scottish Journal of Geology*, **20**, 129–134.

ANDREWS, J. E. & NABI, G. 1998. Palaeoclimatic significance of calcretes in the Dinantian of the Cockburnspath Outlier (East Lothian-North Berwickshire). *Scottish Journal of Geology*, **34**, 155–164.

ANDREWS, J. E. & WALTON, W. 1990. Depositional environments within Middle Jurassic oyster-dominated lagoons: an integrated litho-, bio- and palynofacies study of the Duntulm Formation (Great Estuarine Group, Inner Hebrides). *Transactions of the Royal Society of Edinburgh: Earth Sciences*, **81**, 1–22.

ANDREWS, J. E., HAMILTON, P. J. & FALLICK, A. E. 1987. The geochemistry of early diagenetic dolostones from a low-salinity Jurassic lagoon. *Journal of the Geological Society, London*, **144**, 687–698.

ANDREWS, J. E., TURNER, M. S., NABI, G. & SPIRO, B. 1991. The anatomy of an early Dinantian floodplain: palaeoenvironment and early diagenesis. *Sedimentology*, **38**, 271–287.

ANDREWS, J. T. & DUGDALE, R. E. 1970. Age prediction of glacio-isostatic strandlines based on their gradients. *Geological Society of America Bulletin*, **81**, 3769–3771.

ANDREWS, S. M. 1978. A possible occurrence of *Remingolepis* in the topmost Old Red Sandstone of Berwickshire. *Scottish Journal of Geology*, **14**, 311–315.

ANDREWS, S. M. 1982. *The Discovery of Fossil Fishes in Scotland up to 1845 with Checklists of Agassiz's Figured Specimens*. Royal Scottish Musem, Edinburgh.

ANDREWS, S. M. 1983. Altyre and Lethan Bar, two Middle Old Red Sandstone fish localities? *Scottish Journal of Geology*, **19**, 243–264.

ANON 1826. Petrified fishes. *Edinburgh Philosophical Journal*, **14**, 191.

ANON 1933. The Scottish shale oil industry. Reprinted by The Almond Valley Heritage Trust, Livingston, West Lothian from *Wonders of World Engineering*, The Amalgamated Press Limited.

ARMSTRONG, D. 1957. Dating some of the minor intrusions of Ayrshire. *Nature, London*, **180**, 1277.

ARMSTRONG, H. A. & COE, A. L. 1997. Deep-sea sediments record the geophysiology of the late Ordovician glaciation. *Journal of the Geological Society, London*, **154**, 929–934.

ARMSTRONG, H. A. & OWEN, A. W. 2000a. Age and provenance of limestone clasts in Lower Old Red Sandstone conglomerates: implications for the geological history of the Midland Valley Terrane. In: FRIEND, P. F. & WILLIAMS, B. P. J. (eds) *New Perspectives on the Old Red Sandstone*. Geological Society, London, Special Publications, **180**, 459–471.

ARMSTRONG, H. A. & OWEN, A. W. 2000b. Plate tectonics and the Caledonian orogeny. *Teaching Earth Sciences*, **25**, 143–152.

ARMSTRONG, H. A. & OWEN, A. W. 2001. Terrane evolution of the paratectonic Caledonides of northern Britain. *Journal of the Geological Society, London*, **158**, 475–486.

ARMSTRONG, H. A., CLARKSON, E. N. K. & OWEN, A. W. 1990. A new lower Ordovician conodont faunule from the Northern Belt of the Southern Uplands. *Scottish Journal of Geology*, **26**, 47–52.

ARMSTRONG, H. A., OWEN, A. W., SCRUTTON, C. T., CLARKSON, E. N. K. & TAYLOR, M. 1996. Evolution of the Northern Belt, Southern Uplands: Implications for the Southern Uplands controversy. *Journal of the Geological Society, London*, **153** 197–205.

ARMSTRONG, H. A., OWEN, A. W. & FLOYD, J. D. 1999. Rare earth geochemistry of Arenig cherts from the Ballantrae Ophiolite and Leadhills Imbricate Zone, southern Scotland: implications for origin and significance to the Caledonian. *Journal of the Geological Society, London*, **156**, 549–560.

ARMSTRONG, L. A., TEN HAVE, A. & JOHNSON, H. D. 1987. The Geology of the Gannet Fields, Central North Sea, UK sector. In: BROOKS, J. & GLENNIE, K. (eds) *Petroleum Geology of Northwest Europe*. Graham & Trotman, London, 533–548.

ARMSTRONG, M. 1977. The Old Red Sandstone of Easter Ross and the Black Isle. In: GILL, G. (ed.) *The Moray Firth Area – Geological Studies*. Inverness Field Club.

ARMSTRONG, M. & PATERSON, I. B. 1970. The Lower Old Red Sandstone of the Strathmore Region. *Institute of Geological Science Report 70/12*, 1–23.

ARMSTRONG, M., DONOVAN, R. N. & MYKURA, W. 1978a. Western Moray Firth and Caithness. In: FRIEND, P. F. & WILLIAMS, B. P. J. (eds) *A Field Guide to Selected Outcrop Areas of the Devonian of Scotland, the Welsh Borderland and South Wales*. Palaeontological Association, London, 32–37.

ARMSTRONG, M., DONOVAN, R. N. & PATERSON, I. B. 1978b. Angus and Kincardine. In: FRIEND, P. F. & WILLIAMS, B. P. J. (eds) *A Field Guide to Selected Outcrop Areas of the Devonian of Scotland, the Welsh Borderland and South Wales*, Palaeontological Association, London, 13–22.

ARMSTRONG, M., PATERSON, I. B. & BROWNE, M. A. E. 1985. Geology of the Perth and Dundee District. *Memoir of the British Geological Survey* (Sheets 48E, 48W, 49).

ARUP ECONOMICS AND PLANNING 1991. *Occurrence and Utilisation of Mineral and Construction Wastes*. Department of the Environment Geological and Minerals Planning Research Programme, London, HMSO.

ARUP ECONOMICS AND PLANNING 1992. *Coastal Superquarries to Supply South-East Aggregate Requirements*. Department of the Environment.

ASHCROFT, W. A. & BOYD, R. 1976. The Belhelvie mafic igneous intrusion, Aberdeenshire – a reinvestigation. *Scottish Journal of Geology*, **2**, 1–14.

ASHCROFT, W. A. & MUNRO, M. 1978. The structure of the eastern part of the Insch mafic intrusion, Aberdeenshire. *Scottish Journal of Geology*, **14**, 55–79.

ASHCROFT, W. A., KNELLER, B. C., LESLIE, A. G. & MUNRO, M. 1984. Major shear zones and autochthonous Dalradian in the northeast Scottish Caledonides. *Nature, London*, **310**, 760–762.

ASHWORTH, J. R. 1975. The sillimanite zones of the Huntly-Portsoy area in the northeast Dalradian, Scotland. *Geological Magazine*, **112**, 113–136.

ASHWORTH, J. R. 1976. Petrogenesis of migmatites in the Huntly-Portsoy area in the north-east Dalradian. *Mineralogical Magazine*, **40**, 661–682.

ASHWORTH, J. R. 1979. Textural and mineralogical evolution of migmatites. *In*: HARRIS, A. L., HOLLAND, C. H. & LEAKE, B. E. (eds) *The Caledonides of the British Isles – Reviewed*. Geological Society, London, Special Publications, **8**, 357–362.

ASHWORTH, J. R. & TYLER, I. M. 1983. The distribution of temperatures around the Strontian Granodiorite. *Geological Magazine*, **120**, 281–290.

ASTIN, T. R. 1982. *The Devonian Geology of the Walls Peninsula, Shetland*. PhD thesis, University of Cambridge.

ASTIN, T. R. 1983. Discussion on implications for Caledonian plate tectonic models of chemical data from volcanic rocks of the British Old Red Sandstone. *Journal of the Geological Society, London*, **140**, 315–318.

ASTIN, T. R. 1985. The palaeogeography of the Middle Devonian Lower Eday Sandstone of Orkney. *Scottish Journal of Geology*, **21**, 353–375.

ASTIN, T. R. 1990. The Devonian lacustrine sediments of Orkney, Scotland; implications for climatic cyclicity, basin structure and maturation history. *Journal of the Geological Society, London*, **147**, 141–157.

ASTIN, T. R. & ROGERS, D. A. 1991. 'Subaqueous shrinkage cracks' in the Devonian of Scotland re-interpreted. *Journal of Sedimentary Petrology*, **61**, 850–859.

ATHERTON, M. P. 1977. The metamorphism of the Dalradian rocks of Scotland. *Scottish Journal of Geology*, **13**, 331–370.

ATHERTON, M. P. & GHANI, A. A. 2002. Slab breakoff: a model for Caledonian, Late Granite syn-collisional magmatism in the orthotectonic (metamorphic) zone of Scotland and Donegal. *Lithos*, **62**, 65–85.

ATKINSON, T. C., BRIFFA, K. R. & COOPE, G. R. 1987. Seasonal temperatures in Britain during the past 22,000 years reconstructed using beetle remains. *Nature, London*, **325**, 587–592.

ATTFIELD, P. 1987. The structural history of the Canisp Shear Zone. *In*: PARK, R. G. & TARNEY, J. (eds) *Evolution of the Lewisian and Comparable Precambrian High Grade Terrains*. Geological Society, London, Special Publications, **27**, 165–173.

BABA, S. 1999. Sapphirine-bearing orthopyroxene-kyanite/sillimanite granulites from South Harris, NW Scotland: evidence for Proterozoic UHT metamorphism in the Lewisian. *Contributions to Mineralogy and Petrology*, **136**, 33–47.

BABTIE GEOTECHNICAL 1997. *Management of coal mine effluents*. Scottish Natural Heritage Review series, No. 33.

BACON, M. & CHESHER, J. 1975. Evidence against post-Hercynian transcurrent movement on the Great Glen Fault. *Scottish Journal of Geology*, **11**, 79–82.

BAILEY, E. B. 1910a. Recumbent folds in the schists of the Scottish Highlands. *Quarterly Journal of the Geological Society of London*, **66**, 586–620.

BAILEY, E. B. 1910b. The geology of East Lothian. *Memoir of the Geological Survey, Scotland*.

BAILEY, E. B. 1912. The Glen-Orchy anticline (Argyllshire). *Quarterly Journal of the Geological Society of London*, **68**, 164–179.

BAILEY, E. B. 1913. The Loch Awe syncline (Argyllshire). *Quarterly Journal of the Geological Society of London*, **69**, 280–307.

BAILEY, E. B. 1914. The Ballachulish fold near the head of Loch Creran (Argyllshire). *Quarterly Journal of the Geological Society of London*, **70**, 321–327.

BAILEY, E. B. 1922. The structure of the South-west Highlands of Scotland. *Quarterly Journal of the Geological Society of London*, **78**, 82–127.

BAILEY, E. B. 1923. The metamorphism of the South-West Highlands. *Geological Magazine*, **60**, 317–331.

BAILEY, E. B. 1930. On the chronological order of deposition of the Highland Schists, *Geological Magazine*, **67**, 68–73.

BAILEY, E. B. 1934. The Glencoul Nappe and the Assynt Culmination. *Geological Magazine*, **72**, 151–165.

BAILEY, E. B. 1950. The structural history of Scotland. *International Geological Congress. Report of the Eighteenth Session Great Britain 1948. Part I General Proceedings*, 230–255.

BAILEY, E. B. 1960. *Geology of Ben Nevis and Glencoe*. Memoir of the Geological Survey of Great Britain (2nd edition).

BAILEY, E. B. & MCCALLIEN, W. J. 1934. Precambrian Association Excursion to Scotland. *Geological Magazine*, **71**, 553–555.

BAILEY, E. B. & MCCALLIEN, W. J. 1957. The Ballantrae serpentine, Ayrshire. *Transactions of the Edinburgh Geological Society*, **17**, 33–53.

BAILEY, E. B. & MAUFE, H. B. 1916. *The Geology of Ben Nevis and Glen Coe, and the Surrounding Country (Explanation of Sheet 53)*. HMSO, Edinburgh.

BAILEY, E. B. & WEIR, J. 1932. Submarine faulting in Kimmeridgian Times: East Sutherland. *Transactions of the Royal Society of Edinburgh*, **57**, 429–467.

BAILEY, E. B., CLOUGH, C. T., WRIGHT, W. B., RICHEY, J. E. & WILSON, G. V. 1924. *Tertiary and post-Tertiary Geology of Mull, Loch Aline and Oban*. Memoir of the Geological Survey of Great Britain.

BAILEY, N. J. L., BURWOOD, R. & HARRIMAN, G. 1990. Application of pyrolysate carbon isotope and biomarker technology to organofacies definition and oil correlation problems in North Sea basins. *In*: DURAND, B. & BEHAR, F. (eds) *Advances in Organic Geochemistry. Organic Geochemistry*, **16**, 1157–1172.

BAIN, J. S. 1993. Historical overview of exploration of Tertiary plays in the UK North Sea. *In*: PARKER, J. R. (ed.) *Petroleum Geology of Northwest Europe: Proceedings of the 4th Conference*. Geological Society, London, 5–13.

BAIRD, A. W. 1982. The Sgurr Beag Slide within Moine rocks at Loch Eilt, Inverness-shire. *Journal of the Geological Society, London*, **139**, 647–654.

BAIRD, W. J. 1991. *The Scenery of Scotland*. National Museums of Scotland.

BAKER, A. J. 1985. Pressures and temperatures of metamorphism in the eastern Dalradian. *Journal of the Geological Society, London*, **142**, 137–148.

BAKER, P. & KASTNER, M. 1981. Constraints on the formation of sedimentary dolomite. *Science*, **213**, 214–216.

BALD, R. 1812. *A General View of the Coal Trade of Scotland*. W. Turnbull, Glasgow; F. Charnley, Newcastle; Hurst, Rees, Orme & Brown, London.

BALIN, D. F. 2000. Calcrete morphology and karst development in the Upper Old Red Sandstone at Milton Ness, Scotland. *In*: FRIEND, P. F. & WILLIAMS, B. P. J. (eds) *New perspectives on the Old Red Sandstone*. Geological Society, London, Special Publications, **180**, 485–501.

BALLANTYNE, C. K. 1986. Landslides and slope failures in Scotland: a review. *Scottish Geographical Magazine*, **102**, 134–150.

BALLANTYNE, C. K. 1987. The present day periglaciation of upland Britain. *In*: BOARDMAN, J. (ed.) *Periglacial Landforms and Processes in Great Britain and Ireland*. Cambridge University Press, 113–126.

BALLANTYNE, C. K. 1999. Maximum altitude of the late Devensian glaciation on the Isle of Mull and Isle of Jura. *Scottish Journal of Geology*, **35**, 97–106.

BALLANTYNE, C. K. & WHITTINGHAM, G. 1987. Niveo-aeolian sand deposits on An Teallach, Wester Ross, Scotland. *Transactions of the Royal Society Edinburgh: Earth Sciences*, **78**, 51–64.

BALSILLIE, D. 1932. The Ballantrae Igneous Complex. *Geological Magazine*, **69**, 107–131.

BALSILLIE, D. 1937a. Further observations on the Ballantrae igneous complex, south Ayrshire (Scotland). *Geological Magazine*, **877**, 20–33.

BALSILLIE, D. 1937b. The Girvan–Ballantrae serpentine (Scotland). *Geological Magazine*, **877**, 336.

BAMFORD, D. 1979. Seismic constraints on the deep geology of the Caledonides of northern Britain. *In*: HARRIS, A. L, HOLLAND, C. H. & LEAKE, B. E. (eds) *The Caledonides of the British Isles – Reviewed*. Geological Society, London, Special Publications, **8**, 93–100.

BAMFORD, D., NUNN, K., PROEDEHL, C. & JACOB, B. 1978. LISPB-IV. Crustal studies of northern Britain. *Geophysical Journal of the Royal Astronomical Society*, **54**, 43–60.

BARBER, A. J. & MAY, F. 1976. The history of the Western Lewisian in the Glenelg inlier, Lochalsh, Northern Highlands. *Scottish Journal of Geology*, **12**, 35–50.

BARENDREGT, R. W. & IRVING, E. 1998. Changes in the extent of the North American ice sheets during the late Cenozoic. *Canadian Journal of Earth Sciences*, **35**, 504–509.

BARLING, J., MARKER, M. & BREWER, T. 1996. A juvenile ~1.95–1.93 Ga magmatic arc complex northeast of the Lapland Granulite belt in the Lapland-Kola orogen, northern Baltic shield – geochemical and isotopic study. *Proceedings, 2nd DLC Workshop on Nagssugtoqidian geology*, Danish Lithosphere Centre, Copenhagen, 66–70.

BARNES, R. P. 1989. *Geology of the Whithorn District*. Memoir of the British Geological Survey, Sheet 2 Scotland.

BARNES, R. P. 2000. *The Geology of the Kirkcowan, Wigtown and Whithorn Districts*. Memoir of the British Geological Survey, Sheets 4W and 4E (Scotland).

BARNES, R. P., ROCK, N. M. S. & GASKARTH, J. W. 1986. Late Caledonian dyke swarms in Southern Scotland: new field, petrological and geochemical data for the Wigtown peninsula, Galloway. *Journal of Geology*, **21**, 101–205.

BARNES, R. P., LINTERN, B. C. & STONE, P. 1989. Timing and regional implications of deformation in the Southern Uplands of Scotland. *Journal of the Geological Society, London*, **77**, 203–222.

BARNES, R. P., PHILLIPS, E. R. & BOLAND, M. P. 1995. The Orlock Bridge Fault in the Southern Uplands of SW Scotland: a terrane boundary? *Geological Magazine*, **132**, 523–529.

BARNETT, J. A. M. 1985. Fracture patterns related to volcanic rocks and pipes in an Upper Limestone Group (Namurian) coal seam in the Kincardine Basin, West Fife, Scotland. *Proceedings of the Yorkshire Geological Society*, **45**, 249–259.

BARR, D. 1985. Migmatites in the Moine. *In*: ASHWORTH, J. R. (ed.) *Migmatites*. Blackie, Glasgow, 226–264.

BARR, D., ROBERTS, A. M., HIGHTON, A. J., PARSON, L. M. & HARRIS, A. L. 1985. Structural setting and geochronological significance of the West Highland Granitic Gneiss, a deformed early granite within the Proterozoic, Moine rocks of NW Scotland. *Journal of the Geological Society, London*, **142**, 663–675.

BARR, D., HOLDSWORTH, R. E. & ROBERTS, A. M. 1986. Caledonian ductile thrusting in a Precambrian metamorphic complex: the Moine of north-western Scotland. *Geological Society of America Bulletin*, **97**, 754–764.

BARRET, T. J., JENKYNS, H. C., LEGGETT, J. K. & ROBERTSON, A. H. F. 1982. Comment and reply on 'Age and origin of Ballantrae ophiolite and its significance to the Caledonian orogeny and the Ordovician time-scale'. *Geology*, **9**, 331–333.

BARRON, H. F. 1989a. Dinoflagellate cyst biostratigraphy and palaeoenvironments of the Upper Jurassic (Kimmeridgian to basal Portlandian) of the Helmsdale region, east Sutherland, Scotland. *In*: BATTEN, D. J. (ed.) *Studies in NW European micropalaeontology and palynology*. British Micropalaeontology Society Series, Ellis Horwood, Chichester, 192–213.

BARRON, H. F. 1989b. Mid-Wenlock acritarchs from a Silurian inlier in the Cheviot Hills, NE England. *Scottish Journal of Geology*, **25**, 81–98.

BARROW, G. 1893. On an intrusion of muscovite biotite gneiss in the southeast Highlands of Scotland and its accompanying metamorphism. *Quarterly Journal of the Geological Society of London*, **49**, 330–358.

BARROW, G. 1901. On the occurrence of Silurian(?) Rocks in Forfarshire and Kincardineshire along the eastern border of the High-

lands. *Quarterly Journal of the Geological Society of London*, **57**, 328–345.

BARROW, G. 1912. On the geology of lower Deeside and the southern Highland Border. *Proceedings of the Geologists' Association*, **23**, 268–273.

BARROW, G. n.d. Unpublished typescript, ca. 1930. British Geological Survey archives, Edinburgh, LSA 326. (Reproduced on CD © NERC 1999).

BARTON, P. J. 1992. LISPB revisited: a new look under the Caledonides of northern Britain. *Geophysical Journal International*, **110**, 371–391.

BASSETT, M. G., BLUCK, B. J., CAVE, R., HOLLAND, C. H. & LAWSON, J. D. 1992. Silurian. *In*: COPE, J. C. W., INGHAM, J. K. & RAWSON, P. F. (eds) *Atlas of Palaeogeography and Lithofacies*. Geological Society, London, Memoir, **13**, 37–56.

BATCHELOR, R. A. 1987. Geochemical and petrological characteristics of the Etive granitoid complex, Argyll. *Scottish Journal of Geology*, **23**, 227–249.

BATCHELOR, R. A. 1998. Metabentonites from the Silurian Inliers of the southern Midland Valley of Scotland: distribution and geochemistry. *Scottish Journal of Geology*, **35**, 71–77.

BATCHELOR, R. A. & CLARKSON, E. N. K. 1993. Geochemistry of a Silurian metabentonite and associated apatite from the North Esk Inlier, Pentland Hills. *Scottish Journal of Geology*, **29**, 123–130.

BATCHELOR, R. A. & WEIR, J. A. 1988. Metabentonite geochemistry; magmatic cycles and graptolite extinctions at Dob's Linn, Southern Scotland. *Transactions of the Royal Society of Edinburgh: Earth Sciences*, **79**, 19–41.

BATTEN, D. J., TREWIN, N. H. & TUDHOPE, A. W. 1986. The Triassic-Jurassic junction at Golspie, Inner Moray Firth Basin. *Scottish Journal of Geology*, **22**, 85–98.

BAXTER, A. N. 1987. Petrochemistry of late Palaeozoic lamprophyre dykes from N Scotland. *Transactions of the Royal Society of Edinburgh*, **77**, 267–277.

BAXTER, A. N. & MITCHELL, J. G. 1984. Camptonite-monchiquite dyke swarms of Northern Scotland; age relationships and their implications. *Scottish Journal of Geology*, **20**, 297–308.

BAXTER, E. F., AGUE, J. J. & DEPAOLO, D. J. 2002. Prograde temperature–time evolution in the Barrovian type-locality constrained by Sm/Nd garnet ages from Glen Clova, Scotland. *Journal of the Geological Society, London*, **159**, 71–82.

BEACH, A., COWARD, M. P. & GRAHAM, R. H. 1974. An interpretation of the structural evolution of the Laxford front. *Scottish Journal of Geology*, **9**, 297–308.

BEAMISH, D. R. & SMYTHE, D. K. 1986. Geophysical images of the deep crust; the Iapetus suture. *Journal of the Geological Society, London*, **143**, 489–497.

BECKINSALE, R D., PANKHURST, R. J., SKELHORN, R. R. & WALSH, J. N. 1978. Geochemistry and Petrogenesis of the Early Tertiary Lava Pile of the Isle of Mull, Scotland. *Contibutions to Mineralogy and Petrology*, **66**, 415–427.

BEDDOE-STEPHENS, B. 1990. Pressures and temperatures of Dalradian metamorphism and the andalusite-kyanite transformation in the north-east Grampians. *Scottish Journal of Geology*, **26**, 3–14.

BELL, B. R. 1983. Significance of ferrodioritic liquids in magma mixing processes. *Nature, London*, **306**, 323–327.

BELL, B. R. 1985. The pyroclastic rocks and rhyolitic lavas of the Eastern Red Hills district, Isle of Skye. *Scottish Journal of Geology*, **21**, 57–70.

BELL, B. R. & CLAYDON, R. V. 1992. The cumulus and post-cumulus evolution of chrome-spinels in ultrabasic layered intrusions: evidence from the Cuillin Igneous Complex, Isle of Skye, Scotland. *Contributions to Mineralogy and Petrology*, **112**, 242–253.

BELL, B. R. & HARRIS, J. W. 1986. *An Excursion Guide to the Geology of the Isle of Skye*. Geological Society of Glasgow.

BELL, B. R. & JOLLEY, D. W. 1997. Application of palynological data to the chronology of Palaeogene lava fields of the British Province: implications for magnetic stratigraphy. *Journal of the Geological Society, London*, **154**, 701–708.

BELL, B. R. & PANKHURST, R. J. 1993. Sr-isotope variations in a composite sill: crystal-liquid processes and the origin of Skye granites. *Journal of the Geological Society, London*, **150**, 121–124.

BELL, B. R., CLAYDON, R. V. & ROGERS, G. 1994. The petrology and geochemistry of cone-sheets from the Cuillin Igneous Igneous Complex, Isle of Skye: evidence for combined assimilation and fractional crystallization during lithospheric extension. *Journal of Petrology*, **35**, 1055–1094.

BELL, B. R., WILLIAMSON, I. T., HEAD, F. E. & JOLLEY, D. W. 1996. On the origin of a reddened interflow bed within the Palaeogene lava field of North Skye. *Scottish Journal of Geology*, **32**, 117–126.

BELL, J. D. 1976. The Tertiary intrusive complex on the Isle of Skye. *Proceedings of the Geologists' Association*, **87**, 247–271.

BENNETT, K. D. 1995. Insularity and the Quaternary tree and shrub flora of the British Isles. *In*: PREECE, R. C. (ed.) *Island Britain: A Quaternary Perspective*. Geological Society, London, Special Publications, **96**, 173–180.

BENNETT, K. D. & BOULTON, G. S. 1993a. A reinterpretation of Scottish 'hummocky moraine' and its significance for the deglaciation of the Scottish Highlands during the Younger Dryas or Loch Lomond Stadial. *Geological Magazine*, **130**, 301–318.

BENNETT, K. D. & BOULTON, G. S. 1993b. Deglaciation of the Younger Dryas or Loch Lomond Stadial ice-field in the northern Highlands, Scotland. *Journal of Quaternary Science*, **8**, 133–145.

BENNETT, R. B. & DOYLE, P. 1997. *Environmental Geology – Geology and the Human Environment*. Wiley, Chichester.

BENTLEY, M. R. 1988. The Colonsay Group. *In*: WINCHESTER, J. A. (ed.) *Later Proterozoic Stratigraphy of the Northern Atlantic Regions*. Blackie, Glasgow, 119–130.

BENTON, M. J. 1982. Trace fossils from Lower Palaeozoic ocean-floor sediments of the Southern Uplands of Scotland, *Transactions of the Royal Society of Edinburgh: Earth Sciences*, **73**, 67–87.

BENTON, M. J. & SPENCER, P. S. 1995. British Permian fossil reptile sites. *In*: BENTON, M. J. & SPENCER, P. S. (eds) *Fossil Reptiles of Great Britain*. Geological Conservation Review Series, **10**, Chapman & Hall, London, 27–29.

BENTON, M. J. & TREWIN, N. H. 1980. *Dictyodora* from the Silurian of Peebleshire, Scotland. *Palaeontology*, **23**, 501–513.

BENTON, M. J. & WALKER, A. D. 1985. Palaeoecology, taphonomy, and dating of Permo-Triassic reptiles from Elgin, north-east Scotland. *Palaeontology*, **28**, 207–234.

BENTON, M. J., COOK, E. & TURNER, P. 2002. *Permian and Triassic Red Beds and the Penarth Group of Great Britain*. Joint Nature Conservation Committee, Peterborough.

BERGSTROM, S. M. & ORCHARD, M. J. 1985. Conodonts of the Cambrian and Ordovician systems from the British Isles. *In*: HIGGINS, A. C. & AUSTIN, R. L. (eds) *A stratigraphical Index of Conodonts*. Ellis Horwood, Chichester, 32–67.

BERNARD-GRIFFITHS, J., PEUCAT, J. J., POSTAIRE, B., VIDAL, PH., CONVERT, PH. & MOREAU, B. 1984. Isotopic data (U–Pb, Rb–Sr, Pb–Pb and Sm–Nd) on mafic granulites from Finnish Lapland. *Precambrian Research*, **23**, 325–348.

BERRIDGE, N. G. 1969. A summary of the mineral resources of the 'Crofter Counties' of Scotland. *Institute of Geological Sciences*, Report **69/5**.

BERRIDGE, N. G. & IVIMEY-COOK, H. C. 1967. The geology of a Geological Survey borehole at Lossiemouth, Morayshire. *Bulletin Geological Survey, G.B.*, **27**, 155–169.

BERTHELSEN, A. & MARKER, M. 1986. Tectonics of the Kola collision suture and adjacent Archaean and Early Proterozoic terrains in the northeastern region of the Baltic shield. *Tectonophysics*, **126**, 31–55.

BESSA, J. L. 1991. *A Reinterpretation of Devonian Carbonates found in Well 30/16–5, Auk Field, North Sea*. MSc thesis, University of Aberdeen.

BEVAN, J. C. & HUTCHISON, R. 1984. Layering in the Gars-bheinn ultrabasic sill, Isle of Skye: a new interpretation, and its implications. *Scottish Journal of Geology*, **20**, 329–342.

BEVERIDGE, R., BROWN, S., GALLAGHER, M. J. & MERRITT, J. W. 1991. Economic Geology. *In*: CRAIG, G. Y. (ed.) *Geology of Scotland* (3rd edition). Geological Society, London, 545–595.

BHATTACHARJEE, C. C. 1968. The structural history of the Lewisian rocks north-west of Loch Tollie, Ross-shire, Scotland. *Scottish Journal of Geology*, **4**, 235–264.

BICKERMAN, M., BOWES, D. R. & VAN BREEMEN, O. 1975. Rb–Sr whole rock isotopic studies of Lewisian metasediments and gneisses in the Loch Maree region, Ross-shire. *Journal of the Geological Society, London*, **131**, 237–254.

BINGEN, B., DEMAIFFE, D. & VAN BREEMEN, O. 1998. The 616 Ma old Egursund basaltic dike swarm, SW Norway and late Neoproterozoic opening of the Iapetus ocean. *Journal of Geology*, **106**, 565–574.

BINNS, P. E., MCQUILLAN, R., FANNIN, N. G. T., KENOLTY, N. & ARDUS, D. A. 1975. Structure and stratigraphy of sedimentary basins in the sea of the Hebrides and Minches. *In*: WOODLAND, A. W. (ed.) *Petroleum and the Continental Shelf of North-West Europe*, **1**, 93–102.

BIRKS, H. J. B. 1973. *Past and Present Vegetation of the Isles of Skye. A Palaeoecological Study*. Cambridge University Press.

BIRKS, H. J. B. 1977. The Flandrian forest history of Scotland: a preliminary synthesis. *In*: SHOTTON, F. W. (ed.) *British Quaternary Studies: Recent Advances*. Clarendon, Oxford, 119–135.

BIRKS, H. J. B. & MATHEWES, R. W. 1978. Studies in the vegetational history of Scotland. V. Late Devensian and Early Flandrian pollen and macrofossil stratigraphy at Abernethy Forest, Invernesshire. *New Phytologist*, **80**, 455–484.

BIRKS, H. J. B. & PEGLAR, S. M. 1979. Interglacial pollen spectra from Sel Ayre, Shetland. *New Phytologist*, **83**, 559–575.

BISHOP, W. W. & COOPE, G. R. 1977. Stratigraphical and faunal evidence for Lateglacial and early Flandrian environments in south-west Scotland. *In*: GRAY, J. M. & LOWE, J. J. (eds) *Studies in the Scottish Lateglacial Environment*, 61–68. Pergamon, Oxford.

BJERRUM, C. J., SURLYK, F., CALLOMON. J. H. & SLINGERLAND, R. L. 2001. Numerical paleoceanographic study of the Early Jurassic transcontinental Laurasian seaway. *Paleoceanography*, **16**, 390–404.

BLACK, G. P. 1966. *Arthur's Seat. A History of Edinburgh's Volcano*. Oliver and Boyd, Edinburgh.

BLACK, M. 1933. The algal sediments of Andros Island, Bahamas. *Philosophical Transactions of the Royal Society, London*, **B222**, 165–192.

BLACK, R. C., POELEN, H. J., ROBERTS, M. J. & RODDY, S. E. 1999. Tern Field development: a marriage of new technologies for business benefit. *In*: FLEET, A. J. & BOLDY, S. A. R. (eds) *Petroleum Geology of Northwest Europe: Proceedings of the 5th Conference*, Geological Society, London, 1063–1073.

BLACKBOURN, G. 1981. Probable Old Red Sandstone conglomerates around Tongue and adjacent areas, north Scotland. *Scottish Journal of Geology*, **17**, 103–118.

BLACKBOURN, G. 1987. Sedimentary environments and stratigraphy of the Late Devonian-Early Carboniferous Clair Basin, west of Shetland. *In*: MILLER, J., ADAMS, A. E. & WRIGHT, V. P. (eds) *European Dinantian Environments. Geological Journal, Special Issue*, **12**, 75–91.

BLAKE, D. H., ELWELL, R. W. D., GIBSON, I. L., SKELHORN, R. R. & WALKER, G. P. L. 1965. Some relationships resulting from the intimate association of acid and basic magmas. *Quarterly Journal of the Geological Society of London*, **121**, 31–49.

BLAKE, J. F. 1902. On a remarkable inlier among the Jurassic rocks of Sutherland and its bearing on the origin of the breccia-beds. *Quarterly Journal of the Geological Society, London*, **57**, 290–312.

BLEHAUT, J. F., VAN BEEK, F., BILLEAU, C., GAUSE, J. K., *et al.* 1999. Shearwater prospect development: a high pressure/high temperature challenge. *In*: FLEET, A. J. & BOLDY, S. A. R. (eds) *Petroleum Geology of Northwest Europe: Proceedings of the 5th Conference*, Geological Society, London, 1021–1027.

BLOCK VAGLE, G., HURST, A. & DYPVIK, H. Origin of quartz cements in some sandstones from the Jurassic of the Inner Moray Firth (UK). *Sedimentology*, **41**, 363–377.

BLOXAM, T. W. 1968. The petrology of Byne Hill, Ayrshire. *Transactions of the Royal Society of Edinburgh: Earth Sciences*, **68**, 105–122.

BLUCK, B. J. 1978. Sedimentation in a late orogenic basin: the Old Red Sandstone of the Midland Valley of Scotland. *In*: BOWES, D. R. & LEAKE, B. E. (eds) *Crustal Evolution in Northwestern Britain and Adjacent Regions. Geological Journal, Special Issue*, **10**, 249–278.

BLUCK, B. J. 1980. Structure, generation and preservation of upward fining, braided stream cycles in the Old Red Sandstone of Scotland. *Transactions of the Royal Society of Edinburgh*, **17**, 29–46.

BLUCK, B. J. 1982. Hyalotuff delta deposits in the Ballantrae ophiolite of SW Scotland: evidence for crustal position of the lava sequence. *Transactions of the Royal Society of Edinburgh: Earth Sciences*, **72**, 217–228.

BLUCK, B. J. 1983. Role of the Midland Valley of Scotland in the Caledonian orogeny. *Transactions of the Royal Society of Edinburgh: Earth Sciences*, **74**, 119–136.

BLUCK, B. J. 1984. Pre-Carboniferous history of the Midland Valley of Scotland. *Transactions of the Royal Society of Edinburgh: Earth Sciences*, **75**, 297–295.

BLUCK, B. J. 1985. The Scottish paratectonic Caledonides. *Scottish Journal of Geology*, **21**, 437–464.

BLUCK, B. J. 1986. Upward coarsening sedimentation units and facies lineages, Old Red Sandstone, Scotland. *Transactions of the Royal Society of Edinburgh: Earth Sciences*, **77**, 251–246.

BLUCK, B. J. 1992a. Excursion 9. Balmaha. *In*: LAWSON, J. D. & WEEDON, D. S. (eds) *Geological Excursions around Glasgow and Girvan*. Geological Society of Glasgow, 110–129.

BLUCK, B. J. 1992b. Excursion 25. Pinbain Block. *In*: LAWSON, J. D. & WEEDON, D. S. (eds) *Geological Excursions around Glasgow and Girvan*. Geological Society of Glasgow, 319–338.

BLUCK, B. J. 1995. W. Q. Kennedy, the Great Glen Fault and strike-slip motion. *In*: LE BAS, M. J. (ed.) *Milestones in Geology*, Geological Society, London, Memoir, **16**, 57–65.

BLUCK, B. J. 2000. Old Red Sandstone basins and alluvial systems of Midland Scotland. *In*: FRIEND, P. F. & WILLIAMS, B. P. J. (eds) *New perspectives on the Old Red Sandstone*. Geological Society, London, Special Publications, **180**, 417–437.

BLUCK, B J. 2001. Caledonian and related events in Scotland. *Transactions of the Royal Society of Edinburgh: Earth Sciences*, **91**, 375–404.

BLUCK, B. J. & INGHAM, J. K. 1992. The Girvan-Ballantrae Complex, Introduction. *In*: LAWSON, J. D. & WEEDON, D. S. (eds) *Geological Excursions around Glasgow and Girvan*. Geological Society of Glasgow, 301–306.

BLUCK, B. J. & INGHAM, J. K. 1997. The Highland Border controversy: a discussion of 'New evidence that the Lower Cambrian Leny Limestone at Callander, Perthshire, belongs to the Dalradian Supergroup, and a reasseement of the 'exotic' status of the Highland Border Complex'. *Geological Magazine*, **134**, 563–570.

BLUCK, B. J., HALLIDAY, A. N., AFTALION, M. & MACINTYRE, R. M. 1980. Age and origin of the Ballantrae Complex and its significance to the Caledonian orogeny and the Ordovician time scale. *Geology*, **8**, 492–495.

BLUCK, B. J., INGHAM, J. K., CURRY, G. B. & WILLIAMS, A. 1984. Stratigraphy and tectonic setting of the Highland Border Complex. *Transactions of the Royal Society of Edinburgh: Earth Sciences*, **75**, 124–133.

BLUCK, B. J., HAUGHTON, P. D. W., HOUSE, M. R., SELWOOD, E. B. & TUNBRIDGE, I. P. 1988. Devonian of England, Wales and Scotland. *In*: MCMILLAN, N. J., EMBRY, A. F. & GLASS, D. J. (eds) *Devonian of the World*. Canadian Society of Petroleum Geologists, Memoir, **14**, Vol. I, 305–324.

BLUCK, B. J., COPE, J. C. W. & SCRUTTON, C. T. 1992. Devonian. *In*: COPE, J. C. W., INGHAM, J. K. & RAWSON, P. F. (eds) *Atlas of Palaeogeography and Lithofacies*. Geological Society, London, Memoir, **13**, 57–66.

BLUCK, B. J., DEMPSTER, T. J. & ROGERS, G. 1997. Allochthonous metamorphic blocks on the Hebridean passive margin, Scotland. *Journal of the Geological Society, London*, **154**, 921–924.

BOAST, A. M., HARRIS, M. & STEFFE, D. 1990. Intrusive-hosted gold mineralization at Hare Hill, Southern Uplands, Scotland. *Transactions of the Institute of Mining and Metallurgy*, **99**, B106–B112.

BONNEY, T. G. 1878. On the serpentine and associated igneous rocks of the Ayrshire coast. *Quarterly Journal of the Geological Society of London*, **34**, 769–785.

BOR, L. 1951. *The Glen More Ring-dyke*. DPhil thesis, University of Cambridge.

BORRADAILE, G. J. 1979. Pretectonic reconstructions of the Islay anticline: implications for the depositional history of Dalradian rocks in the S. W. Highlands. *In*: HARRIS, A. L., HOLLAND, C. H. & LEAKE, B. E. (eds) *The Caledonides of the British Isles – Reviewed*. Geological Society, London, Special Publications, **8**, 229–239.

BOTT, M. H. P. & MASSON-SMITH, D. 1960. A gravity survey of the Criffel Granodiorite and the New Red Sandstone deposits near Dumfries. *Proceedings of the Yorkshire Geological Society*, **32**, 317–332.

BOTT, M. H. P. & TANTRIGODA, D. A. 1987. Interpretation of the gravity and magnetic anomalies over the Mull Tertiary intrusive complex, NW Scotland. *Journal of the Geological Society, London*, **144**, 17–28.

BOTT, M. H. P. & TUSON, J. 1973. Deep structure beneath the Tertiary volcanic regions of Skye, Mull and Ardnamurchan, north-west Scotland. *Nature (Physical Sciences)*, **242**, 114–116.

BOUÉ, A. 1820. *Essai Géologique sur l'Écosse*. Courcier, Paris.

BOULTER, M. C. & KVACEK, Z. 1989. *The Palaeocene Flora of the Isle of Mull*. Special Papers in Palaeontology, **42**.

BOULTON, G. S. 1993. Ice Ages and Climatic Change. *In*: DUFF, P. MCL. D. (ed.) *Holmes' Principles of Physical Geology* (3rd Edition) Chapman & Hall, London, 439–469.

BOULTON, G. S., SMITH, G. D., JONES, A. S. & NEWSOME, J. 1985. Glacial geology and glaciology of the last mid-latitude ice sheets. *Journal of the Geological Society, London*, **142**, 447–474.

BOULTON, G. S., PEACOCK, J. D. & SUTHERLAND, D. G. 1991. Quaternary. *In*: CRAIG, G. Y. (ed.) *Geology of Scotland* (3rd edition). Geological Society, London, 503–543.

BOULTON, G. S., DONGELMANS, P., PUNKARI, M. & BROADGATE, M. 2001. Palaeoglaciology of an ice sheet through a glacial cycle: the European ice sheet through the Weichselian. *Quaternary Science Reviews*, **20**, 591–625.

BOWEN, J. M. 1975. The Brent oilfield. *In*: WOODLAND, A. W. (ed.) *Petroleum and the Continental Shelf of North-west Europe*, Vol. 1. Applied Science Publishers, Barking, Essex, 353–360.

BOWEN, J. M. 1992. Exploration of the Brent Province. *In*: MORTON, A. C., HASZELDINE, R. S., GILES, M. R. & BROWN, S. (eds) *Geology of the Brent Group*. Geological Society, London, Special Publications, **61**, 3–14.

BOWEN, N. 1928. *The Evolution of Igneous Rocks*. Princeton University Press, Princeton.

BOWES, D. R. 1968a. The absolute time scale and the subdivision of Precambrian rocks in Scotland. *Geologiska Föreningens i Stockholm Förhandlingar*, **90**, 175–188.

BOWES, D. R. 1968b. An orogenic interpretation of the Lewisian of Scotland. *XXIII International Geological Congress*, **4**, 225–236.

BOWES, D. R. & WRIGHT, A. E. 1967. The explosion-breccia pipes near Kentallen, Scotland, and their geological setting. *Transactions of the Royal Society of Edinburgh*, **67**, 109–143.

BOWES, D. R., WRIGHT, A. E. & PARK, R. G. 1964. Layered intrusive rocks in the Lewisian of the north-west Highlands of Scotland. *Quarterly Journal of the Geological Society, London*, **120**, 153–184.

BOWIE, S. H. U., DAWSON, J. GALLAGHER, M. J., OSTLE, D., LAMBERT, R. ST. J. & LAWSON, R. I. 1966. Potassium-rich sediments in the Cambrian of north west Scotland. *Institute of Mining and Metallurgy Bulletin*, **714**, 125–145.

BOWMAN, M. J. B. 1998. Cenozoic. *In*: GLENNIE, K. W. (ed.) *Petroleum Geology of the North Sea*, 4th edition, Blackwell, Oxford, 350–375.

BOYD, R. & MUNRO, M. 1978. Deformation of the Belhelvie mass, Aberdeenshire. *Scottish Journal of Geology*, **14**, 29–44.

BRADBURY, H. J. 1979. Migmatization, deformation and porphyroblast growth in the Dalradian of Tayside, Scotland. *In*: HARRIS, A. L., HOLLAND, C. H. & LEAKE, B. E. (eds) *The Caledonides of the British Isles – Reviewed*. Geological Society, London, Special Publications, **8**, 351–356.

BRADBURY, H. J., SMITH, R. A. & HARRIS, A. L. 1976. 'Older Granites' as time-markers in Dalradian evolution. *Journal of the Geological Society, London*, **132**, 677–684.

BRADSHAW, A. D. & CHADWICK, M. J. 1980. *The Restoration of Land – the Reclamation of Derelict and Degraded Land*. Blackwell, Oxford.

BRADSHAW, M. J. & 7 OTHERS. 1992. Jurassic. *In*: COPE, J. C. W., INGHAM, J. K. & RAWSON, P. F. (eds) *Atlas of Palaeogeography and Lithofacies*. Geological Society, London, Memoir, **13**, 107–129.

BRALEY, S. 1990. *Sedimentology, Palaeoecology and Stratigraphy of the Cretaceous Rocks in NW Scotland*. PhD thesis, Polytechnic SW, Plymouth.

BRAND, P. J. 1977. *The fauna and distribution of the Queenslie Marine Band (Westphalian) in Scotland*. Institute of Geolological Sciences Report **77/18.**

BRAND, P. J. 1983. Stratigraphical palaeontology of the Westphalian of the Ayrshire Coalfield, Scotland. *Transactions of the Royal Society of Edinburgh*, **73**, 173–190.

BRAND, P. J. 1998. The genus *Paracarbonicola* and associated forms in the Carboniferous rocks of Scotland. *Scottish Journal of Geology*, **34**, 139–143.

BRAND, P. J., ARMSTRONG, M. & WILSON, R. B. 1980. *The Carboniferous Strata at the Westfield Opencast Site, Fife, Scotland*. Institute of Geolological Sciences Report **79/11.**

BRASIER, M. D. 1977. An Early Cambrian chert biota and its implications. *Nature, London*, **268**, 719–720.

BRASIER, M. D. & SHIELDS, G. 2000. Neoproterozoic chemostratigraphy and correlation of the Port Askaig glaciation, Dalradian Supergroup of Scotland. *Journal of the Geological Society, London*, **157**, 909–914.

BRAZIER, M. D. & SHIELDS, G. 2000. Neoproterozoic chemostratigraphy and correlation of the Port Askaig glaciation, Dalradian, Supergroup of Scotland. *Journal of the Geological Society, London*, **155**, 2–12.

BRAZIER, V., WHITTINGTON, G. & BALLANTYNE, C. K. 1988. Holocene debris cone evolution in Glen Etive, western Grampian Highlands, Scotland. *Earth Surface Processes and Landforms*, **13**, 525–531.

BREWER, J. A. & SMYTHE, D. K. 1984. MOIST and the continuity of crustal reflector geometry along the Appalachian–Caledonian orogen. *Journal of the Geological Society, London*, **141**, 105–120.

BREWER, J. A., MATHEWS, D. H., WARNER, M. R., HALL, J., SMYTHE, D. K. & WHITTINGTON, R. J. 1983. BIRPS deep seismic reflection studies of the British Caledonides. *Nature, London*, **305**, 206–210.

BREWER, M. S., BROOK, M. & POWELL, D. 1979. Dating of the tectonometamorphic history of the southwestern Moine. *In*: HARRIS, A. L., HOLLAND, C. H. & LEAKE, B. E. (eds) *The Caledonides of the British Isles – Reviewed*. Geological Society, London, Special Publications, **8**, 129–137.

BREWSTER, J. 1991. The Frigg Field, Block 10/1, UK North Sea and 25/1, Norwegian North Sea. *In*: ABBOTTS, I. L. (ed.) *United Kingdom Oil and Gas Fields 25 Years Commemorative Volume*. Geological Society, London, Memoir, **14**, 117–126.

BRICKENDEN, L. B. 1850. Fossil foot-prints of Moray, *Elgin Courier*, 18 October, 2.

BRIDEN, J. C., TURNELL, H. B. & WATTS, D. R. 1984. British paleomagnetism, Iapetus Ocean and the Great Glen Fault. *Geology*, **12**, 136–139.

BRIDGE, M. C., HAGGART, B. A. & LOWE, J. J. 1990. The history and palaeoclimatic significance of subfossil remains of *Pinus sylvestris* in blanket peats from Scotland. *Journal of Ecology*, **78**, 77–99.

BRIDGWATER, D., MARKER, M. & MENGEL, F. 1991. The eastern extension of the Early Proterozoic Torngat orogenic zone across the Atlantic. *In*: WARDLE, R. J. & HALL, J. (eds), *Eastern Canadian Shield Onshore-Offshore Transect (ECSOOT)*, Lithoprobe report 27, Memorial University, Newfoundland, 76–91.

BRIDGWATER, D., CAMPBELL, L., MENGEL, F., MARKER, M. & SCOTT, D. 1996. The Nagssugtoqidian of West Greenland in the light of comparative studies of juvenile components in the Palaeoproterozoic Torngat, SE Greenland Nagssugtoqidian, and Lapland-Kola 'collisional' belts. *Proceedings of the 2nd DLC Workshop on Nagssugtoqidian Geology*, Danish Lithosphere Centre, Copenhagen, 8–19.

BRITISH GEOLOGICAL SURVEY 1972 et seq. *United Kingdom Minerals Yearbook*. NERC.

BRITISH GEOLOGICAL SURVEY 1992a. *Airdrie. Scotland Sheet 31W. Solid.* 1:50 000. British Geological Survey, Keyworth, Nottingham.

BRITISH GEOLOGICAL SURVEY 1992b. *Kirkcowan, Scotland Sheet 4W. Solid.* 1:50 000 Ordnance Survey, Southampton.

BRITISH GEOLOGICAL SURVEY 1992c. *Mull, Sheet 44W and part of 44E*. Solid. 1:50 000. British Geological Society, Keyworth, Nottingham.

BRITISH GEOLOGICAL SURVEY 1993. *Regional Geochemistry of Southern Scotland and Part of Northern England*. British Geological Survey Report, Keyworth, Nottingham.

BRITISH GEOLOGICAL SURVEY 1996. *Foyers. Scotland Sheet 73E. Solid Geology. 1:50 000*. British Geological Survey, Keyworth, Nottingham.

BRITISH GEOLOGICAL SURVEY 1997a. *Tongue. Scotland Sheet 114E. Solid Geology. 1:50 000*. British Geological Survey, Keyworth, Nottingham.

BRITISH GEOLOGICAL SURVEY 1997b. Colour shaded relief gravity anomaly map of Britain, Ireland and adjacent areas. SMITH, I. F. & EDWARDS, J. W. F. (compilers) 1:1 500 000 Scale. British Geological Survey, Keyworth, Nottingham.

BRITISH GEOLOGICAL SURVEY 1998a. Colour shaded relief magnetic anomaly map of Britain, Ireland and adjacent areas. ROYLES, C. P. & SMITH, I. F. (compilers) 1:1 500 000 Scale. British Geological Survey, Keyworth, Nottingham.

BRITISH GEOLOGICAL SURVEY 1998b. *Guide to Sources of Earth Science Information for Planning and Development*. Report to Department of the Environment, Transport and the Regions, London, HMSO.

BRITISH GEOLOGICAL SURVEY 1999a. *Aviemore. Scotland Sheet 84E. Solid Geology. 1:50 000*. British Geological Survey, Keyworth, Nottingham.

BRITISH GEOLOGICAL SURVEY 1999b. *United Kingdom minerals yearbook 1998*, Keyworth.

BRITISH GEOLOGICAL SURVEY 2000a. *Dalwhinnie. Scotland Sheet 63E. Solid Geology. 1:50 000*. British Geological Survey, Keyworth, Nottingham.

BRITISH GEOLOGICAL SURVEY 2000b. *Minginish, Sheet 70*. Solid and Drift Geology. 1:50 000. British Geological Society, Keyworth, Nottingham.

BRITISH STANDARDS INSTITUTION 1985. *Use of Industrial By-Products and Waste Materials in Building and Civil Engineering*. **BS 6543.**

BROOK, M., POWELL, D. & BREWER, M. S. 1976. Grenville age for rocks in the Moine of north-western Scotland. *Nature, London*, **260**, 515–517.

BROOKFIELD, M. E. 1976. The age of the Allt na Cuile Sandstones (Upper Jurassic, Sutherland). *Scottish Journal of Geology*, **12**, 181–186.

BROOKFIELD, M. E. 1978. Revision of the Stratigraphy of Permian and supposed Permian rocks of Southern Scotland. *Geologische Rundschau*, **67**, 110–149.

BROOKFIELD, M. E. 1979. Anatomy of a Lower Permian aeolian sandstone complex, Southern Scotland. *Scottish Journal of Geology*, **15**, 81–96.

BROOKFIELD, M. E. 1980. Permian intermontane basin sedimentation in southern Scotland. *Sedimentary Geology*, **27**, 167–194.

BROOKS, C. K. & JAKOBSEN, S. P. 1974. Petrochemistry of the volcanic rocks of the North Atlantic ridge system. *In*: KRISTJANSSON, L. (ed.) *Geodynamics of Iceland and the North Atlantic Area*. Dordrecht: Reidel. 139–154.

BROOKS, D. & MARKER, B. R. 1987. Thematic geological mapping as an essential tool in land-use planning. *In*: CULSHAW, M. G., BELL, F. G., CRIPPS, J. C. & O'HARA, M. (eds) *Planning and Engineering Geology*. Geological Society, London, Engineering Geology Special Publications, **4**, 211–214.

BROWN, D. J. & HENDERSON, J. 1870. On the Silurian rocks of the Pentland Hills. With notes on the brachiopoda. By THOS. DAVIDSON, F. G. S. *Transactions of the Edinburgh Geological Society*, **1**, 23–33.

BROWN, G. C. 1979. Geochemical and geophysical constraints on the origin and the evolution of Caledonian granites. *In*: HARRIS, A. L., HOLLAND, C. H. & LEAKE, B. E. (eds) *The Caledonides of the British Isles – Reviewed*. Geological Society, London, Special Publications, **8**, 645–652.

BROWN, G. C., FRANCIS, E. H., KENNAN, P. & STILLMAN, C. J. 1985. Caledonian igneous rocks of Britain and Ireland. *In*: HARRIS, A. L. (ed.) *The Nature and Timing of Orogenic Activity in the Caledonian Rocks of the British Isles*. Geological Society, London, Memoirs, **9**, 1–15.

BROWN, G. M. 1956. The layered ultrabasic rocks of Rhum, Inner Hebrides. *Philosophical Transactions of the Royal Society of London*, **240B**, 1–53.

BROWN, G. M. 1963. Melting relations of Tertiary granitic rocks in Skye and Rhum. *Mineralogical Magazine*, **33**, 533–562.

BROWN, P. E. 1991. Caledonian and earlier magmatism. *In*: CRAIG, G. Y. (ed.) *Geology of Scotland* (3rd edition). Geological Society, London, 229–295.

BROWN, R. L., DALZIEL, I. W. D. & JOHNSON, M. R. W. 1970. A review of the structure and stratigraphy of the Moinian of Ardgour, Moidart and Sunart, Argyll- and Inverness-shire. *Scottish Journal of Geology*, **6**, 309–335.

BROWNE, M. A. E. & MCMILLAN, A. A. 1984. Shoreline inheritance and coastal history in the Firth of Clyde. *Scottish Journal of Geology*, **19**, 321–325.

BROWNE, M. A. E. & MCMILLAN, A. A. 1991. British Geological Survey thematic geology maps of Quaternary deposits in Scotland. *In*: FOSTER, A., CULSHAW, M. G., CRIPPS, J. C., LITTLE, J. A. & MOON, C. F. (eds) *Quaternary Engineering Geology*. Geological Society, London, Engineering Geology Special Publications, **7**, 511–518.

BROWNE, M. A. E. & MONRO, S. K. 1989. Evolution of the coal basins of Central Scotland. *Compte Rendu XIme Congrès International de Stratigraphie et de Géologie du Carbonifère, Beijing 1987*, **5**, 1–19.

BROWNE, M. A. E. & THIRLWALL, M. F. 1981. An occurrence of Lower Carboniferous lava at Monksgrave (Powmill), near Dollar. *Scottish Journal of Geology*, **17**, 275–279.

BROWNE, M. A. E. & WOODHALL, D. G. 1999. Geology of the Kirkcaldy district – a brief explanation of the geological map. *Sheet Explanation of the British Geological Survey* 1:50 000 Sheet 40E Kirkcaldy (Scotland).

BROWNE, M. A. E., HARGREAVES, R. L. & SMITH, I. F. 1985. *The Upper Palaeozoic Basins of the Midland Valley of Scotland. Investigation of the geothermal potential of the UK*. British Geological Survey, Keyworth, Nottingham.

BROWNE, M. A. E., FORSYTH, I. H. & MCMILLAN, A. A. 1986. Glasgow, a case study in urban geology. *Journal of the Geological Society, London*, **143**, 509–520.

BROWNE, M. A. E., DEAN, M. T., HALL, I. H. S., MCADAM, A. D., MONRO, S. K. & CHISHOLM, J. I. 1996. *A Lithostratigraphical Framework for the Carboniferous Rocks of the Midland Valley of Scotland*. British Geological Survey Technical Report **WA/96/29**.

BROWNE, M. A. E., SMITH, R. A. & AITKEN, A. M. (In Press). A lithostratigraphic framework for the Devonian (Old Red Sandstone) rocks of Scotland south of a line from Fort William to Aberdeen. British Geological Survey Research Report WA/00/63.

BRUCK, P. M., DEDMAN, R. E. & WILSON, R. C. L. 1967. The New Red Sandstone of Raasay and Scalpay, Inner Hebrides. *Scottish Journal of Geology*, **3**, 168–180.

BRYCE, J. 1859. *Geology of Clydesdale and Arran, Embracing also the Marine Zoology and the Flora of Arran*. Richard Griffin & Co., London & Glasgow.

BRYCE, J. 1877. On the granite of Strath-Errick, Lough Ness. *Report of the Forty-Sixth Meeting of the British Association for the Advancement of Science; Held at Glasgow in September 1876*, 87. John Murray, London.

BUCHAN, K. L., MERTANEN, S., PARK, R. G., PESONEN, L. J., ELMING, S.-A., ABRAHAMSEN, N. & BYLUND, G. 2000. Comparing the drift of Laurentia and Baltica in the Proterozoic: the importance of key palaeomagnetic poles. *Tectonophysics*, **319**, 169–198.

BUCHANAN, P. G., BISHOP, D. J. & HOOD, D. N. 1996. Development of salt-related structures in the Central North Sea. Results from section balancing. *In*: ALSOP, G. I., BLUNDELL, D. J. & DAVISON, I. (eds) *Salt Tectonics*, Geological Society, London, Special Publications, **100**, 111–128.

BUDDING, M. C. & INGLIN, H. F. 1981. A reservoir geological model of the Brent sands in Southern Cormorant. *In*: ILLING, L. V. & HOBSON, G. P. (eds) *Petroleum Geology of the Continental Shelf of North-West Europe*. Heyden, 326–334.

BURLEY, S. D. 1993. Models of burial diagenesis for deep exploration in Jurassic fault traps of the Central and Northern North Sea. *In*: PARKER, J. R. (ed.) *Petroleum Geology of Northwest Europe: Proceedings of the 4th Conference*. Geological Society, London, 1353–1375.

BURNS, I. M. 1994. *Tectonothermal Evolution and Petrogenesis of the Naver and Kirtomy Nappes, North Sutherland*. PhD thesis, Oxford Brookes University.

BURTON, C. J. & CURRY, G. B. 1984. Chitinozoa and Miscellanea from the Highland Border Complex. *Transactions of the Royal Society of Edinburgh: Earth Sciences*, **75**, 119–121.

BUSREWIL, M. T., PANKHURST, R. J. & WADSWORTH, W. J. 1975. The origin of the Kennethmont granite-diorite series. *Mineralogical Magazine*, **40**, 367–376.

BUTCHER, A. R., PIRRIE, P., PRICHARD, H. M. & FISHER, P. 1999. Platinum-group mineralization in the Rum layered intrusion, Scottish Hebrides, UK. *Journal of the Geological Society, London*, **156**, 213–216.

BUTLER, C. A., HOLDSWORTH, R. E. & STRACHAN, R. A. 1995. Evidence for Caledonian sinistral strike-slip motion and associated fault zone weakening, Outer Hebrides Fault Zone, NW Scotland. *Journal of the Geological Society, London*, **152**, 743–746.

BUTLER, R. W. H. 1982a. A structural analysis of the Moine Thrust zone between Loch Eriboll and Foinaven, NW Scotland. *Journal of Structural Geology*, **4**, 19–29.

BUTLER, R. W. H. 1982b. The terminology of structures in thrust belts. *Journal of Structural Geology*, **4**, 239–245.

BUTLER, R. W. H. 1997. Late Proterozoic rift faults and basement–cover relationships within the Ben More thrust sheet, NW Scotland. *Journal of the Geological Society, London*, **154**, 761–764.

BUTLER, R. W. H. & COWARD, M. P. 1984. Geological constraints, structural evolution and the deep geology of the NW Scottish Caledonides. *Tectonics*, **3**, 347–365.

BUTLER, R. W. H. & HUTTON, D. H. W. 1994. Basin structure and Tertiary magmatism on Skye, NW Scotland. *Journal of the Geological Society, London*, **151**, 931–944.

BYERS, P. N. 1972. *Correlation and Provenance of the Precambrian Moine and Torridonian Rocks of Morar, Raasay, Rhum, and Skye, Northwest Scotland*. PhD thesis, University of Reading.

CADELL, H. M. 1886. Recent advances in West Lothian Geology. *Report of the Fifty-fifth Meeting of the British Association for the Advancement of Science; Held at Aberdeen in September 1885*. John Murray, London, 1037–1038.

CADELL, H. M. 1913. *The Story of the Earth*. James Maclehose & Sons, Glasgow.

CALLAWAY, C. 1883. The age of the newer gneissic rocks of the Northern Highlands. With notes on the lithology, by Prof. T. G. Bonney. *Quarterly Journal of the Geological Society of London*, **39**, 355–422.

CALVER, M. A. 1968. Distribution of Westphalian marine faunas in northern England and adjoining areas. *Proceedings of the Yorkshire Geological Society*, **37**, 1–72.

CAMERON, E. M. 1994. Depletion of gold and LILE in the lower crust: Lewisian Complex, Scotland. *Journal of the Geological Society, London*, **151**, 747–754.

CAMERON, I. B. & MCADAM, A. D. 1978. *The Oil-shales of the Lothians: Present Resources and Former Workings*. Institute of Geological Sciences Report 78/2.

CAMERON, I. B. & STEPHENSON, D. 1985. *British Regional Geology: The Midland Valley of Scotland*. 3rd edition. HMSO, London.

CAMERON, I. B., AITKEN, A. M., BROWNE, M. A. E. & STEPHENSON, D. 1998. *Geology of the Falkirk District*. Memoir of the Geological Survey of Great Britain.

CAMERON, T. D. J. 1993. Triassic, Permian and Pre-Permian of the Central and Northern North Sea. *In*: KNOX, R. W. O'B. & CORDEY, W. G. (eds) *Lithostratigraphic Nomenclature of the North Sea, vol. 4*. British Geological Survey. On behalf of UK Offshore Operators Association.

CAMERON, T. D. J., CROSBY, A., BALSON, P. S., JEFFREY, D. H., LOTT, G. K., BULAT, J. & HARRISON, D. J. 1992. *The Geology of the Southern North Sea*. United Kingdom Offshore Regional Report, British Geological Survey. HMSO, London.

CAMERON, T. G. J. 1981. The history of Caledonian deformation in East Lecale, County Down. *Journal of Earth Sciences: Royal Dublin Society*, **4**, 53–74.

CAMERON, T. G. J. & ANDERSON, T. B. 1980. Silurian metabentonites in County Down, Northern Ireland. *Geological Journal*, **15**, 59–75.

CAMPBELL, G., DUKE OF ARGYLL 1851a. On a fossiliferous deposit underlying basalt in the Island of Mull. *Report on the Twentieth Meeting of the British Association for the Advancement of Science; Held at Edinburgh in July and August 1850*. John Murray, London, 70–71.

CAMPBELL, G., DUKE OF ARGYLL 1851b. On Tertiary leaf-beds in the Isle of Mull. With a note on the vegetable remains from Ardtun Head. By Professor E. Forbes. *Quarterly Journal of the Geological Society of London*, **7**, 89–103.

CAMPBELL, L. M., BRIDGWATER, D. & FARMER, G. L. 1994. A comparison of Proterozoic crustal formation along the Torngat–Nagssugtoqidian–Lapland–Kola collision belts: preliminary constraints from Nd and Pb isotopic studies in Northern Labrador. *In*: WARDLE, R. J. & HALL, J. (eds) *Lithoprobe Report No. 45*, University of British Columbia, 22–36.

CAMPBELL, R. 1913. The geology of south-eastern Kincardineshire. *Transactions of the Royal Society of Edinburgh*, **42**, 923–960.

CANDE, S. C. & KENT, D. V. 1995. Revised calibration of the geomagnetic polarity timescale for the Late Cretaceous and Cenozoic. *Journal of Geophysical Research B, Solid Earth Sciences*, **100** (B4), 6093–6095.

CANNING, J. C., HENNEY, P. J., MORRISON, M. A. & GASKARTH, J. W. 1996. Geochemistry of late Caledonian minettes from Northern Britain: Implications for the Caledonian sub-continental lithospheric mantle. *Mineralogical Magazine*, **128**, 385–388.

CANNING, J. C., HENNEY, P. J., MORRISON, M. A., VAN CALSTEREN, P. W., GASKARTH, J. W. & SWARBRICK, A. 1998. The Great Glen Fault: A major lithospheric boundary. *Journal of the Geological Society, London*, **155**, 424–427.

CANZ 1996. *'Undersea New Zealand'* (New Zealand Region Physiography) 1 : 4 000 000, 2nd edition. NZ Oceanography Institute, Miscellaneous Chart Series, no. 74.

CAREY, P. J. & PLATTEN, I. M. 2000. Discussion on the influence of country rock structural architecture during pluton emplacement: the Loch Loyal Syenites, Scotland. *Journal of the Geological Society, London*, **157**, 509–510.

CARRICK MOORE, J. 1838–1842 (1840). On the rocks which form the west shore of the bay of Loch Ryan in Wigtownshire. *Proceedings of the Geological Society of London*, **3**, 277–278.

CARROLL, S. 1991. *Terrestrial, Fluvial and Marginal Lacustrine Ecosystems of the Old Red Sandstone of the Orcadian Basin*. PhD thesis, University of Aberdeen.

CARROLL, S. & TREWIN, N. H. 1995. *Cornulatichnus*: a new trace fossil from the Old Red Sandstone of Orkney. *Scottish Journal of Geology*, **37**, 37–41.

CARRUTHERS, R. G., CALDWELL, W., BAILEY, E. M. & CONACHER, H. R. J. 1927. *The Oil-shales of the Lothians*. Memoir, Geological Survey of Scotland.

CARRUTHERS, R. G., BURNETT, G. A., ANDERSON, W. & THOMAS, H. H. 1932. *The Geology of the Cheviot Hills*. Memoir of the Geological Survey of Great Britain. Sheets 3 and 5, England and Wales.

CARTWRIGHT, I. & BARNICOAT, A. C. 1987. Petrology of Scourian supracrustal rocks and orthogneisses from Stoer, NW Scotland: implications for the geological evolution of the Lewisian complex. *In*: PARK, R. G. & TARNEY, J. (eds) *Evolution of the Lewisian and Comparable Precambrian High-grade Terrains*. Geological Society, London, Special Publications, **27**, 93–107.

CARTWRIGHT, I., FITCHES, W. R., O'HARA, M. J., BARNICOAT, A. C. & O'HARA, S. 1985. Archaean supracrustals from the Lewisian near Stoer, Sutherland. *Scottish Journal of Geology*, **21**, 187–196.

CARTY, J., CONNELLY, J., GALE, J. & HUDSON, N. 2002. Kinematics and timing of deformation in the Portsoy shear zone, NE Scotland. *Tectonic Studies Group Annual Meeting Abstracts*, University of Leicester, 54.

CASELDINE, C. J. 1980 A Lateglacial site at Stormont Loch, near Blairgowrie, eastern Scotland. *In*: LOWE, J. J., GRAY, J. M. & ROBINSON, J. E. (eds) *Studies in the Lateglacial of North-west Europe*. Pergamon, Oxford and New York, 69–88.

CASEY, D. M. 1983. *Geological Studies in the Central Belt of the Eastern Southern Uplands of Scotland*. PhD thesis, University of Oxford.

CATER, J. M., BRIGGS, D. E. G. & CLARKSON, E. N. K. 1989. Shrimp-bearing sedimentary successions in the Lower Carboniferous (Dinantian) Cementstone and Oil Shale Groups of northern Britiain. *Transactions of the Royal Society of Edinburgh: Earth Sciences*, **80**, 5–15.

CAWOOD, P. A., NEMCHIN, A. A., SMITH, M. & LOEWY, S. (In Press). Source of the Dalradian Supergroup constrained by U/Pb dating of detrital zircon and implications for the East Laurentian margin. *Journal of the Geological Society, London*.

CHADWICK, R. A. & EVANS, D. J. 1995. The timing and direction of Permo-Triassic extension in southern Britain. *In*: BOLDY, S. A. R. (ed.) *Permian and Triassic Rifting in Northwest Europe*. Geological Society, London, Special Publications, **91**, 161–192.

CHADWICK, R. A., HOLLIDAY, D. W., HOLLOWAY, S. & HULBERT, A. G. 1995. *The Structure and Evolution of the Northumberland-Solway Basin and Adjacent Areas*. Subsurface Memoir of the Geological Survey, GB, HMSO, London.

CHALLONER, W. G. 1972. Devonian plants from Fair Isle, Scotland. *Reviews of Palaeobotany and Palynology*, **14**, 44–61.

CHAMBERS, L. M. & PRINGLE, M. S. 2001. Age and duration of activity at the Mull Tertiary igneous centre, Scotland, and confirmation of the existence of subchrons during anomaly 26r. *Earth and Planetary Science Letters*, **193**, 333–345.

CHAMBERS, L. M. & PRINGLE, M. (In Press). Initiation of magmatism in the North Atlantic Igneous Province. *Earth and Planetary Science Letters*.

CHAMBERS, L. M. & FITTON, J. G. 2000. Geochemical transitions in the ancestral Iceland plume: evidence from the Isle of Mull Tertiary volcano, Scotland. *Journal of the Geological Society, London*, **157**, 261–263.

CHAMBERS, R. 1844. *Vestiges of the Natural History of Creation*. John Churchill, London.

CHAPMAN, H. J. 1979. 2390 Myr. Rb–Sr whole-rock age for the Scourie dykes of north-west Scotland. *Nature, London*, **277**, 642–643.

CHAPMAN, N. A. 1976. Inclusions and megacrysts from undersaturated tuffs and basanites, East Fife, Scotland. *Journal of Petrology*, **16**, 29–35.

CHAPMAN, N. A. & McKINLEY, I. G. 1987. *The Geological Disposal of Nuclear Waste*. Wiley, Chichester.

CHARLEY, M. J., HAZELTON, R. E. & TEAR, S. J. 1989. Precious-metal mineralisation associated with Fore Burn igneous complex, Ayrshire, southwest Scotland. *Transactions of the Institution of Mining and Metallurgy*, **98**, B48.

CHEN, P-J. & HUDSON, J. D. 1991. The conchostracan fauna of the Great Estuarine Group, Middle Jurassic, Scotland. *Palaeontology*, **34**, 515–545.

CHESHIRE, J. A., DEEGAN, C. E., ARDUS, D. A., BINNS, P. E. & FANNIN, N. G. T. 1972. *IGS Marine Drilling with m.v. Whitehorn in Scottish Waters 1970–71*. HMSO for Institute of Geological Sciences.

CHEW, K. J. 1978. Crystalline manganese oxides in till, from Bridge of Don, Aberdeen. *Scottish Journal of Geology*, **14**, 329–334.

CHINNER, G. A. 1966. The distribution of pressure and temperature during Dalradian metamorphism. *Quarterly Journal of the Geological Society of London*, **122**, 159–186.

CHINNER, G. A. 1978. Metamorphic zones and fault displacements in the Scottish Highlands. *Geological Magazine*, **115**, 37–45.

CHINNER, G. A. & HESELTINE, F. J. 1979. The Grampian andalusite-kyanite isograd. *Scottish Journal of Geology*, **15**, 117–127.

CHISHOLM, J. I. & DEAN, J. M. 1974. The upper Old Red Sandstone of Fife and Kinross: a fluviatile sequence with evidence of marine incursion. *Scottish Journal of Geology*, **10**, 1–30.

CHISHOLM, J. I. C., McADAM, A. D. & BRAND, P. J. 1989. *Lithostratigraphical classification of Upper Devonian and Lower Carboniferous rocks in the Lothians*. Geological Survey Technical Report, **WA/89/26**.

CHUNG, P. Y. M. 1991. *Silver Mineralisation in Scotland: Genesis and Exploration*. MPhil thesis, University of Glasgow.

CHURCH, W. R. & GAYER, R. A. 1973. The Ballantrae ophiolite. *Geological Magazine*, **110**, 497–510.

CLAPPERTON, C. M. & SUGDEN, D. E. 1977. The Late Devensian glaciation of north-east Scotland. *In*: GRAY, J. M. & LOWE, J. J. (eds) *Studies in the Scottish Lateglacial Environment*. Pergamon, Oxford, 1–13.

CLARK, N. D. L. 1999. The Elgin Marvel. *Open University Geological Society Journal*, **20**, 16–18.

CLARK, N. D. L. & BARCO RODROGUEZ, J. L. 1998. The first dinosaur trackway from the Valtos Sandstone Formation (Bathonian, Jurassic) of the Isle of Skye, Scotland, UK. *Geogaceta*, **24**, 79–82.

CLARK, N. D. L., NIMMO, F. & NICHOLAS, C. J. 1993. A new occurrence of Scottish plesiosaurian remains from the Island of Skye. *Scottish Journal of Geology*, **29**, 197–199.

CLARK, N. D. L., BOYD, J. D., DIXON, R. J. & ROSS, D. A. 1995. The first Middle Jurassic dinosaur from Scotland: a cetiosaurid? (Sauropoda) from the Bathonian of the Isle of Skye. *Scottish Journal of Geology*, **31**, 171–176.

CLARKE, P. & PARNELL, J. 1999. Facies analysis of a back-tilted lacustrine basin in a strike-slip zone, Lower Devonian, Scotland. *Palaeogeography, Palaeoclimatology, Palaeoecology*, **151**, 167–190.

CLARKSON, E. N. K. 1986. Pease Bay to Cove. *In*: McADAM, A. D. & CLARKSON, E. N. K. (eds) *Lothian Geology: An Excursion Guide*. Scottish Academic Press, Edinburgh, 140–145.

CLARKSON, E. N. K. & TAYLOR, C. M. 1993. Dob's Linn, Moffat. *In*: McADAM, A. D., CLARKSON, E. N. K. & STONE, P. (eds) *Scottish Borders Geology. An excursion guide*. Scottish Academic Press, Edinburgh, 159–172.

CLARKSON, E. N. K., HARPER, D. A. T., OWEN, A. W. & TAYLOR, C. M. 1992. Ordovician faunas in mass-flow deposits, southern Scotland. Proceedings of the VI meeting of the European Union of Geological Sciences on fossils in fold belts. *Terra Nova*, **4**, 245–253.

CLARKSON, E. N. K., MILNER, A. R. & COATES, M. I. 1994. Palaeoecology of the Visean of East Kirkton, West Lothian, Scotland. *Transactions of the Royal Society of Edinburgh: Earth Sciences*, **84**, 417–425.

CLARKSON, E. N. K., HARPER, D. A. T. & HOEY, A. N. 1998. Wenlock biofacies from the Girvan DISTRICT, S. W. Scotland. *Scottish Journal of Geology*, **34**, 61–71.

CLAYBURN, J. A. P., HARMON, R. S., PANKHURST, R. J. & BROWN, J. F. 1983. Sr, O and Pb isotope evidence for the origin and evolution of the Etive Igneous Complex, Scotland. *Nature, London*, **303**, 492–497.

CLAYDON, R. V. & BELL, B. R. 1992. The structure and petrology of ultrabasic rocks in the southern part of the Cuillin Igneous Complex, Isle of Skye. *Transactions of the Royal Society of Edinburgh: Earth Sciences*, **83**, 635–653.

CLEAL, C. J. & THOMAS, B. A. 1995. Palaeozoic palaeobotany of Great Britain. *Geological Conservation Review Series*, **9**. Chapman and Hall.

CLEAL, C. J. & THOMAS, B. A. 1999. *Plant Fossils*. Boydell, Woodbridge.

CLEEVELY, R. J., TRIPP, R. P. & HOWELL, Y. 1989. Mrs Elizabeth Grey (1831–1924): a passion for fossils. *Bulletin of the British Museum (Natural History). Historical Series*, **17**, 167–258.

CLEMMENSEN, L. B. 1987. Complex star dunes and associated bed forms, Hopeman Sandstone (Permo-Triassic), Moray Firth Basin, Scotland. *In*: FROSTICK, L & REID, I. (eds) *Desert Sediments, Ancient and Modern*. Geological Society, London, Special Publications, **35**, 35–231.

CLIFF, R. A. & REX, D. 1989. Evidence for a 'Grenville' event in the Lewisian of the northern Outer Hebrides. *Journal of the Geological Society, London*, **146**, 921–924.

CLIFF, R. A., GRAY, C. M. & HUHMA, H. 1983. A Sm–Nd isotopic study of the South Harris Igneous Complex, the Outer Hebrides. *Contributions to Mineralogy and Petrology*, **82**, 91–98.

CLIFF, R. A., REX, D. & GUISE, P. G. 1998. Geochronological studies of Proterozoic crustal evolution in the northern Outer Hebrides. *Precambrian Research*, **91**, 401–418.

CLIFFORD, P. 1960. The geological structure of the Loch Luichart area, Ross-shire. *Quarterly Journal of the Geological Society of London*, **115**, 365–388.

CLIFFORD, T. N. 1957. The stratigraphy and structure of part of the Kintail district of southern Ross-shire – its relationship to the Northern Highlands. *Quarterly Journal of the Geological Society of London*, **113**, 57–92.

CLOUD, P. & GERMS, A. 1971. New pre-Paleozoic nannofossils from the Stoer Formation (Torridonian), northwest Scotland. *Bulletin of the Geological Society of America*, **82**, 3469–3474.

CLOUGH, C. T., MAUFE, H. B. & BAILEY, E. B. 1909. The cauldron-subsidence of Glencoe and associated igneous phenomena. *Quarterly Journal of the Geological Society, London*, **65**, 611–676.

CLYMO, R. S. 1987. Rainwater-fed peat as a precursor of coal. *In*: SCOTT, A. C. (ed.) *Coal and Coal-Bearing Strata: Recent Advances*. Geological Society, London, Special Publications, **32**, 17–23.

COATS, J. S., SMITH, C. G., FORTEY, N. J., GALLAGHER, M. J., MAY, F. & McCOURT, W. J. 1980. Stratabound barium-zinc mineralisation in Dalradian schist near Aberfeldy. *Transactions of the Institution of Mining and Metallurgy*, **89**, B110–B122.

COATS, J. S., SMITH, C. G., GALLAGHER, M. J., MAY, F., McCOURT, W. G., PARKER, M. E. & FORTEY, N. J. 1981. Stratabound barium-zinc mineralisation in Dalradian schist near Aberfeldy. *Institute of Geological Sciences, Mineral Reconnaissance Programme*, Report **40**.

COATS, J. S., FORTEY, N. J., GALLAGHER, M. J. & GROUT, A. 1984*a*. Stratiform barium enrichment in the Dalradian of Scotland. *Economic Geology*, **79**, 1585–1595.

COATS, J. S., PEASE, S. F. & GALLAGHER, M. J. 1984*b*. Exploration of the Scottish Dalradian. *In*: *Prospecting in Areas of Glaciated Terrain*. Institution of Mining and Metallurgy, London, 21–34.

COATS, J. S., FORTEY, N. J., GALLAGHER, M. J. & PEASE, S. F. 1987. Mineral exploration for zinc, lead and baryte in Middle Dalradian rocks of the Glenshee area, Grampian Highlands. *Institute of Geological Sciences, Mineral Reconnaissance Programme*, Report **88**.

COATS, J. S., SHAW, M. H., GALLAGHER, M. J., ARMSTRONG, M., GREENWOOD, P. G., CHACKSFIELD, B. C., WILLIAMSON, J. P. & FORTEY, N. J. 1991. Gold in the Ochil Hills, Scotland. *British Geological Survey Technical Report WF/91/1. Mineral Reconnaissance Programme*, Report **116**.

COCKS, L. R. M. 2000. The Early Palaeozoic geography of Europe. *Journal of the Geological Society, London*, **157**, 1–10.

COCKS, L. R. M. & FORTEY, R. A. 1982. Faunal evidence for oceanic separations in the Palaeozoic of Britain. *Journal of the Geological Society, London*, **139**, 465–478.

COCKS, L. R. M. & TOGHILL, P. 1973. The biostratigraphy of the Silurian rocks of the Girvan District, Scotland. *Journal of the Geological Society, London*, **129**, 209–243.

COHEN, A. S., O'NIONS, R. K. & O'HARA, M. J. 1991. Chronology and mechanism of depletion in Lewisian granulites. *Contributions to Mineralogy and Petrology*, **106**, 142–153.

COLLIE, M. 1991. *Huxley at Work: With the Scientific Correspondence of T. H. Huxley and the Rev. Dr. George Gordon of Birnie, near Elgin.* Macmillan, London.

COLLIE, M. 1995. George Gordon (1801–1893), Man of Science. *Archives of Natural History*, **22**, 29–49.

COLLIE, M. & BENNETT, S. 1996. *The Scientific Correspondence of George Gordon: An Annotated Bibliography.* Scolar, London.

COLLIE, M. & DIEMER, J. 1995. *Murchison in Moray: A Geologist on Home Ground. With the Correspondence of Roderick Impey Murchison and the Rev. Dr. George Gordon of Birnie.* The American Philosophical Society, Philadelphia.

COLLINS, A. G. & DONOVAN, R. N. 1977. The age of two Old Red Sandstone sequences in southern Caithness. *Scottish Journal of Geology*, **13**, 53–57.

COLMAN-SADD, S. P., STONE, P., SWINDEN, H. S. & BARNES, R. P. 1992. Parallel geological development in the Dunnage Zone of Newfoundland and the Lower Palaeozoic terranes of southern Scotland; an assessment. *Transactions of the Royal Society of Edinburgh: Earth Sciences*, **83**, 571–594.

COLTER, V. S. & BARR, K. W. 1975. Recent developments in the geology of the Irish Sea and Cheshire Basins. *In*: WOODLAND, A. W. (ed.) *Petroleum and the Continental Shelf of North West Europe.* Applied Science Publishers, Barking, 61–73.

COMPSTON, W. 2000. Interpretation of SHRIMP and isotope dilution zircon ages for the Palaeozoic time-scale: Part 2, Silurian to Devonian. *Mineralogical Magazine*, **64**, 1127–1146.

CONDON, D. J. & PRAVE, A. R. 2000. Two from Donegal: Neoproterozoic glacial episodes on the northeast margin of Laurentia. *Geology*, **28**, 951–954.

CONEY, P. J., JONES, D. L. & MONGER, J. W. H. 1980. Cordilleran suspect terranes. *Nature, London*, **288**, 329–333.

CONEY, D., FYFE, T. B., RETAIL, P. & SMITH, P. J. 1993. Clair appraisal: the benefits of a co-operative approach. *In*: PARKER, J. R. (ed.) *Petroleum Geology of Northwest Europe: Proceedings of the 4th Conference.* Geological Society, London, 1409–1420.

CONNELL, E. R. & HALL, A. M. 1987. The periglacial history of Buchan, Scotland. *In*: BOARDMAN, J. (ed.) *Field Guide to Periglacial Landforms of Northern England.* Quaternary Research Association, Cambridge.

CONNELLY, J. N. & MENGEL, F. C. 1996. Definition and refinement of Archaean and Palaeoproterozoic magmatic and tectonic events in the Nagssugtoqidian orogen: a summary of conventional U–Pb geochronology results. *Proceedings of the 2nd Workshop on Nagssugtoqidian Geology*, Danish Lithosphere Centre, Copenhagen, 71–73.

CONWAY MORRIS, S. & RUSHTON, A. W. A. 1988. Precambrian to Tremadoc biotas in the Caledonides. *In*: HARRIS, A. L. & FETTES, D. J. (eds) *The Caledonides-Appalachian Orogen.* Geological Society, London, Special Publications, **38**, 93–109.

CONYBEARE, W. D. 1833. Report on the progress, actual state, and ulterior prospects of geological science. *Report of the First and Second Meetings of the British Association for the Advancement of Science; At York in 1831, and at Oxford in 1832*, 365–414. John Murray, London.

COOPE, G. R. 1962. *Coleoptera* from a peat interbedded between two boulder clays at Burnhead near Airdrie. *Transactions of the Geological Society of Glasgow*, **24**, 279–286.

COOPE, G. R. 1977. Fossil coleopteran assemblages as sensitive indicators of climatic change during the Devensian (last) cold stage. *Philosophical Transactions of the Royal Society*, **B280**, 313–337.

COOPER, M. M., EVANS, A. C., LYNCH, D. J., NEVILLE, G. & NEWLEY, T. 1999. The Foinaven Field: managing reservoir development uncertainty prior to start-up. *In*: FLEET, A. J. & BOLDY, S. A. R. (eds) *Petroleum Geology of Northwest Europe: Proceedings of the 5th Conference*, Geological Society, London, 675–682.

COPE, J. C. W., INGHAM, J. K. & RAWSON, P. F. (eds) 1992. *Atlas of Palaeogeography and Lithofacies.* Geological Society, London, Memoirs, **13**.

CORFIELD, S. M., GAWTHORPE, R. L., GAGE, M., FRASER, A. J. & BESLY, B. M. 1996. Inversion tectonics of the Variscan foreland of the British Isles. *Journal of the Geological Society, London*, **153**, 17–32.

CORFU, F., HEAMAN, L. M. & ROGERS, G. 1994. Polymetamorphic evolution of the Lewisian complex, NW Scotland, as recorded by U–Pb isotopic compositions of zircon, titanite and rutile. *Contributions to Mineralogy and Petrology*, **117**, 215–228.

CORFU, F., CRANE A., MOSER, D. & ROGERS, G. 1998. U–Pb zircon systematics at Gruinard Bay, northwest Scotland: implications for the early orogenic evolution of the Lewisian complex. *Contributions to Mineralogy and Petrology*, **133**, 329–345.

COTTON, W. R. 1968. *A Geophysical Survey of the Clyde Plateau Lavas.* PhD thesis, University of Glasgow.

COUPLES, G. D., MCKEOWN, C., HASZELDINE, R. S. & SMYTHE, D. K. 1998. The role of the academic geoscientist in radioactive waste disposal assessment. *In*: BENNETT, M. R. & DOYLE, P. (eds) *Issues in Environmental Geology: a British Perspective.* Geological Society, London, 243–276.

COWARD, M. P. 1972. The eastern gneisses of South Uist. *Scottish Journal of Geology*, **8**, 1–12.

COWARD, M. P. 1973 Heterogeneous deformation in the development of the Laxfordian complex of South Uist, Outer Hebrides. *Journal of the Geological Society, London*, **129**, 139–160.

COWARD, M. P. 1982. Surge zones in the Moine Thrust zone of NW Scotland. *Journal of Structural Geology*, **4**, 247–256.

COWARD, M. P. 1984a. Major shear zones in the Precambrian crust; examples from NW Scotland and southern Africa and their significance. *In*: KRONER, A. & GREILING, S. R. (eds) *Precambrian Tectonics Illustrated.* Stuttgart, 207–235.

COWARD, M. P. 1984b. The strain and textural history of thin-skinned tectonic zones: examples from the Assynt region of the Moine Thrust Zone, NW Scotland. *Journal of Structural Geology*, **6**, 89–99.

COWARD, M. P. 1985. The thrust structures of southern Assynt, Moine Thrust Zone. *Geological Magazine*, **122**, 595–607.

COWARD, M. P. 1990. The Precambrian, Caledonian and Variscan framework to NW Europe. *In*: HARDMAN, R. F. P. & BROOKS, J. (eds) *Tectonic Events Responsible for Britain's Oil and Gas Reserves.* Geological Society, London, Special Publications, **55**, 1–34.

COWARD, M. P. 1993. The effect of Late Caledonian and Variscan continental escape tectonics on basement structure, Palaeozoic basin kinematics and subsequent Mesozoic basin development in NW Europe. *In*: PARKER, J. R. (ed.) *Petroleum Geology of Northwest Europe: Proceedings of the 4th Conference.* Geological Society, London, 1095–1108.

COWARD, M. P. 1995. Structural and tectonic setting of the Permo-Triassic basins of northwest Europe. *In*: BOLDY, S. A. R. (ed.) *Permian and Triassic Rifting in Northwest Europe.* Geological Society, London, Special Publications, **91**, 7–39.

COWARD, M. P. & PARK, R. G. 1987. The role of mid-crustal shear zones in the Early Proterozoic evolution of the Lewisian. *In*: PARK, R. G. & TARNEY, J. (eds) *Evolution of the Lewisian and Comparable Precambrian High Grade Terrains.* Geological Society, London, Special Publications, **27**, 127–138.

COWARD, M. P., FRANCIS, P. W., GRAHAM, R. H., MYERS, J. S. & WATSON, J. 1969. Remnants of an early metasedimentary assemblage in the Lewisian Complex of the Outer Hebrides. *Proceedings of the Geologists' Association*, **80**, 387–408.

COWARD, R. N., CLARK, N. M. & PINNOCK, S. J. 1991. The Tartan Field, Block 15/16, UK North Sea. *In*: ABBOTTS, I. L. (ed.) *United Kingdom Oil and Gas Fields 25 Years Commemorative Volume.* Geological Society, London, Memoir, **14**, 377–384.

COWIE, J. & MCNAMARA, K. J. 1978. *Olenellus* (Trilobita) from the Lower Cambrian strata of north-west Scotland. *Palaeontology*, **21**, 615–634.

COWIE, J. W. 1974. The Cambrian of Spitzbergen and Scotland. *In*: HOLLAND, C. H. (ed.) *Cambrian of the British Isles, Norden and Spitzbergen.* Wiley, Chichester.

COWIE, J. W., RUSHTON, A. W. A. & STUBBLEFIELD, C. J. 1972. *A Correlation of Cambrian Rocks in the British Isles*. Geological Society, London, Special Reports, **2**.

CRAIG, G. Y. (ed.) 1991. *Geology of Scotland* (3rd edition). Geological Society, London.

CRAIG, G. Y. & WALTON, E. K. 1959. Sequence and structure in the Silurian rocks of Kirkcudbrightshire. *Geological Magazine*, **96**, 209–220.

CRAIG, G. Y., MCINTYRE, D. B. & WATERSTON, C. D. (eds). 1978. *James Hutton's Theory of the Earth and the Lost Drawings*. Scottish Academic Press, Edinburgh.

CRAIG, P. M. 1980. *Volcanic Geology of the Campsie Fells area, Stirlingshire*. PhD thesis, University of Lancaster.

CRAIG, P. M. & HALL, I. H. S. 1975. The Lower Carboniferous rocks of the Campsie–Kilpatrick area. *Scottish Journal of Geology*, **11**, 171–174.

CRAMPTON, C. B. & CARRUTHERS, R. E. 1914. *The Geology of Caithness (Sheets 110 and 116 with Parts of 109, 115 and 117)*. Geological Survey of Scotland Memoir.

CRANE, A. 1978. Correlation of metamorphic fabrics and the age of Lewisian metasediments near Loch Maree. *Scottish Journal of Geology*, **14**, 225–246.

CRANE, A., GOODMAN, S., KRABBENDAM, M., LESLIE, A. G. & ROBERTSON, S. 2002. *Geology of Sheet 56W and adjacent areas (Scotland)*. Memoir of the British Geological Survey, HMSO.

CRAW, D. 1990. Regional fluid and metal mobility in the Dalradian metamorphic belt, Southern Grampian Highlands, Scotland. *Mineralium Deposita*, **25**, 281–288.

CRAW, D. & CHAMBERLAIN, C. P. 1996. Meteoric incursion and oxygen fronts in the Dalradian metamorphic belt, southwest Scotland: a new hypothesis for regional gold mobility. *Mineralium Deposita*, **31**, 365–373.

CRAWFORD, R., LITTLEFAIR, R. W. & AFFLECK, L. G. 1991. The Arbroath and Montrose Fields, Blocks 22/17, **18**, UK North Sea. *In*: ABBOTTS, I. L. (ed.) *United Kingdom Oil and Gas Fields 25 Years Commemorative Volume*. Geological Society, London, Memoir, **14**, 211–217.

CRESSWELL, D. 1972. The structural development of the Lewisian rocks on the north shore of Loch Torridon, Ross-shire. *Scottish Journal of Geology*, **8**, 293–308.

CROWELL, J. C. 1961. Depositional structures from the Jurassic boulder beds, East Sutherland. *Transactions of the Edinburgh Geological Society*, **18**, 202–220.

CROWELL, J. C. 1995. The ending of the Late Paleozoic Ice Age During the Permian Period. *In*: SCHOLLE, P. A. PERYT, T. M. & ULMER-SCHOLLE, D. S. (eds) *The Permian of Northern Pangea vol. 1. Paleogeography, Paleoclimates, Stratigraphy*. Springer, Berlin, 62–74.

CROWLEY, S. F., BOTTRELL, S. H., MCCARTHY, B., WARD, J. & YOUNG, B. 1997. ^{34}S of Lower Carboniferous anhydrite, Cumbria and its implications for barite mineralisation in the northern Pennines. *Journal of the Geological Society, London*, **154**, 597–600.

CRUMMY, J. 1993. *Geological Processes of Gold Concentration and Depletion in Caledonian Terrains*. PhD thesis, University of Glasgow.

CRUMMY, J., HALL, A. J., HAZELDINE, R. S. & ANDERSON, I. K. 1997. Potential for epithermal gold mineralization in east and central Sutherland, Scotland: indications from River Brora headwaters. *Transactions of the Institution of Mining and Metallurgy*, **106**, B9–B14.

CULLINGFORD, R. A. 1977. Lateglacial raised shorelines and deglaciation in the Earn-Tay area. *In*: GRAY, J. M. & LOWE, J. E. (eds) *Studies in the Scottish lateglacial environment*. Oxford, 15–32.

CULLINGFORD, R. A. & SMITH, D. E. 1980. Late Devensian raised shorelines in Angus and Kincardineshire, Scotland. *Boreas*, **9**, 21–38.

CUMMING, J. 1985. John Macculloch: blackguard, thief and high priest. *In*: WHEELER, J. H. & PRICE, J. H. (eds) *From Linnaeus to Darwin: Commentaries on the History of Biology and Geology*. Society for the History of Natural History, London, 77–88.

CUNNINGHAM, H. R. J. 1841. Geognostical Account of the County of Sutherland. *Transactions of the Highland and Agricultural Society of Scotland*, **13**.

CURRIE, S. 1996. The development of the Ivanhoe, Rob Roy and Hamish Fields, Block 15/21a, UK North Sea. *In*: HURST, A., JOHNSON, H. D., BURLEY, S. D., CANHAM, A. C. & MACKERTICH, D. S. (eds) *Geology of the Humber Group: Central Graben and Moray Firth, UKCS*. Geological Society, London, Special Publications, **114**, 329–341.

CURRY, G. B., INGHAM, J. K., BLUCK, B. J. & WILLIAMS, A. 1982. The significance of a reliable Ordovician age for some Highland Border rocks in Central Scotland. *Journal of the Geological Society, London*, **139**, 451–454.

CURTIS, C. D. & SPEARS, D. A. 1968. The formation of sedimentary iron minerals. *Economic Geology*, **63**, 257–270.

CURTIS, S. C., PATTRICK, R. A. D., JENKINS, G. T. R., BOYCE, A. J., FALLICK, A. E. & TREAGUS, J. E. 1993. A stable isotope and fluid inclusion study of fault related mineralization in the Tyndrum area, Scotland. *Transactions of the Institution of Mining and Metallurgy*, **102**, B39–B47.

CURTIS, S. F. 1990. *Fault Movement History, Related Mineralization and Age Dating of the Tyndrum Fault, the Grampian Highlands of Scotland*. PhD thesis, University of Manchester.

CUVIER, G. L. C. F. D. de. 1813. *Essay on the Theory of the Earth. Translated by Robert Kerr. With Mineralogical Notes, and an Account of Cuvier's Geological Discoveries, by Professor Jameson*. William Blackwood, Edinburgh; Robert Kerr, London.

DALLMEYER, R. D., STRACHAN, R. A., ROGERS, G., WATT, G. R. & FRIEND, C. R. L. 2001. Dating deformation and cooling in the Caledonian thrust nappes of north Sutherland, Scotland: insights from ^{40}Ar/^{39}Ar and Rb–Sr chronology. *Journal of the Geological Society, London*, **158**, 501–512.

DALY, J. S. 1996. Pre-Caledonian history of the Annagh Gneiss Complex, North-western Ireland, and correlation with Laurentia-Baltica. *Irish Journal of Earth Sciences*, **15**, 5–18.

DALY, J. S. 2000. Precambrian. *In*: HOLLAND, C. H. (ed.) *The Geology of Ireland*. Dunedin Academic Press, Edinburgh, 7–45.

DALY, J. S. & BOGDANOVA, S. 1991. Timing of metamorphism in the Lapland granulite belt, Finland (abstr.). *In*: TUISKU, P. & LAAJOKI, K. (eds) *Metamorphism, deformation and structure of the crust. Report of joint meeting of IGCP projects 275 and 304*, University of Oulu, Finland, 11.

DALY, J. S., MUIR, R. J. & CLIFF, R. A. 1991a. A precise U–Pb zircon age for the Inishtrahull syenitic gneiss, County Donegal, Ireland. *Journal of the Geological Society, London*, **148**, 639–642.

DALY, J. S., AITCHESON, S. J., CLIFF, R. A., GAYER, R. A. & RICE, A. N. 1991b. Geochronological evidence from discordant plutons for a late-Proterozoic orogen in the Caledonides of Finnmark, northern Norway. *Journal of the Geological Society, London*, **148**, 29–40.

DALZIEL, I. W. D. 1963. Zircons from the granite gneiss of western Ardgour, Argyll: their bearing on its origin. *Transactions of the Edinburgh Geological Society*, **19**, 349–362.

DALZIEL, I. W. D. 1966. A structural study of the granitic gneiss of western Ardgour, Argyll and Inverness-shire. *Scottish Journal of Geology*, **2**, 125–152.

DALZIEL, I. W. D. 1997. Neoproterozoic-Paleozoic geography and tectonics: Review, hypothesis, environmental speculation. *Bulletin of the Geological Society of America*, **109**, 16–42.

DALZIEL, I. W. D. & SOPER, N. J. 2001. Neoproterozoic extension on the Scottish promontory of Laurentia: paleogeographic and tectonic implications. *Journal of Geology*, **109**, 299–317.

DANSGAARD, A. N., JOHNSEN, S. J., CLAUSEN, H. B., DAHL-JENSEN, D., GUNDESTRUP, N. S., HAMMER, C. U., HVIDBERG, C. S., STEFFENSEN, J. P., SVEINBJORNSDOTTIR, A. E., JOUZEL, J. & BOND, G. 1993. Evidence for general instability of past climate from a 250-kyr ice-core record. *Nature, London*, **364**, 218–220.

DARWIN, F. (ed.). 1887. *The Life and Letters of Charles Darwin, Including an Autobiographical Chapter*. 3 vols. John Murray, London.

DASH, B. 1969. Structure of the Lewisian rocks between Strath Dionard and Rhiconich, Sutherland, Scotland. *Scottish Journal of Geology*, **5**, 347–374.

DAVID, M. J. 1996. History of hydrocarbon exploration in the Moray Firth. *In*: HURST, A., JOHNSON, H. D., BURLEY, S. D., CANHAM,

A. C. & MACKERTICH, D. S. (eds) *Geology of the Humber Group: Central Graben and Moray Firth, UKCS.* Geological Society, London, Special Publications, **114**, 47–80.

DAVIDEK, K., LANDING, E., BOWRING, S. A., WESTROP, S. R., RUSHTON, A. W. A., FORTEY, R. A. & ADRAIN, J. M. 1998. New uppermost Cambrian U–Pb date from Avalonian Wales and age of the Cambrian-Ordovician boundary. *Geological Magazine*, **135**, 303–309.

DAVIDSON, K. A. S., SOLA, M., POWELL, D. W. & HALL, J. 1984. Geophysical model for the Midland Valley of Scotland. *Transactions of the Royal Society of Edinburgh: Earth Sciences*, **75**, 175–181.

DAVIES, A. 1970. Carboniferous rocks of the Sanquhar Outlier. *Bulletin of the Geological Survey of Great Britain*, **31**, 37–87.

DAVIES, A., MCADAM, A. D. & CAMERON, I. B. 1986. *Geology of the Dunbar District.* Memoir of the British Geological Survey, Sheet 33E and part of 41 (Scotland).

DAVIES, F. B. 1974. A layered basic complex in the Lewisian, south of Loch Laxford, Sutherland. *Journal of the Geological Society, London*, **130**, 270–284.

DAVIES, F. B. 1978. Progressive simple shear deformation of the Laxford shear zone, Sutherland. *Proceedings of the Geologists' Association*, **89**, 177–196.

DAVIES, G. R. & MACDONALD, R. 1987. Crustal influences in the petrogenesis of the Naivasha basalt-rhyolite complex: combined trace element and Sr-Nd-Pb isotope constraints. *Journal of Petrology*, **28**, 1009–1031.

DAVIES, H. C., DOBSON, M. R. & WHITTINGTON, R. J. 1984. A revised seismic stratigraphy for Quaternary deposits on the inner continental shelf of Scotland between 55°30′N and 57°30′N. *Boreas*, **13**, 48–66.

DAVIES, J. M. & KINGSTON, P. F. 1992. Sources of environmental disturbance associated with offshore oil and gas developments. *In*: CAIRNS, W. J. (ed.) *North Sea Oil and the Environment-Developing Oil and Gas Resources, Environmental Impacts and Responses.* Elsevier Applied Science, 417–457.

DAVIES, J. M. & TOPPING, G. (eds.) 1997. *The Impact of an Oil Spill in Turbulent Waters: The Braer.* The Stationery Office, Edinburgh.

DAVIES, J. M., BEDBOROUGH, D. R., BLACKMAN, K., ADDY, J. M., APPLEBEE, J. F., GROGAN, W. C., PARKER, J. G. & WHITEHEAD, A. 1988. The environmental effects of oil based mud drilling in the North Sea. *Proceedings of the International Conference on Drilling Wastes, Calgary, Alberta, Canada. April 1988.* Elsevier Science Publishers, 59–89.

DAVIES, P. 1990. The geology of the Rhinns of Galloway, SW Scotland: the west coast between Killantringan Bay and Clanyard Bay. *British Geological Survey Technical Report*, WA/90/67.

DAVIS, D. W. & PACES, J. B. 1990. Time resolution of geologic events on the Keweenaw Peninsula and implications for development of the Midcontinent Rift system. *Earth & Planetary Science Letters*, **97**, 54–64.

DAVISON, I., ALSOP, I., BIRCH, P., ELDERS, C., EVANS, N., NICHOLSON, H., RORISON, P., WADE, D., WOODWARD, J. & YOUNG, M. 2000. Geometry and late stage structural evolution of Central Graben salt diapirs, North Sea. *Marine and Petroleum Geology*, **17**, 499–522.

DAVISON, S. & HAMBREY, M. J. 1996. Indications of glaciation at the base of the Proterozoic Stoer Group (Torridonian), NW Scotland. *Journal of the Geological Society, London*, **153**, 139–149.

DAVISON, S. & HAMBREY, M. J. 1997. Discussion on indications of glaciation at the base of the Proterozoic Stoer Group (Torridonian), NW Scotland. *Journal of the Geological Society, London*, **154**, 1087–1088.

DAWSON, A. G. 1980. Interglacial marine erosion in western Scotland. *Proceedings of the Geologists' Association, London*, **91**, 339–344.

DAWSON, A. G. 1982. Late-glacial sea-level changes and ice limits in Islay, Jura and Scarba, Scottish Inner Hebrides. *Scottish Journal of Geology*, **18**, 253–266.

DAWSON, A. G. 1988. The Main Rock Platform (Main Lateglacial Shoreline) in Ardnamurchan and Moidart, western Scotland. *Scottish Journal of Geology*, **24**, 163–174.

DAWSON, A. G., LONG, D. & SMITH, D. E. 1988. The Storegga Slides: evidence from eastern Scotland for a possible tsunami. *Marine Geology*, **82**, 271–276.

DAWSON, J. & GALLACHER, M. J. 1965. Alluvial gold in Scotland. *Mining Journal*, **264**, 193.

DAY, J. B. 1970. *Geology of the Country around Bewcastle.* Memoir of the Geological Survey of Great Britain.

DE SOUZA, H. A. F. 1979. *The Geochronology of Scottish Carboniferous Volcanism.* PhD thesis, University of Edinburgh.

DE SOUZA, H. A. F. 1982. Age data from Scotland and the Carboniferous time scale. *In*: ODIN, G. S. (ed.) *Numerical Dating in Stratigraphy.* Wiley, Chichester, 456–465.

DEAN, D. R. 1992. *James Hutton and the History of Geology.* Cornell University Press, Ithaca & London.

DEAN, M. T. 1992. Conodont colour maturation indices for the Carboniferous of west-central Scotland. *In*: PARNELL, J. (ed.) *Basins of the Atlantic Seaboard: Petroleum Geology, Sedimentology and Basin Evolution.* Geological Society, London, Special Publications, **62**, 21–23.

DEAN, W. E. & FOUCH, T. D. 1983. Lacustrine Environment, *In*: SCHOLLE, P. A., BEBOUT, D. G. & MOORE, C. H. (eds) *Carbonate Depositional Environments.* American Association of Petroleum Geologists, Memoir, **33**, 98–130.

DEANS, T., GARSON, M. S. & COATS, J. S. 1971. Fenite-type soda metasomatism in the Great Glen, Scotland. *Nature, Physical Sciences*, **234**, 145–147.

DEARNLEY, R. 1962. An outline of the Lewisian complex of the Outer Hebrides in relation to that of the Scottish mainland. *Quarterly Journal of the Geological Society, London*, **118**, 143–176.

DEARNLEY, R. 1963. The Lewisian complex of South Harris. *Quarterly Journal of the Geological Society, London*, **119**, 243–307.

DEARNLEY, R. 1967. Metamorphism of minor intrusions associated with the Newer Granites of the Western Highlands of Scotland. *Scottish Journal of Geology*, **3**, 449–457.

DEC, T. 1992. Textural characteristics and interpretation of second-cycle, debris-flow dominated alluvial fans (Devonian of Northern Scotland). *Sedimentary Geology*, **77**, 269–296.

DEEGAN, C. E. 1973. Tectonic control of sedimentation at the margin of a Carboniferous basin, Kirkudbright. *Scottish Journal of Geology*, **9**, 371–412.

DEEGAN, C. E. & SCULL, B. J. 1977. *A Standard Lithostratigraphic Nomenclature for the Central and Northern North Sea.* Institute of Geological Science Report No. 77/25, HMSO.

DEMPSTER, T. J. 1985. Uplift patterns and orogenic evolution in the Scottish Dalradian. *Journal of the Geological Society, London*, **142**, 111–128.

DEMPSTER, T. J. & BLUCK, B. J. 1989. The age and origin of boulders in the Highland Border Complex: constraints on terrane movements. *Journal of the Geological Society, London*, **146**, 377–379.

DEMPSTER, T. J. & BLUCK, B. J. 1991a. Age and tectonic significance of the Bute Amphibolite, Highland Border Complex, Scotland. *Geological Magazine*, **128**, 77–80.

DEMPSTER, T. J. & BLUCK, B. J. 1991b. Xenoliths in the lamprophyre dykes, Lomondside; constraints on the nature of the crust beneath the southern Dalradian. *Scottish Journal of Geology*, **27**, 157–165.

DEMPSTER, T. J. & HARTE, B. 1986. Polymetamorphism in the Dalradian of the Central Scottish Highlands. *Geological Magazine*, **123**, 95–104.

DEMPSTER, T. J., HUDSON, N. F. & ROGERS, G. 1995. Metamorphism and cooling of the NE Dalradian. *Journal of the Geological Society, London*, **152**, 383–390.

DEMPSTER, T. J., PRESTON, R. J. & BELL, B. R. 1999. The origin of Proterozoic massif-type anorthosites: evidence from interactions between crustal xenoliths and basaltic magma. *Journal of the Geological Society, London*, **156**, 41–46.

DEMPSTER, T. J., ROGERS, G., TANNER, P. W. G., BLUCK, B. J., MUIR, R. J., REDWOOD, S. D., IRELAND, T. R. & PATERSON, B. A. 2002. Timing and deposition, orogenesis and glaciation within the Dalradian rocks of Scotland: constraints from U-Pb ages. *Journal of the Geological Society, London*, **159**, 83–94.

DEMYTTENAERE, R. R. A., SLUIJK, A. H. & BENTLEY, M. R. 1993. A fundamental reappraisal of the structure of the Cormorant Field and its impact on field development strategy. *In*: PARKER, J. R. (ed.) *Petroleum Geology of Northwest Europe: Proceedings of the 4th Conference*. Geological Society, London, 1151–1157.

DENTITH, M. C. & HALL, J. 1989. MAVIS-an upper crustal seismic refraction experiment in the Midland Valley of Scotland. *Geophysical Journal International*, **99**, 627–643.

DENTITH, M. C. & HALL, J. 1990. MAVIS: geophysical constraints on the structure of the Carboniferous basin of West Lothian, Scotland. *Transactions of the Royal Society of Edinburgh: Earth Sciences*, **81**, 117–126.

DENTITH, M., TRENCH, A. & BLUCK, B. J. 1992. Geophysical constraints on the nature of the Highland Boundary Fault zone in Western Scotland. *Geological Magazine*, **129**, 411–419.

DEPARTMENT OF ENERGY 1989. *The Development of Oil and Gas Resources of the United Kingdom*. HMSO, London.

DEPARTMENT OF THE ENVIRONMENT 1990. *Landfilling Wastes. A Technical Memorandum for the Disposal of Wastes on Landfill Sites*. Department of the Environment Waste Management paper, **26**, HMSO, London.

DEPARTMENT OF THE ENVIRONMENT 1992a. *The Use of Land for Amenity Purposes*. HMSO, London.

DEPARTMENT OF THE ENVIRONMENT 1992b. *Mining Instability in Great Britain*. HMSO, London.

DEPARTMENT OF THE ENVIRONMENT 1994a. *Landsliding in Great Britain*. HMSO, London.

DEPARTMENT OF THE ENVIRONMENT 1994b. *Sustainable Development – The UK Strategy*. HMSO, London.

DEPARTMENT OF THE ENVIRONMENT 1996a. *Reclamation of Damaged Land for Nature Conservation*. HMSO, London.

DEPARTMENT OF THE ENVIRONMENT 1996b. *Landslide Investigation and Management in Great Britain: A Guide for Planners and Developers*. Rendal Geotechnics. The Stationery Office.

DEPARTMENT OF THE ENVIRONMENT 1996c. *Assessment of Subsidence Arising from Gypsum Dissolution (with particular reference to Ripon, North Yorkshire)* Symonds Travers Morgan, The Stationery Office.

DEPARTMENT OF THE ENVIRONMENT, TRANSPORT AND THE REGIONS 2000a. *Potential UK Adaptation Strategies for Climate Change*, ERM, London.

DEPARTMENT OF THE ENVIRONMENT, TRANSPORT AND THE REGIONS 2000b. *Climate Change: Assessing the Impacts – Identifying the Response*. London.

DEPARTMENT OF THE ENVIRONMENT, TRANSPORT AND THE REGIONS 2000c. *Climate Change and UK Nature Conservation*. London.

DEPARTMENT OF TRADE & INDUSTRY 1998. *The Energy Report: Oil and Gas Resources of the United Kingdom*.

DEWEY, H., FLETT, J. S. & WILSON, G. V. 1920. Arsenic and antimony ores. *Memoir Geological Survey Special Report, Mineral Resources Great Britain*, **15**.

DEWEY, J. F. 1969. Evolution of the Caledonian/Appalachian orogen. *Nature, London*, **222**, 124–129.

DEWEY, J. F. 1971. A model for the Lower Palaeozoic evolution of the southern margin of the early Caledonides of Scotland and Ireland. *Scottish Journal of Geology*, **7**, 219–240.

DEWEY, J. F. 1974. The geology of the southern terminations of the Caledonides. *In*: NAIRN, A. (ed.) *The Ocean Basins and their Margins*. Vol. 2 The North Atlantic. 205–231. Wiley, New York.

DEWEY, J. F. & MANGE, M. 1999. Petrography of Ordovician and Silurian sediments in the western Irish Caledonides: tracers of a short-lived Ordovician continent-arc collision orogeny and the evolution of the Laurentian–Appalachian–Caledonian margin. *In*: MACNIOCIALL, C. & RYAN, P. D. (eds) *Continental Tectonics*. Geological Society, London, Special Publications, **164**, 55–107.

DEWEY, J. F. & PANKHURST, R. J. 1970. The evolution of the Scottish Caledonides in relation to their radiometric age pattern. *Transactions of the Royal Society of Edinburgh*, **68**, 361–389.

DEWEY, J. F. & RYAN, P. D. 1990. The Ordovician evolution of the South Mayo Trough, western Ireland. *Tectonics*, **9**, 887–903.

DEWEY, J. F. & RYAN, P. D. 1991. A geological cross section of the Caledonides of western Ireland. *Journal of the Geological Society, London*, **148**, 137–180.

DEWEY, J. F. & SHACKLETON, R. J. 1984. A model for the evolution of the Grampian tract in the early Caledonides and Appalachians. *Nature, London*, **312**, 115–120.

DICKIN, A. P. 1981. Isotope geochemistry of Tertiary igneous rocks from the Isle of Skye, N.W. Scotland. *Journal of Petrology*, **22**, 155–189.

DICKIN, A. P. & BOWES, D. R. 1991. Isotopic evidence for the extent of early Proterozoic basement in Scotland and northwest Ireland. *Geological Magazine*, **128**, 385–388.

DICKIN, A. P. & EXLEY, R. A. 1981. Isotopic and geochemical evidence for magma mixing in the peterogenesis of the Coire Uaigneich Granophyre, Isle of Skye, N.W. Scotland. *Contributions to Mineralogy and Petrology*, **76**, 98–108.

DICKIN, A. P., MOORBATH, S. & WELKE, H. J. 1981. Isotope, trace-element and major-element geochemistry of Tertiary igneous rocks, Isle of Arran, Scotland. *Transactions of the Royal Society of Edinburgh: Earth Sciences*, **72**, 159–170.

DICKIN, A. P., BROWN, J. L., THOMPSON, R. N., HALLIDAY, A. N. & MORRISON, M. A. 1984. Crustal contamination and the granite problem in the British Tertiary Volcanic Province. *Philosophical Transactions of the Royal Society of London*, **310A**, 755–780.

DICKIN, A. P., JONES, N. W., THIRLWALL, M. F. & THOMPSON, R. N. 1987. A Ce/Nd isotope study of crustal contamination processes affecting Palaeocene magmas in Skye, NW Scotland. *Contributions to Mineralogy and Petrology*, **96**, 455–464.

DICKINSON, B. B. & WATSON, J. 1976. Variations in crustal level and geothermal gradient during the evolution of the Lewisian complex of northwest Scotland. *Precambrian Research*, **3**, 363–374.

DICKINSON, W. R. & SUCZEK, C. A. 1978. Plate tectonics and sandstone composition. *AAPG Bulletin*, **63**, 2164–2182.

DICKS, B. M. & WHITE, I. C. 1992. Oil spills – effect and response. *In*: CAIRNS, W. J. (ed.) *North Sea and the Environment-Developing Oil and Gas Resources, Environmental Impacts and Resources*. Elsevier Applied Science, 441–457.

DICKSON, J. H., JARDINE, W. G. & PRICE, R. J. 1976. Three Late-Devensian sites in west-central Scotland. *Nature*, London, **262**, 43–44.

DIEMER, J. 1997. Old or New Red Sandstone? Evolution of a nineteenth century stratigraphic debate. *Earth Sciences History*, **15**, 151–166.

DIKIN, A. & BOWES, D. 1991. Isotopic evidence for the extent of early Proterozoic basement in Scotland and northwest Ireland. *Geological Magazine*, **128**, 385–388.

DINELEY, D. L. & METCALF, S. J. 1999. *Fossil Fishes of Great Britain*. Geological Conservation Review Series, **16**. Joint Nature Conservation Committee, Peterborough.

DIXON, J. E., FITTON, J. G. & FROST, R. T. C. 1981. The tectonic significance of post-Carboniferous igneous activity in the North Sea Basin. *In*: ILLING, L. V. & HOBSON, G. P. (eds) *Petroleum Geology of the Continental Shelf of North-West Europe*. Heyden, London, 121–137.

DONALDSON, C. H. 1977. Petrology of anorthite-bearing gabbro anorthosite dykes in north-west Skye. *Journal of Petrology*, **18**, 595–620.

DONG, H., HALL, C. M., HALLIDAY, A. N., PEACOR, D. R., MERRIMAN, R. J. & ROBERTS, B. 1997. $^{40}Ar/^{39}Ar$ dating of Late Caledonian (Acadian) metamorphism and cooling of K-bentonites and slates from the Welsh Basin, U.K. *Earth and Planetary Science Letters*, **150**, 337–351.

DONNER, J. J. 1957. The geology and vegetation of late-glacial retreat stages in Scotland. *Transactions of the Royal Society Edinburgh*, **63**, 221–264.

DONOVAN, A. L. & PRENTISS, J. 1980. James Hutton's *Dissertatio Physico-Medica Inauguralis De Sanguine et Circulatione Microcosmi*. Leyden Academy, 1749, with English translation. *Transactions of the American Philosophical Society*, **70** (Part 6).

DONOVAN, R. N. 1973. Basin margin deposits of the Middle Old Red Sandstone at Dirlot, Caithness. *Scottish Journal of Geology*, **8**, 203–211.

DONOVAN, R. N. 1975. Devonian lacustrine limestones at the margin of the Orcadian Basin, Scotland. *Journal of the Geological Society, London*, **131**, 489–510.

DONOVAN, R. N. 1978. The Middle O. R. S. of the Orcadian Basin. *In*: FRIEND, P. F. & WILLIAMS, B. P. J. (eds) *A Field Guide to Selected Outcrop Areas of the Devonian of Scotland, the Welsh Borderland and South Wales*. The Palaeontological Association, London, 37–53.

DONOVAN, R. N. 1980. Lacustrine cycles, fish ecology and stratigraphic zonation in the Middle Devonian of Caithness. *Scottish Journal of Geology*, **16**, 35–50.

DONOVAN, R. N. 1993. Evaporites in the Middle Devonian of the Orcadian Basin near Berriedale, Caithness. *Scottish Journal of Geology*, **29**, 45–54.

DONOVAN, R. N. & FOSTER, R. J. 1972. Subaqueous shrinkage cracks from the Caithness Flagstone Series (Middle Devonian) of north-east Scotland. *Journal of Sedimentary Petrology*, **42**, 309–317.

DONOVAN, R. N., FOSTER, R. J. & WESTOLL, T. S. 1974. A stratigraphical revision of the Old Red Sandstone of north-eastern Caithness. *Transactions of the Royal Society of Edinburgh*, **69**, 167–201.

DONOVAN, R. N., COLLINS, A., ROWLANDS, M. A. & ARCHER, R. 1978. The age of sediments on Foula, Shetland. *Scottish Journal of Geology*, **14**, 87–88.

DONOVAN, S. K. & PAUL, C. R. C. 1985. Coronate echinoderms from the Lower Palaeozoic of Britain. *Palaeontology*, **28**, 527–543.

DORÉ, A. G., LUNDIN, E. R., JENSEN, L. N., BIRKELAND, Ø., ELIASSEN, P. E. & FICHLER, C. 1999. Principal tectonic events in the evolution of the northwest European Atlantic margin. *In*: FLEET, A. J. & BOLDY, S. A. (eds) *Petroleum Geology of Northwest Europe: Proceedings of the 5th Conference*. Geological Society, London, 41–61.

DOTT, R. H. JR. 1999. Closing remarks for the Hutton bicentenary, Edinburgh. *In*: CRAIG, G. Y. & HULL J. H. (eds) *James Hutton-Present and Future*. Geological Society, London, Special Publications, **150**, 157–167.

DOWNIE, C. 1962. So-called spores from the Torridonian. *Proceedings of the Geological Society of London*, **160**, 127–128.

DOWNIE, C. 1982. Lower Cambrian acritarchs from Scotland, Norway, Greenland and Canada. *Transactions of the Royal Society of Edinburgh: Earth Sciences*, **72**, 257–285.

DOYLE, P. & MACDONALD, D. I. M. 1993. Belemnite battlegrounds. *Lethaia*, **26**, 65–80.

DRAPER, L. & DRAPER, P. 1990. *The Raasay Iron Mine 1912–1942; where Enemies became Friends*. L. & P. Draper, Dingwall, Ross-shire.

DROOP, G. T. R. & CHARNLEY, N. R. 1985. Comparative geobarometry of pelitic hornfelses associated with the Newer Gabbros: a preliminary study. *Journal of the Geological Society, London*, **122**, 53–62.

DROOP, G. T. R. & TRELOAR, P. J. 1981. Pressures of metamorphism in the thermal aureole of the Etive Granite Complex. *Scottish Journal of Geology*, **17**, 85–102.

DROOP, G. T. R., FERNANDES, L. A. D. & SHAW, S. 1998. Laxfordian metamorphic conditions of the Palaeoproterozoic Loch Maree Group, Lewisian Complex, NW Scotland. *Scottish Journal of Geology*, **35**, 31–50.

DRURY, S. A. 1972. The tectonic evolution of a Lewisian complex on Coll, Inner Hebrides. *Scottish Journal of Geology*, **8**, 309–333.

DTI 2000. *Development of UK Oil and Gas Resources 2000*. The Stationary Office, London.

DUFF, P. McL. D. 1965. Economic Geology. *In*: CRAIG, G. Y. (ed.) *Geology of Scotland* (1st edition).Oliver & Boyd, Edinburgh, 506–534.

DUINDAM, P. & VAN HOORN, B. 1987. Structural evolution of the West Shetland continental margin. *In*: BROOKS, J. & GLENNIE, K. (eds) *Petroleum Geology of North West Europe*. Graham & Trotman, London. 765–774.

DULLER, P. R. & FLOYD, J. D. 1995. Turbidite geochemistry and provenance studies in the Southern Uplands of Scotland *Geological Magazine*, **132**, 557–569.

DULLER, P. R., GALLAGHER, M. J., HALL, A. J. & RUSSELL, M. J. 1997. Glendinning deposit-an example of turbidite-hosted arsenic–antimony–gold mineralization in the Southern Uplands, Scotland. *In*: SMITH, C. G. (ed.) *Mineralization in the Caledonides. Transactions of the Institution of Mining and Metallurgy*, **106**, B119–B134.

DUNCAN, A. D. & HAMILTON, R. F. M. 1988. Palaeolimnology and organic geochemistry of the Middle Devonian in the Orcadian Basin. *In*: FLEET, A. J., KELTS, K. & TALBOT, M. R. (eds) *Lacustrine Petroleum Source Rocks*. Geological Society, London, Special Publications, **40**, 173–201.

DUNCAN, G. J. C. 1848. *Memoir of the Rev. Henry DUNCAN, D. D., Minister of Ruthwell Founder of Savings Banks, Author of 'Sacred Philosophy of the Seasons' &c. &c*. William Oliphant & Sons, Edinburgh; Hamilton, Adams & Co., London.

DUNCAN, H. 1831. An account of the tracks and footprints of animals found impressed on sandstone in the quarry of Corncockle Muir in Dumfries-shire. *Transactions of the Royal Society of Edinburgh*, **11**, 194–209.

DUNCAN, W. I. & BUXTON, N. W. K. 1995. New evidence for evaporitic Middle Devonian lacustrine sediments with hydrocarbon source potential on the East Shetland Platform, North Sea. *Journal of the Geological Society, London*, **152**, 251–258.

DUNHAM, A. C. 1968. The felsites, granophyres, explosion breccias and tuffisites of the north-eastern margin of the Tertiary igneous complex of Rhum, Inverness-shire. *Quarterly Journal of the Geological Society of London*, **123**, 327–352.

DUNHAM, A. C. & STRASSER-KING, V. E. H. 1982. Late Carboniferous intrusions of northern Britain. *In*: SUTHERLAND, D. S. (ed.) *Igneous Rocks of the British Isles*, John Wiley, Chichester.

DUNHAM, K. C., BEER, K. E., ELLIS, R. A., GALLAGHER, M. J., NUTT, M. J. C. & WEBB, B. C. 1979. United Kingdom. *In*: BOWIE, S. H. U., KVALHEIM, A. & HASLAM, H. W. (eds). *Mineral Deposits of Europe*, **1**. Institution of Mining and Metallurgy & Mineralogical Society, London, 263–317.

DUNNING, F. W. (ed.) 1985. *Geological Structure of Great Britain, Ireland and Surrounding Seas*. Mapchart, Geological Society of London.

DUNNING, G. R. & KROGH, T. E. 1985. Geochronology of ophiolites of the Newfoundland Appalachians. *Canadian Journal of Earth Sciences*, **22**, 1659–1670.

DUNNING, G. R. & PEDERSEN, R. B. 1988. U/Pb ages of ophiolites and arc-related plutons of the Norwegian Caledonides: implications for the development of Iapetus. *Contributions to Mineralogy and Petrology*, **98**, 13–23.

DURRANT, G. P., KOKELAAR, B. P. & WHITTINGTON, R. J. 1982. The Blackstones Bank Igneous Centre, Western Scotland. *In*: BLANCHARD, J., MAIR, J. & MORRISON, I. (eds) *Proceedings 6th Symposium Coned. Mondiale des Activities subaquatique, September 1980*. Published by NERC, Swindon, 297–308.

DYMOKE, P. L. 1989. *Geochronological and Petrological Studies of the Thermal Evolution of the Dalradian, Southwest Scottish Highlands*. PhD thesis, University of Edinburgh.

EAGAR, R. M. C. 1977. Some new Namurian bivalve faunas and their significance in the origin of *Carbonicola* and the colonisation of Carboniferous deltaic environments. *Philosophical Transactions of the Royal Society, London*, **B280**, 535–570.

EAGAR, R. M. C. & VAN AMEROM, H. W. J. 1999. A new highly variable non-marine bivalve fauna and a new species from basal Westphalian D near Osnabruck, Germany. *Transactions of the Royal Society of Edinburgh: Earth Sciences*, **90**, 67–86.

EARLS, G., PARKER, R. T. G., CLIFFORD, J. A. & MELDRUM, A. H. 1992. The geology of the Cononish gold-silver deposit, Grampian Highlands of Scotland. *In*: EARLS, G. (ed.) *The Irish Minerals Industry – A Review of the Decade*. Irish Association of Economic Geology, Galway, 287–300.

EDWARDS, C. W. 1991. The Buchan Field, Blocks 20/5a and 21/1a, UK North Sea. *In*: ABBOTTS, I. L. (ed.) *United Kingdom Oil and Gas Fields 25 Years Commemorative Volume*. Geological Society, London, Memoir, **14**, 253–259.

EDWARDS, D. 1975. Some observations on the fertile parts of *Zosterophyllum myretonianum* Penhallow from the Lower Old Red Sandstone of Scotland. *Transactions of the Royal Society of Edinburgh*, **69**, 251–265.

EDWARDS, K. J. & SMOUT, T. C. 2000. Perspectives on human–environment interaction in pre-historic and historical times. *In*: HOLMES, G. & CROFTS, R. (eds) *Scotland's Environment: The Future*. Tuckwell Press in association with the Royal Society of Edinburgh and Scottish Natural Heritage.

EDWARDS, K. J. & WHITTINGTON G. 1997. A 12 000 year record of environmental change in the Lomond Hills, Fife, Scotland: *vegetational and climatic variability*. *Vegetation History and Archaeobotany*, **6**, 133–152.

EL FEGI, M. S. 1989. *Petrography and Geochemistry of Lower Palaeozoic Sandstone Sequence, Girvan*. PhD thesis, University of Glasgow.

ELDERS, C. F. 1987. The provenance of granite boulders in conglomerates of the Northern and Central Belts of the Southern Uplands of Scotland. *Journal of the Geological Society, London*, **144**, 853–863.

ELLES, G. L. & TILLEY, C. E. 1930. Metamorphism in relation to structure in the Scottish Highlands. *Transactions of the Royal Society of Edinburgh*, **56**, 621–646.

ELLIOTT, D. & JOHNSON, M. R. W. 1980. Structural evolution in the northern part of the Moine thrust belt, NW Scotland. *Transactions of the Royal Society of Edinburgh: Earth Sciences*, **71**, 69–96.

ELLIS, N. V. (ed.), BOWEN, D. Q., CAMPBELL, S., KNILL, J. L., MCKIRDY, A. P., PROSSER, C. D., VINCENT, M. A. & WILSON, R. C. L. 1996. *An Introduction to the Geological Conservation Review*. Geological Conservation Review Series, **1**, Joint Nature Conservation Committee, Peterborough.

ELLIS, R. A., COATS, J. S., HASLAM, H. W., MICHIE, U. McL., FORTEY, N. J., JOHNSON, C. E. & PARKER, M. E. 1977. Investigation of disseminated copper mineralization near Kilmelford, Argyllshire, Scotland. *Institute of Geological Sciences, Mineral Reconnaissance Programme*, Report **9**.

ELLIS, R. A., MARSDEN, G. R. & FORTEY, N. J. 1978. Disseminated sulphide mineralization at Garbh Achadh, Argyllshire, Scotland. *Institute of Geological Sciences, Mineral Reconnaissance Programme*, Report **23**.

ELSENHEIMER, D. & VALLEY, J. W. 1993. Submillimetre scale zonation of ^{18}O in quartz and feldspar, Isle of Skye, Scotland. *Geochimica et Cosmochimica Acta*, **57**, 3669–3676.

EMELEUS, C. H. 1973. Granophyre pebbles in Tertiary conglomerate on the Isle of Canna, Inverness-shire. *Scottish Journal of Geology*, **9**, 157–159.

EMELEUS, C. H. 1983. Tertiary Igneous Activity. *In*: CRAIG, G. Y. (ed.) *Geology of Scotland* (2nd edition). Scottish Academic Press, Edinburgh, 357–397.

EMELEUS, C. H. 1985. The Tertiary lavas and sediments of northwest Rhum, Inner Hebrides. *Geological Magazine*, **122**, 419–437.

EMELEUS, C. H. 1991. Tertiary Igneous Activity. *In*: CRAIG, G. Y. (ed.) *Geology of Scotland* (3rd Edition). Geological Society, London, 455–502.

EMELEUS, C. H. 1997. *Geology of Rum and the Adjacent Islands*. Memoirs of the British Geological Survey, Sheet 60, with parts of 61 and 70 (Scotland) HMSO, London.

EMELEUS, C. H. & GYOPARI, M. C. 1992. *British Tertiary Igneous Province*. Geological Conservation Review, **4**, Joint Nature Conservation Committee, Peterborough.

EMELEUS, C. H., ALLWRIGHT, E. A., KERR, A. C. & WILLIAMSON, I. T. 1996a. Red tuffs in the Palaeocene lava successions of the Inner Hebrides. *Scottish Journal of Geology*, **32**, 83–89.

EMELEUS, C. H., CHEADLE, M. J., HUNTER, R. H., UPTON, B. G. J. & WADSWORTH, W. J. 1996b. The Rum Layered Suite. *In*: CAWTHORN, R. G. (ed.) *Layered Intrusions*. Vol. 15, Developments in Petrology, Elsevier, Amsterdam, 403–439.

EMELEUS, C. H. & BELL, B. R. 2003. *Scotland: The Tertiary Volcanic Districts*. British Regional Geology, 4th Edition (London: HMSO for the British Geological Survey).

ENGLAND, R. W. 1988. The early Tertiary stress regime in NW Britain: evidence from patterns of volcanic activity. *In*: MORTON, A. C. & PARSON, L. M. (eds) *Early Tertiary Volcanism and the Opening of the NE Atlantic*. Geological Society, London, Special Publications, **39**, 381–389.

ENGLAND, R. W. 1992a. The role of Palaeocene magmatism in the tectonic evolution of the Sea of the Hebrides Basin: implications for basin evolution on the NW Seaboard. *In*: PARNELL, J. (ed.) *Basins on the Atlantic Seaboard: Petroleum Geology, Sedimentology and Basin Evolution*. Geological Society, London, Special Publications, **62**, 163–174.

ENGLAND, R. W. 1992b. The genesis, ascent and emplacement of the Northern Arran Granite, Scotland: Implications for granitic diapirism. *Geological Society of America Bulletin*, **104**, 606–614.

ENGLAND, R. W. 1994. The structure of the Skye Lava Field. *Scottish Journal of Geology*, **30**, 33–38.

ENGLISH NATURE (Quarry Products Association and Silica & Moulding Sands Association) 1999. *Biodiversity and minerals – Extracting the benefits for wildlife*. Entec UK Ltd.

EPSTEIN, A. G., EPSTEIN, J. B & HARRIS, L. D. 1977. Conodont colour alteration – an index to organic metamorphism. *United States Geological Survey Professional Paper* No. **995**, 1–27.

ERNST, R. & BUCHAN, K. L. 1997. Giant radiating dyke swarms; their use in identifying pre-Mesozoic large igneous provinces and mantle plumes. *In*: MAHONEY, J. J. & COFFIN, M. F. (eds) *Large Igneous Provinces; Continental, Oceanic and Planetary Flood Volcanism*. Geophysical Monograph **100**. American Geophysical Union. Washington DC. 297–333.

ESANG, C. B. & PIPER, J. D. A. 1984. Palaeomagnetism of the Carboniferous E–W dyke swarm in Argyllshire. *Scottish Journal of Geology*, **20**, 309–314.

ESSON, J., DUNHAM, A. C. & THOMPSON, R. N. 1975. Low alkali, high calcium olivine tholeiite lavas from the Isle of Skye, Scotland. *Journal of Petrology*, **16**, 488–497.

ETHINGTON, R. L & AUSTEN, R. 1991. Conodonts of the Dounans limestone, Highland Border Complex, Scotland. *Journal of Micropalaeontology*, **10**, 51–56.

EVANS, A. M. & EL-NIKHELY, A. 1982. Palaeomagnetic age for mineralisation at Auchenstilloch, Lanarkshire, Scotland. *Transactions of the Institution of Mining and Metallurgy*, **91**, B43–B44.

EVANS, A. H., HASLAM, H. M. & SHAW, R. P. 1980. Porphyry style copper-molybdenum mineralization in Ballachulish igneous complex, Argyllshire, with special reference to the fluid inclusions. *Proceedings of the Geologists' Association*, **91**, 47–51.

EVANS, C. R. 1965. Geochronology of the Lewisian basement near Lochinver, Sutherland. *Nature, London*, **204**, 638–641.

EVANS, C. R. & LAMBERT, R. St.-J. 1974. The Lewisian of Lochinver, Sutherland; the type area for the Inverian metamorphism. *Journal of the Geological Society, London*, **130**, 125–150.

EVANS, C. R. & TARNEY, J. 1964. Isotopic ages of Assynt dykes. *Nature, London*, **204**, 638–641.

EVANS, D., CHESHER, J. A., DEEGAN, C. E. & FANNIN, N. G. T. 1982. The offshore geology of Scotland in relation to the ICS shallow drilling program 1970–1978. *Report of the Institute of Geological Sciences*, **81/12**, 1–36.

EVANS, D., GRAHAM, C., ARMOUR, A. & BATHURST, P. (eds) 2003. *The Millennium Atlas: petroleum geology of the central and northern North Sea*. The Geological Society, London.

EVANS, D. J. & WHITE, S. H. 1984. Microstructural and fabric studies from the Moine rocks of the Moine Nappe, Eriboll, NW Scotland. *Journal of Structural Geology*, **6**, 369–389.

EVANS, J. A. & SOPER, N. J. 1997. A discussion of 'metamorphism and cooling of the NE Dalradian' and U–Pb and Rb–Sr geochronology of magmatism and metamorphism in the Dalradian of Conemarra, western Ireland. Comment. *Journal of the Geological Society, London*, **154**, 357–358.

EVANS, J. A., STONE, P. & FLOYD, J. D. 1991. Isotope characteristics of Ordovician greywacke provenance in the Southern Uplands of Scotland. *In*: MORTON, A. C. (ed.) *Developments in Sedimentary*

Provenance Studies. Geological Society, London, Special Publications, **57**, 161–172.

EVANS, J. A., FITCHES, W. R. & MUIR, R. J. 1998. Laurentian clasts from a Neoproterozoic Tillite from Scotland. *Journal of Geology*, **106**, 361–366.

EVANS, N., RORISON, P. & SYKES, G. 1999. Banff Field, UK Central Graben – evaluation of a steeply dipping, fractured reservoir. *In*: FLEET, A. J. & BOLDY, S. A. R. (eds) *Petroleum Geology of Northwest Europe: Proceedings of the 5th Conference*, Geological Society, London, 975–988.

EVANS, R. H. S. & TANNER, P. W. G. 1996. A late Vendian age for the Kinlochlaggan Boulder Bed (Dalradian?). *Journal of the Geological Society, London*, **153**, 823–826.

EVANS, S. E. & WALDMAN, M. 1996. Small reptiles and amphibians from the Middle Jurassic of Skye, Scotland. *In*: MORALES, M. (ed.) *The Continental Jurassic*. Museum of Northern Arizona, Bulletin **60**, 219–226.

EXLEY, R. A. 1980. Microprobe studies of REE-rich accessory minerals: implications for Skye granite petrogenesis and REE mobility in hydrothermal systems. *Earth and Planetary Science Letters*, **48**, 97–110.

EYLES, V. A. 1948. Louis Albert Necker, of Geneva, and his geological map of Scotland. *Transactions of the Edinburgh Geological Society*, **14**, 93–127.

EYLES, V. A., SIMPSON, J. B. & MACGREGOR, M. C. 1949. Geology of central Ayrshire, 2nd Edition. *Memoir of the Geological Survey of Scotland*.

FAIRCHILD, I J. 1980. Stages in a Precambrian dolomitization, Scotland: cementing versus replacement textures. *Sedimentology*, **27**, 631–650.

FAIRCHILD, I J. 1985. Petrography and carbonate chemistry of some Dalradian dolomitic metasediments: preservation of diagenetic textures. *Journal of the Geological Society, London*, **142**, 167–185.

FANNIN, N. G. T. 1970. *The Sedimentary Environment of the Old Red Sandstone of Western Orkney*. PhD thesis, University of Reading.

FARRIS, M. A., OATES, M. J. & TORRENS, H. S. 1999. New evidence on the origin and Jurassic age of palaeokarst and limestone breccias, Loch Slapin, Isle of Skye. *Scottish Journal of Geology*, **35**, 25–29.

FENNER, C. N. 1937. A view of magmatic differentiation. *Journal of Geology*, **18**, 158–168.

FERRY, J. M. 1985*a*. Hydrothermal alteration of Tertiary igneous rocks from the Isle of Skye, northwest Scotland. I. Gabbros. *Contributions to Mineralogy and Petrology*, **91**, 264–282.

FERRY, J. M. 1985*b*. Hydrothermal alteration of Tertiary igneous rocks from the Isle of Skye, northwest Scotland. II. Granites. *Contributions to Mineralogy and Petrology*, **91**, 283–304.

FERRY, J. M., MUTTI, L. J. & ZUCCALA, G. J. 1987. Contact metamorphism/hydrothermal alteration of Tertiary basalts from the Isle of Skye, northwest Scotland. *Contributions to Mineralogy and Petrology*, **95**, 166–181.

FETTES, D. J. 1970. The structural and metamorphic state of the Dalradian rocks and their bearing on the age of emplacement of the basic sheet. *Scottish Journal of Geology*, **6**, 108–118.

FETTES, D. J. 1979. A metamorphic map of the British and Irish Caledonides. *In*: HARRIS, A. L., HOLLAND, C. H. & LEAKE, B. E. (eds) *The Caledonides of the British Isles – Reviewed*. Geological Society, London, Special Publications, **8**, 307–321.

FETTES, D. J. & MACDONALD, R. 1978. The Glen Garry vein complex. *Scottish Journal of Geology*, **14**, 335–358.

FETTES, D. J. & MENDUM, J. R. 1987. The evolution of the Lewisian complex in the Outer Hebrides. *In*: PARK, R. G. & TARNEY, J. (eds) *Evolution of the Lewisian and Comparable Precambrian High Grade Terrains*. Geological Society, London, Special Publications, **27**, 27–44.

FETTES, D. J., GRAHAM, C. M., SASSI, F. P. & SCHOLARI, A. 1976. The basal spacing of potassic white micas and facies series variation across the Caledonides. *Scottish Journal of Geology*, **12**, 227–236.

FETTES, D. J., LONG, C. B., MAX, M. D. & YARDLEY, B. W. D. 1985. Grade and time of metamorphism in the Caledonide Orogen of Britain and Ireland. *In*: HARRIS, A. L. (ed.) *The Nature and Timing of Orogenic Activity in the Caledonian Rocks of the British Isles*. Geological Society of London, Memoirs, **9**, 41–53.

FETTES, D. J., GRAHAM, C. M., HARTE, B. & PLANT, J. A. 1986. Lineaments and basement domains: an alternative view of Dalradian evolution. *Journal of the Geological Society, London*, **143**, 453–464.

FETTES, D. J., LESLIE, A. G., STEPHENSON, D. & KIMBELL, S. F. 1991. Disruption of Dalradian stratigraphy along the Portsoy Lineament from new geological and magnetic surveys. *Scottish Journal of Geology*, **27**, 57–73.

FETTES, D. J., MENDUM, J. R., SMITH, D. I. & WATSON, J. 1992. *The Geology of the Outer Hebrides*. Memoir of the British Geological Survey.

FIELDING, C. R., Al-RUBAII, M. & WALTON, E. K. 1988. Deltaic sedimentation in an unstable tectonic environment – the Lower Limestone Group (Lower Carboniferous) of East Fife, Scotland. *Geological Magazine*, **125**, 241–255.

FINLAY, T. M. 1926. The Old Red Sandstone of Shetland Part 1. South-eastern area. *Transactions of the Royal Society of Edinburgh*, **54**, 553–572.

FISHER, I. ST. J. & HUDSON, J. D. 1987. Pyrite formation in shales of contrasting biofacies. *In*: BROOKS, J. & Fleet, A. J. (eds) *Marine Petroleum Source Rocks*. Geological Society, London, Special Publications, **26**, 69–78.

FISHER, M. J. & MUDGE, D. C. 1998. Triassic. *In*: GLENNIE, K. W. (ed.) *Petroleum Geology of the North Sea*. Blackwell, Oxford, 212–244.

FISK, S. 1986. *An Oxygen Isotope Study of Siliceous Rocks Associated with Stratabound Mineralisation in Scotland and Ireland*. PhD thesis, University of Strathclyde.

FITCH, F. J., MILLER, J. A. & BROWN, P. E. 1964. Age of Caledonian orogeny and metamorphism in Britain. *Nature, London*, **203**, 275–278.

FITCHES, W. R. & MALTMAN, A. J. 1984. Tectonic development and stratigraphy at the western margin of the Caledonides: Islay and Colonsay. *Transactions of the Royal Society of Edinburgh: Earth Sciences*, **75**, 365–382.

FITCHES, W. R., MUIR, R. J., MALTMAN, A. J. & BENTLEY, M. R. 1990. Is the Colonsay-west Islay block of SW Scotland an allochthonous terrane? Evidence from Dalradian tillite clasts. *Journal of the Geological Society, London*, **147**, 417–420.

FITTON, J. G., SAUNDERS, A. D., NORRY, M. J., HARDARSON, B. S. & TAYLOR, R. N. 1997. Thermal and chemical structure of the Iceland Plume. *Earth and Planetary Science Letters*, **153**, 197–208.

FLEET, A. J. & BOLDY, S. A. R. (eds) 1999. *Petroleum Geology of Northwest Europe: Proceedings of the 5th Conference*. Geological Society, London.

FLETCHER, T. A. & RICE, C. M. 1989. Geology, mineralisation (Ni–Cu) and precious metal geochemistry of Caledonian mafic and ultramafic intrusions near Huntly, northeast Scotland. *Transactions of the Institution of Mining and Metallurgy*, **98**, B185–B200.

FLETCHER, T. A., BOYCE, A. J. & FALLICK, A. E. 1989. A sulphur isotope study of Ni–Cu mineralisation in the Huntly–Knock Caledonian mafic and ultramafic intrusions of northeast Scotland. *Journal of the Geological Society, London*, **146**, 675–684.

FLETCHER, T. A., BOYCE, A. J., FALLICK, A. E., RICE, C. M. & KAY, R. L. F. 1997. Geology and stable isotope study of Arthrath mafic intrusion and Ni–Cu mineralization, northeast Scotland. *In*: SMITH, C. G. (ed.) *Mineralization in the Caledonides. Transactions of the Institution of Mining and Metallurgy*, **106**, B169–B178.

FLETT, J. S. 1905. *On the Petrographic Characters of the Inliers of Lewisian Rocks among the Moine Gneisses of the North of Scotland*. Memoirs of the Geological Survey, Summary of Progress for 1905, 155–167.

FLETT, J. S. & READ, H. H. 1921. Tertiary gravels of the Buchan district of Aberdeenshire. *Geological Magazine*, **58**, 215–225.

FLINN, D. 1958. The nappe structure of north-east Shetland. *Quarterly Journal of the Geological Society of London*, **114**, 107–136.

FLINN, D. 1961. Continuation of the Great Glen Fault beyond the Moray Firth. *Nature, London*, **191**, 589–591.

FLINN, D. 1969. A geological interpretation of the aeromagnetic maps of the continental shelf around Orkney and Shetland. *Geological Journal*, **6**, 279–292.

FLINN, D. 1977. Transcurrent faults and associated cataclasis in Shetland. *Journal of the Geological Society, London*, **133**, 231–248.

FLINN, D. 1985. The Caledonides of Shetland. In: GEE, D. G. & STURT, B. A. (eds) *The Caledonide Orogen – Scandinavia and Related Areas*. Wiley, New York, 1159–1172.

FLINN, D. 1988. The Moine rocks of Shetland. In: WINCHESTER, J. A. (ed.) *Later Proterozoic Stratigraphy of the Northern Atlantic Regions*. Blackie, Glasgow, 74–85.

FLINN, D. 1992. Late Caledonian northeastward thrusting in the Shetland Islands, UK–Refutation. *Tectonophysics*, **216**, 387–389.

FLINN, D. 1993. Discussion on the location and history of the Walls Boundary fault and Moine thrust north and south of Shetland. *Journal of the Geological Society, London*, **150**, 1003–1008.

FLINN, D. 2000. The architecture of the Shetland Ophiolite. *Scottish Journal of Geology*, **36**, 123–135.

FLINN, D., FRANK, P. L., BROOK, M. & PRINGLE, I. R. 1979. Basement-cover relations in Shetland. In: HARRIS, A. L., HOLLAND, C. H. & LEAKE, B. E. (eds) *The Caledonides of the British Isles – Reviewed*. Geological Society, London, Special Publications, **8**, 109–115.

FLINN, D., MILLER, J. A. & RODDOM, D. 1991. The age of the Norwick hornblende schists of Unst and Fetlar and the obduction of the Shetland ophiolite. *Scottish Journal of Geology*, **27**, 11–19.

FLOYD, J. D. 1982. Stratigraphy of a flysch succession: the Ordovician of W Nithsdale, SW Scotland. *Transactions of the Royal Society of Edinburgh: Earth Sciences*, **73**, 1–9.

FLOYD, J. D. 1994. The derivation and definition of the 'Southern Upland Fault'; a review of the Midland Valley–Southern Uplands terrane boundary. *Scottish Journal of Geology*, **30**, 51–62.

FLOYD, J. D. 1996. Lithostratigraphy of the Ordovician rocks in the Southern Uplands: Crawford Group, Moffat Shale Group, Leadhills Supergroup *Transactions of the Royal Society of Edinburgh: Earth Sciences*, **86**, 153–165.

FLOYD, J. D. 1999. *Geology of the Carrick-Loch Doon District*. Memoir of the British Geological Survey. Sheets 8W and 8E (Scotland).

FLOYD, J. D. 2001. The Southern Uplands Terrane: a stratigraphical review. *Transactions of the Royal Society of Edinburgh: Earth Sciences*, **91**, 349–362.

FLOYD, J. D. & KIMBELL, G. S. 1995. Magnetic and tectonostratigraphic correlation at a terrane boundary–the Tappins Group of the Southern Uplands. *Geological Magazine*, **132**, 515–521.

FLOYD, J. D. & PHILLIPS, E. R. 1998. Xenoliths of Southern Uplands 'basement ?' in a lamprophyre dyke, Central Belt, Glen Luce, SW Scotland. *Scottish Journal of Geology*, **35**, 57–62.

FLOYD, J. D. & RUSHTON, A. W. A. 1993. Ashgill greywackes in the Southern Uplands: An extension of the Ordovician succession in the Northern Belt. *Transactions of the Royal Society of Edinburgh: Earth Sciences*, **78**, 79–85.

FLOYD, J. D. & STIVEN, G. 1991. Rare temporary exposure of the Southern Upland Fault near Abington, Strathclyde. *Scottish Journal of Geology*, **27**, 75–80.

FLOYD, J. D. & TRENCH, A. 1989. Magnetic susceptibility contrasts in Ordovician greywackes of the Southern Uplands of Scotland. *Journal of the Geological Society, London*, **146**, 77–83.

FLOYD, J. D., STONE, P., BARNES, R. P. & LINTERN, B. C. 1987. Constraints on the significance of the Orlock Bridge Fault within the Scottish Southern Uplands – a discussion of 'The Orlock Bridge Fault: a major late Caledonian sinistral fault in the Southern Uplands terrane, British Isles'. *Transactions of the Royal Society of Edinburgh: Earth Sciences*, **78**, 219–221.

FLOYD, J. D., WILLIAMS, M. & RUSHTON, A. W. A. 1999. Late Ordovician (Ashgill) ostracodes from the Drummuck group, Craighead Inlier, Girvan District, southwest Scotland. *Scottish Journal of Geology*, **35**, 15–24.

FLOYD, P. A., WINCHESTER, J. A. & PARK, R. G. 1989. Geochemistry and tectonic setting of Lewisian clastic metasediments from the early Proterozoic Loch Maree Group of Gairloch, NW Scotland. *Precambrian Research*, **45**, 203–214.

FORBES, E. 1851. On the Estuary Beds and the Oxford Clay at Loch Staffin, in Skye. *Quarterly Journal of the Geological Society of London*, **7**, 104–113.

FORBES, J. D. 1846. Notes on the topography and geology of the Cuchullin Hills in Skye, and on the traces of ancient glaciers which they present. *The Edinburgh New Philosophical Journal*, **40**, 76–99.

FORESTER, R. W. & TAYLOR, H. P. 1977. $^{18}O/^{16}O$, D/H and $^{13}C/^{12}C$ studies on the Tertiary igneous complex of Skye, Scotland. *American Journal of Science*, **277**, 136–177.

FORSTER, M. W. C. 1998. *Fossils and Other Collectable Earth Heritage Materials in Scotland: their Use and Conservation*. Scottish Natural Heritage, Research, Survey and Monitoring Series, No. 115.

FORSTER, S. C. & WARRINGTON, G. 1985. Geochronology of the Carboniferous, Permian and Triassic. In: SNELLING, N. J. (ed.) *The Chronology of the Geological Record*. Geological Society, London, Memoirs, **10**, 99–113.

FORSYTH, I. H. 1970. Geological Survey Boreholes in the Lower Carboniferous of West Fife (1965–6). *Bulletin of the Geological Survey of Great Britain*, **31**, 1–18.

FORSYTH, I. H. 1979. *The* Lingula *Bands in the Upper Part of the Limestone Coal Group (E1 Stage of the Namurian) in the Glasgow District*. Institute of Geological Sciences Report **79/16**.

FORSYTH, I. H. 1982. The *stratigraphy of the Upper Limestone Group (E1 and E2 stages of the Namurian) in the Glasgow District*. Institute of Geolological Sciences Report **82/4**.

FORSYTH, I. H. & BRAND, P. J. 1986. *Stratigraphy and Stratigraphical Palaeontology of Westphalian B and C in the Central Coalfield of Scotland*. British Geological Survey Report, **18**, No. 4.

FORSYTH, I. H. & CHISHOLM, J. I. 1977. *The Geology of East Fife*. Memoir of the Geological Survey of Great Britain.

FORSYTH, I. H. & RUNDLE, C. C. 1978. The age of the hypabyssal rocks of east Fife. *Bulletin of the Geological Survey of Great Britain*, **60**, 23–29.

FORSYTH, I. H. & WILSON, R. B. 1965. Recent sections in the Lower Carboniferous of the Glasgow Area. *Bulletin of the Geological Survey of Great Britain*, **22**, 65–79.

FORSYTH, I. H., HALL, I. H. S. & MCMILLAN, A. A. 1996. *Geology of the Airdrie District*. Memoir of the British Geological Survey.

FORTEY, N. J. 1980. Hydrothermal mineralization associated with minor late Caledonian intrusions in northern Britain: preliminary comments. *Transactions of the Institution of Mining and Metallurgy*, **89**, B173–B176.

FORTEY, N. J. & BEDDOE-STEPHENS, B. 1982. Barium silicates in stratabound Ba–Zn mineralisation in the Scottish Dalradian. *Mineralogical Magazine*, **46**, 63–72.

FORTEY, N. J. & SMITH, C. G. 1986. Stratabound mineralisation in Dalradian rocks near Tyndrum, Perthshire. *Scottish Journal of Geology*, **22**, 377–393.

FORTEY, N. J., NANCARROW, P. M. A. & GALLAGHER, M. J. 1991. Armenite from the Middle Dalradian of Scotland. *Mineralogical Magazine*, **378**, 135–138.

FORTEY, N. J., MERRIMAN, R. J. & HUFF, W. D. 1995. Silurian and Late Ordovician K-bentonites as a record of late Caledonian volcanism in the British Isles. *Transactions of the Royal Society of Edinburgh: Earth Sciences*, **86**, 167–180.

FOSTER, P. T. & RATTEY, P. R. 1993. The evolution of a fractured Chalk reservoir: Machar Field, UK North Sea. In: PARKER J. R. (ed.) *Petroleum Geology of Northwest Europe: Proceedings of the 4th Conference*. Geological Society, London, 1445–1452.

FOWLER, J. D. 1976. *Geochemical and V. L. F. Investigation in the Region of the Knipes Stibnite Deposit, Ayrshire*. MSc thesis, University of St Andrews.

FOWLER, M. B. 1988a. Ach'uaine hybrid appinite pipes: evidence for mantle-derived shoshonitic parent magmas in Caledonian granite genesis. *Geology*, **16**, 1026–1030.

FOWLER, M. B. 1988b. Elemental evidence for crustal contamination of mantle-derived Caledonian syenite by metasediment anatexis and magma mixing. *Chemical Geology*, **69**, 1–16.

FOWLER, M. B. 1992. Elemental and O-Sr-Nd isotope geochemistry of the Glen Dessary syenite, NW Scotland. *Journal of the Geological Society, London*, **149**, 209–220.

FOWLER, M. B. & HENNEY, P. J. 1996. Mixed Caledonian appinite magmas: implications for lamprophyre fractionation and high

Ba-Sr granite genesis. *Contributions to Mineralogy and Petrology*, **126**, 199–215.

FOWLER, M. B., HENNEY, P. J., DARBYSHIRE, D. P. F. & GREENWOOD, P. B. 2001. Petrogenesis of high Ba-Sr granites: the Rogart pluton, Sutherland. *Journal of the Geological Society, London*, **158**, 521–534.

FRANCES, J. M., GOODIER, R. & FERGUSON, M. P. 1992. Safeguarding Environmental interests *In*: CAIRNS, W. J. (ed.) *North Sea and the Environment-Developing Oil and Gas Resources, Environmental Impacts and Resources*. Elsevier Applied Science, 239–263.

FRANCIS, E. H. 1957. New evidence of volcanicity in Fife. *Transactions of the Edinburgh Geological Society*, **17**, 71–80.

FRANCIS, E. H. 1959. A volcanic vent in the Bogside Mines, Fife. *Geological Magazine*, **96**, 457–469.

FRANCIS, E. H. 1965. Carboniferous. *In*: CRAIG, G. Y. (ed.) *The Geology of Scotland* (1st edition). Oliver & Boyd, Edinburgh, 309–357.

FRANCIS, E. H. 1970. Bedding in Scottish (Fifeshire) tuff-pipes and its relevance to maars and calderas. *Bulletin Volcanologique*, **34**, 697–712.

FRANCIS, E. H. 1982. Emplacement mechanism of late Carboniferous tholeiite sills in north Britain. *Journal of the Geological Society, London*, **139**, 1–20.

FRANCIS, E. H. 1983. Carboniferous. *In*: Craig, G. Y. (ed.) *Geology of Scotland* (2nd edition). Scottish Academic Press, Edinburgh, 253–296.

FRANCIS, E. H. 1991a. Carboniferous. *In*: CRAIG, G. Y. (ed.) *Geology of Scotland* (3rd edition). Geological Society, London, 347–392.

FRANCIS, E. H. 1991b. Carboniferous–Permian igneous rocks. *In*: CRAIG, G. Y. (ed.) *Geology of Scotland* (3rd edition). Geological Society, London, 393–420.

FRANCIS, E. H. & EWING, C. J. C. 1961. Coal Measures and volcanism off the Fife coast. *Geological Magazine*, **98**, 501–510.

FRANCIS, E. H. & HOPGOOD, A. M. 1970. Volcanism and the Ardross Fault, Fife, Scotland. *Scottish Journal of Geology*, **6**, 162–185.

FRANCIS, E. H. & WALKER, B. H. 1987. Emplacement of alkali-dolerite sills relative to extrusive volcanism and sedimentary basins in the Carboniferous of Fife, Scotland. *Transactions of the Royal Society of Edinburgh: Earth Sciences*, **77**, 309–323.

FRANCIS, E. H., FORSYTH, I. H., READ, W. A. & ARMSTRONG, M. 1970. The geology of the Stirling district (sheet 39). *Memoirs of the Geological Survey, Great Britain*.

FREDERIKSEN, K. S., CLEMMENSEN, L. B. & LAWÆTZ, H. S. 1998. Sequential architecture and cyclicity in Permian desert deposits, Brodick Beds, Arran, Scotland. *Journal of the Geological Society, London*, **155**, 677–683.

FREEMAN, B., KLEMPERER, S. L. & HOBBS, R. W. 1988. The deep structure of Northern England and the Iapetus suture zone from BIRPS deep seismic reflection profiles. *Journal of the Geological Society, London*, **145**, 727–740.

FREEMAN, S. R., BUTLER, R. W. H., CLIFF, R. A. & REX, D. C. 1998. Dating mylonite evolution: an Rb–Sr and K–Ar study of the Moine mylonites, NW Scotland. *Journal of the Geological Society, London*, **155**, 745–758.

FRENCH, P. W. 1997. *Coastal and Estuarine Management*. Routledge, London.

FREY, M. & MERRIMAN, D. 1999. *Low Grade Metamorphism*. Blackwell, Oxford.

FRIEDRICH, A. M., HODGES, K. V., BOWRING, S. A. & MARTIN, M. W. 1999. Geochronological constraints on the magmatic, metamorphic and thermal evolution of the Connemara Caledonides, western Ireland. *Journal of the Geological Society, London*, **156**, 1217–1230.

FRIEND, C. R. L. & KINNY, P. D. 1995. New evidence for protolith ages of Lewisian granulites, northwest Scotland. *Geology*, **23**, 1027–1030.

FRIEND, C. R. L. & KINNY, P. D. 2001. A reappraisal of the Lewisian Gneiss Complex: geochronological evidence for its tectonic assembly from disparate terranes in the Proterozoic. *Contributions to Mineralogy and Petrology*, **142**, 198–218.

FRIEND, C. R. L., KINNY, P. D., ROGERS, G., STRACHAN, R. A. & PATERSON, B. A. 1997. U–Pb zircon geochronological evidence for Neoproterozoic events in the Glenfinnan Group (Moine Supergroup): the formation of the Ardgour granite gneiss, northwest Scotland. *Contributions to Mineralogy and Petrology*, **128**, 101–113.

FRIEND, C. R. L., JONES, K. A. & BURNS, I. M. 2000. New high-pressure granulite facies event in the Moine Supergroup, northern Scotland: implications for Taconic (early Caledonian) crustal evolution. *Geology*, **28**, 543–546.

FRIEND, C. R. L., KINNY, P. D. & STRACHAN, R. A. 2002a. The basement inliers in the Moine Supergroup of NW Scotland: what do they represent? *Tectonic Studies Group Highlands Workshop Abstracts*, University of St Andrews, Scotland, 5.

FRIEND, C. R. L., STRACHAN, R. A., KINNY, P. D. & WATT, G. R. 2003. Provenance of the Moine Supergroup of NW Scotland: evidence from geochronology of detrital and inherited zircons from sediments, granites and migmatites. *Journal of the Geological Society*, **160**, in press.

FRIEND, P. F. & MACDONALD, R. 1968. Volcanic sediments, stratigraphy and tectonic background of the Old Red Sandstone of Kintyre, W. Scotland. *Scottish Journal of Geology*, **4**, 265–282.

FRIEND, P. F. & WILLIAMS, B. P. J. (eds) 1978. *A Field Guide to Selected Outcrop Areas of the Devonian of Scotland, the Welsh Borderland and South Wales*. Palaeontological Association, London.

FRIEND, P. F., WILLIAMS, B. J. P., FORD, M. & WILLIAMS, E. A. 2000. Kinematics and dynamics of Old Red Sandstone basins. *In*: FRIEND, P. F. & WILLIAMS, B. J. P. (eds) *New Perspectives on the Old Red Sandstone*. Geological Society, London, Special Publications, **180**, 29–60.

FRITZ, W. H. & YOCHELSON, E. l. 1988. The status of *Salterella* as a Lower Cambrian index fossil. *Canadian Journal of Earth Sciences*, **25**, 403–416.

FRÖDIN, G. 1920–1922. On the analogies between the Scottish and Scandinavian portions of the Caledonian mountain range. *Bulletin of the Geological Institution of the University of Uppsala*, **18**, 199–238.

FROSTICK, L., REID, I., JARVIS, J. & EARDLEY, H. 1988. Triassic sediments of the Inner Moray Firth, Scotland: Early rift deposits. *Journal of the Geological Society, London*, **145**, 235–248.

FYFE, T. B. & OSBORNE, P. L. 1996. The Atlantic Frontier – an introduction. *Proceedings of the Offshore Technology Conference, Houston*, OTC 8030.

FYFE, T. B. & WEIR, J. A. 1976. The Ettrick Valley Thrust and the upper limit of the Moffat Shales in Craigmichael Scaurs (Dumfries and Galloway Region: Annandale & Eskdale District). *Scottish Journal of Geology*, **12**, 93–102.

FYFE, J. A., LONG, D. & EVANS, D. 1993. *The Geology of the Malin-Hebrides Sea Area*. United Kingdom Offshore Report, **4**.

GALLAGHER, M. J. 1964. Rock alteration in some mineralised basic dykes in Britain. *Transactions of the Institution of Mining and Metallurgy*, **73**, 825–840.

GALLAGHER, M. J., MICHIE, U. McL., SMITH, R. T. & HAYNES, L. 1971. New evidence of uranium and other mineralisation in Scotland. *Transactions of the Institution of Mining and Metallurgy*, **80**, B150–B173.

GALLAGHER, M. J., SMITH, R. T., PEACOCK, J. D. & HAYNES, L. 1974. Molybdenite mineralisation in Precambrian rocks near Lairg, Scotland. *Transactions of the Institution of Mining and Metallurgy*, **83**, B81–B87.

GALLAGHER, M. J., HALL, I. H. S. & STEPHENSON, D. 1982. Controls and genesis of baryte veins in central Scotland. *Bulletin du Bureau de Recherches Geologiques et Minieres*, Section **II**, no. 2, 143–148.

GALLAGHER, M. J., STONE, P., KEMP, A. E. S., HILLS, M. G., JONES, R. C., SMITH, R. T., PEACHEY, D., VICKERS, B. P., PARKER, M. E., ROLLIN, K. E. & SKILTON, B. R. H. 1983. Stratabound arsenic and vein antimony mineralisation in Silurian greywackes at Glendinning, south Scotland. *Institute of Geological Sciences, Mineral Reconnaissance Programme*, Report **59**.

GALLAGHER, M. J., SMITH, C. G., COATS, J. S., GREENWOOD, P. G., CHACKSFIELD, B. J., FORTEY, N. J. & NANCARROW, P. H. A. 1989a. Stratabound barium and base metal mineralisation in Middle Dalradian metasediments near Braemar, Scotland. *Institute of Geological Sciences, Mineral Reconnaissance Programme*, Report **104**.

GALLAGHER, M. J., BASHAM, I. R. & 10 OTHERS. 1989b. Marine deposits of chromite and olivine, Inner Hebrides of Scotland. *Institute of Geological Sciences, Mineral Reconnaissance Programme*, Report **106**.

GARDNER, J. S. 1884–1885. On the evidence of fossil plants regarding the age of the Tertiary basalts of the north-east Atlantic. *Proceedings of the Royal Society of London*, **38**, 14–23.

GARDNER, J. S. 1887. On the leaf-beds and gravels of Ardtun, Carsaig, etc., in Mull. *Quarterly Journal of the Geological Society of London*, **43**, 270–300.

GARSON, M. S. & MAY, F. 1976. Copper mineralization at Vidlin, Shetland. *Transactions of the Institution of Mining and Metallurgy*, **85**, B153–B157.

GARSON, M. S. & PLANT, J. A. 1973. Alpine type ultramafic rocks and episodic mountain building in the Scottish Highlands. *Nature, London*, **242**, 34–38.

GARSON, M. S., COATS, J. S., ROCK, N. M. S. & DEANS, T. 1984. Fenites, breccia dykes, albitites and carbonatitic veins near the Great Glen Fault, Inverness, Scotland. *Journal of the Geological Society, London*, **141**, 711–732.

GASS, I. G. & THORPE, R. S. 1976. *Igneous Case Study: The Tertiary Igneous Rocks of Skye*. Open University, Milton Keynes.

GATLIFF, R. W., HITCHEN, K., RITCHIE, J. D. & SMYTHE, D. K. 1984. Internal structure of the Erlend volcanic complex, north of Shetland, revealed by seismic reflection. *Journal of the Geological Society, London*, **141**, 555–562.

GATLIFF, R. W., RICHARDS, P. C., SMITH, K., GRAHAM, C. C., McCORMAC, M., SMITH, N. J. P., LONG, D., CAMERON, T. D. J., EVANS, D., STEVENSON, A. G., BULAT, J. & RITCHIE, J. D. 1994. *The Geology of the Central North Sea*. British Geological Survey Offshore Regional Report, HMSO, London.

GEBELEIN, C. D. & HOFFMAN, P. 1973. Algal origin of dolomite laminations in stromatolitic limestone. *Journal of Sedimentary Petrology*, **43**, 603–613.

GEE, D. & ROBERTS, D. 1983. Timing of deformation in the Scandinavian Caledonides. *In*: SCHENK, W. (ed.) *Regional Trends in the Geology of the Appalachian-Caledonian Orogen*. NATO ASI Series c, Reidel, 116–125.

GEIKIE, A. 1865. *The Scenery of Scotland Viewed in Connection with its Physical Geology*. Macmillan, London & Cambridge.

GEIKIE, A. 1869. Opening address – Thursday, 4th November 1869. *Transactions of the Edinburgh Geological Society Session 1869–70*, **2**, 1–13.

GEIKIE, A. 1875. *Life of Sir Roderick Murchison*. 2 vols. John Murray, London.

GEIKIE, A. 1884. The crystalline schists of the Scottish Highlands. *Nature, London*, **31**, 29–31.

GEIKIE, A. 1888. Report on the recent work of the Geological Survey in the north-west Highlands of Scotland based on the field notes and maps of Messers. B. N. Peach, J. Horne, W. Gunn, C. T Clough, L. Hinxman and H. M. Cadell. *Quarterly Journal of the Geological Society of London*, **44**, 378–439.

GEIKIE, A. 1891. Anniversary address of the President. *Proceedings of the Geological Society of London*, **47**, 48–162.

GEIKIE, A. 1893a. *Annual Report of the Geological Survey and Museum of Practical Geology for the Year Ending December 31, 1892*. Eyre & Spottiswoode, London.

GEIKIE, A. 1893b. On the pre-Cambrian rocks of the British Isles. *Journal of Geology*, **1**, 1–14.

GEIKIE, A. 1894. On the relations of the basic and acidic rocks of the Tertiary volcanic series of the Inner Hebrides. *Quarterly Journal of the Geological Society of London*, **50**, 212–231.

GEIKIE, A. 1895. *Report of the Geological Survey and Museum for 1894*.

GEIKIE, A. 1897a. *Annual Report of the Geological Survey and Museum of Practical Geology for the Year Ending December 31, 1896*. Eyre & Spottiswoode, London.

GEIKIE, A. 1897b. *The Ancient Volcanoes of Great Britain*. 2 vols. Macmillan, London & New York.

GEIKIE, A. 1905. *The Founders of Geology*. Macmillan, London & New York.

GEIKIE, A. 1906. The history of the geography of Scotland. *Scottish Geographical Magazine*, **22**, 117–134.

GEIKIE, J. 1885. The physical features of Scotland. *The Scottish Geographical Magazine* **1**, 26–41 & map.

GELDMACHER, J., HAASE, K. M., DEVEY, C. W. & GARBE-SCHONBERG, C. D. 1998. The petrogenesis of Tertiary cone-sheets in Ardnamurchan, NW Scotland: petrological and geochemical constraints on crustal contamination and partial melting. *Contributions to Mineralogy and Petrology*, **131**, 196–209.

GELUK, M. C. & RÖHLING, H-G. 1999. High-resolution sequence stratigraphy of the Lower Triassic Buntsandstein: a new tool for basin analysis. *Epicontinental Triassic*. Zentralblatt für Geologie und Paläontologie. **1**, 727–745.

GEOLOGICAL SURVEY OF GREAT BRITAIN 1959. *Summary of progress of the Geological Survey of Great Britain and the Museum of Practical Geology 1959*. London, HMSO.

GEORGE, T. N. 1955. Drainage in the Southern Uplands: Clyde, Nith, Annan. *Transactions of the Geological Society of Glasgow*, **22**, 1–34.

GEORGE, T. N. 1960. The stratigraphical evolution of the Midland Valley. *Transactions of the Geological Society of Glasgow*, **24**, 32–107.

GEORGE, T. N. 1965. The geological growth of Scotland. *In*: CRAIG, G. Y. (ed.) *The Geology of Scotland* (1st edition). Oliver & Boyd, Edinburgh, 1–48.

GEORGE, T. N., JOHNSON, G. A. L., MITCHELL, M., PRENTICE, J. E., RAMSBOTTOM, W. H. C., SEVASTOPULO, G. D. & WILSON, R. B. 1976. *A Correlation of Dinantian Rocks in the British Isles*. Geological Society, London, Special Report, **7**.

GIBB, F. G. F. & GIBSON, S. A. 1989. The Little Minch Sill Complex. *Scottish Journal of Geology*, **20**, 21–29.

GIBB, F. G. F. & HENDERSON, C. M. B. 1978. The petrology of the Dippin Sill, Isle of Arran. *Scottish Journal of Geology*, **14**, 1–27.

GIBB, F. G. F. & HENDERSON, C. M. B. 1996. The Shiant Isles Main Sill: structure and mineral fractionation trends. *Mineralogical Magazine*, **60**, 67–98.

GIBB, F. G. F. & KANARIS-SOTIRIOU, R. 1988. The geochemistry and origin of the Faeroe-Shetland Sill Complex. *In*: MORTON, A. C. & PARSON, L. M. (eds) *Early Tertiary Volcanism and the Opening of the NE Atlantic*. Geological Society, London, Special Publications, **39**, 241–252.

GIBB, F. G. F., KANARIS-SOTIRIOU, R. & NEVES, R. 1986. A new Tertiary sill complex of mid-ocean ridge basalt type NNE of the Shetland Isles: a preliminary report. *Transactions of the Royal Society of Edinburgh: Earth Sciences*, **77**, 223–230.

GIBBONS, W. & GAYER, R. A. 1985. British Caledonian Terranes. *In*: GAYER, R. A. (ed.) *The Tectonic Evolution of the Caledonian-Appalachian Orogen*. Viewseg, Brunswick, 3–16.

GIBSON, S. A. 1990. The geochemistry of the Trotternish sills, Isle of Skye: crustal contamination in the British Tertiary Volcanic Province. *Journal of the Geological Society, London*, **147**, 1071–1081.

GIBSON, S. A. & JONES, A. P. 1991. Igneous stratigraphy and internal structure of the Little Minch Sill Complex, Trotternish Peninsula, northern Skye, Scotland. *Geological Magazine*, **128**, 51–66.

GIBSON, W. 1922. Cannel coals, lignite and mineral oil in Scotland. *Special Report on Mineral Resources of Great Britain*, HMSO, **24**, 56–63.

GILETTI, B., MOORBATH, S. & LAMBERT, R. ST. J. 1961. A geochronological study of the metamorphic complexes of the Scottish Highlands. *Quarterly Journal of the Geological Society, London*, **117**, 233–264.

GILLANDERS, R. J. 1981. The Leadhills–Wanlockhead mining district, Scotland. *The Mineralogical Record*, **12**, 235–250.

GILLEN, C. 1987. Huntly, Elgin and Lossiemouth. *In*: TREWIN, N. H., KNELLER, B. C. & GILLEN, C. (eds) *Excursion Guide to the Geology of the Aberdeen Area*. Geological Society of Aberdeen, Scottish Academic Press, Edinburgh, 149–160.

GILLEN, C. & TREWIN, N. H. 1987a. Dunnottar to Stonehaven and the Highland Boundary Fault. *In*: TREWIN, N. H., KNELLER, B. C. & GILLEN, C. (eds) *Excursion Guide to the Geology of the Aberdeen Area*. Geological Society of Aberdeen, Scottish Academic Press, Edinburgh, 265–273.

GILLEN, C. & TREWIN, N. H. 1987b. Excursion 23: Dunnottar to Stonehaven and the Highland Boundary Fault. *In*: TREWIN, N. H., KNELLER, B. C. & GILLEN, C. (eds) *Excursion Guide to the Geology of the Aberdeen Area*. Geological Society of Aberdeen, Scottish Academic Press, Edinburgh.

GILLISPIE, C. C. 1959. *Genesis and Geology: A Study of Scientific Thought, Natural Theology, and Social Opinion in Great Britain, 1790–1850*. Harper & Brothers, New York.

GLAZNER, A. F. 1991. Plutonism, oblique subduction and continental growth: An example from the Mesozoic of California. *Geology*, **19**, 784–786.

GLENDINNING, N. R. W. 1988. Sedimentary structures and sequences within a late Proterozoic tidal shelf deposit: the Upper Morar Psammite Formation of northwestern Scotland. *In*: WINCHESTER, J. A. (ed.) *Later Proterozoic Stratigraphy of the Northern Atlantic Regions*. Blackie, Glasgow, 14–31.

GLENDINNING, N. R. W. 1989. *Sedimentology of Proterozoic, Moine Rocks of West Scotland*. PhD thesis, University of London.

GLENNIE, K. W. 1972. Permian Rotliegendes of Northwest Europe interpreted in light of modern desert sedimentation studies. *AAPG Bulletin*, **56**, 1048–1071.

GLENNIE, K. W. 1997. Recent advances in understanding the southern North Sea Basin: a summary. *In*: ZIEGLER, K., TURNER, P. & DAINES, S. R. (eds) *Petroleum Geology of the Southern North Sea: Future Potential*. Geological Society, London, Special Publications, **123**, 17–29.

GLENNIE, K. W. (ed.) 1998a. *Petroleum Geology of the North Sea*. 4th Edition, Blackwell, Oxford.

GLENNIE, K. W. 1998b. Lower Permian-Rotliegend. *In*: GLENNIE, K. W. (ed.) *Petroleum Geology of the North Sea*. 4th Edition, Blackwell, Oxford, 137–173.

GLENNIE, K. W. 2000. Contribution of the Scottish offshore to the advancement of geology. *Scottish Journal of Geology*, **36**, 17–32.

GLENNIE, K. W. & ARMSTRONG, L. A. 1991. The Kittiwake Field, Block 21/18, UK North Sea. *In*: ABBOTTS, I. L. (ed.) *United Kingdom Oil and Gas Fields 25 years Commemorative Volume*. Geological Society of London, Memoir, **14**, 339–345.

GLENNIE, K. W. & BULLER, A. T. 1983. The Permian Weissliegend of NW Europe: the partial deformation of aeolian dune sands caused by the Zechstein transgression. *Sedimentary Geology*, **35**, 43–81.

GLENNIE, K. W. & UNDERHILL, J. R. 1998. Origin, development and evolution of structural styles. *In*: GLENNIE, K. W. (ed.) *Petroleum Geology of the North Sea*. Blackwell, Oxford, 42–84.

GLENNIE, K. W., HIGHAM, J. & STEMMERIK, L. 2003. Permian. *In*: EVANS, D., GRAHAM. C., ARMOUR, A. & BATHURST, P. (eds) *Millennium Atlas: Petroleum Geology of the Northern North Sea*, 91–103.

GLOVER, B. W. 1993. The sedimentology of the Neoproterozoic Grampian Group and the significance of the Fort William Slide between Spean Bridge and Rubha Cuil-cheanna, Inverness-shire. *Scottish Journal of Geology*, **29**, 29–43.

GLOVER, B. W. & McKIE, T. 1996. A sequence stratigraphic approach to the understanding of basin history in orogenic Neoproterozoic successions: an example from the central Highlands of Scotland. *In*: HESSELBO, S. P. & PARKINSON, D. N. (eds) *Sequence Stratigraphy in British Geology*. Geological Society, London, Special Publications, **103**, 257–269.

GLOVER, B. W. & WINCHESTER, J. A. 1989. The Grampian Group: a major Late Proterozoic clastic sequence in the Central Highlands of Scotland. *Journal of the Geological Society, London*, **146**, 85–97.

GLOVER, B. W., KEY, R. M., MAY, F., CLARK, G. C., PHILLIPS, E. R. & CHACKSFIELD, B. C. 1995. A Neoproterozoic multiphase rift sequence: the Grampian and Appin groups of the southern Monadhliath Mountains of Scotland. *Journal of the Geological Society, London*, **152**, 391–406.

GOBBETT, D. J. & WILSON, C. B. 1960. The Oslobreen Series, Upper Hecla Hoek of Ny Friesland, Spitsbergen. *Geological Magazine*, **97**, 441–457.

GODCHAUX, M. M., BONNISCHSEN, W. & JENKS, M. D. 1992. Types of phreatomagmatic volcanoes in the western Snake River Plain, Idaho, USA. *Journal of Volcanology and Geothermal Research*, **52**, 1–25.

GOLDSMITH, P. J., RICH, B. & STANDRING, J. 1995. Triassic correlation and stratigraphy in the South Central Graben, UK North Sea. *In*: BOLDY, S. A. R. (ed.) *Permian and Triassic Rifting in Northwest Europe*. Geological Society, London, Special Publications, **91**, 123–143.

GOODLET, G. A. 1957. Lithological variations in the Lower Limestone Group in the Midland Valley of Scotland. *Bulletin of the Geological Survey of Great Britain*, **12**, 52–65.

GOODMAN, S. & WINCHESTER, J. A. 1993. Geochemical variations within metavolcanic rocks of the Dalradian Farragon Beds and adjacent formations. *Scottish Journal of Geology*, **29**, 131–141.

GOODMAN, S., CRANE, A., KRABBENDAM, M. & LESLIE, A. G. 1997. Correlation of lithostratigraphic sequences in a structurally complex area: Gleann Fearnach to Glen Shee, Scotland. *Transactions of the Royal Society of Edinburgh*, **87**, 503–513.

GORDON, J. E. 1996. *Restoration and Management of Mineral Extraction Sites in Quaternary Landforms and Deposits*. Information and Advice Note, No. 41, Scottish Natural Heritage, Edinburgh.

GORDON, J. E. & CAMPBELL, S. 1992. Conservation of glacial deposits in Great Britain: a framework for assessment and protection of sites of special scientific interest. *Geomorphology*, **6**, 89–97.

GORDON, J. E. & MACFADYEN, C. C. J. 2001. Earth heritage conservation in Scotland: state, pressure and issues. *In*: GORDON, J. E. & LEYS, K. F. (eds) *Earth Sciences and the Natural Heritage: Interactions and Integrated Management*. The Stationery Office, Edinburgh.

GORDON, J. E. & SUTHERLAND, D. G. (eds) 1994. *Quaternary of Scotland*. Geological Conservation Review, **6**, Joint Nature Conservation Committee, Peterborough.

GOROKHOV, I. M., SIEDLECKA, A., ROBERTS, D., MELNIKOV, N. N. & TURCHENKO, T. L. 2001. Rb–Sr dating of diagenetic illite in Neoproterozoic shales, Varanger Peninsula, northern Norway. *Geological Magazine*, **138**, 541–562.

GOULD, D. 1997. *Geology of the Country around Inverurie and Alford*. Memoir of the British Geological Survey, Sheets 76W and 76E (Scotland).

GOWER, C. F. 1988. The Double Mer Formation. *In*: WINCHESTER, J. A. (ed.) *Later Proterozoic Stratigraphy of the northern Atlantic regions*. Blackie, Glasgow, 113–118.

GOWLAND, S. 1996. Facies characteristics and depositional models of highly bioturbated shallow marine siliciclastic strata: an example from the Fulmar Formation Late Jurassic, UK Central Graben. *In*: HURST, A., JOHNSON, H. D., BURLEY, S. D., CANHAM, A. C. & MACKERTICH, D. S. (eds) *Geology of the Humber Group: Central Graben and Moray Firth, UKCS*. Geological Society, London, Special Publications, **114**, 185–214.

GRABAU, A. W. 1916. Comparison of American and European Lower Ordovician Formation. *Bulletin of the Geological Society of America*, **27**, 562–563.

GRACIE, A. J. & STEWART, A. D. 1967. Torridonian sediments at Enard Bay, Ross-shire. *Scottish Journal of Geology*, **3**, 181–194.

GRADSTEIN, F. M. & OGG, J. 1996. A Phanerozoic time scale. *Episodes*, **19**, 3–4.

GRADSTEIN, F. M., KRISTIANSEN, I. L., LOEMO, L. & KAMINSKI, M. A. 1992. Cenozoic foraminiferal and dinoflagellate cyst biostratigraphy of the central North Sea. *Micropalaeontology*, **38**, 101–137.

GRAHAM, A. M. & UPTON, B. G. J. 1978. Gneisses in diatremes, Scottish Midland Valley: petrology and tectonic implications. *Journal of the Geological Society, London*, **135**, 219–228.

GRAHAM, C. M. 1983. High-pressure greenschist to epidote-amphibolite facies metamorphism of Dalradian rocks of the SW Scottish Highlands: isograds and P-T conditions. *Newsletter, Geological Society, London*, **12**, 23.

GRAHAM, C. M. 1986a. Petrochemistry and tectonic significance of Dalradian metabasaltic rocks of the SW Scottish Highlands. *Journal of the Geological Society, London*, **132**, 61–84.

GRAHAM, C. M. 1986b. The role of the Cruachan Lineament during Dalradian evolution. *Scottish Journal of Geology*, **22**, 257–270.

GRAHAM, C. M. & HARTE, B. 1985. Conditions of Dalradian metamorphism. *Journal of the Geological Society, London*, **142**, 1–3.

GRAHAM, R. H. 1980. The role of shear belts in the structural evolution of the South Harris igneous complex. *Journal of Structural Geology*, **2**, 29–37.

GRAHAM, J. R., WRAFTER, J. P., DALY, J. S. & MENUGE, J. F. 1991. A local source for the Ordovician Derryveeny Formation, western Ireland: implications for the Connemara Dalradian. *In*: MORTON, A. C, TODD, S. P. & HAUGHTON, P. D. W. (eds) *Develoments in Sedimentary Provenance Studies*. Geological Society, London, Special Publications, **57**, 199–213.

GRAY, J. 1865. *Biographical Details of the Rev. David Ure; with an Examination Critical and Detailed of his History of Rutherglen and East Kilbride*. Hugh Hopkins, Glasgow.

GRAY, J. M. 1974. Lateglacial and postglacial shorelines in western Scotland. *Boreas*, **3**, 129–138.

GRAY, J. M. 1978. Low-level shore platforms in the south-west Scottish Highlands: altitude, age and correlation. *Transactions of the Institute of British Geographers*, **3**, 151–164.

GRAY, J. M. 1998. Hills of waste: a policy conflict in environmental geology *In*: BENNETT, M. R. & DOYLE, P. (eds) *Issues in Environmental Geology: A British Perspective*. Geological Society, London, 173–195.

GRAY, J. M. & IVANOVICH, M. 1988. Age of the Main Rock Platform, western Scotland. *Palaeogeography, Palaeoecology, Palaeoclimatology*, **68**, 337–345.

GRAY, J. M. & LOWE, J. J. 1977. The Scottish lateglacial environment: a synthesis. *In*: GRAY, J. M. & LOWE, J. J. (eds) *Studies in the Scottish Lateglacial Environment*. Oxford, 163–181.

GRAYSON, A. 1992. *Rock Solid*. Natural History Museum, London.

GREENWOOD, R. C., DONALDSON, C. H. & EMELEUS, C. H. 1990. The contact zone of the Rhum ultrabasic intrusion: evidence of peridotite formation from magnesian magmas. *Journal of the Geological Society, London*, **147**, 209–212.

GREGORY, J. W. 1910. Work for Glasgow geologists – The problems of the South-western Highlands. *Transactions of the Geological Society of Glasgow*, **14**, 1–29.

GREGORY, J. W. 1915. Moine pebbles in Torridonian conglomerates. *Geological Magazine* Decade 6, **2**, 447–450.

GREGORY, J. W. 1928. The nickel-cobalt ore of Talnotry, Kirkcudbrightshire. *Transactions of the Institution of Mining and Metallurgy*, **37**, 178–195.

GREGORY, J. W. 1931. *Dalradian Geology: The Dalradian Rocks of Scotland and their Equivalents in other Countries*. Methuen, London.

GREIG, D. C. 1971. *British Regional Geology: The South of Scotland* (3rd edition). HMSO, London.

GREIG, D. C. 1988. *Geology of the Eyemouth District*. British Geological Survey, Keyworth.

GREILING, R. O. & SMITH, A. G. 2000. The Dalradian of Scotland: Missing link between the Vendian of Northern & Southern Scandinavia? *Physics and Chemistry of the Earth (A)*, **25**, 495–498.

GRIBBLE, C. D. 1968. The cordierite-bearing rocks of the Haddo House and Arnage districts, Aberdeen-shire. *Contributions to Mineralogy and Petrology*, **17**, 315–330.

GRIBBLE, C. D. 1970. The role of partial fusion in the genesis of certain cordierite-bearing rocks. *Scottish Journal of Geology*, **6**, 75–82.

GRIBBLE, C. D. 1980. The geological case for large coastal quarries. *Quarry management and Products*, **8**.

GRIBBLE, C. D. 1981. The geological case for large coastal quarries. *Quarry Management and Products*, **8**, 268–270.

GRIBBLE, C. D. 1983. Mineral resources of the Inner Hebrides. *Proceedings of the Royal Society of Edinburgh*, **83B**, 611–625.

GRIBBLE, C. D. 1989. UK aggegate production and coastal quarries. *Quarry Management*, **16**, 31–33.

GRIBBLE, C. D. 1990. The sand and gravel deposits of the Strathkelvin Valley. *Quarry Management*, **17**, 29–31.

GRIBBLE, C. D. 1991. Coastal quarries – an update. *Quarry Management*, **18**, 23–24.

GRIBBLE, C. D. 1995. *Geological and other issues relevant to coastal superquarries*. Report (ref SNH/Lingarabay/RASD/ESB) Scottish Natural Heritage.

GRIBBLE, C. D. & O'HARA, M. J. 1967. Interaction of basic magma and pelitic materials. *Nature, London*, **214**, 1198–1201.

GRIBBLE, C. D. & WILSON, I. 1980. *Potential for Large Scale Coastal Quarries in Scotland*. Report to the Scottish Development Department.

GUIRDHAM, C. 1998. *Regional Stratigraphy, Lithofacies, Diagenesis and Dolomitisation of Microbial Carbonates in the Lower Carboniferous, West Lothian Oil-Shale Formation*. PhD thesis, University of East Anglia.

GUN, A. G., LEAKE, R. C. & STYLES, M. T. 1985. Platinum-group element mineralization in the Unst ophiolite, Shetland. *Institute of Geological Sciences, Mineral Reconnaissance Programme*, Report **73**.

GUST, D. A., BIDDLE, K. T., PHELPS, D. W. & ULIANA, M. A. 1985. Associated middle to late Jurassic volcanism and extension in southern South America. *Tectonophysics*, **116**, 223–253.

HADFIELD, P. 2002. Destroyer of worlds. *New Scientist*, No. **2327**, 11.

HALDANE, D. & EYLES, V. A. 1945. Diatomite. Wartime pamphlet, Geological Survey of England and Wales, **5**.

HALL, A. J. 1993. Stratiform mineralisation in the Dalradian of Scotland. *In*: PATTRICK, R. A. D. & POLYA, D. A. (eds). *Mineralisation in the British Isles*. Chapman and Hall, London, 38–101.

HALL, A. J., BOYCE, A. J. & FALLICK, A. E. 1988. A sulphur isotope study of iron sulphides in the Late Precambrian Dalradian Easdale Slate Formation, Argyll, Scotland. *Mineralogical Magazine*, **52**, 483–490.

HALL, A. J., BOYCE, A. J., FALLICK, A. E. & HAMILTON, P. J. 1991. Isotopic evidence of the depositional environment of Late Proterozoic stratiform barite mineralization, Aberfeldy, Scotland. *Chemical Geology*, **87**, 99–114.

HALL, A. M. 1984. Introduction. *In*: HALL, A. M. (ed.) *Buchan Field Guide*. Quaternary Research Association, Cambridge, 1–26.

HALL, A. M. 1985. Cenozoic weathering covers in Buchan, Scotland and their significance. *Nature, London*, **315**, 392–395.

HALL, A. M. 1991. Pre-Quaternary landscape evolution in the Scottish Highlands. *Transactions of the Royal Society of Edinburgh; Earth Sciences*, **82**, 1–26.

HALL, A. M. & JARVIS, J. 1989. A preliminary report on the Late Devensian glaciomarine deposits at St. Fergus, Grampian region. *Quaternary Newsletter*, **59**, 5–7.

HALL, A. M. & JARVIS, J. 1993a. Kirkhill. *In*: GORDON, J. E. & SUTHERLAND, D. G. (eds) *Quaternary of Scotland*. Chapman and Hall, London, 225–230.

HALL, A. M. & JARVIS, J. 1993b. A concealed Lower Cretaceous outlier at Moss of Cruden, Grampian Region. *Scottish Journal of Geology*, **30**, 163–166.

HALL, A. M. & WHITTINGTON, G. 1989. Late Devensian Glaciation of southern Caithness. *Scottish Journal of Geology*, **25**, 307–324.

HALL, A. M., WHITTINGTON, G. & GORDON, J. E. 1993. Interglacial peat at Fugla Ness, Shetland. *In*: BIRNIE, J., GORDON, J. E., BENNETT, K. D. & HALL, A. M. (eds) *The Quaternary of Shetland*: Field Guide. Quaternary Research Association, London, 62–76.

HALL, I. H. S. & CHISHOLM, J. I. 1987. Aeolian sediments in the late Devonian of the Scottish Midland valley. *Scottish Journal of Geology*, **23**, 203–208.

HALL, I. H. S., GALLAGHER, M. J., SKILTON, B. R. H. & JOHNSON, C. E. 1982. *Investigation of Polymetallic Mineralisation in Lower*

Devonian Volcanics near Alva, Central Scotland. Mineral Reconnaissance Report, Institute of Geological Sciences, **53**.

HALL, I. H. S., BROWNE, M. A. E. & FORSYTH, I. H. 1998. *Geology of the Glasgow District*. Memoir of the British Geological Survey.

HALL, J. 1805. Experiments on whinstone and lava. *Transactions of the Royal Society of Edinburgh*, **5**, 43–76.

HALL, J. 1812. Account of a series of experiments, showing the effects of compression in modifying the action of heat. *Transactions of the Royal Society of Edinburgh*, **6**, 71–186.

HALL, J. 1826. On the consolidation of the strata of the earth. *Transactions of the Royal Society of Edinburgh*, **10**, 314–329.

HALL, J. 1974. A seismic reflection survey of the Clyde Plateau lavas in north Ayrshire and Renfrewshire. *Scottish Journal of Geology*, **9**, 253–279.

HALL, J. 1985. Geophysical constraints on crustal structure in the Dalradian region of Scotland. *Journal of the Geological Society, London*, **142**, 149–155.

HALL, J. 1987. Physical properties of Lewisian rocks: implications for deep crustal structure. *In*: PARK, R. G. & TARNEY, J. (eds) *Evolution of the Lewisian and Comparable Precambrian High Grade Terrains*. Geological Society, London, Special Publications, **27**, 185–192.

HALL, J. & AL-HADDAD, F. M. 1976. Seismic velocities in the Lewisian metamorphic complex, northwest Britain – 'in situ' measurements. *Scottish Journal of Geology*, **12**, 305–314.

HALL, J., POWELL, D. W., WARNER, M. R., EL-ISA, Z. H. M., ADESANYA, O. & BLUCK, B. J. 1983. Seismological evidence for shallow crystalline basement in the Southern Uplands of Scotland. *Nature, London*, **305**, 418–420.

HALL, J., BREWER, J. A., MATHEWS, D. H. & WARNER, M. R. 1984. Crustal structure across the Caledonides from the WINCH seismic reflection profile: influences on the evolution of the Midland Valley of Scotland. *Transactions of the Royal Society of Edinburgh: Earth Sciences*, **75**, 97–109.

HALL, S. 1910. *Dr. Duncan of Ruthwell*. Oliphant, Anderson & Ferrier, London & Edinburgh.

HALLAM, A. 1959. Stratigraphy of the Broadford Beds of Skye, Raasay and Applecross. *Proceedings of the Yorkshire Geological Society*, **32**, 165–184.

HALLAM, A. 1965. Jurassic, Cretaceous and Tertiary sediments. *In*: CRAIG, G. Y. (ed.) *The Geology of Scotland* (1st edition). Oliver & Boyd, Edinburgh, 401–444.

HALLAM, A. 1969. Faunal realms and facies in the Jurassic. *Palaeontology*, **12**, 1–18.

HALLAM, A. 1975. *Jurassic Environments*. Cambridge University Press.

HALLAM, A. 1983. Jurassic, Cretaceous and Tertiary sediments. *In*: CRAIG, G. Y. (ed.) *Geology of Scotland* (2nd Edition). Scottish Academic Press, Edinburgh, 343–356.

HALLAM, A. 1991. Jurassic, Cretaceous and Tertiary sediments. *In*: CRAIG, G. Y. (ed.) *Geology of Scotland* (3rd Edition). Geological Society, London, 439–453.

HALLAM, A. & BRADSHAW, M. J. 1979. Bituminous shales and oolite ironstones as indicators of transgressions and regressions. *Journal of the Geological Society, London*, **136**, 157–164.

HALLETT, D., DURANT, G. P. & FARROW, G. E. 1985. Oil exploration and production in Scotland. *Scottish Journal of Geology*, **21**, 547–570.

HALLIDAY, A. N. 1977. K-Ar dating of mineralisation episodes – a discussion. *Economic Geology*, **72**, 870–871.

HALLIDAY, A. N. 1984. Coupled Sm–Nd and U–Pb systematics in late Caledonian granites and basement under northern Britain. *Nature, London*, **307**, 229–233.

HALLIDAY, A. N., AFTALION, M., VAN BREEMEN, O. & JOCELYN, J. 1979. Petrogenesis and significance of Rb–Sr and U–Pb isotopic systems in the 400 Ma old British Isles granitoids and their hosts. *In*: HARRIS, A. L., HOLLAND, C. H. & LEAKE, B. E. (eds) *The Caledonides of the British Isles – Reviewed*. Geological Society, London, Special Publications, **8**, 653–662.

HALLIDAY, A. N., STEPHENS, W. E. & HARMON, R. S. 1980. Rb–Sr and O isotopic relationships in zoned Caledonian granitic plutons, Southern Uplands, Scotland: evidence for varied sources

and hybridization of magmas. *Journal of the Geological Society, London*, **137**, 329–348.

HALLIDAY, A. N., AFTALION, M., UPTON, B. G. J., ASPEN, P. & JOCELYN, J. 1984. U–Pb isotopic ages from a granulite-facies xenolith from Partan Craig in the Midland Valley of Scotland. *Transactions of the Royal Society of Edinburgh: Earth Sciences*, **75**, 71–74.

HALLIDAY, A. N., STEPHENS, W. E., HUNTER, R. H., MENZIES, M. A., DICKIN, A. P. & HAMILTON, P. J. 1985. Isotopic and chemical constraints on the building of the deep Scottish lithosphere. *Scottish Journal of Geology*, **21**, 456–491.

HALLIDAY, A. N., AFTALION, M., PARSONS, I., DICKIN, A. P. & JOHNSON, M. R. W. 1987. Syn-orogenic alkaline magmatism and its relationship to the Moine Thrust Zone and the thermal state of the lithosphere in Northwest Scotland. *Journal of the Geological Society, London*, **144**, 611–617.

HALLIDAY, A. N., DICKIN, A. P., HUNTER, R. H., DAVIES, G. R., DEMPSTER, T. J., HAMILTON, J. P. & UPTON, B. G. J. 1993. Formation and composition of the lower continental crust: Evidence from Scottish xenolith suites. *Journal of Geophysical Research*, **98**, 581–607.

HAMBREY, M. J., FAIRCHILD, I. J., GLOVER, B. W., STEWART, A. D., TREAGUS, J. E. & WINCHESTER, J. A. 1991. The late Precambrian geology of the Scottish Highlands and islands. *Geologists' Association Guide*, **44**, 1–130.

HAMILTON, B. M. 1989. British geologists' changing perceptions of Precambrian time in the nineteenth century. *Earth Sciences History*, **8**, 141–149.

HAMILTON, M. A., PEARSON, D. G., THOMPSON, R. N., KELLEY, S. P. & EMELEUS, C. H. 1998. Rapid eruption of Skye lavas inferred from precise U–Pb and Ar–Ar dating of the Rum and Cuillin plutonic complexes. *Nature, London*, **394**, 260–263.

HAMILTON, M. A., PEARSON, D. G., EMELEUS, C. H. & THOMPSON. R. N. 1999. Precise U–Pb zircon dating of Hebredian igneous centres and their implications for lithospheric evolution and magnetostratigraphy: a progress report. Conference Proceedings. *The North Atlantic Igneous Province: Magmatic Controls on Sedimentation*. Geological Society of London, April 1999.

HAMILTON, P. J., EVENSEN, N. M., O'NIONS, R. K. & TARNEY, J. 1979. Sm–Nd systematics of Lewisian gneisses: implications for the origin of granulites. *Nature, London*, **277**, 25–28.

HAMILTON, P. J., BLUCK, B. J. & HALLIDAY, A. N. 1984. Sm–Nd ages from the Ballantrae Complex, SW Scotland. *Transactions of the Royal Society of Edinburgh: Earth Sciences*, **75**, 183–187.

HAMILTON, R. F. M. & TREWIN, N. H. 1988. Environmental controls on fish faunas of the Middle Devonian Orcadian Basin. *In*: MCMILLAN, N. J., EMBRY, A. F. & GLASS, D. J. (eds) *Devonian of the World*. Canadian Society of Petroleum Geologists, Memoir **14**, Vol. III, 589–600.

HAMILTON, R. F. M. & TREWIN, N. H. 1994. Taphonomy of fish beds from the Upper Flagstone Group of the Middle Old Red Sandstone, Caithness. *Scottish Journal of Geology*, **30**, 175–181.

HAMPSON, G., STOLLHOFEN, H. & FLINT, S. 1999. A sequence stratigraphic model for the Lower Coal Measures (Upper Carboniferous) of the Rhur district, north-west Germany. *Sedimentology*, **46**, 1119–1131.

HANCOCK, J. M. 2000. The Gribun Formation: clues to the latest Cretaceous history of western Scotland. *Scottish Journal of Geology*, **36**, 137–141.

HANCOCK, J. M. & RAWSON, P. F. 1992. Cretaceous. *In*: COPE, J. C. W., INGHAM, J. K. & RAWSON, P. F. (eds) *Atlas of Palaeogeography and Lithofacies*. Geological Society, London, Memoir, **13**, 113–139.

HANSEN, B. T. & KALSBEEK, F. 1989. Precise age for the Ammassalik intrusive complex. *Gronlands Geologiske Undersogelse Rapport*, **146**, 46–47.

HANSOM, J. D. 1999. The coastal geomorphology of Scotland: understanding sediment budgets for effective coastal management. *In*: BAXTER, J. M., DUNCAN, K., ATKINS, S. M. & LEES, G. (eds) *Scotland's Living Coastline*. The Stationery Office, Edinburgh, 34–44.

HARCOMBE-SMEE, B. J., PIPER, J. D. A., ROLPH, T. C. & THOMAS, D. N. 1996. A palaeomagnetic and palaeointensity study of the Mauchline lavas, south-west Scotland. *Physics of the Earth and Planetary Interiors*, **94**, 63–74.

HARDIE, L. A., SMOOT, J. P. & EUGSTER, H. P. 1978. Saline lakes and their deposits: a sedimentological approach. *Special Publications of the International Association of Sedimentologists*, **2**, 7–41.

HARDIE, W. G. 1968. Volcanic breccia and the Lower Old Red Sandstone unconformity, Glencoe, Argyll. *Scottish Journal of Geology*, **4**, 291–299.

HARDING, R. R. 1983. Zr-rich pyroxenes and glauconitic minerals in the Tertiary alkali granite of Ailsa Craig. *Scottish Journal of Geology*, **19**, 219–227.

HARDING, R. R., MERRIMAN, R. J. & NANCARROW, P. H. A. 1984. *St. Kilda: an Illustrated Account of the Geology*. Report of the British Geological Survey, **16**. HMSO, London.

HARKER, A. 1904. *The Tertiary Igneous Rocks of Skye*. Memoir of the Geological Survey: Scotland. Sheets 70 and 71.

HARKER, A. 1908. *The Geology of the Small Isles of Inverness-shire*. Memoir of the Geological Survey: Scotland. Sheet 60.

HARKER, A. 1917. Some aspects of igneous action in Britain. *Quarterly Journal of the Geological Society of London*, **73**, lxvii–xcvi.

HARKER, A. & CLOUGH, C. T. 1904. *The Tertiary Igneous Rocks of Skye*. HMSO, Glasgow.

HARKER, S. D. 1998. The palingenesy of the Piper oil field, UK North Sea. *Petroleum Geoscience*, **4**, 271–286.

HARKER, S. D. & CHERMAK, A. 1992. Detection and prediction of Lower Cretaceous sandstone distribution in the Scapa Field, North Sea. *In*: HARDMAN, R. F. P. (ed.) *Exploration Britain: Geological Insights for the Next Decade*. Geological Society, London, Special Publications, **67**, 221–246.

HARKER, S. D., GUSTAV, S. H. & RILEY, L. A. 1987. Triassic to Cenomanian stratigraphy of the Witch Ground Graben. *In*: BROOKS, J. & GLENNIE, K. (eds) *Petroleum Geology of Northwest Europe*, Graham & Trotman, London, 809–818.

HARKER, S. D., GREEN, S. C. H. & ROMANI, R. S. 1991. The Claymore Field, Block 14/19, UK North Sea. *In*: ABBOTTS, I. L. (ed.) *United Kingdom Oil and Gas Fields 25 Years Commemorative Volume*. Geological Society, London, Memoir, **14**, 269–278.

HARKER, S. D., MANTELL, K. A., MORTON, D. J. & RILEY, L. A. 1993. The stratigraphy of Oxfordian-Kimmeridgian late Jurassic reservoir sandstones in the Witch Ground Graben, United Kingdom North Sea. *AAPG Bulletin*, **77**, 1693–1709.

HARKNESS, R. 1850. On the New Red Sandstone of the southern Portion of the vale of the Nith. *Quarterly Journal of the Geological Society of London*, **6**, 389–399.

HARKNESS, R. 1851. On the Silurian rocks of Dumfriesshire and Kirkcudbrightshire. *Quarterly Journal of the Geological Society of London*, **7**, 46–58.

HARKNESS, R. 1861. On the rocks of the portions of the Highlands of Scotland south of the Caledonian Canal; and on their equivalents in the north of Ireland. *Quarterly Journal of the Geological Society of London*, **17**, 256–271.

HARLAND, W. B. & GAYER, R. A. 1972. The arctic Caledonides and earlier oceans. *Geological Magazine*, **109**, 289–314.

HARLAND, W., ARMSTRONG, R. L., COX, A. V., CRAIG, L. E., SMITH, A. G. & SMITH, D. G. 1990. *A Geologic Time Scale 1989*. Cambridge University Press.

HARMON, R. S. 1983. Oxygen and strontium isotope evidence regarding the role of continental crust in the origin and evolution of the British Caledonian granites. *In*: ATHERTON, M. P. & GRIBBLE, C. D. (eds) *Migmatites, Melting and Metamorphism*. Shiva, Orpington, 62–79.

HARMON, R. S., MACLEOD, S., HOERNES, S., WEISS, S., TROLL, G. & PATTISON, D. 1985. Oxygen and hydrogen isotope geochemistry of the Ballachulish igneous complex, associated porphyry-style mineralization, and contact metamorphic aureole. *In*: TAYLOR, R. P. & STRONG, D. F. (eds) *Granite-Related Mineral Deposits*. Canadian Institution of Mining Conference, Halifax, Nova Scotia, 132–136.

HARPER, C. T. 1967. The geological interpretation of potassium–argon ages of metamorphic rocks from the Scottish Caledonides. *Scottish Journal of Geology*, **3**, 46–66.

HARPER, D. A. T. 1982. The Stratigraphy of the Drummuck Group (Ashgill), Girvan. *Geological Journal*, **17**, 251–277.

HARRIS, A. L. 1991. The growth and structure of Scotland. *In*: CRAIG, G. Y. (ed.) *Geology of Scotland* (3rd edition). Geological Society, London, 1–24.

HARRIS, A. L. 1995. The nature and timing of orogenesis in the Scottish Highlands and the role of the Great Glen Fault. *In*: HIBBARD, J., VAN STAAL, C. R. & CAWOOD, P. A. (eds) *Current Perspectives in the Appalachian-Caledonian Orogen*. Geological Association of Canada, Special Paper, **41**, 65–79.

HARRIS, A. L. & FETTES, D. J. 1972. Stratigraphy and structure of Upper Dalradian rocks at the Highland Border. *Scottish Journal of Geology*, **8**, 253–264.

HARRIS, A. L. & JOHNSON, M. R. W. 1991. Moine. *In*: CRAIG, G. Y. (ed.) *Geology of Scotland* (3rd edition). Geological Society, London, 87–123.

HARRIS, A. L. & PITCHER, W. S. 1975. The Dalradian Supergroup. *In*: HARRIS, A. L., SHACKLETON, R. M., WATSON, J. V., DOWNIE, C., HARLAND, W. B. & MOORBATH, S. (eds) *A Correlation of Precambrian Rocks in the British Isles*. Geological Society, London, Special Report, **6**, 52–75.

HARRIS, A. L., BRADBURY, H. J. & McGONIGAL, M. H. 1976. The evolution and transport of the Tay Nappe. *Scottish Journal of Geology*, **12**, 103–113.

HARRIS, A. L., BALDWIN, C. T., BRADBURY, H. J., JOHNSON, H. D. & SMITH, R. A. 1978. Ensialic basin sedimentation: the Dalradian Supergroup: *In*: BOWES, D. R. & LEAKE, B. E. (eds) *Crustal Evolution in Northwestern Britain and Adjacent Regions*. Geological Journal Special Issue, **10**, 115–138.

HARRIS, A. L., HIGHTON, A. J., ROBERTS, A. M. & STOKER, M. S. 1983. Discussion on the Glen Kyllachy Granite and its bearing on the Caledonian Orogeny in Scotland. *Journal of the Geological Society, London*, **140**, 961–963.

HARRIS, A. L., HASELOCK, P. J., KENNEDY, M. J. & MENDUM, J. R. 1994. The Dalradian Supergroup in Scotland, Shetland and Ireland. *In*: GIBBONS, W. & HARRIS, A. L. (eds) *A Revised Correlation of Precambrian Rocks in the British Isles*. Geological Society, London, Special Report, **22**, 33–53.

HARRIS, A. L., FETTES, D. J. & SOPER, N. J. 1998. Age of the Grampian event: a discussion of 'New evidence that the Lower Cambrian Leny Limestone at Callander, Perthshire, belongs to the Dalradian Supergroup, and a re-assessment of the 'exotic' status of the Highland Border Complex'. *Geological Magazine*, **135**, 575–579.

HARRIS, J. P. 1989. The sedimentology of a Middle Jurassic lagoonal delta system: Elgol Formation (Great Estuarine Group), NW Scotland. *In*: WHATELY, M. K. & PICKERING, K. (eds) *Deltas: Sites and Traps for Fossil Fuels*. Geological Society, London, Special Publications, **41**, 147–166.

HARRIS, J. P. 1992. Mid-Jurassic lagoonal delta systems in the Hebridean basins: thickness and facies distribution patterns of potential reservoir sand bodies. *In*: PARNELL, J. (ed.) *Basins on the Atlantic Seaboard: Petroleum Geology, Sedimentology and Basin Evolution*. Geological Society, London, Special Publications, **62**, 111–144.

HARRIS, J. P. & HUDSON, J. D. 1980. Lithostratigraphy of the Great Estuarine Group (Middle Jurassic), Inner Hebrides. *Scottish Journal of Geology*, **16**, 231–250.

HARRIS, M., KAY, E. A., WIDNALL, M. A., JONES, E. M. & STEELE, G. B. 1988a. Geology and mineralisation of the Lagalochan intrusive complex, western Argyll, Scotland. *Transactions of the Institution of Mining and Metallurgy*, **97**, B15–B21.

HARRIS, M., WIDNALL, M. A., JONES, E. M. & STEELE, G. B. 1988b. Application of top-of-bedrock geochemical sampling techniques at the Lagalochan intrusive complex, western Argyll, Scotland. *Transactions of the Institution of Mining and Metallurgy*, **97**, B22–B28.

HARRIS, P. M., FARRAR, E., MacINTYRE, R. M., MILLER, J. A. & YORK, D. 1965. Potassium–argon age measurements on two igneous rocks from the Ordovician system of Scotland. *Nature, London*, **205**, 352–353.

HARRISON, D. J. 1985. Mineralogical and chemical appraisal of Corrycharmaig serpentinite intrusion, Glen Lochay, Perthshire. *Transactions of the Institution of Mining and Metallurgy*, **94**, B147–B151.

HARRISON, R. K., STONE, P., CAMERON, I. B., ELLIOT, R. W. & HARDING, R. R. 1987. *Geology, Petrology and Geochemistry of Ailsa Craig, Ayrshire*. British Geological Survey Report **16(9)**.

HARRISON, T. N. 1987. The granitoids of eastern Aberdeenshire. *In*: TREWIN, N. H., KNELLER, B. C. & GILLEN, C. (eds) *Excursion Guide to the Geology of the Aberdeen area*. Scottish Academic Press, Edinburgh, 243–250.

HARRISON, T. N. & HUTCHINSON, J. 1987. The age and origin of the eastern Grampian Newer Granites. *Scottish Journal of Geology*, **23**, 269–282.

HARRY, W. T. 1953. The composite granitic gneiss of western Ardgour, Argyll. *Quarterly Journal of the Geological Society, London*, **109**, 285–308.

HARTE, B. 1988. Lower Palaeozoic metamorphism in the Moine-Dalradian belt of the British Isles. *In*: HARRIS, A. L. & FETTES, D. J. (eds) *The Caledonian-Appalachian Orogen*. Geological Society, London, Special Publications, **38**, 123–134.

HARTE, B. & HUDSON, N. F. C. 1979. Pelite facies series and the temperatures and pressures of Dalradian metamorphism. *In*: HARRIS, A. L., HOLLAND, C. H. & LEAKE, B. E. (eds) *The Caledonides of the British Isles – Reviewed*. Geological Society, London, Special Publications, **8**, 323–337.

HARTE, B. & JOHNSON, M. R. W. 1969. Metamorphic history of Dalradian rocks in Glens Clova, Esk and Lethnot, Angus, Scotland. *Scottish Journal of Geology*, **5**, 54–80.

HARTE, B., BOOTH, J. E., DEMPSTER, T. J., FETTES, D. J., MENDUM, J. R. & WATTS, D. 1984. Aspects of the post-depositional evolution of Dalradian and Highland Border Complex rocks in the Southern Highlands of Scotland. *Transactions of the Royal Society of Edinburgh: Earth Sciences*, **75**, 151–163.

HARTOG JAGER, D. DEN, GILES, M. R. & GRIFFITHS, G. R. 1993. Evolution of Paleogene submarine fans of the North Sea in space and time. *In*: PARKER, J. R. (ed.) *Petroleum Geology of Northwest Europe: Proceedings of the 4th Conference*. Geological Society, London, 59–71.

HASLAM, H. W. & CAMERON, D. G. 1985. Disseminated molybdenum mineralization in the Etive plutonic complex in the western Highlands of Scotland. *Institute of Geological Sciences, Mineral Reconnaissance Programme*, Report **76**.

HASLAM, H. W. & KIMBELL, G. S. 1981. Disseminated copper-molybdenum mineralization near Ballachulish, Highland Region. *Institute of Geological Sciences, Mineral Reconnaissance Programme*, Report **43**.

HASWELL, G. C. 1865. *On the Silurian Formations in the Pentland Hills*. William P. Nimmo, Edinburgh.

HASZELDINE, R. S., RITCHIE, J. D. & HITCHEN, K. 1987. Seismic and well evidence for the early development of the Faeroe-Shetland Basin. *Scottish Journal of Geology*, **23**, 283–300.

HAUBOLD, H. 1971. Ichnia Amphibiorum et Reptilorum fossilium. *In*: KUHN, O. (ed.). *Handbuch der Palaeoherpetologie*, Fisher, Stuttgart, **18**, 1–124.

HAUGHTON, P. D. W. 1988. A cryptic Caledonian flysch terrane in Scotland. *Journal of the Geological Society, London*, **145**, 685–703.

HAUGHTON, P. D. W. & BLUCK, B. J. 1988. Diverse alluvial sequences from the Lower Old Red Sandstone of the Strathmore Region, Scotland. Implications for the relationship between late Caledonian tectonics and sedimentation. *In*: MCMILLAN, N. J., EMBRY, A. F. & GLASS, D. J. (eds) *Devonian of the World*. Canadian Society of Petroleum Geologists, Memoir, **14**, Vol. II, 269–293.

HAUGHTON, P. D. W. & HALLIDAY, A. N. 1991. Significance of a late Caledonian igneous complex revealed by clasts in the Lower Old Red Sandstone conglomerates, central Scotland. *Geological Society of America, Bulletin*, **103**, 1476–1492.

HAUGHTON, P. D. W., ROGERS, G. & HALLIDAY, A. N. 1990. Provenance of Lower Old Red Sandstone conglomerates, SE Kincardineshire: evidence for the timing of Caledonian terrane accretion in central Scotland. *Journal of the Geological Society, London*, **147**, 105–120.

HAWKES, J. R., MERRIMAN, R. J., HARDING, R. R. & DARBYSHIRE, D. P. F. 1975. Rockall Island: new geological, petrological, chemical and Rb–Sr age data. *In*: HARRISON, R. K. (ed.) *Expeditions to Rockall 1971–72*. Institute of Geological Sciences Report **75/1**, 11–51.

HAWSON, C. A. & HALL, A. J. 1987. Middle Dalradian Corrycharmaig serpentinite, Perthshire, Scotland: an ultramafic intrusion. *Transactions of the Institution of Mining and Metallurgy*, **96**, B173–B177.

HAY CUNNINGHAM, R. J. 1831–1837. On the geology of the Lothians. *Memoirs of the Wernerian Natural History Society*, **7**, 1–158.

HAY CUNNINGHAM, R. J. 1838. *Essay on the Geology of the Lothians*. Neill & Co., Edinburgh.

HAY CUNNINGHAM, R. J. 1841. Geognostic account of the County of Sutherland. *Transactions of the Highland and Agricultural Society of Scotland*, New Series, **7**, 73–114.

HAYNES, V. M. 1995. Scotland's landforms: a review. *Scottish Association of Geography Teachers' Journal*, **24**, 18–37.

HEAMAN, L. M. & TARNEY, J. 1989. U–Pb baddeleyite ages for the Scourie dyke swarm, Scotland: evidence for two distinct intrusion events. *Nature, London*, **340**, 705–708.

HEBDON, N. J., ATKINSON, T. C. & LAWSON, T. J. 1997. Rate of glacial valley deepening during the late Quaternary in Assynt, Scotland. *Earth Surface Processes and Landforms*, **22**, 307–315.

HEDDLE, M. F. 1923–1924. GOODCHILD, J. G. (ed.) *The Mineralogy of Scotland*, Vols 1–2, Vol. 1, 1923; Vol. 2, 1924, David Douglas, Edinburgh.

HEINZ, W. & LOESCHKE, J. 1988. Volcanic clasts in Silurian conglomerates of the Midland Valley (Hagshaw Hills Inlier) Scotland, and their meaning for Caledonian plate tectonics. *Geologische Rundschau*, **77**, 453–466.

HEMSLEY, A. R. 1990. *Parka decipiens* and land plant spore evolution. *Historical Biology*, **4**, 39–50.

HENDERSON, C. M. B. & GIBB, F. G. F. 1987. The petrology of the Lugar Sill, SW Scotland. *Transactions of the Royal Society of Edinburgh*, **77**, 115–126.

HENDERSON, C. M. B., FOLLAND, K. A. & GIBB, F. G. F. 1987. The age of the Lugar sill and a discussion of the Late Carboniferous/Early Permian sill complex of SW Scotland. *Geological Journal*, **22**, 43–52.

HENDERSON, W. G. & FORTEY, N. J. 1982. The Highland Border rocks at Loch Lomond and Aberfoyle. *Scottish Journal of Geology*, **18**, 227–245.

HENDERSON, W. G. & ROBERTSON, A. H. F. 1982. The Highland Border rocks and their relationship to marginal basin development in the Scottish Caledonides. *Journal of the Geological Society, London*, **139**, 433–450.

HENDERSON, W. G., FORTEY, N. J., JOHNSON, C. E. & GROUT, A. 1983. Mineral reconnaissance at the Highland Boundary with special reference to the Loch Lomond and Aberfoyle areas. *Institute of Geological Sciences, Mineral Reconnaissance Programme*, Report **61**.

HENDRY, J. P., PERKINS, W. T. & BANE, T. 2001. Short-term environmental change in a Jurassic lagoon deduced from geochemical trends in aragonite bivalve shells. *Geological Society of America, Bulletin*, **113**, 790–798.

HENNEY, P. J. 1991. *The Geochemistry and Petrogenesis of the Minor Intrusive Suite Associated with the Late Caledonian Criffell-Dalbeattie Pluton, SW Scotland*. PhD thesis, University of Aston in Birmingham.

HENRY, J. 1996. Palaeontology and theodicy: religion, politics and the *Asterolepis* of Stromness. *In*: SHORTLAND, M. E. (ed.), *Hugh Miller and the Controversies of Victorian Science*. Clarendon, Oxford, 151–170.

HENSEN, B. J. & ZHOU, B. 1995. Retention of isotopic memory in garnets partially broken down during an overprinting granulite facies metamorphism: Implications for the Sm–Nd closure temperature. *Geology*, **23**, 225–228.

HEPWORTH, B. C., OLIVER, G. J. H. & MCMURTRY, M. J. 1982. Sedimentology, volcanism, structure and metamorphism of the northern margin of a Lower Palaeozoic accretionary complex; Bail Hill–Abington area of the Southern Uplands of Scotland. *In*: LEGGETT, J. K. (ed.) *Trench-Fore-arc Geology*. Geological Society, London, Special Publications, **10**, 521–534.

HERRIES, R., PODDUBIUK, R. & WILCOCKSON, P. 1999. Solan, Strathmore and the back basin play, west of Shetland. *In*: FLEET, A. J. & BOLDY, S. A. R. (eds) *Petroleum Geology of Northwest Europe: Proceedings of the 5th Conference*. Geological Society, London, 693–712.

HESSELBO, S. P. & COE, A. L. 2000. Jurassic sequences of the Hebrides Basin, Isle of Skye, Scotland. *In*: GRAHAM, J. R. & RYAN, A. (eds) *Field Trip Guidebook, International Association of Sedimentologists Meeting, Dublin, 2000* (University of Dublin, Dublin, Ireland), 41–58.

HESSELBO, S. P. & JENKYNS, H. C. 1998. British Lower Jurassic sequence stratigraphy. *Society of Economic Palaeontologists and Mineralogists, Special Publications*, **60**, 561–581.

HESSELBO, S. P., OATES, M. J. & JENKYNS, H. C. 1998. The Lower Lias Group of the Hebrides Basin. *Scottish Journal of Geology*, **34**, 23–60.

HEWARD, A. P. 1991. Inside Auk – the anatomy of an eolian oil reservoir. *In*: MIALL, D. & TYLER, N. (eds) *The Three Dimensional Facies Architecture of Clastic Sediments and its Implications for Hydrocarbon Discovery and Recovery*, Concepts and Models in Sedimentology and Paleontology 3, SEPM, Tulsa, OK: 44–56.

HIBBERT, S. 1836. On the fresh-water Limestone of Burdiehouse in the neighbourhood of Edinburgh, belonging to the Carboniferous group of rocks. *Transactions of the Royal Society of Edinburgh*, **8**, 169–282.

HICKLING, G. 1912. On the geology and palaeontology of Forfarshire. *Proceedings of the Geologists' Association*, **23**, 302–311.

HICKMAN, A. H. 1975. The stratigraphy of late Precambrian metasediments between Glen Roy and Lismore. *Scottish Journal of Geology*, **11**, 227–245.

HICKMAN, A H. 1978. Recumbent folds between Glen Roy and Lismore. *Scottish Journal of Geology*, **14**, 191–212.

HIGGINS, A. C. 1967. The age of the Durine Member of the Durness Limestone Formation of Durness. *Scottish Journal of Geology*, **3**, 382–388.

HIGGINS, A. K., SMITH, M. P., SOPER, N. J., LESLIE, A. G., RASMUSSEN, J. A. & SØNDERHOLM, M. 2001. The Neoproterozoic Hekla Sund Basin, Eastern North Greenland: a pre-Iapetan extensional sequence thrust across its rift shoulders during the Caledonian orogeny. *Journal of the Geological Society, London*, **158**, 487–499.

HIGHTON, A J. 1992. The tectonostratigraphical significance of pre-750 Ma metagabbros within the northern Central Highlands, Inverness-shire. *Scottish Journal of Geology*, **28**, 71–76.

HIGHTON, A. J. 1999. *Geology of the country around Aviemore*. Memoir of the British Geological Survey, Sheet 74E (Scotland).

HIGHTON, A. J., HYSLOP, E. K. & NOBLE, S. J. 1999. U–Pb geochronology of migmatisation in the Northern Central Highlands: evidence for pre-Caledonian (Neoproterozoic) tectonometamorphism in the Grampian block, Scotland, *Journal of the Geological Society, London*, **156**, 1195–1204.

HILL, J. B. & KYNASTON, H. 1900. On kentallenite and its relations to other igneous rocks in Argyllshire. *Quarterly Journal of the Geological Society of London*, **56**, 531–558.

HILLIER, S. J. & MARSHALL, J. E. A. 1992. Organic maturation, thermal history and hydrocarbon generation in the Orcadian Basin, Scotland. *Journal of the Geological Society, London*, **149**, 491–502.

HIMSWORTH, E. M. 1973. *Marine Geophysical Studies between Northwest Scotland and the Faeroe Plateau*. PhD thesis, University of Durham.

HINE, P., THOMPSON, A. & GREIG, J. 1998. *Land Use Planning for the New Millennium: the Role of Environmental Geology*. Department of the Environment, Transport and the Regions Report.

HITCHEN, C. S. 1929. Unst and its chromite deposits, *Mining Magazine*, **40**, 18–24.

HITCHEN, K. & RITCHIE, J. D. 1987. Geological Review of the West Shetland Area. *In*: BROOKS, J. & GLENNIE, K. (eds) *Petroleum Geology of North West Europe*. Graham & Trotman, London, 737–749.

HITCHEN, K. & RITCHIE, J. D. 1993. New K–Ar ages, and a provisional chronology, for the offshore part of the British Tertiary Igneous Province. *Scottish Journal of Geology*, **29**, 73–85.

HITCHIN, K., STOKER, M. S., EVANS, D. & BEDDOE-STEPHENS, B. 1995. Permo-Triassic sedimentary and volcanic rocks in basins to the north and west of Scotland. *In*: BOLDY, S. A. R. (ed.) *Permian and Triassic Rifting in Northwest Europe*. Geological Society, London, Special Publications, **91**, 87–102.

HODGSON, N. A., FARNSWORTH, J. & FRASER, A. J. 1992. Salt-related tectonics, sedimentation and hydrocarbon plays in the Central Graben, North Sea, UKCS. *In*: HARDMAN, R. F. P. (ed.) *Exploration Britain: Geological Insights for the Next Decade*. Geological Society, London, Special Publications, **67**, 31–63.

HOEY, T. B., SMART, D. W. J., PENDER, G. & METCALFE, H. 1998. *Engineering Methods for Scottish Gravel Bed Rivers*. Scottish Natural Heritage, Research, Survey and Monitoring, No. 47, Battleby.

HOFFMAN, P. F. 1989. Precambrian geology and tectonic history of North America. *In*: BALLY, A. W. & PALMER, A. R. (eds), *The Geology of North America*, **A**, Geological Society of America, Boulder, 447–512.

HOLDSWORTH, R. E. 1989. The geology and structural evolution of a Caledonian fold and ductile thrust zone, Kyle of Tongue region, Sutherland, northern Scotland. *Journal of the Geological Society, London*, **146**, 809–823.

HOLDSWORTH, R. E. 1990. Progressive deformation structures associated with ductile thrusts in the Moine Nappe, Sutherland, N. Scotland. *Journal of Structural Geology*, **12**, 443–452.

HOLDSWORTH, R. E. & ROBERTS, A. M. 1984. A study of early curvilinear fold structures and strain in the Moine of the Glen Garry region, Inverness-shire. *Journal of the Geological Society, London*, **141**, 327–338.

HOLDSWORTH, R. E. & STRACHAN, R. A. 1988. The structural age and possible origin of the Vagastie Bridge granite and associated intrusions, central Sutherland. *Geological Magazine*, **125**, 613–620.

HOLDSWORTH, R. E., HARRIS, A. L. & ROBERTS, A. M. 1987. The stratigraphy, structure and regional significance of the Moine rocks of Mull, Argyllshire, W Scotland. *Geological Journal*, **22**, 83–107.

HOLDSWORTH, R. E., STRACHAN, R. A. & HARRIS, A. L. 1994. Precambrian rocks in northern Scotland east of the Moine Thrust: the Moine Supergroup. *In*: GIBBONS, W. & HARRIS, A. L. (eds) *A Revised Correlation of Precambrian Rocks in the British Isles*. Geological Society, London, Special Report, **22**, 23–32.

HOLDSWORTH, R. E., MCERLEAN, M. A. & STRACHAN, R. A. 1999. The influence of country rock structural architecture during pluton emplacement: the Loch Loyal syenites, Scotland. *Journal of the Geological Society, London*, **156**, 163–175.

HOLDSWORTH, R. E., WOODCOCK, N. H. & STRACHAN, R. A. 2000. Geological framework of Britain and Ireland. *In*: WOODCOCK, N. H. & STRACHAN, R. A. (eds) *Geological History of Britain and Ireland*. Blackwell Science Ltd., Oxford, 19–37.

HOLDSWORTH, R. E., STRACHAN, R. A. & ALSOP, G. I. 2001. *Geology of the Tongue District*. Memoir of the British Geological Survey, HMSO.

HOLE, M. J. 1988. Post-subduction alkaline volcanism along the Antarctic Peninsula. *Journal of the Geological Society, London*, **145**, 985–998.

HOLE, M. J. & MORRISON, M. A. 1992. The differentiated boss, Cnoc Rhaonastil, Islay: a natural experiment in the low pressure differentiation of an alkali olivine basalt magma. *Scottish Journal of Geology*, **28**, 55–70.

HOLGATE, N. 1969. Palaeozoic and Tertiary transcurrent movement along the Great Glen Fault. *Scottish Journal of Geology*, **5**, 97–139.

HOLLAND, J. G. & LAMBERT, R. ST. -J. 1973. Comparative major element geochemistry of the Lewisian of the mainland of Scotland. *In*: PARK, R. G. & TARNEY, J. (eds) *The Early Precambrian of Scotland and Related Rocks of Greenland*. University of Keele, 51–62.

HOLLAND, J. G. & LAMBERT, R. ST. -J. 1995. The geochemistry and geochronology of the gneisses and pegmatites of the Tollie antiform in the Lewisian complex of northwestern Scotland. *Canadian Journal of Earth Science*, **32**, 496–507.

HOLLOWAY, S. 1986. The natural gas occurrences of the United Kingdom landward area. *In*: SCHROEDER, L. & SCHONEICH, H. (compilers) *International Map of Natural Gas Fields in Europe, Explanatory Notes*. U. N. Economic Commission in Europe, 737–749.

HOLM, G. M. 1996. The Central Graben: a dynamic overpressure system. *In*: GLENNIE, K. & HURST, A. (eds) *AD1995: NW Europe's Hydrocarbon Industry*, Geological Society, London, 107–122.

HOLMDEN, C. & HUDSON, J. D. 2000. Strontium isotope investigation of paleosalinity in the Great Estuarine Group. Jurassic, Scotland. Goldschmidt Meeting, Oxford, September 2000. *Journal of Conference Abstracts*, **5**, 527.

HOLMES, A. 1936. The idea of contrasted differentiation. *Geological Magazine*, **73**, 228–238.

HOLMES, A. 1944. *Principles of Physical Geology*. Thomas Nelson & Sons, London & Edinburgh.

HOLMES, G. 1984. *Rock Slope Failure in Part of the Scottish Highlands*. PhD thesis, University of Edinburgh.

HOLMES, R. 1977. *Quaternary Deposits of the Central North Sea 5. The Quaternary Geology of the UK Sector of the North Sea between 56° and 58°*. Report of the Institute of Geological Sciences, No. **77/14**.

HOLNESS, M. B., BICKLE, M. J. & HARTE, B. 1989. Textures of forsterite-calcite marbles from the Beinn an Dubhaich aureole, Skye, and implications for the structure of metamorphic porosity. *Journal of the Geological Society, London*, **146**, 917–920.

HOLROYD, J. 1978. *The Sedimentologic and Geotectonic Significance of Lower Palaeozoic Flysch Rudites*. PhD thesis, University of Wales, Swansea.

HOLROYD, J. D. 1994. *The Structure and Stratigraphy of the Suardal Area, Isle of Skye, North-west Scotland: An Investigation of Tertiary Deformation in the Skye Volcanic Complex*. PhD thesis, University of Manchester.

HOLUB, F. V., KLAPOVA, H., BLUCK, B. J. & BOWES, D. R. 1984. Petrology and geochemistry of post-obduction dykes of the Ballantrae Complex, SW Scotland. *Transactions of the Royal Society of Edinburgh: Earth Sciences*, **75**, 211–223.

HOPKINS, C. 1999. New finds in the Hopeman Sandstone. *Open University Geological Society Journal*, **20**, 10–15.

HORNE, J. & HINXMAN, L. W. 1914. The geology of the country around Beauly and Inverness: including a part of the Black Isle. *Memoir of the Geological Society of the United Kingdom* (Sheet 83).

HORNE, J., ROBERTSON, G., JAMIESON, T. F., FRASER, J., KENDALL, P. F. & BELL, D. 1893. The character of the high-level shell-bearing deposits at Clava, Chapelhall and other localities. *Report of the British Association*, 483–514.

HORSFIELD, W. B. 1983. *The Deglaciation Pattern of the Western Grampians, Scotland*. PhD thesis, University of East Anglia.

HOWARD HUMPHRIES & PARTNERS 1994. *Demolition and Construction Wastes in the UK*. Department of the Environment Report, London.

HOWARD, M. 1999. *The Geochemistry of Late-Palaeozoic Quartz Tholeiite Intrusions in Northern Britain*. MRes thesis, University of Edinburgh.

HOWELL, H. & GEIKIE, A. 1861. *The Geology of the Neighbourhood of Edinburgh (Map 32)*. Longman, Green, Longman & Roberts, London.

HOWIE, R. A. & WALSH, J. N. 1981. Reibeckite, arfvedsonite and aenigmatite from the Ailsa Craig microgranite. *Scottish Journal of Geology*, **17**, 123–128.

HR WALLINGFORD 1991. *A guide to the Selection of Appropriate Coast Protection Works for Geological Sites of Special Scientific Interest*, **EX 2112**, Wallingford.

HR WALLINGFORD 1997. *Coastal Cells in Scotland*. Scottish Natural Heritage, Research, Survey and Monitoring, No. 56, Battleby.

HR WALLINGFORD 2000a. *Coastal Cells in Scotland. Cell 1-St. Abbs Head to Fife Ness*. Scottish Natural Heritage, Research Survey and Monitoring, No. 143, Battleby.

HR WALLINGFORD 2000b. *A Guide to Managing Erosion in Beach/Dune Systems*. Scottish Natural Heritage, Natural Heritage Management Series, Battleby.

HUBERT, J. F., REED, A. A., DOWDALL, W. L. & GILCHRIST, J. M. 1978. Guide to the Mesozoic redbeds of central Connecticut. *State Geological and Natural History Survey of Connecticut Guidebook*, **4**, 1–128.

HUBERT, J. F., FESHBACH-MERINEY, P. E. & SMITH, M. A. 1992. The Triassic–Jurassic Hartford rift basin, Connecticut and Massachusetts: evolution, sandstone diagenesis, and hydrocarbon history. *AAPG Bulletin*, **76**, 1710–1734.

HUDSON, J. D. 1963. The recognition of salinity-controlled mollusc assemblages in the Great Estuarine Series (Middle Jurassic) of the Inner Hebrides. *Palaeontology*, **6**, 318–326.

HUDSON, J. D. 1970. Algal limestones with pseudomorphs after gypsum from the Middle Jurassic of Scotland. *Lethaia*, **3**, 11–40.

HUDSON, J. D. 1983. Mesozoic sedimentation and sedimentary rocks in the Inner Hebrides. *Proceedings of the Royal Society of Edinburgh*, **83B**, 47–63.

HUDSON, J. D. & ANDREWS, J. E. 1987. The diagenesis of the Great Estuarine Group, Middle Jurassic, Inner Hebrides, Scotland. *In*: MARSHALL, J. D. (ed.) *Diagenesis of Sedimentary Sequences*. Geological Society, London, Special Publications, **36**, 259–278.

HUDSON, J. D. & PALMER, T. J. 1976. A euryhaline oyster from the Middle Jurassic and the origin of the true oysters. *Palaeontology*, **19**, 79–93.

HUDSON, J. D., RIDING, J. B., WAKEFIELD, M. I. & WALTON, W. 1995. Jurassic paleosalinities and brackish-water communities – A case study. *Palaios*, **10**, 392–407.

HUDSON, N. F. C. 1980. Regional metamorphism of some Dalradian pelites in the Buchan area, NE Scotland. *Contributions to Mineralogy and Petrology*, **73**, 39–51.

HUDSON, N. F. C. 1985. Conditions of Dalradian metamorphism in the Buchan area, NE Scotland. *Journal of the Geological Society, London*, **142**, 63–76.

HUDSON, T. A. & DALLMEYER, R. D. 1982. Age of mineralized greisens in the Irish Creek tin district, Virginia Blue Ridge. *Economic Geology*, **77**, 189–192.

HUFF, W. D., WHITEMAN, J. A. & CURTIS C. D. 1988. Investigation of a K-bentonite by X-ray powder diffraction and analytical transmission electron microscopy. *Clays and Clay Minerals*, **36**, 83–93.

HUFF, W. D., ANDERSON, T. B., RUNDLE, C. C. & ODIN, G. S. 1991. Chemostratigraphy, K–Ar ages and illitisation of Silurian K-bentonites from the Central Belt of the Southern Uplands–Down-Longford terrane, British Isles. *Journal of the Geological Society, London*, **148**, 861–868.

HULME, M. & JENKINS, G. J. 1998. *Climate change scenarios for the UK: scientific report*. UKCIP Technical Report, **1**, Climatic Research Unit, Norwich.

HUNTER, R. H., UPTON, B. G. J. & ASPEN, P. 1984. Meta-igneous granulite and ultramafic xenoliths from basalts of the Midland Valley of Scotland: petrology and mineralogy of the lower crust and upper mantle. *Transactions of the Royal Society of Edinburgh: Earth Sciences*, **75**, 75–84.

HURST, A. 1981. Mid Jurassic stratigraphy and facies at Brora, Sutherland. *Scottish Journal of Geology*, **17**, 169–177.

HURST, A. 1985. The implications of clay mineralogy to palaeoclimate and provenance during the Jurassic in N.E. Scotland. *Scottish Journal of Geology*, **21**, 143–160.

HURST, A. 1993. Bathonian to Oxfordian strata of the Brora area. *In*: TREWIN, N. H. & HURST, A. (eds) *Excursion Guide to the Geology of East Sutherland and Caithness*. Scottish Academic Press, Edinburgh, 49–74.

HUSELBEE, M. Y. & THOMAS, A. T. 1998. *Olenellus* and conodonts from the Durness group, NW Scotland, and the correlation of the Durness succession. *Scottish Journal of Geology*, **34**, 83–88.

HUTCHESON, A. R. & OLIVER, G. J. H. 1998. Garnet provenance studies, juxtaposition of Laurentian marginal terranes and timing of the Grampian Orogeny in Scotland. *Journal of the Geological Society, London*, **155**, 541–550.

HUTCHINSON, A. D. 1928. A lava flow at the base of the Kincardineshire Downtownian. *Transactions of the Geological Society of Edinburgh*, **12**, 69–73.

HUTCHINSON, J. N., MILLAR, D. L. & TREWIN, N. H. 2001. Coast erosion at a nuclear waste shaft, Dounreay, Scotland. *Quarterly Journal of Engineering Geology and Hydrogeology*, **34**, 245–268.

HUTCHISON, A. R. & OLIVER, G. J. H. 1998. Garnet provenance studies, juxtaposition of Laurentian marginal terranes and timing of the Grampian Orogeny in Scotland. *Journal of the Geological Society, London*, **155**, 541–550.

HUTCHISON, R. 1968. Origin of the White Allivalite, Western Cuillin, Isle of Skye. *Geological Magazine*, **105**, 338–347.

HUTTON, A. C. 1982. Petrographic classification of oil shales. *International Journal of Coal Geology*, **8**, 203–231.

HUTTON, D. H. W. 1979. Tectonic slides: a review and reappraisal. *Earth Science Reviews*, **15**, 151–172.

HUTTON, D. H. W. 1987. Strike-slip terranes and a model for the evolution of the British and Irish Caledonides. *Geological Magazine*, **124**, 405–425.

HUTTON, D. H. W. 1988a. Granite emplacement mechanisms and tectonic controls: inferences from deformation studies. *Transactions of the Royal Society of Edinburgh: Earth Sciences*, **79**, 245–255.

HUTTON, D. H. W. 1988b. Igneous emplacement in a shear-zone termination: the biotite granite at Strontian, Scotland. *Geological Society of America, Bulletin*, **100**, 1392–1399.

HUTTON, D. H. W. & McERLEAN, M. 1991. Silurian and early Devonian sinistral deformation of the Ratagain granite, Scotland: constraints on the age of Caledonian movements on the Great Glen Fault system. *Journal of the Geological Society, London*, **148**, 1–4.

HUTTON, D. H. W. & REAVY, R. J. 1992. Strike-slip tectonics and granite petrogenesis. *Tectonics*, **11**, 960–967.

HUTTON, D. H. W., AFTALION, M. & HALLIDAY, A. N. 1985. An Ordovician ophiolite in County Tyrone, Ireland. *Nature, London*, **315**, 210–212.

HUTTON, D. H. W., STEPHENS, W. E., YARDLEY, B. W. D., McERLEAN, M. & HALLIDAY, A. N. 1993. The Ratagain Plutonic Complex. *In*: MAY, F. (ed.) *Geology of the Kintail District*. Memoir of the British Geological Survey, HMSO.

HUTTON, J. 1785. *Abstract of a Dissertation Read in the Royal Society of Edinburgh, upon the Eleventh of March, and Fourth of April, M,DCC,LXXXV, Concerning the System of the Earth, its Duration, and Stability*. Edinburgh.

HUTTON, J. 1788. Theory of the earth; or an investigation of the laws observable in the composition, dissolution, and restoration of land upon the globe. *Transactions of the Royal Society of Edinburgh*, **1**, 209–304.

HUTTON, J. 1795. *Theory of the Earth. With Proofs and Illustrations. I and II*. Cadell & Davies, London; William Creech, Edinburgh.

HUTTON, J. 1899. *Theory of the Earth. With Proofs and Illustrations.* Vol. 3, edited by Sir Archibald Geikie. London: Geological Society.

HUXLEY, T. H. 1869. On *Hyperodapedon. Quarterly Journal of the Geological Society of London*, **25**, 138–152, 157–158.

HYSLOP, E. K. 1992. *Strain-Induced Metamorphism and Pegmatite Development in the Moine Rocks of Scotland*. PhD thesis, University of Hull.

HYSLOP, E. K. & PIASECKI, M. A. J. 1999. Mineralogy, geochemistry and the development of ductile shear zones in the Grampian Slide zone of the Scottish Central Highlands. *Journal of the Geological Society, London*, **156**, 577–589.

HYSLOP, E. K., GILLANDERS, R. J., HILL, P. G. & FAKES, R. D. 1999. Rare-earth-bearing minerals fergusonite and gadolinite from the Arran granite. *Scottish Journal of Geology*, **35**, 65–69.

IMRIE, N. 1806. A description of the strata which occur in ascending from the plains of Kincardineshire to the summit of Mount Battoc, one of the most elevated points in the eastern district of the Grampian mountains. *Transactions of the Royal Society of Edinburgh*, **6**, 1–18.

INCE, D. 1984. Sedimentation and tectonism in the Middle Ordovician of the Girvan District, SW Scotland. *Transactions of the Royal Society of Edinburgh: Earth Sciences*, **75**, 225–237.

INESON, P. R. & MITCHELL, J. G. 1974. K–Ar isotopic age determinations from some Scottish mineral localities. *Transactions of the Institution of Mining and Metallurgy*, **83**, B13–B18.

INGHAM, J. K. 1978. Geology of a continental margin 2: middle and late Ordovician transgression, Girvan. *In*: BOWES, D. R & LEAKE, B. E. (eds) *Crustal Evolution in Northwest Britain and Adjacent Regions*. Seel House, Liverpool, 163–176.

INGHAM, J. K. 1992. Excursion 29. Upper Stinchar Valley and adjacent areas. *In*: LAWSON, J. D. & WEEDON, D. S. (eds) *Geological Excursions around Glasgow and Girvan*. Geological Society of Glasgow, 378–395.

INGHAM. J. K. 2000. Scotland: the Midland Valley Terrane – Girvan. *In*: FORTEY, R. A., HARPER, D. A. T., INGHAM, J. K., OWEN, A. W., PARKES, M. A., RUSHTON, A. W. A. & WOODCOCK, N. H. (eds) *A Revised Correlation of Ordovician rocks in the British Isles*. Geological Society, London, Special Report, **24**, 43–47.

INGHAM, J. K. & TRIPP, R. P. 1991. The trilobite fauna of the middle Ordovician Doularg Formation of the Girvan District, Scotland. *Transactions of the Royal Society of Edinburgh: Earth Sciences*, **82**, 27–54.

INGHAM, J. K., CURRY, G. B. & WILLIAMS, A. 1985. Early Ordovician Dounans Limestone fauna, Highland Border Complex, Scotland. *Transactions of the Royal Society of Edinburgh: Earth Sciences*, **76**, 481–513.

INNES, J. 1983. Lichenometric dating of debris flow deposits in the Scottish Highlands. *Earth Surface Processes and Landforms*, **8**, 579–588.

IRVING, E. & RUNCORN, S. K. 1957. Analysis of the palaeomagnetism of the Torridonian sandstone series of north-west Scotland. *Philosophical Transactions of the Royal Society of London*, **A250**, 83–99.

IXER, R. A., PATTRICK, R. A. D. & STANLEY, C. J. 1997. Geology, mineralogy and genesis of gold mineralization at Calliachar–Urlar Burn, Scotland. *In*: SMITH, C. G. (ed.) Mineralization in the Caledonides. *Transactions of the Institution of Mining and Metallurgy*, **106**, B99–B108.

JACKSON, D. I. & MULHOLLAND, P. 1993. Tectonic and stratigraphic aspects of the East Irish Sea Basin and adjacent areas: contrasts in their post-Carboniferous structural styles. *In*: PARKER, J. R. (ed.) *Petroleum Geology of Northwest Europe: Proceedings of the 4th Conference*. Geological Society, London, 791–808.

JACKSON, D. I., MULHOLLAND, P., JONES, S. M. & WARRINGTON, G. 1987. The geological framework of the East Irish Sea Basin. *In*: BROOKS, J. & GLENNIE, K. (eds) *Petroleum Geology of North West Europe*. Graham & Trotman, London 191–203.

JACQUE, M. & THOUVENIN, J. 1975. Lower Tertiary tuffs and volcanic activity in the North Sea. *In*: WOODLAND, A. W. (ed.) *Petroleum and the Continental Shelf of North West Europe* (Vol. 1: Geology). Applied Science Publishers, London, 455–465.

JACQUES, J. M. & REAVY, R. J. 1994. Caledonian plutonism and major lineaments in the SW Scottish Highlands. *Journal of the Geological Society, London*, **151**, 955–969.

JAMES, N. P., BARNES, C. R., STEVENS, R. K. & KNIGHT, I. 1989. A Lower Paleozoic continental margin carbonate platform, northern Canadian Appalachians, *In*: CREVELLO, T., SARG, R., READ, J. F. & WILSON, J. L. (eds) *Controls on Carbonate Platforms and Basin Development*. Society of Economic Paleontologists and Mineralogists, Special Publications, **44**, 123–146.

JAMES, S., PRONK, D., ABBOTS, F., WARD, V., VAN DIERENDONCK, A. & STEVENS, D. 1999. The Brent Field: improving subsurface characterization for late life field management. *In*: FLEET, A. J. & BOLDY, S. A. R. (eds) *Petroleum Geology of Northwest Europe: Proceedings of the 5th Conference*, Geological Society, London, 1039–1049.

JAMESON, J. 1987. Carbonate sedimentation on a mid-basin high: the Petershill Formation, Midland Valley of Scotland. *In*: MILLER, J., ADAMS, A. E. & WRIGHT, V. P. (eds) *European Dinantian Environments*. Geological Journal Special Issue **12**. Wiley, Chichester, 309–327.

JAMESON, R. 1796. Is the volcanic opinion of the formation of the basaltes founded on truth? *Dissertations of the Royal Medical Society*, **20**, 218–224.

JAMESON, R. 1805. *A Mineralogical Description of the County of Dumfries*. Bell & Bradfute & W. Blackwood, Edinburgh; Longman, Hurst, Rees & Orme, London.

JAMESON, R. 1818. On the geology of the Lothians. *Memoirs of the Wernerian Natural History Society*, **2**, 618–633.

JAMESON, R. 1821. Geognosy of East Lothian. *Memoirs of the Wernerian Natural History Society*, **3**, 225–244.

JAMIESON, T. F. 1865. The history of the last geological changes in Scotland. *Quarterly Journal of the Geological Society, London*, **21**, 161–203.

JAMIESON, T. F. 1866. On the glacial phenomena of Caithness. *Quarterly Journal of the Geological Society of London*, **22**, 261–281.

JANAWAY, T. M. & PARNELL, J. 1989. Carbonate production within the Orcadian Basin, northern Scotland: a petrographic and geochemical study. *Palaeogeography, Palaeoclimatology, Palaeoecology*, **70**, 89–105.

JARDINE, W. 1853. *The Ichnology of Annandale; Or, Illustrations of Footmarks Impressed on the New Red Sandstone of Corncockle Muir*. The Author, Edinburgh.

JARDINE, W. G. 1980. Holocene raised coastal sediments and former shorelines of Dumfriesshire and eastern Galloway. *Transactions of the Dumfriesshire and Galloway Natural History and Antiquarian Society*, **55**, 1–59.

JARDINE, W. G., DICKSON, J. H. & HAUGHTON, R. D. W. 1988. A late Middle Devensian site at Sourlie, near Irvine, Strathclyde. *Scottish Journal of Geology*, **24**, 288–295.

JARVIK, E. 1948. On the morphology and taxonomy of the Middle Devonian Osteolepid fishes of Scotland. *Kungliga Svenska Vetenskapsakademiens Handlingar*, **3**, (25), 1, 1–301.

JASSIM, R. Z., PATTRICK, R. A. D. & RUSSELL, M. J. 1983. On the origin of the silver + copper + cobalt + baryte mineralisation of Ochil Hills, Scotland; a sulphur isotopic study. *Transactions of the Institution of Mining and Metallurgy*, **92**, B213–B216.

JASSIM, S. Z. & GASS, I. G. 1970. The Loch na Creitheach volcanic vent, Isle of Skye. *Scottish Journal of Geology*, **6**, 285–294.

JEHU, T. J. & CAMPBELL, R. 1917. The Highland Border rocks of the Aberfoyle district. *Transactions of the Royal Society of Edinburgh*, **52**, 175 212.

JEHU, T. J. & CRAIG, R. M. 1923–34. Geology of the Outer Hebrides, Parts I–V. Transactions of the Royal Society of Edinburgh, **53**, 419–411 (1923); **53**, 615–641 (1925); **54**, 46–89 (1926); **55**, 457–488 (1927); **57**, 839–874 (1934).

JELINEK, E., SOUCEK, J., BLUCK, B. J., BOWES, D. R. & TRELOAR, P. J. 1980. Nature and significance of beerbachites in the Ballantrae ophiolite, SW Scotland. *Transactions of the Royal Society of Edinburgh: Earth Sciences*, **71**, 159–179.

JELINEK, E., SOUCEK, J., RANDA, Z., JAKES, P., BLUCK, B. J. & BOWES, D. R. 1984. Geochemistry of peridotites, gabbros and trondjemites of the Ballantrae complex, SW Scotland. *Transactions of the Royal Society of Edinburgh: Earth Sciences*, **75**, 193–209.

JENYON, M. K., CRESSWELL, P. M. & TAYLOR, J. C. M. 1984. The nature of the connection between the Northern and Southern Zechstein Basins across the Mid North Sea High. *Marine and Petroleum Geology*, **1**, 355–363.

JESSEN, A. 1905. On the shell-bearing clay in Kintyre. *Transactions of the Geological Society of Edinburgh*, **8**, 76–86.

JIN, YUGAN, WARDLAW, B. R., GLENISTER, B. F. & KOTLYAR, G. V. 1997. Permian chronostratigraphic subdivisions. *Episodes*, **20**, 10–15.

JOASS, J. M. 1869. Notes on the Sutherland gold field. *Quarterly Journal of the Geological Society of London*, **25**, 314–326.

JOHNES, L. H. & GAUER, M. B. 1991. The Northwest Hutton Field, Block 211/27, UK North Sea. In: ABBOTTS, I. L. (ed.) *United Kingdom Oil and Gas Fields 25 Years Commemorative Volume*. Geological Society, London, Memoir, **14**, 145–151.

JOHNSEN, S. J., CLAUSEN, H. B. & DANSGAARD, W. 1992. Irregular glacial interstadials recorded in a new Greenland ice core. *Nature, London*, **359**, 311–313.

JOHNSON, H. D. & FISHER, M. J. 1998. North Sea plays: geological controls on hydrocarbon distribution. In: GLENNIE, K. W. (ed.) *Petroleum Geology of the North Sea*, 4th edition, Blackwell, Oxford, 463–547.

JOHNSON, H. & LOTT, G. K. 1993. 2. Cretaceous of the Central and Northen North Sea. In: CORDEY, G. W. & KNOX, R. W. O'B. (eds) *Lithostratigraphic Nomenclature of the UK Northern North Sea*. British Geological Survey and UKOOA, Nottingham.

JOHNSON, H., RICHARDS, P. C., LONG, D. & GRAHAM, C. C. 1993. *The Geology of the Northern North Sea*. British Geological Survey Offshore Regional Report, HMSO, London.

JOHNSON, M. R. W. 1962. Relations of movement and metamorphism in the Dalradian of Banffshire. *Transactions of the Royal Society of Edinburgh*, **19**, 29–64.

JOHNSON, M. R. W. 1963. Some time relations of movement and metamorphism in the Scottish Highlands. *Geologie en Mijnbouw*, **42**, 121–142.

JOHNSON, M. R. W. & DALZIEL, I. W. D. 1963. Metamorphosed lamprophyres and the late thermal history of the Moine. *Geological Magazine*, **103**, 240–249.

JOHNSON, M. R. W. & FROST, R. T. C. 1977. Fault and lineament pattern in the Southern Highlands of Scotland. *Geologie en Mijnbouw*, **56**, 287–294.

JOHNSON, M. R. W. & HARRIS, A. L. 1967. Dalradian-?Arenig relations in part of the Highland Border, Scotland, and their significance in the chronology of the Caledonian orogeny. *Scottish Journal of Geology*, **3**, 1–16.

JOHNSON, M. R. W. & PARSONS, I. 1979. *Geological Excursion Guide to the Assynt District of Sutherland*. Edinburgh Geological Society.

JOHNSON, M. R. W., KELLEY, S. P., OLIVER, G. J. H. & WINTER, D. A. 1985. Thermal effects and timing of thrusting in the Moine Thrust zone. *Journal of the Geological Society, London*, **142**, 863–874.

JOHNSON, Y., PARK, R. G. & WINCHESTER, J. 1987. Geochemistry, petrogenesis and tectonic significance of the Early Proterozoic Loch Maree amphibolites. In: PHAROAH, T. C., BECKINSALE, R. D. & RICKARD, D. T (eds) *Geochemistry and Mineralization of Proterozoic Volcanic Suites*. Geological Society, London, Special Publications, **33**, 255–269.

JOHNSTON, D. R. 1996. A reassessment of the age and form of the Broadford Gabbro, Isle of Skye: new evidence from Creag Strollamus. *Scottish Journal of Geology*, **32**, 51–58.

JOHNSTON, S. C., SMITH, R. I. & UNDERHILL, J. R. 1995. The Clair Discovery, west of the Shetland Isles. *Scottish Journal of Geology*, **31**, 187–190.

JOHNSTONE, G. S. 1965. The volcanic rocks of the Misty Law-Knockside Hills district, Renfrewshire. *Bulletin of the Geological Survey of Great Britain*, **22**, 53–64.

JOHNSTONE, G. S. 1966. *British Regional Geology: The Grampian Highlands* (3rd Edition) HMSO.

JOHNSTONE, G. S. 1972. *British Regional Geology: The Grampian Highlands* (4th Edition) HMSO.

JOHNSTONE, G. S. 1975. The Moine Succession. In: HARRIS, A. L., SHACKLETON, R. M., WATSON, R. M., WATSON, J. V., DOWNIE, C., HARLAND, W. B. & MOORBATH, S. (eds) *A Correlation of Precambrian Rocks in the British Isles*. Geological Society, London, Special Report, **6**, 30–42.

JOHNSTONE, G. S. & MYKURA, W. 1989. *The Northern Highlands of Scotland*. British Regional Geology (4th Edition) British Geological Survey, HMSO London.

JOHNSTONE, G. S., SMITH, D. I. & HARRIS, A. L. 1969. The Moinian Assemblage of Scotland. In: KAY, M. (ed.) *North Atlantic Geology and Continental Drift*. American Association of Petroleum Geologists, Memoirs, **12**, 159–180.

JOLLEY, D. W. 1997. Palaeosurface palynofloras of the Skye Lava Field, and the age of the British Tertiary Volcanic Province. In: WIDDOWSON, M. (ed.) *Palaeosurfaces: Recognition, Reconstruction and Palaeoenvironmental Interpretation*. Geological Society, London, Special Publications, **120**, 67–94.

JOLLY, R. J. H. & SANDERSON, D. J. 1995. Variation in the form and distribution of dykes of the Mull swarm, Scotland. *Journal of Structural Geology*, **17**, 1543–1557.

JONES, E. M., RICE, C. M. & TWEEDIE, J. R. 1987. Lower Proterozoic stratiform sulphide deposits in Loch Maree Group, Gairloch, northwest Scotland. *Transactions of the Institution of Mining and Metallurgy*, **96**, B128–140.

JONES, J. 1985. James Hutton's agricultural researches and his life as a farmer. *Annals of Science*, **42**, 573–601.

JONES, L. S., GARRETT, S. W., MACLEOD, M., GUY, M., CONDON, P. J., NOTMAN, L. 1999. Britannia Field, UK Central North Sea: modelling heterogeneity in usual deep water deposits. *In*: FLEET, A. J. & BOLDY, S. A. R. (eds) *Petroleum Geology of Northwest Europe: Proceedings of the 5th Conference*, Geological Society, London, 1115–1124.

JUDD, J. W. 1873. The secondary rocks of Scotland. *Quarterly Journal of the Geological Society, London*, **29**, 97–195.

JUDD, J. W. 1874. The Secondary rocks of Scotland. Second paper. On the ancient volcanoes of the Highlands and the relations of their products to the Mesozoic strata. *Quarterly Journal of the Geological Society of London*, **30**, 220–302.

JUDD, J. W. 1878. The secondary rocks of Scotland. III. The strata of the western coast and islands. *Quarterly Journal of the Geological Society, London*, **34**, 660–743.

JUDD, J. W. 1889. The Tertiary volcanoes of the Western Isles of Scotland. *Quarterly Journal of the Geological Society of London*, **46**, 341–385.

JUDD, J. W. 1893. On inclusions of Tertiary granite in the gabbro of the Cuillin Hills, Skye, and on the products resulting from the partial fusion of the acid by the basic rock. *Quarterly Journal of the Geological Society of London*, **49**, 175–195.

KALALIDDEN, Z. A. R. 1991. *Seismic Interpretation of the Southern Uplands Terrane*. PhD thesis, University of Glasgow.

KALSBEEK, F. (ed.) 1989. Geology of the Ammassalik region, South-East Greenland. *Gronlands Geologiske Undersogelse, Rapport*, **146**.

KALSBEEK, F. & TAYLOR, P. N. 1985. Isotopic and chemical variation across a Proterozoic continental margin – the Ketilidian mobile belt of South Greenland. *Earth and Planetary Science Letters*, **73**, 65–80.

KALSBEEK, F., BRIDGWATER, D. & ZECK, H. 1987. A 1950 ± 60 Ma Rb–Sr isochron age from two Kangamiut dykes and the timing of the Nagssugtoqidian (Hudsonian) orogeny in West Greenland. *Canadian Journal of Earth Science*, **15**, 1122–1128.

KALSBEEK, F., AUSTRHEIM, H., BRIDGWATER, D., HANSEN, B. T., PEDERSEN, S. & TAYLOR, P. N. 1993. Geochronology of the Ammassalik area, South-East Greenland, and comparisons with the Lewisian of Scotland and the Nagssugtoqidian of West Greenland. *Precambrian Research*, **62**, 239–270.

KANARIS-SOTIRIOU, R. 1997 Graphite-bearing peraluminous dacites from the Erland volcanic complex, Faeroe-Shetland Basin, North Atlantic. *Mineralogical Magazine*, **61**, 175–184.

KANARIS-SOTIRIOU, R. & GIBB, F. G. F. 1985. Hybridisation and the petrogenesis of composite intrusions: the dyke at An Cumhann, Isle of Arran, Scotland. *Geological Magazine*, **122**, 361–372.

KANARIS-SOTIRIOU, R., MORTON, A. C. & TAYLOR, P. N. 1993. Palaeocene peraluminous magmatism, crustal melting and continental break-up: the Erlend complex, Faeroe-Shetland Basin, NE Atlantic. *Journal of the Geological Society, London*, **150**, 903–914.

KASSI, A. M. & WEIR, J. A. 1993. Depositional and geotectonic history of the Gala area, eastern Southern Uplands, Scotland. *Transactions of the Royal Society of Edinburgh: Earth Sciences*, **84**, 161–173.

KASSI, A. M., WEIR, J. A., MCMANUS, J. & BROWNE, M. A. E. (in press). Lithofacies and sedimentary cycles within the Late Dinantian of Fife and East Lothian: is a sequence stratigraphical approach valid? *Transactions of the Royal Society of Edinburgh: Earth Sciences*.

KAY, E. A. 1985. *Hydrothermal Mineralization and Alteration of the Lagalochan Au–Cu–Mo Prospect, W. Scotland*. PhD thesis, University of London.

KEILLAR, I. & SMITH, J. S. (eds). 1995. *George Gordon: Man of Science*. Centre for Scottish Studies, University of Aberdeen, Aberdeen.

KELLEY, S. P. 1988. The relationship between K–Ar mineral ages, mica grain sizes and movement on the Moine Thrust Zone, NW Highlands, Scotland. *Journal of the Geological Society, London*, **145**, 1–10.

KELLEY, S. P. & BLUCK, B. J. 1989. Detrital mineral ages from the Southern Uplands using $^{40}Ar/^{39}Ar$ laser probe. *Journal of the Geological Society, London*, **146**, 401–403.

KELLEY, S. P. & POWELL, D. 1985. Relationships between marginal thrusting and movement on major, internal shear zones in the N. Highland Caledonides, Scotland. *Journal of Structural Geology*, **7**, 43–56.

KELLEY, S. P., REDDY, S. M. & MADDOCK, R. 1994. Laser-probe $^{40}Ar/^{39}Ar$ investigation of a pseudotachylite and its host rock from the Outer Isles thrust, Scotland. *Geology*, **22**, 443–446.

KELLING, G. 1961. The stratigraphy and structure of the Ordovician rocks of the Rhinns of Galloway. *Quarterly Journal of the Geological Society, London*, **117**, 37–75.

KELLING, G. 1962. The petrology and sedimentation of Upper Ordovician rocks of the Rhinns of Galloway, South-West Scotland. *Transactions of the Royal Society of Edinburgh*, **65**, 107–137.

KELLING, G., DAVIES, P. & HOLYROYD, J. 1987. Style, scale and significance of sand bodies in the Northern and Central Belts, southwest Southern Uplands. *Journal of the Geological Society, London*, **144**, 787–805.

KELLOCK, E. 1969. Alkaline basic igneous rocks in the Orkneys. *Scottish Journal of Geology*, **5**, 140–153.

KELLY, S. B. 1992. Milankovitch cyclicity recorded from Devonian non-marine sediments. *Terra Nova*, **4**, 578–584.

KEMP, A. E. S. 1986. Tectonostratigraphy of the Southern Belt of the Southern Uplands. *Scottish Journal of Geology*, **22**, 241–256.

KEMP, A. E. S. 1987. Evolution of Silurian depositional systems in the Southern Uplands, Scotland. *In*: LEGGETT, J. K. & ZUFFA, G. G. (eds) *Marine Clastic Sedimentology*. Graham & Trotman 124–155.

KEMP, A. E. S. & WHITE, D. E. 1985. Silurian trench sedimentation in the Southern Uplands, Scotland: implications of new age data. *Geological Magazine*, **122**, 275–277.

KEMP, A. E. S., OLIVER, G. J. H. & BALDWIN, J. R. 1985. Low-grade metamorphism and accretion tectonics: Southern Uplands terrain, Scotland. *Mineralogical Magazine*, **49**, 335–344.

KEMP, D. D. 1971. *The stratigraphy and sub-carse morphology of an area on the northern side of the River Forth, between the Lake of Menteith and Kincardine-on-Forth*. PhD thesis, University of Edinburgh.

KENNEDY, M. J. 1975. The Fleur de Lys Supergroup: stratigraphic comparison of Moine and Dalradian equivalents in Newfoundland with the British Caledonides. *Journal of the Geological Society, London*, **131**, 305–310.

KENNEDY, W. Q. 1930. The parent magma of the British Tertiary Province. *Geological Survey of Great Britain Summary of Progress*, **II**, 61–73.

KENNEDY, W. Q. 1933. Trends in differentiation of basaltic magmas. *American Journal of Science*, **25**, 239–256.

KENNEDY, W. Q. 1946. The Great Glen Fault. *Quarterly Journal of the Geological Society of London*, **102**, 41–76.

KENNEDY, W. Q. 1948. On the significance of thermal structure in the Scottish Highlands. *Geological Magazine*, **85**, 229–234.

KENNEDY, W. Q. 1949. Zones of progressive regional metamorphism in the Moine schists of the western Highlands of Scotland. *Geological Magazine*, **86**, 43–56.

KENNEDY, W. Q. 1951. Sedimentary differentiation as a factor in the Moine–Torridonian correlation. *Geological Magazine*, **88**, 257–266.

KENNEDY, W. Q. 1958. Tectonic evolution of the Midland Valley of Scotland. *Transactions of the Geological Society of Glasgow*, **23**, 107–133.

KENT, R. W. & FITTON, J. G. 2000. Mantle sources and melting dynamics in the British Palaeogene Igneous Province. *Journal of Petrology*, **41**, 1023–1040.

KENT, R. W., THOMSON, B. A., SKELHORN, R. R., KERR, A. C., NORRY, M. J. & WALSH, J. N. 1998. Emplacement of Hebridean Tertiary flood basalts: evidence from an inflated pahoehoe lava flow on Mull, Scotland. *Journal of the Geological Society, London*, **155**, 599–607.

KERLOGUE, A., CHERRY, S., DAVIES, H., QUINE, M. & SPOTTI, G. 1994. The Tiffany and Toni oil fields, Upper Jurassic submarine fan reservoirs, South Viking Graben, UK North Sea. *Petroleum Geoscience*, **1**, 279–286.

KERR, A. C. 1995a. The geochemical stratigraphy, field relations and temporal variation of the Mull-Morvern lava succession, NW Scotland. *Transactions of the Royal Society of Edinburgh: Earth Sciences*, **86**, 35–47.

KERR, A. C. 1995b. Elemental evidence for an enriched small-fraction-melt input into Tertiary Mull basalts, Western Scotland. *Journal of the Geological Society, London*, **150**, 763–769.

KERR, A. C. 1998. On the nature of the parental magma of the Tertiary Staffa magma sub-Type, Isle of Mull, Scotland. *Transactions of the Royal Society of Edinburgh: Earth Sciences*, **89**, 87–93.

KERR, A. C., KEMPTON, P. D. & THOMPSON, R. N. 1995. Crustal assimilation during turbulent magma ascent (ATA); new isotopic evidence from the Mull Tertiary lava succession, N. W. Scotland. *Contributions to Mineralogy and Petrology*, **119**, 142–154.

KERR, A. C., KENT, R. W., THOMSON, B., SEEDHOUSE, J. K. & DONALDSON, C. H. 1999. Geochemical evolution of the Tertiary Mull Volcano, Western Scotland. *Journal of Petrology*, **40**, 873–908.

KEY, R. M., CLARK, G. C., MAY, F., PHILLIPS, E. R., CHACKSFIELD, B. C. & PEACOCK, J. D. 1997. *Geology of the Glen Roy district.* Memoir of the British Geological Survey, HMSO.

KIDSTON, R. & LANG, W. H. 1916–1921. On Old Red Sandstone plants showing structure, from the Rhynie chert bed, Aberdeenshire: parts I–V. *Transactions of the Royal Society of Edinburgh*, **51** 1916–1917, 761–784, **52**, 1917–1921, 603–627, 643–680, 831–854, 855–902.

KILLE, I. C., THOMPSON, R. N., MORRISON, M. A. & THOMPSON, R. F. 1986. Field evidence for turbulence during flow of magma through conduits from southwest Mull. *Geological Magazine*, **123**, 693–697.

KIMBELL, G. S. & STONE, P. 1995. Crustal magnetization variations across the Iapetus Suture Zone. *Geological Magazine*, **132**, 599–609.

KING, B. C. 1942. The Cnoc nan Cuilean area of the Ben Loyal Igneous Complex. *Quarterly Journal of the Geological Society of London*, **98**, 149–182.

KING, B. C. 1955. The Ard Bheinn area of the central igneous complex of Arran. *Quarterly Journal of the Geological Society of London*, **110**, 323–355.

KING, P. M. 1977. *The Secondary Minerals in the Tertiary Lavas of Northern and Central Skye – Zeolite Zonation Patterns, their Origin and Formation.* PhD thesis, University of Aberdeen.

KINNY, P. D. & FRIEND, C. R. L. 1997. U/Pb isotopic evidence for the accretion of different crustal blocks to form the Lewisian complex of northwest Scotland. *Contributions to Mineralogy and Petrology*, **129**, 326–340.

KINNY, P. D., FRIEND, C. R. L., STRACHAN, R. A., WATT, G. R. & BURNS, I. M. 1999. U–Pb geochronology of regional migmatites, East Sutherland, Scotland: evidence for crustal melting during the Caledonian orogeny. *Journal of the Geological Society, London*, **156**, 1143–1152.

KINNY, P. D., STRACHAN, R. A., ROGERS, G. R., FRIEND, C. R. L. & KOCKS, H. 2003. U–Pb geochronology of deformed meta-granites in central Sutherland, Scotland: evidence for widespread Silurian metamorphism and ductile deformation of the Moine Supergroup during the Caledonian orogeny. *Journal of the Geological Society, London*. In press.

KIRBY, R. P. 1969. Till fabric analyses from the Lothians, central Scotland. *Geografiska Annaler, Stockholm*, **51A**, 48–60.

KIRK, M. 1983. *Sedimentology and Palaeogeography in the Westphalian A and B coalfields of Scotland.* PhD thesis, University of Strathclyde.

KIRK, M. 1989. Westphalian alluvial plain sedimentation, Isle of Arran, Scotland. *Geological Magazine*, **126**, 407–421.

KISCH, H. J. 1987. Correlation between indicators of very-low-grade metamorphism. *In*: FREY, M, (ed.) *Low Temperature Metamorphism.* Blackie & Son, Glasgow, 227–300.

KISSIN, S. A. 1988. Nickel–cobalt–native silver five element veins: a rift-related ore type. *In*: KISVARSANYO, G. & GRANT, S. K. (eds). *Proceedings of the North American Conference on Tectonic Control of Ore Deposits and the Vertical and Horizontal Extent of Ore Systems*, University of Missouri, Rolla, Missouri, 268–279.

KITCHEN, D. E. 1985. The parental magma on Rhum: evidence from alkaline segregations and veins in the peridotite from Salisbury's Dam. *Geological Magazine*, **122**, 529–537.

KLEMPERER, S. L., RYAN, P. D. & SNYDER, D. B. 1991. A deep seismic reflection transect across the Irish Caledonides. *Journal of the Geological Society, London*, **148**, 149–164.

KNELLER, B. C. 1985. Dalradian basin evolution and metamorphism (abstract). *Journal of the Geological Society, London*, **142**, 4.

KNELLER, B. C. 1987. A geological history of N. E. Scotland. *In*: TREWIN, N. H., KNELLER, B. C. & GILLEN, C. (eds) *Excursion Guide to the Geology of the Aberdeen area.* Scottish Academic Press, Edinburgh, 1–50.

KNELLER, B. C. 1991. A foreland basin on the southern margin of Iapetus. *Journal of the Geological Society, London*, **148**, 207–210.

KNELLER, B. C. & AFTALION, M. 1987. The isotopic and structural age of the Aberdeen granite. *Journal of the Geological Society, London*, **144**, 717–722.

KNELLER, B. C. & LESLIE, A. G. 1984. Amphibolite facies metamorphism in shear zones in the Buchan area of NE Scotland. *Journal of Metamorphic Geology*, **2**, 83–94.

KNELLER, B. C., KING, L. M. & BELL, A. M. 1993. Foreland basin development and tectonics on the northwest margin of eastern Avalonia. *Geological Magazine*, **130**, 691–697.

KNIGHT, I. 1978. Platformal sediments on the Great Northern Peninsula: stratigraphic studies and geological mapping of the north St. Barbe District. *Newfoundland Department of Mines and Energy, Mineral Development Division, Report*, **78–1**, 140–150.

KNIGHT, I. & BOYCE, W. D. 1987. Lower to Middle Cambrian terrigenous-carbonate rocks of Chimney Arm, Canada Bay: lithostratigraphy, preliminary biostratigraphy and regional significance. *In*: BLACKWOOD, R. F., WALSH, D. G. & GIBBONS, R. V. (eds) *Current Research.* Newfoundland Department of Mines and Energy, Mineral Development Division, 359–365.

KNIGHT, I. & JAMES, N. P. 1987. Stratigraphy of the St. George Group, (Lower Ordovician) western Newfoundland; the interaction between eustasy and tectonics. *Canadian Journal of Earth Sciences*, **24**, 1927–1952.

KNILL, J L. 1963. A sedimentary history of the Dalradian Series. *In*: JOHNSON, M. R. W. & STEWART, F. H. (eds). *The British Caledonides.* Oliver & Boyd, Edinburgh, 99–121.

KNIPE, R. J. & NEEDHAM, D. T. 1986. Deformation processes in accretionary wedges-examples from the SW margin of the Southern Uplands, Scotland. *In*: COWARD, M. P. & RIES, A. C. (eds) *Collision Tectonics.* Geological Society, London, Special Publications, **9**, 51–65.

KNIPE, R. J., CHAMBERLAIN, M. I., PAGE, A. & NEEDHAM, D. T. 1988. Structural histories in the SW Southern Uplands, Scotland. *Journal of the Geological Society, London*, **145**, 679–684.

KNOX, R. W. O'B. 1977. Upper Jurassic pyroclastic rocks in Skye, west Scotland. *Nature, London*, **265**, 323–324.

KNOX, R. W. O'B. & HOLLOWAY, S. 1992. 1. Paleogene of the Central and Northern North Sea. *In*: KNOX, R. W. O'B. & CORDEY, W. G. (eds) *Lithostratigraphic Nomenclature of the UK North Sea.* British Geological Survey, Nottingham.

KNOX, R. W. O'B. & MORTON, A. C. 1983. Stratigraphical distribution of early Palaeogene pyroclastic deposits in the North Sea Basin. *Proceedings of the Yorkshire Geological Society*, **44**, 355–363.

KNOX, R. W. O'B. & MORTON, A. C. 1988. The record of early Tertiary North Atlantic volcanism in sediments of the North Sea Basin. *In*: MORTON, A. C. & PARSON, L. M. (eds) *Early Tertiary Volcanism and the Opening of the NE Atlantic.* Geological Society, London, Special Publications, **39**, 407–420.

KNOX, R. W. O'B., CORFIELD, R. M. & DUNAY, R. E. (eds) 1996. *Correlation of the Early Paleogene in Northwest Europe.* Geological Society, London, Special Publications, **101**.

KNOX, R. W. O'B., HOLLOWAY, S., KIRBY, G. A. & BAILY, H. E. 1997. *Stratigraphic Nomenclature of the UK North West Margin. 2. Early Paleogene Lithostratigraphy and Sequence Stratigraphy.* British Geological Survey, Nottingham.

KOKELAAR, B. P. 1982. Fluidization of wet sediments during the emplacement and cooling of various igneous bodies. *Journal of the Geological Society, London,* **139**, 21–34.

KOOMANS, C. & KUENEN, P. H. 1938. On the differentiation of the Glen More ring-dyke, Mull. *Geological Magazine,* **75**, 145–160.

KOZUR, H. W. 1999. The correlation of the Germanic Bundstein and Muschelkalk with the Tethyan scale. *In*: BACHMANN, G. H. & LERCHE, I. (eds.) *Epicontinental Triassic.* Zentralblatt für Geologie und Paläontologie, **1**, 701–725.

KRABBENDAM, M., LESLIE, A. G., CRANE, A. & GOODMAN, S. 1997. Generation of the Tay Nappe, Scotland, by large-scale SE-directed shearing. *Journal of the Geological Society, London,* **154**, 15–24.

KRIZ, J. & POJETA, J. 1974. Barrande's colonies concept and a comparison of his stratigraphy with the modern stratigraphy of the Middle Bohemian Lower Paleozoic rocks (Barrandian) of Czechoslovakia. *Journal of Paleontology,* **48**, 489–494.

KROON, D., AUSTIN, W. E. N., CHAPMAN, M. R. & GANSSEN, G. M. 1997. Deglacial surface circulation changes in the northeast Atlantic: temperature and salinity records off NW Scotland on a century scale. *Palaeoceanography,* **12**, 755–763.

KÜBLER, B. 1968. Evaluation quantatitive du metamorphism par la cristallinite de l'illite. *Bulletin Centre Research Pau- SNPA* **2**, 385–397.

KURSTEN, M. 1957. The metamorphic and tectonic history of parts of the Outer Hebrides. *Transactions of the Edinburgh Geological Society,* **17**, 1–31.

KVENVOLEN, K. A. & VON HEUNE, R. 1985. Natural gas generation in sediments of the convergent margin of the eastern Aleutian trench arc. *In*: HOWELL, D. G. (ed.) *Tectonostratigraphic terranes of the circum-Pacific region.* Circum–Pacific Council for Energy and Mineral Resources, Earth Science Series, 31–49.

LAILEY, M., STEIN, A. M. & RESTON, T. J. 1989. The Outer Hebrides fault, Scotland: a major Proterozoic structure in NW Britain. *Journal of the Geological Society, London,* **146**, 253–260.

LAM, K. & PORTER, R. 1977. The distribution of palynomorphs in the Jurassic rocks of the Brora Outlier, N.E. Scotland. *Journal of the Geological Society, London,* **134**, 45–55.

LAMBECK, K. 1993. Glacial rebound of the British Isles. *Geophysical Journal International,* **115**, 941–990.

LAMBERT, R. ST.-J. & HOLLAND, J. G. 1972. A geochronological study of the Lewisian from Loch Laxford to Durness, Sutherland, NW Scotland. *Journal of the Geological Society, London,* **128**, 3–19.

LAMBERT, R. ST. J., HOLLAND, J. G. & LEGGETT, J. K. 1981. Petrology and tectonic setting of some Ordovician volcanic rocks from the Southern Uplands of Scotland. *Journal of the Geological Society, London,* **138**, 421–436.

LAMBERT, R. ST.-J. 1969. Isotopic studies relating to the Pre-Cambrian history of the Moinian of Scotland. *Proceedings of the Geological Society, London,* **1652**, 243–245.

LAMBERT, R. ST.-J. & MCKERROW, W. S. 1976. The Grampian Orogeny. *Scottish Journal of Geology,* **12**, 271–292.

LAMBERT, R. ST.-J., MYERS, J. S. & WATSON, J. 1970. An apparent age for a member of the Scourie dyke suite in Lewis, Outer Hebrides. *Scottish Journal of Geology,* **6**, 214–220.

LAMONT, A. & LINDSTROM, M. 1957. Arenigian and Llandeilian cherts identified in the Southern uplands by means of conodonts. *Transactions of the Royal Society of Edinburgh,* **17**, 60–70.

LAND, D. 1997. Culross moat shaft: a Scottish 'first' in mining technology. *The Edinburgh Geologist,* **No. 29**, 5–7.

LANDING, E., BOWRING, S. A, DAVIDEK., K. L., WESTROP, S. R., GEYER, G. & HELDMAIER, W. 1998. Duration of the Early Cambrian: U–Pb ages of volcanic ashes from Avalon and Gondwana. *Canadian Journal of Earth Science,* **35**, 329–335.

LANG, W. H. 1927. Contributions to the study of the Old Red Sandstone flora of Scotland. VI. On *Zosterophyllum myretonianum* Penhallow and some other plant remains from the Carmyllie Beds

of the Lower Old Red Sandstone. *Transactions of the Royal Society of Edinburgh,* **55**, 443–452.

LAPWORTH, C. 1870. On the Silurian rocks of Galashiels. *Geological Magazine,* Decade 1, **7**, 204–209, 279–284.

LAPWORTH, C. 1874. On the Silurian rocks of the south of Scotland. *Transactions of the Glasgow Geological Society,* **4**, 164–174.

LAPWORTH, C. 1878. The Moffat Series. *Quarterly Journal of the Geological Society of London,* **34**, 240–346.

LAPWORTH, C. 1882. The Girvan succession. Part I. Stratigraphy. *Quarterly Journal of the Geological Society of London,* **38**, 537–664.

LAPWORTH, C. 1883. The secret of the Highlands. *Geological Magazine,* Decade 2, **10**, 120–128 193–199, 337–144.

LAPWORTH, C. 1888. On the discovery of the *Olenellus* fauna in the Lower Cambrian rocks of Britain. *Geological Magazine* **5**, 484–487.

LAPWORTH, C. 1889. On the Ballantrae Rocks of the South of Scotland and their place in the Upland Sequence. *Geological Magazine,* **26**, 20–24, 59–69.

LAPWORTH, C. & WILSON, J. 1871. On the Silurian Rocks of the Counties of Roxburgh and Selkirk. *Geological Magazine,* **8**, 456–464.

LASOCKI, J., GUEMENE, J. M., HEDAYATI, A., LEGORJUS, C. & PAGE, W. M. 1999. The Elgin and Franklin fields in UK Blocks 22/30c, 22/30b and 29/5b. *In*: FLEET, A. J. & BOLDY, S. A. R. (eds) *Petroleum Geology of Northwest Europe: Proceedings of the 5th Conference,* Geological Society, London, 1007–1020.

LATIN, D. M., DIXON, J. E. & FITTON, J. G. 1990*a*. Rift-related magmatism in the North Sea basin. *In*: BLUNDELL, D. J. & GIBBS, A. D. (eds) *Tectonic Evolution of the North Sea Rifts.* Oxford Scientific Publications, Oxford, 104–144.

LATIN, D. M., DIXON, J. E., FITTON, J. G. & WHITE, N. 1990*b*. Mesozoic magmatic activity in the North Sea Basin: implications for stretching history. *In*: HARDMAN, R. P. F. & BROOKS, J. (eds) *Tectonic Events Responsible for Britain's Oil and Gas Reserves.* Geological Society, London, Special Publications, **55**, 207–227.

LAW, A., RAYMOND, A., WHITE, G., ATKINSON, A., CLIFTON, M., ATHERTON, T., DAWES, I., ROBERTSON, E., MELVIN, A. & BRAYLEY, S. 2000. The Kopervik fairway, Moray Firth, UK. *Petroleum Geoscience,* **6**, 265–274.

LAWSON, D. E. 1972. Torridonian volcanic sediments. *Scottish Journal of Geology,* **8**, 345–362.

LAWSON, D. E. 1976. Sandstone boulder conglomerates and a Torridonian cliffed shoreline between Gairloch and Stoer, northwest Scotland. *Scottish Journal of Geology,* **12**, 67–88.

LAWSON, T. J. 1984. Reindeer in the Scottish Quaternary. *Quaternary Newsletter,* **42**, 1–7.

LAWSON, T. J. & BONSALL, C. 1986. Early settlement in Scotland: the evidence from Reindeer Cave, Assynt. *Quaternary Newsletter,* **49**, 1–7.

LE MAITRE, R. W. (ed.) 1989. *A classification of igneous rocks and glossary of terms. Recommendations of the International Union of Geological Science Subcommission on the Systematics of Igneous Rocks.* Blackwell, Oxford.

LEACH, H. M., HERBERT, N., LOS, A. & SMITH, R. L. 1999. The Schiehallion development. *In*: FLEET, A. J. & BOLDY, S. A. R. (eds) *Petroleum Geology of Northwest Europe: Proceedings of the 5th Conference,* Geological Society, London, 683–692.

LEAKE, B. E. 1990. Granite magmas: their sources, initiation and consequences of emplacement. *Journal of the Geological Society, London,* **147**, 579–589.

LEAKE, R. C. & BROWN, M. J. 1979. Porphyry-style copper mineralization at Black Stockarton Moor, southwest Scotland. *Transactions of the Institution of Mining and Metallurgy,* **88**, B177–B181.

LEAKE, R. C. & COOPER, D. C. 1983. The Black Stockarton Moor subvolcanic complex, Galloway, *Journal of the Geological Society, London,* **140**, 665–676.

LEAKE, R. C., AULD, H. A., STONE, P. & JOHNSON, C. E. 1981. Gold mineralisation at the southern margin of the Loch Doon granitoid complex, Southwest Scotland. *Institute of Geological Sciences, Mineral Reconnaissance Programme,* Report **46**.

LEAKE, R. C., CHAPMAN, R. J., BLAND, D. J., STONE, P., CAMERON, D. G. & STYLES, M. T. 1998. The origin of alluvial gold in the Leadhills area of Scotland; evidence from internal characteristics. *Journal of Geochemical Exploration*, **63**, 7–36.

LEE, G. W. 1913. The occurrence of oil-shale among the Jurassic rocks of Raasay and Skye. *Nature, London*, October 9 1913, 169.

LEE, G. W. 1920. The Mesozoic rocks of Applecross, Raasay and north-east Skye. *Memoir Geological Survey of Scotland*.

LEE, G. W. 1925. Mesozoic rocks of East Sutherland and Ross. *In*: READ, H. H., ROSS, G. & PHEMISTER, J. *The Geology of the Country around Golspie, Sutherland*. Memoirs of the Geological Survey, 65–115.

LEE, G. W. & BAILEY, E. B. 1925. The pre-Tertiary geology of Mull, Lock Aline and Oban. *Memoir of the Geological Society of Great Britain*. Sheet 44 (Scotland).

LEEDAL, G. P. 1952. The Cluanie igneous intrusion, Inverness-shire and Ross-shire. *Quarterly Journal of the Geological Society of London*, **108**, 35–63.

LEEDER, M. G. 1973. Sedimentology and palaeogeography of the Upper Old Red Sandstone in the Scottish Border Basin. *Scottish Journal of Geology*, **9**, 117–145.

LEEDER, M. G. & BRIDGES, P. H. 1978. Upper Old Red Sandstone near Kirkbean, Dumfries and Galloway. *Scottish Journal of Geology*, **14**, 267–272.

LEEDER, M. R. 1974. Lower Border Group (Tournaisian) fluviodeltaic sedimentation and the palaeogeography of the Northumberland Basin. *Proceedings of the Yorkshire Geological Society*, **40**, 129–180.

LEEDER, M. R. 1988. Recent developments in Carboniferous geology: a critical review with implications for the British Isles and N.W. Europe. *Proceedings of the Geologists' Association*, **99**, 73–100.

LEEDER, M. R. & BOLDY, S. R. 1990. The Carboniferous of the Outer Moray Firth Basin, quadrants 14 and 15, Central North Sea. *Marine and Petroleum Geology*, **7**, 29–37.

LEEDER, M. R., FAIRHEAD, D., LEE, A., STUART, G., CLEMMY, H., AL-HADDEH, B. & GREEN, C. 1989. Sedimentary and tectonic evolution of the Northumberland Basin. *In*: ARTHURTON, R. S., GUTTERIDGE, P. & NOLAN, S. C. (eds) *The role of tectonics in Devonian and Carboniferous sedimentation in the British Isles*. Occasional Publications of the Yorkshire Geological Society, **6**, 143–152.

LEES, R. G., GORDON, J. E. & McKIRDY, A. P. 1998. Coastal erosion, coastal defence and earth heritage in Scotland. *In*: HOOKE, J. (ed.) *Coastal defence and earth science conservation*. Geological Society, 133–150.

LEGGETT, J. K. 1980. Palaeogeographic setting of the Wrae Limestone; an Ordovician submarine-slide deposit in Tweeddale. *Scottish Journal of Geology*, **16**, 91–104.

LEGGETT, J. K. 1987. The Southern Uplands as an accretionary prism; the importance of analogues in reconstructing palaeogeography. *Journal of the Geological Society, London*, **144**, 737–752.

LEGGETT, J. K., McKERROW, W. S. & EALES, M. H. 1979. The Southern Uplands of Scotland; a lower Palaeozoic accretionary prism. *Journal of the Geological Society, London*, **136**, 755–770.

LEGGETT, J. K., McKERROW, W. S. & SOPER, N. J. 1983. A model for the crustal evolution of southern Scotland. *Tectonics*, **2**, 187–210.

LEITH, C. K. 1913. *Structural Geology*. H. Holt & Co., New York.

LERVIK, K. S., SPENCER, A. M. & WARRINGTON, G. 1989. Correlation in Hydrocarbon Exploration. Norwegian Petroleum Society (Graham & Trotman), 173–189.

LESLIE, A. G. 1984. Field relations in the north-eastern part of the Insch mafic igneous mass, Aberdeenshire. *Scottish Journal of Geology*, **20**, 215–235.

LESPERANCE, P. J. 1988. Trilobites. *In*: COX, L. R. M. & RICKARDS, R. B. (eds) *A Global Analysis of the Ordovician–Silurian boundary*. *Bulletin of the British Museum (Natural History)*, **43**, 359–376.

LEVESON, D. J. 1996. What was James Hutton's methodology? *Archives of Natural History*, **23**, 61–77.

LEWIS, A. D. & BLOXAM, T. W. 1977. Petrotectonic environments of the Girvan–Ballantrae lavas from rare-earth element distributions. *Scottish Journal of Geology*, **13**, 211–222.

LEWIS, C. L. E., CARTER, A. & HURFORD, A. J. 1992. Low-temperature effects of the Skye Tertiary intrusions on Mesozoic sediments in the Sea of the Hebrides Basin. *In*: PARNELL, J. (ed.) *Basins on the North Atlantic Seaboard: Petroleum Geology, Sedimentology and Basin Evolution*. Geological Society, London, Special Publications, **62**, 175–188.

LINDLEY, I., McKIRDY, A. P. & McMILLAN, A. A. 2001. Sustainability and use of non-energy minerals. *In*: GORDON, J. E. & LEYS, K. (eds) *Earth Sciences and the Natural Heritage: Interactions and Integrated Management*. The Stationery Office, Edinburgh, 5–16.

LINDSAY, N. G., HASELOCK, P. J. & HARRIS, A. L. 1989. The extent of Grampian orogenic activity in the Scottish Highlands. *Journal of the Geological Society, London*, **146**, 733–735.

LINSLEY, P. N. 1972. *The Stratigraphy and Sedimentology of the Kimmeridgian Deposits of Sutherland, Scotland*. PhD thesis, University of London.

LINSLEY, P. N., POTTER, H. C., McNAB, G. & RACHER, D. 1980. The Beatrice field, Inner Moray Firth, U.K. North Sea. *In*: HALBOUTY, M. T. (ed.) *Giant Oil and Gas Fields of the Decade 1968–1978*. American Association of Petroleum Geologists, Memoir, **30**, 117–129.

LINTERN, B. C. & FLOYD, J. D. 2000. The geology of the Dalbeattie-Kirkcudbright district. *Memoir of the British Geological Survey*, sheets 5, E&W (Scotland).

LINTERN, B. C., BARNES, R. P. & STONE, P. 1992. Discussion on Silurian and Early Devonian sinistral deformation of the Ratagain Granite, Scotland; constraints on the age of Caledonian movements on the Great Glen system. *Journal of the Geological Society, London*, **149**, 858.

LINTON, D. L. 1959. Morphological contrasts between eastern and western Scotland. *In*: MILLER, R. & WATSON, J. W. (eds) *Geographical Essays in Memory of Alan G. Ogilvie*. Edinburgh, 16–45.

LIPPMANN, F. 1973. *Sedimentary Carbonate Minerals*. Berlin, Springer.

LISS, D., HUTTON, D. H. W & OWEN, W. H. 2001. Macroscopic and magnetic magma flow indicators from the Whin Sill, England (abstract). *Tectonic Studies Group Annual Meeting, University of Leeds, 3–6 January 2001*.

LITHERLAND, M. 1980. The stratigraphy of the Dalradian rocks around Loch Creran, Argyll. *Scottish Journal of Geology*, **16**, 105–123.

LIVERA, S. E. 1989. Facies associations and sand body geometries in the Ness Formation of the Brent Group, Brent Field. *In*: WHATELEY, M. K. G. & PICKERING, K. T. (eds) *Deltas: Sites and Traps for Fossil Fuels*. Geological Society, London, Special Publications, **41**, 269–286.

LOBJOIT, W. M. 1959. On the form and mode of emplacement of the Ben Buie Intrusion, Isle of Mull, Argyllshire. *Geological Magazine*, **96**, 393–402.

LOESCHKE, J. 1985. Geochemistry of acidic volcanic clasts in Silurian conglomerates of the Midland Valley of Scotland:Implications on the Caledonian orogeny. *Geologische Rundschau*, **74**, 537–546.

LOFTUS, G. W. L. 1985. *The Petrology and Depositional Environments of the Dinantian Burdiehouse Limestone Formation of Scotland*. PhD thesis, University of London.

LOFTUS, G. W. L. & GREENSMITH, J. T. 1988. The lacustrine Burdiehouse Limestone Formation – a key to the deposition of the Dinantian Oil Shales of Scotland. *In*: FLEET, A. J. & TALBOT, M. R. (eds), *Lacustrine Petroleum Source Rocks*. Geological Society, London, Special Publications, **40**, 219–234.

LONG, D., SMITH, D. E. & DAWSON, A. G. 1989. A Holocene tsunami deposit in eastern Scotland. *Journal of Quaternary Science*, **4**, 61–66.

LONG, L. E. & LAMBERT, R. St. J. 1963. Rb-Sr isotopic ages from the Moine series. *In*: JOHNSON, M. R. W. & STEWART, F. H. (eds) *The British Caledonides*. Oliver & Boyd, Edinburgh, 217–246.

LONGMAN, C. D., BLUCK, B. J. & VAN BREEMEN, O. 1979. Ordovician conglomerates and the evolution of the Midland Valley. *Nature, London*, **280**, 578–581.

LORD, R. A. & PRICHARD, H. M. 1997. Exploration and origin of stratigraphically controlled platinum-group element mineralization in crustal-sequence ultramafics, Shetland ophiolite complex. *In*:

SMITH, C. G. (ed.) Mineralization in the Caledonides. *Transactions of the Institution of Mining and Metallurgy*, **106**, B179–B193.

LORENZ, V. 1973. On the formation of maars. *Bulletin Volcanologique*, **37**, 183–204.

LORENZ, V. 1986. On the growth of maars and diatremes and its relevance to the formation of tuff rings. *Bulletin of Volcanology*, **48**, 265–274.

LOUGHLIN, S. C. & STEPHENSON, D. (In Press) Tholeiitic sills and dykes of Scotland and northern England: Introduction. *In*: STEPHENSON, D., LOUGHLIN, S. C., MILLWARD, D., WATERS, C. N. & WILLIAMSON, I. T. *Carboniferous and Permian Igneous Rocks of Great Britain*. Geological Conservation Review Series, **27**. (Peterborough: Joint Nature Conservation Committee).

LOVELL, J. P. B. 1974. Sand volcanoes in the Silurian rocks of Kirkcudbrightshire. *Scottish Journal of Geology*, **10**, 161–162.

LOVELL, J. P. B. 1991. Permian and Triassic. *In*: CRAIG, G. Y. (ed.) *Geology of Scotland* (3rd Edition). Geological Society, London, 421–438.

LOWDEN, B., BRALEY, S., HURST, A. & LEWIS, J. 1992. Sedimentological studies of the Cretaceous Lochaline Sandstone, NW Scotland. *In*: PARNELL, J. (ed.) *Basins on the Atlantic Seaboard: Petroleum Geology, Sedimentology and Basin Evolution*. Geological Society, London, Special Publications, **62**, 159–162.

LOWRY, D., BOYCE, A. J., FALLICK, A. E. & STEPHENS, W. E. 1997. Sources of sulphur, metals and fluids in granitoid-related mineralization of the Southern Uplands, Scotland. *In*: SMITH, C. G. (ed.) Mineralization in the Caledonides. *Transactions of the Institution of Mining and Metallurgy*, **106**, B157–B168.

LUMSDEN, G. I. 1964. The Limestone Coal Group of the Douglas Coalfield, Lanarkshire. *Bulletin of the Geological Survey of Great Britain*, **21**, 37–71.

LUMSDEN, G. I. 1967. The Upper Limestone Group and Passage Group of Douglas, Lanarkshire. *Bulletin of the Geological Survey of Great Britain*, **27**, 17–48.

LUMSDEN, G. I. & CALVER, M. A. 1958. The stratigraphy and palaeontology of the Coal Measures of the Douglas Coalfield, Lanarkshire. *Bulletin of the Geological Survey of Great Britain*, **15**, 32–70.

LUMSDEN, G. I. & WILSON, R. B. 1961. The stratigraphy of the Archerbeck Borehole, Canonbie, Dumfriesshire. *Bulletin of the Geological Survey of Great Britain*, **18**, 1–89.

LUMSDEN, G. I., TULLOCH, W., HOWELLS, M. F. & DAVIES, A. 1967. *The Geology of the Neighbourhood of Langholm*. Memoir of the Geological Survey of Great Britain.

LYELL, C. 1825. On a dike of serpentinite, cutting through sandstone, in the County of Forfar. *Edinburgh Journal of Science*, **5**, 112–126.

LYELL, C. 1829. On a recent formation of freshwater limestone in Forfarshire. *Transactions of the Geological Society of London*, 2nd series, **2**, 73–96.

LYELL, C. 1830–1833. *Principles of Geology, Being an Attempt to Explain the Former Changes of the Earth's Surface, by Reference to Causes now in Operation*. 3 vols. John Murray, London.

LYELL, C. 1838. *Elements of Geology*. John Murray, London.

LYELL, C. 1838–1840 (1840). On the geological evidence of the former existence of glaciers in Forfarshire. *Proceedings of the Geological Society of London*, **3**, 337–345.

LYELL, C. 1841. *Elements of Geology*. 2nd edition. John Murray, London.

LYELL, C. 1863. *The Geological Evidences of the Antiquity of Man with Remarks on Theories of the Origin of Species by Variation*. John Murray, London.

LYELL, K. M. (ed.) 1881. *Life Letters and Journals of Sir Charles Lyell, Bart.* 2 vols. John Murray, London.

LYON, A. G. & EDWARDS, D. 1991. The first zosterophyll from the Lower Devonian Rhynie Chert, Aberdeenshire. *Transactions of the Royal Society of Edinburgh: Earth Sciences*, **82**, 323–332.

LYON, T. B. D., PIDGEON, R. T., BOWES, D. R. & HOPGOOD, A. 1973. Geochronological investigation of the quartzofeldspathic rocks of the Lewisian of Rona, Inner Hebrides. *Journal of the Geological Society, London*, **129**, 389–402.

MACCULLOCH, J. 1814*a*. Miscellaneous remarks accompanying a catalogue of specimens [of the mineral productions and rocks of Scotland] transmitted to the Geological Society. *Transactions of the Geological Society*, **2**, 388–449.

MACCULLOCH, J. 1814*b*. Remarks on several parts of Scotland which exhibit quartz rock, and on the nature and connexions of this rock in general. *Transactions of the Geological Society*, **2**, 450–487.

MACCULLOCH, J. 1816. Sketch of the mineralogy of Sky. *Transactions of the Geological Society*, **3**, 1–111.

MACCULLOCH, J. 1817. Corrections and additions to the sketch of the mineralogy of Sky, published in the third volume of the Transactions of the Geological Society. *Transactions of the Geological Society*, **4**, 156–192.

MACCULLOCH, J. 1819. *A Description of the Western Islands of Scotland, Including the Isle of Man, Comprising an Account of their Geological Structure; With Remarks on their Agriculture, Scenery, and Antiquities*. 3 vols. Constable, London.

MACCULLOCH, J. 1824. On the limestone of Clunie, in Perthshire, with remarks on Trap and Serpentinite. *Edinburgh Journal of Science*, **1**, 1–16.

MACCULLOCH, J. 1831. *A System of Geology, With a Theory of the Earth and an Explanation of its Connection with Ancient Records*. 2 vols. Longman, Rees, Orme, Brown & Green, London.

MACCULLOCH, J. 1836. *A Geological Map of Scotland by Dr. Macculloch, F.R.S. &c. &c. &c. Published by Order of the Lords of the Treasury by S. Arrowsmith. Hydrographer to the King*. London.

MACDONALD, A. C. & TREWIN, N. H. 1993. The Upper Jurassic of the Helmsdale area. *In*: TREWIN, N. H. & HURST, A. (eds) *Excursion Guide to the Geology of East Sutherland and Caithness*. Scottish Academic Press, Edinburgh, 75–114.

MACDONALD, J. G. 1973. Carbon-dioxide metasomatism in the Campsie lavas. *Mineralogical Magazine*, **39**, 119–120.

MACDONALD, R. 1975. Petrochemistry of the Early Carboniferous (Dinantian) lavas of Scotland. *Scottish Journal of Geology*, **11**, 269–314.

MACDONALD, R. 1980. Trace element evidence for mantle heterogeneity beneath the Scottish Midland Valley in the Carboniferous and Permian. *Philosophical Transactions of the Royal Society, London*, **A297**, 245–257.

MACDONALD, R., GOTTFRIED, D., FARRINGTON, M. J., BROWN, F. & SKINNER, N. G. 1981. Geochemistry of a continental tholeiite suite: Late Palaeozoic quartz dolerite dykes of Scotland. *Transactions of the Royal Society of Edinburgh: Earth Sciences*, **72**, 57–74.

MACDONALD, R., WILSON, L., THORPE, R. S. & MARTIN, A. 1988. Emplacement of the Cleveland Dyke: evidence from geochemistry, mineralogy and physical modelling. *Journal of Petrology*, **29**, 559–583.

MACFADYEN, C. J. 1999. *Fossil Collecting in Scotland*. Scottish Natural Heritage, Information and Advisory Note, No. 110, Battleby.

MACGREGOR, A. G. 1928. The classification of Scottish Carboniferous olivine basalts and mugearites. *Transactions of the Geological Society of Glasgow*, **18**, 324–360.

MACGREGOR, M. & PHEMISTER, J. 1972. *Geological Excursion Guide to the Assynt District of Sutherland (Third Edition)*. Edinburgh Geological Society.

MACGREGOR, A. G., MACGREGOR, M. & ROBERTSON, T. 1944. Barytes in Central Scotland. *Wartime Pamphlet, Geological Survey of Great Britain*, **38**.

MACGREGOR, M. 1928–1929 (1931). Scottish Carboniferous stratigraphy; an introduction to the study of the Carboniferous rocks of Scotland. *Transactions of the Geological Society of Glasgow*, **18**, 442–558.

MACGREGOR, M. 1954. The Coalfields of Scotland. *In*: TRUEMAN, A. (ed.) *The Coalfields of Great Britain*, Edward Arnold, London, 325–381.

MACGREGOR, M., LEE, G. W. & WILSON, G. V. 1920. The iron ores of Scotland. *Special Report Mineral Resources of Great Britain*, **XI**.

MACINTYRE, R. M., CLIFF, R. A. & CHAPMAN, N. A. 1981. Geochronological evidence for phased volcanic activity in Fife and Caithness necks, Scotland. *Transactions of the Royal Society of Edinburgh: Earth Sciences*, **72**, 1–7.

MACKAY, R. A. 1959. The Leadhills Wanlockhead mining district. In: Future of Non-Ferrous Mining in Great Britain and Ireland. Institution of Mining and Metallurgy, London, 49–64.

MACKIE, W. 1913. The rock series of Craigbeg and Ord Hill, Rhynie, Aberdeenshire. Transactions of the Edinburgh Geological Society, 10, 205–236.

MACKIE, W. 1923a. The principles that regulate the distribution of heavy minerals in sedimentary rocks, as illustrated by the sandstones of the North-East of Scotland. Transactions of the Edinburgh Geological Society, 11, 138–164.

MACKIE, W. 1923b. The source of purple zircons in the sedimentary rocks of Scotland. Transactions of the Edinburgh Geological Society, 11, 200–213.

MACKLIN, M. G. & LEWIN, J. 1993. Holocene alluviation in Britain. In: DOGLAS, I. & HAGEDORN, J. (eds) Geomorphology and Geoecology. Fluvial geomorphology. Zeitschrift für Geomorphologie, Suppl. Bd, 88, 109–122.

MACKNIGHT, T. 1811. On the mineralogy and local scenery of certain districts in the Highlands of Scotland. Memoirs of the Wernerian Natural History Society, 1, 274–369.

MACLAREN, C. 1839. A Sketch of the Geology of Fife and the Lothians, Including Detailed Descriptions of Arthur's Seat and Pentland Hills. Adam & Charles Black, Edinburgh; Longman, Orme, Brown, Green & Longman, London.

MACLENNAN, A. M. & TREWIN, N. H. 1989. Palynofacies and sedimentology of the Late Bathonian–Mid. Callovian in the Inner Moray Firth. In: BATTEN, D. J. (ed.) Studies in NW European micropalaeontology and palynology. British Micropalaeontology Society Series, Ellis Horwood, Chichester. 92–117.

MACNAIR, P. 1896. The altered clastic rocks of the Southern Highlands: their structure and succession. Geological Magazine, Decade 4, 3, 167–174, 211–217.

MACPHERSON, J. B. 1980. Environmental change during the Loch Lomond Stadial: evidence from a site in the upper Spey Valley, Scotland. In: LOWE, J. J., GRAY, J. M. & ROBINSON, J. E. (eds) Studies in the Lateglacial of North-West Europe, 89–102. Pergamon, Oxford.

MACPHERSON, K. A. T. 1986. Special sand resources (silica sands). Resource Planning, Central Scotland Mineral Portfolio. British Geological Survey (Scotland).

MACPHERSON, K. A. T., SMITH, R. A. & AKHURST, M. C. 2001. Geology of the Kilmarnock district-a brief explanation of the geological map. Sheet Explanation of the British Geological Survey, 1:50 000 Series. Sheet 22E (Scotland).

MACQUEEN, J. A. & POWELL, D. 1977. Relationships between deformation and garnet growth in Moine (Precambrian) rocks of western Scotland. Geological Society of America Bulletin, 88, 235–240.

MADDOX, S. J. & ANDREWS, J. E. 1987. Lithofacies and stratigraphy of a Dinantian non-marine dolostone from the Lower Oil–Shale Group of Fife and West Lothian. Scottish Journal of Geology, 23, 129–147.

MADDOX, S. J., BLOW, R. A. & O'BRIEN, S. R. 1997. The geology and hydrocarbon prospectivity of the North Channel Basin. In: MEADOWS, N. S., TRUEBLOOD, S. P., HARDMAN, M. & COWAN, G. (eds) Petroleum Geology of the Irish Sea and Adjacent Areas. Geological Society, London, Special Publications, 124, 95–111.

MAGNUSSON, M. 1992. Sense and sensibility, Homage to Frank Fraser Darling. The 1992 NERC Annual Lecture by Magnus Magnusson. NERC News, January 1993.

MAGUIRE, K., THOMPSON, J. & GOWLAND, S. 1996. Dinantian depositional environments along the northern margin of the Solway Basin, UK. In: STROGEN, P., SOMERVILLE, I. D. & JONES, G. LL. (eds) Recent Advances in Lower Carboniferous Geology. Geological Society, London, Special Publications, 107, 163–182.

MAHER, C. E. 1981. The Piper oil field. In: ILLING, L. V. & HOBSON, G. P. (eds) Petroleum Geology of the Continental Shelf of North-West Europe. Heyden, London. 358–370.

MANGERUD, J., ANDERSON, S. T., BERGLAND, B. E. & DONNER, J. J. 1974. Quaternary stratigraphy of Norden, a proposal for terminology and classification. Boreas, 3, 109–128.

MANN, M. E., BRADLEY, R. S. & HUGHES, M. K. 1999. Northern hemisphere temperatures during the past millenium: inferences, uncertainties, and limitations. Geophysical Research Letters, 26, 759–762.

MANTELL, G. A. & BRICKENDEN, L. 1852. Notice of the discovery of reptilian foot-tracks and remains in the Old Red or Devonian strata of Moray. With a description of the Telerpeton Elginense, and observations on supposed fossil ova of Batrachians in the Lower Devonian strata of Forfarshire. Quarterly Journal of the Geological Society of London, 8, 97–109.

MARCANTONIO, F., DICKIN, A. P., MCNUTT, R. H. & HEAMAN, L. M. 1988. A 1800-million-year-old Proterozoic gneiss terrane in Islay with implications for the crustal structure and evolution of Britain. Nature, London, 335, 62–64.

MARR, J. E. 1880. On the predevonian rocks of Bohemia, Quarterly Journal of the Geological Society of London, 36, 591–619.

MARSHALL, J. E. A. & HEWITT, A. J. 2003. Devonian. In: EVANS, D., GRAHAM, C. G., ARMOUR, A. & BATHURST, P. (eds) The Millennium Atlas: petroleum geology of the central and northern North Sea. The Geological Society, London, 65–81.

MARSHALL, J. E. A. 1988. Devonian miospores from Papa Stour, Shetland. Transactions of the Royal Society of Edinburgh: Earth Sciences, 79, 13–18.

MARSHALL, J. E. A. 1991. Palynology of the Stonehaven Group, Scotland; evidence for a Mid-Silurian age and its geological implications. Geological Magazine, 128, 283–286.

MARSHALL, J. E. A. 1998. The recognition of multiple hydrocarbon generation episodes: an example from Devonian lacustrine sedimentary rocks in the Inner Moray Firth, Scotland. Journal of the Geological Society, London, 155, 335–352.

MARSHALL, J. E. A. 2000. Devonian (Givetian) miospores from the Walls Group, Shetland. In: FRIEND, P. F. & WILLIAMS, B. P. J. (eds) New perspectives on the Old Red Sandstone. Geological Society, London, Special Publications, 180, 473–483.

MARSHALL, J. E. A. & ALLEN, K. C. 1982. Devonian miospore assemblages from Fair Isle, Shetland. Palaeontology, 25, 277–312.

MARSHALL, J. E. A., BROWN, J. F. & HINDMARSH, S. 1985. Hydrocarbon source rock potential of the Devonian rocks of the Orcadian basin. Scottish Journal of Geology, 21, 301–320.

MARSHALL, J. E. A., HAUGHTON, P. D. W. & HILLIER, S. J. 1994. Vitrinite reflectivity and the structure and burial history of the Old Red Sandstone of the Midland Valley of Scotland. Journal of the Geological Society, London, 151, 425–438.

MARSHALL, J. E. A., ROGERS, D. A. & WHITELEY, M. J. 1996. Devonian marine incursions into the Orcadian Basin, Scotland. Journal of the Geological Society, London, 153, 451–466.

MARSHALL, L. A. & SPARKS, R. S. J. 1984. Origins of some mixed-magma and net-veined ring intrusions. Journal of the Geological Society, London, 141, 171–182.

MARSTON, R. J. 1971. The Foyers granitic complex, Inverness-shire. Quarterly Journal of the Geological Society of London, 126, 331–368.

MARTIGNOLE, J., MACHADO, N. & INDARES, A. 1994. The Wakeham terrane: a Mesoproterozoic terrestrial rift in the eastern part of the Grenville Province. Precambrian Research, 68, 291–306.

MARTIN, M. A. & POLLARD, J. E. 1996. The role of trace fossil ichnofabric analysis in the development of depositional models for the Upper Jurassic Fulmar Formation of the Kittiwake Field Quadrant 21 UKCS. In: HURST, A., JOHNSON, H. D., BURLEY, S. D., CANHAM, A. C. & MACKERTICH, D. S. (eds) Geology of the Humber Group: Central Graben and Moray Firth, UKCS. Geological Society, London, Special Publications, 114, 163–183.

MASON, P. W. & MASON, J. E. 1984. The Strontian barytes project – a case study. Transactions of the Institution of Mining and Metallurgy, 93, A133–A135.

MATTEY, D. P., GIBSON, I. L., MARRINER, G. F. & THOMPSON, R. N. 1977. The diagnostic geochemistry, relative abundance and spatial distribution of high-calcium, low-alkali olivine tholeiite dykes in the Lower Tertiary regional swarm of the Isle of Skye, N.W. Scotland. Mineralogical Magazine, 41, 273–285.

MATTHEWS, D. W. & WOOLEY, A. R. 1977. Layered ultramafic rocks within the Borralan complex, Scotland. *Scottish Journal of Geology*, **13**, 223–236.

MAUFE, H. B. 1910. The geological structure of Ben Nevis. *In*: *Memoirs of the Geological Survey. Summary of Progress of the Geological Survey of Great Britain and the Museum of Practical Geology for 1909*. HMSO, London, 80–89.

MAX, M. D. 1976. The pre-Palaeozoic basement in southeastern Scotland and the Southern Uplands Fault. *Nature, London*, **264**, 485–486.

MAY, F. & HIGHTON, A. J. 1997. *Geology of the Invermoriston District*. Memoir of the British Geological Survey, HMSO.

MAY, F., PEACOCK, J. D., SMITH, D. I. & BARBER, A. J. 1993. *Geology of the Kintail District*. Memoir of the British Geological Survey, HMSO.

MAYNARD, J., PRICHARD, H. M., IXER, R. A., LORD, R. A., WRIGHT, I. P., PILLINGER, C. T., McCONVILLE, P., BOYCE, A. J. & FALLICK, A. E. 1997. Sulphur isotope study of Ni–Fe–Cu mineralization in the Shetland ophiolite. *Transactions of the Institution of Mining and Metallurgy*, **106**, B215–B226.

MAYNARD, J. R., HOFMAN, W., DUNAY, R. E., BENTHAM, P. N., DEAN, K. P. & WATSON, I. 1997. The Carboniferous of western Europe: the development of a petroleum system. *Petroleum Geoscience*, **3**, 97–115.

McADAM, A. D. & TULLOCH, W. 1985. *Geology of the Haddington district*. Memoir of the British Geological Survey, Sheet 33W and part of 41 (Scotland).

McALPINE, A. 1977. *The Upper Old Red Sandstone deposits of Hoy and Dunnet Head, Northern Scotland*. PhD thesis, University of Newcastle-on-Tyne.

McBRIDE, J. H. 1994. Investigating the crustal structure of a strike-slip 'step-over' zone along the Great Glen Fault. *Tectonics*, **13**, 1150–1160.

McCLAY, K. R. & COWARD, M. P. 1981. The Moine Thrust zone: an overview. *In*: McCLAY, K. R. & PRICE, N. J. (eds) *Thrust and Nappe Tectonics*. Geological Society, London, Special Publications, **9**, 241–260.

McCLAY, K. R., NORTON, M. G., CONEY, P. & DAVIS, G. H. 1986. Collapse of the Caledonian orogen and the Old Red Sandstone. *Nature, London*, **323**, 147–159.

McCLURG, J. E. 1982. *Petrology and evolution of the northern part of the Rhum ultrabasic complex*. PhD thesis, University of Edinburgh.

McCURRY, J. A. 1987. *The Geology of the Rhins of Galloway (south of Portayew area)*. British Geological Survey. Southern Uplands project. British Geological Survey, open file, Edinburgh.

McCURRY, J. A. 1990. The geology of the Rhins of Galloway, south of the Porayew area. British Geological Survey Technical Report, WA/90/66.

McCURRY, J. A. & ANDERSON, T. B. 1989. Landward vergence in the lower Paleozoic Southern Uplands–Down–Longford Terrane, British Isles. *Geology*, **17**, 630–633.

McGHEE, G. R. 1990. Frasnian–Fammenian. *In*: BRIGGS, E. G. & CROWTHER, P. R. (eds) *Palaeobiology, a synthesis*. Blackwell, Oxford, 184–187.

McGIVEN, A. 1967. *Sedimentation and provenance of the post Valentian conglomerates up to and including the basal conglomerate of the Old Red Sandstone in the southern part of the Midland Valley of Scotland*. PhD thesis, University of Glasgow.

McGREGOR, M. & ANDERSON, E. M. 1923. The economic geology of the Central Coalfield of Scotland, Area VI. Memoir of the Geological Survey of Scotland.

McINTYRE, B. D. 1951. The tectonics of the area between Grantown and Tomintoul (mid-Strathspey). *Quarterly Journal of the Geological Society of London*, **107**, 1–22.

McINTYRE, D. B. & McKIRDY, A. 1997. *James Hutton: The Founder of Modern Geology*. The Stationery Office, Edinburgh.

McINTYRE, D. B. & McKIRDY, A. P. 2001. *James Hutton: The Founder of Modern Geology*. National Museums of Scotland, Edinburgh.

McKEE, E. D., REYNOLDS, M. A. & BAKER, C. H. 1962. Experiments on intraformational recumbent folds in crossbedded sand. *US Geological Survey*, Professional Paper **450D**, D 151–160.

McKEEVER, P. J. 1994. A new vertebrate trackway from the Permian of Dumfries and Galloway. *Scottish Journal of Geology*, **30**, 11–14.

McKENZIE, D. P. & BICKLE, M. J. 1988. The volume and composition of melt generated by extension of the lithosphere. *Journal of Petrology*, **29**, 625–679.

McKERROW, W. S. & ATKINS, F. B. 1985. *Isle of Arran*. Geologists' Association Guide.

McKERROW, W. S., LEGGETT, J. K. & EALES, M. H. 1977. Imbricate thrust model of the Southern Uplands of Scotland. *Nature, London*, **267**, 237–239.

McKERROW, W. S., LAMBERT, R. St-J. & COCKS, L. 1985. The Ordovician, Silurian and Devonian periods. *In*: SNELLING, N. J. (ed.) *The chronology of the geological record*. Memoir of the Geological Society of London, **10**, 73–79.

McKERROW, W. S., DEWEY, J. F. & SCOTESE, C. R. 1991. The Ordovician and Silurian development of the Iapetus Ocean. *Special Papers in Palaeontology*, **44**, 165–178.

McKERROW, W. S., BRASIER, M. D. & SCOTESE, C. R. 1992. Early Cambrian continental reconstructions. *Journal of the Geological Society, London*, **149**, 599–606.

McKERROW, W. S., MacNIOCAILL, C. & DEWEY, J. F. 2000. The Caledonian Orogeny redefined. *Journal of the Geological Society, London*, **157**, 1149–1154.

McKIE, T. 1989. Barrier island to tidal shelf transition in the early Cambrian Eriboll Sandstone. *Scottish Journal of Geology*, **25**, 273–293.

McKIE, T. 1990. Tidal and storm influenced sedimentation from a Cambrian transgressive passive margin sequence. *Journal of the Geological Society, London*, **147**, 785–794.

McKIRDY, A. P. 1994. Development of our physical resources – sustainability in practice? *In*: BAXTER, J. M. & USHER, M. B. (eds) *The Islands of Scotland- a Living Marine Heritage*. HMSO, Edinburgh, 239–254.

McKIRDY, A. P. 2000. Environmental geology – reaching out to a wider audience. *Scottish Journal of Geology*, **36**, 105–109.

McKIRDY, A. P. & McKIRDY, M. F. 1995. *Scottish Rocks and Fossils*. National Museums of Scotland, Edinburgh.

McKIRDY, A. P. & WRIGHT, J. R. 1990. Engineering for conservation. *Institution of Mining and Metallurgy. Transactions A: Mining Industry*, **99**, 125–132.

McKIRDY, A. P., THOMPSON, A. & POOLE, J. 1998. Dissemination of information on earth sciences to planners and other decision-makers. *In*: DOYLE, P. & BENNETT M. (eds) *Issues in Environmental Geology: a British Perspective*. Geological Society, 22–37.

McLEAN, A. C. 1966. A gravity survey in Ayrshire and its geological interpretation. *Transactions of the Royal Society of Edinburgh*, **66**, 239–265.

McLEAN, A. C. & DEEGAN, C. E. 1978. A synthesis of the solid geology of the Firth of Clyde region. *In*: McLEAN, A. C. & DEEGAN, C. E. (eds) *The Solid Geology of the Clyde Sheet (55 N/6 W)*. Institute of Geolological Sciences Report **78/9**, 93–114.

McLEOD, A. E. & UNDERHILL, J. R. 1999. Processes and products of footwall degradation, northern Brent Field, Northern North Sea. *In*: FLEET, A. J. & BOLDY, S. A. R. (eds) *Petroleum Geology of Northwest Europe: Proceedings of the 5th Conference*, Geological Society, London, 91–106.

McMILLAN, A. A. 1996. Thornhill: a small Permo-Carboniferous basin, Excursion 2. *In*: STONE, P. (ed.) *Geology in South-West Scotland: an Excursion Guide*. British Geological Survey, Keyworth, 80–87.

McMILLAN, A. A. & AITKEN, A. M. 1981. The sand and gravel resources of the country west of Peterhead, Grampian region. *Mineral Assessment Report of the Institute of Geological Sciences*, No. **58**.

McMILLAN, A. A. & BRAND, P. J. 1995. Depositional setting of Permian and Upper Carboniferous strata of the Thornhill Basin, Dumfriesshire. *Scottish Journal of Geology*, **31**, 43–52.

McMILLAN, A. A. & MERRITT, J. W. 1980. *A Reappraisal of the 'Tertiary' Deposits of Buchan, Grampian Region*. Institute of Geological Sciences Report **80/1**.

McQUILLIN, R. & TUSON, J. 1963. Gravity measurements over the Rhum Tertiary plutonic complex. *Nature, London*, **199**, 1276–1277.

McQUILLIN, R., BACON, M. & BINNS, P. E. 1975. The Blackstones Tertiary igneous complex. *Scottish Journal of Geology*, **11**, 179–192.

MEADOWS, N. S., MACCHI, L., CUBITT, J. M. & JOHNSON, B. 1987. Sedimentology and reservoir potential in the west of Shetland, UK, exploration area. *In*: BROOKS, J. & GLENNIE, K. W. (eds) *Petroleum Geology of North West Europe*. Graham & Trotman, London, 723–736.

MEIGHAN, I. G. 1979. The acid igneous rocks of the Tertiary Province. *Bulletin of the Geological Survey of Great Britain*, **70**, 10–22.

MEIGHAN, I. G., HUTCHISON, R., WILLIAMSON, I. T. & MACINTIRE, R. M. 1982. Geological evidence for the different relative ages of the Rhum and Skye Tertiary central complexes. *Journal of the Geological Society, London*, **139**, 659.

MEIGHAN, I. G., FALLICK, A. E. & McCORMICK, A. G. 1992. Anorogenic granite magma genesis: new isotopic data from the southern sector of the British Tertiary Volcanic Province. *Transactions of the Royal Society of Edinburgh: Earth Sciences*, **83**, 227–233.

MEIKLE, T. K. 1994. Native silver from Hilderston mine, West Lothian, Scotland. *Journal of the Russell Society*, **5**, 83–90.

MEISSNER, R., MATTHEWS, D. & WEVER, T. 1986. The 'Moho' in and around Great Britain. *Annales Geophysicae*, 4, **B6**, 659–664.

MELLERE, D. & STEEL, R. J. 1996. Tidal sedimentation in the Inner Hebrides half grabens, Scotland: the Mid-Jurassic Bearreraig Sandstone Formation. *In*: DE BATIST, M. & JACOBS, P. (eds) *Geology of Siliclastic Shelf Seas*. Geological Society, London, Special Publications, **117**, 49–79.

MELVIN, J. 1985. Walls Formation, Western Shetland, distal alluvial plain deposits within a tectonically active Devonian Basin. *Geological Journal*, **21**, 23–40.

MENDUM, J. R. & FETTES, D. J. 1985. The Tay nappe and associated folding in the Ben Ledi–Loch Lomond area. *Scottish Journal of Geology*, **21**, 41–56.

MENNING, M. 1995. A numerical time scale for the Permian and Triassic Periods: an integrated time analysis. *In*: SCHOLLE, P. A., PERYT, T. M. & ULMER-SCHOLLE, D. S. (eds) *The Permian of Northern Pangea. 1*. Springer, Berlin, 77–97.

MENNING, M., WEYER, D., DOZDZEWSKI, G., VAN ANEROM, H. W. J. & WENDT, I. 2001. A Carboniferous time scale 2000: discussion and use of geological parameters as time indicators from Central and Western Europe. *Geologisches Jahrbuch, Hannover*, **A 156**, 3–44.

MENZIES, M. A., HALLIDAY, A. N., HUNTER, R. H., MACINTIRE, R. M. & UPTON, B. G. J. 1989. The age, composition and significance of a xenolith-bearing monchiquite dike, Lewis, Scotland. *In*: ROSS, J., JACQUES, A. L., FERGUSON, J., GREEN, D. H., O'REILLY, S. Y., DANCHIN, R. V. & JANSE, A. J. A. (eds) *Kimberlites and Related Rocks*. 2 volumes. Proceedings of the Fourth International Kimberlite Conference, Geological Society of Australia, Special Publications, **14**.

MERCY, E. L. P. 1963. The geochemistry of some Caledonian granitic and metasedimentary rocks. *In*: JOHNSON, M. R. W. & STEWART, F. H. (eds) *The British Caledonides*. Oliver & Boyd, Edinburgh, 189–215.

MERRIMAN, R. J. & FREY, M. 1999. *Low Grade Metamorphism*. Blackwell, Oxford, University Press, Cambridge.

MERRIMAN, R. J. & ROBERTS, B. 1985. A survey of white mica crystallinity and polytypes in pelitic rocks of Snowdonia and Llyn, N. Wales. *Mineralogical Magazine*, **49**, 305–319.

MERRIMAN, R. J. & ROBERTS, B. 1990. Metabentonites in the Moffat Shale Group, Southern Uplands of Scotland; geochemical evidence of ensialic marginal basin volcanism. *Geological Magazine*, **127**, 259–271.

MERRIMAN, R. J. & ROBERTS, B., PEACOR, D. R. & HIRONS, S. R. 1995a. Strain-related differences in the crystal growth of white mica and chlorite; a TEM and XRD study of the development of metapelitic microfabrics in the Southern Uplands thrust terrane, Scotland. *Journal of Metamorphic Geology*, **13**, 559–576.

MERRIMAN, R. J., REX, D. C., SOPER, N. J. & PEACOR, D. R. 1995b. The age of Acadian cleavage in Northern England, UK: K–Ar and TEM analysis of a Silurian metabentonite. *Proceedings of the Yorkshire Geological Society*, **50**, 255–265.

MERRITT, J. W., AUTON, C. A. & FIRTH, C. R. 1995. Ice proximal glaciomarine sedimentation and sea-level change in the Inverness area, Scotland: a review of the deglaciation of a major ice stream of the British late Devensian. *Quaternary Science Reviews*, **14**, 289–329.

MIALL, A. D. 1977. A review of the braided river depositional environment. *Earth Science Reviews*, **13**, 1–62.

MILES, R. S. 1968. The Old Red Sandstone Antiarchs of Scotland: Family Bothriolepidae. *Palaeontographical Society (Monograph)*, **122**, 1–130.

MILES, R. S. & WESTOLL, T. S. 1963. Two new genera of Coccosteid Arthrodira from the Middle Old Red Sandstone of Scotland and their stratigraphic distribution. *Transactions of the Royal Society of Edinburgh*, **65**, 179–210.

MILLAR, I. L. 1999. Neoproterozoic extensional basic magmatism associated with emplacement of the West Highland granite gneiss in the Moine Supergroup of NW Scotland. *Journal of the Geological Society, London*, **156**, 1153–1162.

MILLER, G. H., SEJRUP, H. P., MANGERUD, J. & ANDERSON, B. G. 1987. Amino-acid ratios in Quaternary molluscs and foraminifera from western Norway. *Boreas*, **12**, 107–124.

MILLER, H. 1841. *The Old Red Sandstone; Or, New Walks in an Old Field*. J. Johnstone, Edinburgh.

MILLER, H. 1849. *Footprints of the Creator; Or, The Asterolepis of Stromness*. Johnstone & Hunter, London.

MILLER, H. 1854. The fossiliferous deposits of Scotland. *Proceedings of the Royal Physical Society, Edinburgh*, **1**, 1–29.

MILLER, H. 1858. *The Cruise of the Betsey, with Rambles of a Geologist*. Constable, Edinburgh.

MILLER, J. A. & MOHR, P. A. 1965. Potassium-argon age determination on rocks from St. Kilda and Rockall. *Scottish Journal of Geology*, **1**, 93–99.

MILLER, J. M. & TAYLOR, K. 1966. Uranium mineralization near Dalbeattie, Kirkcudbrightshire. *Bulletin of the Geological Survey of Great Britain*, **25**, 1–18.

MINISTRY OF AGRICULTURE, FISHERIES AND FOOD 1995. *Shoreline Management Plans. A Guide for Coastal Defence Authorities*. MAFF PB 2197. London.

MITCHELL, A. H. G. & McKERROW, W. S. 1975. Analogous evolution of the Burma Orogen and the Scottish Caledonides. *Geological Society of America Bulletin*, **86**, 305–315.

MITCHELL, G. H. & MYKURA, W. 1962. The Geology of the neighbourhood of Edinburgh. *Memoir of the Geological Survey UK* (Sheet 32).

MITCHELL, J. G. & HALLIDAY, A. N. 1976. Extent of Triassic/Jurassic hydrothermal ore deposits on the North Atlantic margins. *Transactions of the Institution of Mining and Metallurgy*, **85**, B159–B161.

MOHAMMED, H. A. 1987. *Petrography, Mineral Chemistry, Geochemistry and Sulphur Isotope Studies of the Abhainn Srathain Copper Mineralisation, Meall Mor, South Knapdale, Scotland*. PhD thesis, University of Strathclyde.

MOLES, N. R. 1983. Sphalerite composition in relation to deposition and metamorphism of the Foss stratiform Ba–Zn–Pb deposit, Aberfeldy, Scotland, *Mineralogical Magazine*, **47**, 487–500.

MOLES, N. R. 1985. *Geology, Geochemistry, and Petrology of the Foss Stratiform Barite-Base Metal Deposit and Adjacent Dalradian Metasediments near Aberfeldy, Scotland*. PhD thesis, University of Edinburgh.

MOLES, N. R. 1986. Geological setting and origin of the Foss celsian–barite–Zn–Pb sulphide deposit, Central Scottish Highlands. *Irish Association of Economic Geologists, Annual Review*, 34–40.

MOLYNEUX, S. G. 1987. Possible early Wenlock acritarchs from the Linkum Beds of the Southern Uplands. *Scottish Journal of Geology*, **23**, 301–313.

MOLYNEUX, S. G. 1998. An upper Dalradian microfossil reassessed. *Journal of the Geological Society, London*, **155**, 740–743.

MONGKOLTIP, P. & ASHWORTH, J. R. 1986. Amphibolitization of metagabbros in the Scottish Highlands. *Journal of Metamorphic Geology*, **4**, 261–283.

MONRO, S. K. 1985. Sedimentation controls in the Midland Valley of Scotland – the Dalry Basin case study. *Compte Rendu Xme Congrès International de Stratigraphie et de Géologie du Carbonifère, Madrid 1983*, **10**, 343–353.

MONRO, S. K. 1999. *Geology of the Irvine District.* Memoir of the Geological Survey of Great Britain.

MONRO, S. K. & HULL, J. H. 1986. Environmental geology in Great Britain. *In*: BENDER, F. (ed.) *Proceedings of the Fourth International Symposium, Schweizerbart'sche Verlagsbuchhandlung.* (Nagele u obermiller) Stuttgart, 107–124.

MONRO, S. K., LOUGHNAN, F. C. & WALKER, M. C. 1983. The Ayrshire Bauxitic Clay – an allochthonous deposit? *In*: WILSON, R. C. L. (ed.) *Residual Deposits.* Geological Society, London, Special Publications, **11**, 47–58.

MONTY, C. L. V. 1967. Distribution and structure of recent stromatolitic algal mats, eastern Andros Island, Bahamas. *Annales de la Société geologique Belgique*, **90**, Bulletin 3, B55–100.

MONTY, C. L. V. & HARDIE, L. A. 1976. The geological significance of the freshwater algal marsh. *In*: WALTER, M. R. (ed.) *Stromatolites.* Developments in Sedimentology, **20**, Elsevier, Amsterdam, 447–477.

MOORBATH, S. & BELL, J. D. 1965. Strontium isotope abundance studies and Rb/Sr age measurements of Tertiary igneous rocks of Skye. *Journal of Petrology*, **6**, 37–66.

MOORBATH, S. & PARK, R. G. 1972. The Lewisian chronology of the southern region of the Scottish Mainland. *Scottish Journal of Geology*, **8**, 51–74.

MOORBATH, S. & TAYLOR, P. N. 1974. Lewisian age for the Scardroy Mass. *Nature, London*, **250**, 41–43.

MOORBATH, S. & THOMPSON, R. N. 1980. Strontium isotope geochemistry and petrogenesis of the Early Tertiary lava pile of the Isle of Skye, and other basic rocks of the British Tertiary Province: an example of magma-crust interaction. *Journal of Petrology*, **21**, 295–321.

MOORBATH, S. & WELKE, H. 1969. Lead isotope studies on igneous rocks from the Isle of Skye, northwest Scotland. *Earth and Planetary Science Letters*, **5**, 217–230.

MOORBATH, S., STEWART, A. D., LAWSON, D. E. & WILLIAMS, G. E. 1967. Geochronological studies on the Torridonian sediments of north-west Scotland. *Scottish Journal of Geology*, **3**, 389–412.

MOORBATH, S., POWELL, J. L. & TAYLOR, P. N. 1975. Isotopic evidence for the age and origin of the 'grey gneiss' complex of the southern Outer Hebrides, north-west Scotland. *Journal of the Geological Society, London*, **131**, 213–222.

MOORE, D. J. 1979. *The Baryte Deposits of Central and Southern Scotland.* PhD thesis, University of Leeds.

MOORE, I. & KOKELAAR, P. 1997. Tectonic influences in piecemeal caldera collapse at Glencoe volcano, Scotland. *Journal of the Geological Society, London*, **154**, 765–768.

MOORE, I. & KOKELAAR, P. 1998. Tectonically controlled piecemeal caldera collapse: A case study of Glencoe volcano, Scotland. *Geological Society of America, Bulletin*, **110**, 1448–1466.

MOORHOUSE, S. J. & MOORHOUSE, V. E. 1979. The Moine amphibolite suites of central and northern Sutherland. *Mineralogical Magazine*, **43**, 211–225.

MOORHOUSE, S. J. & MOORHOUSE, V. E. 1988. The Moine Assemblage in Sutherland. *In*: WINCHESTER, J. A. (ed.) *Later Proterozoic Stratigraphy in the Northern Atlantic Regions.* Blackie, Glasgow, 54–73.

MOORHOUSE, V. E. 1979. *The Geology and Geochemistry of the Bettyhill–Strathy Area of North-East Sutherland.* PhD thesis, University of Hull.

MOORHOUSE, V. E. & MOORHOUSE, S. J. 1983. The geology and geochemistry of the Strathy complex of north-east Sutherland, Scotland. *Mineralogical Magazine*, **47**, 123–137.

MORETON, S., ASPEN, P., GREEN, D. I. & INGRAM, S. M. 1998. The silver and cobalt mineralization near Alva, Central Region, Scotland. *Journal of the Russell Society*, **7**, 23–30.

MORRIS, G. A. & HUTTON, D. H. W. 1993. Evidence for sinistral shear associated with the emplacement of the early Devonian Etive dyke swarm. *Scottish Journal of Geology*, **29**, 69–72.

MORRIS, J. H. 1987. The Northern Belt of the Longford-Down Inlier, Ireland and Southern Uplands, Scotland: an Ordovician back-arc basin. *Journal of the Geological Society, London*, **144**, 773–786.

MORRISON, M. A., THOMPSON, R. N., GIBSON, I. L. & MARRINER, G. F. 1980. Lateral chemical heterogeneity in the Palaeocene upper mantle beneath the Scottish Hebrides. *Philosophical Transactions of the Royal Society of London*, **297A**, 229–244.

MORRISON, M. A., HENDRY, G. L. & LEAT, P. T. 1987. Regional and tectonic implications of parallel Caledonian and Permo-Carboniferous lamprophyre dyke swarms from Lismore, Ardgour. *Transactions of the Royal Society of Edinburgh: Earth Sciences*, **77**, 279–288.

MORTON, A. C. & KNOX, R. W. O'B. 1990. Geochemistry of the late Palaeocene and early Eocene tephras from the North Sea Basin. *Journal of the Geological Society, London*, **147**, 425–437.

MORTON, A. C., DIXON, J. E., FITTON, J. G., MACINTYRE, R. M., SMYTHE, D. K. & TAYLOR, P. N. 1988. Early Tertiary rocks in well 163/6–1A, Rockall Trough. *In*: MORTON, A. C. & PARSON, L. M. (eds) *Early Tertiary Volcanism and the Opening of the NE Atlantic.* Geological Society, London, Special Publications, **39**, 293–308.

MORTON, D. J. 1979. Palaeogeographical evolution of the Lower Old Red Sandstone basin in the Western Midland Valley. *Scottish Journal of Geology*, **15**, 97–116.

MORTON, N. 1965. The Bearreraig Sandstone Series (Middle Jurassic) of Skye and Raasay. *Scottish Journal of Geology*, **1**, 189–216.

MORTON, N. 1983. Palaeocurrents and palaeo-environments of part of the Bearreraig Sandstone (Middle Jurassic) of Skye and Raasay, Inner Hebrides. *Scottish Journal of Geology*, **19**, 87–95.

MORTON, N. 1987. Jurassic subsidence history in the Hebrides, NW Scotland, *Marine and Petroleum Geology*, **4**, 226–242.

MORTON, N. 1989. Jurassic sequence stratigraphy in the Hebrides Basin, NW Scotland. *Marine and Petroleum Geology*, **6**, 243–260.

MORTON, N. 1990. Tectonic and eustatic controls of Jurassic genetic sequences in the Hebrides Basin, NW Scotland. *Bulletin de la Société Geologique de France*, **8**, 1001–1009.

MORTON, N. 1992. Dynamic stratigraphy of the Triassic and Jurassic of the Hebrides Basin, NW Scotland. *In*: PARNELL, J. (ed.) *Basins on the Atlantic Seaboard: Petroleum Geology, Sedimentology and Basin Evolution.* Geological Society, London, Special Publications, **62**, 97–110.

MORTON, N. 1994. Stratigraphical markers in the Aalenian–Bajocian boundary section at Bearreraig, Isle of Skye, Scotland. *In*: Proceedings 3rd International Meeting on Aalenian-Bajocian Stratigraphy. *Miscellanea del Servizio Geologico Nazionale*, **5**, 79–90.

MORTON, N. 1999a. Discussion: The lower Lias Group of the Hebrides Basin. (reply by S. P. HESSELBO, M. J. OATES & H. C. JENKYNS). *Scottish Journal of Geology*, **35**, 85–88.

MORTON, N. 1999b. Middle Hettangian (lower Jurassic) ammonites from Isle of Raasay, Inner Hebrides, and correlation of the Hettangian–lowermost Sinemurian Breakish Formation in the Skye area, NW Scotland. *Scottish Journal of Geology*, **35**, 119–130.

MORTON, N. & HUDSON, J. D. 1995. Field guide to the Jurassic of the Isles of Raasay and Skye, Inner Hebrides, NW Scotland. *In*: TAYLOR, P. D. (ed.) *Field Geology of the British Jurassic*, Geological Society, London, 209–280.

MOSELEY, B. 1999. Downthrown closures of the Outer Moray Firth. *In*: FLEET, A. J. & BOLDY, S. A. R. (eds) *Petroleum Geology of Northwest Europe: Proceedings of the 5th Conference*, Geological Society, London, 861–878.

MOSELEY, F. 1971. A reconnaissance of the Wadi Beihan, South Yemen. *Proceedings of the Geologists' Association*, **82**, 61–69.

MOULD, A. S., SMITH, I. F., HITCHEN, K. & EVANS, J. R. 1996. *Geophysical Image Atlas, Volume 11G: Hatton Bank (Gravity).* British Geological Survey, Edinburgh.

MUDGE, D. C. & RASHID, B. 1987. The Geology of the Faeroe Basin area. *In*: Brooks, J & GLENNIE, K. (eds) *Petroleum Geology of North West Europe*. Graham & Trotman, London, 751–763.

MUIR, R. J. 1990. *The Precambrian Basement and Related Rocks of the Southern Inner Hebrides, Scotland*. PhD thesis, University of Wales.

MUIR, R. J., EVANS, J. A. & FITCHES, W. R. 1993. Mafic dykes within the Lewisian Complex on Tiree and Coll, Inner Hebrides. *Scottish Journal of Geology*, **29**, 167–176.

MUIR, R. J, FITCHES, W. R., MALTMAN, A. J. & BENTLEY, M. R. 1994a. Precambrian rocks of the southern Inner Hebrides–Malin Sea region: Colonsay, West Islay, Inishtrahull and Iona. *In*: GIBBONS, W. & HARRIS, A. L. (eds) *A Revised Correlation of Precambrian Rocks in the British Isles*. Geological Society of London, Special Report, **22**, 54–58.

MUIR, R. J., FITCHES, W. R. & MALTMAN, A. J. 1994b. The Rhinns Complex: Proterozoic basement on Islay and Colonsay, Inner Hebrides, Scotland, and on Inishtrahull, NW Ireland. *Transactions of the Royal Society of Edinburgh: Earth Sciences*, **85**, 77–90.

MUIR, R. O. 1963. Petrography and provenance of the Millstone Grit of central Scotland. *Transactions of the Edinburgh Geological Society*, **19**, 439–485.

MUNRO, M. 1973. Structures in the south-eastern part of the Strontian Granite Complex, Argyllshire. *Scottish Journal of Geology*, **9**, 99–108.

MUNRO, M. 1984. Cumulate relations in the 'Younger Basic' masses of the Huntly–Portsoy area, Grampian Region. *Scottish Journal of Geology*, **20**, 343–359.

MUNRO, M. & GALLAGHER, J. W. 1984. Disruption of the 'Younger Basic' masses in the Huntly-Portsoy area, Grampian region. *Scottish Journal of Geology*, **20**, 361–382.

MURCHISON, D. G & RAYMOND, A. C. 1989. Igneous activity and organic maturation in the Midland Valley of Scotland. *International Journal of Coal Geology*, **14**, 47–82.

MURCHISON, R. I. 1827. On the coal-field of Brora in Sutherlandshire. *Transactions of the Geological Society, London*, **2**, 293–326.

MURCHISON, R. I. 1839. *The Silurian System*. London.

MURCHISON, R. I. 1851. On the Silurian rocks of the south of Scotland. *Quarterly Journal of the Geological Society of London*, **7**, 139–178.

MURCHISON, R. I. 1859a. On the sandstones of Morayshire (Elgin &c.) containing reptilian remains; and on their relations to the Old Red Sandstone of that country. *Quarterly Journal of the Geological Society of London*, **15**, 419–439.

MURCHISON, R. I. 1859b. *Siluria: The History of the Oldest Known Rocks Containing Organic Remains, With a Brief Sketch of the Distribution of Gold over the Earth*. 3rd edition. John Murray, London.

MURCHISON, R. I. 1859c. Some results of recent researches among the older rocks of the Highlands of Scotland. *Report of the Twenty-Eighth Meeting of the British Association for the Advancement of Science; Held at Leeds in September 1858*. John Murray, London.

MURCHISON, R. I. 1859d. On the succession of the older rocks in the northernmost counties of Scotland. *Quarterly Journal of the Geological Society, London*, **15**, 353–418.

MURCHISON, R. I. 1867. *Siluria: A History of the Oldest Rocks in the British Isles and other Countries; with Sketches of the Origin and Distribution and Nature of Gold, the General Succession of Geological Formations. and Changes of the Earth's Surface*. 4th edition. John Murray, London.

MURCHISON, R. I. & GEIKIE, A. 1861. On the altered rocks of the western islands of Scotland, and the north-western and central Highlands. *Quarterly Journal of the Geological Society of London*, **17**, 171–229.

MURPHY, F. C. & HUTTON, D. H. W. 1986. Is the Southern Uplands of Scotland really an accretionary prism? *Geology*, **14**, 354–357.

MUSSETT, A. E. 1984. Time and duration of Tertiary igneous activity of Rhum and adjacent areas. *Scottish Journal of Geology*, **20**, 273–293.

MUSSETT, A. E., DAGLEY, P., HODGSON, B. & SKELHORN, R. R. 1987. Palaeomagnetism and age of the quartz-porphyry intrusions, Isle of Arran. *Scottish Journal of Geology*, **23**, 9–22.

MUSSETT, A. E., DAGLEY, P. & SKELHORN, R. R. 1988. Time and duration of activity in the British Tertiary Igneous Province. *In*: MORTON, A. C. & PARSON, L. M. (eds) *Early Tertiary Volcanism and the Opening of the NE Atlantic*. Geological Society, London, Special Publications, **39**, 337–348.

MYERS, J. S. 1970. Gneiss types and their significance in the repeatedly deformed and metamorphosed Lewisian complex of Western Harris, Outer Hebrides. *Scottish Journal of Geology*, **6**, 186–199.

MYERS, J. S. 1971. The Late Laxfordian granite-migmatite complex of western Harris, Outer Hebrides. *Scottish Journal of Geology*, **7**, 254–284.

MYERS, J. S. 1987. The East Greenland Nagssugtoqidian mobile belt compared with the Lewisian complex. *In*: PARK, R. G. & TARNEY, J. (eds) *Evolution of the Lewisian and Comparable Precambrian High Grade Terrains*. Geological Society, London, Special Publications, **27**, 235–246.

MYKURA, W. 1960a. The replacement of coal by limestone and the reddening of Coal Measures in the Ayrshire Coalfield. *Bulletin of the Geological Survey of Great Britain*, **16**, 69–109.

MYKURA, W. 1960b. The Lower Old Red Sandstone igneous rocks of the Pentland Hills, *Bulletin, Geological Survey of Great Britain*, **16**, 131–155.

MYKURA, W. 1967. The Upper Carboniferous rocks of south-west Ayrshire. *Bulletin of the Geological Survey of Great Britain*, **26**, 23–98.

MYKURA, W. 1972. The Old Red Sandstone sediments of Fair Isle, Shetland Islands. *Bulletin, Geological Survey of Great Britain*, **41**, 1–31.

MYKURA, W. 1976. *Orkney and Shetland*. British Regional Geology. Institute of Geological Sciences, Edinburgh.

MYKURA, W. 1982. The Old Red Sandstone east of Loch Ness, Inverness-shire. *Institute of Geological Sciences, Report* **82–13**, Edinburgh.

MYKURA, W. 1991. Old Red Sandstone. *In*: Craig. G. Y. (ed.) *Geology of Scotland* (3rd edition). Geological Society, London, 297–346.

MYKURA, W. & OWENS, B. 1983. The Old Red Sandstone of the Meal fuorvonie outlier, west of Loch Ness, Inverness-shire. *Institute of Geological Sciences, Report*, 83/7.

NADEN, J. & CAULFIELD, J. B. D. 1989. Fluid inclusion and isotopic studies of gold mineralisation in the southern Uplands of Scotland. *Transactions of the Institution of Mining and Metallurgy*, **98**, B46–B48.

NAUMOVA, S. N. & PAVLOVSKY, E. V. 1961. The discovery of plant remains (spores) in the Torridonian shales of Scotland. *Doklady Akademii Nauk SSSR*, **141**, 181–182.

NECKER DE SAUSSURE, L. A. 1821. *Voyage en Écosse et aux Îsles Hébrides*. J. J. Paschoud, Geneva.

NECKER DE SAUSSURE, L. A. 1822. *A Voyage to the Hebrides, Or Western Isles of Scotland*. Sir Richard Phillips & Co., London.

NEEDHAM, D. T. & KNIPE, R. J. 1985. Accretion- and collision-related deformation in the Southern Uplands accretionary wedge, southwest Scotland. *Geology*, **14**, 303–306.

NEVES, R. & SELLEY, R. C. 1975. A review of the Jurassic rocks of North-East Scotland. *In*: FINSTAD, K. G. & SELLEY, R. C. (eds) *Proceedings Jurassic Northern North Sea Symposium*, Stavanger, Sept. 1975. Norsk Petroleum-forening. JNNSS/5, 1–29.

NEVES, R., READ, W. A. & WILSON, R. B. 1965. Note on recent spore and goniatite evidence from the Passage Group of the Scottish Upper Carboniferous succession. *Scottish Journal of Geology*, **1**, 185–188.

NEWEY, W. W. 1970. Pollen analysis of Late-Weichselian deposits at Corstorphine, Edinburgh. *New Phytologist*, **69**, 1167–1177.

NEWMAN, M. ST. J., REEDER, M. L., WOODRUFF, A. H. W. & HATTON, I. R. 1993. The geology of the Gryphon Oil Field. *In*: PARKER, J. R. (ed.) *Petroleum Geology of Northwest Europe: Proceedings of the 4th Conference*. Geological Society, London, 123–133.

NEWMAN, M. J. & TREWIN, N. H. 2001. A new jawless vertebrate from the Middle Devonian of Scotland. *Palaeontology*, **44**, 43–51.

NEWTON, S. K. & FLANAGAN, K. P. 1993. The Alba Field: evolution of the depositional model. *In*: PARKER, J. R. (ed.) *Petroleum Geology of Northwest Europe: Proceedings of the 4th Conference*. Geological Society, London, 161–171.

NICHOLAS, C. J. 1994. New stratigraphical constraints on the Durness Group of NW Scotland. *Scottish Journal of Geology*, **30**, 73–85.

NICHOLSON, H. A. 1872. *A Manual of Palaeontology: With a General Introduction on the Principles of Palaeontology*. W. Blackwood, Edinburgh.

NICHOLSON, K. 1986. Mineralogy and geochemistry of manganese and iron veins, Arndilly, Banffshire. *Scottish Journal of Geology*, **22**, 213–224.

NICHOLSON, K. 1989. Early Devonian geothermal systems in northeast Scotland: Exploration targets for epithermal gold. *Geology*, **17**, 568–571.

NICHOLSON, K. 1990. Stratiform manganese mineralization near Inverness, Scotland: A Devonian sublacustrine hot spring deposit? *Mineralium Deposita*, **25**, 126–131.

NICHOLSON, K. & ANDERTON, R. 1989. The Dalradian rocks of the Lecht, NE Scotland: stratigraphy, faulting, geochemistry and mineralization. *Transactions of the Royal Society of Edinburgh: Earth Science*, **80**, 143–157.

NICHOLSON, P. G. 1993. A basin reappraisal of the Proterozoic Torridon Group, northwest Scotland. *In*: FROSTICK, L. E. & STEEL, R. J. (eds) *Tectonic Controls and Signatures in Sedimentary Successions*. International Association of Sedimentologists, Special Publications, **20**, 183–202.

NICHOLSON, R. 1978. The Camas Malag Formation: an interbedded rhythmite conglomerate sequence of probable Triassic age, Loch Slapin, Isle of Skye. *Scottish Journal of Geology*, **14**, 301–309.

NICKLESS, E. F. P. 1982. *Environmental Geology of the Glenrothes District, Fife Region*. Description of 1:25,000 sheet No. 20, Institute of Geological Sciences, Report 82/15.

NICOL, J. 1843. On the Geology of Peeblesshire. *Transactions of the Highland and Agricultural Society*, **8**, 149–206.

NICOL, J. 1844. *Guide to the Geology of Scotland: Containing an Account of the Character, Distribution, and More Interesting Appearances of its Rocks and Minerals. With a Geological Map and Engravings by Jackson and Bruce*. Oliver & Boyd, Edinburgh.

NICOL, J. 1848. On the geology of the Silurian rocks in the valley of the Tweed. [With] notice on the fossils collected by Mr. Nicol, in Peeblesshire [by J. W. Salter]. *Quarterly Journal of the Geological Society of London*, **4**, 195–209.

NICOL, J. 1850. Observations on the Silurian strata of the south-east of Scotland. [With] notes on the fossils. *Quarterly Journal of the Geological Society of London*, **6**, 53–69.

NICOL, J. 1855. Observations on the Silurian Strata of the south-east of Scotland. *Quarterly Journal of the Geological Society, London*, **6**, 53–65.

NICOL, J. 1857. On the red sandstone and conglomerate, and the superposed quartz-rocks, limestones, and gneiss of the north-west coast of Scotland. *Quarterly Journal of the Geological Society of London*, **13**, 17–39.

NICOL, J. 1859. On the age and relations of the gneiss rocks in the north of Scotland. *Report of the Twenty-Eighth Meeting of the British Association for the Advancement of Science; Held at Leeds in September 1858*, 94–96. John Murray, London.

NICOL, J. 1860. On the relations of the gneiss, red sandstone, and quartzite in the northwest Highlands. *Report of the Twenty-Ninth Meeting of the British Association for the Advancement of Science; Held at Aberdeen in September 1859*, 119–120. John Murray, London.

NICOL, J. 1863. On the geological structure of the southern Grampians. *Quarterly Journal of the Geological Society of London*, **19**, 180–209.

NICOL, J. 1866. *The Geology and Scenery of the North of Scotland: being Two Lectures Given at the Philosophical Institution, Edinburgh, with Notes and an Appendix*. Edinburgh, 1–96.

NIREX 1989. *Deep Repository Project, Preliminary Environmental and Radiological Assessment and Preliminary Safety Report*. UK Harwell NIREX Ltd., Report No. 71, Harwell, UK.

NIREX 1992. *The Physical and Chemical Characteristics of UK Radioactive Wastes*. UK NIREX Ltd., Report No. 286, Harwell, UK.

NIREX 1994. *An Assessment of the Impact of the Rock Characterisation Facility on Groundwater Flow and on Risk from the Groundwater Pathway*. UK NIREX Ltd., Report No. 560, Harwell, UK.

NIRONEN, M. 1997. The Svecofennian Orogen: a tectonic model. *Precambrian Research*, **86**, 21–44.

NOBLE, S. R., HYSLOP, E. K. & HIGHTON, A. J. 1996. High-precision U–Pb monazite geochronology of the *c.* 806 Ma Grampian Shear Zone of the Central Highlands of Scotland. *Journal of the Geological Society, London*, **153**, 511–514.

NOBLE, S. R., HIGHTON, A. J. & HYSLOP, E. K. 1998. U–Pb constraints on the tectonometamorphic evolution of the Central highlands, Scotland. *Geological Society of America, Annual Meeting*. Toronto, Ontario, Abstract A-215.

NORTON, M. G, McCLAY, K. R. & WAY, N. A. 1987. Tectonic evolution of Devonian basins in northern Scotland and southern Norway. *Norsk Geolgisk Tidsskrift*, **67**, 323–338.

OAKMAN, C. D. & MARTIN, J. H. 1993. Core workshop and discussion forum. *In*: PARKER, J. R. (ed.) *Petroleum Geology of Northwest Europe: Proceedings of the 4th Conference*. Geological Society, London, 1541–1542.

O'BRIEN, W. 1996. *Bronze Age copper mining in Britain and Ireland*. Shire Publications.

O'CONNOR, S. J. & WALKER, D. 1993. Palaeocene reservoirs of the Everest trend. *In*: PARKER, J. R. (ed.) *Petroleum Geology of Northwest Europe: Proceedings of the 4th Conference*. Geological Society, London, 145–160.

ODLING, N. E. 1984. Strain analysis and strain path modelling in the Loch Tollie gneisses, Gairloch, NW Scotland. *Journal of Structural Geology*, **6**, 543–562.

OEYNHAUSEN, C. VON 1826–1833 (1829). Observations on the mountain Ben Nevis, and on some other places in Scotland. *Proceedings of the Geological Society of London*, **1**, 94–96.

OEYNHAUSEN, C. VON & DECHEN, H. VON 1829. Die Insel Skye. *Archive für Mineralogie, Geognosie, Bergbau und Hüttenkunde*, **1**, 56–104.

OEYNHAUSEN, C. VON 1830. Der Ben Nevis am Loch Eil. *Archive für Mineralogie, Geognosie, Bergbau und Hüttenkunde*, **2**, 38–55, 95–96.

OFOEGBU, C. O. & BOTT, M. H. P. 1985. Interpretation of the Minch linear magnetic anomaly and of a similar feature on the shelf north of Lewis by non-linear optimization. *Journal of the Geological Society, London*, **141**, 1077–1087.

OGAWA, Y. 1998. Tectonostratigraphy of the Glen App area, Southern Uplands, Scotland: anatomy of an Ordovician accretionary complex. *Journal of the Geological Society, London*, **155**, 651–662.

O'HARA, M. J. 1961. Petrology of the Scourie dyke, Sutherland. *Mineralogical Magazine*, **32**, 848–865.

OKEKE, P. O., BORLEY, G. D. & WATSON, J. 1983. A geochemical study of Lewisian metasedimentary granulites and gneisses in the Scourie–Laxford area of north-west Scotland. *Mineralogical Magazine*, **47**, 1–9.

OLDROYD, D. R. 1971. The Vulcanist–Neptunist dispute reconsidered. *Journal of Geological Education*, **19**, 124–129.

OLDROYD, D. R. 1990. *The Highlands Controversy: Constructing Geological Knowledge through Fieldwork in Nineteenth-Century Britain*. Chicago University Press, Chicago & London.

OLDROYD, D. R. 1996a. [Hugh Miller:] The geologist from Cromarty. *In*: SHORTLAND, M. E. (ed), *Hugh Miller and the Controversies of Victorian Science*, 87–134. Clarendon, Oxford.

OLDROYD, D. R. 1996b. Sir Archibald Geikie: new archival sources for the history of British geology in the nineteenth century. *Earth Sciences History*, **15**, 141–150.

OLDROYD, D. R. & HAMILTON, B. M. 1997. Geikie and Judd, and controversies about the igneous rocks of the Scottish Hebrides: theory, practice, and power in the geological community. *Annals of Science*, **54**, 221–268.

OLIVER, G. J. H. 1978. Prehnite–pumpellyite facies metamorphism in County Cavan, Ireland. *Nature, London*, **274**, 242–243.

OLIVER, G. J. H. 1988. Arenig to Wenlock metamorphism in the paratectonic Caledonides of the British Isles. *In*: HARRIS, A. L. & FETTES, D. J. (eds) *The Caledonian/Appalachian Orogen*. Geological Society, London, Special Publications, **38**, 347–363.

OLIVER, G. J. H. 2001. Reconstruction of the Grampian episode in Scotland: its place in the Caledonian Orogeny. *Tectonophysics*, **332**, 23–49.

OLIVER, G. J. H. & LEGGETT, J. K. 1980. Metamorphism in an accretionary prism: prehnite–pumpellyite facies metamorphism in the Southern Uplands of Scotland. *Transactions of the Royal Society of Edinburgh: Earth Sciences*, **71**, 235–246.

OLIVER, G. J. H. & MCALPINE R. R. 1998. Occurrence of a sheeted dolerite dyke complex in the Ballantrae Ophiolite, Scotland. *Geological Magazine*, **135**, 509–517.

OLIVER, G. J. H. & MCKERROW, W. S. 1984. Seismological evidence for shallow basement in the Southern Uplands. *Nature, London*, **309**, 89–90.

OLIVER, G. J. H., SMELLIE, J. L., THOMAS, L. J., CASEY, D. M., KEMP, A. E. S., EVANS, L. J., BALDWIN, J. R. & HEPWORTH, B. C. 1984. Early Palaeozoic metamorphic history of the Midland Valley, Southern Uplands–Longford–Down massif and the Lake District, British Isles. *Transactions of the Royal Society of Edinburgh: Earth Sciences*, **75**, 245–258.

OLIVER, G. J. H., CHEN, F. BUCHWALD, R. & HEGER, E. 2000. Fast tectonothermal metamorphism and exhumation in the type area of the Barrovian and Buchan zones. *Geology*, **28**, 459–462.

OLIVER, G. J. H., MARTIN, M. & BANKS, G. 2002. Origin of the tectonised 470 Ma Portsoy 'Older Basic' Complex, NE Scotland. *Tectonic Studies Group Annual Meeting*, University of Leicester, 55.

O'NIONS, R. K., HAMILTON, P. J. & HOOKER, P. J. 1983. A Nd isotope investigation of sediments related to crustal development in the British Isles. *Earth and Planetary Science Letters*, **63**, 229–240.

OWEN, A. W. & RUSHTON, A. W. A. 1999. Scotland: Ordovician of the Midland Valley terrane. *In*: RUSHTON, A. W. A., OWEN, A. W., OWENS, R. M. & PRIGMORE, J. K. (eds) *British Cambrian to Ordovician Stratigraphy*. Joint Nature Conservation Committee, 327–347.

OWEN, A. W., ARMSTRONG, H. A. & FLOYD, J. D. 1999. Rare earth element geochemistry of Upper Ordovician cherts from the Southern Uplands of Scotland. *Journal of the Geological Society, London*, **156**, 191–204.

OWEN, G. 1995. Soft-sediment deformation in upper Proterozoic Torridonian sandstones (Applecross Formation) at Torridon, northwest Scotland. *Journal of Sedimentary Research*, **A65**, 495–504.

OWEN, G. 1996a. Anatomy of a water-escape cusp in Upper Proterozoic Torridon Group sandstones, Scotland. *Sedimentary Geology*, **103**, 117–128.

OWEN, G. 1996b. Experimental soft-sediment deformation: structures formed by the liquefaction of unconsolidated sands and some ancient examples. *Sedimentology*, **43**, 279–293.

OWEN, J. S. 1995. *Coal Mining at Brora 1529–1974*. Inverness Highland Libraries.

OWENS, B., NEVES, R., GUEINN, K. J., MISHELL, D. R. F., SABRY, H. S. M. Z. & WILLIAMS, J. E. 1977. Palynological division of the Namurian of northern England and Scotland. *Proceedings of the Yorkshire Geological Society*, **41**, 381–398.

PAGE, K. N. 1996. Mesozoic ammonoids in space and time. *In*: LANDMAN, N., TANABE, K. & DAVIS, R. A. (eds) *Ammonoid Paleobiology*. Topics in Geobiology, **13**, 755–793.

PAITHANKAR, M. G. 1967. Tuffisite and volcanic phenomena associated with the Glas Eilean Vent, Ardnamurchan, Argyllshire, Scotland. *Geologiska Foreningens i Stockholm Forhandlingar*, **89**, 15–28.

PALMER, T. J., MCKERROW, W. S. & COWIE, J. W. 1980. Sedimentological evidence for a stratigraphic break in the Durness Group. *Nature, London*, **287**, 720–722.

PANKHURST, R. J. 1970. The geochronology of the basic igneous complexes. *Scottish Journal of Geology*, **6**, 83–107.

PANKHURST, R. J. 1974. Rb–Sr whole-rock chronology of Caledonian events in northeast Scotland. *Bulletin of the Geological Society of America*, **85**, 345–350.

PANKHURST, R. J. 1979. Isotope and trace element evidence for the origin and evolution of Caledonian granites in the Scottish Highlands. *In*: ATHERTON, M. P. & TARNEY, J. (eds) *Origin of Granitic Batholiths*. Shiva, Orpington, 18–33.

PARK, A. F. 1991. Continental growth by accretion: a tectonostratigraphic terrane analysis of the evolution of the western and central Baltic SHIELD, 2. 50 to 1. 75 Ga. *Geological Society of America Bulletin*, **103**, 522–537.

PARK, R. G. 1964. The structural history of the Lewisian rocks of Gairloch, Wester Ross. *Quarterly Journal of the Geological Society, London*, **120**, 397–434.

PARK, R. G. 1965. Early metamorphic complex of the Lewisian northeast of Gairloch, Ross-shire, Scotland. *Nature, London*, **207**, 66–68.

PARK, R. G. 1966. Nature and origin of Lewisian basic rocks at Gairloch, Ross-shire. *Scottish Journal of Geology*, **2**, 179–199.

PARK, R. G. 1970. Observations on Lewisian chronology. *Scottish Journal of Geology*, **6**, 379–399.

PARK, R. G. 1994. Early Proterozoic tectonic overview of the northern British Isles and neighbouring terrains in Laurentia and Baltica. *Precambrian Research*, **68**, 65–79.

PARK, R. G. & CRESSWELL, D. 1972. Basic dykes in the early Precambrian (Lewisian) of NW Scotland: their structural relations, conditions of emplacement and orogenic significance. *Proceedings of the 24th International Geological Congress, Montreal 1972*, **1**, 238–245.

PARK, R. G. & CRESSWELL, D. 1973. The dykes of the Laxfordian belts. *In*: PARK, R. G. & TARNEY, J. (eds) *The Early Precambrian of Scotland and related rocks of Greenland*. University of Keele, 119–130.

PARK, R. G. & TARNEY, J. 1987. The Lewisian complex: a typical Precambrian high-grade terrain? *In*: PARK, R. G. & TARNEY, J. (eds) *Evolution of the Lewisian and Comparable Precambrian High-Grade Terrains*. Geological Society, London, Special Publications, **27**, 13–25.

PARK, R. G., CRANE, A. & NIAMATULLAH, M. 1987. Early Proterozoic structure and kinematic evolution of the southern mainland Lewisian. *In*: PARK, R. G. & TARNEY, J. (eds) *Evolution of the Lewisian and Comparable Precambrian High-Grade Terrains*. Geological Society, London, Special Publications, **27**, 139–151.

PARK, R. G., CLIFF, R. A., FETTES, D. G. & STEWART, A. D. 1994. Lewisian and Torridonian. *In*: GIBBONS, F. C. & HARRIS, A. L. (eds) *A Revised Correlation of Precambrian Rocks in the British Isles*. Geological Society of London, Special Report, **22**, 6–22.

PARK, R. G., TARNEY, J. & CONNELLY, J. N. 2001. The Loch Maree Group: Palaeoproterozoic subduction-accretion complex in the Lewisian of NW Scotland. *Precambrian Research*, **105**, 205–226.

PARKER, J. R. (ed.) 1993. *Petroleum Geology of Northwest Europe: Proceedings of the 4th Conference*. Geological Society, London.

PARKER, M. E. 1980. VLF electromagnetic mapping of strata-bound mineralisation in Dalradian schist near Aberfeldy, Scotland. *Transactions of the Institution of Mining and Metallurgy*, **89**, B123–B129.

PARNELL, J. 1984. Hydrocarbon minerals in the Midland Valley of Scotland with particular reference to the Oil-shale Group. *Proceedings of the Geologists' Association*, **95**, 275–285.

PARNELL, J. 1985. Hydrocarbon source rocks, reservoir rocks and migration in the Orcadian Basin. *Scottish Journal of Geology*, **21**, 321–336.

PARNELL, J. (ed.) 1992. *Basins on the Atlantic Seaboard: Petroleum Geology, Sedimentology and Basin Evolution*. Geological Society, London, Special Publications, **62**.

PARRISH, J. T. 1982. Upwelling and petroleum source beds, with reference to the Paleozoic. *AAPG Bulletin*, **66**, 750–774.

PARRISH, J. T. 1993. Climate of the supercontinent Pangea. *Journal of Geology*, **101**, 215–233.

PARSONS, I. 1965a. The feldspathic syenites of the Loch Ailsh intrusion, Assynt, Scotland. *Journal of Petrology*, **6**, 365–394.

PARSONS, I. 1965b. The sub-surface shape of part of the Loch Ailsh intrusion, Assynt, as deduced from magnetic anomalies across the contact, with a note on traverses across the Loch Borralan complex. *Geological Magazine*, **102**, 46–58.

PARSONS, I. 1968. The origin of the basic and ultrabasic rocks of the Loch Ailsh intrusion, Assynt. *Scottish Journal of Geology*, **4**, 221–234.

PARSONS, I. 1972. Comparative petrology of the leucocratic syenites of the Northwest Highlands of Scotland. *Geological Journal*, **8**, 71–82.

PARSONS, I. 1979. The Assynt alkaline suite. *In*: HARRIS, A. L., HOLLAND, C. H. & LEAKE, B. E. (eds) *The Caledonides of the British Isles-Reviewed*. Geological Society, London, Special Publications, **8**, 677–681.

PARSONS, I. & MCKIRDY, A. P. 1983. Inter-relationship of igneous activity and thrusting in Assynt: excavations at Loch Borralan. *Scottish Journal of Geology*, **19**, 59–66.

PARTINGTON, M. A., MITCHENER, B. C., MILTON, N. & FRASER, A. J. 1993. Genetic sequence stratigraphy for the North Sea Late Jurassic and Early Cretaceous: distribution and prediction of Kimmeridgian–Late Rhyazanian reservoirs in the North Sea and adjacent areas. *In*: PARKER, R. J. (ed.) *Petroleum Geology of Northwest Europe: Proceedings of the 4th Conference*. Geological Society, London, 347–370.

PATERSON, B. A., ROGERS, G., STEPHENS, W. E. & HINTON, R. W. 1993. The longevity of acid-basic magmatism associated with a major transcurrent fault. *Geological Society of America, Abstracts with Programs*, **25**, 642.

PATERSON, I. B. & HALL, I. H. S. 1986. Lithostratigraphy of the late Devonian and early Carboniferous rocks of the Midland Valley of Scotland. *Report of the British Geological Survey*, **18**, No. 3.

PATERSON, I. B., BROWNE, M. A. E. & ARMSTRONG, M. 1976. Upper Old Red Sandstone palaeogeography. *Scottish Journal of Geology*, **12**, 89–91.

PATERSON, I. B., ARMSTRONG, M. & BROWNE, M. A. E. 1981. Quaternary estuarine deposits in the Tay–Earn area, Scotland. *Report of the Institute of Geological Sciences*, **81/7**.

PATERSON, I. B., HALL, I. H. S. & STEPHENSON, D. 1990. *Geology of the Greenock District*. Memoir of the British Geological Survey.

PATERSON, I. B., MCADAM, A. D. & MACPHERSON, K. A. T. 1998. *Geology of the Hamilton District*. Memoir of the British Geological Survey.

PATON, R. L., SMITHSON, T. R. & CLACK, J. A. 1999. An amniote-like skeleton from the Early Carboniferous of Scotland. *Nature, London*, **398**, 508–513.

PATTERSON, W. P. 1999. Oldest isotopically characterized fish otoliths provide insight to Jurassic continental climate of Europe. *Geology*, **27**, 199–202.

PATTISON, D. R. M. & HARTE, B. 1989. Evolution of structurally contrasting anatectic migmatites in the 3-kbar Ballachulish aureole, Scotland. *Journal of Metamorphic Petrology*, **6**, 475–494.

PATTISON, D. R. M. & TRACEY, D. E. 1991. Phase equilibria and thermobarometry of metapelites. *In*: KERRICK, D. M. (ed.) *Contact Metamorphism*. Mineralogical Society of America, Reviews in Mineralogy, **26**, 105–206.

PATTRICK, R. A. D. 1984. Sulphide mineralogy of the Tomnadashan copper deposit and the Corrie Buie lead veins, south Loch Tayside, Scotland. *Mineralogical Magazine*, **48**, 85–91.

PATTRICK, R. A. D. 1985. Pb–Zn and minor U mineralisation at Tyndrum, Perthshire. *Mineralogical Magazine*, **49**, 671–681.

PATTRICK, R. A. D. & POLYA, D. A. 1993. The Mineralisation and Tectonic Evolution of the British Isles. *In*: PATTRICK, R. A. D. & POLYA, D. A. (eds) *Mineralization in the British Isles*. Chapman and Hall, London, 1–37.

PATTRICK, R. A. D. & RUSSELL, M. J. 1989. Sulphur isotopic investigation of Lower Carboniferous vein deposits of the British Isles. *Mineralium Deposita*, **24**, 148–153.

PATTRICK, R. A. D., BOYCE, A. J. & MACINTYRE, R. M. 1988. Gold-silver vein mineralisation at Tyndrum, Scotland. *Mineralogy and Petrology*, **38**, 61–76.

PAVLOVSKY, Y. E. 1958. Precambrian and Lower Palaeozoic history of the Scottish Highlands and the role of abyssal fractures. *Izvestiya Akademii Nauk SSSR. Seriya geologicheskaya*, **7** (in translation), 1–16.

PEACH, B. N. & HORNE, J. 1884. Report on the geology of the north-west of Scotland. *Nature, London*, **31**, 31–35.

PEACH, B. N. & HORNE, J. 1899. *The Silurian Rocks of Britain. Volume I: Scotland. With Petrological Chapters and Notes by J. J. H. Teall*. HMSO, Glasgow.

PEACH, B. N. & HORNE, J. 1930. *Chapters on the Geology of Scotland*. Oxford University Press, London.

PEACH, B. N., HORNE, J., GUNN, W., CLOUGH, C. T. & HINXMAN, L. W. 1907. *The Geological Structure of the Northwest Highlands of Scotland*. Memoirs of the Geological Survey of Great Britain.

PEACH, B. N., CLOUGH, C. T., HINXMAN, L. W., GRANT WILSON, J. S., CRAMPTON, C. B., MAUFF, B. A. & BAILEY, E. B. 1910a. *The geology of the neighbourhood of Edinburgh*. (Sheet 32, with part of 31). Memoir of the Geological Survey of Scotland.

PEACH, B. N., HORNE, J., WOODWARD, H. B., CLOUGH, C. T., HARKER, A. & WEDD, C. D. 1910b. *The Geology of Glenelg, Lochalsh and south-east part of Skye*. Memoirs of the Geological Survey of Great Britain.

PEACH, B. N., GUNN, W., CLOUGH, C. T., HINXMAN, L. W., CRAMPTON, C. B., ANDERSON, E. M. & FLETT, J. S. 1912. *The Geology of Ben Wyvis, Carn Chuinneag, Inchbae and the surrounding country*. Memoirs of the Geological Survey of Great Britain.

PEACH, B. N., HORNE, J., HINXMAN, L. W., CRAMPTON, C. B., ANDERSON, E. M. & CARRUTHERS, R. G. 1913. *The Geology of Central Ross-shire (Explanation of Sheet 82.) With Petrological Notes by J. S. Flett*. HMSO, Edinburgh.

PEACH, C. W. 1858. Notice of the discovery of fossils in the limestones of Durness, in the county of Sutherland. *Proceedings of the Royal Physical Society of Edinburgh*, **1**, 23–24.

PEACOCK, J. D. 1966a. *Contorted Beds in the Permo-Triassic Aeolian Sandstones of Morayshire*. Bulletin, Geological Survey Great Britain, **24**, 157–162.

PEACOCK, J. D. 1966b. Note on the drift sequence near Portsoy, Banffshire. *Scottish Journal of Geology*, **2**, 35–57.

PEACOCK, J. D. 1971. A re-interpretation of the coastal deposits of Banffshire and their place in the late-glacial history of N.E. Scotland. *Geological Survey of Great Britain, Bulletin*, **37**, 81–89.

PEACOCK, J. D. 1973. Sodic rocks of metasomatic origin in the Moine nappe. *Scottish Journal of Geology*, **9**, 96–97.

PEACOCK, J. D. 1975. Depositional environment of glacical deposits at Clava, north-east Scotland. *Bulletin of the Geological Survey Great Britain*, **49**, 31–37.

PEACOCK, J. D. 1981. Scottish Late-glacial marine deposits and their environmental significance. *In*: NEALE, J. & FLENLEY, J. (eds) *The Quaternary in Britain*. Pergamon, Oxford, 222–236.

PEACOCK, J. D. 1983. A model for Scottish interstadial marine palaeo-temperature 13 000 to 11 000 BP. *Boreas*, **12**, 73–82.

PEACOCK, J. D. 1989. Marine molluscs and Late-Quaternary environmental studies with particular reference to the Late-glacial period in north-west Europe: a review. *Quaternary Science Reviews*, **8**, 179–192.

PEACOCK, J. D. & BROWNE, M. A. E. 1998. Radiocarbon dates from the Errol Beds (pre-Windemere Interstadial raised marine deposits) in eastern Scotland. *Quaternary Newsletter*, **86**, 1–7.

PEACOCK, J. D. & GRAHAM, D. K. 1977. Evolution of lateglacial marine environments at Lochgilphead, Scotland. *In*: GRAY, J. M. & LOWE, J. J. (eds) *Studies in the Scottish Lateglacial Environment*. Oxford, 89–100.

PEACOCK, J. D. & HARKNESS, D. D. 1990. Radiocarbon ages and the full-glacial to Holocene transition in seas adjacent to Scotland and southern Scandinavia: a review. *Transactions of the Royal Society of Edinburgh: Earth Sciences*, **81**, 385–396.

PEACOCK, J. D. & LONG, D. L. 1994. Late Devensian glaciation and deglaciation of Shetland. *Quaternary Newsletter*, **74**, 16–21.

PEACOCK, J. D., BERRIDGE, N. G., HARRIS, A. L. & MAY, F. 1968. *The Geology of the Elgin District*. Memoir of the Geological Survey of Scotland. HMSO, Edinburgh.

PEACOCK, J. D., GRAHAM, D. K. & WILKINSON, I. P. 1978. Late-glacial and post-glacial marine environments at Ardyne, Scotland and their significance in the interpretation of the history of the Cyde Sea area. *Report of the Institute Geological Sciences*, **78/17**.

PEACOCK, J. D., HARKNESS, D. D., HOUSLEY, R. A., LITTLE, J. & PAUL, M. A. 1989. Radiocarbon ages for a glaciomarine bed associated with the maximum of the Loch Lomond Readvance in west Benderloch. *Scottish Journal of Geology*, **25**, 69–79.

PEACOCK, J. D., MENDUM, J. R. & FETTES, D. J. 1992. *Geology of the Glen Affric District*. Memoir of the British Geological Survey, HMSO.

PEARCE, G. R. & BESLY, B. M. 1997. End-Carboniferous fold-thrust structures, Oxfordshire, UK: implications for the structural evolution of the late Variscan foreland of south-central England. *Journal of the Geological Society, London*, **154**, 225–237.

PEARCE, R. B. & CLAYTON, T. 1995. Tschermak substitution as an indicator of palaeotemperature in Silurian K-bentonites from the Southern Uplands of Scotland and Northern Ireland. *Clay Minerals*, **30**, 15–25.

PEARCE, R. B., CLAYTON, T. & KEMP, A. E. S. 1991. Illitization and organic maturity in Silurian sediments from the Southern Uplands of Scotland. *Clay Minerals*, **26**, 199–210.

PEARSON, M. J. 1979. Geochemistry of the Hepworth Carboniferous sediment sequence and origin of the diagenetic iron minerals and concretions. *Geochimica et Cosmochimica Acta*, **43**, 927–941.

PEASE, S. F., COATS, J. S. & FORTEY, N. J. 1986. Exploration for sediment-hosted exhalative mineralisation in the Middle Dalradian at Glenshee, Scotland. *In: Prospecting in Areas of Glaciated Terrain 1986*. Institution of Mining and Metallurgy, London, 95–108.

PEAT, C. & DIVER, W. 1982. First signs of life on Earth. *New Scientist*, **95**, 776–781.

PEGLAR, S. M. 1979. A radiocarbon-dated pollen diagram from Loch of Winles, Caithness, north-east Scotland. *New Phytologist*, **82**, 245–263.

PENGE, J., MUNNS, J. W., TAYLOR, B. & WINDLE, T. M. F. 1999. Rift-raft tectonics: examples of gravitational tectonics from the Zechstein basins of northwest Europe. *In: FLEET, A. J. & BOLDY, S. A. R. (eds) Petroleum Geology of Northwest Europe: Proceedings of the 5th Conference*. Geological Society, London, 201–213.

PENN, I. E., HOLLIDAY, D. W., KIRBY, G. A., KUBALA, M., SOBEY, R. A., MITCHELL, W. I., HARRISON, R. K. & BECKINSALE, R. D. 1983. The Larne No. 2 Borehole: discovery of a new Permian volcanic centre. *Scottish Journal of Geology*, **19**, 333–346.

PENNINGTON, J. J. 1975. The Geology of the Argyll Field. *In: WOODLAND, A. W. (ed.) Petroleum and the Continental Shelf of North West Europe*. Applied Science Publishers, Barking, 285–291.

PENNINGTON, W. 1975. A chronostratigraphic comparison of Late-Weichselian and Late-Devensian subdivisions, illustrated by two radiocarbon dated profiles from western Britain. *Boreas*, **4**, 157–171.

PENNINGTON, W. 1977. Lake sediments and the lateglacial environment in northern Scotland. *In: GRAY, J. M. & LOWE, J. J (eds) Studies in the Lateglacial Environment*. Oxford, 119–141.

PENNINGTON, W., TUTIN, T. G., HAWORTH, E. Y., BONNY, A. P. & LISHMAN, J. P. 1972. Lake sediments in northern Scotland. *Philosophical Transactions of the Royal Society, London*, **B264**, 191–294.

PERNER, J. 1937. Les 'colonies de Barrande'. *Bulletin de la Société Géologique de France*, **7**, Series 5, 513–526.

PESGB 2000. *Structural Framework of the North Sea and Atlantic Margin*. 2000 Edition. Petroleum Exploration Society of Great Britain, London.

PETERS, D., HIGHTON, A. J., NOBLE, S. R., HORSTWOOD, M. S. A. & WINCHESTER, J. A. 2001. U–Pb detrital zircon geochronology of Precambrian coarse clastic formations in the Northern and Central Highlands of Scotland. *Tectonic Studies Group Highlands Workshop Abstracts*, Oxford Brookes University, 6.

PETERS, K. E., MOLDOWAN, J., DRISCOLE, A. & DEMAISON, G. J. H. 1989. Origin of Beatrice Oil by co-sourcing from Devonian and Middle Jurassic source rocks, Inner Moray Firth, UK. *AAPG Bulletin*, **73**, 454–471.

PETHICK, J. 1999. Future sea-level changes in Scotland: options for coastal management. *In: BAXTER, J. M., DUNCAN, K., ATKINS, S. M. & LEES, G. (eds) Scotland's Living Coastline*. HMSO, Edinburgh, 45–62.

PETIT, J. R. & 18 OTHERS 1999. Climate and atmospheric history of the past 420,000 years from the Vostok ice core, Antarctica. *Nature, London*, **399**, 429–436.

PHEMISTER, J. 1926. The alkaline igneous rocks of the Loch Ailsh District. *In: READ, H. H., PHEMISTER, J. & ROSS, G. (eds) The Geology of Strath Oykell and Lower Loch Shin*. Memoir of the Geological Survey of Great Britain.

PHEMISTER, J. 1960. *Scotland: The Northern Highlands*. Department of Scientific and Industrial Research, Geological Survey and Museum.

PHILLIPS, E. R., CLARK, G. C. & SMITH, D. I. 1993. Mineralogy, petrology, and microfabric analysis of the Eilrig Shear Zone, Fort Augustus, Scotland. *Scottish Journal of Geology*, **29**, 143–158.

PHILLIPS, E. R., BARNES, R. P., MERRIMAN, R. J. & FLOYD, J. D. 1995. Tectonic significance of Ordovician basic igneous rocks in the Southern Uplands, southwest Scotland. *Geological Magazine*, **132**, 549–556.

PHILLIPS, E. R., SMITH, R. A. & CARROLL, S. 1997. Strike-slip terrane accretion and pre- Carboniferous evolution of the Midland Valley of Scotland. *Transactions of the Royal Society of Edinburgh: Earth Sciences*, **89**, 209–224.

PHILLIPS, E. R., HIGHTON, A. J., HYSLOP, E. K. & SMITH, M. 1999a. The timing and P-T conditions of regional metamorphism in the Central Highlands, Scotland. *Journal of the Geological Society, London*, **156**, 1175–1193.

PHILLIPS, E. R., SMITH, R. A. & FLOYD, J. D. 1999b. The Bail Hill Volcanic Group: alkaline within-plate volcanism during Ordovician sedimentation in the Southern Uplands, Scotland. *Transactions of the Royal Society of Edinburgh: Earth Sciences*, **89**, 233–247.

PHILLIPS, F. C. 1951. Apparent coincidences in the life-history of the Moine Schists. *Geological Magazine*, **88**, 225–235.

PHILLIPS, T. L. & PEPPERS, R. A. 1984. Changing patterns of Pennsylvanian coal-swamp vegetation and implications of climate control on coal occurrence. *International Journal of Coal Geology*, **3**, 205–255.

PHILLIPS, W. 1818. *Geology of England and Wales*. London.

PHILLIPS, W. E. A., STILLMAN, C. J. & MURPHY, T. 1976. A Caledonian plate-tectonic model. *Journal of the Geological Society, London*, **132**, 579–609.

PHILLIPS, W. J., PEASE, S. F., GREENWOOD, P. G., HOLSTEIN, H., KELLY, D., LEWIS, T. P. & FROMBERG, A. 1986. Relationship between impedance and phase measurements and magnetic, SP, IP, and VLF-EM parameters over the calcareous schist-graphitic schist boundary near Moulin, Scotland. *Prospecting in Areas of Glaciated Terrain 1986*. Institute of Mining and Metallurgy, London, 119–128.

PIASECKI, M. A. J. 1980. New light on the Moine rocks of the Central Highlands of Scotland. *Journal of the Geological Society, London*, **137**, 47–59.

PIASECKI, M. A. J. 1984. Ductile thrusts as time markers in orogenic evolution: an example from the Scottish Caledonides. *In: GALSON, D. & MUELLER, S. E. (eds) First European Geotraverse Workshop: the Northeastern Segment*. Publication of the European Science Foundation, Strasbourg, 109–114.

PIASECKI, M. A. J. & TEMPERLEY, S. 1988a. Central Highland Division. *In: WINCHESTER, J. A. (ed.) Later Proterozoic Stratigraphy of the Northern Atlantic Regions*. Blackie, Glasgow, 46–53.

PIASECKI, M. A. J. & TEMPERLEY, S. 1988b. The Northern Sector of the Central Highlands. *In: ALLISON, I, MAY, F & STRACHAN, R. A. (eds) An Excursion Guide to the Moine Geology of the Scottish Highlands*, Scottish Academic Press. 51–68.

PIASECKI, M. A. J. & VAN BREEMEN, O. 1979. A Morarian age for the 'younger Moines' of central and western Scotland. *Nature, London*, **78**, 734–736.

PIASECKI, M. A. J. & VAN BREEMEN, O. 1983. Field and isotopic evidence for a c. 750 Ma tectonothermal event in the Moine rocks of the central Highland region of the Scottish Caledonides. *Transactions of the Royal Society of Edinburgh: Earth Sciences*, **73**, 119–134.

PIASECKI, M. A. J., VAN BREEMEN, O. & WRIGHT, A. E. 1981. Late Precambrian geology of Scotland, England and Wales. *In: KERR, J. W. & FERGUSSON, A. J. (eds) Geology of the North Atlantic Borderlands*. Memoir of the Canadian Society of Petroleum Geologists, **7**, 57–94.

PICKARD, N. A. H. 1992. Depositional controls on Lower Carboniferous microbial buildups, eastern Midland Valley of Scotland. *Sedimentology*, **39**, 1081–1100.

PICKARD, N. A. H. 1994. Sedimentology of the upper Dinantian Charlestown Main Limestone: implications for the controls on cyclothem deposition, eastern Midland Valley of Scotland. *Scottish Journal of Geology*, **30**, 15–31.

PICKEN, G. S. 1988. The concealed coalfield at Canonbie: an interpretation based on boreholes and seismic surveys. *Scottish Journal of Geology*, **24**, 61–71.

PICKERING, K. T. 1984. The Upper Jurassic 'Boulder Beds' and related deposits: a fault-controlled submarine slope, N.E. Scotland. *Journal of the Geological Society, London*, **141**, 357–374.

PICKERING, K. T., BASSETT, M. G. & SIVETER, D. J. 1988. Late Ordovician–Early Silurian destruction of the Iapetus Ocean: Newfoundland, British Isles and Scandinavia-a discussion. *Transactions of the Royal Society of Edinburgh: Earth Sciences*, **79**, 361–382.

PIDGEON, R. T. & AFTALION, M. 1978. Cogenetic and inherited zircon U–Pb systems in granites: Palaeozoic granites of Scotland and England. *In*: BOWES, D. R. & LEAKE, B. E. (eds) *Crustal Evolution in Northwestern Britain and Adjacent Regions*, Geological Journal Special Issue, **10**, 183–220.

PIDGEON, R. T. & BOWES, D. R. 1972. Zircon U–Pb ages of granulites from the central region of the Lewisian of north-western Scotland. *Geological Magazine*, **109**, 247–258.

PIEDA PLC 1995. *Scottish Minerals Recycling*. Scottish Natural Heritage. Review series, No. 36.

PIPER, D. J. W. 1970. Eolian sediments in the basal New Red Sandstone of Arran. *Scottish Journal of Geology*, **6**, 295–308.

PIPER, J. D. A. 1992. Post-Laxfordian magnetic imprint in the Lewisian metamorphic complex and strike-slip motion in the Minches, NW Scotland. *Journal of the Geological Society, London*, **149**, 127–137.

PIPER, J. D. A. & POPPLETON, T. J. 1991. Palaeomagnetic conglomerate tests on basal Stoer Group sediments, NW Scotland. *Scottish Journal of Geology*, **27**, 97–106.

PIRRIE, D., POWER, M. R., ANDERSEN, J. C. & BUTCHER, A. R. 2000. Platinum-group mineralization in the Tertiary Igneous Province: new data from Mull and Skye, Scottish Inner Hebrides, UK. *Geological Magazine*, **137**, 651–658.

PITCHER, W. S., ELWELL, R. W. D., TOZER, C. F. & CAMBRAY, F. W. 1964. The Leannan Fault. *Quarterly Journal of the Geological Society of London*, **120**, 241–273.

PITTY, A. F., DOWNING, R. A. & SMITH, G. M. 1989. *Hydrogeological, Geomorphological and Other Environmental Characteristics of the Low-Level Solid Radioactive Waste Disposal Site at Dounreay*. INTERA-ECL report prepared for UKAEA I1903–6, Version 2.

PLANT, J. A. 1984. Regional geochemical maps of the United Kingdom. *NERC News Journal*, **3**, 1 & 5–7.

PLANT, J. A. 1986. Models for granites and their mineralising systems in the British and Irish Caledonides. *In*: ANDREW, C. J. (ed.) *Geology and Genesis of Mineral Deposits in Ireland*. Irish Association for Economic Geology, Dublin, 121–156.

PLANT, J. A. & COLEMAN, R. F. 1972. Application of neutron activation analysis to the evaluation of placer gold concentrations. *In*: JONES, M. J. (ed.) *Geochemical Exploration 1972*. Institute of Mining and Metallurgy, London, 373–387.

PLANT, J. A. & SLATER, D. 1986. Regional geochemistry-potential developments. *In*: Min-Ex 2000. London 1985. *Transactions of the Institution of Mining and Metallurgy*, **95**, B63–B70.

PLANT, J. A., BROWN, G. C., SIMPSON, P. R. & SMITH, R. T. 1980. Signatures of metalliferous granites in the Scottish Caledonides. *Transactions of the Institution of Mining and Metallurgy*, **89**, B198–B210.

PLANT, J. A., SIMPSON, P. R., GREEN, P. M., WATSON, J. V. & FOWLER, M. B. 1983. Metalliferous and mineralised Caledonian granites in relation to regional metamorphism and fracture systems in Northern Scotland. *Transactions of the Institution of Mining and Metallurgy*, **92**, B33–B42.

PLANT, J. A., SMITH, R. T., STEVENSON, A. G., FORREST, M. D. & HODGSON, J. F. 1984. Regional geochemical mapping for mineral exploration in northern Scotland. *In*: *Prospecting in areas of glaciated terrain*. Institution of Mining and Metallurgy, London, 103–120.

PLANT, J. A., BREWARD, N., FOREST, M. D. & SMITH, R. T. 1989. The gold pathfinder elements As, Sb and Bi – their distribution and significance in the southwest Highlands of Scotland. *Transactions of the Institution of Mining and Metallurgy*, **98**, B91–B101.

PLANT, J. A., HENNEY, P. J. & SIMPSON, P. R. 1990. The genesis of tin-uranium granites in the Scottish Caledonides: implications for metallogenesis. *Geological Journal*, **25**, 431–442.

PLATTEN, I. M. 2000. Incremental dilation of magma-filled fractures: evidence from dykes on the Isle of Skye, Scotland. *Journal of Structural Geology*, **22**, 1153–1164.

PLATTEN, I. M. & MONEY, M. S. 1987. Formation of late Caledonian breccia pipes at Curachan Cruinn, Grampian Highlands, Scotland. *Transactions of the Royal Society of Edinburgh: Earth Sciences*, **78**, 85–103.

PLATTEN, I. M. & WATTERSON, J. 1987. Magma flow and crystallization in dyke fissures. *In*: HALLS, H. C. & FAHRIG, W F. (eds) Mafic dyke swarms. *Geological Association of Canada* Special Paper **34**, 65–73.

PLAYFAIR, J. 1802. *Illustrations of the Huttonian Theory of the Earth*. Cadell & Davies, London; William Creech, Edinburgh.

PLAYFAIR, J. 1805. Biographical account of the late Dr James Hutton, F.R.S. Edin. *Transactions of the Royal Society of Edinburgh*, **5** (Part 3), 39–99.

POLLARD, S. J. T. & HERBERT, S. M. 1998. Contaminated land regulations in the UK: The role of the Environment Agency (EA) and the Scottish Environment Protection Agency. *In*: *Proceedings of the Sixth International FZK/TNO Conference on Contaminated Soil*, 17–21 May 1998, Edinburgh, **1**, Thomas Telford, London.

POLLARD, J. E. & STEEL, R. J. 1978. Intertidal sediments in the Achenhew Beds (Triassic) of Arran. *Scottish Journal of Geology*, **14**, 317–328.

POOLER, J. & AMORY, M. 1999. A subsurface perspective on ETAP – an integrated development of seven North Sea fields. *In*: FLEET, A. J. & BOLDY, S. A. R. (eds) *Petroleum Geology of Northwest Europe: Proceedings of the 5th Conference*, Geological Society, London, 993–1006.

PORTEOUS, W. G. 1973. A breccia pipe in the Dalradian series, East Kincardineshire. *Scottish Journal of Geology*, **9**, 233–237.

POTTS, G. J. 1990. A palaeomagnetic study of recumbently folded and thermally metamorphosed Torridon Group sediments, Eishort anticline, Skye, Scotland. *Journal of the Geological Society, London*, **147**, 999–1007.

POULSEN, C. 1951. The position of East Greenland Cambro-Ordovician in the palaeogeography of the North Atlantic region. *Meddelelser fra Dansk Geologisk Forening*, **12**, 161–162.

POWELL, C. L., EDWARDS, D. & TREWIN, N. H. 2000a. A new vascular plant from the Lower Devonian Windyfield chert, Rhynie, NE Scotland. *Transaction of the Royal Society of Edinburgh: Earth Sciences*, **90**, 331–349.

POWELL, C. L., TREWIN, N. H. & EDWARDS, D. 2000b. Palaeoecology and plant succession in a borehole through the Rhynie cherts, Lower Old Red Sandstone, Scotland. *In*: FRIEND, P. F. & WILLIAMS, B. P. J. (eds) *New Perspectives on the Old Red Sandstone*. Geological Society, London, Special Publications, **180**, 439–457.

POWELL, D. 1966. The Structure of the South-Eastern Part of the Morar Antiform, Inverness-shire. *Proceedings of the Geologists' Association*, **77**, 79–100.

POWELL, D. 1974. Stratigraphy and structure of the western Moine and the problem of Moine orogenesis. *Journal of the Geological Society, London*, **130**, 575–593.

POWELL, D. & GLENDINNING, R. 1988. Excursion 4: Glenfinnan to Morar. *In*: ALLISON, I., MAY, F. & STRACHAN, R. A. (eds) *An Excursion Guide to the Moine Geology of the Scottish Highlands*. Scottish Academic Press, Edinburgh, 80–102.

POWELL, D. & PHILLIPS, W. E. A. 1985. Time of deformation in the Caledonide orogen of Britain and Ireland. *In*: HARRIS, A. L. (ed.) *The Nature and Timing of Orogenic Activity in the Caledonian Rocks of the British Isles*. Geological Society, London, Memoirs, **9**, 17–39.

POWELL, D., BAIRD, A. W., CHARNLEY, N. R. & JORDAN, P. J. 1981. The metamorphic environment of the Sgurr Beag Slide: a major crustal displacement zone in Proterozoic, Moine rocks of Scotland. *Journal of the Geological Society, London*, **138**, 661–673.

POWELL, D., BROOK, M. & BAIRD, A. W. 1983. Structural dating of a Precambrian pegmatite in Moine rocks of northern Scotland and its bearing on the status of the 'Morarian Orogeny'. *Journal of the Geological Society, London*, **140**, 813–823.

POWELL, D., ANDERSEN, T. B., DRAKE, A. A., HALL, L. & KEPPIE, J. D. 1988. The age and distribution of basement rocks in the Caledonide orogen of the N Atlantic. *In*: HARRIS, A. L. & FETTES, D. J. (eds) *The Caledonian-Appalachian Orogen*. Geological Society, London, Special Publications, **38**, 63–74.

POWER, G. M. & PARK, R. G. 1969. A chemical study of five amphibolite bodies from the Lewisian of Gairloch, Ross-shire. *Scottish Journal of Geology*, **5**, 26–41.

POWER, M. R. & PIRRIE, D. 2000. Platinum-Group mineralization within ultramafic rocks at Corrycharmaig, Perthshire: implications for the origin of the complex. *Scottish Journal of Geology*, **36**, 143–150.

PRAEG, D. 1996. *Morphology, Stratigraphy and Genesis of Buried Mid-Pleistocene Tunnel Valleys in the Southern North Sea Basin*. PhD thesis, University of Edinburgh.

PRAEGEL, N-O. 1981. Origin of ultramafic inclusions and megacrysts in a monchiquite dyke at Streap, Inverness-shire, Scotland. *Lithos*, **14**, 305–322.

PRAVE, A. 1999. The Neoproterozoic Supergroup of Scotland: an alternative hypothesis. *Geological Magazine*, **136**, 609–617.

PRAVE, A. & ALSOP, G. I. A. 1998. Evidence for the stratigraphical discontinuities in the Dalradian succession: implications for Neoproterozoic tectonics. *Tectonic Studies Group Annual Meeting*, University of St Andrews. 69.

PRAVE, A., OLIVER, G. J. H., STEPHENS, W. E., PARRISH, R. & PRINGLE, M. 2001. The Scottish Highlands: a Revisionist Neoproterozoic tectonostratigraphic template. *Tectonic Studies Annual Meeting Abstracts*, University of Leeds, UK, 45.

PRESTON, R. J. 2001. Composite minor intrusions as windows into subvolcanic magma reservoir processes: mineralogical and geochemical evidence for complex magmatic plumbing systems in the British Tertiary Igneous Province. *Journal of the Geological Society, London*, **158**, 47–58.

PRESTON, R. J. & BELL, B. R. 1997. Cognate gabbroic xenoliths from a tholeiitic subvolcanic sill complex: implications for fractional crystallization and crustal contamination processes. *Mineralogical Magazine*, **61**, 329–349.

PRESTON, R. J., BELL, B. R. & ROGERS, G. 1997. The Loch Scridain Xenolithic Sill Complex, Isle of Mull, Scotland: Fractional Crystallization, Assimilation, Magma-Mixing and Crustal Anatexis in Subvolcanic Conduits. *Journal of Petrology*, **39**, 519–550.

PRESTON, R. J., HOLE, M. J., BOUCH, J. & STILL, J. 1998. The occurrence of zirconiun aegirine and calcic catapleiite (CaZrSi$_3$O$_9$. 2H$_2$O) within a nepheline syenite, British Tertiary Igneous Province. *Scottish Journal of Geology*, **34**, 173–180.

PRESTON, R. J., DEMPSTER, T. J., BELL, B. R. & ROGERS, G. 1999. The Petrology of Mullite-bearing Peraluminous Xenoliths: Implications for Contamination Processes in Basaltic Magmas. *Journal of Petrology*, **40**, 549–573.

PRESTON, R. J., HOLE, M. J. & STILL, J. 2000*a*. The occurrence of Zr-bearing amphiboles and their relationships with the pyroxenes and biotites in the teschenite and nepheline syenites of a differentiated dolerite boss, Islay, NW Scotland. *Mineralogical Magazine*, **64**, 459–468.

PRESTON, R. J., HOLE, M. J. & STILL, J. 2000*b*. Exceptional REE-enrichment in apatite during the low pressure fractional crystallisation of alkali olivine basalt: an example from the British Tertiary Igneous Province. *Transactions of the Royal Society of Edinburgh: Earth Sciences*, **90**, 273–285.

PRICHARD, H. M. 1985. The Shetland ophiolite. *In*: GEE, D. G. & STURT, B. A. (eds) *The Caledonide Orogen: Scandinavia and Related Areas*. Wiley, New York, 1173–1184.

PRICHARD, H. M. & LORD, R. A. 1993. An overview of the PGE concentrations in the Shetland ophiolite complex. *In*: PRICHARD, H. M., ALABASTER, T., HARRIS, N. B. W. & NEARY, C. R. (eds) *Magmatic Processes and Plate Tectonics*. Geological Society, London, Special Publications, **76**, 273–294.

PRICHARD, H. M. & NEARY, C. R. 1985. Field Guide 'The Unst Ophiolite'. Conference '*Metallogeny of Basic and Ultrabasic Rocks*', Institution of Mining & Metallurgy, Edinburgh.

PRICHARD, H. M., NEARY, C. R. & POTTS, P. J. 1986. Platinum-group minerals in the Shetland ophiolite complex. *In*: GALLAGHER, M. J., IXER, R. A., NEARY, C. R. & PRICHARD, H. M. (eds) *Metallogeny of Basic and Ultrabasic Rocks*. Symposium volume for 1985 conference. Institution of Mining & Metallurgy, Edinburgh, 395–414.

PRINGLE, J. 1940. The discovery of Cambrian trilobites in the Highland Border rocks near Callander, Perthshire (Scotland). *Report of the British Association for the Advancement of Science*, **1**, 252.

PRINGLE, J. 1941. On the relationship of the green conglomerate to the Margie Grits in the North Esk, near Edzell; and on the probable age of the Margie Limestone. *Transactions of the Geological Society of Glasgow*, **20**, 136–140.

PURI, G. & GORDON, J. E. 1998. Soils and sustainability – A natural heritage perspective. *In*: *Proceedings of the Sixth International FZK/TNO Conference on Contaminated Soil*, 17–21 May 1998, Edinburgh, **1**, Thomas Telford, London, 1–5.

QUARRY PRODUCTS ASSOCIATION & ENGLISH NATURE 1999. Biodiversity and minerals, English Nature, Peterborough.

QURESHI, I. R. 1970. A gravity survey in the region of the Highland Boundary Fault, Scotland. *Quarterly Journal of the Geological Society, London*, **125**, 481–502.

RAINBIRD, R. H., HAMILTON, M. A. & YOUNG, G. M. 2001. Detrital zircon geochronology and provenance of the Torridonian, NW Scotland. *Journal of the Geological Society, London*, **158**, 15–27.

RAMSAY, A. C. 1841. *The Geology of the Island of Arran, from Original Survey*. Richard Griffin & Co., Glasgow; Thomas Tegg, London.

RAMSAY, A. C. 1865. The glacial theory of lake basins. *Philosophical Magazine*, **29**, 285.

RAMSAY, J. G. 1958. Moine-Lewisian relations at Glenelg, Inverness-shire. *Quarterly Journal of the Geological Society of London*, **113**, 487–523.

RAMSAY, J. G. 1963. Structure and metamorphism of the Moine and Lewisian rocks of the North-West Caledonides. *In*: JOHNSON, M. R. W. & STEWART, F. H. (eds). *The British Caledonides*. Oliver & Boyd, Edinburgh, 143–170.

RAMSBOTTOM, W. H. C., CALVER, M. A., EAGAR, R. M. C., HODSON, F., HOLLIDAY, D. W., STUBBLEFIELD, C. J. & WILSON, R. B. 1978. *A Correlation of Silesian rocks in the British Isles*. Geological Society, London, Special Report, **10**.

RAST, N. 1958. Metamorphic history of the Schiehallion complex, Perthshire. *Transactions of the Royal Society of Edinburgh*, **64**, 413–431.

RAST, N., DIGGENS, J. N. & RAST, D. E. 1968. Triassic rocks of the Isle of Mull: their sedimentation, facies, structure and relationship to the Great Glen fault and the Mull caldera. *Proceedings of the Geological Society, London*, **1645**, 299–304.

RATHBONE, P. A. & HARRIS, A. L. 1979. Basement-cover relationships at Lewisian inliers in the Moine rocks. *In*: HARRIS, A. L., HOLLAND, C. H. & LEAKE, B. E. (eds) *The Caledonides of the British Isles – Reviewed*. Geological Society, London, Special Publications, **8**, 101–107.

RATHBONE, P. A. & HARRIS, A. L. 1980. Moine and Lewisian near the Great Glen Fault in Easter Ross. *Scottish Journal of Geology*, **16**, 51–64.

RATHBONE, P. A., COWARD, M. P. & HARRIS, A. L. 1983. Cover and basement: A contrast in style and fabrics. *In*: HARRIS, L. D. & WILLIAMS, H. (eds) *Tectonics and Geophysics of Mountain Chains*. Geological Society of America Memoir, **158**, 213–223.

RAWSON, P. F. & RILEY, L. A. 1982. Latest Jurassic–Early Cretaceous events and the 'Late Cimmerian Unconformity' in the North Sea area. *AAPG Bulletin*, **66**, 2628–2648.

RAYMOND, A. C. 1991. *Carboniferous Rocks of the Eastern and Central Midland Valley of Scotland: Organic Petrology, Organic Geochemistry and Effects of Igneous Activity*. PhD thesis, University of Newcastle upon Tyne.

RAYMOND, A. C. & MURCHISON, D. G. 1991. The relationship between organic maturation, the widths of thermal aureoles and the thicknesses of sills in the Midland Valley of Scotland and northern England. *Journal of the Geological Society, London*, **148**, 215–218.

RAYNER, D. H. 1963. The Achanarras Limestone of the Middle Old Red Sandstone, Caithness, Scotland. *Proceedings of the Yorkshire Geological Society*, **34**, 1–44.

READ, H. H. 1923a. The petrology of the Arnage district in Aberdeenshire: a study of assimilation. *Quarterly Journal of the Geological Society of London*, **79**, 446–484.

READ, H. H. 1923b. Geology of the country around Banff, Huntly and Turriff. *Memoir of the Geological Survey of Scotland*.

READ, H. H. 1931. *The Geology of Central Sutherland*. Memoir of the Geological Survey of Great Britain.

READ, H. H. 1934a. Age problems of the Moine series of Scotland. *Geological Magazine*, **71**, 302–317.

READ, H. H. 1934b. The metamorphic geology of Unst in the Shetland Islands. *Quarterly Journal of the Geological Society of London*, **90**, 637–688.

READ, H. H. 1935. The gabbros and associated xenolithic complexes of the Haddo House district, Aberdeenshire. *Quarterly Journal of the Geological Society of London*, **91**, 591–635.

READ, H. H. 1952. Metamorphism in the Ythan Valley, Aberdeenshire. *Transactions of the Geological Society of Edinburgh*, **15**, 265–279.

READ, H. H. 1955. The Banff Nappe. *Proceedings of the Geologists' Association*, **66**, 1–29.

READ, H. H. 1956. The dislocated south-western margin of the Insch igneous mass, Aberdeenshire. *Proceedings of the Geologists' Association*, **67**, 73–86.

READ, H. H. 1957. *The Granite Controversy*. Thomas Murby & Sons, London.

READ, H. H. 1961. Aspects of the Caledonian magmatism in Scotland. *Proceedings of the Liverpool and Manchester Geological Society*, **2**, 653–683.

READ, H. H. & FARQUHAR, O. C. 1956. The Buchan anticline of the Banff nappe of Dalradian rocks in north-east Scotland. *Quarterly Journal of the Geological Society of London*, **112**, 131–154.

READ, H. H. & HAQ, B. T. 1965. Notes, mainly geochemical, on the granite-diorite complex of the Insch igneous mass, with an addendum on the Aberdeenshire quartz-dolerites. *Proceedings of the Geologists' Association*, **76**, 13–19.

READ, H. H., ROSS, G., PHEMISTER, J. & LEE, G. W. 1925. *The Geology of the Country around Golspie, Sutherlandshire*. Memoir of the Geological Survey, Scotland.

READ, H. H., SADASHIVAIAH, M. S. & HAQ, B. T. 1961. Differentiation in the olivine-gabbro of the Insch mass, Aberdeenshire. *Proceedings of the Geologists' Association*, **72**, 391–413.

READ, H. H., SADASHIVAIAH, M. S. & HAQ, B. T. 1965. The hypersthene-gabbro of the Insch complex, Aberdeenshire. *Proceedings of the Geologists' Association*, **76**, 1–11.

READ, W. A. 1959. The Economic Geology of the Stirling and Clackmannan Coalfield, Scotland: Area South of the River Forth. *Coalfield Papers of the Geological Survey of Great Britain*, **2**.

READ, W. A. 1965. Shoreward facies changes and their relation to cyclical sedimentation in part of the Namurian east of Stirling. *Scottish Journal of Geology*, **1**, 69–96.

READ, W. A. 1988. Controls on Silesian sedimentation in the Midland Valley of Scotland. *In*: BESLY, B. M. & KELLING, G. (eds) *Sedimentation in a Synorogenic Basin Complex*. Blackie, Glasgow, 222–241.

READ, W. A. 1989. The interplay of sedimentation, volcanicity and tectonics in the Passage Group (Arnsbergian, E2 to Westphalian A) in the Midland Valley of Scotland. *In*: ARTHURTON, R. S., GUTTERIDGE, P. & NOLAN, S. C. (eds) *The Role of Tectonics in Devonian and Carboniferous Sedimentation in the British Isles*. Occasional Publications of the Yorkshire Geological Society, **6**, 143–152.

READ, W. A. 1992. Evidence of tidal influences in Arnsbergian rhythmites in the Kincardine Basin. *Scottish Journal of Geology*, **28**, 135–142.

READ, W. A. 1994a. The frequencies of Scottish Pendleian allocycles. *Scottish Journal of Geology*, **30**, 91–94.

READ, W. A. 1994b. High-frequency, glacial-eustatic sequences in early Namurian coal-bearing fluviodeltaic deposits, central Scotland. *In*: DE BOER, P. L. & SMITH, D. G. (eds) Orbital Forcing and Cyclical Sequences. *Special Publication International Association of Sedimentologists*, **19**, 413–428.

READ, W. A. 1995. Sequence stratigraphy and lithofacies geometry in an early Namurian coal-bearing succession in central Scotland. *In*: WHATELEY, M. K. G. & SPEARS, D. A. (eds) *European Coal Geology*. Geological Society, London, Special Publications, **82**, 285–297.

READ, W. A. & DEAN, J. M. 1982. Quantitative relationships between numbers of fluvial cycles, bulk lithological composition and net subsidence in a Scottish Namurian basin. *Sedimentology*, **29**, 181–200.

READ, W. A. & FORSYTH, I. H. 1989. Allocycles and autocycles in the upper part of the Limestone Coal Group (Pendleian, E1) in the Glasgow–Stirling region of the Midland Valley of Scotland. *Geological Journal*, **24**, 121–137.

READ, W. A. & FORSYTH, I. H. 1991. Allocycles in the upper part of the Limestone Coal Group (Pendleian, E1) of the Glasgow–Stirling Region viewed in the light of sequence stratigraphy. *Geological Journal*, **26**, 85–89.

READ, W. A. & JOHNSON, S. R. H. 1967. The sedimentology of sandstone formations within the Upper Old Red Sandstone and lowest Calciferous Sandstone measures west of Stirling. *Scottish Journal of Geology*, **3**, 247–267.

REED, F. R. C. 1935. Palaeontological evidence of the age of the Craighead Limestone. *Transactions of the Geological Society of Glasgow*, **19**, 341–372.

REMY, W., GENSEL, P. G. & HASS, H. 1993. The gametophyte generation of some early Devonian land plants. *International Journal of Plant Science*, **154**, 35–58.

RETALLACK, G. J. & MINDSZENTY, A. 1994. Well preserved late Precambrian paleosols from northwest Scotland. *Journal of Sedimentary Research*, **A64**, 264–281.

RICE, C. M. 1993. Mineralisation associated with Caledonian magmatism. *In*: PATTRICK, R. A. D. & POLYA, D. A. (eds) *Mineralisation in the British Isles*. Chapman and Hall, London, 102–186.

RICE, C. M. & DAVIES, B. 1979. Copper mineralization associated with an appinite pipe in Argyll, Scotland. *Transactions of the Institution of Mining and Metallurgy*, **88**, B154–B160.

RICE, C. M. & TREWIN, N. H. 1988. Lower Devonian gold-bearing hot spring system near Rhynie, Scotland. *Transactions of the Institution of Mining and Metallurgy*, **97**, B141–B144.

RICE, C. M., ASHCROFT, W. A., BATTEN, D. J., BOYCE, A. J., CAULFIELD, J. B. D., FALLICK, A. E., HOLE, M. J., JONES, E. M., ROGERS, G. E., PEARSON, M. J., SAXTON, J. M., STUART, F. M., TREWIN, N. H. & TURNER, G. 1995. A Devonian auriferous hot spring system, Rhynie, Scotland. *Journal of the Geological Society, London*, **152**, 229–250.

RICE, C. M., TREWIN, N. H. & ANDERSON, L. I. 2002. Geological setting of the Early Devonian Rhynie cherts, Aberdeenshire, Scotland: An early terrestrial hot spring system. *Journal of the Geological Society, London*, **159**, 203–214.

RICE, R. 1975. Geochemical exploration in an area of glacial overburden at Arthrath, Aberdeenshire. *In*: JONES, M. J. (ed.) *Prospecting in Areas of Glaciated Terrain*. Institution of Mining & Metallurgy, London, 82–86.

RICHARDS, P. C. 1985a. A Lower Old Red Sandstone lake in the offshore Orcadian Basin. *Scottish Journal of Geology*, **21**, 381–383.

RICHARDS, P. C. 1985b. Upper Old Red Sandstone sedimentation in the Buchan oilfield, North Sea. *Scottish Journal of Geology*, **21**, 227–237.

RICHARDS, P. C. 1992. An introduction to the Brent Group: a literature review. *In*: MORTON, A. C., HASZELDINE, R. S., GILES, M. R.

& BROWN, S. (eds) *Geology of the Brent Group*. Geological Society, London, Special Publications, **61**, 15–26.

RICHARDS, P. C., LOTT, G. K., JOHNSON, H., KNOX, R. W. O'B. & RIDING, J. B. 1993. Jurassic of the Central and Northern North Sea. *In*: KNOX, R. W. O'B. & CORDEY, W. G. (eds) *Lithstratigraphic Nomenclature of the UK North Sea*. BGS, Nottingham.

RICHARDSON, J. B. 1967. Some British Lower Devonian spore assemblages and their stratigraphical significance. *Reviews of Palaeobotany and Palynology*, **1**, 111–129.

RICHARDSON, J. B. & MCGREGOR, D. C. 1986. Silurian and Devonian spore zones of the Old Red Sandstone continent and adjacent regions. *Geological Survey of Canada Bulletin*, **364**, 1–79.

RICHARDSON, J. B., FORD, J. H. & PARKER, F. 1984. Miospores, correlation and age of some Scottish Lower Old Red Sandstone sediments from the Strathmore Region (Fife and Angus). *Journal of Micropalaeontology*, **3**, 109–124.

RICHARDSON, S. W. 1968. The petrology of the metamorphosed syenite in Glen Dessary, Inverness-shire. *Quarterly Journal of the Geological Society of London*, **124**, 9–51.

RICHARDSON, S. W. & POWELL, R. 1976. Thermal causes of the Dalradian metamorphism in the central Highlands of Scotland. *Scottish Journal of Geology*, **12**, 237–268.

RICHARDSON, W. 1805. Remarks on the basaltes of the coast of Antrim. *Transactions of the Royal Society of Edinburgh*, **5** (Part 3), 15–20.

RICHEY, J. E. 1932. Tertiary ring structures in Britain. *Transactions of the Geological Society of Glasgow*, **19**, 42–140.

RICHEY, J. E. 1937. Areas of sedimentation of Lower Carboniferous age in the Midland Valley of Scotland. *Geological Survey of Great Britain Summary of Progress (1935)*, **II**, 93–110.

RICHEY, J. E. 1961. *Scotland: The Tertiary Volcanic Districts*. British Regional Geology, HMSO, London.

RICHEY, J. E. & KENNEDY, W. Q. 1939. *The Moine and Sub-Moine Series of Morar, Inverness-shire*, Memoir of the British Geological Survey, Scotland, **2**, 26–45.

RICHEY, J. E. & THOMAS, H. H. 1930. *The Geology of Ardnamurchan, North-West Mull and Coll (A Description of Sheet 51 and Part of Sheet 52 of the Geological Map)*. HMSO, Edinburgh.

RICHEY, J. E., STEWART, F. H. & WAGER, L. R. 1946. Age relations of certain granites and marscoite in Skye. *Geological Magazine*, **83**, 293.

RICHTHOFEN, F. VON. 1868. Principles of the natural system of volcanic rocks. *Memoirs Presented to the California Academy of Science*, **1** (part 2), 1–136.

RIDD, M. F. 1981. Petroleum geology west of the Shetlands. *In*: ILLING, L. V. & HOBSON, G. D. (eds) *Petroleum Geology of the Continental Shelf of North-West Europe*. Heyden, London, 414–425.

RIDD, M. F. 1983. Aspects of the Tertiary geology of the Faeroe–Shetland Channel. *In*: BOTT, M. H. P., SAXOV, S., TALWANI, M. & THIEDE, J. (eds) *Structure and Development of the Greenland-Scotland Ridge: New Methods and Concepts*. Plenum, New York, 91–108.

RIDING, J. B. 1992. On the age of the Upper Ostrea Member, Staffin Bay Formation (Middle Jurassic) of north-west Skye. *Scottish Journal of Geology*, **28**, 155–158.

RIDING, J. B. & THOMAS, J. 1997. Marine palynomorphs from the Staffin Bay and Staffin Shale Formations (Middle–Upper Jurassic) of the Trotternish Peninsula, NW Skye. *Scottish Journal of Geology*, **33**, 59–74.

RIDING, J. B., WALTON, W. & SHAW, D. 1991 Toarcian to Bathonian (Jurassic) palynology of the Inner Hebrides, north-west Scotland. *Palynology*, **15**, 115–179.

RIGBY, S. & DAVIES, S. J. 2001. Volcanically mediated plankton blooms in the Central Belt of the Southern Uplands, Scotland, during the Llandovery. *Transactions of the Royal Society of Edinburgh: Earth Sciences*, **91**, 457–470.

RILEY, L. A. 1980. Palynological evidence of an early Portlandian age for the uppermost Helmsdale Boulder Beds, Sutherland. *Scottish Journal of Geology*, **16**, 29–31.

RILEY, N. J., CLAOUÉ-LONG, J., HIGGINS, A. C., OWENS, B., SPEARS, A., TAYLOR, L. & VARKER, W. J. 1994. Geochronometry and geochemistry of the European Mid-Carboniferous Boundary Global Stratotype proposal, Stonehead Beck, North Yorkshire, UK. *Annales de Societé Géologique de Belgique*, **116**, 275–289.

RIPPON, J. H. 1996. Sand body orientation, palaeoslope analysis and basin-fill implications in the Westphalian A–C of Great Britain. *Journal of the Geological Society, London*, **153**, 881–900.

RIPPON, J. H. 1997. *Variations in Tectonic Style and Setting in British Coalfields*. PhD thesis, University of Keele.

RIPPON, J. H. 1998. The identification of syn-depositionally active structures in the coal-bearing Upper Carboniferous of Great Britain. *Proceedings of the Yorkshire Geological Society*, **52**, 73–93.

RIPPON, J. H., READ, W. A. & PARK, R. G. 1996. The Ochil Fault and the Kincardine Basin: key structures in the tectonic evolution of the Midland Valley of Scotland. *Journal of the Geological Society, London*, **153**, 573–587.

RITCHIE, J. D. & HITCHEN, K. 1993. Discussion on the location and history of the Walls Boundary fault and Moine thrust north and south of Shetland. *Journal of the Geological Society, London*, **150**, 1003–1008.

RITCHIE, J. D. & HITCHEN, K. 1996. Early Paleogene offshore igneous activity to the northwest of the UK and its relationship to the North Atlantic Igneous Province. *In*: KNOX, R. W. O'B., CORFIELD, R. M. & DUNAY, R. E. (eds) *Correlation of the Early Paleogene in Northwest Europe*. Geological Society, London, Special Publications, **101**, 63–78.

RITCHIE, J. D., HITCHEN, K. & MITCHELL, J. G. 1987. The offshore continuation of the Moine thrust north of Shetland as deduced from basement isotope ages. *Scottish Journal of Geology*, **23**, 163–173.

RITCHIE, J. D., SWALLOW, J. L., MITCHELL, J. G. & MORTON, A. C. 1988. Jurassic ages for intrusives and extrusives within the Forties Igneous Province. *Scottish Journal of Geology*, **24**, 81–88.

RITCHIE, J. D., GATLIFF, R. W. & RIDING, J. B. 1996. 1. Pre-Tertiary lithostratigraphy. *In*: KNOX, R. W. O'B. (ed.) *Stratigraphic Nomenclature of the UK North West Margin*. British Geological Survey, Nottingham.

RITCHIE, J. D., GATLIFF, R. W. & RICHARDS, P. C. 1999. Early Tertiary magmatism in the offshore NW UK margin and surrounds. *In*: FLEET, A. J. & BOLDY, S. A. R. (eds) *Petroleum Geology of Northwest Europe: Proceedings of the 5th Conference*. Geological Society, London, 573–584.

RITCHIE, M. & ECKFORD, R. J. A. 1936. The 'Haggis rock' of the Southern Uplands. *Transactions of the Edinburgh Geological Society*, **13**, 371–377.

RITCHIE, W. & O'SULLIVAN, M. 1994. *The Environmental Impact of the Wreck of the Braer*. The Scottish Office, Edinburgh.

RIVERS, T. 1994. A revised crustal-scale cross-section of the Grenville province in western Labrador and eastern Quebec – evidence of tectonic thickening and orogenic collapse. *GAC/MAC Annual Meeting. Program with Abstracts*, A94.

ROBERTS, A. M. 1989. Fold and thrust structures in the Kintradwell 'Boulder Beds', Moray Firth. *Scottish Journal of Geology*, **25**, 173–186.

ROBERTS, A. M. & HARRIS, A. L. 1983. The Loch Quoich Line – a limit of early Palaeozoic crustal reworking in the Moine of the northern Highlands of Scotland. *Journal of the Geological Society, London*, **140**, 883–892.

ROBERTS, A. M. & HOLDSWORTH, R. E. 1999. Linking onshore and offshore structures: Mesozoic extension in the Scottish Highlands. *Journal of the Geological Society, London*, **156**, 1061–1064.

ROBERTS, A. M., SMITH, D. I. & HARRIS, A. L. 1984. The structural setting and tectonic significance of the Glen Dessary syenite, Inverness-shire. *Journal of the Geological Society, London*, **141**, 1033–1042.

ROBERTS, A. M., STRACHAN, R. A., HARRIS, A. L., BARR, D. & HOLDSWORTH, R. E. 1987. The Sgurr Beag nappe: a reassessment of the northern Highland Moine. *Bulletin of the Geological Society of America*, **98**, 497–506.

ROBERTS, A. M., BRADLEY, M. E., PRICE, J. D. & HUCK, I. W. 1990. Structural history of a transtensional basin: Inner Moray Firth, N E Scotland. *Journal of the Geological Society*, London, **147**, 87–103.

ROBERTS, J. D., MATHIESON, A. S. & HAMPSON, J. M. 1987. Statfjord. In: SPENCER, A. M. et al. (eds) *Geology of the Norwegian Oil and Gas Fields*. Graham & Trotman, London, 319–340.

ROBERTS, J. L. 1974. The evolution of the Glencoe cauldron. *Scottish Journal of Geology*, **10**, 269–282.

ROBERTS, J. L. & TREAGUS, J. E. 1977a. The Dalradian rocks of the Loch Leven area. *Scottish Journal of Geology*, **13**, 165–184.

ROBERTS, J. L. & TREAGUS, J. E. 1977b. Polyphase generation of nappe structures in the Dalradian rocks of the southwest Highlands of Scotland. *Scottish Journal of Geology*, **13**, 237–254.

ROBERTS, J. L. & TREAGUS, J. E. 1979. Stratigraphical and structural correlation between the Dalradian rocks of the SW and Central Highlands of Scotland. In: HARRIS, A. L., HOLLAND, C. H. & LEAKE, B. E. (eds) *The Caledonides of the British Isles – Reviewed*. Geological Society, London, Special Publications, **8**, 199–204.

ROBERTSON, G. 1989. A palaeoenvironmental interpretation of the Silurian rocks in the Pentland Hills, near Edinburgh, Scotland. *Transactions of the Royal Society of Edinburgh; Earth Sciences*, **80**, 127–144.

ROBERTSON, G. 1993. Beryl Field: geological evolution and reservoir behaviour. In: PARKER, J. R. (ed.) *Petroleum Geology of Northwest Europe: Proceedings of the 4th Conference*. Geological Society, London, 1491–1502.

ROBERTSON, R. C. R. & PARSONS, I. 1974. The Loch Loyal Syenites. *Scottish Journal of Geology*, **10**, 129–146.

ROBERTSON, R. H. S. 1945. The raw materials of Scotland: Diatomite. *Quarry Manager's Journal* (Special Issue). **28**, 453–458.

ROBERTSON, S. 1994. Timing of Barrovian metamorphism and 'Older Granite' emplacement in relation to Dalradian deformation. *Journal of the Geological Society, London*, **151**, 5–8.

ROBERTSON, S. & SMITH, M. 1999. The significance of the Geal Charn–Ossian Steep Belt in basin development in the Central Scottish Highlands. *Journal of the Geological Society, London*, **156**, 1175–1182.

ROBINSON, M. & BALLANTYNE, C. K. 1979. Evidence for a glacial readvance pre-dating the Loch Lomond Advance in Wester Ross. *Scottish Journal of Geology*, **15**, 271–277.

ROBINSON, M. A. & MCCLELLAND, E. A. 1987. Palaeomagnetism of the Torridonian of Rhum, Scotland: evidence for limited uplift of the Central Intrusive Complex. *Earth and Planetary Science Letters*, **85**, 473–487.

ROBSON, D. 1991. The Argyll, Duncan and Innes Fields, Blocks 30/24 and 30/25a, UK North Sea. In: ABBOTTS, I. L. (ed.) *United Kingdom Oil and Gas Fields 25 years Commemorative Volume*. Geological Society, London, Memoir, **14**, 219–225.

ROCK, N. M. S. 1983. *The Permo-Carboniferous Camptonite-Monchiquite Dyke-Suite of the Scottish Highlands: Distribution, Field and Petrological Aspects*. Institute of Geological Sciences Report, **82/14**.

ROCK, N. M. S. & MACDONALD, R. 1986. Petrology, chemistry and origin of a peculiar lens of pelites, limestones and possible para-amphibolites from the Moines of the Ross of Mull, Scotland. *Proceedings of the Geologists' Association*, **97**, 249–258.

ROCK, N. M. S. & RUNDLE, C. C. 1986. Lower Devonian age for the 'Great (basal) Conglomerate' Scottish Borders. *Scottish Journal of Geology*, **22**, 285–288.

ROCK, N. M. S., JEFFREYS, L. A. & MACDONALD, R. 1984. The problem of anomalous limestone-pelite successions within the Moine outcrop; I: metamorphic limestones of the Great Glen area, from Ardgour to Nigg. *Scottish Journal of Geology*, **20**, 383–406.

ROCK, N. M. S., MACDONALD, R., WALKER, B. H., MAY, F., PEACOCK, J. D. & SCOTT, P. 1985. Intrusive metabasite belts within the Moine assemblage, west of Loch Ness, Scotland: evidence for metabasite modification by country rock interactions. *Journal of the Geological Society, London*, **142**, 643–661.

ROCK, N. M. S., GASKARTH, J. W. & RUNDLE, C. C. 1986. Late Caledonian dyke-swarms in southern Scotland; a regional zone of primitive K-rich lamprophyres and associated vents. *Journal of Geology*, **94**, 505–522.

ROCK, N. M. S., DULLER, P., HASZELDINE, R. S. & GROVES, D. I. 1987. Lamprophyres as potential gold exploration targets: some preliminary observations and speculations. In: GROVES, D. I. & HO, S. E. (eds) *Recent Advances in Understanding Archaean Gold Deposits*. University of W. Australia extension publication, **11**, 1–16.

RODD, J. A. & STEWART, A. D. 1992. Geochemistry, weathering and diagenesis of the Diabaig Formation (Torridon Group) in NW Scotland. *Scottish Journal of Geology*, **28**, 27–35.

RODDICK, J. C. & MAX, M. D. 1983. A Laxford age from the Inishtrahull Platform, Co Donegal, Ireland. *Scottish Journal of Geology*, **19**, 97–102.

RODDOM, D., MILLER, J. A. & FLINN, D. 1989. Permo-Carboniferous mylonite formation in the Walls Boundary fault system, Shetland. *Proceedings of the Yorkshire Geological Society*, **47**, 339–343.

ROGERS, D. A. 1987. *Devonian Correlations, Environments and Tectonics Across the Great Glen Fault*. PhD thesis, University of Cambridge.

ROGERS, D. A. 1990. Probable tetrapod tracks rediscovered in the Devonian of northern Scotland. *Journal of the Geological Society, London*, **147**, 746–748.

ROGERS, D. A. & ASTIN, T. R. 1991. Ephemeral lakes, mud pellet dunes and wind-blown sand and silt: re-interpretations of Devonian lacustrine cycles in north Scotland. In: ANADON, P., CABRERA, L. & KELTS, K. (eds) *Lacustrine Facies Analysis*. International Association of Sedimentologists Special Publications, **12**, 201–223.

ROGERS, D. A., MARSHALL, J. E. A. & ASTIN, T. R. 1989. Devonian and later movements on the Great Glen Fault system, Scotland. *Journal of the Geological Society, London*, **146**, 369–372.

ROGERS, G. & DUNNING, G. R. 1991. Geochronology of appinitic and related granitic magmatism in the W. Highlands of Scotland: constraints on the timing of transcurrent fault movement. *Journal of the Geological Society, London*, **148**, 17–27.

ROGERS, G., DEMPSTER, T. J., BLUCK, B. J. & TANNER, P. W. G. 1989. A high-precision age for the Ben Vuirich granite: implications for the evolution of the Scottish Dalradian Supergroup. *Journal of the Geological Society, London*, **146**, 789–798.

ROGERS, G., KROUGH, T. E., BLUCK, B. J. & KWOK, Y. Y. 1990. Provenance ages of the Torridonian Sandstone of NW Scotland using single grain U–Pb zircon analysis. *Geological Society of Australia Abstracts*, **27**, 84.

ROGERS, G., HYSLOP, E. K., STRACHAN, R. A., PATERSON, B. A. & HOLDSWORTH, R. E. 1998. The structural setting and U–Pb geochronology of Knoydartian pegmatites in W. Inverness-shire: evidence for Neoproterozoic tectonothermal events in the Moine of NW Scotland. *Journal of the Geological Society, London*, **155**, 685–696.

ROGERS, G., KINNEY, P. D., STRACHAN, R. A., FRIEND, C. R. & PATERSON, B. 2001. U–Pb chronology of the Fort Augustus granite gneiss: constraints on the timing of Neoproterozoic and palaeozoic tectonothermal events in the NW Highlands of Scotland, *Journal of the Geological Society, London*, **158**, 7–14.

ROGERS, J. J. W. 1996. A history of continents in the past three billion years. *Journal of Geology*, **104**, 91–107.

ROGERS, J. J. W. & SANTOSH, M. 2002. Configuration of Columbia, a Mesoproterozoic Supercontinent. *Gondwana Research*, **5**, 5–22.

ROLFE, W. D. I. 1960. The Silurian inlier of Carmichael, Lanarkshire. *Transactions of the Royal Society of Edinburgh*, **64**, 245–260.

ROLFE, W. D. I. 1961. The geology of the Hagshaw Hills Silurian Inlier, Lanarkshire. *Transactions of the Edinburgh Geological Society*, **18**, 240–269.

ROLFE, W. D. I. 1966. Woolly rhinoceros from the Scottish Pleistocene. *Scottish Journal of Geology*, **2**, 253–258.

ROLFE, W. D. I. 1980. Early invertebrate terrestrial faunas. In: PANCHEN, A. L. (ed.) *The Terrestrial Environment and the Origin of Land Vertebrates*. Systematics Association Special Volume 15. Academic, London and New York, 117–157.

ROLFE, W. D. I. 1992. Excursion 21, Hagshaw Hills. *In*: LAWSON, J. D. & WEEDON, D. S (eds) *Geological Excursions around Glasgow and Girvan*. Geological Society of Glasgow, 265–279.

ROLFE, W. D. I., DURRANT, G. P., FALLICK, A. E., HALL, A. J., LARGE, D. J., SCOTT, A. C., SMITHSON, T. R. & WALKDEN, G. M. 1990. An early terrestrial biota preserved by Viséan volcanicity in Scotland. *In*: LOCKLEY, M. G. & RICE, A. (eds) *Volcanism and Fossil Biotas: Implications for Preservation, Evolution and Extinction*. Geological Society of America Special Paper, **244**, 13–24.

ROLFE, W. D. I., DURRANT, G. P., BAIRD, W. J., CHAPLIN, C., PATON, R. L. & REEKIE, R. J. 1994. The East Kirkton Limestone, Viséan, of West Lothian, Scotland: introduction and stratigraphy. *Transactions of the Royal Society of Edinburgh: Earth Sciences*, **84**, 177–188.

ROLLIN, K. E. 1994. Geophysical correlation of Precambrian rocks in northern Britain. *In*: GIBBONS, W. & HARRIS, A. L. (eds) *A Revised Correlation of Precambrian Rocks in the British Isles*. Geological Society, London, Special Report, **22**, 65–74.

ROOKSBY, S. 1991. The Miller Field, Blocks 16/7b & 16/8b, UK North Sea. *In*: ABBOTTS, I. L. (ed.) *United Kingdom Oil and Gas Fields 25 Years Commemorative Volume*. Geological Society, London, Memoir, **14**, 159–164.

ROSE, P. T. S. 1999. Reservoir characterisation in the Captain Field: integration of horizontal and vertical well data. *In*: FLEET, A. J. & BOLDY, S. A. R. (eds) *Petroleum Geology of Northwest Europe: Proceedings of the 5th Conference*, Geological Society, London, 1101–1113.

ROSE, P. T. S. & HARRIS, A. L. 2000. Evidence for the Lower Palaeozoic age of the Tay Nappe: the timing and nature of Grampian events in the Scottish Highland sector of the Laurentian margin. *Journal of the Geological Society, London*, **157**, 381–391.

ROYAL COMMISSION ON ENVIRONMENTAL POLLUTION 1996. *Sustainable Use of Soils*. 19th. Report, London, HMSO.

ROYAL SOCIETY FOR THE PROTECTION OF BIRDS 1990. *Gravel Pit Restoration for Wildlife – a Practical Manual*. RSPB, Sandy.

ROYAL SOCIETY FOR THE PROTECTION OF BIRDS & SCOTTISH NATURAL HERITAGE 2000. *Biodiversity and Opencast Coal Mining – A Good Practice Guide*. Edinburgh.

RUDDIMAN, W. F. & MACINTYRE, A. 1973. Time-transgressive deglacial retreat of polar waters from the North-Atlantic. *Quaternary Research*, **3**, 117–130.

RUDWICK, M. J. S. 1962. Hutton and Werner compared: George Greenough's geological tour of Scotland in 1805. *The British Journal for the History of Science*, **1**, 117–135.

RUSHTON, A. W. A. & OWEN, A. W. 1999. Scotland: Cambrian and Ordovician of the Grampian Terrane and Highland Border Subterrane. *In*: RUSHTON, A. W. A., OWEN, A. W., OWENS, R. M. & PROGMORE, J. K. (eds) *British Cambrian to Ordovician Stratigraphy*. Geological Conservation Review Series, **18**. Joint Nature Conservation Committee, 319–322.

RUSHTON, A. W. A. & STONE, P. 1991. Terrigenous input to the Moffat Shale sequence, Southern Uplands. *Scottish Journal of Geology*, **27**, 167–169.

RUSHTON, A. W. A. & TRIPP, R. P. 1979. A fossiliferous Lower Canadian (Tremadoc) boulder from the Benan conglomertae of the Girvan district. *Scottish Journal of Geology*, **15**, 321–327.

RUSHTON, A. W. A., STONE, P., SMELLIE, J. L. & TUNNICLIFF, S. P. 1986. An early Arenig age for the Pinbain sequence of the Ballantrae Complex. *Scottish Journal of Geology*, **22**, 41–54.

RUSHTON, A. W. A., STONE, P. & HUGHES, R. A. 1996*a*. Biostratigraphical control of thrust models for the Southern Uplands of Scotland. *Transactions of the Geological Society of Edinburgh: Earth Sciences*, **86**, 137–152.

RUSHTON, A. W. A., TUNNICLIFF, S. P. & Tripp, R. P. 1996*b*. The faunas of the Albany Group in the Girvan area, and their palaeogeographical implications. *Scottish Journal of Geology*, **32**, 23–32.

RUSHTON, A. W. A., OWEN, A. W., OWENS, R. M. & PRIGMORE, J. K. (eds) 1999. *British Cambrian to Ordovician Stratigraphy*. Geological Conservation Review Series, **18**, Joint Nature Conservation Committee, 327–347.

RUSSELL, M. J. 1976. Incipient plate separation and possible related mineralization in lands bordering the North Atlantic. *In*: STRONG, D. F. (ed.) *Metallogeny and Plate Tectonics*. Geological Association of Canada Special Paper, **14**, 339–349.

RUSSELL, M. J. 1985. The evolution of the Scottish mineral subprovince. *Scottish Journal of Geology*, **21**, 513–546.

RUSSELL, M. J. 1988*a*. A model for the genesis of sediment-hosted exhalative (SEDEX) ore deposits. *Proceedings of the Seventh Symposium of the International Association on the Genesis of Ore Deposits, Stuttgart*, 59–66.

RUSSELL, M. J. 1988*b*. Chimneys, chemical gardens and feldspar horizons +/− pyrrhotine in some SEDEX deposits: aspects of alkaline environments of deposition. *Proceedings of the Seventh Symposium of the International Association on the Genesis of Ore Deposits, Stuttgart*, 183–190.

RUSSELL, M. J. & SMYTHE, D. K. 1983. Origin of the Oslo Graben in relation to the Hercynian Alleghanian orogeny and lithospheric rifting in the North Atlantic. *Tectonophysics*, **94**, 457–472.

RUSSELL, M. J., HALL, A. J., WILLAN, R. C. R., ALLISON, I., ANDERTON, R. & BOWES, G. E. 1984. On the origin of the Aberfeldy celsian + baryte + base-metal deposits, Scotland. *In*: *Prospecting in Areas of Glaciated Terrain*. Institution of Mining and Metallurgy, London, 159–170.

RUST, B. R. 1965. The stratigraphy and structure of the Whithorn area of Wigtownshire, Scotland, *Scottish Journal of Geology*, **2**, 159–164.

RYAN, P. D. & SOPER, N. J. 2002. Modelling anatexis in intra-cratonic rift basins: an example from the Neoproterozoic rocks of the Scottish Highlands. *Geological Magazine*, **138**, 577–588.

SABINE, P. A. 1953. The petrology and geological significance of the post-Cambrian minor intrusions of Assynt and the adjoining districts of north-west Scotland. *Quarterly Journal of the Geological Society of London*, **109**, 137–171.

SABINE, P. A. 1963. The Strontian granite complex, Argyllshire. *Bulletin of the Geological Survey of Great Britain*, **20**, 6–41.

SADASHIVAIAH, M. S. 1954. The granite–diorite complex of the Insch Igneous Mass, Aberdeenshire. *Geological Magazine*, **91**, 286–292.

SALLOMY, J. T. & PIPER, J. D. A. 1973. Palaeomagnetic studies in the British Caledonide – II. The Younger Gabbros of Aberdeenshire, Scotland. *Geophysical Journal of the Royal Astronomical Society*, **34**, 13–26.

SAMSON, I. M. & BANKS, D. A. 1988. Epithermal base-metal vein mineralization in the Southern Uplands of Scotland: Nature and origin of the fluids. *Mineralium Deposita*, **23**, 1–8.

SANDERS, I. S. & JOHNSTON, J. D. 1989. The Torridonian Stac Fada Member: an extrusion of fluidized peperite? *Transactions of the Royal Society of Edinburgh: Earth Sciences*, **80**, 1–4.

SANDERS, I. S. & JOHNSTON, J. D. 1990. Reply to: the Torridonian Stac Fada Member: a discussion. *Transactions of the Royal Society of Edinburgh: Earth Sciences*, **80**, 249–250.

SANDERS, I. S., VAN CALSTEREN, P. W. C. & HAWKESWORTH, C. J. 1984. A Grenville Sm–Nd age for the Glenelg eclogite in northwest Scotland. *Nature, London*, **312**, 439–440.

SARJEANT, W. A. S. 1974. A history and bibliography of the study of fossil vertebrate footprints in the British Isles. *Palaeogeography, Palaeoclimatology, Palaeoecology*, **16**, 265–378.

SAUNDERS, A. D., ROGERS, G., MARRINERR, G. F., TERRELL, D. J. & VERMA, S. P. 1987. Geochemistry of Cenozoic volcanic rocks, Baja California, Mexico: Implications for the petrogenesis of post-subduction magmas. *Journal of Volcanology and Geothermal Research*, **32**, 223–245.

SAUNDERS, A. D., FITTON, J. G., KERR, A. C., NORRY, M. J. & KENT, R. W. 1997. The North Atlantic Igneous Province. *In*: MAHONEY, J. J. & COFFIN, M. F. (eds) Large Igneous Provinces: Continental, Oceanic, and Planetary Volcanism. *Geophysical Monograph*, **100**, 45–93.

SCARROW, J. H., CURRAN, J. M. & KERR, A. C. 2000. Major Element Records of Variable Plume Involvement in the North Atlantic Province Tertiary Flood Basalts. *Journal of Petrology*, **41**, 1 155–1 176.

SCARROW, J. H. & COX, K. G. 1995. Basalt generated by decompressive adiabatic melting of a mantle plume: a case study from the Isle of Skye, NW Scotland. *Journal of Petrology*, **36**, 3–22.

SCHNEIDER, J. W., SCHRETZENMAYR, ST. & GAITSCH, B. G. 1998. Excursion Guide: Rotliegend Reservoirs at the margin of the Southern Permian Basin. *Leipziger Geowissenschaften*, **7**, S: 15–44.

SCHUMM, S. A. 1968. Speculations concerning paleohydrologic controls of terrestrial sedimentation. *Bulletin of the Geological Society of America*, **79**, 1573–1588.

SCOTESE, C. R. & MCKERROW, W. S. 1990. Revised World maps and introduction. *In*: MCKERROW, W. S. & SCOTESE, C. R. (eds) *Palaeozoic Palaeogeography and Biogeography*, Geological Society, London, Memoir, **12**, 1–21.

SCOTT, A. C. 1977. A review of the ecology of Upper Carboniferous plant assemblages, with new data from Strathclyde. *Palaeontology*, **20**, 447–473.

SCOTT, A. C. 1979. The ecology of Coal Measures floras from northern Britain. *Proceedings of the Geologists' Association*, **90**, 97–117.

SCOTT, A. C. 1980. The ecology of some Upper Palaeozoic floras. *In*: PANCHEN, A. L. (ed.) *The Terrestrial Environment and the Origin of Land Vertebrates*. Systematics Association Special Volume **15**, 87–115.

SCOTT, A. C. 1990. Preservation, evolution and extinction of plants in Lower Carboniferous volcanic sequences in Scotland. *In*: LOCKLEY, M. & RICE, A. (eds) *Volcanism and fossil biotas: Implications for Preservation, Evolution and Extinction*. Geological Society of America Special Paper, **244**, 25–38.

SCOTT, A. C. 1999. The distribution of megaspores from the upper Carboniferous (Namurian A) coal-bearing sequence of Dalquhandy, Douglas Coalfield, Lanarkshire, Scotland. *Palynology*, **23**, 3–14.

SCOTT, A. C. 2001. Roasted alive in the Carboniferous. *Geoscientist*, **11**, 4–7.

SCOTT, A. C. & GALTIER, J. 1985. Distribution and ecology of early ferns. *Proceedings of the Royal Society of Edinburgh*, **86B**, 141–149.

SCOTT, A. C. & GALTIER, J. 1996. A review of the problems in the stratigraphical, palaeoecological and palaeobiogeographical interpretation of the Lower Carboniferous (Dinantian) floras of Western Europe. *Reviews of Palaeobotany and Palynology*, **90**, 141–153.

SCOTT, A. C. & REX, C. M. 1987. The accumulation and preservation of Dinantian plants from Scotland and its Borders. *In*: MILLER, J., ADAMS, A. E. & WRIGHT, W. B. (eds) *European Dinantian Environments*. Wiley, Chichester, 329–344.

SCOTT, A. C., GALTIER, J. & CLAYTON, G. 1984. Distribution of anatomically-preserved floras in the Lower Carboniferous in Western Europe. *Transactions of the Royal Society of Edinburgh: Earth Sciences*, **75**, 311–340.

SCOTT, A. C., PARSONS, D. & HEMSLEY, A. 1993. The distribution of megaspores from the Upper Carboniferous coal-bearing sequence of Westfield, Fife. *Compte Rendu XIIme Congres International de Stratigraphie et de Geologie du Carbonifere, Buenos Aires*, **1**, 161–166.

SCOTT, A. C., BROWN, R., GALTIER, J. & MEYER-BERTHAUD, B. 1994. Fossil plants from the Viséan of East Kirkton, West Lothian, Scotland. *Transactions of the Royal Society of Edinburgh: Earth Sciences*, **84**, 249–260.

SCOTT, B. 1967. Barytes mineralisation at Gasswater mine, Ayrshire, Scotland. *Transactions of the Institution of Mining and Metallurgy*, **76**, B40-B45.

SCOTT, D. J. & GAUTHIER, G. 1996. Ages of detrital zircons in Palaeoproterozoic sediments from northeastern Laurentia using TIMS (U–Pb) and Laser Ablation Microprobe ICP-MS (Pb–Pb). Comparison of techniques and implications for the tectonic evolution of the region. *Chemical Geology*, **131**, 127–142.

SCOTT, D. J. & MACHADO, N. 1995. U-Pb geochronology of the northern Torngat orogen, Labrador, Canada: a record of Palaeoproterozoic magmatism and deformation. *Precambrian Research*, **70**, 169–190.

SCOTT, E. S. 1992. The palaeoenvironments and dynamics of the Rannoch–Etive nearshore and coastal succession, Brent Group, Northern North Sea. *In*: MORTON, A. C., HASZELDINE, R. S., GILES, M. R. & BROWN, S. (eds) *Geology of the Brent Group*. Geological Society, London, Special Publications, **61**, 129–147.

SCOTT, R. A. 1987. *Lithostratigraphy, Structure and Mineralization of the Argyll Group Dalradian near Tyndrum, Scotland*. PhD thesis, University of Manchester.

SCOTT, R. A., PATTRICK, R. A. D. & POLYA, D. A. 1986. Sulphur isotopic and related studies on Dalradian stratabound mineralization in the Tyndrum region, Scotland. *Stable Isotope Report*, **30**, British Geological Survey, London.

SCOTT, R. A., POLYA, D. A. & PATTRICK, R. A. D. 1988. Proximal Cu + Zn exhalites in the Argyll Group Dalradian, Creag Bhocan, Perthshire. *Scottish Journal of Geology*, **24**, 97–112.

SCOTT, R. A., PATTRICK, R. A. D. & POLYA, D. A. 1991. Origin of sulphur in metamorphosed stratabound rnineralisation from the Argyll Group Dalradian of Scotland. *Transactions of the Royal Society of Edinburgh, Earth Sciences*, **82**, 91–98.

SCOTTISH ENVIRONMENTAL PROTECTION AGENCY 1999. *State of the Natural Heritage Report-Improving Scotland's Water Environment*.

SCOTTISH EXECUTIVE, DEVELOPMENT DEPARTMENT 1999a. *Environmental Impact Assessment*. Planning and Advice Note, No. 58.

SCOTTISH EXECUTIVE 1999b. *Natural Heritage*. National Planning Policy Guidelines, No. 14.

SCOTTISH EXECUTIVE 1999c. *Opencast Coal and Related Minerals*. National Planning Policy Guidelines, No. 16.

SCOTTISH EXECUTIVE 2000. *Planning for Natural Heritage*. Planning Advice Note, No. 60.

SCOTTISH NATURAL HERITAGE & BRITISH GEOLOGICAL SURVEY 1993–2001. *A landscape fashioned by geology* series. Edinburgh, Skye, Cairngorms, Loch Lomond to Stirling, Orkney and Shetland, East Lothian and the Borders, Arran and the Clyde Islands, Scotland –the creation of its natural landscape, Fife and Tayside, North West Highlands.

SCOTTISH NATURAL HERITAGE 1996. *Restoration and Management of Mineral Extraction Sites in Quaternary Landforms and Deposits*. Information and Advisory Note, No. 41, Battleby.

SCOTTISH NATURAL HERITAGE 2000. *Minerals and the Natural Heritage in Scotland's Midland Valley*. SNH, Battleby.

SCOTTISH OFFICE 1988. *Environmental Assessment (Scotland) Regulations 1988*, 1221.

SCOTTISH OFFICE 1992. *Land for Mineral Working*. National Planning Policy Guidelines, No. 4.

SCOTTISH OFFICE 1997. *Coastal Planning*. National Planning Policy Guidelines, No. 13.

SEARL, A. 1989. Sedimentology and early diagenesis of the Lower Jurassic, Applecross, Wester Ross. *Scottish Journal of Geology*, **25**, 45–62.

SEARL, A. 1992. Sedimentology and early diagenesis of the Broadford Beds (Lower Jurassic), Skye, north-west Scotland. *Geological Journal*, **27**, 243–270.

SEARL, A. 1994. Diagenetic destruction of reservoir potential in shallow marine sandstones of the Broadford Beds (Lower Jurassic), north-west Scotland: depositional versus burial and thermal history controls on porosity destruction. *Marine and Petroleum Geology*, **11**, 131–147.

SECORD, J. E. 1991. Edinburgh Lamarckians: Robert Jameson and Robert E. Grant. *Journal of the History of Biology*, **24**, 1–18.

SEDGWICK, A. 1831. On the general structure of the Lake mountains of the north of England, and on the great dislocations by which they have been separated from the neighbouring chains. *Philosophical Magazine*, **9**, 211–213, 377–379.

SEDGWICK, A. 1850. On the geological structure and relations of the frontier chain of Scotland. *Report on the Twentieth Meeting of the British Association for the Advancement of Science; Held at Edinburgh in July and August 1850*. John Murray, London, 103–107.

SEDGWICK, A. 1851. On the geological structure and relations of the frontier chain of Scotland. *Edinburgh New Philosophical Journal*, **51**, 250–288.

SEDGWICK, A. & MURCHISON, R. I. 1828a. On the geological relations of the Secondary strata in the Isle of Arran. *Transactions of the Geological Society of London*, 2nd series, **3**, 21–36.

SEDGWICK, A. & MURCHISON, R. I. 1828b. On the old conglomerates and other Secondary deposits on the north coasts of Scotland. *Proceedings of the Geological Society of London*, **1**, 77–88.

SEDGWICK, A. & MURCHISON, R. I. 1828c. On the structure and relations of the deposits contained between the Primary rocks and the Oolitic series in the north of Scotland. *Transactions of the Geological Society of London* 2nd series, **3**, 125–160.

SEDGWICK, A. & MURCHISON, R. I. 1835. On the Geological relations of the Secondary Strata in the Isle of Arran. *Transactions of the Geological Society*, 2nd Series, **3**, 21–36.

SEDGWICK, A. & MURCHISON, R. I. 1839. On the classification of the older rocks of Devon and Cornwall. *Proceedings of the Geological Society, London*, **3**, 121–123.

SEJRUP, H. P., HAFLIDASON, H. & AARSETH, I. 1994. Late Weichselian glaciation history of the northern North Sea. *Boreas*, **23**, 1–13.

SEJRUP, H. P., LARSEN, E., LANDVIK, J., KING, E. L., HAFLIDSON, H. & NESJE, A. 2000. Quaternary glaciations in southern Fennoscandia: evidence from southwestern Norway and the northern North Sea region. *Quaternary Science Reviews*, **19**, 667–685.

SELBY, I. 1989. *Quaternary Geology of the Hebridean Continental Margin*. PhD thesis, University of Nottingham.

SELLEY, R. C. 1965a. Diagnostic characters of fluviatile sediments of the Torridonian formation (Precambrian) of northwest Scotland. *Journal of Sedimentary Petrology*, **35**, 366–380.

SELLEY, R. C. 1965b. The Torridonian succession on the islands of Fladday, Raasay, and Scalpay, Inverness-shire. *Geological Magazine*, **102**, 361–369.

SELLEY, R. C. 1969. Torridonian alluvium and quicksands. *Scottish Journal of Geology*, **5**, 328–346.

SELLWOOD, B. W. 1972. Regional environmental change across a Lower Jurassic stage-boundary in Britain. *Palaeontology*, **15**, 125–157.

SELLWOOD, B. W., VALDES, P. J. & PRICE, G. D. 2000. Geological evaluation of multiple general circulation model simulations of Late Jurassic palaeoclimate. *Palaeogeography, Palaeoclimatology, Palaeoecology*, **156**, 147–160.

ŞENGÖR, A. M. C. 2001. *Is the Present the Key to the Past or the Past the Key to the Present? James Hutton and Adam Smith versus Abraham Gottlob Werner and Karl Marx in Interpreting History*. Geological Society of America, Boulder, Special paper **355**.

SHACKLETON, N. J. 1987. Oxygen isotopes, ice volume and sea level. *Quaternary Science Review*, **6**, 193–190.

SHACKLETON, R. M. 1949. Tectonics of the older mountain systems of northern Europe, Greenland, and North America [Comments on *International Geological Congress Eighteenth Session — Great Britain 1948*]. *Geological Magazine*, **86**, 28–29.

SHACKLETON, R. M. 1958. Downward-facing structures of the Highland Border. *Quarterly Journal of the Geological Society of London*, **113**, 361–392.

SHACKLETON, R. M. 1979. The British Caledonides: comments and summary. *In*: HARRIS, A. L., HOLLAND, C. H. & LEAKE, B. E. (eds), *The Caledonides of the British Isles-Reviewed*. Geological Society, London, Special Publications, **8**, 299–304.

SHAND, S. J. 1910. On Boralanite and its associates in Assynt. *Transactions of the Edinburgh Geological Society*, **9**, 202–215.

SHAND, S. J. 1939. Loch Borolan laccolith, north-west Scotland. *Journal of Geology*, **47**, 408–410.

SHELTON, R. 1995. Mesozoic basin evolution of the North Channel: preliminary results. *In*: CROKER, P. F. & SHANNON, P. M. (eds), *The Petroleum Geology of Ireland's Offshore Basins*. Geological Society, London, Special Publications, **93**, 17–20.

SHENNAN, I., INNES, J. B., LONG, A. J. & YONGQIANG ZONG 1994. Late Devensian and Holocene relative sea level changes at Loch nan Eala, near Arisaig, northwest Scotland. *Journal of Quaternary Science*, **9**, 261–283.

SHENNAN, I., INNES, J. B., LONG, A. J. & YONGQIANG ZONG 1995. Holocene relative sea-level changes and coastal vegetation history at Kentra Moss, Argyll, northwest Scotland. *Marine Geology*, **124**, 43–59.

SHEPHERD, J. 1973. The structure and structural dating of the Carn Chuinneag intrusion, Ross-shire. *Scottish Journal of Geology*, **9**, 63–88.

SHEPHERD, M. 1991. The Magnus Field, Blocks 211/7a, **12a**, UK North Sea. *In*: ABBOTTS, I. L. (ed.) *United Kingdom Oil and Gas Fields 25 Years Commemorative Volume*. Geological Society, London, Memoir, **14**, 153–157.

SHERATON, J. W., TARNEY, J., WHEATLEY, T. H. & WRIGHT, A. E. 1973. The structural history of the Assynt district. *In*: PARK, R. G. & TARNEY, J. (eds) *The Early Precambrian of Scotland and Related Rocks of Greenland*. University of Keele, 31–44.

SHIELLS, K. A. G. & DEARMAN, W. R. 1963. Tectonics of the Coldingham Bay area of Berwickshire in the Southern Uplands of Scotland. *Proceedings of the Yorkshire Geological Society*, **34**, 209–234.

SHIELLS, K. A. G. & DEARMAN, W. R. 1966. On the possible occurrence of Dalradian rocks in the Southern Uplands of Scotland. *Scottish Journal of Geology*, **2**, 231–242.

SHORTLAND, M. E. (ed.). 1996. *Hugh Miller and the Controversies of Victorian Science*. Clarendon., Oxford.

SIBSON, R. H. 1977. Fault rocks and fault mechanisms. *Journal of the Geological Society, London*, **133**, 191–214.

SIDE, J. C. 1992. Decommissioning and abandonment of offshore installations. *In*: CAIRNS, W. J. (ed.) *North Sea Oil and the Environment – Developing Oil and Gas Resources, Environmental Impacts and Responses*. Elsevier Applied Science, 523–545.

SILLS, J. D. & ROLLINSON, H. R. 1987. Metamorphic evolution of the mainland Lewisian complex. *In*: PARK, R. G. & TARNEY, J. (eds) *Evolution of the Lewisian and Comparable Precambrian High Grade Terrains*. Geological Society, London, Special Publications, **27**, 81–92.

SIMONY, P. S. 1973. Lewisian sheets within the Moines around 'The Saddle' of northwest Scotland. *Journal of the Geological Society, London*, **129**, 191–201.

SIMPSON, P. R., GALLAGHER, M. J., GREEN, P. M., MIDDLETON, R. S., RAISWELL, R. & WILLIAMS, R. A. C. 1989. Gold mineralization in relation to the evolution of extensional volcano-sedimentary basins in the Scottish Dalradian and Abitibi belt, Canada. *Transactions of the Institution of Mining and Metallurgy*, **98**, B102–B117.

SINCLAIR, I. K., SHANNON, P. M., WILLIAMS, B. P. J., HARKER, S. D. & MOORE, J. G. 1994. Tectonic control and evolution of three Mesozoic basins, North Atlantic borderlands. *Basin Research*, **6**, 193–217.

SINTON, C. W., HITCHEN, K. & DUNCAN, R. A. 1998. ^{40}Ar–^{39}Ar geochronology of silicic and basic volcanic rocks on the margins of the N Atlantic. *Geological Magazine*, **135**, 161–170.

SISSONS, J. B. 1966. Relative sea-level changes between 10 300 and 8300 BP in part of the Carse of Stirling. *Transactions of the Institute of British Geographers*, **39** 19–21.

SISSONS, J. B. 1969. Drift stratigraphy and buried morphological features in the Grangemouth-Falkirk-Airth area, central Scotland. *Transactions of the Institute of British Geographers*, **62**, 95–114.

SISSONS, J. B. 1976a. *Scotland*. Methuen, London.

SISSONS, J. B. 1976b. Lateglacial marine erosion in South-east Scotland. *Scottish Geographical Magazine*, **92**, 17–29.

SISSONS, J. B. 1978. The parallel roads of Glen Roy and adjacent glens. *Boreas*, **7**, 229–244.

SISSONS, J. B. 1979. Palaeoclimatic inferences from former glaciers in Scotland and the Lake District. *Nature, London*, **278**, 518–521.

SISSONS, J. B. 1980. The Loch Lomond advance in the Lake District, northern England. *Transactions of the Royal Society of Edinburgh: Earth Sciences*, **71**, 13–27.

SISSONS, J. B. 1982. The so-called high 'interglacial' rock shoreline of western Scotland. *Transactions of the Institute of British Geographers*, NS **7**, 205–216.

SISSONS, J. B. 1983. Quaternary. *In*: CRAIG, G. Y. (ed.) *The Geology of Scotland* (2nd Edition). Scottish Academic Press, Edinburgh.

SISSONS, J. B. & BROOKS, C. L. 1971. Dating of early postglacial land and sea level changes in the western Forth valley. *Nature, London*, **234**, 124–127.

SISSONS, J. B. & SMITH, D. E. 1965. Peat bogs in a postglacial sea and a buried raised beach in the western part of the Carse of Stirling. *Scottish Journal of Geology*, **1**, 247–255.

SISSONS, J. B., SMITH, D. E. & CULLINGFORD, R. A. 1966. Lateglacial and postglacial shorelines in South-East Scotland. *Transactions of the Institute of British Geographers*, **39**, 9–18.

SKELHORN, R. R. 1969. *The Tertiary Igneous Geology of the Isle of Mull*. Geologists' Association Guide, **20**.

SKELHORN, R. R. & ELWELL, R. W. D. 1966. The structure and form of the granophyric quartz-dolerite intrusion, Centre II, Ardnamurchan, Argyllshire. *Transactions of the Royal Society of Edinburgh*, **66**, 286–306.

SKELHORN, R. R., HENDERSON, P., WALSH, J. N. & LONGLAND, P. J. N. 1979. The chilled margin of the Ben Buie layered gabbro, Isle of Mull. *Scottish Journal of Geology*, **15**, 161–167.

SKIPSEY, E. 1989. Geological excursion guide 6: the Eden Valley, Cumbria. *Geology Today*, **5**, 175–178.

SLAUGHTER, M. & HILL, R. J. 1991. The influence of organic matter in organogenic dolomitization. *Journal of Sedimentary Petrology*, **61**, 296–303.

SMEDLEY, P. L. 1986a. Petrochemistry of Dinantian volcanism in northern Britain. PhD thesis, University of Edinburgh.

SMEDLEY, P. L. 1986b. The relationship between calc-alkaline volcanism and within-plate continental rift volcanism: evidence from Scottish Palaeozoic lavas. *Earth and Planetary Science Letters*, **77**, 113–128.

SMEDLEY, P. L. 1988a. Trace element and isotopic variations in Scottish and Irish Dinantian volcanism; evidence for an OIB-like mantle source. *Journal of Petrology*, **29**, 414–443.

SMEDLEY, P. L. 1988b. The geochemistry of Dinantian volcanism in south Kintyre and the evidence for provincialism in the southern Scottish mantle. *Contributions to Mineralogy and Petrology*, **99**, 374–384.

SMELLIE, J. L. 1984. Accretionary lapilli and highly vesiculated pumice in the Ballantrae ophiolite complex: ash-fall products of sub-aerial eruptions. *Report of the British Geological Survey*, **16**, 36–40.

SMELLIE, J. L. & STONE, P. 1984. 'Eclogite' in the Ballantrae Complex; a garnet-clinopyroxenite segregation in mantle harzburgite? *Scottish Journal of Geology*, **20**, 315–327.

SMELLIE, J. L. & STONE, P. 1992. Geochemical control on the evolutionary history of the Ballantrae Complex, SW Scotland, from comparisons with recent analogues. *In*: PARSONS, L, MURTON, B. J. & BROWNING, P. (eds) *Ophiolites and their Modern Oceanic Analogues*. Geological Society, London, Special Publications, **60**, 171–178.

SMELLIE, J. L., STONE, P. & EVANS, J. 1995. Petrogenesis of boninites in the Ordovician Ballantrae Complex ophiolite, southwest Scotland. *Journal of Volcanology and Geothermal Research*, **69**, 323–342.

SMITH, A. & ELLISON, R. A. 1999. *Applied Geological Maps for Planning and Development – a Review of Examples from England and Wales 1983 to 1996*. Quarterly Journal of Engineering Geology, London, **32**, May Supplement.

SMITH, C. G. 1985. Recent investigations of manganese mineralisation in the Scottish Highlands. *Transactions of the Institution of Mining and Metallurgy*, **94**, A159–A162.

SMITH, C. G. 1992. *Stratabound Baryte-Base Metal Deposits and Gold Veins in Dalradian Metasediments of the Grampian Highlands, Scotland: An Excursion Guide*. British Geological Survey, Edinburgh.

SMITH, C. G. & GALLAGHER, M. J. 1994. *Syngenetic and Epigenetic Baryte, Base and Precious Metal Mineralization in the Central and Eastern Grampian Highlands, Scotland: An Excursion Guide*. British Geological Survey, Edinburgh.

SMITH, C. G. & MARSDEN, G. R. 1977. Report on geophysical and geological surveys at Blackmount, Argyllshire. *Institute of Geological Sciences, Mineral Reconnaissance Programme*, Report **16**.

SMITH, C. G., PITFIELD, P. E. J., BURLEY, A. J., HOWARD, S. H. D., PARKER, M. E., MICHIE, U. McL. & FORTEY, N. J. 1977. Investigations of stratiform sulphide mineralization in parts of central Perthshire. *Institute of Geological Sciences, Mineral Reconnaissance Programme*, Report **8**.

SMITH, C. G., McCOURT, W. G., FORTEY, N. J., JOHNSON, C. E., PARKER, M. E., COATS, J. S. & MICHIE, U. McL. 1978. Investigation of stratiform sulphide mineralisation at Meall Mor, South Knapdale, Argyllshire. *Institute of Geological Sciences, Mineral Reconnaissance Programme*, Report **15**.

SMITH, C. G., GALLAGHER, M. J., COATS, J. S. & PARKER, M. E. 1984. Detection and general characteristics of stratabound mineralisation in the Dalradian of Scotland. *Transactions of the Institution of Mining and Metallurgy*, **93**, B125–B133.

SMITH, C. G., GALLAGHER, M. J., GROUT, A., COATS, J. S., VICKERS, B. P., PEACHEY, D., PEASE, S. F., PARKER, M. E. & FORTEY, N. J. 1988. Stratabound base-metal mineralisation in Dalradian rocks near Tyndrum, Scotland. *Institute of Geological Sciences, Mineral Reconnaissance Programme*, Report **93**.

SMITH, D. B. 1970. The Palaeogeography of the British Zechstein. *In*: RAU, J. L. & DELLWIG, L. F. (eds) *Third Symposium on salt*. Northern Ohio Geological Society, 20–23.

SMITH, D. B. & TAYLOR, J. C. M. 1989. A north-west passage to the southern Zechstein Basin of the UK North Sea. *Proceedings of the Yorkshire Geological Society*, **47**, 313–320.

SMITH, D. B. & TAYLOR, J. C. M. 1992. Permian. *In*: COPE, J. C. W., INGHAM, J. K. & RAWSON, P. F. (eds) *Atlas of Palaeogeography and Lithofacies*. Geological Society of London, Memoir, **13**, 87–96.

SMITH, D. B., BRUNSTROM, R. G. W., MANNING, P. I., SIMPSON, S. & WEST, R. G. 1975. *A Correlation of Permian Rocks in the British Isles*. Geological Society, London, Special Report, **5**, 1–45.

SMITH, D. E., CULLINGFORD, R. A. & BROOKS, C. I. 1983. Flandrian relative sea level changes in the Ythan Valley, north-east Scotland. *Earth Surface Processes and Landforms*, **8**, 423–438.

SMITH, D. E., DAWSON, A. G., CULLINGFORD, R. A. & HARKNESS, D. D. 1985. The stratigraphy of Flandrian relative sea level changes at a site in Tayside, Scotland. *Earth Surface Processes and Landforms*, **10**, 17–25.

SMITH, D. G. W. 1969. Pyrometamorphism of phyllites by a dolerite plug. *Journal of Petrology*, **10**, 20–55.

SMITH, D. I. 1979. Caledonian minor intrusions of the N Highlands of Scotland. *In*: HARRIS, A. L., HOLLAND, C. H. & LEAKE, B. E. (eds) *The Caledonides of the British Isles – Reviewed*. Geological Society, London, Special Publications, **8**, 129–137.

SMITH, D. I. & HARRIS, A. L. 1972. Microcline porphyroblasts in the Moinian rocks of the Western Highlands. *Scottish Journal of Geology*, **8**, 193–202.

SMITH, D. I. & WATSON, J. V. 1983. Scale and timing of movements on the Great Glen Fault, Scotland. *Geology*, **11**, 523–526.

SMITH, J. 1909. *Upland Fauna of the Old Red Sandstone Formation of Carrick, Ayrshire*. A. W. Cross, Kilwinning.

SMITH, L. B. & READ, J. F. 2000. Rapid onset of late Paleozoic glaciation on Gondwana: evidence from Upper Mississippian strata of the Midcontinent, United States. *Geology*, **28**, 279–282.

SMITH, M., ROBERTSON, S. & ROLLIN, K. E. 1999. Rift basin architecture and stratigraphical implications for basement-cover relationships in the Neoproterozoic Grampian Group of the Scottish Caledonides. *Journal of the Geological Society, London*, **156**, 1163–1173.

SMITH, N. D. 1970. The braided stream depositional environment: comparison of the Platte River with some Silurian clastic rocks, north-central Appalachians. *AAPG Bulletin*, **81**, 2993–3014.

SMITH, N. J. 1985. The age and structural setting of limestones and basalts on the Main Ring Fault of southeast Rhum. *Geological Magazine*, **122**, 439–445.

SMITH, R. A. 1995. The Siluro-Devonian evolution of the Southern Midland Valley of Scotland. *Geological Magazine*, **132**, 503–513.

SMITH, R. A. 1996. *Geology of the Gas Water Area*. British Geological Survey Technical Report, WA/96/22.

SMITH, R. A. & HARRIS, A. L. 1976. The Ballachulish rocks of the Blair Atholl District. *Scottish Journal of Geology*, **12**, 153–157.

SMITH, R. A., STEPHENSON, D. & MONRO, S. K. 1994. The geological setting of the southern Bathgate Hills, West Lothian, Scotland. *Transactions of the Royal Society of Edinburgh: Earth Sciences*, **84**, 189–196.

SMITH, R. L., STEARNS, J. E. F. & PIPER, J. D. A. 1983. Palaeomagnetic studies of the Torridonian sediments, NW Scotland. *Scottish Journal of Geology*, **19**, 29–45.

SMITH, T. E. 1967. A preliminary study of sandstone sedimentation in the Carboniferous of Berwickshire. *Scottish Journal of Geology*, **3**, 282–305.

SMITHSON, T. R., CARROLL, R. L., PANCHEN, A. L. & ANDREWS, S. M. 1994. *Westlothiana lizziae* from the Visean of East Kirkton, West Lothian, Scotland and the amniote stem. *Transactions of the Royal Society of Edinburgh: Earth Sciences*, **84**, 383–412.

SMYTHE, D. K. 1994. Geophysical evidence for ultrawide dykes of the late Carboniferous quartz-dolerite swarm of northern Britain. *Geophysical Journal International*, **119**, 20–30.

SMYTHE, D. K., DOBINSON, A., McQUILLIN, R., BREWER, J. A., MATTHEWS, D. H., BLUNDELL, D. J. & KELK, B. 1982. Deep structure of the Scottish Caledonides revealed by the MOIST reflection profile. *Nature, London*, **299**, 338–340.

SMYTHE, D. K., CHALMERS, J., SKUCE, A. G., DOBINSON, A. & MOULD, A. S. 1983. Early opening of the North Atlantic-I. Structure and origin of the Faeroe-Shetland Escarpment. *Geophysical Journal of the Royal Astronomical Society*, **72**, 373–398.

SMYTHE, D. K., RUSSELL, M. J. & SKUCE, A. G. 1995. Intra-continental rifting inferred from the major late Carboniferous quartz-dolerite dyke swarms of NW Europe. *Scottish Journal of Geology*, **31**, 151–162.

SNYDER, D. B. & FLACK, C. A. 1990. A Caledonian age for reflectors within the mantle lithosphere north and west of Scotland. *Tectonics*, **9**, 903–922.

SOPER, N. J. 1963. The structure of the Rogart igneous complex, Sutherland, Scotland. *Quarterly Journal of the Geological Society of London*, **119**, 445–478.

SOPER, N. J. 1986. The Newer Granite problem: a geotectonic view. *Geological Magazine*, **123**, 227–236.

SOPER, N. J. 1994a. Was Scotland a Vendian RRR junction? *Journal of the Geological Society, London*, **151**, 579–582.

SOPER, N. J. 1994b. Neoproterozoic sedimentation on the northeast margin of Laurentia and the opening of Iapetus. *Geological Magazine*, **131**, 291–299.

SOPER, N. J. & BROWN, P. E. 1971. Relationship between metamorphism and migmatisation in the northern part of the Moine Nappe. *Scottish Journal of Geology*, **7**, 305–325.

SOPER, N. J. & ENGLAND, R. W. 1995. Vendian and Riphean rifting in NW Scotland. *Journal of the Geological Society, London*, **152**, 11–14.

SOPER, N. J. & HARRIS, A. L. 1997. Report: Highland field workshops 1995–1996. *Scottish Journal of Geology*, **33**, 187–190.

SOPER, N. J. & HUTTON, D. H. W. 1984. Late Caledonian sinistral displacements in Britain: Implications for a three-plate model. *Tectonics*, **3**, 781–794.

SOPER, N. J. & WILKINSON, P. 1975. The Moine Thrust and Moine Nappe at Loch Eriboll, Scotland. *Scottish Journal of Geology*, **11**, 239–259.

SOPER, N. J., WEBB, B. C. & WOODCOCK, N. C. 1987. Late Caledonian (Arcadian) transpression in north-west England: timing, geometry and geotectonic significance. *Proceedings of the Yorkshire Geological Society*, **46**, 175–192.

SOPER, N. J., ENGLAND, R. W., SNYDER, D. B. & RYAN, P. D. 1992a. The Iapetus suture zone in England, Scotland, and eastern Ireland; a reconciliation of geological and deep seismic data. *Journal of the Geological Society, London*, **149**, 697–700.

SOPER, N. J., STRACHAN, R. A., HOLDSWORTH, R. E., GAYER, R. A. & GREILING, R. O. 1992b. Sinistral transpression and the Silurian closure of Iapetus. *Journal of the Geological Society, London*, **149**, 871–880.

SOPER, N. J., HARRIS, A. L. & STRACHAN, R. A. 1998. Tectonostratigraphy of the Moine Supergroup: a synthesis. *Journal of the Geological Society, London*, **155**, 13–24.

SOPER, N. J., RYAN, P. D. & DEWEY, J. F. 1999. Age of the Grampian orogeny in Scotland and Ireland. *Journal of the Geological Society, London*, **156**, 1231–1236.

SORJONEN-WARD, P., CLAOUE-LONG, J. C. & HUHMA, H. 1994. SHRIMP isotope studies of granulite zircons and their relevance to early Proterozoic tectonics in northern Fennoscandia. *Abstracts, 8th International Conference on Geochronology, Cosmochronology and Isotope Geology, US Geological Survey Circular*, **1107**, 299.

SPAAK, P., ALMOND, J., SALAHUDIN, S., MOHD SALLEH, Z. & TOSUN, O. 1999. Fulmar, a mature field revisited. *In*: FLEET, A. J. & BOLDY, S. A. R. (eds) *Petroleum Geology of Northwest Europe: Proceedings of the 5th Conference*, Geological Society, London, 1089–1100.

SPARKS, R. S. J. 1988. Petrology of the Loch Ba ring dyke, Mull (NW Scotland): an example of the extreme differentiation of tholeiitic magmas. *Contributions to Mineralogy and Petrology*, **100**, 446–461.

SPEIGHT, J. M., SKELHORN, R. R., SLOAN, T. & KNAAP, R. J. 1982. The dyke swarms of Scotland. *In*: SUTHERLAND, D. S. (ed.) *Igneous Rocks of the British Isles*. Wylie, Chicester.

SPENCER, A M. 1971. *Late Precambrian Glaciation in Scotland*. Geological Society, London, Memoirs, **6**.

SPENCER, A. M. & SPENCER, M. O. 1972. The late Precambrian/Lower Cambrian Bonahaven Dolomite of Islay and its stromatolites. *Scottish Journal of Geology*, **8**, 269–282.

SPENCER, A. M., LECKIE, G. G. & CHEW, K. J. 1996. North Sea hydrocarbon plays and their resources. *In*: GLENNIE, K. & HURST, A. (eds) *AD1995: NW Europe's Hydrocarbon Industry*. Geological Society, London, 25–41.

SPRAY, J. G. 1988. Thrust-related metamorphism beneath the Shetland Islands oceanic fragment, northeast Scotland. *Canadian Journal of Earth Sciences*, **25**, 1760–1776.

SPRAY, J. G. & DUNNING, G. R. 1991. A U/Pb age for the Shetland Islands oceanic fragment, Scottish Caledonides: evidence from anatectic plagiogranites in 'layer 3' shear zones. *Geological Magazine*, **128**, 667–671.

SPRAY, J. G. & WILLIAMS, G. D. 1980. The sub-ophiolite metamorphic rocks of the Ballantrae Igneous Complex, SW Scotland. *Journal of the Geological Society, London*, **137**, 359–368.

SRIVASTAVA, S. K. 1975. Maastrichtian microspore assemblages from the interbasaltic lignites of Mull, Scotland. *Palaeontographica*, **18**, 125–156.

STANLEY, C. J., SYMES, R. F. & JONES, G. C. 1987. Nickel–copper mineralisation at Talnotry, Newton Stewart, Scotland. *Mineralogy and Petrology*, **37**, 293–313.

STAUFFER, P. H. 1985. Continental terranes in southeast Asia: pieces of which puzzle? *In*: HOWELL, D. G. (ed.) *Tectonostratigraphic Terranes of the Circum-Pacific Region*. Circum-Pacific Council for Energy and Mineral Resources Earth Science Series, No. 1, 529–539.

STEAVENSON, A. 1928. Some Geological Notes on Three Districts in Northern Scotland. *Transactions of the Geological Society of Glasgow*, **18**, 193–233.

STEDMAN, C. 1988. Namurian E1 tectonics and sedimentation in the Midland valley of Scotland: rifting versus strike-slip influence. *In*: BESLEY, B. M & KELLING, G. (eds) *Sedimentation in a Synorogenic Basin Complex: the Upper Carboniferous of Northwest Europe*. Blackie, Glasgow, 245–252.

STEEL, R. J. 1971. New Red Sandstone movement on the Minch Fault. *Nature, London*, **234**, 158–159.

STEEL, R. J. 1974. New Red Sandstone floodplain and piedmont sedimentation in the Hebridean province, Scotland. *Journal of Sedimentary Petrology*, **44**, 336–357.

STEEL, R. J. & RYSETH, A. 1990. The Triassic-Jurassic succession in the northern North Sea: megasequence stratigraphy and intra-Triassic tectonics. *In*: HARDMAN, R. F. P. & BROOKS, J. (eds) *Tectonic Events Responsible for Britain's Oil and Gas Reserves*. Geological Society, London, Special Publications, **55**, 139–168.

STEEL, R. J. & WILSON, A. C. 1975. Sedimentation and tectonism (?Permo-Triassic) on the margin of the North Minch Basin, Lewis. *Journal of the Geological Society, London*, **131**, 183–202.

STEEL, R. J., NICHOLSON, R. & KALANDER, L. 1975. Triassic sedimentation and palaeogeography in Central Skye. *Scottish Journal of Geology*, **11**, 1–13.

STEIN, A. M. 1992. Basin development and petroleum potential in The Minches and Sea of the Hebrides basins. *In*: PARNELL, J. (ed.) *Basins on the Atlantic Seaboard: Petroleum Geology, Sedimentology and Basin Evolution*. Geological Society, London, Special Publications, **62**, 17–20.

STEMMERIK, L., INESON, J. R. & MITCHELL, J. G. 2000. Stratigraphy of the Rotliegend Group in the Danish part of the Northern Basin, North Sea. *Journal of the Geological Society, London*, **157**, 1127–1136.

STEPHEN, K. J., UNDERHILL, J. R., PARTINGTON, M. A. & HEDLEY, R. J. 1993. The genetic sequence stratigraphy of the Hettangian to Oxfordian succession, Inner Moray Firth. *In*: PARKER, J. R. (ed.) *Petroleum Geology of Northwest Europe: Proceedings of the 4th Conference*, Geological Society, London, 485–505.

STEPHENS, W. E. 1988. Granitoid plutonism in the Caledonian orogen of Europe. *In*: HARRIS, A. L. & FETTES, D. J. (eds) *The Caledonian–Appalachian Orogen*. Geological Society, London, Special Publications, **38**, 389–403.

STEPHENS, W. E. & HALLIDAY, A. N. 1979. Compositional variation in the Galloway plutons. *In*: ATHERTON, M. P. & TARNEY, J. (eds), *Origins of Granite Batholiths*. Shiva, Orpington.

STEPHENS, W. E. & HALLIDAY, A. N. 1984. Geochemical contrasts between late Caledonian granitoid plutons of northern, central and southern Scotland. *Transactions of the Royal Society of Edinburgh: Earth Sciences*, **75**, 259–273.

STEPHENSON, D. 1983. Polymetallic mineralisation in Carboniferous rocks at Hilderston, near Bathgate, central Scotland. *Mineral Reconnaissance Programme Report, Institute of Geological Sciences*, No. 68.

STEPHENSON, D. (In Press) Alkaline basic sills and dykes of Scotland: Introduction. *In*: STEPHENSON, D., LOUGHLIN, S. C., MILLWARD, D., WATERS, C. N. & WILLIAMSON, I. T. *Carboniferous and Permian Igneous Rocks of Great Britain*. Geological Conservation Review Series, **27**. (Peterborough: Joint Nature Conservation Committee).

STEPHENSON, D. & COATS, J. S. 1983. Baryte and copper rnineralisation in the Renfrewshire Hills, central Scotland. *Institute of Geological Sciences, Mineral Reconnaissance Programme*, Report **67**.

STEPHENSON, D. & GOULD, D. 1995. *The Grampian Highlands*. British Regional Geology, British Geological Survey, HMSO London.

STEPHENSON, D., FORTEY, N. J. & GALLAGHER, M. J. 1983. Polymetallic mineralisation in Carboniferous rocks at Hilderston, near Bathgate, central Scotland. *Institute of Geological Sciences, Mineral Reconnaissance Programme*, Report **68**.

STEPHENSON, D., BEVINS, R. E., MILLWARD, D., HIGHTON, A. J., PARSONS, I., STONE, P. & WADSWORTH, W. J. 1999. *Caledonian Igneous Rocks of Great Britain*. Geological Conservation Review Series, **17**. Joint Nature Conservation Committee, 1–648.

STEPHENSON, D., LOUGHLIN, S. C., MILLWARD, D., WATERS, C. N. & WILLIAMSON, I. T. (In Press). *Carboniferous and Permian Igneous Rocks of Great Britain*. Geological Conservation Review Series, **27**. (Peterborough: Joint Nature Conservation Committee).

STEPHENSON, M. A. 1991. The North Brae Field, Block 16/7a, UK North Sea. *In*: ABBOTTS, I. L. (ed.) *United Kingdom Oil and Gas Fields 25 Years Commemorative Volume*. Geological Society, London, Memoir, **14**, 43–48.

STEVENS, V. 1991. The Beatrice Field, Block 11/30a, UK North Sea. *In*: ABBOTTS, I. L. (ed.) *United Kingdom Oil and Gas Fields 25 Years Commemorative Volume*. Geological Society, London, Memoir, **14**, 245–252.

STEVENSON, R. K. & PATCHETT, P. J. 1990. Implications for the evolution of continental crust from Hf isotope systematics of Archaean detrital zircons. *Geochimica Cosmochimica Acta*, **54**, 1683–1697.

STEWART, A. D. 1962. On the Torridonian sediments of Colonsay and their relationship to the main outcrop in north-west Scotland. *Liverpool and Manchester Geological Journal*, **3**, 121–156.

STEWART, A. D. 1969. Torridonian rocks of Scotland reviewed. *In*: KAY, M. (ed.) *North Atlantic Geology and Continental Drift: a Symposium*. American Association of Petroleum Geologists Memoirs, **12**, 595–608.

STEWART, A. D. 1972. Pre-Cambrian landscapes in northwest Scotland. *Geological Journal*, **8**, 111–124.

STEWART, A. D. 1982. Late Proterozoic rifting in NW Scotland: the genesis of the 'Torridonian'. *Journal of the Geological Society, London*, **139**, 413–420.

STEWART, A. D. 1990. The Torridonian Stac Fada Member: a discussion. *Transactions of the Royal Society of Edinburgh: Earth Sciences*, **81**, 247.

STEWART, A. D. 1991a. Geochemistry, provenance and climate of the Upper Proterozoic Stoer Group in Scotland. *Scottish Journal of Geology*, **26**, 89–97.

STEWART, A. D. 1991b. Geochemistry, provenance and palaeoclimate of the Sleat and Torridon Groups in Skye. *Scottish Journal of Geology*, **27**, 81–95.

STEWART, A. D. 1993. Late Proterozoic and late Palaeozoic movement on the Coigach fault in NW Scotland. *Scottish Journal of Geology*, **29**, 21–28.

STEWART, A. D. 1995a. Well preserved late Precambrian paleosols from northwest Scotland – discussion. *Journal of Sedimentary Research*, **A65**, 444.

STEWART, A. D. 1995b. Possible sources of clastic sediment in the late Proterozoic Torridon Group, from geochemical mass balance. *Transactions of the Royal Society of Edinburgh: Earth Sciences*, **85**, 303–309.

STEWART, A. D. 1997. Discussion of the evidence for glaciation in the Proterozoic Stoer Group of Scotland. *Journal of the Geological Society, London*, **154**, 375–376.

STEWART, A. D. & HACKMAN, B. D. 1973. Precambrian sediments of western Islay. *Scottish Journal of Geology*, **9**, 43–51.

STEWART, A. D. & DONNELLAN, N. C. B. 1992. Geochemistry and provenance of red sandstones in the Upper Proterozoic Torridon Group of Scotland. *Scottish Journal of Geology*, **28**, 143–153.

STEWART, A. D. & IRVING, E. 1974. Palaeomagnetism of Precambrian sedimentary rocks from NW Scotland and the apparent polar wandering path of Laurentia. *Geophysical Journal of the Royal Astronomical Society*, **37**, 51–72.

STEWART, A. D. & PARKER, A. 1979. Palaeosalinity and environmental interpretation of red beds from the late Precambrian ('Torridonian') of Scotland. *Sedimentary Geology*, **22**, 229–241.

STEWART, F. W. 1965. Tertiary Igneous Activity. *In*: CRAIG, G. Y. (ed.) *The Geology of Scotland* (1st edition). Oliver & Boyd, Edinburgh, 417–465.

STEWART, M. 1997. *Kinematic Evolution of the Great Glen Fault Zone, Scotland*. PhD thesis, Oxford Brookes University.

STEWART, M., STRACHAN, R. A. & HOLDSWORTH, R. E. 1997. Direct field evidence for sinistral displacements along the Great Glen Fault Zone: late Caledonian reactivation of a regional basement structure? *Journal of the Geological Society, London*, **154**, 135–139.

STEWART, M., STRACHAN, R. A. & HOLDSWORTH, R. E. 1999. Structure and early kinematic history of the Great Glen Fault Zone, Scotland. *Tectonics*, **18**, 326–342.

STEWART, M., HOLDSWORTH, R. E. & STRACHAN, R. A. 2000. Deformation processes and weakening mechanisms within the frictional-viscous transition zone of major crustal-scale faults: insights from the Great Glen Fault Zone, Scotland. *Journal of Structural Geology*, **22**, 543–560.

STEWART, M., STRACHAN, R. A., MARTIN, M. W. & HOLDSWORTH, R. E. 2001. Dating early sinistral displacements along the Great Glen Fault Zone, Scotland: structural setting, emplacement and U–Pb geochronology of the syn-tectonic Clunes Tonalite. *Journal of the Geological Society, London*, **158**, 821–830.

STOKER, M. S. 1982. Old Red Sandstone sedimentation and deformation in the Great Glen Fault Zone NW of Loch Linnhe. *Scottish Journal of Geology*, **19**, 369–386.

STOKER, M. S. 1983. The stratigraphy and structure of the Moine rocks of eastern Ardgour. *Scottish Journal of Geology*, **19**, 369–385.

STOKER, M. S., LONG, D. & FYFE, D. A. 1985. A revised Quaternary stratigraphy for the central North Sea. *Report of the British Geological Survey*, No. **17** (2).

STOKER, M. S. & BENT, A. J. A. 1987. Lower Pleistocene deltaic and marine sediments in boreholes from the central North Sea. *Journal of Quaternary Science*, **2**, 87–96.

STOKER, M. S., HITCHEN, K. & GRAHAM, C. C. 1993. *The Geology of the Hebrides and West Shetland Shelves, and Adjacent Deep-Water Basins*. British Geological Survey Offshore Regional Report. HMSO, London.

STOKER, M. S., HOWE, J. A. & STOKER, S. J. 1999. Late Vendian-?Cambrian glacially influenced deep-water sedimentation, Macduff Slate Formation (Dalradian), NE Scotland. *Journal of the Geological Society, London*, **156**, 55–61.

STONE, P. 1982. Clastic rocks within the Ballantrae complex. Borehole evidence. *Report of the Institute of Geological Sciences*, No. **82/1**, 45–47.

STONE, P. 1984. Constraints on genetic models for the Ballantrae complex, SW Scotland. *Transactions of the Royal Society of Edinburgh: Earth Sciences*, **75**, 189–191.

STONE, P. 1995. *Geology of the Rhinns of Galloway*. Memoir of the British Geological Survey, HMSO.

STONE, P. & EVANS, J. 1995. Nd-isotope study of provenance patterns across the British sector of the Iapetus Suture. *Geological Magazine*, **132**. 571–580.

STONE, P. & EVANS, J. 2001. Silurian provenance variation in the Southern Uplands terrane, Scotland, assessed using neodynium isotopes and linked with regional tectonic evolution. *Transactions of the Royal Society of Edinburgh: Earth Sciences*, **91**, 447–455.

STONE, P. & RUSHTON, A. W. A. 1983. Graptolite faunas from the Ballantrae ophiolite complex and their structural implications. *Scottish Journal of Geology*, **19**, 297–310.

STONE, P. & SMELLIE, J. L. 1988. *Classical Areas of British Geology: The Ballantrae area* (Sheets NX 08, 18 & 19). British Geological Survey. HMSO, London.

STONE, P. & SMELLIE, J. L. 1990. The Ballantrae ophiolite, Scotland: an Ordovician island arc-marginal basin assemblage. *In*: MALPAS, J., MOORES, E. M., PANATIOTOU, A. & XENOPHONTES, C. (eds) *Ophiolites: Ocean Crustal Analogues*. Proceedings of the Symposium 'Troodos 1987'. Geological Survey Department, Nicosia, Cyprus, 535–546.

STONE, P. & STRACHAN, I. 1981. A fossiliferous borehole section within the Ballantrae ophiolite. *Nature, London*, **293**, 455–456.

STONE, P., FLOYD, J. D., BARNES, R. P. & LINTERN, B. C. 1987. A sequential back-arc and foreland basin thrust duplex model for the Southern Uplands. *Journal of the Geological Society, London*, **144**, 753–764.

STONE, P., GREEN, P. M., LINTERN, B. C., PLANT, J. A., SIMPSON, P. R. & BREWARD, N. 1991. Geochemistry characterizes provenance in southern Scotland. *Geology Today*, **7**, 177–181.

STONE, P., GREEN, P. M., LINTERN, B. C., SIMPSON, P. R. & PLANT, J. A. 1993. Regional geochemical variation across the Iapetus Suture zone: tectonic implications. *Scottish Journal of Geology*, **29**, 113–121.

STONE, P., COOK, J. M., McDERMOTT, C., ROBINSON, J. J. & SIMPSON, P. R. 1995. Lithostratigraphic and structural controls on distribution of As and Au in Southwest Southern Uplands, Scotland. *Transactions of the Institution of Mining and Metallurgy*, Section B, **104**, 111–119.

STONE, P., GREEN, P. M. & WILLIAMS, T. M. 1997a. Relationship of source and drainage geochemistry in the British partectonic Caledonides – an exploratory regional assessment. *Transactions of the Institution of Mining and Metallurgy*, Section B, **106**, B79–84.

STONE, P., KIMBELL, G. S. & HENNEY, P. J. 1997b. Basement control on the location of strike-slip shear in the Southern Uplands of Scotland. *Journal of the Geological Society, London*, **154**, 141–144.

STONE, P., EVANS, J. A., HUTCHISON, A. R. & OLIVER, G. J. H. 1999a. Garnet provenance studies, juxtaposition of Laurentian marginal terranes and timing of the Grampian Orogeny in Scotland; discussion and reply. *Journal of the Geological Society, London*, **156**, 205–207.

STONE, P., PLANT, J. A., MENDUM, J. R. & GREEN, P. M. 1999b. A regional geochemical assessment of some terrane relationships in the British Caledonides. *Scottish Journal of Geology*, **35**, 145–156.

STOPES, M. C. 1907. The flora of the Inferior Oolite of Brora. *Quarterly Journal of the Geological Society, London*, **63**, 375–382.

STORETVEDT, K. M. & STEEL, R. J. 1977. Palaeomagnetic evidence for the age of the Stornoway Formation. *Scottish Journal of Geology*, **13**, 263–269.

STOREY, C., BREWER, T., PARRISH, R. & TEMPERLEY, S. 2002. The nature of the sub-Moinian basement, its relationship with the Moine Supergroup and its bearing on Late Proterozoic tectonics in the NW Highlands: a case study from the Glenelg–Attadale Inlier. *Tectonic Studies Group Highland Workshop Abstracts*, University of St Andrews, Scotland, 17.

STOUGE, S. & BOYCE, W. D. 1983. Fossils of northwestern Newfoundland and southeastern Labrador: conodonts and trilobites. *Newfoundland Department of Mines and Energy, Mineral Development Division, Report*, **83–3**.

STRACHAN, R. A. 1985. The stratigraphy and structure of the Moine rocks of the Loch Eil area, West Inverness-shire. *Scottish Journal of Geology*, **21**, 9–22.

STRACHAN, R. A. 1986. Shallow marine sedimentation in the Proterozoic Moine succession, northern Scotland. *Precambrian Research*, **32**, 17–33.

STRACHAN, R. A. 1988. The metamorphic rocks of the Scaraben° area, East Sutherland and Caithness. *Scottish Journal of Geology*, **24**, 1–13.

STRACHAN, R. A. 2000. The Grampian Orogeny: Mid-Ordovician arc-continent collision along the Laurentian margin of Iapetus. *In*: WOODCOCK, N. H. & STRACHAN, R. A. (eds) *Geological History of Britain and Ireland*. Blackwell Science Ltd, Oxford, 88–106.

STRACHAN, R. A. & HOLDSWORTH, R. E. 1988. Basement-cover relationships and structure within the Moine rocks of central and southeast Sutherland. *Journal of the Geological Society, London*, **145**, 23–36.

STRACHAN, R. A. & HOLDSWORTH, R. E. 2000. Late Neoproterozoic (<750 Ma) to Early Ordovician passive margin sedimentation along the Laurentian margin of Iapetus. *In*: WOODCOCK, N. H. & STRACHAN, R. A. (eds) *Geological History of Britain and Ireland*. Blackwell Science Ltd, Oxford, 73–87.

STRACHAN, R. A., MAY, F. & BARR, D. 1988. The Glenfinnan and Loch Eil Divisions of the Moine Assemblage. *In*: WINCHESTER, J. A. (ed.) *Later Proterozoic Stratigraphy of the Northern Atlantic Regions*. Blackie, Glasgow, 32–45.

STRINGER, P. & TREAGUS, J. E. 1980. Non-planar S1 cleavage in the Hawick Rocks of the Galloway area, Southern Uplands, Scotland. *Journal of Structural Geology*, **2**, 317–331.

STUART, F. M., ELLAM, R. M., HARROP, P. J., FITTON, J. G. & BELL, B. R. 2000. Constraints on mantle plumes from helium isotopic composition of basalts from the British Tertiary Igneous Province. *Earth and Planetary Science Letters*, **177**, 273–285.

STUART, F. M., BLUCK, B. J. & PRINGLE, M. S. 2001. Detrital muscovite ^{40}Ar/^{39}Ar ages from Carboniferous sandstones of the British Isles: Provenance and implications for the uplift history of orogenic belts. *Tectonics*, **20**, 255–267.

STUBBLEFIELD, C. J. 1956. Cambrian palaeogeography in Britain. *In*: Rodgers, J. (ed.) *El Sistema Cambrico, su paleogeografia y el problema de su base*. Report of the International Geological Congress, **20**, Mexico, 1–43.

STURT, B. A. 1961. The geological structure of the area south of Loch Tummel. *Quarterly Journal of the Geological Society of London*, **117**, 131–156.

STURT, B. A. & HARRIS, A. L. 1961. The metamorphic history of the Loch Tummel area, Central Perthshire. *Liverpool and Manchester Geological Journal*, **2**, 689–711.

STYLES, M. T., PEREZALVAREZ, M. & FLOYD, J. D. 1995. Pyroxenous greywackes in Southern Uplands of Scotland and their petrotectonic implications. *Geological Magazine*, **132**, 539–547.

STYLES, M. T., STONE, P. & FLOYD, J. D. 1989. Arc detritus in the Southern Uplands; mineralogical characterization of a 'missing' terrane. *Journal of the Geological Society, London*, **146**, 397–400.

SUTHERLAND, D. G. 1981. The high-level marine shell beds of Scotland and the build-up of the last Scottish ice-sheet. *Boreas*, **10**, 247–254.

SUTHERLAND, D. G. 1984. The Quaternary deposits and landforms of Scotland and the neighbouring shelves: a review. *Quaternary Science Reviews*, **3**, 79–92.

SUTHERLAND, D. G. 1986. The Quaternary deposits and landforms of Scotland and the neighbouring shelves – a review reply. *Quaternary Science Reviews*, **4(2)**, R5–R9.

SUTTON, J. 1963. Some events in the evolution of the Caledonides. *In*: JOHNSON, M. R. W. & STEWART, F. H. (eds) *The British Caledonides*, Oliver & Boyd, Edinburgh, 249–269.

SUTTON, J. & WATSON, J. 1951. The pre-Torridonian metamorphic history of the Loch Torridon and Scourie areas in the North-west Highlands and its bearing on the chronological classification of the Lewisian. *Quarterly Journal of the Geological Society, London*, **106**, 241–307.

SUTTON, J. & WATSON, J. V. 1953. The supposed Lewisian inlier of Scardroy, central Ross-shire and its relations with the surrounding Moine rocks. *Quarterly Journal of the Geological Society of London*, **108**, 99–126.

SUTTON, J. & WATSON, J. V. 1954. The structural and stratigraphic succession of Fannich Forest and Strath Bran, Ross-shire. *Quarterly Journal of the Geological Society of London*, **110**, 21–54.

SUTTON, J. & WATSON, J. V. 1956a. The deposition of the Upper Dalradian rocks of the Banffshire coast. *Proceedings of the Geologists' Association*, **66**, 101–133.

SUTTON, J. & WATSON, J. V. 1956b. The Boyndie syncline of the Dalradian of the Banffshire coast. *Quarterly Journal of the Geological Society of London*, **112**, 103–130.

SUTTON, J. & WATSON, J. 1960. Sedimentary structures in the Epidotic Grits of Skye. *Geological Magazine*, **97**, 106–122.

SUTTON, J. & WATSON, J. 1964. Some aspects of Torridonian stratigraphy in Skye. *Proceedings of the Geologists' Association*, **75**, 251–289.

SUTTON, J. & WATSON, J. 1987. The Lewisian complex: questions for the future. *In*: PARK, R. G. & TARNEY, J. (eds) *Evolution of the Lewisian and Comparable Precambrian High Grade Terrains*. Geological Society, London, Special Publications, **27**, 7–11.

SWAINBANK, I. G. & FORTEY, N. J. 1981. Lead isotope ratios of galena from stratabound mineralization in the Scottish Dalradian. *In*: HALL, A. J. & GALLAGHER, M. J. (eds) *Caledonian–Appalachian Stratabound Sulphides, Scotland 1981*. Department of Applied Geology, University of Strathclyde, 20–23.

SWEET, I. P. 1985. Sedimentology of the Lower Old Red Sandstone near New Aberdour, Grampian Region. *Scottish Journal of Geology*, **21**, 239–259.

SWEET, J. M. & WATERSTON, C. D. 1967. Robert Jameson's approach to the Wernerian theory of the earth. *Annals of Science*, **23**, 81–95.

SWETT, K. 1965. *Petrology of the Cambro-Ordovician succession of the north west highlands of Scotland*. D. Phil thesis, University of Edinburgh.

SWETT, K. 1969. Interpretation of depositional and diagenetic history of Cambrian-Ordovician Succession of northwest Scotland. *In*: KAY, M. (ed.) *North Atlantic Geology and Continental Drift*. American Association of Petroleum Geologists, Memoirs, **12**, 630–646.

SWETT, K. 1981. Cambro-Ordovician strata in Ny Friesland, Spitzbergen and their palaeotectonic significance. *Geological Magazine*, **118**, 325–336.

SWETT, K. & SMIT, D. E. 1972. Cambro-Ordovician shelf sedimentation of western Newfoundland, north west Scotland and central east Greenland. *Proceedings of the 24th International Geological Congress*, 33–41.

SWIECICKI, T., WILCOCKSON, P., CANHAM, A., WHELAN, G. & HOMANN, H. 1995. Dating, correlation and stratigraphy of the Triassic sediments in the West Shetlands area. *In*: BOLDY, S. A. R. (ed.) *Permian and Triassic Rifting in Northwest Europe*. Geological Society, London, Special Publications, **91**, 57–85.

SYBA, E. 1989. *The Sedimentation and Provenance of the Greywacke Conglomerate, Southern Midland Valley, Scotland*. PhD thesis, University of Glasgow.

SYKES, R. M. 1975. The stratigraphy of the Callovian and Oxfordian stages (Middle-Upper Jurassic) in Northern Scotland. *Scottish Journal of Geology*, **11**, 51–78.

SYKES, R. M. & CALLOMON, J. H. 1979. The *Amoeboceras* zonation of the Boreal Upper Oxfordian. *Palaeontology*, **22**, 839–903.

TAIT, D. 1910. On a large, glacially transported mass of Lower Cretaceous rock at Leavad in the county of Caithness. *Transactions of the Edinburgh Geological Society*, **10**, 1–9.

TALBOT, C. J. 1983. Microdiorite sheet intrusions as incompetent time- and strain-markers in the Moine assemblage NW of the Great Glen Fault, Scotland. *Transactions of the Royal Society of Edinburgh: Earth Sciences*, **74**, 137–152.

TANNER, P. W. G. 1970. The Sgurr Beag Slide – a major tectonic break within the Moinian of the western Highlands of Scotland. *Quarterly Journal of the Geological Society of London*, **126**, 435–463.

TANNER, P. W. G. 1976. Progressive regional metamorphism of thin calcareous bands from the Moinian rocks of NW Scotland. *Journal of Petrology*, **17**, 100–134.

TANNER, P. W. G. 1995. New evidence that the Lower Cambrian Leny Limestone at Callander, Perthshire, belongs to the Dalradian Supergroup, and a reassessment of the 'exotic' status of the Highland Border Complex. *Geological Magazine*, **132**, 473–483.

TANNER, P. W. G. 1996. Significance of the early fabric in the contact metamorphic aureole of the 590 Ma Ben Vuirich Granite, Perthshire, Scotland. *Geological Magazine*, **133**, 683–695.

TANNER, P. W. G. & BLUCK, B. J. 1999. Current controversies in the Caledonides. *Journal of the Geological Society, London*, **156**, 1137–1141.

TANNER, P. W. G. & LESLIE, A. G. 1994. A pre-D2 age for the 590 Ma Ben Vuirich Granite in the Dalradian of Scotland. *Journal of the Geological Society, London*, **151**, 209–212.

TANNER, P. W. G. & PRINGLE, M. 1999. Testing for the presence of a terrane boundary within Neoproterozoic (Dalradian) to Cambrian siliceous turbidites at Callander, Perthshire, Scotland. *Journal of the Geological Society, London*, **156**, 1205–1216.

TANNER, P. W. G. & TOBISCH, O. T. 1972. Sodic and ultra-sodic rocks of metasomatic origin from part of the Moine Nappe. *Scottish Journal of Geology*, **8**, 151–178.

TANNER, P. W. G., JOHNSTONE, G. S., SMITH, D. I. & HARRIS, A. L. 1970. Moinian Stratigraphy and the problem of the Central Ross-shire Inliers. *Bulletin of the Geological Society of America*, **81**, 299–306.

TANTON, T. L. 1930. Determination of age-relations in folded rocks. *Geological Magazine*, **67**, 73–76.

TARLING, D. H. 1985. Palaeomagnetic studies of the Orcadian Basin. *Scottish Journal of Geology*, **21**, 261–273.

TARLO, L. B. H. 1961. Psammosteids from the Middle and Upper Devonian of Scotland. *Quarterly Journal of the Geological Society, London*, **117**, 193–211.

TARNEY, J. 1963. Assynt dykes and their metamorphism. *Nature, London*, **199**, 672–674.

TARNEY, J. & JONES, C. E. 1994. Trace element geochemistry of orogenic igneous rocks and crustal growth models. *Journal of the Geological Society, London*, **151**, 855–868.

TARNEY, J. & WEAVER, B. L. 1987a. Geochemistry of the Scourian complex: petrogenesis and tectonic models. *In*: PARK, R. G. & TARNEY, J. (eds) *Evolution of the Lewisian and Comparable Precambrian High-Grade Terrains*. Geological Society, London, Special Publications, **27**, 45–56.

TARNEY, J. & WEAVER, B. L. 1987b. Mineralogy, petrology and geochemistry of the Scourie dykes: petrogenesis and crystallisation processes in dykes intruded at depth. *In*: PARK, R. G. & TARNEY, J.

(eds) *Evolution of the Lewisian and Comparable Precambrian High-Grade Terrains*. Geological Society, London, Special Publications, **27**, 217–233.

TARNEY, J., SKINNER, A. C. & SHERATON, J. W. 1972. A geochemical comparison of major Archaean gneiss units from Northwest Scotland and East Greenland. *Proceedings of the 24th International Geological Congress, Section*, **I**, 162–174.

TATE, M. P. & DOBSON, M. R. 1989. Late Permian to early Mesozoic rifting and sedimentation offshore NW Ireland. *Marine and Petroleum Geology*, **6**, 49–59.

TAUBENECK, W. H. 1967. Notes on the Glen Coe cauldron subsidence, Argyllshire, Scotland. *Bulletin of the Geological Society of America*, **78**, 1295–1316.

TAYLOR, H. P. & FORESTER, R. W. 1971. Low-^{18}O igneous rocks from the intrusive complexes of Skye, Mull and Ardnamurchan, western Scotland. *Journal of Petrology*, **12**, 465–497.

TAYLOR, J. C. M 1998. Upper Permian-Zechstein. *In*: GLENNIE, K. W. (ed.) *Petroleum Geology of the North Sea* (4th Edition). Blackwell, Oxford, 174–211.

TAYLOR, P. N., JONES, N. W. & MOORBATH, S. 1984. Isotopic assessment of relative contributions from crust and mantle sources to the magma genesis of Precambrian granitoid rocks. *Philosophical Transactions of the Royal Society, London*, **A310**, 605–625.

TAYLOR, T. N., HASS, H. & REMY, W. 1992. Devonian fungi: interactions with the green alga *Palaeonitella*. *Mcyologia*, **84**, 901–910.

TAYLOR, T. N., HASS, H. & KERP, H. 1997. A cyanolichen from the Lower Devonian Rhynie chert. *American Journal of Botany*, **84**, 992–1004.

TEMPLE, A. K. 1956. The Leadhills–Wanlockhead lead and zinc deposits. *Transactions of the Royal Society of Edinburgh: Earth Sciences*, **63**, 85–113.

THIRLWALL, M. F. 1979. *The Petrochemistry of the British Old Red Sandstone Volcanic Province*. PhD thesis, University of Edinburgh.

THIRLWALL, M. F. 1981a. Peralkaline rhyolites from the Ordovician Tweeddale lavas, Peeblesshire, Scotland. *Geological Journal*, **16**, 41–44.

THIRLWALL, M. F. 1981b. Implications for Caledonian plate tectonic models of chemical data from volcanic rocks of the British Old Red Sandstone. *Journal of the Geological Society, London*, **138**, 123–138.

THIRLWALL, M. F. 1982. Systematic variation in chemistry and Nd–Sr isotopes across a Caledonian calc alkaline volcanic arc: implications for source materials. *Earth and Planetary Science Letters*, **58**, 27–50.

THIRLWALL, M. F. 1983a. Isotope geochemistry and origin of calc-alkaline lavas from a Caledonian continental margin volcanic arc. *Journal of Volcanology and Geothermal Research*, **18**, 589–631.

THIRLWALL, M. F. 1983b. Reply to discussion by O. van Breeman & B. J. Bluck on: Systematic variation in chemistry and Nd–Sr isotopes across a Caledonian calc-alkaline volcanic arc: implications for source materials. *Earth and Planetary Science Letters*, **65**, 208.

THIRLWALL, M. F. 1986. Lead isotope evidence for the nature of the mantle beneath Caledonian Scotland. *Earth and Planetary Science Letters*, **80**, 55–70.

THIRLWALL, M. F. 1988. Geochronology of Late Caledonian Magmatism in northern Britain. *Journal of the Geological Society, London*, **145**, 951–967.

THIRLWALL, M. F. 1989. Movement on proposed terrane boundaries in northern Britain; constraints from Ordovician–Devonian igneous rocks. *Journal of the Geological Society, London*, **146**, 373–376.

THIRLWALL, M. F. & BLUCK, B. J. 1984. Sm-Nd isotope and chemical evidence that the Ballantrae 'ophiolite', SW Scotland is polygenetic. *In*: GASS, I. G., LIPARD, S. J. & SHELTON, A. W. (eds) *Ophiolites and the Ocean Lithosphere*. Geological Society, London, Special Publications, **13**, 215–230.

THIRLWALL, M. F. & BURNARD, P. 1990. Pb–Sr–Nd isotope evidence and chemical study of the origin of undersaturated and oversaturated shoshonitic magmas from the Borralan pluton, Assynt, NW Scotland. *Journal of the Geological Society, London*, **147**, 259–269.

THIRLWALL, M. F. & JONES, A. P. 1983. Isotope geochemistry and contamination mechanics of Tertiary lavas from Skye, North-west Scotland. *In*: HAWKESWORTH, C. J. & NORRY, M. J. (eds) *Continental Basalts and Mantle Xenoliths*. Shiva, Orpington, 186–208.

THIRLWALL, M. F., SMITH, T. E., GRAHAM, A. M., THEODOROU, N., HOLLINGS, P., DAVIDSON, J. P. & ARCULUS, R. J. 1994. High field strength element anomalies in arc lavas: source or process? *Journal of Petrology*, **35**, 819–838.

THIRLWALL, M. F., GRAHAM, A. M., ARCULUS, R. J., HARMON, R. S. & MACPHERSON, C. G. 1996. Resolution of the effects of crustal assimilation, sediment subduction and fluid transport in island arc magmas: Pb–Sr–Nd–O isotope geochemistry of Grenada, Lesser Antilles. *Geochimica et Cosmochimica Acta*, **60**, 4785–4810.

THOMAS, A. N., WALMSLEY, P. J. & JENKINS, D. A. L. 1975. The Forties Field. *Norsk Geologiske Undersøgelse*, **316**, 105–120.

THOMAS, C. W. 1989. Application of geochemistry to the stratigraphic correlation of Appin and Argyll Group carbonate rocks from the Dalradian of northeast Scotland. *Journal of the Geological Society, London*, **146**, 631–647.

THOMAS, D. N, ROLPH, T. C & SHAW, W. 1995. Palaeointensity results from the P-C (Kiaman) reversed superchron: the Great Whin and Midland Valley sills of the northern United Kingdom. *Geophysical Journal International*, **123**, 798–816.

THOMAS, H. H., HALLIMOND, A. F. & RADLEY, E. G. 1920. Refractory minerals: ganister and silica rock. *Special Report Mineral Resources Great Britain*, **16**.

THOMAS, P. R. 1979. New evidence for a Central Highland root zone. *In*: HARRIS, A. L., HOLLAND, C. H. & LEAKE, B. E. (eds) *The Caledonides of the British Isles – Reviewed*. Geological Society, London, Special Publications, **8**, 205–211.

THOMAS, W. A., ASTINI, R. & BAYONA, G. 2002. Ordovician collision of the Argentine Precordillera with Gondwana, independant of Laurentian Taconic orogeny. *Tectonophysics*, **345**, 131–152.

THOMPSON, A., HINE, P. D., POOLE, J. S. & GREIG, J. R. 1998. *Environmental Geology in Land Use Planning: a Guide to Good Practice*. Department of Environment, Transport and the Regions Report, London, HMSO.

THOMPSON, R. N. 1969. Tertiary granites and associated rocks of the Marsco area, Isle of Skye. *Quarterly Journal of the Geological Society of London*, **124**, 349–385.

THOMPSON, R. N. 1974. Primary basalts and magma genesis. *Contributions to Mineralogy and Petrology*, **45**, 317–341.

THOMPSON, R. N. 1980. Askja 1875, Skye 56 Ma: basalt-triggered Plinian, mixed-magma eruptions during the emplacement of the Western Redhills Granites, Isle of Skye, Scotland. *Geologische Rundschau*, **69**, 249–262.

THOMPSON, R. N. 1981. Thermal aspects of the origin of Hebridean Tertiary acid magmas. I. An experimental study of partial fusion of Lewisian gneisses and Torridonian sediments. *Mineralogical Magazine*, **44**, 161–170.

THOMPSON, R. N. 1982. Magmatism of the British Tertiary Volcanic Province. *Scottish Journal of Geology*, **18**, 49–107.

THOMPSON, R. N. 1983. Thermal aspects of the origin of Hebridean Tertiary acid magmas. II. Experimental melting behaviour of the granites at 1 kbar PH2O. *Mineralogical Magazine*, **47**, 111–121.

THOMPSON, R. N. & FOWLER, M. B. 1986. Subduction-related shoshonitic and ultrapotassic magmatism: a study of Siluro–Ordovician syenites from the Scottish Caledonides. *Contributions to Mineralogy and Petrology*, **94**, 507–522.

THOMPSON, R. N. & GIBSON, S. A. 1991. Subcontinental mantle plumes, hotspots and pre-existing thinspots. *Journal of the Geological Society, London*, **148**, 973–977.

THOMPSON, R. N., ESSON, J. & DUNHAM, A. C. 1972. Major element chemical variation in the Eocene lavas of the Isle of Skye, Scotland. *Journal of Petrology*, **13**, 219–253.

THOMPSON, R. N., GIBSON, I. L., MARRINER, G. F., MATTEY, D. P. & MORRISON, M. A. 1980. Trace-element evidence of multistage mantle fusion and polybaric fractional crystallization in the Palaeocene lavas of Skye, NW Scotland. *Journal of Petrology*, **21**, 265–293.

THOMPSON, R. N., DICKIN, A. P., GIBSON, I. L. & MORRISON, M. A. 1982. Elemental fingerprints of isotopic contamination of Hebridean Palaeocene mantle-derived magmas by Archaean sial. *Contributions to Mineralogy and Petrology*, **79**, 159–168.

THOMPSON, R. N., MORRISON, M. A., DICKIN, A. P., GIBSON, I. L. & HARMON, R. S. 1986. Two contrasted styles of interaction between basic magmas and continental crust in the British Tertiary Volcanic Province. *Journal of Geophysical Research*, **91**, 5985–5997.

THOMSON, K. & UNDERHILL, J. R. 1993. Controls on the development and evolution of structural styles in the Inner Moray Firth Basin. *In*: PARKER, J. R. (ed.) *Petroleum Geology of North-West Europe, Proceedings of the 4th Conference*. Geological Society, London, 1167–1178.

THOMSON, K., UNDERHILL, J. R., GREEN, P. F., BRAY, R. J. & GIBSON, H. J. 1999. Evidence from fission track analysis for the post-Devonian burial and exhumation history of the northern Highlands, Scotland. *Marine and Petroleum Geology*, **16**, 27–30.

THOMSON, M. E. 1978. *IGS Studies of the Geology of the Firth of Forth and its Approaches*. Institute of Geological Sciences Report **77/17**.

THORPE, R. S. 1978. The parental basaltic magma of granites from the Isle of Skye, NW Scotland. *Mineralogical Magazine*, **42**, 157–158.

THORPE, R. S., POTTS, P. J. & SARRE, M. B. 1977. Rare earth evidence concerning the origin of granites of the Isle of Skye, northwest Scotland. *Earth and Planetary Science Letters*, **36**, 111–120.

THRASHER, J. 1992. Thermal effect of the Cuillin intrusive complex in the Jurassic of the Hebrides: an organic geochemical study. *In*: PARNELL, J. (ed.) *Basins on the North Atlantic Seaboard: Petroleum Geology, Sedimentology and Basin Evolution*. Geological Society of London, Special Publications, **62**, 35–49.

TILLEY, C. E. 1925. A preliminary survey of metamorphic zones in the southern Highlands of Scotland. *Quarterly Journal of the Geological Society of London*, **81**, 100–112.

TILLEY, C. E. 1950. Some aspects of magmatic evolution. *Quarterly Journal of the Geological Society of London*, **106**, 37–61.

TILLEY, C. E. 1951. The zoned contact skarns of the Broadford area of Skye; a study of boron-fluorine metasomatism in dolomites. *Mineralogial Magazine*, **29**, 621–666.

TIMBRELL, G. 1993. Sandstone architecture of the Balder Formation depositional system, UK Quadrant 9 and adjacent areas. *In*: PARKER, J. R. (ed.) *Petroleum Geology of Northwest Europe: Proceedings of the 4th Conference*. Geological Society, London, 107–121.

TINDLE, A. G. & WEBB, P. C. 1989. Niobian wolframite from Glen Gairn in the eastern Highlands of Scotland: a microprobe investigation. *Geochimica et Cosmochimica Acta*, **53**, 1921–1935.

TIPPER, J. C. 1976. The stratigraphy of the North Esk Inlier, Midlothian. *Scottish Journal of Geology*, **12**, 15–22.

TIPPING, R. M. 1985. Loch Lomond Stadial *Artemisia* pollen assemblages and Loch Lomond Readvance regional firn line altitudes. *Quaternary Newsletter*, **46**, 1–11.

TIPPING, R. M. 1986. A late-Devensian pollen site in Cowal, southwest Scotland. *Scottish Journal of Geology*, **22**, 27–40.

TIPPING, R. M. 1988. The recognition of glacial retreat from palynological data: a review of recent work in the British Isles. *Journal of Quaternary Science*, **3**, 171–182.

TIPPING, R. M. 1989. Devensian lateglacial vegetation history at Loch Barnluasgan, Argyllshire, Western Scotland. *Journal of Biogeography*, **16**, 435–447.

TISSOT, B. P. & WELTE, D. H. 1978. *Petroleum Formation and Occurrence*. Springer, Berlin.

TOBISCH, O. T. 1966. Large-scale basin-and-dome pattern arising from the interference of major folds. *Bulletin of the Geological Society of America*, **77**, 393–408.

TOBISCH, O. T., FLEUTY, M. J., MERH, S. S., MUKHOPADHYAY, D. & RAMSAY, J. G. 1970. Deformational and metamorphic history of Moinian and Lewisian rocks between Strathconon and Glen Affric. *Scottish Journal of Geology*, **6**, 243–265.

TODD, S. P., MURPHY, F. C. & KENNAN, P. S. 1991. On the trace of the Iapetus suture in Ireland and Britain. *Journal of the Geological Society, London*, **148**, 869–880.

TOMKEIEFF, S. I. 1937. Petrochemistry of the Scottish Carboniferous-Permian igneous rocks. *Bulletin of Volcanology*, **1**, 59–87.

TOMKEIEFF, S. I. 1962. Unconformity – an historical study. *Proceedings of the Geologists' Association*, **73**, 383–417.

TORRENS, H. S. 1996. 'Mineral engineer' John Williams of Kerry (1732–95): his work in Britain and his mineral surveys in the Veneto and North Italy. *Montgomeryshire Collections*, **84**, 67–102.

TORSVIK, T. H. & STURT, B. A. 1987. On the origin and stability of remanence and the magnetic fabric of the Torridonian red beds, NW Scotland. *Scottish Journal of Geology*, **23**, 23–38.

TORSVIK, T. H., LYSE, O., ATTERAS, G. & BLUCK, B. J. 1989. Palaeozoic palaeomagnetic results from Scotland and their bearing on the British apparent polar wander path. *Physics of the Earth and Planetary Interiors*, **55**, 93–105.

TORSVIK, T. H., SMETHURST, M. A., MEERT, J. G., VAN DER VOO, R., MCKERROW, W. S., BRASIER, M. D., STURT, B. A. & WALDERHAUG, H. J. 1996. Continental break-up and collision in the Neoproterozoic – A tale of Baltica and Laurentia. *Earth Science Reviews*, **40**, 229–258.

TORSVIK, T. H., ANDERSEN, T. B, EIDE, E. A. & WALDERHAUG, H. J. 1997. The age and tectonic significance of dolerite dykes in western Norway. *Journal of the Geological Society, London*, **154**, 961–973.

TRAQUAIR, R. H. 1896. The extinct vertebrate fauna of the Moray Firth area. *In*: HARVEY-BROWN, H. H. & BUCKLEY, T. E. (eds) *Vertebrate Fauna of the Moray Firth*. Vol. 2, Edinburgh.

TRAQUAIR, R. H. 1897. Additional notes on the fossil fishes of the Upper Old Red Sandstone of the Moray Firth area. *Proceedings of the Royal Physical Society of Edinburgh*, **13**, 376–385.

TRAQUAIR, R. H. 1905. On the Fauna of the Upper Old Red Sandstone of the Moray Firth area. *Report of the British Association, Cambridge*, 1904, 547.

TREAGUS, J. E. 1969. The Kinlochlaggan Boulder Bed. *Proceedings of the Geological Society, London*, **1654**, 55–60.

TREAGUS, J. E. 1981. The Lower Dalradian Kinlochlaggan Boulder Bed, Central Scotland. *In*: HAMBREY, J. M. & HARLAND, W. B. (eds) *Earth's pre-Pleistocene Glacial Record*. Cambridge University Press, 637–639.

TREAGUS, J. E. 1987. The structural evolution of the Dalradian of the Central Highlands of Scotland. *Transactions of the Royal Society of Edinburgh: Earth Sciences*, **78**, 1–15.

TREAGUS, J. E. 1991. Fault displacements in the Dalradian of the Central Highlands. *Scottish Journal of Geology*, **27**, 135–145.

TREAGUS, J. E 1999. A structural interpretation of the Tummel belt and a transpressional model for evolution of the Tay Nappe in the Central Highlands of Scotland. *Geological Magazine*, **136**, 643–660.

TREAGUS, J. E. 2000. *Solid Geology of the Schiehallion District*. Memoir of the British Geological Survey, HMSO.

TREAGUS, J. E. & ROBERTS, J. L. 1981. The Boyndie Syncline, a D1 structure in the Dalradian of Scotland. *Geological Journal*, **16**, 125–135.

TREAGUS, J. E., PATTRICK, R. A. D & CURTIS, S. F. 1999. Movement and mineralization in the Tyndrum Fault Zone, Scotland and its regional significance. *Journal of the Geological Society, London*, **156**, 591–604.

TRELOAR, P. J., BLUCK, B. J., BOWES, D. R. & DUDEK, A. 1980. Hornblende-garnet metapyroxenite beneath serpentinite in the Ballantrae complex of S.E. Scotland, and its bearing on the depth of provenance of obducted ocean lithosphere. *Transactions of the Royal Society of Edinburgh: Earth Sciences*, **71**, 201–212.

TRENCH, A. & HAUGHTON, P. D. W. 1990. Palaeomagnetic and geochemical evaluation of a terrane-linking ignimbrite: evidence for the relative position of the Grampian and Midland Valley terranes in late Silurian time. *Geological Magazine*, **127**, 241–57.

TRENCH, A., BLUCK, B. J. & WATTS, D. R. 1988. Palaeomagnetic studies within the Ballantrae Ophiolite; southwest Scotland: magnetotectonic and regional tectonic implications. *Earth and Planetary Science Letters*, **90**, 431–448.

TRENCH, A., DENTITH, M. C., BLUCK, B. J., WATTS, D. R. & FLOYD, J. D. 1989. Palaeomagnetic constraints on the geological terrane models of the Scottish Caledonides. *Journal of the Geological Society, London*, **146**, 1–4.

TREWIN, N. H. 1976*a*. Correlation of the Achanarras and Sandwick fish beds. Middle Old Red Sandstone, Scotland. *Scottish Journal of Geology*, **12**, 205–208.

TREWIN, N. H. 1976*b*. *Isopodichnus* in a trace fossil assemblage from the Old Red Sandstone. *Lethaia*, **9**, 29–37.

TREWIN, N. H. 1986. Palaeoecology and sedimentology of the Achanarras fish bed of the Middle Old Red Sandstone, Scotland. *Transactions of the Royal Society of Edinburgh: Earth Sciences*, **77**, 21–46.

TREWIN, N. H. 1987*a*. Pennan, unconformity within the Old Red Sandstone. *In*: TREWIN, N. H., KNELLER, B. C. & GILLEN, C. (eds) *Excursion Guide to the Geology of the Aberdeen Area*, Scottish Academic Press, Edinburgh, 127–130.

TREWIN, N. H. 1987*b*. Devonian of St Cyrus and Milton Ness. *In*: TREWIN, N. H., KNELLER, B. C. & GILLEN, C. (eds) *Excursion Guide to the Geology of the Aberdeen Area*, Scottish Academic Press, Edinburgh, 251–258.

TREWIN, N. H. 1987*c*. Crawton: lavas and conglomerates of the Lower ORS. *In*: TREWIN, N. H., KNELLER, B. C. & GILLEN, C. (eds) *Excursion Guide to the Geology of the Aberdeen Area*, Scottish Academic Press, Edinburgh, 259–264.

TREWIN, N. H. 1987*d*. Macduff, Dalradian turbidite fan and glacial deposits. *In*: TREWIN, N. H., KNELLER, B. C. & GILLEN, C. (eds) *Excursion Guide to the Geology of the Aberdeen Area*. Scottish Academic Press, 79–88.

TREWIN, N. H. 1989. Petroleum potential of the ORS of Northern North Scotland. *Scottish Journal of Geology*, **25**, 201–225.

TREWIN, N. H. 1991. *Jurassic Sedimentation and Tectonics in the Brora-Helmsdale Area and Old Red Sandstones Fluvial and Lacustrine Facies in N. Scotland*. Field Guide No. 8 compiled for the 13th International Sedimentological Congress, Nottingham UK 1990, 1–86, British Sedimentological Research Group, Cambridge.

TREWIN, N. H. 1992. 'Subaqueous shrinkage cracks' in the Devonian of Scotland re-interpreted – Discussion. *Journal of Sedimentary Petrology*, **62**, 921–922.

TREWIN, N. H. 1993*a*. The Lower Old Red Sandstone and Helmsdale Granite of the Ousdale area. *In*: TREWIN, N. H. & HURST, A. (eds) *Excursion Guide to the Geology of East Sutherland and Caithness*. Scottish Academic Press, Edinburgh, 115–122.

TREWIN, N. H. 1993*b*. The Old Red Sandstone of Caithness. *In*: TREWIN, N. H. & HURST, A. (eds) *Excursion Guide to the Geology of East Sutherland and Caithness*. Scottish Academic Press, Edinburgh, 123–166.

TREWIN, N. H. 1993*c*. The Triassic and Lower Jurassic of Golspie. *In*: TREWIN, N. H. & HURST, A. (eds) *Excursion Guide to the Geology of East Sutherland and Caithness*. Scottish Academic Press, Edinburgh, 41–47.

TREWIN, N. H. 1993*d*. Geological history of East Sutherland and Caithness. *In*: TREWIN, N. H. & HURST, A. (eds) *Excursion Guide to the Geology of East Sutherland and Caithness*. Scottish Academic Press, Edinburgh, 1–35.

TREWIN, N. H. 1994. Depositional environment and preservation of biota in the Lower Devonian hot-springs of Rhynie, Aberdeenshire, Scotland. *Transactions of the Royal Society of Edinburgh: Earth Sciences*, **84**, 433–442.

TREWIN, N. H. 1996. The Rhynie Cherts: an early Devonian ecosystem preserved by hydrothermal activity. *In*: BOCK, G. R. & GOODE, J. (eds) *Evolution of Hydrothermal Ecosystems on Earth (and Mars?)*. Ciba Foundation Symposium 202, 131–149.

TREWIN, N. H. 2001. The Rhynie chert. *In*: BRIGGS, D. E. G. & CROWTHER, P. R. (eds) *Palaeobiology II*. Blackwell Science Ltd, Oxford, 342–346.

TREWIN, N. H. & BRAMWELL, M. G. 1991. The Auk Field, Block 30/16, UK North Sea. *In*: ABBOTTS, I. L. (ed.) *United Kingdom Oil and Gas Fields 25 Years Commemorative Volume*. Geological Society, London, Memoir, **14**, 227–236.

TREWIN, N. H. & DAVIDSON, R. G. 1996. An Early Devonian lake and its associated biota in the Midland Valley of Scotland. *Transactions of the Royal Society of Edinburgh: Earth Sciences*, **86**, 233–246.

TREWIN, N. H. & DAVIDSON, R. G. 1999. Lake-level changes, sedimentation and faunas in a Middle Devonian basin-margin fish bed. *Journal of the Geological Society, London*, **156**, 535–548.

TREWIN, N. H. & KNELLER, B. C. 1987*a*. Old Red Sandstone and Dalradian of Gamrie Bay. *In*: TREWIN, N. H., KNELLER, B. C. & GILLEN, C. (eds) *Excursion Guide to the Geology of the Aberdeen Area*, Scottish Academic Press, Edinburgh, 113–126.

TREWIN, N. H. & KNELLER, B. C. 1987*b*. The Lower Old Red Sandstone of New Aberdour. *In*: TREWIN, N. H., KNELLER, B. C. & GILLEN, C. (eds) *Excursion Guide to the Geology of the Aberdeen Area*, Scottish Academic Press, Edinburgh, 131–142.

TREWIN, N. H. & KNOLL, A. H. 1999. Preservation of Devonian chemotropic filamentous bacteria in calcite veins. *Palaios*, **14**, 288–294.

TREWIN, N. H. & RICE, C. M. 1992. Stratigraphy and sedimentology of the Devonian Rhynie chert locality. *Scottish Journal of Geology*, **28**, 37–47.

TRIPP, R. P. 1954. Caradocian trilobites from mudstones at Craighead Quarry, near Girvan, Ayrshire. *Transactions of the Royal Society of Edinburgh: Earth Sciences*, **62**, 655–693.

TROLL, V. R., EMELEUS, C. H. & DONALDSON, C. H. 2000. Caldera formation in the Rum Central Igneous Complex, Scotland. *Bulletin of Volcanology*, **62**, 301–317.

TRUEBLOOD, S. & MORTON, N. 1991. Comparative sequence stratigraphy and structural styles of the Slyne Trough and Hebrides Basin. *Journal of the Geological Society, London*, **148**, 197–201.

TUCKER, R. D. & MCKERROW, W. S. 1995. Early Palaeozoic chronology: a review in light of new U-Pb zircon ages from Newfoundland and Britain. *Canadian Journal of Earth Sciences*, **32**, 368–379.

TUCKER, R. D., BRADLEY, D. C., VER STRAETEN, G. A., HARRIS, A. G., EBERT, J. R. & MCCUTCHEON, S. R. 1998. New U–Pb zircon ages and the duration and division of Devonian time. *Earth and Planetary Science Letters*, **158**, 175–186.

TURNBULL, M. J. M., WHITEHOUSE, M. J. & MOORBATH, S. 1996. New isotope age determinations for the Torridonian, NW Scotland. *Journal of the Geological Society, London*, **153**, 955–964.

TURNER, B. R. 1991. The hydrocarbon potential of the Northumberland Basin. *Journal of the Open University Geological Society*, **12**, 49–65.

TURNER, B. R. & SCRUTON, C. 1995. The Carboniferous rocks around Berwick-upon-Tweed. *In*: SCRUTON, C. (ed.) *Northumbrian Rocks and Landscape*. Ellenbank Press, Maryport, Cumbria, for Yorkshire Geological Society, 42–52.

TURNER, B. R., YOUNGER, P. L. & FORDHAM, C. E. 1993. Fell Sandstone Group lithostratigraphy south-west of Berwick-upon-Tweed: implications for the regional development of the Fell Sandstone. *Proceedings of the Yorkshire Geological Society*, **49**, 269–281.

TURNER, B. R., DEWEY, C. & FORDHAM, C. E. 1997. Marine ostracods in the Lower Carboniferous fluvial Fell Sandstone Group: evidence for base level changes and marine flooding of the central graben, Northumberland Basin. *Proceedings of the Yorkshire Geological Society*, **51**, 297–306.

TURNER, F. J. 1981. *Metamorphic Petrology – Mineralogical, Field and Tectonic Aspects*. 2nd Edition. McGraw-Hill, New York.

TURNER, P. J. 1993. Clyde: reappraisal of a producing field. *In*: PARKER, J. R. (ed.) *Petroleum Geology of Northwest Europe: Proceedings of the 4th Conference*. Geological Society, London, 1503–1512.

TWEEDIE, J. R. 1979. Origin of uranium and other metal enrichments in Helmsdale Granite: east Sutherland, Scotland. *Transactions of the Institution of Mining and Metallurgy*, **88**, B145–B153.

TWENHOFEL, W. 1926. *Treatise on Sedimentation*. 2 vols. Williams & Wilkins, Baltimore.

TYSON, R. V. 1995. Sequence stratigraphical interpretation of organic facies variations in marine siliclastic systems: general principles and application to the onshore Kimmeridge Clay Formation, UK. *In*: HESSELBO, S. P. & PARKINSON, D. N. (eds) *Sequence Stratigraphy in British Geology*. Geological Society, London, Special Publications, **103**, 75–96.

UNDERHILL, J. R. 1993. Discussion on the location and history of the Walls Boundary fault and Moine thrust north and south of Shetland. *Journal of the Geological Society, London*, **150**, 1003–1008.

UNDERHILL, J. R. 1994. Discussion on the palaeoecology and sedimentology across a Jurassic fault scarp, NE Scotland. *Journal of the Geological Society, London*, **151**, 729–731.

UNDERHILL, J. R. 1998. Jurassic. *In*: GLENNIE, K. W. (ed.) *Petroleum Geology of the North Sea*. 4th Edition. Blackwell, Oxford. 245–293.

UNDERHILL, J. R. & BRODIE, J. A. 1993. Structural geology of Easter Ross, Scotland: implications for movement on the Great Glen fault zone. *Journal of the Geological Society, London*, **150**, 515–527.

UNDERHILL, J. R. & PARTINGTON, M. A. 1993. Jurassic thermal doming and deflation in the North Sea: implications of the sequence stratigraphic evidence. *In*: PARKER, J. R. (ed.) *Petroleum Geology of Northwest Europe: Proceedings of the 4th Conference*. Geological Society, London, 337–346.

UNDERHILL, J. R. & PARTINGTON, M. A. 1994. Use of maximum flooding surfaces in determining a regional control on the Intra-Aalenian Mid Cimmerian sequence boundary: implications of North Sea basin development and Exxon's Sea-Level Chart. *In*: POSAMENTIER, H. W. & WEIMER, P. J. (eds) *Recent Advances in Siliciclastic Sequence Stratigraphy*. American Association of Petroleum Geologists, Memoir, **58**, 449–484.

UNDERHILL, J. R., SAWYER, M. J., HODGSON, P., SHALLCROSS, M. D. & GAWTHORPE, R. L. 1997. Implications of fault scarp degradation for Brent Group prospectivity, Ninian Field, Northern North Sea. *AAPG Bulletin*, **81**, 295–311.

UPFOLD, R. L. 1984. Tufted microbial (cyanobacterial) mats from the Proterozoic Stoer Group, Scotland. *Geological Magazine*, **121**, 351–355.

UPTON, B. G. J. 1982. Carboniferous to Permian volcanism in the stable foreland. *In*: SUTHERLAND, D. S. (ed.) *Igneous Rocks of the British Isles*. Wiley, Chichester, 255–275.

UPTON, B. G. J. 1984. Regional setting of Carboniferous volcanism in the Midland Valley of Scotland. *In*: ROLFE, W. D. I., CLARKSON, E. N. K. & PANCHEN, A. L. (eds) Volcanism and early terrestrial biotas. *Transactions of the Royal Society of Edinburgh: Earth Sciences*, **84**, 209–212.

UPTON, B. G. J., ASPEN, P. & CHAPMAN, N. A. 1983. The upper mantle and deep crust beneath the British Isles: evidence from inclusions in volcanic rocks. *Journal of the Geological Society, London*, **140**, 105–122.

UPTON, B. G. J., ASPEN, P. & HUNTER, R. H. 1984. Xenoliths and their implication for the deep geology of the Midland Valley of Scotland and adjacent regions. *Transactions of the Royal Society of Edinburgh: Earth Science*, **75**, 65–70.

UPTON, B. G. J., FITTON, J. G. & MACINTYRE, R. M. 1987. The Glas Eilean lavas: evidence of a Lower Permian volcano-tectonic basin between Islay and Jura, Inner Hebrides. *Transactions of the Royal Society of Edinburgh: Earth Sciences*, **77**, 289–293.

UPTON, B. G. J., MITCHELL, R. H., LONG, A. & ASPEN, P. 1992. Primitive olivine melanephelinite dykes from the Orkney Islands, Scotland. *Geological Magazine*, **129**, 319–324.

UPTON, B. G. J., ASPEN, P., REX, D. C., MELCHER, F. & KINNY, P. D. 1998. Lower crustal and shallow mantle samples from beneath the Hebrides: evidence from a xenolithic dyke at Gribun, western Mull. *Journal of the Geological Society, London*, **155**, 813–828.

UPTON, B. G. J., HINTON, R. W., ASPEN, P., FINCH, A. & VALLEY, J. W. 1999. Megacrysts and associated xenoliths: evidence for migration of geochemically enriched melts in the Upper Mantle beneath Scotland. *Journal of Petrology*, **40**, 935–956.

UPTON, B. G. J., ASPEN, P. & HINTON, R. W. 2001. Pyroxenite and granulite xenoliths from beneath the Scottish Northern Highlands Terrane: evidence of lower-crust/upper-mantle relationships. *Contributions to Mineralogy and Petrology*, **142**, 178–197.

UPTON, P. S. 1986. *A Structural Cross-Section of the Moine and Dalradian Rocks of the Braemar Area*. Report of the British Geological Survey.

URE, D. 1793. *The History of Rutherglen and East-Kilbride. Published with a View to Promote the Study of Antiquity and Natural History*. David Niven, Glasgow.

VAIL, P. R., MITCHUM, R. M. & THOMPSON, S. 1977. Global cycles of relative changes in sea level. *In*: PAYTON, C. E. (ed.) Seismic stratigraphy – applications to hydrocarbon exploration. *American Association of Petroleum Geologists, Memoir*, **26**, 83–97.

VALEN, V., MANGERUD, J. & LARSEN, E. 1996. Sedimentology and stratigraphy in the cave Hamnsundhelleren, western Norway. *Journal of Quaternary Science*, **11**, 185–201.

VAN BREEMEN, O. & BLUCK, B. J. 1981. Episodic granite plutons in the Scottish Caledonides. *Nature, London*, **291**, 113–117.

VAN BREEMEN, O. & BOYD, R. 1972. A radiometric age for pegmatite cutting the Belhelvie mafic intrusion, Aberdeenshire. *Scottish Journal of Geology*, **8**, 115–120.

VAN BREEMEN, O. & HAWKESWORTH, C. J. 1980. Sm–Nd isotopic study of garnets and their metamorphic host rocks. *Transactions of the Royal Society of Edinburgh: Earth Sciences*, **71**, 97–102.

VAN BREEMEN, O. & PIASECKI, M. A. J. 1983. The Glen Kyllachy granite and its bearing on the Caledonian orogeny in Scotland. *Journal of the Geological Society, London*, **140**, 47–62.

VAN BREEMEN, O., AFTALION, M. A. & PIDGEON, R. T. 1971. The age of the granite injection-complex of Harris, Outer Hebrides. *Scottish Journal of Geology*, **5**, 269–285.

VAN BREEMEN, O., PIDGEON, R. T. & JOHNSON, M. R. W. 1974. Precambrian and Palaeozoic pegmatites in the Moines of northern Scotland. *Journal of the Geological Society, London*, **130**, 493–507.

VAN BREEMEN, O., HALLIDAY, A. N., JOHNSON, M. R. W. & BOWES, D. R. 1978. Crustal additions in late Precambrian times. *In*: BOWES, D. R. & LEAKE, B. E. (eds) *Crustal Evolution in Northwestern Britain and Adjacent Regions*. Geological Journal Special Issue, **10**, 81–106.

VAN BREEMEN, O., AFTALION, M. & JOHNSON, M. R. W. 1979a. Age of the Loch Borrolan complex, Assynt, and late movements along the Moine Thrust zone. *Journal of the Geological Society, London*, **136**, 489–496.

VAN BREEMEN, O., AFTALION, M., PANKHURST, R. J. & RICHARDSON, S. W. 1979b. Age of the Glen Dessary syenite, Inverness-shire: diachronous Palaeozoic metamorphism across the Great Glen. *Scottish Journal of Geology*, **15**, 49–62.

VAN DE KAMP, P. C. & LEAKE, B. E.. 1996. Petrology, geochemistry, and Na metasomatism of Triassic–Jurassic non-marine clastic sediments in the Newark, Hartford, and Deerfield rift basins, northeastern USA. *Chemical Geology*, **133**, 89–124.

VAN DE KAMP, P. C. & LEAKE, B. E. 1997. Mineralogy, geochemistry, provenance and sodium metasomatism of Torridonian rift basin clastic rocks, NW Scotland. *Scottish Journal of Geology*, **33**, 105–124.

VAN DER BURGH, J. & VAN KONIJNENBURG-VAN CITTERT, J. H. A. 1984. A drifted flora from the Kimmeridgian (Upper Jurassic) of Lothbeg Point, Sutherland, Scotland. *Reviews of Palaeobotany and Palynology*, **43**, 359–396.

VAN DER VOO, R. & SCOTESE, C. 1981. Palaeomagnetic evidence for a large (c. 2000 km) sinistral offset along the Great Glen Fault during Carboniferous times. *Geology*, **9**, 583–584.

VAN GOOL, J., MARKER, M,, MENGEL, F. & FIELD PARTY 1995. The Palaeoproterozoic Nagssugtoqidian orogen in West Greenland: current status of work by the Danish Lithosphere Centre. *Bulletin Gronlands Geologiske Undersogelse*, **172**, 88–94.

VAN KRANENDONK, M. J. & WARDLE, R. J. 1994. Promontory indentation, transpression and disharmonic folding in the formation of the Palaeoproterozoic Torngat orogen, Northeastern Canada. *Terra Abstracts*, **6**, 20.

VAN STAAL, C. R., DEWEY, J. F. C., MACNIOCAILL, C. & MCKERROW, W. S. 1998. The Cambrian–Silurian tectonic evolution of the northern Appalachians and the British Caledonides: history of a complex west and southwest Pacific-type segment of Iapetus. *In*: BLUNDELL, D. J. & SCOTT, A. C. (eds) *Lyell: the Past is the Key to the Present*. Geological Society, London, Special Publications, **143**, 199–242.

VAN VESSEM, E. J. & GAN, T. L. 1991. The Ninian Field, blocks 3/3 & 3/8, UK North Sea. *In*: ABBOTTS, I. L. (ed.) *United Kingdom Oil and Gas Fields 25 Years Commemorative Volume*. Geological Society, London, Memoir, **14**, 175–182.

VANCE, D., STRACHAN, R. A. & JONES, K. A. 1998. Extensional versus compressional settings for metamorphism: garnet chronometry and pressure–temperature–time histories in the Moine Supergroup, northwest Scotland. *Geology*, **26**, 927–930.

VAUGHAN, T. E. 1974. *The Bailgill Mining District, N. E. Leadhills*. PhD thesis, University of Strathclyde.

VERNEY COMMITTEE: ADVISORY COMMITTEE ON AGGREGATES 1976. *Aggregates: the Way Ahead*. HMSO, London.

VOGT, T. 1930. On the chronological order of deposition in the Highlands. *Geological Magazine*, **67**, 68–76.

VOLKER, J. A. & UPTON, B. G. J. 1990. The structure and peterogenesis of the Trallval and Ruinsival areas of the Rhum ultrabasic complex. *Transactions of the Royal Society of Edinburgh: Earth Sciences*, **81**, 69–88.

VON KNORRING, O. & DEARNLEY, R. 1960a. The Lewisian pegmatites of South Harris, Outer Hebrides, *Mineralogical Magazine*, **32**, 366–378.

VON KNORRING, O. & DEARNLEY, R. 1960b. Molybdenite associated with Laxfordian gneisses at Loch Stack, Sutherlandshire. *Mineralogical Magazine*, **32**, 344–345.

WADSWORTH, W. J. 1961. The layered ultrabasic rocks of south-west Rhum, Inner Hebrides. *Philosophical Transactions of the Royal Society of London*, **244B**, 21–64.

WADSWORTH, W. J. 1982. The basic plutons. *In*: SUTHERLAND, D. (ed.) *Igneous Rocks of the British Isles*. Wiley, Chichester, 135–148.

WADSWORTH, W. J. 1992. Ultrabasic breccias of the Long Loch area, Isle of Rum. *Scottish Journal of Geology*, **28**, 103–113.

WADSWORTH, W. J. 1994. The peridotite plugs of northern Rum. *Scottish Journal of Geology*, **30**, 167–174.

WAGER, L. R. 1956. A chemical definition of fractionation stages as a basis for comparison of Hawaiian, Hebridean and other basic lavas. *Geochimica et Cosmochimica Acta*, **9**, 217–248.

WAGER, L. R. & BROWN, G. M. 1968. *Layered Igneous Rocks*. Oliver and Boyd, Edinburgh.

WAGER, L. R., WEEDON, D. S. & VINCENT, E. A. 1953. A granophyre from Coire Uaigneich, Isle of Skye, containing quartz paramorphs after tridymite. *Mineralogical Magazine*, **30**, 263–276.

WAGER, L. R., BROWN, G. M. & WADSWORTH, W. J. 1960. Types of igneous cumulates. *Journal of Petrology*, **1**, 73–85.

WAGER, L. R., VINCENT, E. A., BROWN, G. M. & BELL, J. D. 1965. Marscoite and related rocks of the Western Redhills Complex, Isle of Skye. *Philosophical Transactions of the Royal Society of London*, **257A**, 273–307.

WAGNER, R. H. 1983. A lower Rotliegend flora from Ayrshire. *Scottish Journal of Geology*, **19**, 135–155.

WAKEFIELD, M. I. 1995. Ostracoda and salinity variations in the Middle Jurassic Lealt Shale Formation, Inner Hebrides, Scotland. *Palaeontology*, **38**, 583–617.

WALKER, A. D. 1973. The age of the Cuttie's Hillock Sandstone (Permo-Triassic) of the Elgin area. *Scottish Journal of Geology*, **9**, 177–183.

WALKER, B. H. 1986. *Emplacement Mechanism of High-Level Dolerite Sills and Related Eruptions in Sedimentary Basins, Fife, Scotland*. PhD thesis, University of Leeds.

WALKER, B. H. & FRANCIS, E. H. 1987. High-level emplacement of an olivine dolerite sill into Namurian sediments near Cardenden, Fife. *Transactions of the Royal Society of Edinburgh: Earth Sciences*, **77**, 295–307.

WALKER, E. F. 1985. Arthropod ichnofauna of the Old Red Sandstone at Dunure and Montrose, Scotland. *Transactions of the Royal Society of Edinburgh: Earth Sciences*, **76**, 287–297.

WALKER, G. P. L. 1970. Distribution of amygdale minerals in Mull and Morvern (Western Scotland). *In*: MURTY, T. V. V. G. R. K. & RAO, S. S. (eds) *Studies in Earth Sciences, West Commemoration Volume*. Today & Tomorrow's Printers & Publishers, Faridabad, India, 181–194.

WALKER, G. P. L. 1975. A new concept of the evolution of the British Tertiary intrusive centres. *Journal of the Geological Society, London*, **131**, 121–141.

WALKER, G. P. L. 1993a. Basaltic-volcano systems. *In*: PRICHARD, H. M., ALABASTER, T., HARRIS, N. B. W. & NEARY, C. R. (eds) *Magmatic Processes and Plate Tectonics*. Geological Society, London, Special Publications, **76**, 3–38.

WALKER, G. P. L. 1993b. Re-evaluation of inclined intrusive sheets and dykes in the Cuillins volcano, Isle of Skye. *In*: PRICHARD, H. M., ALABASTER, T., HARRIS, N. B. W. & NEARY, C. R. (eds) *Magmatic Processes and Plate Tectonics*. Geological Society, London, Special Publications, **76**, 589–497.

WALKER, G. P. L. 1995. Flood basalts versus central volcanoes and the British Tertiary Volcanic Province. *In*: LE BAS, M. J. (ed.) *Milestones in Geology*. Geological Society, London, Memoir, **16**, 195–202.

WALKER, G. P. L. & SKELHORN, R. R. 1966. Some associations of acid and basic igneous rocks. *Earth-Science Reviews*, **2**, 93–109.

WALKER, M. J. C. 1984. Pollen analysis and Quaternary research in Scotland. *Quaternary Science Reviews*, **3**, 369–404.

WALKER, M. J. C. & LOWE, J. J. 1997. Vegetation and climate in Scotland, 13 000 to 7000 radiocarbon years ago. *In*: GORDON, J. E. (ed.) *Reflections on the Ice Age in Scotland*. Scottish Natural Heritage, 105–115.

WALKER, M. J. C. & LOWE, J. J. 1981. Postglacial history of Rannoch Moor, Scotland. *Journal of Biogeography*, **8**, 475–491.

WALLIS, S. M. 1989. *Petrology and Geochemistry of Upper Carboniferous–Lower Permian Volcanic Rocks in Scotland*. PhD thesis, University of Edinburgh.

WALSH, J. N., BECKINSALE, R. D., SKELHORN, R. R. & THORPE, R. S. 1979. Geochemistry and petrogenesis of Tertiary granitic rocks from the Isle of Mull, Northwest Scotland. *Contributions to Mineralogy and Petrology*, **71**, 99–116.

WALTON, E. K. 1955. Silurian greywackes in Peebleshire. *Proceedings of the Royal Society of Edinburgh*, **B65**, 327–357.

WALTON, E. K. 1961. Some aspects of the succession and structure in the Lower Palaeozoic rocks of the Southern Uplands of Scotland. *Geologische Rundschau*, **50**, 63–77.

WALTON, E. K. 1983. Lower Palaeozoic-Structure and Palaeogeography. *In*: CRAIG, G. Y. (ed.) *Geology of Scotland* (2nd edition). Scottish Academic Press, Edinburgh, 139–166.

WALTON, E. K. & OLIVER, G. J. H. 1991. Lower Palaeozoic Stratigraphy, Structure & Palaeogeography. *In*: CRAIG, G. Y. (ed.) *Geology of Scotland* (3rd edition). Geological Society, London, 161–228.

WARD, J. 1997. Early Dinantian evaporites of the Easton-1 well, Solway Basin, onshore, Cumbria, England. *In*: MEADOWS, N. S., TRUEBLOOD, S. P., HARDMAN, M. & COWAN, G. (eds) *Petroleum Geology of the Irish Sea and Adjacent Areas*. Geological Society, London, Special Publications, **124**, 277–296.

WARDLAW, B. R. 2000. Notes from the SPS Chair. *Permophiles*, **36**, 1–3.

WARDLE, R. J., RYAN, B. & ERMANOVICS, I. F. 1990. The eastern Churchill province, Torngat and New Quebec orogens: an overview. *Geoscience, Canada*, **17**, 217–222.

WARR, L. N. 2000. The Variscan Orogeny: the Welding of Pangea. *In*: WOODCOCK, N. & STRACHAN, R. (eds) *Geological History of Britain and Ireland*. Blackwell, Oxford, 271–294.

WARREN, P. T. 1964. The stratigraphy and structure of the Silurian rocks southeast of Hawick, Roxburghshire. *Quarterly Journal of the Geological Society, London*, **120**, 193–218.

WARRINGTON, D. & IVIMEY-COOK, H. C. 1992. Triassic. *In*: COPE, J. C. W., INGHAM, J. K. & RAWSON, P. F. 1992. *Atlas of Palaeogeography and Lithofacies*. Geological Society of London, Memoir, **13**, 97–106.

WARRINGTON, G. & POLLARD, J. E. 1985. Late Triassic miospores from Gribun, Western Mull. *Scottish Journal of Geology*, **21**, 218–221.

WARRINGTON, G., AUDLEY-CHARLES, M. G., ELLIOTT, R. E., EVANS, W. B., IVIMEY-COOK, H. C., KENT, P. E., ROBINSON, P. L., SHOTTON, F. W. & TAYLOR, F. M. 1980. *A Correlation of Triassic Rocks in the British Isles*. Geological Society, London, Special Report, **13**.

WATERSTON, C. D. 1957. Robert James Hay Cunningham (1815–1842). *Transactions of the Edinburgh Geological Society*, **17**, 260–272.

WATERSTON, C. D. 1965. The Old Red Sandstone. *In*: CRAIG, G. Y. (ed.) *The Geology of Scotland* (1st Edition). Scottish Academic Press, Edinburgh, 270–310.

WATKINS, K. P. 1983. Petrogenesis of Dalradian albite porphyroblast schists. *Journal of the Geological Society, London*, **140**, 601–618.

WATKINS, K. P. 1985. Geothermometry and geobarometry of inverted metamorphic zones in the W. Central Scottish Dalradian. *Journal of the Geological Society, London*, **142**, 157–165.

WATSON, D. M. S. & HICKLING, G. 1914. On the Triassic and Permian Rocks of Moray. *Geological Magazine*, **1**, 399–402.

WATSON, J. 1969. The Precambrian gneiss complex of Ness, Lewis, in relation to the effects of Laxfordian regeneration. *Scottish Journal of Geology*, **5**, 269–285.

WATSON, J. 1983. Lewisian. *In*: CRAIG, G. Y. (ed.) *Geology of Scotland* (2nd edition). Scottish Academic Press, Edinburgh, 23–47.

WATSON, J. V. 1984. The ending of the Caledonian orogeny in Scotland. *Journal of the Geological Society, London*, **141**, 193–214.

WATSON, S. W. 1976. *The Sedimentary Geochemistry of the Moffat Shales, a Carbonaceous Sequence in the Southern Uplands of Scotland*. PhD thesis, University of St Andrews.

WATT, G. R., BURNS, I. M. & GRAHAM, G. M. 1996. Chemical characteristics of migmatites: accessory phase distribution and evidence for fast melt segregation rates. *Contributions to Mineralogy and Petrology*, **125**, 100–111.

WEAVER, B. L. & TARNEY, J. 1980. Rare-earth geochemistry of Lewisian granulite-facies gneisses, northwest Scotland: implications for the petrogenesis of the Archaean lower continental crust. *Earth and Planetary Science Letters*, **51**, 279–296.

WEBB SEYMOUR, LORD. 1815. An account of observations, made by Lord Webb Seymour and Professor Playfair, upon some geological appearances at Glen Tilt, and the adjacent country. Drawn up by Lord Webb Seymour. *Transactions of the Royal Society of Edinburgh*, **7**, 203–375.

WEBB, B., RUSHTON, A. W. A. & WHITE, D. E. 1993. *Classical Areas of British geology. Moffatdale and the Upper Ettrick Valley*. British Geological Survey, London, HMSO.

WEBB, P. C., TINDLE, A. G. & IXER, R. A. 1992. W–Sn–Mo–Bi–Ag mineralization associated with zinnwaldite-bearing granite from Glen Gairn, Scotland. *Transactions of the Institution of Mining and Metallurgy*, **101**, B59–B72.

WEBER, K. 1972. Note on the determination of illite crystallinity. *Neues Jahrbuuch für Mineralogie Monatshefte*, **6**, 267–276.

WEEDON, D. S. 1960. The Gars-bheinn ultrabasic sill, Isle of Skye. *Quarterly Journal of the Geological Society of London*, **116**, 37–54.

WEEDON, G. P. & READ, W. A. 1995. Orbital forcing of Namurian cyclic sedimentation from spectral analysis of the Limestone Coal Formation, Central Scotland. *In*: HOUSE, M. R. & GALE, A. S. (eds) *Orbital Forcing Timescales and Cyclostratigraphy*. Geological Society, London, Special Publications, **85**, 51–66.

WEISS, S. & TROLL, G. 1989. The Ballachulish Igneous Complex, Scotland: Petrography, Mineral Chemistry and Order of Crystallization in the Monzodiorite-Quartz Diorite Suite and in the Granite. *Journal of Petrology*, **30**, 1069–1115.

WELLMAN, C. H. 1991. *Land-Derived Palynomorphs from Silurian and Lower Devonian Deposits of Scotland*. PhD thesis, University of Wales, College of Cardiff.

WELLMAN, C. H. 1993. A land plant microfossil assemblage of Mid Silurian age from the Stonehaven Group, Scotland. *Journal of Micropalaeontology*, **12**, 47–66.

WELLMAN, C. H. & RICHARDSON, J. B. 1993. Terrestrial plant microfossils from the Silurian inliers of the Midland Valley of Scotland. *Palaeontology*, **36**, 155–193.

WERNER, A. G. 1971. *Short Classification and Description of the Various Rocks*, translated by A. M. Ospovat. Hafner, New York.

WESTBROOK, G. K. 1972. Structure and metamorphism of the Lewisian of east Tiree, Inner Hebrides. *Scottish Journal of Geology*, **8**, 13–30.

WESTERGARD, A. H. 1931. *Diplocraterion, Monocraterion and Skolithos from the Lower Cambrian of Sweden*. *Sveriges Geologische Undersogelse*, **25**, 1–25.

WESTOLL, T. S. 1951. The vertebrate-bearing strata of Scotland. *Report of the 18th International Geological Congress*, **2**, 5–21.

WESTOLL, T. S. 1977. Northern Britain. *In*: HOUSE, M. R., RICHARDSON, J. B., CHALONER, W. G., ALLEN, J. R. L., HOLLAND, C. H. & WESTOLL, T. S. (eds) *A Correlation of the Devonian Rocks in the British Isles*. Geological Society of London, Special Report, **8**, 66–93.

WHITE, D. E., BARRON, H. F., BARNES, R. P. & LINTERN, B. C. 1991. Biostratigraphy of late Llandovery (Telychian) and Wenlock turbiditic sequences in the SW Southern Uplands, Scotland. *Transactions of the Royal Society of Edinburgh: Earth Sciences*, **82**, 297–322.

WHITE, R. S. 1988. A hot-spot model for early Tertiary volcanism in the North Atlantic. *In*: MORTON, A. C. & PARSON, L. M. (eds) *Early Tertiary Volcanism and the Opening of the NE Atlantic*. Geological Society, London, Special Publications, **39**, 3–13.

WHITE, R. S. 1992. Magmatism during and after continental break-up. *In*: STOREY, B. C., ALABASTER, T. & PANKHURST, R. J. (eds) *Magmatism and the Causes of Continental Break-up*. Geological Society, London, Special Publications, **68**, 1–16.

WHITE, R. S. & LOVELL, J. P. B. 1997. Measuring the pulse of a plume with the sedimentary record. *Nature, London*, **387**, 888–891.

WHITE, R. S. & MCKENZIE, D. P. 1989. Magmatism at rift zones: The generation of volcanic continental margins and flood basalts. *Journal of Geophysical Research*, **94**, 7685–7729.

WHITE, R. S. & MCKENZIE, D. P. 1995. Mantle plumes and flood basalts. *Journal of Geophysical Research*, **100**, 17 543–17 585.

WHITE, S. H. & GLASSER, J. 1987. The Outer Hebrides fault zone: evidence for normal movements. *In*: PARK, R. G. & TARNEY, J. (eds) *Evolution of the Lewisian and Comparable Precambrian High Grade Terrains*. Geological Society, London, Special Publications, **27**, 175–183.

WHITEHOUSE, M. J. 1988. Granulite facies Nd-isotopic homogenization in the Lewisian complex of northwest Scotland. *Nature, London*, **331**, 705–707.

WHITEHOUSE, M. J. 1989. Sm–Nd evidence for diachronous crustal accretion in the Lewisian complex of NW Scotland. *Tectonophysics*, **161**, 245–256.

WHITEHOUSE, M. J. 1990. An early Proterozoic age for the Ness anorthosite, Lewis, Outer Hebrides. *Scottish Journal of Geology*, **26**, 131–136.

WHITEHOUSE, M. J. 1993. Age of the Corodale gneisses, South Uist. *Scottish Journal of Geology*, **29**, 1–7.

WHITEHOUSE, M. J. & BRIDGWATER, D. 1999. Palaeoproterozoic evolution of the Outer Hebridean Lewisian Complex, northwest Scotland: constraints from ion microprobe zircon geochronology. *EUG 10th Session A07:3A. Abstracts*.

WHITEHOUSE, M. J., BRIDGEWATER, D. & PARK, R. G. 1997. Detrital zircon ages from Loch Maree Group, Lewisian Coplex, NW Scotland; confirmation of Palaeoproterozoic Laurentia–Fennoscandia connection. *Terra Nova*, **9**, 260–263.

WHITTINGTON, G., EDWARDS, K. J. & CASELDINE, C. J. 1991. Late- and post-glacial pollen analytical and environmental data from a near-coastal site in north-east Fife, Scotland. *Reviews of Palaeobotany and Palynology*, **68**, 65–85.

WHITTINGTON, G., HALL, A. M. & JARVIS, J. 1993. A pre-late Devensian pollen site from Camp Fauld, Buchan, Grampian Region. *New Phytologist*, **125**, 867–874.

WHYATT, M., BOWEN, J. M. & RHODES, D. N. 1992. The Nelson field: a successful application of a development geoseismic model in North Sea exploration. *In*: HARDMAN, R. F. P. (ed.) *Exploration Britain: Geological Insights for the Next Decade*. Geological Society, London, Special Publications, **67**, 283–305.

WHYTE, F. 1964. The Heads of Ayr Vent. *Transactions of the Geological Society of Glasgow*, **25**, 72–97.

WHYTE, F. & MACDONALD, J. G. 1974. Lower Carboniferous volcanicity in the northern part of the Clyde Plateau. *Scottish Journal of Geology*, **10**, 187–198.

WHYTE, M. A. 1994. Scottish Carboniferous fresh-water limestones in their regional setting. *Transactions of the Royal Society of Edinburgh: Earth Sciences*, **84**, 239–248.

WIGNALL, P. B. & PICKERING, K. T. 1993. Palaeoecology and sedimentology across a Jurassic fault scarp. N E Scotland. *Journal of the Geological Society, London*, **150**, 323–340.

WILKINSON, C. G., BAZLEY, R. A. B. & BOULTER, M. C. 1980. The geology and palynology of the Oligocene Lough Neagh Clays. *Journal of the Geological Society, London*, **137**, 65–75.

WILKINSON, J. M. & CANN, J. R. 1974. Trace elements and tectonic relationships of basaltic rocks in the Ballantrae Igneous Complex, Ayrshire. *Geological Magazine*, **111**, 35–41.

WILKINSON, M. 1991. Concretions of the Bearreraig Sandstone Formation: geometry and geochemistry. *Sedimentology*, **38**, 899–912.

WILKINSON, M. 1992. Concretionary cements in Jurassic sandstones, Isle of Eigg, Inner Hebrides. *In*: PARNELL, J. (ed.) *Basins on the North Atlantic Seaboard: Petroleum Geology, Sedimentology and Basin Evolution*. Geological Society, London, Special Publications, **62**, 145–154.

WILKINSON, M. 1993. Concretions of the Valtos Sandstone Formation of Skye: geochemical indicators of palaeo-hydrology. *Journal of the Geological Society, London*, **150**, 57–66.

WILKINSON, M. & DAMPIER, M. D. 1990. The rate of growth of sandstone-hosted calcite concretions. *Geochimica et Cosmochimica Acta*, **54**, 3391–3399.

WILKINSON, S. B. 1907. *The Geology of Islay, including Oronsay and Portions of Colonsay and Jura*. Memoir, Geological Survey of Scotland.

WILKS, G. F. 1974. Exploration by Consolidated Gold Fields on the western side of the Exploration Ventures Limited project, northeast Scotland 1968–1973. Open-file Report, British Geological Survey.

WILLAN, R. C. R. 1980. Stratabound sulphide mineralization in the Dalradian Supergroup of the Grampian Highlands, Scotland. *Norges Geologiske Undersokelse*, **360**, 241–258.

WILLAN, R. C. R. 1981. Geochemistry of host rocks to the Aberfeldy barite deposit, Scotland. *In*: HALL, A. J. & GALLAGHER, M. J. (eds) *Caledonian–Appalachian Stratabound Sulphides, Scotland 1981*. Department of Applied Geology, University of Strathclyde, 46–53.

WILLAN, R. C. R. 1983. *Stratiform Baryte and Sulphide in Dalradian Metasediments of the Grampian Highlands, Scotland: Geological Setting, Mineralogy, Sulphur Isotopes and Geochemistry*. PhD thesis, University of Strathclyde.

WILLAN, R. C. R. & COLEMAN, M. L. 1983. Sulfur isotope study of the Aberfeldy barite, zinc, lead deposit and minor sulfide mineralisation in the Dalradian metamorphic terrain, Scotland. *Economic Geology*, **78**, 1619–1656.

WILLAN, R. C. R. & HALL, A. J. 1980. Sphalerite geobarometry and trace element studies on stratiform sulphide from McPhun's Cairn, Loch Fyne, Argyll, Scotland. *Transactions of the Institution of Mining and Metallurgy*, **88**, B31–B40.

WILLIAMS, A. 1959. A structural history of the Girvan district, SW Ayrshire. *Transactions of the Royal Society of Edinburgh*, **63**, 629–667.

WILLIAMS, A. 1962. *The Barr and Lower Ardmillan Series (Caradoc) of the Girvan District, South-West Ayrshire, with a Description of the Brachiopoda*. Memoir of the Geological Society of London, **3**.

WILLIAMS, A. 1973. Distribution of brachiopod assemblages in relation to Ordovician palaeogeography, *Special Papers in Palaeontology*, **12**, 241–269.

WILLIAMS, D. M. & HARPER, D. A. T. 1988. A basin model for the Silurian of the Midland Valley of Scotland and Ireland. *Journal of the Geological Society, London*, **145**, 741–748.

WILLIAMS, D. M. & HARPER, D. A. T. 1991. End Silurian modification of Ordovician terranes in western Ireland. *Journal of the Geological Society, London*, **148**, 161–171.

WILLIAMS, D. M., HARKIN, J., ARMSTRONG, H. A. & HIGGS, K. T. 1994. A late Caledonian melange in Ireland: implications for tectonic models. *Journal of the Geological Society, London*, **151**, 307–314.

WILLIAMS, D. M., HARKIN, J. & HIGGS, K. T. 1996. Implications of new microfloral evidence from the Clew Bay Complex for Silurian relationships in the west Irish Caledonides. *Journal of the Geological Society, London*, **153**, 771–777.

WILLIAMS, E. A., FRIEND, P. F. & WILLIAMS, B. P. J. 2000. A review of Devonian time scales: databases, construction and new data.

In: FRIEND, P. F. & WILLIAMS, B. P. J. (eds) *New Perspectives on the Old Red Sandstone*. Geological Society, London, Special Publications, **180**, 1–21.

WILLIAMS, G. E. 1966. Palaeogeography of the Torridonian Applecross Group. *Nature, London*, **209**, 1303–1306.

WILLIAMS, G. E. 1968. Torridonian weathering, and its bearing on Torridonian palaeoclimate and source. *Scottish Journal of Geology*, **4**, 164–184.

WILLIAMS, G. E. 1969a. Characteristics and origin of a Precambrian pediment. *Journal of Geology*, **77**, 183–207.

WILLIAMS, G. E. 1969b. Petrography and origin of pebbles from Torridonian strata (late Precambrian), northwest Scotland. *American Association of Petroleum Geologists, Memoir*, **12**, 609–629.

WILLIAMS, G. E. 1971. Flood deposits of sand-bed ephemeral streams of central Australia. *Sedimentology*, **17**, 1–40.

WILLIAMS, G. E. 2001. Neoproterozoic (Torridonian) alluvial fan succession, northwest Scotland, and its tectonic setting and provenance. *Geological Magazine*, **138**, 161–184.

WILLIAMS, G. E. & SCHMIDT, P. W. 1997. Palaeomagnetic dating of sub-Torridon Group weathering profiles, NW Scotland: verification of Neoproterozoic palaeosols. *Journal of the Geological Society, London*, **154**, 987–997.

WILLIAMS, G. M. & AITKENHEAD, N. 1991. Lessons from Loscoe: the uncontrolled migration of landfill gas. *Quarterly Journal of Engineering Geology*, **24**, 191–207.

WILLIAMS, H. & SMYTH, W. R. 1973. Metamorphic aureoles beneath ophiolite suites and alpine peridotites, tectonic implications with west Newfoundland examples. *American Journal of Science*, **273**, 594–621.

WILLIAMS, J. 1789. *The Natural History of the Mineral Kingdom. In Three Parts*. 2 vols. Thomas Ruddiman, Edinburgh.

WILLIAMS, P. J., TOMKINSON, M. J. & CATTELL, A. C. 1985. Petrology and deformation of metamorphosed volcanic-exhalative sediments in the Gairloch Schist Belt, N.W. Scotland. *Mineralium Deposita*, **20**, 302–308.

WILLIAMS, S. H. 1983. The Ordovician–Silurian graptolite fauna of Dob's Linn, southern Scotland. *Palaeontology*, **26**, 605–639.

WILLIAMS, T. M., HENNEY, P. J., STONE, P. & LINTERN, B. C. 1996. Rare earth element geochemistry of Lower Palaeozoic turbidites in the British trans-Iapetus zone: provenance pattern and basin evolution. *Scottish Journal of Geology*, **32**, 1–8.

WILLIAMSON, I. T. & BELL, B. R. 1994. The Palaeocene lava field of west-central Skye, Scotland: Stratigraphy, palaeogeography and structure. *Transactions of the Royal Society of Edinburgh: Earth Sciences*, **85**, 39–75.

WILLS, J. M. 1991. The Forties Field, Blocks 21/10, 22/6a, UK North Sea. *In*: ABBOTTS, I. L. (ed.) *United Kingdom Oil and Gas Fields 25 Years Commemorative Volume*. Geological Society, London, Memoir, **14**, 301–308.

WILSON, D. 1975. *Structure and Metamorphism of the Ben Wyvis District, Ross-shire*. PhD thesis, Edinburgh University.

WILSON, D. & SHEPHERD, J. 1979. The Carn Chuinneag granite and its aureole. *In*: HARRIS, A. L., HOLLAND, C. H. & LEAKE, B. E. (eds) *The Caledonides of the British Isles – Reviewed*. Geological Society, London, Special Publications, **8**, 669–675.

WILSON, G. V. & FLETT, J. S. 1921. The lead, zinc, copper and nickel ores of Scotland. Memoir of the Geological Survey, *Special Report on the Mineral Resources of Great Britain*, **17**, 1–159.

WILSON, G. V., EDWARDS, W., KNOX, J., JONES, R. C. B. & STEPHENS, J. V. 1935. The Geology of the Orkneys. *Memoir of the Geological Survey of Great Britain*.

WILSON, I. S. G. & HINXMAN, L. W. 1890. Explanation of Sheet 76 – Central Aberdeenshire. *Memoir of the Geological Survey, Scotland*.

WILSON, J. T. 1969. Did the Atlantic close and reopen? *Nature, London*, **211**, 676–681.

WILSON, L. G. 1972. *Charles Lyell, The Years to 1841*. Yale University Press, New Haven.

WILSON, R. B. 1967. A study of some Namurian marine faunas of Central Scotland. *Transactions of the Royal Society of Edinburgh*, **66**, 445–493.

WILSON, R. B. 1974. A study of the Dinantian marine faunas of south-east Scotland. *Bulletin of the Geological Survey of Great Britain*, **46**, 35–65.

WILSON, R. B. 1989. A study of the Dinantian marine macrofossils of central Scotland. *Transactions of the Royal Society of Edinburgh: Earth Sciences*, **80**, 91–126.

WILSON, R. C. L. (ed.), DOYLE, P., EASTERBROOK, G., REID, E. & SKIPSEY, E. 1994. *Earth Heritage Conservation*. Geological Society, London.

WILSON, T. J. 1966. Did the Atlantic close and then re-open? *Nature, London*, **211**, 676–681.

WIMBLEDON, W. A. 1988. Palaeontological site conservation in Britain: facts, form, function and efficiency. *In*: CROWTHER, P. R. & WIMBLEDON, W. A. (eds) *The Use and Conservation of Palaeontological Sites*. Special Papers in Palaeontology, **40**, Palaeontological Association, London, 41–56.

WINCHESTER, J. A. 1974. The zonal pattern of regional metamorphism in the Scottish Caledonides. *Journal of the Geological Society, London*, **130**, 509–524.

WINCHESTER, J. A. 1984. The geochemistry of the Strathconan amphibolites, Northern Scotland. *Scottish Journal of Geology*, **20**, 37–51.

WINCHESTER, J. A. 1988. Later Proterozoic environments and tectonic evolution in the northern Atlantic lands. *In*: WINCHESTER, J. A. (ed.) *Later Proterozoic Stratigraphy of the Northern Atlantic Regions*. Blackie, Glasgow, 253–270.

WINCHESTER, J. A. & FLOYD, P. A. 1983. The geochemistry of the Ben Hope sill suite, northern Scotland, UK. *Chemical Geology*, **43**, 49–75.

WINCHESTER, J. A. & GLOVER, B. W. 1988. The Grampian Group, Scotland. *In*: WINCHESTER, J. A. (ed.) *Later Proterozoic Stratigraphy of the Northern Atlantic Regions*. Blackie, London, 146–161.

WINCHESTER, J. A. & LAMBERT, R. ST. J. 1970. Geochemical distinctions between the Lewisian of Cassley, Durcha and Loch Shin, Sutherland and the surrounding Moinian. *Proceedings of the Geologists' Association*, **81**, 275–301.

WINCHESTER, J. A., PARK, R. G. & FLOYD, P. A. 1980. The geochemistry of Lewisian semipelitic schists from the Gairloch district, Wester Ross. *Scottish Journal of Geology*, **16**, 165–179.

WITZKE, B. J. & HECKEL, P. H. 1988. Palaeoclimatic indicators and inferred Devonian palaeolatitudes of Euramerica. *In*: MCMILLAN, N. J., EMBRY, A. F. & GLASS, D. J. (eds) *Devonian of the World*. Canadian Society of Petroleum Geologists, Memoir, **14**, Vol. I, 49–63.

WOOD, S. & NORMAN, D. 1991. Tynet Burn-on the trail of Orcadian Fish. *Earth Science Conservation*, **29**, 15–17.

WOODCOCK, N. H. 1994. *Geology and the Environment in Britain and Ireland*. UCL Press, London.

WOODCOCK, N. H. & STRACHAN, R. (eds) 2000. *Geological History of Britain and Ireland*. Blackwell, Oxford.

WOODWARD, H. B. 1911. *In*: SEWARD, A. C. The Jurassic flora of Sutherland. *Transactions of the Royal Society of Edinburgh*, **47**, 643–709.

WOOLLEY, A. R. 1970. The structural relationships of the Loch Borralan complex, Scotland. *Geological Journal*, **7**, 171–182.

WOOLLEY, A. R. 1973. The pseudoleucite borolanites and associated rocks of the south-eastern tract of the Borralan complex, Scotland. *Bulletin of the British Museum of Natural History (Mineralogy)*, **2**, 287–333.

WORLD COMMISSION ON ENVIRONMENT AND DEVELOPMENT 1993. *Our Common Future*. Oxford University Press, Oxford.

WRIGHT, A. E., TARNEY, J., PALMER, K. F., MOORLOCK, B. S. P. & SKINNER, A. C. 1973. The geology of the Angmassalik area, East Greenland and possible relationships with the Lewisian of Scotland. *In*: PARK, R. G. & TARNEY, J. (eds) *The Early Precambrian of Scotland and Related Rocks of Greenland*, University of Keele, 157–177.

WRIGHT, D. T. 1993. *Studies of the Cambrian Eilean Dubh Formation of Northwest Scotland*. DPhil thesis, University of Oxford.

WRIGHT, D. T. 1994. The role of benthic microbial communities in widespread dolomite formation (abs.). *In*: AWRAMIK, S. M. (ed.)

Death Valley International Stromatolite Symposium, Laughlin, Nevada, USA, 95.

WRIGHT, D. T. 1997a. An organogenic origin for widespread dolomite in the Cambrian Eilean Dubh Formation, north western Scotland. *Journal of Sedimentary Research*, **67**, 54–64.

WRIGHT, D. T. 1997b. Origin of carbonate in marine stromatolites of the Eilean Dubh Formation, north-western Scotland. *Journal of the Open University Geological Society*, 25th Anniversary Edition, **18**, 3–12.

WRIGHT, D. T. & KNIGHT, I. 1995. A revised chronostratigraphy for the lower Durness Group. *Scottish Journal of Geology*, **31**, 11–22.

WRIGHT, S. C. 1985. *The Study of the Depositional Environments and Diagenesis in the Durness Group of North-West Scotland*. DPhil thesis, University of Oxford.

WRIGHT, V. P. & VANSTONE, S. D. 2001. Onset of Late Palaeozoic glacio-eustacy and the evolving climates of low latitude areas. *Journal of the Geological Society, London*, **158**, 579–582.

YARDLEY, B. W. D & VALLEY, J. W. 1997. The petrologic case for a dry lower crust. *Journal of Geophysical Research*, **106 B6**, 12 173–12 185.

YARDLEY, B. W. D., VINE, F. J. & BALDWIN, C. T. 1982. The plate tectonic setting of NW Britain and Ireland in late Cambrian and early Ordovician times. *Journal of the Geological Society, London*, **139**, 457–463.

YOCHELSON, E. L. 1977. Agmata, a proposed extinct phylum of Early Cambrian age. *Journal of Paleontology*, **51**, 437–454.

YODER, H. S. & TILLEY, C. E. 1962. Origin of basalt magmas: an experimental study of natural and synthetic rock systems. *Journal of Petrology*, **3**, 342–532.

YOUNG, B. N., PARSONS, I. & THREADGOULD, R. 1994. Carbonatite near the Loch Borralan intrusion, Assynt. *Journal of the Geological Society, London*, **151**, 945–954.

YOUNG, G. M. 1999. Some aspects of the geochemistry, provenance and palaeoclimatology of the Torridonian of NW Scotland. *Journal of the Geological Society, London*, **156**, 1097–1111.

YOUNG, H. R. 1979. Evidence of former evaporites in the Cambro-Ordovician Durness Group, northwest Scotland. *Sedimentary Geology*, **22**, 287–303.

YOUNG, T. P. 1989. Phanerozoic ironstones: an introduction and review. *In*: YOUNG, T. P. & TAYLOR, W. E. G. (eds) *Phanerozoic Ironstones*. Geological Society, London, Special Publications, **46**, ix–xxv.

ZABALA, C. M. 1970. *On the Geology, Petrology and Copper Mineralization of the Tomnadashan Igneous Complex and Surrounding Area, Perthshire*. MSc thesis, University of Strathclyde.

ZEH, A. & MILLER, I. L. 2001. Metamorphic Evolution of Garnet-Epidote-Biotite Gneiss from the Moine Supergroup, Scotland, and Geotectonic Implications. *Journal of Petrology*, **42**, 529–554.

ZHANG ZHONGYING 1982. Upper Proterozoic microfossils from the Summer Isles, NW Scotland. *Palaeontology*, **25**, 443–460.

ZHANG ZHONGYING, DIVER, W. L. & GRANT, P. R. 1981. Microfossils from the Aultbea Formation, Torridon Group, on Tanera Beg, Summer Isles. *Scottish Journal of Geology*, **17**, 149–154.

ZHOU, J. 1985. The timing of calc-alkaline magmatism in parts of the Alpine–Himalayan collision zone and its relevance to the interpretation of Caledonian magmatism. *Journal of the Geological Society, London*, **142**, 309–317.

ZHOU, J. 1987a. Geology of a copper-bearing intrusive suite near Kilmelford, Argyllshire, Scotland. *Transactions of the Institution of Mining and Metallurgy*, **96**, B179–B186.

ZHOU, J. 1987b. Lithogeochemical exploration for copper and gold in Kilmelford district, Argyllshire, Scotland. *Transactions of the Institution of Mining and Metallurgy*, **96**, B187–B194.

ZIEGLER, P. A. 1988a. Evolution of the Arctic-North Atlantic and the western Tethys. *American Association of Petroleum Geologists, Memoir*, **43**, 1–198.

ZIEGLER, P. A. 1988b. Laurussia – The Old Red Continent. *In*: MCMILLAN, N. J., EMBRY, A. F. & GLASS, D. J. (eds) *Devonian of the World*. Canadian Society of Petroleum Geologists, Memoir, **14**, Vol. I, 15–48.

ZIEGLER, P. A. 1989. *Evolution of Laurussia: a Study in Late Palaeozoic Plate Tectonics.* Kluwer Academic Publishers, Dordrecht.

ZIEGLER, P. A. 1990a. *Geological Atlas of Western and Central Europe.* Geological Society, London, for Shell Internationale Petroleum Maatschappij.

ZIEGLER, P. A. 1990b. Tectonic and palaeogeographic development of the North Sea rift system. *In*: BLUNDELL, D. J. & GIBBS, A. D.
(eds) *Tectonic Evolution of the North Sea Rifts.* Oxford Science Publications, Oxford, 1–36.

ZIEGLER, P. A. 1992. Plate tectonics, plate moving mechanisms and rifting. *Tectonophysics*, **215**, 9–34.

ZIRKEL, F. 1871. Geologische Skizzen von Westküste Schottlands. *Zeitschrift der Deutschen geologischen Gesellschaft*, **23**, 1–124.

Index

Note: Page numbers in *italic* type refer to illustrations; those in **bold** type refer to tables.